Discovery of Bioactive Compounds from Natural Organisms and Their Molecular Mechanisms Against Diseases

Discovery of Bioactive Compounds from Natural Organisms and Their Molecular Mechanisms Against Diseases

Topic Editors

Jun Dang

Tengfei Ji

Xinxin Zhang

MDPI

Basel • Beijing • Wuhan • Barcelona • Belgrade • Novi Sad • Cluj • Manchester

Topic Editors

Jun Dang
Northwest Institute of Plateau Biology
Chinese Academy of Sciences
Xining
China

Tengfei Ji
Institute of Materia Medica
Chinese Academy of Medical Sciences
Beijing
China

Xinxin Zhang
College of Pharmacy
Xi'an Jiaotong University
Xi'an
China

Editorial Office
MDPI AG
Grosspeteranlage 5
4052 Basel, Switzerland

This is a reprint of the Topic, published open access by the journals *Analytica* (ISSN 2673-4532), *Antioxidants* (ISSN 2076-3921), *Biomedicines* (ISSN 2227-9059), *Nutrients* (ISSN 2072-6643), *Separations* (ISSN 2297-8739) and *International Journal of Molecular Sciences* (ISSN 1422-0067), freely accessible at: https://www.mdpi.com/topics/Bioactive_Compounds.

For citation purposes, cite each article independently as indicated on the article page online and as indicated below:

Lastname, Firstname, Firstname Lastname, and Firstname Lastname. Article Title. *Journal Name* **Year**, *Volume Number*, Page Range.

ISBN 978-3-7258-4899-7 (Hbk)
ISBN 978-3-7258-4900-0 (PDF)
https://doi.org/10.3390/books978-3-7258-4900-0

Contents

About the Editors

Jun Dang

Jun Dang, is a researcher at the Northwest Institute of Plateau Biology, Chinese Academy of Sciences, a postgraduate tutor, Deputy Director of Qinghai Provincial Key Laboratory of Tibetan Medicine Research, and Deputy Director of the Social Development Science and Technology Department of the Qinghai Science and Technology Department (2021–2023). He has been successively selected to be part of the Youth Innovation Promotion Association of the Chinese Academy of Sciences, the top talent of "Kunlun Talents, high-end innovation and entrepreneurship talents" of Qinghai province, and the "leader of natural science and engineering technology" of Qinghai province. In "target" screening of "drugs" and "drug" screening of "targets", the research focuses on new methods and targets for the accurate discovery of functional components from Qinghai–Tibet Plateau characteristic biological resources. The expressed, purified, or identified proteins are used as targets, and the "online chromatographic recognition system of target enzyme or proteins" is built to find natural small molecular functional compounds with target protein interaction. Combined with enzymatic, cellular, and animal level verification, the molecular mechanism of natural products targeting a protein to intervene or treat diseases is scientifically explained. He has presided over and participated in more than 20 projects, including the general project of the National Natural Science Foundation of China, the sub-project of the National Major Science and Technology Special Project of New Drug Creation, the talent project of the Chinese Academy of Sciences, the major special project of Qinghai province, etc. He has published 53 SCI papers as the first author or corresponding author, authorized 26 national invention patents as the first inventor, and obtained 7 provincial scientific and technological achievements as the first completion person.

Tengfei Ji

Tengfei Ji is a Principal Investigator, PhD supervisor at the Department of Natural Medicinal Chemistry, Institute of Materia Medica, Chinese Academy of Medical Sciences and Peking Union Medical College. In 2003, he graduated from the Institute of Materia Medica, Peking Union Medical College, and obtained his PhD degree in medicinal chemistry. After graduation, he stayed at the institute to work and focused on the research of new drug research and development from active natural products. In the last 5 years, more than 500 compounds have been isolated from 10 ethnic herbs by his team; more than 200 ingredients are new compounds; more than 100 compounds have active principles, and their activities include anti-depression, anti-inflammatory, anti-tumor, and anti-fibrosis. Currently, he has published more than 80 peer-reviewed papers, including in *Acta Pharmaceutica Sinica B*, *European Journal of Medicinal Chemistry*, *Chem. Commun.*, *Chemical Communications*, *Journal of Ethnopharmacology*, *Chinese Chemical Letters*, *Journal of Natural Products*, and other world-renowned journals. He has presided over more than 20 projects; 3 national projects and 3 provincial and ministerial projects in the past 5 years. He has applied for more than 30 patents, including 15 authorized patents and 1 international PCT patent. He is also an editor and reviewer of many journals.

Xinxin Zhang

Xinxin Zhang holds a Doctor of Medicine degree. He is an associate professor at Xi'an Jiaotong University, and a visiting scholar at Imperial College London. His main research focuses on the active ingredients of traditional Chinese medicines and natural medicines, including studies on extraction processes, pharmacodynamic material bases, and mechanisms of action. To date, he has published more than 30 SCI papers as the first author or corresponding author in international journals such as *Journal of Cleaner Production*, *Food Chemistry*, *Food and Function*, and *Phytochemistry*. He has also undertaken over 10 national and provincial-level scientific research projects as the principal investigator, including those funded by the National Natural Science Foundation of China, the China Postdoctoral Science Foundation, and the Shaanxi Provincial Natural Science Foundation.

analytica

Article

Evaluation of the Anti-Inflammatory Activity of Microwave Extracts of *Thymus algeriensis*: *In Vitro*, *In Vivo*, and *In Silico* Studies

Nassima Boutaoui [1,2,*], Meryem Acila [3], Nesrine Lariche [4], Redouane Lemoui [2], Asma Khellafi [1], Cristina Campestre [5], Francesco Melfi [5] and Marcello Locatelli [6]

[1] Laboratory of Phytochemistry and Pharmacology, Department of Chemistry, Faculty of Exact Sciences and Computer Science, University of Jijel, B.P. 98 Ouled Aissa, Jijel 18000, Algeria; khellafi.asma97@gmail.com

[2] Research Unit for the Valorization of Natural Resources, Bioactive Molecules, and Physicochemical and Biological Analysis, Frères Mentouri University, Constantine 1, Aïn El Bey Road, Constantine 25000, Algeria; redouanelemoui@gmail.com

[3] Laboratory of Materials-Environment Interactions (LIME), Department of Chemistry, Faculty of Exact Sciences and Computer Science, University of Jijel, B.P. 98 Ouled Aissa, Jijel 18000, Algeria; acila.meryem@univ-jijel.dz

[4] Laboratory of Molecular Toxicology, Faculty of Nature and Life Sciences, University of Jijel, Jijel 18000, Algeria; lariche_nessrine@yahoo.fr

[5] Department of Pharmacy, University "G. d'Annunzio" of Chieti-Pescara, Via dei Vestini 31, 66100 Chieti, Italy; cristina.campestre@unich.it (C.C.); francesco.melfi@unich.it (F.M.)

[6] Department of Science, University "G. d'Annunzio" of Chieti-Pescara, Via dei Vestini 31, 66100 Chieti, Italy; marcello.locatelli@unich.it

* Correspondence: boutaoui.nassima@univ-jijel.dz; Tel.: +213-781-83-35-77

Abstract: The objective of this work is to study the anti-inflammatory effect *in vitro* and *in vivo* of microwave (MW) extracts of *Thymus algeriensis*. The *in vitro* study was performed by the human red blood cell protection test, while the *in vivo* study used the carrageenan-induced rat paw edema model. The experimental results were confirmed by a molecular docking calculation. The results indicated that all the microwave extracts have a moderate anti-inflammatory effect, depending on their richness in phenolic compounds. Among the extracts studied, the one obtained at 100 °C for 15 min exhibited the most pronounced anti-inflammatory effect, with an inhibition of 78.52%, which is attributed to its high flavonoid content. In particular, the flavonoids naringin and catechin showed the best affinity for the target protein, with values of −10.3 kcal/mol and −9.2 kcal/mol, respectively, as well as low inhibition constants of 0.028 μM and 0.18 μM. These results indicate that these flavonoids generate interactions that enhance the stability of the target ligand–protein complex, thus contributing to the observed anti-inflammatory effect.

Keywords: *Thymus algeriensis*; anti-inflammatory activity; phenolic compounds; microwave-assisted extraction; molecular docking

1. Introduction

Medicinal plants contain various types of antioxidants, mostly carotenoids, phenolic compounds, benzoic acid derivatives, flavonoids, proanthocyanidins, stilbenes, coumarins, lignans, and lignins, which exhibit high antioxidant activity [1,2]. Recommendations based on epidemiological studies assessed that fruits, vegetables, and less processed staple foods can ensure the best protection against the development of diseases caused by oxidative stress, such as cancer, coronary heart disease, obesity, type 2 diabetes, hypertension, and cataracts [1]. The explanation for this relies on beneficial health effects, due to their antioxidant agents. Indeed, among 50 analyzed food products with high antioxidant content, 13 were spices, 8 were fruits and vegetables, 5 were berries, 5 were chocolate-based food, 5 were breakfast cereals, and 4 were nuts or seeds [3].

Inflammation is a complex biological response of vascular tissue to harmful stimuli and pathogens, characterized by redness, warmth, swelling, and pain [4]. Prolonged inflammation leads to rheumatoid arthritis, atherosclerosis, hay fever, and ischemic heart diseases, and it is also a common manifestation of infectious diseases [5,6].

In the plant kingdom, the genus Thymus belongs to the Lamiaceae family which comprises about 215 to 400 species according to previous studies [7]. Generally, this genus consists of perennial plants and subshrubs native mainly in Europe, Western Asia, and Mediterranean countries [8]. Historically, the volatile constituent-rich aerial parts of the Thymus species have been commonly used as herbal teas, condiments, and spices. In addition, they have shown many ethnomedicinal properties such as tonic, carminative, digestive, antispasmodic, antimicrobial, antioxidant, and anti-inflammatory ones [9–15]. *T. algeriensis* is the most pervasive North African species, endemic to Morocco, Tunisia, Algeria, and Libya [16–20]. Its essential oil was proposed as being antimicrobial, acridicidal, antioxidant, anti-inflammatory, and neuroprotective after extensive knowledge of its safety, chemical composition, and stability [21–31]. Recent investigations were focused on the polyphenolic and flavonoid contents isolated by classical extraction from the aerial parts of this species as alternative components to exert a valuable pharmacological activity [32–37].

To continue our investigations into the biological activities of Thymus [38], this study was designed to investigate the anti-inflammatory activity of microwave-assisted extracts of Algerian *T. algeriensis* aerial parts. Microwave-assisted (MW) extraction was applied to recover a high-benefit composition from this endemic species.

Furthermore, to support the in vivo results and gain deeper insights into the molecular mechanisms behind the anti-inflammatory activity of the extracts, we have employed in silico studies, specifically molecular docking simulations. Molecular docking allows for the prediction of the binding affinity and interaction of bioactive compounds with specific proteins or receptors involved in inflammatory pathways. This computational technique can provide valuable information regarding the potential mechanisms of action of the compounds extracted from *T. algeriensis* and help identify key targets involved in their anti-inflammatory effects. Recent studies have shown that in silico approaches, including molecular docking, are highly effective in understanding the bioactivity of plant-derived compounds, aiding the drug discovery process by identifying promising candidates for further experimental validation [39,40]. By simulating the binding interactions of compounds with key receptors or enzymes involved in inflammation, molecular docking can provide insights into the mechanisms underlying their therapeutic effects [41,42]. Moreover, this method has been widely used in drug discovery to streamline the identification of promising candidates for further experimental validation.

2. Materials and Methods

2.1. Plant Material and Preparation of Extracts

Thymus algeriensis was collected from the Biskra region (coordinates: 34°51′01″ N/5°43′40″ E), Algeria. The plant was identified by Prof. M. Kaabeche (Biology Department, University of Setif 1, Algeria). A relative specimen voucher has been registered in the Herbarium of Frères Mentouri University, Algeria. The microwave-assisted (MW) extraction of the aerial part of *T. algeriensis* was performed using a single-mode microwave reactor: the automatic Biotage Initiator™ 2.0. (Biotage AB, Uppsala, Sweden) characterized by a power range of 0–300 W and 2.45 GHz microwaves. The MW extraction was performed at discrete temperatures (T = 40, 60, 80, 100, or 120 °C) for 5, 10, or 15 min in water as the solvent as previously reported.

2.2. *Profile of Bioactive Compounds*

We measured the total amount of phenolic acid and flavonoids in *T. algeriensis* extracts that had been microwave-irradiated. We also looked for chlorophylls and carotenoids. We wrote more about the exact steps we took in our previous paper [38]. High-quality standard chemicals for the chromatographic analyses (gallic acid, catechin, chlorogenic acid, epicatechin, 4-hydroxybenzoic acid, *t*-ferulic acid, naringin, vanillic acid, *p*-coumaric acid, rutin, syringic acid, benzoic acid, *o*-coumaric acid, 3-hydroxybenzoic acid, sinapinic acid, 2,3-dimethoxybenzoic acid, quercetin, isovanillin) were purchased from Merck (Milan, Italy). The HPLC-PDA method was used for the quantitative characterization of the compounds in these extracts (Supplementary Table S1).

2.3. *In Vitro Anti-Inflammatory Activity*

The anti-inflammatory activity of MW extracts was evaluated using the human red blood cell (RBC) membrane stabilization method [43]. The blood was collected from a healthy human volunteer who had not taken any NSAIDs for 2 weeks prior to the experiment. The collected blood was then mixed with an equal volume of Alsever solution (2% dextrose, 0.8% sodium citrate, 0.5% citric acid, and 0.42% NaCl) and centrifuged at 1730 g. The packed cells were washed with isosaline, and a 10% suspension was made. Different concentrations of extracts were prepared (250, 500, and 1000 μg/mL) using distilled water. To each concentration, 1 mL of phosphate buffer (0.15 M, pH 7.4), 2 mL of hyposaline (0.36%), and 0.5 mL of HRBC (human red blood cell) suspension (10%) were added. Each sample was incubated at 37 °C for a duration of 30 min, followed by centrifugation at 1730 g for 20 min. The supernatant solution was then analyzed spectrophotometrically at a wavelength of 560 nm to estimate the hemoglobin content.

$$\textbf{Percentage inhibition}(\%) = \left[\mathbf{100} - \frac{\mathbf{A_{test}}}{\mathbf{A_{control}}}\right] \times \mathbf{100} \quad (1)$$

where A_{test} is the absorbance of the sample containing the test extract, and $A_{control}$ is the absorbance of the simple without the extract.

Diclofenac was used as the reference drug (Sigma-Aldrich, St. Louis, MO, USA) and tested at the same concentrations as the extracts (250, 500, and 1000 μg/mL) for comparison.

2.4. *Inflammatory Paw Edema Test in Rats*

In this part of the experiments, the anti-inflammatory activity of the microwave-assisted extract was investigated on the carrageenan-induced inflammatory paw edema [44]. Female Wistar rats (80–125 g) were obtained from the Pasteur Institute (Algeria). Rats were housed in standard polypropylene cages, with four per cage. The extracts were dissolved and dispersed in physiological saline (0.9%) and administered orally to a pre-treated group of rats at a dosage of 50 mg/kg. The control group received physiological saline (0.9%) at the same volume as the vehicle used for administering the extracts. One hour after administration, 0.1 mL of 1% carrageenan solution was injected into the footpad of the hind paws of each rat in all groups. Prior to the carrageenan (Sigma-Aldrich) injection, the rat paw volume was measured. The increase in the carrageenan-induced inflammatory paw volume was measured at 1, 2, and 3 h over the injection. The anti-inflammatory activity of the *T. algeriensis* extracts was compared with that of 50 mg/kg diclofenac. The percentages of inhibition were calculated according to the following formula:

$$\textbf{Inhibition}(\%) = \frac{(\mathbf{V_T} - \mathbf{V_0})_{\textbf{control}} - (\mathbf{V_T} - \mathbf{V_0})_{\textbf{treated group}}}{(\mathbf{V_T} - \mathbf{V_0})_{\textbf{control}}} \times \mathbf{100} \quad (2)$$

where V is the diameter of injected paw, V_0 is the average inflammation (hind paw edema) of the control group at a given time 0, and V_T is the average of diameters of the hind paw edema of the drug-treated rat at the same time.

This test was approved by the ethics committee (the committee of the Algerian Association of Sciences in Animal Experimentation (N°. 8808/1988), associated with veterinary medical activities and animal health protection N° JORA: 004/1988). All experimental procedures were conducted in accordance with established ethical principles to ensure respect for the participants' rights and well-being.

2.5. Molecular Docking Study

The study of the molecular docking of the organic molecules that had been extracted from the plant was performed to complement and confirm the results in the experimental section for the in vitro and in vivo activities using the AutoDock Vina program. The protein used to simulate this activity, named COX2, was obtained from the RCSB database with the code [3LN0] [45]. The active site of the protein used was delimited by a box of dimensions as follows: a volume of $40 \times 40 \times 40$ Å^3 and centers x, y, z of 41, 35, and 47, respectively.

To ensure an effective simulation, the ligands (19 molecules: gallic acid, catechin, chlorogenic acid, epicatechin, 4-hydroxy-benzoic acid, *t*-ferulic acid, naringin, vanillic acid, *p*-coumaric acid, rutin, syringic acid, benzoic acid, *o*-coumaric acid, 3-hydroxy-benzoic acid, sinapinic acid, 2,3-dimethoxy-benzoic acid, quercetin, isovanillin, and dichlofenac) were initially prepared by optimizing them using Chem3D 16.0 to achieve a stable geometry with minimum energy. Next, the receptors (proteins) for the two activities were prepared using Discovery Studio. This involved removing water molecules and heteroatoms and adding polar hydrogen atoms. Afterwards, molecular docking simulations were conducted using the AutoDock Vina program [46]

Also, the molecular interactions between the protein targets and compounds were viewed using BIOVIA Discovery Studio. Amino acids engaging with the ligand, hydrogen bonds (H-bonds), hydrophobic interactions, and individual atoms involved were examined in each ligand cluster (Supplementary Table S2).

2.6. Statistical Analysis

Statistical analysis was performed using IBM SPSS Statistics 27. Comparisons were made using one-way analysis of variance (ANOVA), followed by Tukey's test. The results of both the in vitro and in vivo experiments are presented as mean ± standard deviation (SD) with (n = 3), when the *p*-value was less than 0.05.

3. Results and Discussion

3.1. In Vitro Anti-Inflammatory Activity in Human RBCs (HBRCs)

The microwave-assisted extracts of the *T. algeriensis* were then studied for in vitro anti-inflammatory activity by the HRBC membrane stabilization method. The results are reported in Table 1. The in vitro anti-inflammatory activity of the extracts was concentration-dependent, and again, the higher protection of HRBCs in the hypotonic solution was attributed to extracts obtained at a higher temperature (120 °C) or time of extraction (15 min). All the results were compared with standard diclofenac, which showed 96.67 ± 0.15% protection at the highest concentration.

Table 1. In vitro anti-inflammatory activity of the MW extract of *Thymus algeriensis* using the HRBC method.

	Percentage Inhibition (%)		
	250 μg/mL	500 μg/mL	1000 μg/mL
MW 40 °C	77.18 ± 0.17 ***	84.92 ± 0.30 ***	89.28 ± 0.20 ***
MW 60 °C	78.59 ± 0.18 ***	87.43 ± 0.22 ***	90.67 ± 0.10 ***
MW 80 °C	80.53 ± 0.20 ***	88.12 ± 0.13 ***	91.97 ± 0.15 ***
MW 100 °C	77.06 ± 3.04 ***	88.99 ± 0.31 ***	94.94 ± 0.25 ***
MW 120 °C	86.25 ± 0.12 ns	91.13 ± 0.25 ns	96.88 ± 0.15 ns
MW 100 °C, 5 min	76.92 ± 0.20 ***	85.09 ± 0.22 ***	88.64 ± 0.18 ***
MW 100 °C, 15 min	88.96± 0.17 ns	90.95 ± 0.15 ns	96.85 ± 0.17 ns
Diclofenac	89.91 ± 0.17	91.91 ± 0.2	96.67 ± 0.15

Results are presented as mean ± SD (n = 3): ns: no significant difference; *** $p < 0.001$ compared with diclofenac.

The results show that the in vitro anti-inflammatory activity increases with the treatment temperature, reaching its maximum at 120 °C for all tested concentrations, with more pronounced effects at 0.5 mg/mL and 1 mg/mL. The treatment at 100 °C for 15 min also shows a significant improvement compared to a 5 min exposure. Although the effectiveness of the tested treatments is close to that of diclofenac, it remains slightly lower, but the differences are not always statistically significant. These results suggest that combining high temperature with extended treatment time optimizes the anti-inflammatory activity, offering potential comparable to that of reference anti-inflammatory drugs.

The microwave-assisted extracts exhibited a membrane stabilization effect by inhibiting the hypotonicity-induced lysis of the erythrocyte membrane. The erythrocyte membrane is analogous to the lysosomal membrane [47], and its stabilization implies that the extract may also stabilize the lysosomal membranes. Stabilization of the lysosomal membrane is important in limiting the inflammatory response by preventing the release of the lysosomal constituents of activated neutrophils such as bactericidal enzymes and proteases, which cause further tissue inflammation and damage upon extracellular release [48].

The exact mechanism for the membrane-stabilizing effect of these extracts of *T. algeriensis* and the chemical constituents responsible for this effect is hitherto not known. However, a number of studies have shown that flavonoids exhibit analgesic and anti-inflammatory effects as a result of their membrane stabilizing ability in various experimental models [49]. The extract may inhibit the processes, which may stimulate or enhance the efflux of these intracellular components [50]. It has also been shown that the microwave-assisted extracts of *T. algeriensis* contain flavonoids such as rutin, catechin, and epicatechin [38]. Thus, these extracts showed significant in vitro anti-inflammatory activity as compared to that of the standard. On the basis of the above results, it can be concluded that these MW extracts of *T. algeriensis* have a potential anti-inflammatory activity.

3.2. *Carrageenan-Induced Paw Oedema*

The paw oedema thickness was measured at 1, 2, and 3 h post-inflammation induction in animals pre-treated with the MW extract. The percentage of oedema inhibition by the MW extract was measured. The inflammation induced by carrageenan develops into two distinct phases. The initial phase, occurring within one hour of exposure, is identified by the release of histamine, serotonin, and bradykinin. The late phase, occurring after more than an hour, results from the release of prostaglandin-like substances [51,52]. Research has demonstrated the involvement of free radicals in the initial phase of acute inflammation induced by carrageenan [53].

Table 2 shows the effect of microwave-assisted extracts of *T. algeriensis* on the carrageenin-induced rat paw edema test. After carrageenan induction, there was a significant ($p < 0.001$) increase in edema formation in normal rats. Carrageenan-induced hind paw edema is the standard experimental model of acute inflammation. Moreover, the experimental model exhibits a high degree of reproducibility [54].

Table 2. Effect of microwave-assisted *T. algeriensis* extracts on carrageenan-induced paw edema in rats.

	Mean Increase in Paw Thickness (mm) ± SD		
Group	1 h	2 h	3 h
Control	1.92 ± 0.04	1.74 ± 0.09	1.49 ± 0.07
Diclofenac	1.48 ± 0.04 ***	0.72 ± 0.04 ***	0.24 ± 0.04 ***
MW 40 °C	1.45 ± 0.04 ***	1.05 ± 0.04 ***	0.73 ± 0.01 ***
MW 60 °C	1.28 ± 0.02 ***	1 ± 0.02 ***	0.49 ± 0.04 ***
MW 80 °C	1.41 ± 0.04 ***	0.79 ± 0.04 ***	0.49 ± 0.05 ***
MW 100 °C	1.4 ± 0.03 ***	0.96 ± 0.05 ***	0.53 ± 0.02 ***
MW 120 °C	1.36 ± 0.02 ***	0.99 ± 0.01 ***	0.46 ± 0.04 ***
MW 100 °C 5 min	1.44 ± 0.01 ***	1.17 ± 0.02 ***	0.77 ± 0.02 ***
MW 100 °C 15 min	1.37 ± 0.04 ***	0.76 ± 0.02 ***	0.32 ± 0.02 ***

Results are presented as mean ± SD (n = 3); *** $p < 0.001$ compared with control.

Figure 1 shows the inhibition percentages of the microwave-treated extracts of *Thymus algeriensis* and diclofenac. One hour after the carrageenan injection, all the microwave extracts showed a moderate anti-inflammatory effect comparable to that of the reference drug (diclofenac), with inhibition percentages ranging from 24% to 29% for extracts and 23% for diclofenac. These results suggest that microwave-treated extracts of *Thymus algeriensis* have similar anti-inflammatory activity to that of diclofenac, although moderate.

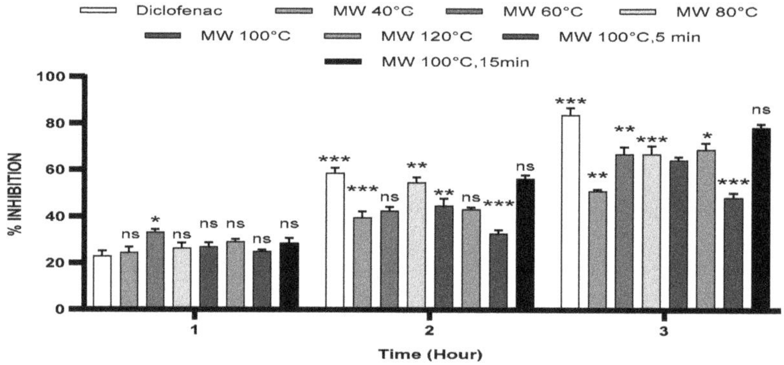

Figure 1. Percentage of inhibition inflammation of MW extracts in rats with carrageenan-induced hind paw edema (values presented as means ± SD (n = 3): ns: not significant difference; * $p < 0.05$ ** $p < 0.01$, and *** $p < 0.001$ considered significant when compared with diclofenac.

After three hours of experimentation, diclofenac showed a marked anti-inflammatory effect, reaching 83.74%, which confirms the efficacy of non-steroidal anti-inflammatories, which act by the inhibition of the COX-1 and COX-2 enzymes [55]. On the other hand, the microwave-treated extracts showed significant inhibition, although lower than that of diclofenac, with percentages ranging between 51% and 70%. However, the extract treated at 100 °C for 15 min showed an anti-inflammatory effect similar to that of diclofenac, with a percentage of 78.52%, suggesting that this treatment could be an interesting alternative with efficacy comparable to that of the reference drug.

Some studies have indicated that the flavonoids contained in plant extracts have anti-inflammatory properties and that they are able to modulate the functioning of the immune system by inhibiting the activity of enzymes which are responsible for inflammation; they may also modulate monocyte adhesion during atherosclerotic inflammation by inhibiting the expression of inflammatory mediators [50]. Our previous phytochemical study of *T. algeriensis* aerial parts revealed the presence of some of these compounds (epicatechin, catechin, rutin, quercetin and naringin), which could be responsible for this anti-inflammatory activity of the extracts. It has been also demonstrated that various biologically active flavonoids (such as rutin and quercetin) produced significant antinociceptive and/or anti-inflammatory activities [56,57].

The extract treated at 100 °C for 15 min (MW 100 °C 15 min) had the most significant anti-inflammatory effects compared to the other extracts tested. The higher efficacy is due to the extract's availability of flavonoids, including quercetin, rutin, catechin, epicatechin, and naringin [38], which are compounds known for their ability to reduce inflammation. These flavonoids, by their action on pro-inflammatory enzymes and their ability to modulate inflammatory mediators, play a key role in reducing inflammatory processes.

The microwave extraction process at 100 °C for 15 min seems to have optimized the extraction of these compounds, which explains the higher efficiency of this extract. Indeed, this method allows a faster and more complete release of flavonoids while preserving their structure and bioactive activity. These results reinforce the idea that microwave extraction can be an effective method to obtain plant extracts rich in anti-inflammatory compounds.

Several researchers have also demonstrated the anti-inflammatory effect of *Thymus algeriensis* extracts, showing that they can reduce inflammation markers and attenuate inflammatory responses in various experimental models.

According to Mensour et al. (2020) [22] and Mahdi et al. (2022) [32], *Thymus algeriensis* has significant anti-inflammatory activities. Extracts from the leaves of *Thymus algeriensis* were evaluated for their ability to inhibit the enzymes cyclooxygenase-1 (COX-1) and cyclooxygenase-2 (COX-2), as well as lipoxygenase (5-LOX). The results indicated that the extract of *Thymus algeriensis* is more selective for COX-2 than for COX-1, with an index of selectivity similar to that of celecoxib, a selective inhibitor of COX-2. The extract also showed anti-inflammatory effects in living things, like rats with leg swelling caused by carrageenan and mice with white blood cells moving into the peritoneal cavity [22,32].

3.3. Molecular Docking

The docking of molecules is a modern bioinformatics method that predicts the probable experimental orientation and the binding affinity needed to produce a stable complex structure between a ligand and a target [58]. The AutoDock Vina tool was used to conduct molecular docking tests to see if each of the identified compounds had an anti-inflammatory effect compared to the standard drug, dichlofenac.

The findings allowed the assessment of the binding energy between the protein (Figure 2) and different ligand positions (Table 3). A negative binding energy indicates a potential for binding between the ligand and the receptor. The inhibition constant (Ki) was calculated using the formula as follows: Ki = exp(ΔG/RT), where ΔG indicates the binding energy, R is the gas constant (1.9872036×10^{-3} kcal. Mol^{-1}), and T represents the ambient temperature (298.15 K) [59]. A smaller inhibition constant signifies a more effective drug derived from the title molecule.

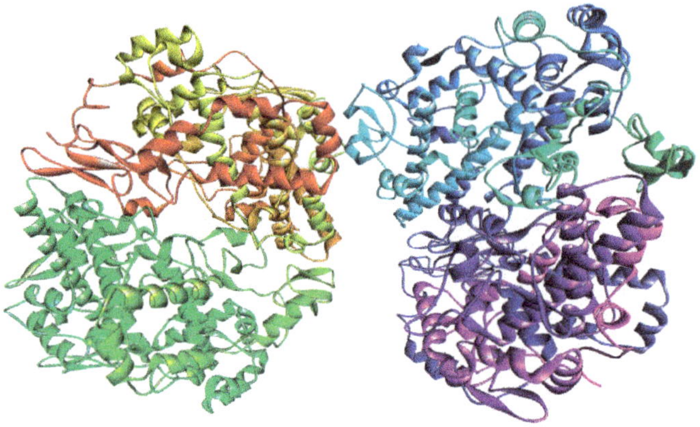

Figure 2. The 3D structure of the inflammatory protein COX-2 [PDB ID: 3LN0].

Table 3. Results for affinity and inhibition constant of ligands with the same protein.

Biomolecules	Anti-Inflammatory Activity	
	Protein: COX-2 (3LN0)	
	ΔG (Kcal/mol)	Ki (μmol)
2,3-dimethoxybenzoic acid	−6.0	39.95
3-hydroxybenzoic acid	−6.1	33.74
4-hydroxybenzoic acid	−5.7	66.28
syringic acid	−5.9	47.29
gallic acid	−6.4	20.33
benzoic acid	−5.5	92.90
catechin	−9.2	0.18
chlorogenic acid	−8.5	0.58
epicatechin	−8.9	0.29
isovanillin	−5.9	47.29
naringin	−10.3	0.028
o-coumaric acid	−6.3	24.07
p-coumaric acid	−6.1	33.74
quercetin	−7.9	1.61
rutin	−8.8	0.35
sinapinic acid	−5.8	55.99
t-ferulic acid	−6.1	33.74
vanillic acid	−6.2	28.50
dichlofenac	−7.1	6.23

It was found that naringin and catechin have the best affinity, with values of −10.3 kcal/ Mol and −9.2 kcal/ Mol, respectively, as well as a low inhibition constants of 0.028 μM and 0.18 μM, respectively. Additionally, we performed molecular docking using a commercialized drug named diclofenac. According to Table 2, catechin, d acid, epicatechin, naringin, quercetin, and rutin have shown favorable results compared to diclofenac (Table 3).

The binding affinity of the fixed ligands to the target proteins in this investigation was affected by non-covalent interactions, including hydrogen bonds and hydrophobic interactions. Several investigations have demonstrated that binding affinity increases when ligands can participate in hydrophobic interactions with a significant amount of hydrophobic residues of amino acids within the binding region of a target protein [60,61]. Stojanovi and Zari [62] emphasized the significance of hydrophobic interactions in various systems characterized by powerful intermolecular forces [63]. This mechanism could be responsible for the significant binding affinity of the active chemicals associated with the proteins selected in this study. The significance of hydrogen bonds in stabilizing molecular interactions between ligands and proteins must not be ignored, because they play a crucial role in enzymatic catalysis and the formation of protein–substrate and protein–inhibitor complexes, contributing to the overall stability of multiple biological molecules [62,63].

For this purpose, the analysis of the molecular interactions of the active compounds, carried out on the basis of their binding energy, hydrogen bonds, and hydrophobic interactions with the surrounding amino acids in the selected protein targets, revealed a significant impact of the ligand–protein complex status. In particular, it was seen that flavonoids taken from *Thymus algeriensis* have incredibly low-free-binding-energy values compared to those of the other polyphenolic compounds being studied. Low free energy indicates a more stable interaction and the strong affinity of flavonoids for their protein targets.

Also, the inhibition constant values (Ki) for these flavonoids were lower than those for other polyphenolic compounds. This means that they had a very strong affinity for binding to the target proteins. Low Ki values are synonymous with a better ability of these flavonoids to effectively inhibit the activity of target enzymes, thus enhancing their role in the modulation of inflammatory pathways. This evidence suggests that flavonoids, including quercetin, rutin, catechin, epicatechin, and naringin, are able to bind stably to the active sites of proteins, which may be the main reason for their anti-inflammatory symptoms noted in this study.

In the *in vivo* test, it was found that the extract treated by the microwave at 100 °C for 15 min (MW 100 °C 15 min) revealed the most powerful anti-inflammatory effect. This result is directly related to the presence of a maximum level of flavonoids in this extract. Extracts with the highest concentrations of flavonoids showed the significant inhibition of inflammatory markers, which confirms that the richness in flavonoids plays a decisive role in the anti-inflammatory efficacy observed. These results are consistent with data from the study of molecular interaction between the different ligands and their target proteins, where flavonoids showed a strong affinity for the active sites of the target proteins, due to low Ki values and particularly low bonding energies.

Figures 3 and 4 show numerous hydrogen bonds between each ligand and the target protein, illustrating the stability and efficacy of these interactions. In addition, non-covalent interactions such as hydrophobic and electrostatic interactions were also observed, further enhancing the stability of ligand–protein complexes. These non-covalent interactions are crucial for the stability of complexes and increase their effectiveness by inhibiting the activity of proteins responsible for inflammation.

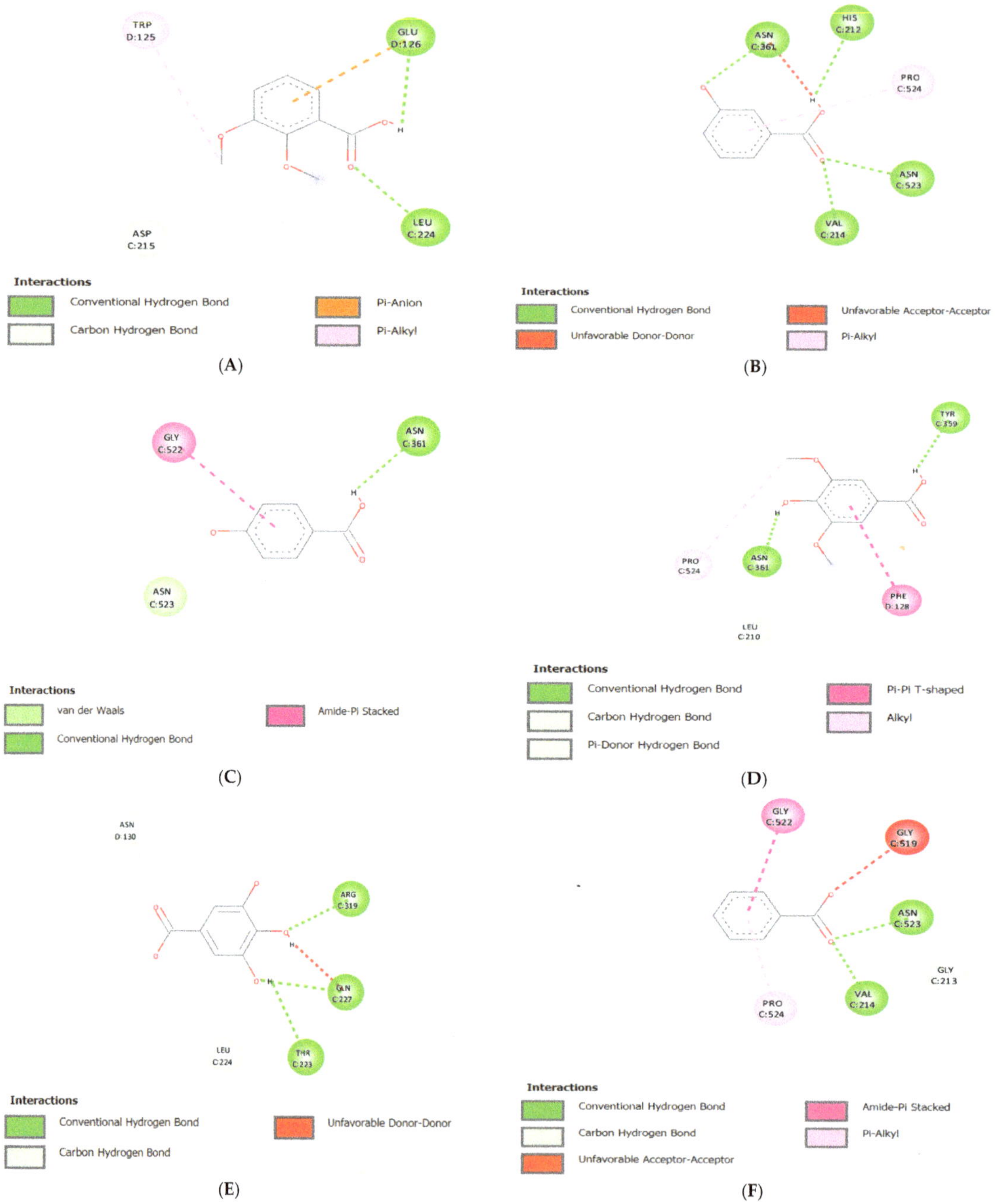

Figure 3. *Cont.*

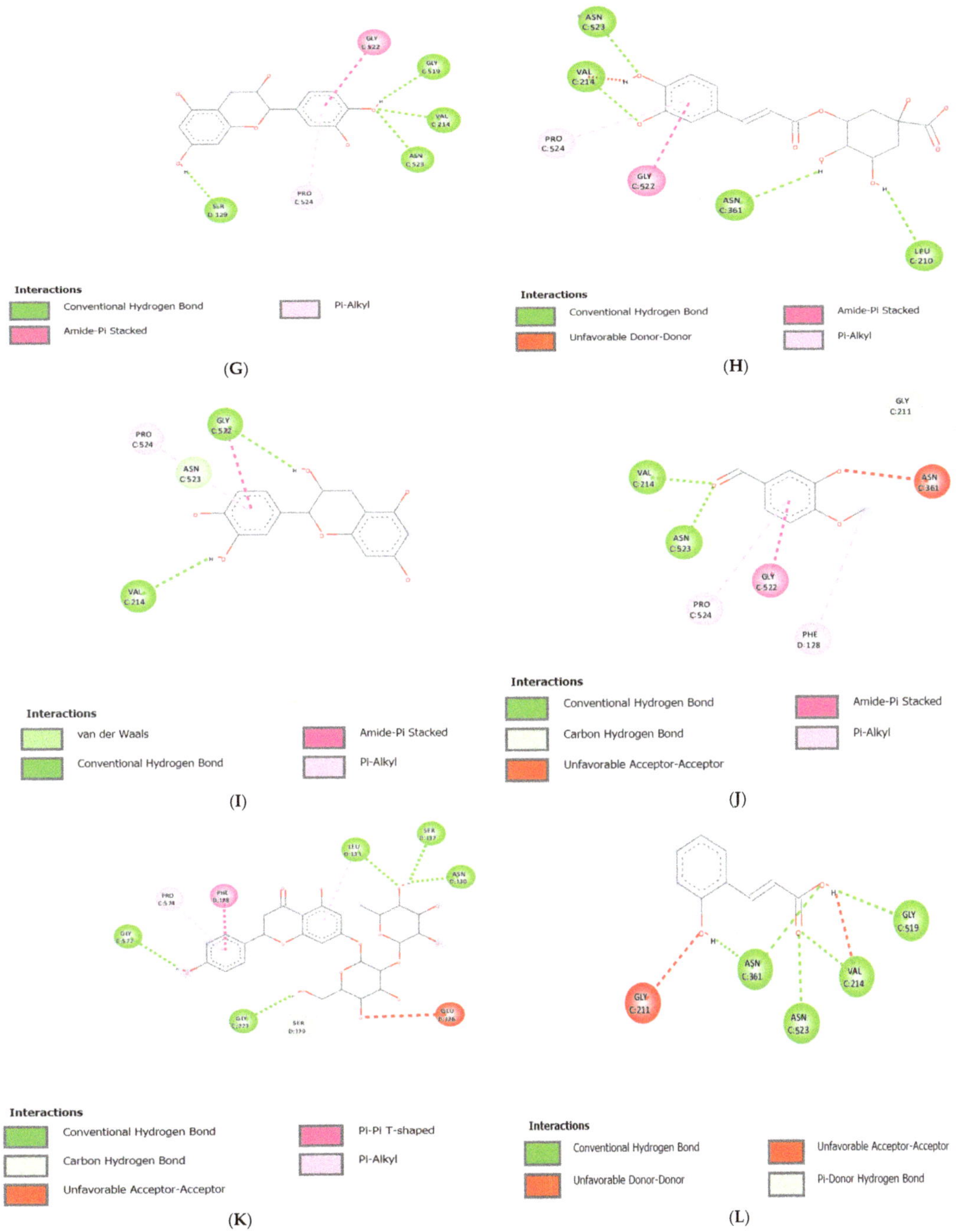

Figure 3. *Cont.*

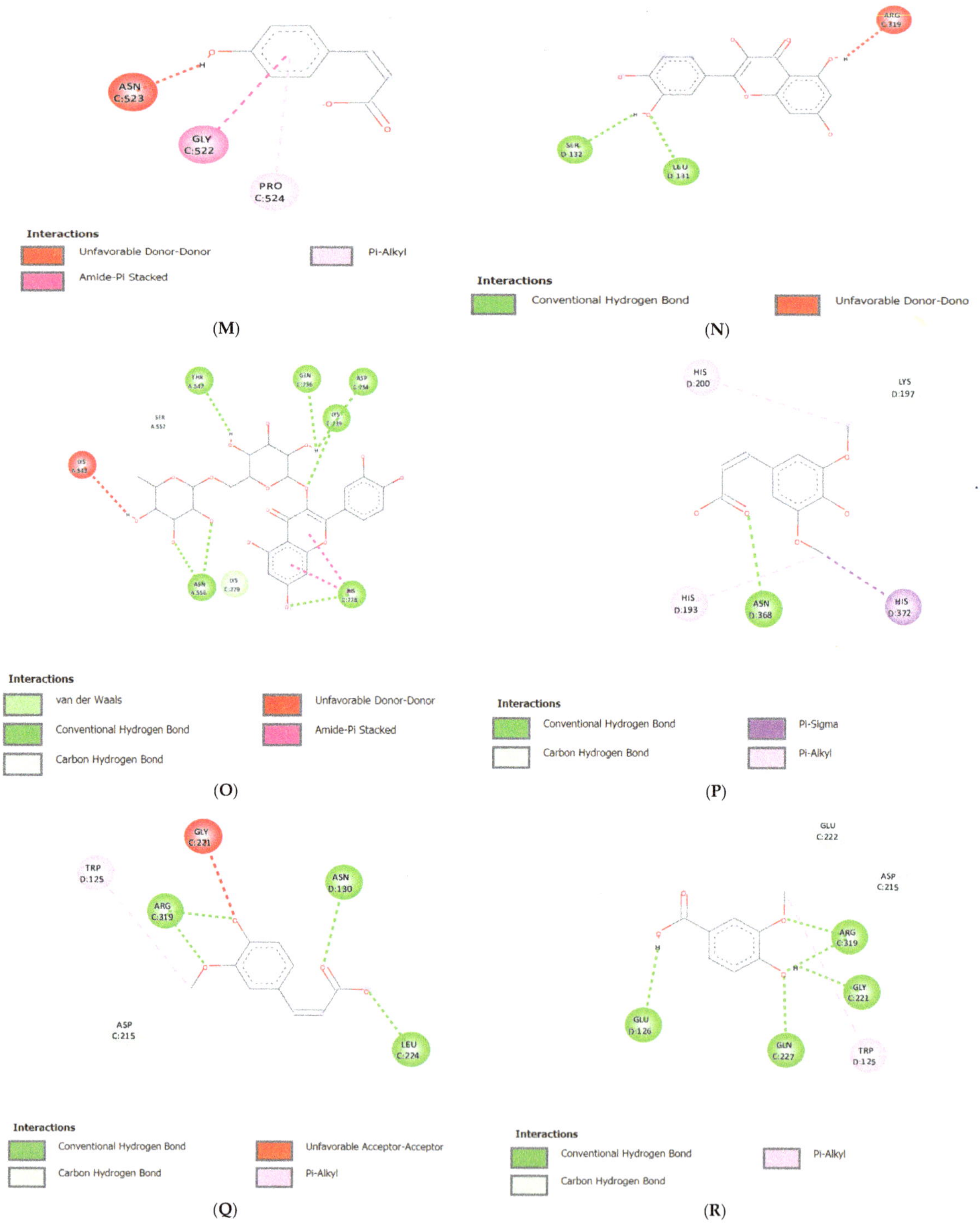

Figure 3. *Cont.*

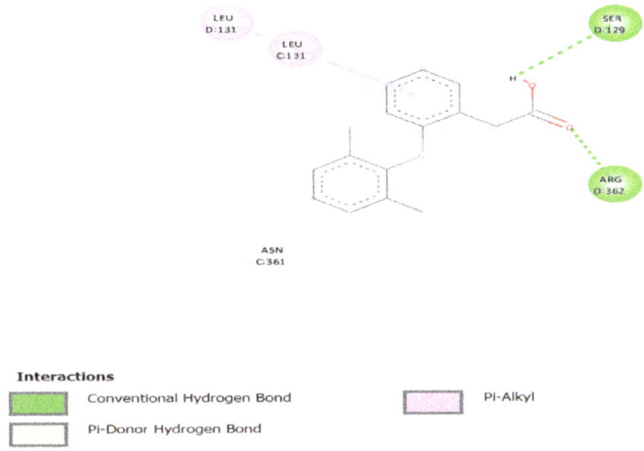

(**S**)

Figure 3. Two-dimensional detailed binding sites of each ligand into the receptor [PDB ID: 3LN0]. (**A**): 2,3-dimethoxybenzoic acid; (**B**): 3-hydroxybenzoic acid; (**C**): 4-hydrobenzoic acid; (**D**): syringic acid; (**E**): gallic acid; (**F**): benzoic acid; (**G**): catechin; (**H**): chlorogenic acid; (**I**): epicatechin; (**J**): isovanillin; (**K**): naringin; (**L**): o-coumaric acid; (**M**): p-coumaric acid; (**N**): quercetin; (**O**): rutin; (**P**): sinapinic acid; (**Q**): t-ferulic acid; (**R**): vanillic acid; (**S**): diclofenac.

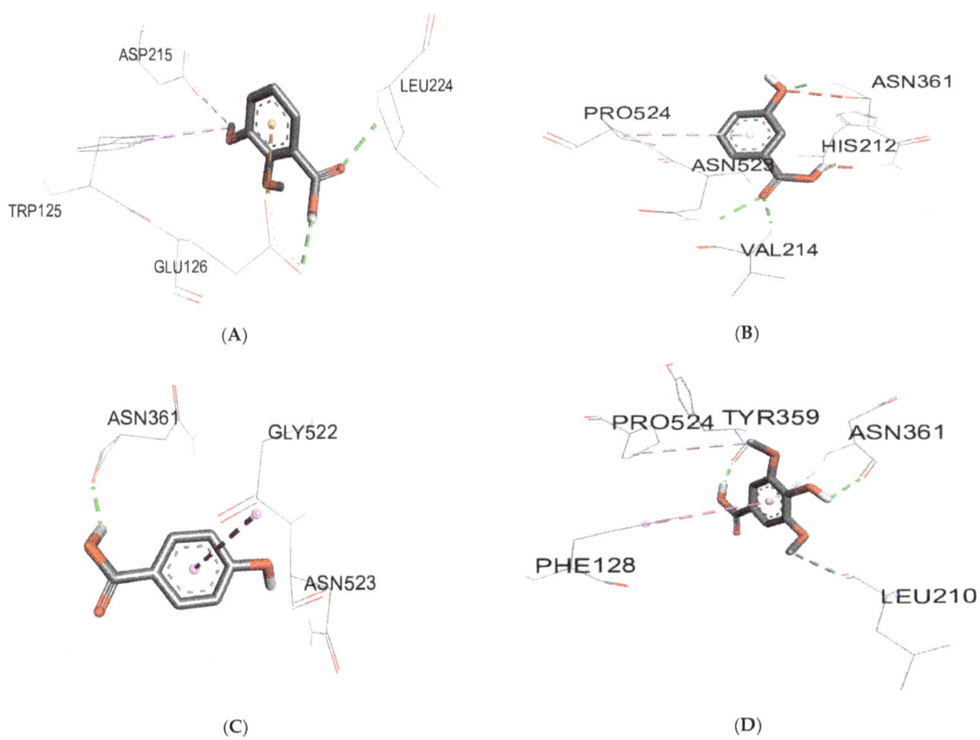

Figure 4. *Cont.*

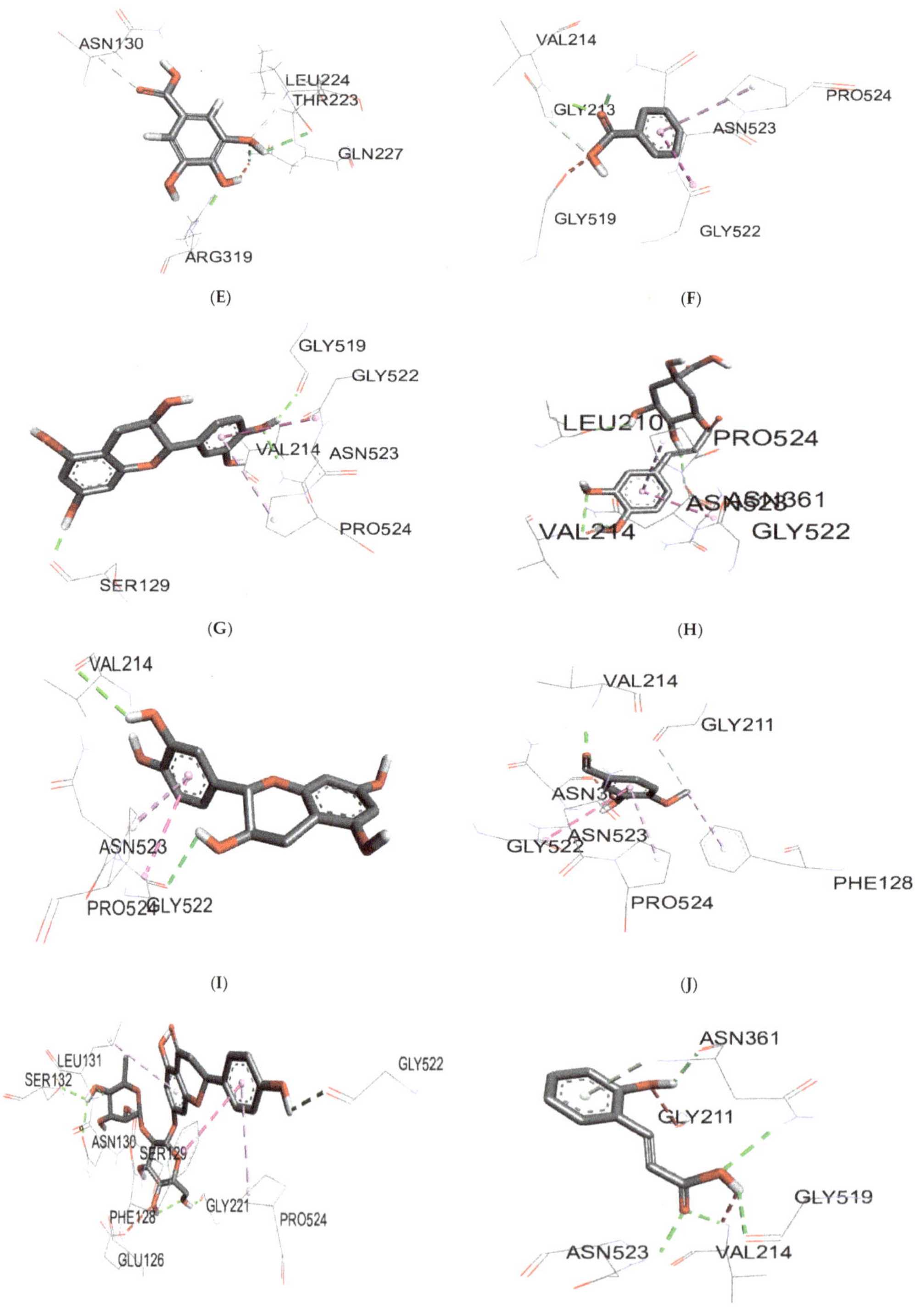

Figure 4. *Cont.*

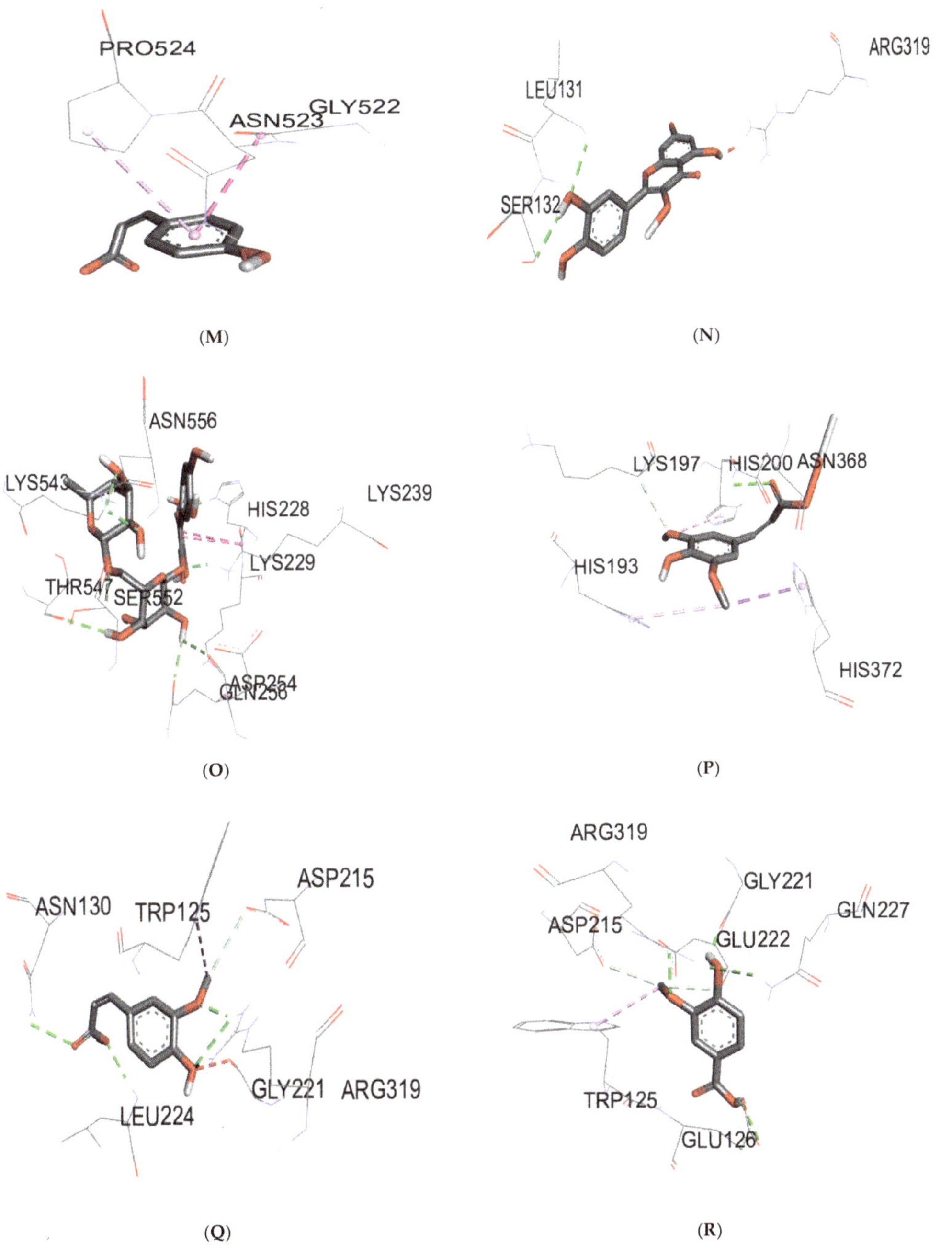

Figure 4. *Cont.*

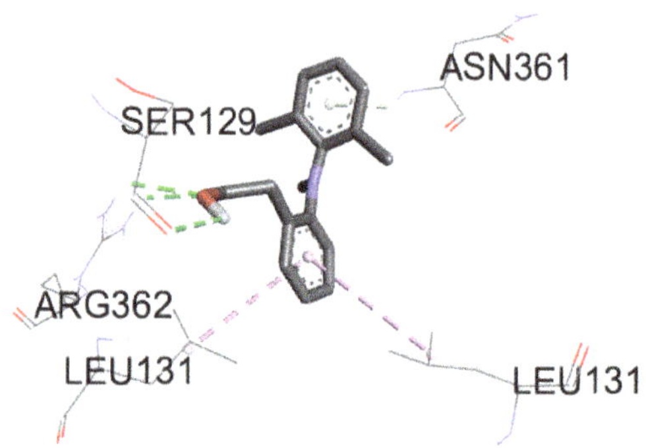

(S)

Figure 4. The 3D detailed binding sites of each ligand into the receptor [PDB ID: 3LN0]. (**A**): 2,3-dimethoxybenzoic acid; (**B**): 3-hydroxybenzoic acid; (**C**): 4-hydrobenzoic acid; (**D**): syringic acid; (**E**): gallic acid; (**F**): benzoic acid; (**G**): catechin; (**H**): chlorogenic acid; (**I**): epicatechin; (**J**): isovanillin; (**K**): naringin; (**L**): o-coumaric acid; (**M**): p-coumaric acid; (**N**): quercetin; (**O**): rutin; (**P**): sinapinic acid; (**Q**): t-ferulic acid; (**R**): vanillic acid; (**S**): dichlofenac.

Based on the results obtained, it appears that each flavonoid (ligand) has the potential to be an effective molecule in the fight against inflammation, thanks to its ability to interact stably with the target proteins. The combined effect of the 18 ligands tested could still produce improved results, suggesting that the use of these flavonoids in combination therapies may have a stronger impact on inflammatory processes.

In addition, the *in silico* results, which were obtained by simulating ligand–protein interactions, fully corroborate the experimental results obtained during in vivo tests. This concordance between the molecular analyses and the experimental results reinforces the validity of the data and highlights the reducing action of the inflammation of the extracts of *Thymus algeriensis*, validating the efficacy of flavonoids as potential therapeutic agents.

4. Conclusions

After the characterization of the *Thymus algeriensis* extracts obtained by the microwave, we focused our study on the anti-inflammatory activity of these extracts (*in vitro* and *in vivo*), evaluating the inhibition of inflammation according to their composition in secondary metabolites. All the extracts showed moderate results, but the extract treated at 100 °C for 15 min had the most pronounced anti-inflammatory effect, effectively reducing inflammatory edema in rats due to its high content of flavonoids, compared to other extracts. These results were corroborated by an *in silico* analysis, which revealed that the flavonoids present in the microwave-processed extracts have a strong affinity for the target protein, thus explaining the efficacy of the extract in reducing inflammation.

Supplementary Materials: The following supporting information can be downloaded at https://www.mdpi.com/article/10.3390/analytica6020016/s1. Table S1: (HPLC-PDA) analysis of the phenolic profile of Thymus algeriensis microwave-assisted extracts. Table S2: Binding interaction.

Author Contributions: Conceptualization, N.B. and M.L.; methodology, N.B. and M.A.; software, N.B. and N.L.; validation, N.B., M.A. and M.L.; formal analysis, N.B. and N.L.; investigation, R.L. and A.K; resources, R.L., A.K. and N.B.; data curation, N.B.; writing—original draft preparation, N.B.; writing—review and editing, C.C. and F.M.; visualization, N.B. and N.L.; supervision, M.L.; project administration, N.B. All authors have read and agreed to the published version of the manuscript.

Funding: This research received no external funding.

Data Availability Statement: Data is contained within the article or Supplementary Material.

Acknowledgments: The authors would like to thank Laboratory of Pharmacy Department, University "G. d'Annunzio" of Chieti-Pescara, for the preparation and characterization of the MAE extracts.

Conflicts of Interest: The authors declare no conflicts of interest.

Abbreviations

The following abbreviations are used in this manuscript:

MW	Microwave extracts
RBC	Red blood cell
NSAIDs	Non-steroidal anti-inflammatory drugs

References

1. Halvorsen, B.L.; Carlsen, M.H.; Phillips, K.M.; Bøhn, S.K.; Holte, K.; Jacobs, D.R., Jr.; Blomhoff, R. Content of redox-active compounds (ie, antioxidants) in foods consumed in the United States. *Am. J. Clin. Nutr.* **2006**, *84*, 95–135. [CrossRef] [PubMed]
2. Halvorsen, B.L.; Holte, K.; Myhrstad, M.C.W.; Barikmo, I.; Hvattum, E.; Remberg, S.F.; Wold, A.-B.; Haffner, K.; Baugerød, H.; Andersen, L.F.; et al. A Systematic Screening of Total Antioxidants in Dietary Plants. *J. Nutr.* **2002**, *132*, 461–471. [CrossRef]
3. Lindsay, D.G.; Astley, S.B. European research on the functional effects of dietary antioxidants—EUROFEDA. *Mol. Asp. Med.* **2002**, *23*, 287–291. [CrossRef] [PubMed]
4. Chen, L.; Deng, H.; Cui, H.; Fang, J.; Zuo, Z.; Deng, J.; Li, Y.; Wang, X.; Zhao, L. Inflammatory responses and inflammation-associated diseases in organs. *Oncotarget* **2018**, *9*, 7204–7218. [CrossRef]
5. Fioranelli, M.; Roccia, M.G.; Flavin, D.; Cota, L. Regulation of inflammatory reaction in health and disease. *Int. J. Mol. Sci.* **2021**, *22*, 5277. [CrossRef] [PubMed]
6. Pezone, A.; Olivieri, F.; Napoli, M.V.; Procopio, A.; Avvedimento, E.V.; Gabrielli, A. Inflammation and DNA damage: Cause, effect or both. *Nat. Rev. Rheumatol.* **2023**, *19*, 200–211. [CrossRef]
7. Cronquist, A. *The Evolution and Classification of Fowering Plants*; New York Botanical Garden: Bronx, NY, USA, 1988; p. 556.
8. Bourlière, F.; Mabberley, D.J. *The Plant Book. A Portable Dictionary of the Higher Plants*; Cambridge University Press: Cambridge, UK, 1987.
9. Benjilali, B.; Hammoumi, M.; M'Hamedi, A.; Richard, H. Essential oil composition of different Moroccan thyme varieties. 2. Principal component analysis. *Sci. Des Aliment.* **1987**, *7*, 275–299.
10. Guesmi, F.; Prasad, S.; Ben Ali, M.; Ismail, I.A.; Landoulsi, A. *Thymus hirtus* sp. algeriensis Boiss. and Reut. volatile oil enhances TRAIL/Apo2L induced apoptosis and inhibits colon carcinogenesis through upregulation of death receptor pathway. *Aging* **2021**, *13*, 21975–21990. [CrossRef]
11. Guesmi, F.; Khantouche, L.; Mehrez, A.; Bellamine, H.; Landoulsi, A. Histopathological and biochemical effects of thyme essential oil on H_2O_2 stress in heart tissues. *Heart Lung Circ.* **2020**, *29*, 308–314. [CrossRef]
12. Bukvicki, D.; Giweli, A.; Stojkovic, D.; Vujisic, L.; Tesevic, V.; Nikolic, M.; Sokovic, M.; Marin, P.D. Short communication: Cheese supplemented with *Thymus algeriensis* oil, a potential natural food preservative. *J. Dairy Sci.* **2018**, *101*, 3859–3865. [CrossRef]
13. Zairi, A.; Nouir, S.; Khalifa, M.A.; Ouni, B.; Haddad, H.; Khelifa, A.; Achour, L.; Trabelsi, M. Phytochemical analysis and assessment of biological properties of essential oils obtained from Thyme and Rosmarinus species. *Curr. Pharm. Biotechnol.* **2020**, *21*, 414–424. [CrossRef]
14. Fatma, G.; Sami, B.H.A.; Ahmed, L. Investigation of extracts from Tunisian ethnomedicinal plants as antioxidants, cytotoxins, and antimicrobials. *Biomed. Environ. Sci.* **2017**, *30*, 811–824.
15. Ouakouak, H.; Benarfa, A.; Messaoudi, M.; Begaa, S.; Sawicka, B.; Benchikha, N.; Simal-Gandara, J. Biological properties of essential oils from *Thymus algeriensis* Boiss. *Plants* **2021**, *10*, 786. [CrossRef] [PubMed]
16. Zouari, N.; Ayadi, I.; Fakhfakh, N.; Rebai, A.; Zouari, S. Variation of chemical composition of essential oils in wild populations of *Thymus algeriensis* Boiss. et Reut., a North African endemic Species. *Lipids Health Dis.* **2012**, *11*, 28. [CrossRef]
17. Maissa, B.J.; Walid, H. Antifungal activity of chemically different essential oils from wild Tunisian *Thymus* spp. *Nat. Prod. Res.* **2015**, *29*, 869–873. [CrossRef]
18. Guesmi, F.; Ben Ali, M.; Barkaoui, T.; Tahri, W.; Mejri, M.; Ben-Attia, M.; Bellamine, H.; Landoulsi, A. Effects of *Thymus hirtus* sp. algeriensis Boiss. et Reut. (Lamiaceae) essential oil on healing gastric ulcers according to sex. *Lipids Health Dis.* **2014**, *13*, 138. [CrossRef] [PubMed]

19. Ait-Ouazzou, A.; Lorán, S.; Bakkali, M.; Laglaoui, A.; Rota, C.; Herrera, A.; Pagán, R.; Conchello, P. Chemical composition and antimicrobial activity of essential oils of *Thymus algeriensis*, *Eucalyptus globulus* and *Rosmarinus officinalis* from Morocco. *J. Sci. Food Agric.* **2011**, *91*, 2643–2651. [CrossRef]
20. Ahmed, S.B.H.; Sghaier, R.; Guesmi, F.; Kaabi, B.; Mejri, M.; Attia, H.; Laouini, D.; Smaali, I. Evaluation of antileishmanial, cytotoxic and antioxidant activities of essential oils extracted from plants issued from the leishmaniasis-endemic region of Sned (Tunisia). *Nat. Prod. Res.* **2011**, *25*, 1195–1201. [CrossRef]
21. Rezq, S.; Alsemeh, A.E.; D'elia, L.; El-Shazly, A.M.; Monti, D.M.; Sobeh, M.; Mahmoud, M.F. *Thymus algeriensis* and *Thymus fontanesii* exert neuroprotective effect against chronic constriction injury-induced neuropathic pain in rats. *Sci. Rep.* **2020**, *10*, 20559. [CrossRef]
22. Sobeh, M.; Rezq, S.; Cheurfa, M.; Abdelfattah, M.A.; Rashied, R.M.; El-Shazly, A.M.; Yasri, A.; Wink, M.; Mahmoud, M.F. *Thymus algeriensis* and *Thymus fontanesii*: Chemical Composition, in vivo antiinflammatory, pain killing and antipyretic activities: A comprehensive comparison. *Biomolecules* **2020**, *10*, 599. [CrossRef]
23. Guesmi, F.; Bellamine, H.; Landoulsi, A. H_2O_2-Induced Oxidative Stress, AChE inhibition and mediated brain injury attenuated by *Thymus algeriensis*. *Appl. Physiol. Nutr. Metab.* **2018**, *43*, 12. [CrossRef] [PubMed]
24. Kouache, B.; Brada, M.; Saadi, A.; Fauconnier, M.L.; Lognay, G.; Heuskin, S. Chemical composition and acaricidal activity of *Thymus algeriensis* essential oil against *Varroa destructor*. *Nat. Prod. Commun.* **2017**, *12*, 135–138. [CrossRef] [PubMed]
25. Guesmi, F.; Tyagi, A.K.; Bellamine, H.; Landoulsi, A. Antioxidant machinery related to decreased MDA generation by *Thymus algeriensis* essential oil-induced liver and kidney regeneration. *Biomed. Environ. Sci.* **2016**, *29*, 639–649.
26. Guesmi, F.; Beghalem, H.; Tyagi, A.K.; Ben Ali, M.; Ben Mouhoub, R.; Bellamine, H.; Landoulsi, A. Prevention of H_2O_2 induced oxidative damages of rat testis by *Thymus algeriensis*. *Biomed. Environ. Sci.* **2016**, *29*, 275–285. [CrossRef]
27. Fatma, G.; Mouna, B.F.; Mondher, M.; Ahmed, L. In-vitro assessment of antioxidant and antimicrobial activities of methanol extracts and essential oil of *Thymus hirtus* sp. algeriensis. *Lipids Health Dis.* **2014**, *13*, 114. [CrossRef]
28. Jayari, A.; Donsì, F.; Ferrari, G.; Maaroufi, A. Nanoencapsulation of thyme essential oils: Formulation, characterization, storage stability, and biological activity. *Foods* **2022**, *11*, 1858. [CrossRef] [PubMed]
29. Nedjimi, B. Trace element quantification in two algerian thymes (*Thymus algeriensis* Boiss & Reut. and *Thymus capitatus* (L.) Hoffm. & Link) using EDXRF spectrometry. *Biol. Trace Element Res.* **2022**, *201*, 455–463. [CrossRef]
30. El Ouahdani, K.; Es-Safi, I.; Mechchate, H.; Al-Zahrani, M.; Qurtam, A.A.; Aleissa, M.; Bari, A.; Bousta, D. *Thymus algeriensis* and Artemisia herba-alba essential oils: Chemical analysis, antioxidant potential and in vivo anti-inflammatory, analgesic activities, and acute toxicity. *Molecules* **2021**, *26*, 6780. [CrossRef]
31. Rezzoug, M.; Bakchiche, B.; Gherib, A.; Roberta, A.; Guido, F.; Kilinçarslan, Ö.; Mammadov, R.; Bardaweel, S.K. Chemical composition and bioactivity of essential oils and Ethanolic extracts of *Ocimum basilicum* L. and *Thymus algeriensis* Boiss. & Reut. from the Algerian Saharan Atlas. *BMC Complement. Altern. Med.* **2019**, *19*, 146. [CrossRef]
32. Mahdi, I.; Ben Bakrim, W.; Bitchagno, G.T.M.; Annaz, H.; Mahmoud, M.F.; Sobeh, M. Unraveling the phytochemistry, traditional uses, and biological and pharmacological activities of *Thymus algeriensis* Boiss. & Reut. *Oxidative Med. Cell. Longev.* **2022**, *2022*, 6487430. [CrossRef]
33. Bouafia, M.; Amamou, F.; Gherib, M.; Benaissa, M.; Azzi, R.; Nemmiche, S. Ethnobotanical and ethnomedicinal analysis of wild medicinal plants traditionally used in Naâma, southwest Algeria. *Vegetos* **2021**, *34*, 654–662. [CrossRef] [PubMed]
34. Righi, N.; Boumerfeg, S.; Fernandes, P.A.; Deghima, A.; Baali, F.; Coelho, E.; Cardoso, S.M.; Coimbra, M.A.; Baghiani, A. *Thymus algeriensis* Bioss & Reut: Relationship of phenolic compounds composition with in vitro/in vivo antioxidant and antibacterial activity. *Food Res. Int.* **2020**, *136*, 109500. [CrossRef] [PubMed]
35. Jaouadi, R.; Silva, A.M.S.; Boussaid, M.; Yahia, I.B.H.; Cardoso, S.M.; Zaouali, Y. Differentiation of phenolic composition among *Tunisian thymus* algeriensis boiss. Et reut.(lamiaceae) populations: Correlation to bioactive activities. *Antioxidants* **2019**, *8*, 515. [CrossRef]
36. Ziani, B.E.; Heleno, S.A.; Bachari, K.; Dias, M.I.; Alves, M.J.; Barros, L.; Ferreira, I.C.F.R. Phenolic compounds characterization by LC-DAD-ESI/MSn and bioactive properties of *Thymus algeriensis* Boiss. & Reut. and *Ephedra alata* Decne. *Food Res. Int.* **2019**, *116*, 312–319.
37. Zairi, A.; Nouir, S.; M'hamdi, N.; Bennani, M.; Bergaoui, I.; Mtiraoui, A.; Chaouachi, M.; Trabelsi, M. Antioxidant, antimicrobial and the phenolic content of infusion, decoction and methanolic extracts of Thyme and Rosmarinus species. *Curr. Pharm. Biotechnol.* **2018**, *19*, 590–599. [CrossRef]
38. Boutaoui, N.; Zaiter, L.; Benayache, F.; Benayache, S.; Carradori, S.; Cesa, S.; Giusti, A.M.; Campestre, C.; Menghini, L.; Innosa, D.; et al. Qualitative and quantitative phytochemical analysis of different extracts from *Thymus algeriensis* aerial parts. *Molecules* **2018**, *23*, 463. [CrossRef]
39. Herowati, R.; Widodo, G.P. *Molecular Docking Analysis: Interaction Studies of Natural Compounds to Anti-Inflammatory Targets Quantitative Structure-Activity Relationship*; IntechOpen: Rijeka, Croatia, 2017. [CrossRef]

40. Thamaraiselvi, L.; Selvankumar, T.; Wesely, E.; Kumar, N.V. In-silico molecular docking analysis of some plant derived molecules for anti-inflammatory inhibitory activity. *Curr. Bot.* **2021**, *12*, 22–27. [CrossRef]
41. Zhang, Q.; Li, X.; Li, J.; Hu, Y.; Liu, J.; Wang, F.; Zhang, W.; Chang, F. Mechanism of anti-inflammatory and antibacterial effects of QingXiaoWuWei decoction based on network pharmacology, molecular docking and in vitro experiments. *Front. Pharmacol.* **2021**, *12*, 678685. [CrossRef]
42. Laloo, D.; Kalita, J.M.; Prasad, S.K. Molecular docking studies of plant-derived bioactive compounds: A comprehensive in silico standardization approach. In *Evidence Based Validation of Traditional Medicines: A Comprehensive Approach*; Springer: Singapore, 2021; pp. 371–404.
43. Brown, J.H.; Mackey, H.K.; Riggilo, D.A. A novel in vitro assay for anti-inflammatory agents based on stabilization of erythrocytes. *Exp. Biol. Med.* **1967**, *125*, 837–843. [CrossRef]
44. Trovato, A.; Raneri, E.; Kouladis, M.; Tzakou, O.; Taviano, M.F.; Galati, E.M. Anti-inflammatory and analgesic activity of *Hypericum empetrifolium* Willd. (Guttiferae). *Il Farm.* **2001**, *56*, 455–457. [CrossRef]
45. Wang, J.L.; Limburg, D.; Graneto, M.J.; Springer, J.; Hamper, J.R.B.; Liao, S.; Pawlitz, J.L.; Kurumbail, R.G.; Maziasz, T.; Talley, J.J.; et al. The novel benzopyran class of selective cyclooxygenase-2 inhibitors. Part 2: The second clinical candidate having a shorter and favorable human half-life. *Bioorganic Med. Chem. Lett.* **2010**, *20*, 7159–7163. [CrossRef] [PubMed]
46. Trott, O.; Olson, A.J. AutoDock Vina: Improving the speed and accuracy of docking with a new scoring function, efficient optimization, and multithreading. *J. Comput. Chem.* **2010**, *31*, 455–461. [CrossRef] [PubMed]
47. Chou, C.-T. The Antiinflammatory Effect of an Extract of *Tripterygium wilfordii* Hook F on Adjuvant-induced Paw Oedema in Rats and Inflammatory Mediators Release. *Phytotherapy Res.* **1997**, *11*, 152–154. [CrossRef]
48. Murugesh, N.; Vembar, S.; Damodaran, C. Studies on erythrocyte membrane IV: In vitro haemolytic activity of oleander extract. *Toxicol. Lett.* **1981**, *8*, 33–38. [CrossRef]
49. David, S. Studies force new view on biology of flavonoids. *Biol. Med.* **2007**, *541*, 737–787.
50. González-Gallego, J.; García-Mediavilla, M.V.; Sánchez-Campos, S.; Tuñón, M.J. Fruit polyphenols, immunity and inflammation. *Br. J. Nutr.* **2010**, *104*, S15–S27. [CrossRef]
51. Rosa, M.D.; Willoughby, D. Screens for anti-inflammatory drugs. *J. Pharm. Pharmacol.* **1971**, *23*, 297–298. [CrossRef]
52. Salvemini, D.; Wang, Z.-Q.; Bourdon, D.M.; Stern, M.K.; Currie, M.G.; Manning, P.T. Evidence of peroxynitrite involvement in the carrageenan-induced rat paw edema. *Eur. J. Pharmacol.* **1996**, *303*, 217–220. [CrossRef]
53. Rayego-Mateos, S.; Morgado-Pascual, J.L.; Opazo-Ríos, L.; Guerrero-Hue, M.; García-Caballero, C.; Vázquez-Carballo, C.; Mas, S.; Sanz, A.B.; Herencia, C.; Mezzano, S.; et al. Pathogenic pathways and therapeutic approaches targeting inflammation in diabetic nephropathy. *Int. J. Mol. Sci.* **2020**, *21*, 3798. [CrossRef]
54. Morris, C.J. Carrageenan-induced paw edema in the rat and mouse. *Methods Mol. Biol.* **2003**, *225*, 115–121. [CrossRef]
55. Tai, F.W.D.; McAlindon, M.E. Non-steroidal anti-inflammatory drugs and the gastrointestinal tract. *Clin. Med.* **2021**, *21*, 131–134. [CrossRef]
56. Srivastava, S.; Singh, P.; Jha, K.K.; Mishra, G.; Srivastava, S.; Khosa, R.L. Antiinflammatory, analgesic and antipyretic activities of aerial parts of *Costus speciosus* Koen. *Indian J. Pharm. Sci.* **2013**, *75*, 83.
57. Silva, G.N.; Martins, F.R.; Matheus, M.E.; Leitão, S.G.; Fernandes, P.D. Investigation of anti-inflammatory and antinociceptive activities of *Lantana trifolia*. *J. Ethnopharmacol.* **2005**, *100*, 254–259. [CrossRef] [PubMed]
58. Kumar, S.; Kumar, S. Molecular docking: A structure-based approach for drug repurposing. In *In Silico Drug Design*; Elsevier: Amsterdam, The Netherlands, 2019; pp. 161–189.
59. Cheng, Y.-C.; Prusoff, W.H. Relationship between the inhibition constant (KI) and the concentration of inhibitor which causes 50 per cent inhibition (I_{50}) of an enzymatic reaction. *Biochem. Pharmacol.* **1973**, *22*, 3099–3108. [CrossRef] [PubMed]
60. Salentin, S.; Schreiber, S.; Haupt, V.J.; Adasme, M.F.; Schroeder, M. PLIP: Fully automated protein–ligand interaction profiler. *Nucleic Acids Res.* **2015**, *43*, W443–W447. [CrossRef] [PubMed]
61. Stojanovic, S.D.; Zaric, S.D. Hydrogen bonds and hydrophobic interactions of porphyrins in porphyrin-containing proteins. *Open Struct. Biol. J.* **2009**, *3*, 34–41. [CrossRef]
62. Omoboyowa, D.A.; Balogun, T.A.; Omomule, O.M.; Saibu, O.A. Identification of terpenoids from *Abrus precatorius* against parkinson's disease proteins using in silico approach. *Bioinform. Biol. Insights* **2021**, *15*, 11779322211050757. [CrossRef]
63. Mohapatra, S.; Prasad, A.; Haque, F.; Ray, S.; De, B.; Ray, S.S. *In silico* investigation of black tea components on α-amylase, α-glucosidase and lipase. *J. Appl. Pharm. Sci.* **2015**, *5*, 42–47. [CrossRef]

International Journal of *Molecular Sciences*

MDPI

Review

Menthol in Livestock: Unveiling Its Multifaceted Properties and Future Potential for Sustainable Agriculture

Brandon Bernard [1], Himani Joshi [2] and Peixin Fan [2,3,*]

[1] Department of Biochemistry, Nutrition & Health Promotion, College of Agriculture and Life Sciences, Mississippi State University, Starkville, MS 39762, USA; bb2842@msstate.edu

[2] Department of Animal and Dairy Sciences, College of Agriculture and Life Sciences, Mississippi State University, Starkville, MS 39762, USA; hj532@msstate.edu

[3] Institute for Genomics, Biocomputing & Biotechnology, Mississippi State University, Starkville, MS 39762, USA

* Correspondence: pf324@msstate.edu

Abstract: Menthol, the primary active compound in the widely cultivated peppermint plant (*Mentha piperita*), is well known for its use in human products such as topical analgesics and cold remedies. Menthol's cooling sensation and ability to locally modulate pain through interactions with transient receptor potential channels make it a valuable bioactive compound. In recent years, menthol's antimicrobial, anti-inflammatory, and antioxidative properties have drawn attention in the livestock industry as a natural alternative to synthetic antibiotics in feed additives. This review comprehensively examines the existing literature to assess menthol's effects on animal growth performance, product quality, immune function, gastrointestinal microbial ecosystems, and metabolism across various livestock species. Notably, menthol shows potential for improving feed efficiency, mitigating chronic inflammation and oxidative stress, inhibiting environmental and gastrointestinal pathogens, and enhancing calcium absorption. However, optimal dosages, treatment durations, synergies with other phytogenic compounds, and regulatory mechanisms require further investigation. Additionally, with increasing global temperatures and growing concerns about animal welfare, menthol's cooling, methane-reducing, and analgesic properties present promising opportunities for advancing sustainable livestock practices.

Keywords: menthol; peppermint; livestock; metabolism; microbiota; transient receptor potential channels

1. Introduction

Menthol is a widely used phytogenic (plant-derived) compound and the principal component of various mint species, including *Mentha arvensis*, *Mentha canadensis*, *Mentha aquatica*, and *Mentha piperita* [1,2]. *Mentha piperita* (*M. piperita*), commonly known as peppermint, is an especially popular hybrid species cultivated worldwide for use in a variety of consumer products [2]. The popularity of *M. piperita* largely stems from its high levels of menthol relative to other species. In addition to natural sources in Mentha species, menthol can also be synthesized chemically at a cost-effective rate (USD 0.2/g for chemical grade; USD 0.1/g for food grade). Worldwide production of menthol is approximately 34,000 metric tons per year, with synthetic menthol accounting for about 60% of this total [3]. Most famously, menthol is capable of exerting potent cooling and analgesic sensations, which are utilized in products such as muscle cooling gels for athletes and cough drops. It exerts potent antimicrobial activity [4–7], as well as possessing anti-inflammatory and antioxidant properties [5,8–12]. Controversially, these properties are exploited in menthol cigarettes, where menthol reduces irritation caused by smoke inhalation [13]. Furthermore, menthol and peppermint have been found to influence appetite and salivation, leading to their common use in gum and candies [14–17].

While menthol has traditionally played a role in a wide array of human-directed applications, it has also received attention for use in livestock such as poultry and ruminants in recent years. Menthol holds several potential uses for increasing the efficiency of livestock production as well as improving animal welfare. Its appetite-modulating properties could contribute to improving animal growth performance and product yields. Menthol also possesses antimicrobial effects that may present a viable alternative to traditional antibiotics, which face increasing regulatory restrictions in livestock production due to rising antimicrobial resistance [18,19]. Through this antimicrobial action, menthol can additionally regulate nutrient digestion and methane emissions by influencing gastrointestinal microbiota [20,21]. Given that ruminants heavily rely on their gastrointestinal microbiota for digestive function, menthol-induced alterations in these microbes could alter the entire metabolic profile of the animal. Furthermore, when combined with other interventions, menthol's cooling properties hold the potential for mitigating heat stress, a challenge increasingly facing livestock production [22,23]. In recent years, the study of phytogenic feed additives in livestock production has become widespread [24–26]. However, despite the well-documented biochemical properties of menthol, research on peppermint and other menthol-containing products in livestock contexts remains limited, with studies utilizing pure menthol being even more scarce. This review systematically summarizes current literature that investigates the effects of menthol and other menthol-rich compounds in livestock and provides insight for future directions of study (Figure 1).

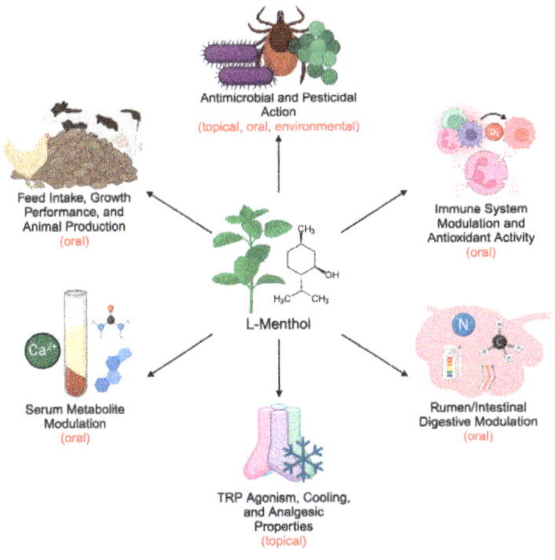

Figure 1. Effects of menthol and menthol-containing compounds such as peppermint oil in humans, livestock, and other animals. Effects of oral supplementation in livestock include regulation of feeding behaviors, increased feed efficiency, and improved milk, meat, and egg production. Oral and topical administration regulates levels of immune cells, immunoglobulins, pro-inflammatory cytokines, and reactive oxygen species, as well as facilitating antibacterial and pesticidal action. Antibacterial action results in modified digestive performance and production of microbial metabolites, such as methane and short-chain fatty acids, in the gastrointestinal tract. Changes in feeding and digestion subsequently affect concentrations of serum parameters, such as glucose, cholesterol, fatty acids, and urea. Additionally, transient receptor potential (TRP) channel agonism increases absorption of cations such as Ca^{2+} and ammonium. In human and mouse models, TRP channel agonism produces cooling and analgesic sensations. This figure was created using BioRender.

2. Physical, Chemical, and Biological Properties of Menthol

Menthol is classified as a monocyclic monoterpene, a molecule derived from two isoprene units [27]. Menthol forms a characteristic solid, white, crystalline form at room temperature and is sparingly water soluble [1]. There are four optical isomers of menthol; however, L-menthol is the most common form found in nature and the most studied for its biological effects. The Food and Drug Administration (FDA) classifies menthol as Generally Recognized as Safe (GRAS) [28]. When ingested, menthol is readily absorbed in the intestines, where it is quickly transported to the liver, glucuronidated to menthol glucuronide, and largely excreted in urine [29]. Several metabolites of menthol have been identified beyond menthol glucuronide, including oxidated, hydroxylated, and sulfated products. Prominent menthol metabolites found in urine include 3,8-dihydroxy-p-menthane-7-carboxylic acid and p-Menthane-3,8-diol. These metabolites are largely considered inert and nontoxic, though most are understudied [29,30]. However, before absorption and metabolism, menthol holds the potential to exert gastroprotective effects [8]. Menthol's antimicrobial activity is partly attributed to its ability to disrupt the lipid membrane of microbial cells [31]. Additionally, menthol's hydroxyl groups allow for reactive oxygen species scavenging and antioxidant activity [8,12,32].

Among menthol's most renowned biological effects is its ability to induce a cooling and pain-relieving sensation, achieved through the activation of transient receptor potential (TRP) cation channels, primarily TRP melastatin 8 (TRPM8), a Ca^{2+} channel [33]. TRPM8 is expressed primarily on the afferent (sensory) neurons of the vagus nerve, the spinal nerve, and the trigeminal nerve [34–36], which are integral pathways for transmitting sensory signals to the central nervous system. Menthol, particularly at concentrations of 60–120 μM in vivo, binds to and activates TRPM8, triggering a cold sensation typically perceived at temperatures below 15 °C [37,38]. The activation of TRPM8 leads to calcium influx, which generates neuronal signals perceived as cold by the brain and spinal cord [37,39,40]. Another TRP channel, TRP vanilloid 1 (TRPV1), is activated by temperatures above 43 °C and plays a key role in detecting noxious heat, which can trigger the burning pain sensation, and is also involved in inflammatory responses [37,38]. Menthol in higher concentrations of 5 mM in vivo and 10 mM in vitro can directly inhibit the activity of TRPV1 channels by eliciting inhibition to the inflammatory response due to reduced Ca^{2+} influx [41]. This modulates the level of pain perception, leading to pain relief [37,38,41–43] (Figure 2). TRPA1, which detects extreme cold (<8 °C) and irritants, is also co-activated through activation of TRPV1 channels, leading to cold hypersensitivity [40,44,45]. High concentrations of menthol (0.3%) can also activate the TRPA1 receptor, leading to greater irritation and nociception [40,41,44,45]. Interestingly, TRPM8, TRPV1, and TRPA1 are co-expressed in certain afferent neurons, enabling the sensation of both cold and hot stimuli, which explains phenomena like paradoxical cold-induced burning pain [33,39,40,45].

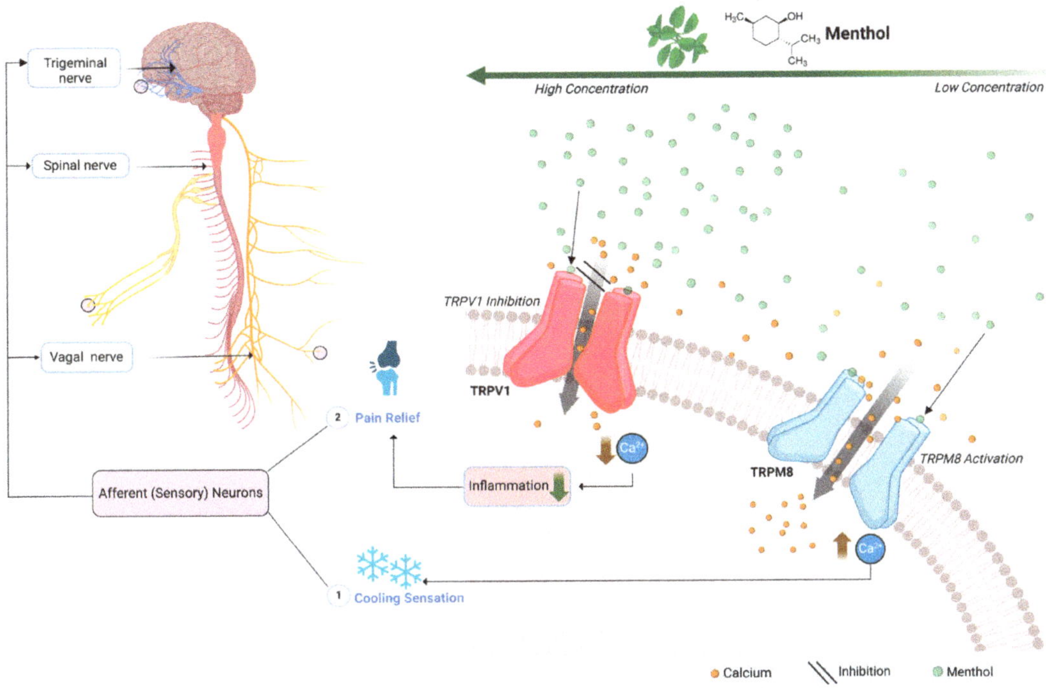

Figure 2. Menthol induces cooling and pain relief by modulating TRP ion channels. At concentrations of 60–120 μM in vivo, menthol binds to and activates TRPM8, a cold-sensitive ion channel expressed on sensory neurons of the vagal, spinal, and trigeminal nerves. This triggers calcium influx, generating neuronal signals perceived as cooling (<15 °C). At higher concentrations (>10 mM in vitro, 5 mM in vivo), menthol inhibits TRPV1, reducing Ca^{2+} influx and suppressing inflammatory responses and thereby modulating pain perception, leading to pain relief. This figure was created using BioRender.

3. Impact of Menthol and Menthol-Rich Supplements on Feed Intake, Growth Performance, and Animal Production

In the livestock industry, maintaining feed intake and optimizing product yield (meat, milk, eggs) are key priorities. While research on menthol and peppermint's effects is substantial, most studies focus on menthol-containing compounds or peppermint as feed additives, with limited investigation into pure menthol as a supplement (Table 1).

Table 1. Impact of menthol and menthol-rich supplements on feed intake, growth performance, and animal production.

Animal	Growth Stage/Condition [1]	Sample Size [2]	Treatment	Dosage [3]	Experiment Duration	Effects of Treatment [4]	Reference
Holstein Cattle	nonlactating, subacute ruminal acidosis conditions	4 CON, 4 per TRT (4 × 4 incomplete Latin square)	Mint or Menthol	T1: 15.3 mg Mnt/kg T2: 153 mg Mnt/kg T3: 6.7 mg Mthl/kg T4: 67 mg Mthl/kg	4 h of supplement	Tendency towards a linear decrease in feed intake from mint, tendency towards a linear increase in feeding time from menthol.	[46]
Holstein Cattle	nonlactating	4 CON, 4 per TRT (4 × 4 incomplete Latin square)	Mint or Menthol	T1: 15.3 mg Mnt/kg T2: 153 mg Mnt/kg T3: 6.7 mg Mthl/kg T4: 67 mg Mthl/kg	4 h of supplement	Increased salivation rate.	[47]
Friesian Cattle	lactating	10 CON, 10 per TRT	Aromix® (133 mg menthol/g)	T1: 3 g/day T2: 6 g/day	3 months	Increased feed intake, milk yield, and milk contents with T1; decrease in same parameters with T2.	[48]
Holstein Cattle	lactating, heat stress conditions	16 CON, 16 TRT	BioHerbal® (contains peppermint)	2 g/day	28 days	Increased feed intake, increased milk yield.	[49]
Holstein–Friesian Cattle	lactating	36 CON, 36 TRT	BTX12 (>80% menthol)	1.2 g/day	Two periods of 20 days	No effect on feed intake, increased milk yield.	[50]
Friesian Cattle	lactating	10 CON, 10 per TRT	Aromix® (133 mg menthol/g)	T1: 3 g/day T2: 6 g/day	3 months	No effect on feed intake, increased milk yield with T1.	[51]
Holstein Cattle	lactating	4 CON, 4 TRT	Peppermint	5%	22 days	Increased feeding time, no effect on feed intake, no effect on milk yield or quality.	[52,53]

Table 1. *Cont.*

Animal	Growth Stage/Condition [1]	Sample Size [2]	Treatment	Dosage [3]	Experiment Duration	Effects of Treatment [4]	Reference
Holstein Cattle	NA	4 CON, 4 TRT (4×4 Latin square)	Peppermint	5%	2 weeks	Increased feed intake.	[54]
Suffolk Sheep	growing	8 CON, 8 per TRT	OAX17 (90% menthol)	T1: 80 mg/day T2: 160 mg/day	28 days	Increased feed intake and feeding time, no effect on body weight.	[55,56]
Sanjabi Sheep	90 days old	6 CON, 6 TRT	Peppermint	3%	90 days	Increased feed intake, no effect on FCR.	[57]
Murrah Buffalo	NA	2 CON, 2 TRT (2×2 switch over)	Garlic Bulb + Peppermint	2.5%	Two periods of 21 days	No effect on feed intake.	[58]
Ross 308 Chickens	1 day old	96 CON, 48 per TRT	Peppermint or Menthol	T1: 5 g Pep/kg T2: 10 g Pep/kg T3: 15 g Pep/kg T4: 26 mg Mthl/kg T5: 52 mg Mthl/kg T6: 78 mg Mthl/kg	Two periods of 35 days	Increased feed intake and body weight, improved FCR, decreased abdominal fat.	[59]
Chickens	18 week old laying hens	20K CON, 20K TRT	Digestarom® (contains menthol)	150 g/t	12 weeks	Decreased mortality and dirty eggs.	[60]
Hubbard Chickens	1 day old	50 CON, 50 per TRT	Phytogenic Blend (garlic, mint, etc.) or Blend + Organic Acids	T1: 3 kg phytogenic blend/ton T2: 3 kg phytogenic blend/ton + organic acids	42 days	Increased feed intake, increased body weight, improved FCR.	[61]
Cobb 500 Chickens	1 day old males	Trial 1: 160 CON, 160 TRT; Trial 2: 40 CON, 40 TRT	Phytogenic Blend (menthol, anethole)	150 mg/kg	Trial 1: 42 days Trial 2: 21 days	No effect on feed intake, body weight, or FCR.	[62]

Table 1. *Cont.*

Animal	Growth Stage/Condition [1]	Sample Size [2]	Treatment	Dosage [3]	Experiment Duration	Effects of Treatment [4]	Reference
Cobb Chickens	1 day old	75 CON, 75 per TRT	Phytogenic Blend (menthol, anethol, and eugenol)	T1: 100 mg/kg T2: 150 mg/kg	42 days	No effect on feed intake, improved FCR.	[63]
Ross 308 Chickens	1 day old	60 CON, 60 per TRT	Phytogenic Blend (ziziphora, oregano, peppermint)	T1: 1% ziziphora, 0.5% others T2: 1% oregano, 0.5% others T3: 1% Pep, 0.5% others	42 days	Decreased feed intake, no change in body weight, improved FCR, and no change to carcass traits with T3. Other groups saw improvements in parameters.	[64]
Hy-Line Brown Chickens	64 week old laying hens	50 CON, 50 per TRT	Peppermint	T1: 5 mg/kg T2: 10 mg/kg T3: 15 mg/kg T4: 20 mg/kg	12 weeks	Increased feed intake, improved FCR, increased egg rate, weight, and Haugh score.	[65]
Hubbard Chickens	1 day old	40 CON, 40 per TRT	Peppermint	T1: 0.25% T2: 0.5% T3: 1% T4: 1.5%	6 weeks	Increased feed intake, increased body weight, improved FCR.	[66]
Chickens	1 week old	104 CON, 104 TRT	Peppermint	0.2% (~70 mg/kg Mthl)	42 days	No effect on feed intake, increased abdominal fat.	[67]
Ross 308 Chickens	240 days old	48 CON, 48 per TRT	Peppermint	T1: 0.1% T2: 0.2% T3: 0.3% (in water)	42 days	No effect on feed intake, improved FCR, increased carcass yield, decreased abdominal fat.	[68]
Ross 308 Chickens	1 day old	48 CON, 48 per TRT	Peppermint	T1: 200 mg/kg T2: 400 mg/kg	6 weeks	No effect on feed intake, improved FCR with T1.	[69]
Chickens	1 day old	9 CON, 9 per TRT	Spearmint	T1: 0.5% T2: 1% T3: 1.5% T4: 2%	42 days	No change in final feed intake, body weight, or FCR, increased production index, decreased abdominal fat.	[70]

Table 1. *Cont.*

Animal	Growth Stage/Condition [1]	Sample Size [2]	Treatment	Dosage [3]	Experiment Duration	Effects of Treatment [4]	Reference
Chickens	1 day old, heat stress conditions	48 CON, 48 per TRT	Peppermint	T1: 1% T2: 2%	42 days	No effect on feed intake, no effect on FCR, reduced heat stress.	[71]
Habcock Chickens	21 week old laying hens	36 CON, 36 per TRT	Peppermint	T1: 50 mg/kg T2: 100 mg/kg T3: 200 mg/kg T4: 50 mg/L T5: 100 mg/L T6: 200 mg/L	56 days	No effect on feed intake, improved FCR, no effect on egg quantity/quality, affected yolk color at 28 days.	[72]
Chickens	60 week old laying hens	54 CON, 54 per TRT	Peppermint	T1: 0.1% T2: 0.2% T3: 0.3% T4: 0.4%	28 days	No effect on feed intake, increased eggshell thickness and egg saturated fatty acids.	[73]
Ross 308 Chickens	1 day old	30 CON, 30 per TRT	Peppermint	T1: 5 g/kg T2: 10 g/kg T3: 15 g/kg	35 days	Decreased feed intake and body weight with T3. No effect on FCR or carcass characteristics.	[74]
Ross 308 Chickens	1 day old	48 CON, 48 per TRT	Peppermint	T1: 4 g/kg T2: 8 g/kg	42 days	Increased body weight and improved FCR with T1, no effect on carcass.	[75]
Ross 308 Chickens	1 day old, heat stress conditions	80 CON, 80 per TRT	Peppermint	T1: 200 ppm ethanolic/kg body weight T2: 200 ppm nano-/kg body weight T3: 200 ppm micro-/kg body weight	42 days	Improved FCR, no effect on feed intake or body weight.	[76]

Table 1. *Cont.*

Animal	Growth Stage/Condition [1]	Sample Size [2]	Treatment	Dosage [3]	Experiment Duration	Effects of Treatment [4]	Reference
Bovans Brown Chickens	32 week old laying hens	40 CON, 40 per TRT	Peppermint	T1: 74 mg/kg T2: 148 mg/kg T3: 222 mg/kg T4: 296 mg/kg	12 weeks	Improved FCR, increased egg production, weight, shell thickness, and Haugh score.	[77]
Lohmann LSL-Lite Chickens	40 week old laying hens, cold stress conditions	30 CON, 30 per TRT	Peppermint or Peppermint + Thyme	T1: 100 mg/kg diet Pep T2: 100 mg/kg diet Pep + thyme	8 weeks	Increased feed intake, improved FCR from combined, increased shell thickness from combined.	[78]
ISA Brown Chickens	28 week old laying hens	24 CON, 24 per TRT	Wild Mint + Geranium	T1: 0.01% T2: 0.05% T3: 0.1%	16 weeks	Increased feed intake, increased egg production, weight, and Haugh score.	[79]
Cobb 500 Chickens	1 day old, heat stress conditions	60 CON, 60 per TRT	Peppermint or Peppermint + Chromium Picolinate	T1: 250 mg Pep/kg T2: 250 mg Pep/kg + chromium picolinate	42 days	No effect on feed intake or body weight, improved FCR with T2.	[80]
Japanese Quail	8 days old	120 CON, 60 per TRT	Peppermint	T1: 10 g/kg T2: 20 g/kg T3: 30 g/kg T4: 40 g/kg	5 weeks	Decreased MDA, cooking loss, and drip loss.	[81]

[1] NA: Not available/not applicable. [2] CON: Control group, TRT: Treatment group. [3] T: Treatment group number, Mthl: Menthol, Pep: Peppermint, Mnt: Mint. [4] FCR: Feed conversion ratio, MDA: Malondialdehyde.

3.1. Feed Intake and Feeding Behavior

The effect of menthol or menthol-containing feed additives on feed intake has been investigated in cattle. In lactating cattle, supplementation with 3 g/day of the menthol-containing blend Aromix® (Masa Egypt Company, Alexandria, Egypt) (133 mg/g) increased lactating cattle's feed intake from 13.4 to 13.8 kg/day, but a higher dose of 6 g/day reduced the intake to 13.0 kg/day [48]. Other cattle studies also reported increased feed intake after supplementation with peppermint [54] or the peppermint-containing supplement BioHerbal® (Pars-Imen-Daru Herbal Medicines Development Co., Tehran, Iran) [49]. In sheep, feed intake improved after supplementation with peppermint [57] and OAX17 (PerformaNat GmbH, Berlin, Germany), a commercial blend comprising about 90% menthol [55,56]. However, several studies reported no significant changes in feed intake after menthol or menthol-containing compound supplementation, including nonlactating Holstein cattle fed with 6.7–67 mg per kg of pure menthol [46], lactating Friesian and Holstein cattle supplemented with 5% peppermint or 1.2 to 6 g/day of menthol-containing commercial supplements [50–52], and male Murrah buffalos supplemented with 2.5% garlic bulb and peppermint over 21 day periods [58].

In poultry, feed intake increased after newborn Ross 308 chickens were supplemented with 26–78 mg/kg of pure menthol during two separate 35 day trial periods [59]. Significant increases in feed intake after mint feeding were observed in a variety of life stages, from 1-day-old chicks to 64-week-old laying hens [61,65,66,78,79]. In contrast, no changes to feed intake were found in most other studies, which supplemented chickens of various life stages with peppermint [62,67–73] or 100–150 mg of a phytogenic blend of menthol, anethol, and eugenol per kg [63]. Narimani et al. even reported a decrease in average feed intake from 160.19 g/d to 147.6 g/d in young chickens fed a blend of 1% peppermint, 0.5% oregano, and 0.5% ziziphora for 42 days [64]. A different study similarly observed a decrease in feed intake in young chickens at 15 g/kg of peppermint supplementation, but not at lower concentrations [74]. These inconsistencies suggest that menthol's effects are dosage-dependent and may be influenced by mixed phytogenic compounds.

Menthol compounds also influence feeding behavior in ruminants. After 6.7–67 mg/kg menthol supplementation, the average feeding time of cattle tended to increase from 39.8 min to 47.2 min [46], and short-term increases in salivation rate were detected [47]. Similar results persist with impure supplements. In a 4-week study using Suffolk sheep, a linear increase in feeding time and frequency was reported after supplementation with 80–160 g/day of OAX17 [55]. Lactating Holstein cattle had an increased feeding time after being supplemented with peppermint at 5% of their diet for 22 days [52]. The potential mechanism of menthol effects on increasing feeding time could be attributed to its reduction in the palatability of the feed and stimulation of TRP channels, with TRPM8 potentially modulating feed intake [52,55].

3.2. Growth Performance and Animal Production

As with increased feed intake, improvement of body weight in young chickens fed menthol was reported [59], and some studies also observed improved weight gain after supplementation with menthol-containing compounds [61,66,75]. However, several other studies found no significant changes to the body weight of sheep [56] or chickens [62,64,70,76,80]. Additionally, Gurbuz and Ismael found that the average chicken body weight decreased over a 35-day trial, with an average of 2413 g for the control group compared to 2178 g for birds supplemented with 15 g of peppermint per kg of feed [74]. This corresponds with their observed decrease in feed intake after peppermint supplementation.

While the effects of menthol on feed intake varied, and few studies observed changes in body weight, evidence for improvements in the feed conversion ratio (FCR) is far more consistent. Pure menthol supplementation at 26–78 mg/kg of feed during the first 21 days of life improved the average chicken FCR [59]. Many other poultry studies at varying life stages also observed FCR improvements after supplementation with peppermint [65,66,68,72,75–78,80] or a combination of compounds including peppermint, menthol, anethol, oregano, etc. [61,63,64]. However, several studies on young chickens reported no difference in chicken FCRs [62,70,71,74]. Khodambashi Emami et al. observed improvements in the FCR of chickens supplemented with 200 mg of peppermint/kg of feed but not when increased to 400 mg/kg, further suggesting the dose-dependent effectiveness of menthol on feed efficiency and growth performance [69]. However, sheep supplemented with 3% peppermint for 90 days showed no FCR improvement [57]. The mechanisms behind improvements in FCRs are not entirely clear, but several studies suggest the antimicrobial and antioxidant qualities of menthol help to stabilize the gut and improve digestion, which will be discussed in detail in the following sections [59,61,71].

Menthol supplementation also led to improvements in meat, milk, and egg production. In chickens, pure menthol supplementation linearly decreased meat abdominal fat and cook loss percentage [59]. Other menthol-containing additives also reduced abdominal fat, increased carcass yield, and enhanced overall production [64,68,70]. Mehri et al. found a decrease in carcass drip loss and malondialdehyde (MDA), which contributes to meat odor and spoilage, in Japanese quail supplemented for 5 weeks with peppermint at 10–40 g/kg feed [81]. These meat-quality improvements are attributed to peppermint's antioxidant activity, which will also be discussed in detail. Other studies found no significant changes in the carcass characteristics of young chickens supplemented with peppermint [67,74,75]. Furthermore, feeding 1 week old chickens 0.2% peppermint (~70 mg menthol/kg feed) for 42 days resulted in an increase in abdominal fat [67]. The researchers attributed this to growth promotion due to the supplement, as fast growth is linked to increased fat. Chicken egg quality followed a similarly positive trend, with improvements in laying rate, cleanliness, weight, and shell thickness found after laying hens were supplemented with peppermint [60,65,73,77–79]. Rahman et al. reported minimal improvements to egg quality after peppermint supplementation up to 200 mg/kg, but improvements in egg yolk color were recorded on day 28 of a 56-day trial period [72].

Improvements in both yield and quality of milk were found after supplementing lactating cows with various commercial products containing menthol, including BTX12 (PerformaNat GmbH, Berlin, Germany) (>80% menthol), Aromix®, and BioHerbal® [48–51]. These trials ranged from 20 days to 3 months. In contrast, other studies did not observe changes in milk production after 5% peppermint supplementation for 22 days [52,53]. These results suggest that effects on milk production may only be observed over long-term supplementation periods. Additionally, commercially formulated supplement blends may be more effective for improving milk performance than peppermint alone. However, some studies reported diminished milk output at higher supplementary concentrations, suggesting menthol's antimicrobial properties may negatively affect digestion and output if not properly dosed [48,51]. There exists evidence suggesting cattle supplemented with herbs, such as oregano and caraway, may positively affect the aroma of produced milk [82]. Menthol and peppermint may confer similar attributes to the milk of supplemented dairy cows, which needs to be further explored.

These results provide strong evidence for menthol's potential to improve livestock production. However, future research is needed to better elucidate the specific mechanisms behind these effects and determine optimal feed supplementation so as to maximize beneficial biochemical effects and minimize detrimental ones.

4. Anti-Inflammation, Immune System Modulation, and Anti-Oxidation Properties of Menthol

4.1. Anti-Inflammation

Inflammation is a crucial component of the immune response, facilitating the removal of harmful stimuli and the repair of damaged tissue. It can be triggered by various stressors, including infection, heat stress, and dietary factors, which stimulate the release of pro-inflammatory cytokines, such as interleukin-6 (IL-6), IL-1β, and tumor necrosis factor-α (TNF-α) [83,84]. While inflammation is essential for immune defense and tissue recovery, excessive production of pro-inflammatory cytokines and leukocytes in response to prolonged stress can lead to chronic inflammation. In livestock, chronic inflammation has been associated with several adverse effects, including impaired growth performance and metabolic function, increased mortality, intestinal barrier dysfunction (leaky gut), reduced egg production in poultry, and decreased milk yield in dairy cows [84–86]. Menthol's anti-inflammatory properties have been extensively studied in vivo and in vitro [1,12], indicating the potential of peppermint and other menthol products to improve livestock health through the reduction of excess inflammation.

In vitro, pure menthol's ability to alleviate mastitis induced by lipopolysaccharide (LPS) challenge in bovine mammary gland epithelial cells (BMECs) was investigated [87]. Pre-treatment with 10 μM of menthol mitigated the negative effects of LPS on milk lipid and protein production in BMECs while also reducing the abundance of pro-inflammatory cytokines, including IL-6, IL-1β, and TNF-α. This effect was attributed to menthol-induced activation of the unc-51 like kinase 1 (ULK1) and nuclear factor-E2 associated factor 2 (Nrf-2) pathways, which initiate and sustain autophagy of proinflammatory cytokines and enzymes, such as cyclooxygenase-2 and inducible nitric oxide synthetase, both of which are involved in the inflammatory response [87]. Similarly, in vivo reductions in pro-inflammatory IL-18 in chickens and the inflammation marker serum amyloid A in cattle were observed after supplementation with 100–150 mg/kg of a menthol-containing blend and 0.04% Digestarom® (DSM GmbH, Grenzach-Whylen, Germany) (menthol, thymol, and eugenol), respectively [63,88]. In contrast, increases in pro-inflammatory IL-6 and TNF-α were observed in the serum of chickens supplemented with a *Mentha arvensis/Geranium thunbergii* mixture at a concentration of 0.01% of feed [79]. Overall, menthol appears to possess modulatory capabilities for the inflammatory response through reductions in pro-inflammatory mediators.

4.2. Immune System Modulation

There is also evidence that menthol influences leukocyte concentrations. In sheep, white blood cell counts significantly increased following supplementation with 30 mL of peppermint oil per kg of feed [89]. Neutrophils are significant producers of reactive oxygen species (ROS) in the immune system and serve as biomarkers for inflammation [10,90,91]. Avians such as poultry lack neutrophils but possess functionally similar heterophils [92,93]. The heterophil to lymphocyte (H/L) ratio has been demonstrated as a marker of avian health, with a lower H/L ratio indicating reduced stress and superior immune response and survival [94–97]. Thus, reducing excess neutrophil and heterophil activity is desirable for animal health. Healthy growing Suffolk sheep exhibited a significant decrease in serum neutrophils supplemented with 160 mg of OAX17 per day over a 28 day trial [56]. The average H/L ratios of healthy Ross 308 chickens supplemented with 200 ppm of peppermint per kg of body weight in the forms of alcoholic extract, encapsulated nanoparticles, and encapsulated microparticles all decreased [76]. Similarly, decreased H/L ratios in young Hubbard chickens supplemented with peppermint at 0.25–1.5% of feed for 6 weeks were observed [66]. In contrast, Fallah et al. reported a significant increase in heterophil concentrations in healthy Ross 308 chickens supplemented with 200 mg/kg peppermint for 42 days, with no significant change in the H/L ratio [98]. Other studies on newborn chickens and laying hens found no significant effect on leukocyte concentrations from peppermint supplements [72,75].

In addition to affecting leukocytes, menthol-containing supplements also influence antibody concentrations. Plasma IgG concentrations reduced after two weeks of 5% peppermint supplementation in Holstein steers [54] and after 56 days of 200 mg/kg peppermint supplementation in Habcock laying hens [72]. An increase in serum IgG and IgA was observed for laying hens supplemented with *Mentha arvensis/Geranium thunbergii* for 16 weeks [79]. Bai et al. observed increased serum IgG but not IgM in peppermint-supplemented laying hens [73]. Another study on newborn chickens reported a significantly reduced secondary antibody response to sheep red blood cells (SRBCs) after 400 mg/kg peppermint supplementation. The study also found evidence of duodenum cell destruction in supplemented animals [69]. The destructive effect at higher peppermint doses may allocate energy usage away from antibody production and into cell repair. Additionally, duodenum cell destruction can impair nutrient absorption, further depriving the host animal of nutrients essential for physiological functions such as immune response. This further supports the need to optimize menthol supplementation, as its antimicrobial effects may adversely affect the animal at high doses. However, some studies found no difference in serum antibody concentrations for young and adult chickens after supplementation [75,98]. Mehri et al. reported a linear increase in the humoral immune response against SRBCs and Newcastle disease virus in Japanese quail supplemented with peppermint at 10 k-40 k mg per kg of feed over a 5 week trial [81]. Further research is needed to understand menthol's effect on livestock antibody production.

4.3. Anti-Oxidation

Reactive oxygen species (ROS) act as chemical messengers in inflammatory signaling and assist neutrophils in pathogen destruction [99–101]. ROS are also formed passively as by-products of oxidative processes in the mitochondria [102]. However, excess ROS are toxic to the host cells, causing DNA damage and lipid peroxidation that leads to cell death [103]. Menthol has been demonstrated to possess antioxidant properties, scavenging excess ROS through its hydroxyl groups [8,12,32]. Multiple studies in chickens [63,73] and cows [48,51] reported a significant elevation in serum antioxidant capacity in animals supplemented with peppermint and other menthol-containing compounds. Additionally, increased activity of ROS-scavenging enzymes, including catalase, glutathione peroxidase, and superoxide dismutase, was detected in supplemented livestock [48,73].

As previously discussed, Mehri et al. observed a decrease in MDA in the carcasses of young Japanese quail supplemented with various concentrations of peppermint, highlighting the antioxidant capacity of menthol-containing substances [81]. Similarly, in young male chickens supplemented with 2% spearmint, thiobarbituric acid reactive substances (TBARS) and 2,2-diphenyl-1-picrylhydrazyl (DPPH) levels were reduced [70]. Notably, these effects were not detected 21 days after birth but were observed at 42 days, potentially due to increased growth rate and oxidative stress during the latter period. In contrast, no significant differences in serum MDA were found in laying hens fed up to 0.4% peppermint for 28 days, though treated groups did possess lower average MDA concentrations than the control group [73]. In ruminants, Kholif et al. observed a reduction in serum MDA in lactating cattle fed 3–6 g Aromix®/day in a 3-month study [48], while they did not find differences in serum MDA, catalase, glutathione peroxidase, or superoxide dismutase in another trial with a similar experimental design [51].

Overall, studies suggest that menthol can reduce chronic inflammation and oxidative stress by regulating cytokine, leukocyte, antibody, and ROS concentrations (Table 2). More research is needed to optimize the menthol dosage and its combination with other plant extracts for different animal species to enhance its efficiency and consistency in enhancing the immunity of livestock.

Table 2. Anti-inflammation, immune system modulation, and anti-oxidation properties of menthol.

Animal	Growth Stage/Condition [1]	Sample Size [2]	Treatment	Dosage [3]	Experiment Duration [4]	Effects of Treatment [5]	Reference
Friesian Cattle	lactating	10 CON, 10 per TRT	Aromix® (133 mg menthol/g)	T1: 3 g/day T2: 6 g/day	3 months	Increased total antioxidant capacity, catalase, superoxide dismutase, and glutathione peroxidase, decreased MDA.	[48]
Friesian Cattle	lactating	10 CON, 10 per TRT	Aromix® (133 mg menthol/g)	T1: 3 g/day T2: 6 g/day	3 months	Increased total antioxidant capacity, no effect on catalase, superoxide dismutase, glutathione peroxidase, or MDA.	[51]
Holstein Cattle	nonlactating	4–5 CON, 4–5 TRT	Digestarom® (contains menthol)	0.04%	Two periods of 6 weeks	Reduced serum amyloid A in week 3.	[88]
Holstein Cattle	NA	4 CON, 4 TRT (4 × 4 Latin square)	Peppermint	5%	2 weeks	Decreased IgG. No significant effect on total antioxidant capacity.	[54]
Suffolk Sheep	growing	8 CON, 8 per TRT	OAX17 (90% menthol)	T1: 80 mg/day T2: 160 mg/day	28 days	Decreased neutrophils. No effect on leukocytes, lymphocytes, monocytes, erythrocytes, or platelets.	[56]
Sheep	3 to 4 years-old	4 CON, 4 per TRT	Peppermint	T1: 10 mL/kg T2: 20 mL/kg T3: 30 mL/kg	NA	Increased white blood cells at higher doses.	[89]

Table 2. *Cont.*

Animal	Growth Stage/Condition [1]	Sample Size [2]	Treatment	Dosage [3]	Experiment Duration [4]	Effects of Treatment [5]	Reference
Cobb Chickens	1 day old	75 CON, 75 per TRT	Phytogenic Blend (menthol, anethol, and eugenol)	T1: 100 mg/kg T2: 150 mg/kg	42 days	Decreased IL-18 in the spleen. No effect on spleen TGF-β4, IFN-γ, IL-10, IL-2, or iNOS. No effect on tonsil cytokines. Tendency to increase total antioxidant capacity.	[63]
Hubbard Chickens	1 day old	40 CON, 40 per TRT	Peppermint	T1: 0.25% T2: 0.5% T3: 1% T4: 1.5%	6 weeks	Decreased H/L ratio. No effect on total white blood cells.	[66]
Ross 308 Chickens	1 day old	48 CON, 48 per TRT	Peppermint	T1: 200 mg/kg T2: 400 mg/kg	6 weeks	Decreased secondary antibody response with T2.	[69]
Chickens	1 day old	9 CON, 9 per TRT	Spearmint	T1: 0.5% T2: 1% T3: 1.5% T4: 2%	42 days	Decreased 2,2-diphenyl-1-picrylhydrazyl and thiobarbituric acid at 42 days.	[70]
Habcock Chickens	21 week old laying hens	36 CON, 36 per TRT	Peppermint	T1: 50 mg/kg T2: 100 mg/kg T3: 200 mg/kg T4: 50 mg/L T5: 100 mg/L T6: 200 mg/L	56 days	Decreased IgG with T6. No effect on lymphocytes, neutrophils, monocytes, or platelets.	[72]
Chickens	60 week old laying hens	54 CON, 54 per TRT	Peppermint	T1: 0.1% T2: 0.2% T3: 0.3% T4: 0.4%	28 days	Increased total antioxidant capacity, IgG, and superoxide dismutase. No effect on MDA or IgM.	[73]

Table 2. *Cont.*

Animal	Growth Stage/Condition [1]	Sample Size [2]	Treatment	Dosage [3]	Experiment Duration [4]	Effects of Treatment [5]	Reference
Ross 308 Chickens	1 day old	48 CON, 48 per TRT	Peppermint	T1: 4 g/kg T2: 8 g/kg	42 days	No effect on white blood cells, heterophils, lymphocytes, or antibodies.	[75]
Ross 308 Chickens	1 day old, heat stress conditions	80 CON, 80 per TRT	Peppermint	T1: 200 ppm ethanolic/kg body weight T2: 200 ppm nano-/kg body weight T3: 200 ppm micro-/kg body weight	42 days	Decreased H/L ratio.	[76]
ISA Brown Chickens	28 week old laying hens	24 CON, 24 per TRT	Wild Mint + Geranium	T1: 0.01% T2: 0.05% T3: 0.1%	16 weeks	Increased serum IgA, IgG, IL-6, and TNF-α.	[79]
Ross 308 Chickens	chicks	75 CON, 75 per TRT	Peppermint or Peppermint + Artichoke	T1: 200 mg Pep/kg water T2: 200 mg Pep/kg water + 1.5% artichoke	42 days	Increased heterophils and lymphocytes. No change to H/L ratio or antibodies.	[98]
Japanese Quail	8 days old	120 CON, 60 per TRT	Peppermint	T1: 10 g/kg T2: 20 g/kg T3: 30 g/kg T4: 40 g/kg	5 weeks	Linear increase in humoral immune response, decreased MDA.	[81]

[1] NA: Not available/not applicable, LPS: Lipopolysaccharide. [2] CON: Control group, TRT: Treatment group. [3] T: Treatment group number, Pep: Peppermint. [4] NA: Not available/not applicable, LPS: Lipopolysaccharide, Mthl: Menthol. [5] LPS: Lipopolysaccharide, MDA: Malondialdehyde, H/L: Heterophil/lymphocyte.

5. Antimicrobial and Pesticidal Action of Menthol

Synthetic antibiotics have seen widespread usage in livestock farming worldwide to protect against illness and improve growth parameters. However, growing concerns have led to the banning or limiting of antibiotic use [18,104]. These concerns have arisen from two main factors. First, the overuse of antibiotics can lead to a buildup of toxic residues in the environment and in humans [104,105]. Second, excessive use of antibiotics promotes the development and propagation of antimicrobial-resistant (AMR) pathogens. AMR pathogens can be transmitted directly from livestock to humans through animal waste and food products. They can also transfer antimicrobial-resistance genes to otherwise susceptible environmental bacteria through horizontal gene transfer [19,104]. Preventing AMR is becoming of increasing importance, with human deaths from AMR pathogens estimated to be 10 million deaths per year by 2050 [106]. The antimicrobial properties of menthol and peppermint oil have been extensively studied in vitro [6,107,108]. These properties are primarily attributed to menthol's ability to disrupt the lipid membrane of microorganisms, causing cellular leakage and subsequent death [31]. Because of this, menthol and other similar phytogenic compounds are garnering increased attention as potential alternatives to synthetic antibiotics, especially for use in livestock production (Table 3).

Table 3. Antimicrobial and pesticidal action of menthol.

Animal	Growth Stage/Condition [1]	Sample Size [2]	Treatment	Dosage [3]	Experiment Duration	Effects of Treatment [4]	Reference
Holstein Cattle	NA	13 CON, 13 TRT	Menthol	0.3%	4 weeks	Increased tetracycline-resistant *E. coli*. No effect on total coliform counts or other antimicrobial resistances.	[109]
Cattle	NA	20 CON, 20 per TRT	Menthol or Menthol + Supra-Nutritional Zinc	T1: 0.3% Mthl T2: 0.3% Mthl + 300 ppm zinc	3 weeks	Tendency for increased tetracycline-resistant *E. coli* and MDR with T2, increased macrolide-resistant *Enterococci* in first 21 days from menthol.	[110]
Cattle	lactating	20 per TRT	Phytogenic Blends (menthol, chavicol, cineol, etc.)	T1: 10 mL/d nasal T2: 20 mL/d vaginal	7 days	Decreased nasal *P. aeruginosa* and *C. albicans*. Reduced vaginal *E. coli*, *P. aeruginosa*, *C. albicans*, and *S. aureus*.	[111]
Cattle	cattle with signs of udder lesions	14 TRT	Phytogenic Blend (*S. sclarea*, *M. canadensis*, *M. piperita* and *C. sativum*)	5–6 mL/nipple/day	7 days	Decreased nipple *Str. uberis*, *P. aeruginosa*, *S. aureus*, *E. coli*, *H. somni*, and *C. albicans*.	[112]

Table 3. *Cont.*

Animal	Growth Stage/Condition [1]	Sample Size [2]	Treatment	Dosage [3]	Experiment Duration	Effects of Treatment [4]	Reference
Chickens	18 week old laying hens	50 CON 50 TRT	Digestarom® (contains menthol)	150 g/t	12 weeks	Decreased gut *Campylobacter*, *Staphylococcus*, *Fusobacterium*, *Desulfovibrio*, *Slackia*, *Saccaropolyspora*, etc. Increased *P. gingivalis* and *Gallibacterium*. No effect on antimicrobial resistance.	[60]
Hubbard Chick-ens	1 day old	50 CON 50 per TRT	Phytogenic Blend (garlic, mint, etc.) or Blend + Organic Acids	T1: 3 kg phytogenic blend/ton T2: 3 kg phytogenic blend/ton + organic acids	42 days	Decreased gut *E. coli* and *Camoylobacter*.	[61]
Ross 308 Chick-ens	1 day old	120 CON 120 TRT	Peppermint	Room fogged with 1 L of 1:250 or 1:500 oil aerosol	42 days	Decreased environmental mesophiles, and *Staphylococci*.	[113]
Japanese Quail	8 days old	72 CON 72 per TRT	Peppermint	T1: 10 g/kg T2: 20 g/kg T3: 30 g/kg T4: 40 g/kg	35 days	Reduced ileal coliform counts.	[114]

[1] NA: Not available/not applicable. [2] CON: Control group, TRT: Treatment group, NA: Not available/not applicable. [3] T: Treatment group number, Mthl: Menthol. [4] MDR: Multidrug resistance, MIC: Minimum inhibitory concentration, LC_{50}: Lethal concentration 50.

5.1. Antimicrobial Activity Against Skin Mucosal, Topical, and Environmental Pathogens

Several studies have found evidence for menthol's efficacy against pathogens causing ruminant mastitis. In vitro antimicrobial activity of peppermint against *Escherichia coli* (*E. coli*) and *Staphylococcus aureus* (*S. aureus*) isolated from camel mastitis was observed, with minimum inhibitory concentrations (MIC) of 1.56% and 3.12% peppermint against *E. coli* and *S. aureus*, respectively [115]. Similarly, antimicrobial activity was observed against *Prototheca zopfii* (*P. zopfii*), a mastitis-causing alga isolated from cattle milk [116]. The alga was found to be susceptible to 50 μL of peppermint essential oil in vitro [117]. In contrast, a similar in vitro study did not identify any inhibitory activity of peppermint against *P. zopfii* at concentrations up to 30 μL/mL [118]. Another study found that peppermint exhibited limited bactericidal activity against *S. aureus* isolates from cow mastitis, though moderate inhibitory effects were observed against seven *S. aureus* strains and five *Staphylococcus chromogenes* strains [119]. In vivo, a decrease in *Pseudomonas aeruginosa* (*P. aeruginosa*) and *Candida albicans* (*C. albicans*) in the nasal mucosa of lactating cattle treated for 7 days with a phytogenic blend containing menthol and other compounds, such as cineol and chavicol (33.27% menthol mass fraction), was observed [111]. A tendency toward a reduction in the presence of *E. coli*, *P. aeruginosa*, *C. albicans*, and *S. aureus* in the vaginal mucosa of cattle treated with a similar blend (22.16% menthol mass fraction) was also detected. Additionally, the presence of several bacterial species, such as *Streptococcus uberis*, *P. aeruginosa*, *S. aureus*, and *C. albicans*, on cow teats was decreased after daily flushing with a blend including *M. piperita* and other phytogenic compounds [112]. In vivo results suggest that menthol-containing compounds hold significant potential as topical antibacterials, though effectiveness against pathogenic algae like *P. zopfii* remains questionable. One 42 day trial showed mesophilic bacteria, particularly Staphylococci, were significantly reduced in the environment after misting broiler houses with peppermint oil, suggesting peppermint could be effective as an aerosolized antimicrobial agent [113].

5.2. Bactericidal Activity Against Gut Pathogens

Gut pathogens can also be inhibited through feed supplementation. In a 12-week study, widespread changes in gastrointestinal bacteria populations were found in laying hens supplemented with Digestarom®, including a reduced abundance of several important pathogenic genera, such as Campylobacter, Staphylococcus, Fusobacterium, Desulfovibrio, Slackia, and Saccaropolyspora, while there was an increased abundance of *Porphyromonas, gingivalis*, and Gallibacterium [60]. Reduced *E. coli* and Campylobacter abundance was reported after Hubbard chickens were fed 3 kg of a phytogenic blend including peppermint per ton of feed after 42 days [61]. In Japanese quail, 10–40 peppermint/kg of feed reduced ileal coliform counts after 35 days [114].

While menthol compounds have shown great antimicrobial effectiveness in livestock, two studies call into question the efficacy of these products as substitutes for traditional antibiotics [109,110]. Aperce et al. reported a minimal reduction in total coliforms after cattle were supplemented with 0.3% menthol, but concerningly, an increase in tetracycline-resistant *E. coli* was observed after 4 weeks [109]. Similarly, Murray et al. found a tendency for increased tetracycline resistance in *E. coli* isolated from cattle supplemented with a blend of 0.3% menthol and 300 ppm of zinc [110]. However, there was no increase in AMR genes in chicken gut bacteria after 12 weeks of Digestarom® supplementation [60]. Further studies are needed to investigate whether menthol specifically induces any AMR genes.

5.3. Pesticidal Activity

There is evidence suggesting that menthol also possesses pesticidal activity. In vitro, larvicidal activity of peppermint was observed 3 days after spraying larva feed with peppermint oil. Fly density showed a 96% decrease around cattle topically treated with a 34.91 μg/μL peppermint formulation [120]. Similarly, 5% peppermint greatly repelled flies around cattle for up to 4 h after application [121]. *M. piperita* was found to be effective against water-buffalo-targeting lice, with a LC_{50} concentration of 12.35% [122], and against ticks with a LC_{50} concentration between 0.39 and 2.85% depending on life stage [123].

In summary, menthol products effectively control surface, mucosal, and gut pathogens, and peppermint shows efficacy against common cattle pests. However, further studies on pure menthol are needed to clarify individual potencies.

6. Impact of Menthol on Digestive Tract Microbial Ecosystem and Function

6.1. Impact on Rumen Microbial Ecosystem and Function

6.1.1. Digestibility in Ruminants

Digestibility in ruminant systems can be tracked by direct methods such as fecal screening or the use of undigestible biomarkers like acid-insoluble ash [124,125]. Alternatively, measuring the total volume of gases produced during in vitro rumen studies serves as an effective indicator of digestive activity [124,126]. Gas production was not affected by the supplementation of up to 0.3% pure crystalline menthol in rumen fluid after 24 h of in vitro culture [127]. Other studies utilizing peppermint in the feed of ruminants, such as cattle, sheep, and buffalo, similarly reported no difference in indicators of digestive performance [52,57,58,128,129]. Despite menthol's antimicrobial activity, potential improvements in ruminant digestion after menthol supplementation were also reported. Holstein steers that consumed 200 g of peppermint per day for 14 days possessed a tendency for increased nutrient digestibility [130]. Corresponding with their observations on feed intake, a pair of studies by Kholif et al. found improvements in the digestibility of various nutrients after lactating Friesian cattle were supplemented with 3 g/day of Aromix® [48,51]. However, when supplementation increased to 6 g/day, digestibility decreased. Another study reported similar findings in vitro, as rumen fluid gas production increased after 1.5 μL/mL of peppermint supplementation but decreased at 3.0 μL/mL [131]. After 24 h in vitro, digestion in buffalo rumen fluid decreased after application of 600 ppm of peppermint; however, no change in digestion was observed at 30 or 300 ppm [132]. The findings of several studies suggest that menthol-containing supplements could impart beneficial effects on digestion at low doses but become detrimental at higher doses. Other researchers reported a decrease in ruminant digestion after peppermint concentrations ranging from 0.1 to 1.2 g/L of rumen fluid in vitro [133,134] and 5% of feed weight in vivo [53]. The decrease in digestion reported by several studies aligns with the observed decreases in commensal microbe populations.

6.1.2. Modulation of Rumen Microbiota

The antimicrobial effects of menthol and other phenolic compounds do not selectively inhibit only pathogens but commensal microbes as well. Studies have observed wide-ranging shifts in rumen function from phytogenic compounds such as *M. piperita*, largely due in part to microbial modifications [135,136]. Alterations in the abundances of most rumen microbial taxa in growing sheep supplemented with OAX17 for 4 weeks were observed [137]. In vitro, peppermint supplementation ranging from 0.33 to 2 μL/mL and from 0.1 to 1 g/L decreased the relative abundance of prominent carbohydrate-degrading species in rumen fluid, including *Ruminococcus flavefaciens*, *Fibrobacter succinogenes*, *Prevotella ruminicola*, and *Ruminococcus albus* [133,138,139]. Overall decreases in bacteria, protozoa, methanogen, and archaea abundances were observed in the rumen in response to varying peppermint concentrations ranging from 0.1 to 1 g/L of digesta in vitro and 200 g/day in vivo [130,133,139]. In contrast, an increase in bacteria and methanogen abundance in vitro at 0.33 μL of peppermint per mL of buffalo rumen fluid was detected, but there was a decrease when peppermint was increased to 1–2 μL/mL [138]. As ruminants heavily rely on rumen microbes for degrading plant material, modifications in their abundances could affect nutrient digestion [140]. However, inhibiting methanogens holds the potential to reduce methane production and combat climate alterations [20,141].

6.1.3. Ruminal pH Modulation

Menthol has the capacity to modulate the pH of the rumen. One of the significant concerns in ruminant nutrition is the development of sub-acute ruminal acidosis (SARA). Cattle can be fed diets high in starch but low in fiber to meet demanding energy requirements in conditions such as the lactating stage in dairy cattle and the fatting stage in beef cattle. However, this diet can often lead to a buildup of excess volatile fatty acids in the rumen and lead to lowered rumen pH (5.2–6.0) [142]. Persistent SARA can lead to a variety of conditions, including decreased feed intake, decreased milk production, poor body condition, diarrhea, and laminitis [142,143]. Aside from reducing the starch content of cattle diets, there is a desire for more productive methods to decrease SARA incidence. Amongst these, the use of essential oils as potential preventatives has garnered attention [144,145]. Nonlactating Holstein cattle under SARA conditions showed higher ruminal pH after 4 h of ad libitum feeding supplemented with 6.7 mg of menthol per kg of feed compared to those fed with a basal diet without menthol supplementation (pH 6.3 vs. pH 6.09), which was attributed to the reduction of volatile fatty acid production, particularly propionate [46]. Their findings on pH are supported by other in vivo and in vitro studies that supplemented ruminants with peppermint and other phytogenic blends [48,49,88,133,134].

Several of the aforementioned studies also found a decrease in propionate, supporting Castillo-Lopez et al.'s explanation for pH modification in cattle [49,88,133] and sheep [134]. However, a 3 month study supplementing lactating cattle with Aromix® observed an increase in ruminal propionate alongside an increase in rumen pH from 6.71 in the control group compared to 6.82–6.85 in supplemented groups [48]. Other studies found no change in ruminal pH after phytogenic supplementation, with or without modified volatile fatty acid profiles [53,54,57,58,128,131,137], and another study found no short-term change to in vitro rumen pH supplemented with pure menthol at up to 0.3% of feed [127]. This suggests that factors other than volatile fatty acid production may also contribute to pH modulation. For example, a buffering effect from peppermint may explain rumen pH stabilization [52]. However, another study found a significant decrease in rumen pH from 14 days of peppermint supplementation at 200 g/day in dairy cattle, with peppermint-fed cows averaging 5.91 pH compared to 6.30 without supplement [130]. Consistent explanations for menthol's pH-modulating abilities remain elusive. As such, while menthol-containing compounds have demonstrated the potential to attenuate rumen pH, more research must be carried out to better understand conflicting results and the mechanisms behind them.

6.1.4. Methane Production and Acetate to Propionate (a/p) Ratio

Because of their antimicrobial activity, essential oils such as peppermint have garnered attention as potential controllers of methane emissions [20,146]. Several previously discussed studies that reported decreased digestibility after supplementation observed a corresponding decrease in methane production [53,131,133,134,138]. Other researchers observed a decrease in methane production without detrimental effects on digestibility. For instance, male buffalo fed a mixture of garlic bulb and peppermint (25 g of garlic bulb per 1 mL of peppermint oil) at 2.5% in feed over a 21-day period showed a 7% decrease in methane production [58]. Similarly, buffalo methane production decreased in vitro over 24 h without significantly affecting digestibility after up to 300 ppm of peppermint was added [132]. In contrast, a 4-week study observed no difference in rumen fermentation or methane production in unsupplemented sheep compared to sheep fed up to 160 mg/day of OAX17 [137]. A quadratic decrease in gas production but no decrease in methane production was observed when 100–400 mg of peppermint/L of rumen fluid collected from nonlactating cattle was supplemented in vitro [129]. These disparate results were attributed to differences in menthol concentration between individual peppermint plants, suggesting less efficiency in methane reduction when using mixed or impure menthol compounds such as peppermint oil.

Another proposed way of estimating digestive efficiency and methane production is based on the acetate to propionate (a/p) ratio. As carbohydrates are degraded by microbes, volatile fatty acids such as acetate, propionate, and butyrate are produced. As the ratio of acetate to propionate decreases, methane production generally decreases [147,148]. Several of the previously discussed studies observed an increase in the a/p ratio after supplementing ruminants with commercial phytogenic blends [49,88] or with peppermint [129,131,133,134,138]. However, as previously discussed, no studies reported an increase in methane production after supplementation, and many reported a decrease, conflicting with previous associations between a/p ratio and methane production. This was suggested to be due to an accumulation of molecular hydrogen due to peppermint reducing the hydrogen utilization efficiency for producing both volatile fatty acids and methane [134,138]. It is also possible that the general decrease in digestive function offsets increased methane production associated with a high a/p ratio. A decreased acetate-to-propionate (a/p) ratio was observed in cattle fed 3 g/day of Aromix® compared to the control group, whereas an increased a/p ratio was reported at a dosage of 6 g/day [48,51]. As with several previous parameters, their studies suggest that menthol's effects on biochemical parameters shift depending on dosage. Regardless, the a/p ratio is likely not a reliable marker for methane production in the context of supplementation with peppermint and other menthol-containing compounds.

6.1.5. Ammonia Production

Another potential benefit of menthol's antimicrobial activity is in modulating the ammonia concentration in the rumen. Proteolytic bacteria aid in the deamination and breakdown of proteins in ruminant guts. Ammonia is produced as a natural by-product of this process. However, when protein deamination produces more ammonia than the host can utilize, the excess ammonia is converted to urea and excreted, resulting in a loss of nitrogen sources. [139]. Excess urea excretion contributes to nitrogen-based pollution, including eutrophication and acid rain, when it is converted to reactive nitrogen compounds in the environment [149]. Many studies observed decreased ammonia concentrations, both in vivo and in vitro. Kholif et al. found a decrease in rumen ammonia after cattle were fed 3–6 g Aromix®/day [48,51]. Similarly, Holstein steers fed 200 g/day of peppermint for 14 days exhibited reduced rumen ammonia levels, which the researchers attributed to menthol's antimicrobial activity [130]. Other cow and sheep studies using *M. piperita* support their findings [57,134]. In cattle supplemented with 0.04% of a menthol-containing blend, ammonia production initially increased compared to the control group after 2 weeks but rapidly declined by the third week [88]. However, Patra et al. reported no changes in ammonia production in sheep supplemented with up to 160 mg/day of OAX17 for 4 weeks [137]. Other ruminant studies utilizing peppermint similarly found no significant changes in ammonia production [52,128,129,132,133,139]. Only one study reported an increase in ruminal ammonia after 5% peppermint supplementation in Holstein steers [54].

Overall, menthol and related supplements have been repeatedly demonstrated to have a significant effect on rumen function. Primarily through their antimicrobial action, evidence suggests that feed digestibility, methane production, ammonia production, and rumen pH are all affected by the consumption of these compounds. However, differing methodologies leave optimal dosages of menthol unclear. Supplementation should be optimized to reduce unwanted by-products of digestion such as methane while minimizing negative effects on digestive performance.

6.2. Impact on Gut Microbial Ecosystem and Function in Poultry

6.2.1. Digestibility in Poultry

In poultry, there is evidence suggesting that menthol could impart beneficial effects on digestion. Linear improvements to digestion in young Cobb chickens with increasing levels of supplementation with a menthol, anethol, and eugenol blend, where up to 150 mg of supplement per kg of feed increased dry matter digestibility, was identified [63]. This was attributed to microbial modulatory effects by Mentha species. Similar improvements to crude protein digestibility were seen after peppermint supplementation to chickens at 200 mg/kg of feed and up to 296 mg/kg, respectively [69,77], which was linked to increases in bile secretion [150]. However, two other studies found no improvements to digestibility, apart from cysteine [62], after chickens were supplemented up to 2% of feed with *Mentha cordifolia* and 150 mg of a menthol/anethol blend per kg of feed [62,70]. Studies on poultry digestion are limited, but the lack of detrimental findings suggests further study on menthol-containing compounds could yield beneficial findings. A single study by [70] also observed improvements in poultry ammonia excretion, where spearmint feeding at 0.5–2% of feed weight for 42 days significantly reduced ammonia excretion in chickens.

6.2.2. Modulation of Gut Microbiota in Poultry

Studies on the effects of menthol on gut microbiota in poultry are relatively limited, though some research has directly reported modifications in specific gut microbial populations. After young Hubbard chickens were supplemented with 3 kg of a mint-containing blend per ton of feed for 42 days, abundances of commensal Lactobacillus and Enterococcus bacteria in the ileum and Enterococcus in the cecum were increased compared to the control group [61]. In another study, decreased abundances of commensal genera such as Lactobacillus and Ruminococcus were reported after the administration of Digestarom® to laying hens [60]. However, the concentration of menthol in this product is unclear. While tracking menthol and peppermint's effects on microbe populations could serve as a helpful predictor of digestive performance, the ultimate value of their modifications is indicated by the resulting effects on digestive function.

Overall, menthol-containing supplements appear to impart beneficial effects on poultry digestion, especially for protein (Table 4). However, other aspects of digestion are largely uninvestigated.

Table 4. Impact of menthol on digestive tract microbial ecosystem and function.

Animal	Growth Stage/Condition [1]	Sample Size [2]	Treatment	Dosage [3]	Experiment Duration	Effects of Treatment [4]	Reference
Holstein Cattle	nonlactating, subacute ruminal acidosis conditions	4 CON, 4 per TRT (4 × 4 incomplete Latin square)	Mint or Menthol	T1: 15.3 mg Mnt/kg T2: 153 mg Mnt/kg T3: 6.7 mg Mthl/kg T4: 67 mg Mthl/kg	4 h of supplement	Increased mean rumen pH from menthol treatment with high-concentrate SARA diet.	[46]
Holstein Cattle	rumen fluid from 17 month olds tested in vitro	5 CON, 5 per TRT	Menthol	T1: 0.003% T2: 0.03% T3: 0.3%	24 h	No effect on gas production, rumen pH, or VFAs.	[127]
Friesian Cattle	lactating	10 CON, 10 per TRT	Aromix® (133 mg menthol/g)	T1: 3 g/day T2: 6 g/day	3 months	Increased nutrient digestibility and VFAs with T1, decreased nutrient digestibility and increased propionate with T2, decreased ammonia production and increased pH at both doses.	[48]
Holstein Cattle	lactating, heat stress conditions	16 CON, 16 TRT	BioHerbal® (contains peppermint)	2 g/day	28 days	Decreased propionate, increased a/p ratio and rumen pH, no effect on total VFAs.	[49]
Friesian Cattle	lactating	10 CON, 10 per TRT	Aromix® (133 mg menthol/g)	T1: 3 g/day T2: 6 g/day	3 months	Increased nutrient digestibility and decreased a/p ratio with T1, decreased nutrient digestibility and increased a/p ratio with T2, decreased ammonia production at both doses.	[51]

Table 4. *Cont.*

Animal	Growth Stage/Condition [1]	Sample Size [2]	Treatment	Dosage [3]	Experiment Duration	Effects of Treatment [4]	Reference
Holstein Cattle	nonlactating	4–5 CON, 4–5 TRT	Digestarom® (contains menthol)	0.04%	Two periods of 6 weeks	Increased rumen pH, decreased propionate and increased a/p ratio and other VFAs at 2 weeks, increased ammonia production at 2 weeks, decreased ammonia production at 3 weeks.	[88]
Holstein Cattle	lactating	4 CON, 4 TRT	Peppermint	5%	22 days	No effect on nutrient digestibility, VFAs, or gas production, immediate decrease in ammonia production but not after 3 h, minor decrease in rumen pH.	[52]
Holstein Cattle	NA	4 CON, 4 TRT (4 × 4 Latin square)	Peppermint	5%	2 weeks	Increased ammonia production, no effect on rumen pH or VFAs.	[54]
Holstein Cattle	lactating	4 CON, 4 TRT	Peppermint	5%	22 days	Decreased nutrient digestibility and methane production per dry/digestible matter intake, no effect on VFAs or pH.	[53]
Cattle	nonlactating cow rumen fluid tested in vitro	3 CON, 3 per TRT	Peppermint	T1: 100 mg/L T2: 200 mg/L T3: 300 mg/L T4: 400 mg/L	48 h	Tendency for decreased digestibility, increased a/p ratio, no effect on methane production or ammonia production.	[129]

Table 4. *Cont.*

Animal	Growth Stage/Condition [1]	Sample Size [2]	Treatment	Dosage [3]	Experiment Duration	Effects of Treatment [4]	Reference
Holstein Cattle	NA	4 CON, 4 TRT	Peppermint	200 g/day	14 days	Tendency for increased nutrient digestibility, decreased ammonia production, VFAs, rumen protozoa, and rumen pH.	[130]
Jersey Cattle	rumen fluid tested in vitro from fistulated lactating cattle	3 CON, 3 per TRT	Peppermint	T1: 0.1 g/L T2: 0.25 g/L T3: 1 g/L	24 h	Decreased archaea, protozoa, methanogens, cellulolytic bacteria, gas production, methane production, and propionate, increased a/p ratio and rumen pH, no change to ammonia production.	[133]
Jersey Cattle	rumen fluid tested in vitro from fistulated lactating cattle	3 CON, 3 TRT	Peppermint	1 g/L	24 h	Decrease in most bacteria and archaea, increase in *S. bovis*, no effect on ammonia production.	[139]
Suffolk Sheep	growing	8 CON, 8 per TRT	OAX17 (90% menthol)	T1:80 mg/day T2: 160 mg/day	4 weeks	Alterations in ruminal abundance of most bacterial taxa, no effect on rumen fermentation, pH, VFAs, ammonia, or methane.	[137]
Sanjabi Sheep	90 days old	6 CON, 6 TRT	Peppermint	3%	90 days	No effect on nutrient digestibility or pH, decreased ammonia production.	[57]
Buffalo	NA	3 CON, 3 TRT (3 × 3 Latin square)	Peppermint	2 mL/100 kg body weight	24 days	No effect on nutrient digestibility, pH, VFAs, ammonia production, or rumen microbes.	[128]

Table 4. *Cont.*

Animal	Growth Stage/Condition [1]	Sample Size [2]	Treatment	Dosage [3]	Experiment Duration	Effects of Treatment [4]	Reference
Buffalo	rumen fluid tested in vitro	5 CON, 5 per TRT	Peppermint	T1: 1.5 µL/mL T2: 3 µL/mL	24 h	Increased gas production with T1, decreased gas production, methane production, dry matter digestibility, and increased a/p ratio with T2, no effect on pH.	[131]
Buffalo	rumen fluid tested in vitro	NA	Peppermint	T1: 30 ppm T2: 300 ppm T3: 600 ppm	24 h	Increased propionate with T3, decreased digestibility and VFAs with T3, decreased methane production with T2 and T3, no effect on ammonia production.	[132]
Sheep	rumen fluid tested in vitro	3 CON, 3 per TRT	Peppermint	T1: 100 mg/L T2: 200 mg/L T3: 400 mg/L T4: 800 mg/L T5: 1200 mg/L	96 h	Decreased organic matter digestibility, methane production, ammonia production, and propionate, increased a/p ratio and pH.	[134]
Buffalo	rumen fluid tested in vitro	6 CON, 6 per TRT	Peppermint	T1: 0.33 µL/mL T2: 1 µL/mL T3: 2 µL/mL	24 h	Decreased bacteria, fungi, and methanogen populations with T2 and T3, increased with T1, increased a/p ratio, decreased feed digestibility and methane production.	[138]
Murrah Buffalo	NA	2 CON, 2 TRT (2 × 2 switch over)	Garlic Bulb + Peppermint	2.5% of dry weight	Two periods of 21 days	Decreased methane production, no effect on dry matter digestibility, rumen pH, or rumen microbes.	[58]

Table 4. *Cont.*

Animal	Growth Stage/Condition [1]	Sample Size [2]	Treatment	Dosage [3]	Experiment Duration	Effects of Treatment [4]	Reference
Chickens	18 week old laying hens	50 CON, 50 TRT	Digestarom® (contains menthol)	150 g/t	12 weeks	Decreased *Lactobacillus* and *Ruminococcus*.	[60]
Hubbard Chickens	1 day old	50 CON, 50 per TRT	Phytogenic Blend (garlic, mint, etc.) or Blend + Organic Acids	T1: 3 kg phytogenic blend/ton T2: 3 kg phytogenic blend/ton + organic acids	42 days	Increased gut *Lactobacillus* in ileum and *Enterococcus* in cecum and ileum.	[61]
Cobb 500 Chickens	1 day old	Trial 1: 160 CON, 160 TRT; Trial 2: 40 CON, 40 TRT	Phytogenic Blend (menthol, anethole)	150 mg/kg diet	Trial 1: 42 days Trial 2: 21 days	Increased cysteine digestibility, no effect on other nutrient digestibility.	[62]
Cobb Chickens	1 day old	75 CON, 75 per TRT	Phytogenic Blend (menthol, anethol, and eugenol)	T1: 100 mg/kg T2: 150 mg/kg	42 days	Linear increase in dry matter digestibility and apparent metabolizable energy corrected for nitrogen, no effect on crude protein or ether extract digestibility.	[63]
Ross 308 Chickens	1 day old	48 CON, 48 per TRT	Peppermint	T1: 200 mg/kg T2: 400 mg/kg	6 weeks	Increased crude protein digestibility with T1, no effect on dry matter or ether extract digestibility.	[69]

Table 4. *Cont.*

Animal	Growth Stage/Condition [1]	Sample Size [2]	Treatment	Dosage [3]	Experiment Duration	Effects of Treatment [4]	Reference
Chickens	1 day old	9 CON, 9 per TRT	Peppermint	T1: 0.5% T2: 1% T3: 1.5% T4: 2%	42 days	Decreased ammonia excretion, no effect on nutrient digestibility.	[70]
Bovans Brown Chickens	32 week old laying hens	40 CON, 40 per TRT	Peppermint	T1: 74 mg/kg T2: 148 mg/kg T3: 222 mg/kg T4: 296 mg/kg	12 weeks	Linear increase in crude protein and ether extract digestibility, no effect on other nutrient digestibility.	[77]

[1] NA: Not available/not applicable. [2] NA: Not available/not applicable, CON: Control group, TRT: Treatment group. [3] T: Treatment group number, Mthl: Menthol, Mnt: Mint. [4] SARA: Subacute ruminal acidosis, VFA: Volatile fatty acid, a/p = Acetate/propionate.

7. Impact of Menthol on Metabolism

Given the alterations to digestion by menthol and peppermint found by many studies, supplementation also leads to changes in the overall metabolic profiles of animals. These include alterations in serum parameters, such as urea, cholesterol, total protein, and others. (Table 5).

Table 5. Impact of menthol on serum parameters.

Animal	Growth Stage/Conditions [1]	Sample Size [2]	Treatment	Dosage [3]	Experiment Duration [4]	Effects of Treatment [5]	Reference
Friesian Cattle	lactating	10 CON, 10 per TRT	Aromix® (133 mg menthol/g)	T1: 3 g/day T2: 6 g/day	3 months	Decreased serum urea, triglycerides, cholesterol, and total lipids, increased serum protein, increased serum glucose with T1, decreased glucose with T2, no effect on serum calcium.	[48]
Holstein–Friesian Cattle	lactating	36 CON, 36 TRT	BTX12 (>80% menthol)	1.2 g/day	Two periods of 20 days	Decreased serum and urine urea, increased serum calcium, no effect on serum protein or urine calcium.	[50]
Friesian Cattle	lactating	10 CON, 10 per TRT	Aromix® (133 mg menthol/g)	T1: 3 g/day T2: 6 g/day	3 months	Increased serum protein and glucose with T1, decreased serum glucose with T2, decreased serum cholesterol and triglycerides, increased serum calcium, no effect on serum urea.	[51]
Holstein Cattle	NA	4 CON, 4 TRT (4 × 4 Latin square)	Peppermint	5%	2 weeks	Increased serum urea, no effect on serum protein or glucose, cholesterol, triglycerides, or lipoproteins.	[54]
Holstein Cattle	4 year olds, transition state pregnancy	10 CON, 10 TRT	Peppermint	400 g/day	15 days + 12 h after calving	Increased serum calcium and decreased urine pH at end of 15 days and 12 h after calving.	[151]

Table 5. *Cont.*

Animal	Growth Stage/Conditions [1]	Sample Size [2]	Treatment	Dosage [3]	Experiment Duration [4]	Effects of Treatment [5]	Reference
Suffolk Sheep	growing	8 CON, 8 per TRT	OAX17 GmbH (90% menthol)	T1: 80 mg/day T2: 160 mg/day	28 days	Tendency for increased serum calcium with T2, increased serum glutamine, glutamate, asparagine, and aspartate, no effect on serum urea, glucose, cholesterol, or triglycerides, tendency for improved Na^+ independent glucose uptake.	[56]
Sanjabi Sheep	90 days old	6 CON, 6 TRT	Peppermint	3%	90 days	Decreased serum urea and increased serum glucose and triglycerides during middle period, no effect on serum protein or cholesterol, increased calcium digestibility.	[57]
Sheep	3 to 4 years-old	4 CON 4 per TRT	Peppermint	T1: 10 mL/kg T2: 20 mL/kg T3: 30 mL/kg	NA	Increased serum glucose with T3, no effect on serum protein, cholesterol, or triglycerides.	[89]
Hubbard Chickens	1 day old	50 CON, 50 per TRT	Phytogenic Blend (garlic, mint, etc.) or Blend + Organic Acids	T1: 3 kg phytogenic blend/ton T2: 3 kg phytogenic blend/ton + organic acids	42 days	Decreased serum cholesterol, no effect on serum protein.	[61]
Cobb Chickens	1 day old	75 CON, 75 per TRT	Phytogenic Blend (menthol, anethol, and eugenol)	T1: 100 mg/kg T2: 150 mg/kg	42 days	No effect on serum protein, glucose, or cholesterol.	[63]
Hy-Line Brown Chickens	64 week old laying hens	50 CON, 50 per TRT	Peppermint	T1: 5 mg/kg T2: 10 mg/kg T3: 15 mg/kg T4: 20 mg/kg	12 weeks	Increased serum protein, decreased serum cholesterol, no effect on serum glucose.	[65]

Table 5. *Cont.*

Animal	Growth Stage/Conditions [1]	Sample Size [2]	Treatment	Dosage [3]	Experiment Duration [4]	Effects of Treatment [5]	Reference
Habcock Chickens	21 week old laying hens	36 CON, 36 per TRT	Peppermint	T1: 50 mg/kg T2: 100 mg/kg T3: 200 mg/kg T4: 50 mg/L T5: 100 mg/L T6: 200 mg/L	56 days	No effect on serum protein, glucose, cholesterol, lipoproteins, or calcium.	[72]
Chickens	60 week old laying hens	54 CON, 54 per TRT	Peppermint	T1: 0.1% T2: 0.2% T3: 0.3% T4: 0.4%	28 days	Increased serum protein, uric acid, and triglycerides, trend towards increased serum cholesterol, no effect on serum lipoproteins or urea.	[73]
Ross 308 Chickens	1 day old	48 CON, 48 per TRT	Peppermint	T1: 4 g/kg T2: 8 g/kg	42 days	No effect on serum protein, cholesterol, or lipoproteins.	[75]
Ross 308 Chickens	1 day old, heat stress conditions	80 CON, 80 per TRT	Peppermint	T1: 200 ppm ethanolic/kg body weight T2: 200 ppm nano-/kg body weight T3: 200 ppm micro-/kg body weight	42 days	Increased serum protein and HDL, decreased serum cholesterol, triglycerides, LDL, and VLDL.	[76]
Bovans Brown Chickens	32 week old laying hens	40 CON, 40 per TRT	Peppermint	T1: 74 mg/kg T2: 148 mg/kg T3: 222 mg/kg T4: 296 mg/kg	12 weeks	Increased serum protein, decreased serum cholesterol, no effect on serum glucose or calcium.	[77]
Lohmann LSL-Lite Chickens	40 week old laying hens, cold stress conditions	30 CON, 30 per TRT	Peppermint or Peppermint + Thyme	T1: 100 mg Pep/kg diet T2: 100 mg Pep/kg + thyme	8 weeks	No effect on serum glucose or uric acid decreased serum triglycerides with T2.	[78]

Table 5. *Cont.*

Animal	Growth Stage/Conditions [1]	Sample Size [2]	Treatment	Dosage [3]	Experiment Duration [4]	Effects of Treatment [5]	Reference
Cobb 500 Chickens	1 day old females, heat stress conditions	60 CON, 60 per TRT	Peppermint or Peppermint + Chromium Picolinate	T1: 250 mg Pep/kg T2: 250 mg Pep/kg + chromium picolinate	42 days	Decreased serum glucose and triglycerides with T2, no effect on serum cholesterol or lipoproteins.	[80]
Ross 308 Chickens	chicks	75 CON, 75 per TRT	Peppermint or Peppermint + Artichoke	T1: 200 mg Mnt/kg water T2: 200 mg Mnt/kg water + 1.5% artichoke	42 days	Decreased serum cholesterol and triglycerides, no effect on serum urea, protein, glucose, or lipoproteins.	[98]
Cobb Chickens	1 day old	20 CON, 20 per TRT	Peppermint or Peppermint + Black Seed	T1: 300 mg/kg Pep T2: 300 mg/kg Pep + 1 mL/kg black seed	42 days	No effect on serum urea or protein.	[152]
Japanese Quail	8 days old	120 CON, 60 per TRT	Peppermint	T1: 10 g/kg T2: 20 g/kg T3: 30 g/kg T4: 40 g/kg	5 weeks	Decreased serum cholesterol, triglycerides, and LDL, increased serum HDL.	[81]
Japanese Quail	7 days old	60 CON, 60 per TRT	Spearmint	T1: 1% T2: 2% T3: 3% T4: 4%	28 days	Decreased serum cholesterol, triglycerides, and LDL.	[153]

[1] NA: Not available/not applicable. [2] NA: Not available/not applicable, CON: Control group, TRT: Treatment group. [3] T: Treatment group number, Pep: Peppermint, Mnt: Mint. [4] NA: Not available/not applicable. [5] HDL: High-density lipoprotein, LDL: Low-density lipoprotein, VLDL: Very low-density lipoprotein, TRP: Transient receptor potential.

7.1. Serum Urea

The presence of urea in blood serum is inextricably linked to ammonia. Ammonia is either produced by protein breakdown in the body or absorbed through the gastrointestinal tract [154]. A buildup of ammonia is toxic to the body, so the urea cycle in the liver converts ammonia to urea, which is then excreted in urine [155]. As previously discussed, several studies reported decreased ammonia in the rumens of livestock after feed supplementation. Thus, it is possible that serum urea levels could be affected in turn. Some results support this notion in ruminants. When Kholif et al. supplemented cattle with 3 or 6 g/day of Aromix® for 3 months, they observed a significant decrease in serum urea (20.3–21.4 g/dL) at both doses compared to the control group (22.8 g/dL), which they attributed to reduced protein catabolism [48]. Similarly, sheep supplemented with 3% dried peppermint over a 90-day period had lower serum urea concentrations throughout the trial, reaching significance during the middle period, which was attributed to a reduction in rumen ammonia [57]. In another study, lactating Holstein–Friesian cattle supplemented with 1.2 g/day of BTX12 had reduced serum urea and urinary ammonia levels, also likely due to antimicrobial activity against proteolytic bacteria [50]. It is speculated that a TRP channel-stimulated increase in protonated ammonium cation absorption over ammonia could reduce blood pH, stimulating glutamine synthesis through liver glutamine synthetase. An increase in glutamine, as a key form of ammonia transport for excretion and amino acid synthesis, could facilitate protein synthesis for lactating cattle [50]. This explanation aligns with other observed effects of menthol, such as increased serum protein levels and TRP-facilitated ion absorption. In contrast, another study found that serum urea levels increased after 5% peppermint supplementation to Holstein steers over 2 weeks, aligning with an observed increase in rumen ammonia [54]. While differing in results, the study affirms the link between levels of rumen ammonia and serum urea. Other studies found no difference in serum urea concentration in cattle and sheep [51,56]; however, despite not reporting a significant difference in serum urea, Patra et al. reported an increase in serum amino acids such as glutamine, glutamate, and aspartate in supplemented Suffolk sheep. They also attributed this to ammonium absorption upregulating glutamine synthetase, lending further evidence to menthol's potential to improve protein efficiency.

7.2. Serum Protein and Amino Acids

Coinciding with serum urea reduction, there is evidence suggesting serum protein concentration is increased by menthol-containing compound supplementation. As discussed previously, Patra et al. observed an increase in serum amino acids after supplementing sheep with OAX17 [56]. In agreement with their findings on blood urea, Kholif et al. also found an increase in blood protein levels compared to controls for lactating cattle fed 3–6 g/day of Aromix® [48]. In a related study, serum protein levels after 3 g/day of Aromix® treatment were increased, even with no change to serum urea concentration [51]. However, other ruminant studies found no effect on serum protein after peppermint feeding [54,89], even with reduced blood urea [50,57]. These discrepancies could be due to factors such as animal breed, supplement differences, and other physiological variables [89].

Poultry studies similarly show evidence of the regulation of blood protein concentration by menthol. Chickens supplemented with peppermint ranging from 74 to 296 mg per kg of feed showed a linear increase in serum protein levels [77]. Other studies similarly reported increased serum protein in chickens after peppermint supplementation [65,73,76]. These results reflect improvements in poultry feed digestibility, specifically for protein, as discussed previously. However, like ruminants, several studies found no changes in serum protein, suggesting other factors also play a role [61,63,72,75,98,152].

7.3. Serum Glucose

Menthol impacts on another important blood metabolite, glucose, were also investigated in several studies. Consistent with their findings on feed intake and nutrient digestibility, Kholif et al. reported dose-dependent effects of Aromix® on cattle serum glucose levels, where cattle fed 3 g daily had higher serum glucose levels than the control group, and an increase to 6 g/day led to a decrease in serum glucoses [48,51]. Specifically, they attribute the increased level of serum glucose to an increase in precursor molecules such as propionate after 3 g of supplementation, suggesting menthol's effect on serum glucose is mediated through the regulation of carbohydrate digestion in the rumen. Another study observed an increase in serum glucose from 54.57 mg/dL in control animals to 70.73 mg/dL in rams fed 30 mL of peppermint oil per kg of feed [89]. However, increased serum glucose or rumen volatile fatty acid concentrations were not found in another study supplementing cattle with peppermint at 5% of diet [54]. Similarly, Patra et al. found no difference in the serum glucose levels of sheep supplemented with up to 160 mg of OAX17 per day [56]. However, they found that sheep fed menthol-containing compounds before slaughter displayed a tendency for improved glucose uptake in the absence of Na^+. Thus, they suggest menthol may have stimulatory effects on Na^+ independent glucose transporters (GLUT), such as GLUT-2 and GLUT-5. Given menthol's action on TRP ion channels, stimulatory effects on other transporters may be possible [156]. Unlike protein concentrations, poultry studies generally found no difference in serum glucose levels after supplementation [63,65,72,77,78,98]. Overall, evidence suggests menthol compounds may significantly increase blood glucose levels through various mechanisms in ruminants, but evidence suggests the same may not be the case in poultry.

7.4. Serum Triglycerides and Cholesterol

Like humans, livestock are susceptible to lipid-related diseases. These diseases are often associated with serum levels of cholesterol and triglycerides. Dairy cattle are particularly susceptible to fatty liver disease, where fat is directed to the liver in response to lactation energy deficits. Decreased serum cholesterol and triglyceride levels have been associated with fatty liver disease in cattle [157]. In poultry, decreased serum lipid profiles are considered preferable for the quality and health of the meat [158,159].

Studies suggest menthol-containing compounds can impact cholesterol and related biomolecules in ruminants. Kholif et al.'s studies on cattle found significant decreases in serum cholesterol levels, as well as triglycerides and total lipids, after Aromix® supplementation [48,51]. 3-hydroxy-3-methylglutaryl-CoA reductase (HMGCR) catalyzes the reaction converting HMG-CoA to mevalonate, a key precursor to cholesterol [160]. As a key irreversible reaction in cholesterol synthesis, the reaction catalyzed by HMGCR is the primary site of cholesterol regulation. Menthol and other monoterpenes have demonstrated the ability to suppress the activity and synthesis of HMGCR [161–164]. While Kholif et al. treated cattle with the blended supplement Aromix®, they concluded that the phytogenic compounds in the supplement must impart most of the cholesterol-suppressing effect, based on previous studies [48]. Some other ruminant studies did not find significant changes in the serum levels of cholesterol or related lipoproteins after supplementation with peppermint [54,89] or OAX17 [56], suggesting that factors other than menthol are likely to contribute to the regulation of these molecules as well.

However, there exists an even greater body of evidence for menthol's cholesterol-modulating activity in poultry studies. Serum cholesterol level was lower in quail supplemented with 10–40 g of peppermint supplementation per kg of feed compared with control birds (2.92–3.47 nmol/L vs. 3.85–3.00 nmol/L) [81]. A decrease in low-density lipoprotein (LDL) and triglycerides and an increase in high-density lipoprotein (HDL) were also observed in supplemented quail [81]. Reduced serum cholesterol and other lipid metabolites after peppermint and menthol-containing blended supplements were also observed in numerous chicken trials at various life stages [65,76,77,98]. One study reported significantly decreased cholesterol, triglyceride, and lipoprotein profiles in quail fed 1–4% spearmint or *Mentha spicata* (*M. spicata*) for 28 days [153]. While the study also acknowledged the possible role of HMGCR suppression in these effects, it also reported an increase in Lactobacillus species in the guts of quail supplemented with the plant. Prior research associated Lactobacillus presence in the gut with an improved cholesterol profile [165]. *M. spicata* possesses relatively little menthol compared to *M. piperita*, but a different study achieved similar results for chickens supplemented with 3 kg of a peppermint-containing phytogenic blend per ton of feed for 42 days, supporting menthol's role in the observed effects of *M. spicata* [61]. The study reported decreased blood cholesterol and increased Lactobacillus presence in the small intestine of treated animals compared to controls. Thus, it is likely that menthol's effects on cholesterol also stem from its gut bacteria modulation activity. Other chicken studies observed a decrease in cholesterol and triglyceride levels when peppermint supplementation was paired with thyme and chromium [78,80]. A few poultry studies did not find a decrease in cholesterol and lipid levels from peppermint and other menthol-containing supplements [63,72,75]. In contrast to most studies, Bai et al. reported that 28 days of 0.1–0.4% peppermint supplementation in laying hens tended to increase serum cholesterol and significantly increased triglycerides compared to control hens [73]. The reason for this increase is not entirely clear. Despite this, there is a significant body of evidence suggesting that menthol can serve as an effective mediator of serum cholesterol and lipid profiles in ruminants and poultry.

7.5. Serum Calcium

Finally, menthol has been shown to improve calcium absorption and serum calcium levels in ruminants. Ruminants, especially dairy cattle, often experience a condition known as hypocalcemia, or milk fever. Hypocalcemia occurs from a disruption in calcium homeostasis, causing a deficiency in blood calcium levels [166]. A lack of available calcium can cause a range of physiological dysfunctions, especially with muscle function. Hypocalcemia often occurs around calving and lactation periods due to the high calcium demands of milk production [167]. Menthol's agonistic activity on TRP channels, such as the cold-sensing TRPM8 channel, has been extensively demonstrated [8]. TRP channel signaling is carried out through cations such as Ca^{2+} and has been found to play a significant role in calcium absorption and homeostasis [168,169]. As such, menthol has been investigated as a potential preventer of hypocalcemia. A pair of in vitro studies demonstrated pure menthol's ability to stimulate calcium absorbance in cow and sheep rumen epithelia [170,171]. It was found that 10–100 μmol/L applied to epithelial cells was able to increase the absorption of Ca^{2+} ions. Through overexpressing the ion channel bTRPV3, intracellular Ca^{2+} levels rose in response to menthol stimulation, likely by binding to and stabilizing the channel's open state [171]. Another study affirmed these findings, finding a prominent presence of TRPV3 in the rumen of sheep [172]. They also demonstrated enhanced transcellular Ca^{2+} transport through rumen epithelial cells treated with 50 μM menthol. Additionally, rumen epithelial cells from sheep fed 80–160 mg of OAX17 per day before slaughter showed an enhanced response to menthol stimulation in vitro, with greater tissue conductivity. The study suggests that extended exposure to menthol can prime these TRP channels for greater future cation absorption. Significant Ca^{2+} absorption and TRPV3 channels were not detected in the jejunum, suggesting that menthol's calcium stimulatory effects occur primarily in the rumen, as opposed to the intestines [172].

In vivo studies found a rise in serum calcium, coinciding with Ca^{2+} absorption observed in vitro. Serum calcium levels were significantly higher in cattle fed 1.2 g/day of BTX12 over two 20-day periods (2.53 nmol/L) compared to the control group (2.46 nmol/L), but urine calcium levels did not differ between the groups, indicating enhanced calcium absorption without substantially increased excretion [50]. Other studies of cattle supplemented with 400 g/day of peppermint [151] and 3–6/day of Aromix® [51] found a significant increase in serum calcium levels, suggesting this effect can be produced with a wide range of menthol-containing supplements. A 28-day trial reported a tendency for serum calcium to increase in sheep fed 160 g/day of OAX17, but not in sheep fed only 80 g/day [56]. Furthermore, increased calcium digestibility was observed in the rumens of sheep fed 3% peppermint [57]. The results of these studies suggest that menthol can stimulate calcium absorption not only through direct interaction with TRP channels but also through the modulation of pH and nutrient digestibility. However, a different study by Kholif et al. did not observe effects on serum calcium [48], and poultry studies did not observe significant alterations in serum calcium profiles after peppermint supplementation [65,72,77].

Overall, several serum parameters can be altered by the consumption of menthol-containing compounds. Calcium and various lipids are chief among them, with urea, protein, and glucose also potentially being regulated.

8. Current Gaps and Future Directions

Despite current studies on menthol's effects in livestock, many future avenues for study and elaboration still exist. There is a particularly notable gap in the current literature investigating the use of menthol for its cooling and pain-relieving properties in livestock. As previously discussed, one of menthol's most established properties is its ability to stimulate TRPM8 cold receptors [8,173]. When used in conjunction with other cooling strategies such as fans and misters, menthol holds the potential to further offset animal heat stress. Some of the previous studies utilized phytogenic supplementation in animals under heat stress conditions, where subsequent improvements in behavior, immunity, nutrition, and serum were observed [49,71,76,80]. However, the quantity of literature investigating the effects of menthol and heat stress together is limited, and menthol's effects on stress biomarkers such as cortisol remain unreported. There is evidence for heat stress in cattle resulting in increased cortisol, adrenaline, and various pro-inflammatory cytokines [86,174]. Furthermore, human and animal trials suggest that menthol can mitigate the physiological effects of heat stress, including elevated cortisol [175–177]. As such, topical or oral administration of menthol holds the potential to improve livestock welfare in hot climates. Furthermore, menthol's analgesic properties [37] may possess utility in painful procedures such as cattle dehorning and castration.

Another limitation of previous studies arises from the use of Mentha products and mixed phytogenic blends over pure menthol. While peppermint's primary active ingredient is menthol, the plant also contains prominent compounds such as menthone and menthyl acetate, as well as numerous others such as acetaldehyde, pinene, etc. [178,179]. Additionally, menthol concentration varies, even between individual plants of the same species, with one study reporting concentrations ranging from 35.01 to 47.50% [180]. Furthermore, the percentage of menthol correlates with the plant's antibacterial effectiveness [107,119]. While most studies utilizing these "impure" supplements obtained results comparable to those using pure menthol, their results may be unreliable in the context of elucidating the effects of menthol alone.

There are other yet-unknown factors that may contribute to menthol's effects on livestock, such as understudied metabolites of menthol, especially oxidized products, and their potential impacts on animals. As previously discussed, menthol is primarily absorbed in the small intestine [29]. Differences in digestive system physiology and gastrointestinal microbiomes between ruminants and monogastric animals may influence their responses to menthol supplementation. For instance, while menthol's antimicrobial properties are well established, it remains largely unexplored whether microbes in the rumen or hindgut can degrade menthol into specific metabolites, which may then be absorbed through the rumen, small intestine, or large intestine and subsequently regulate host physiology.

Finally, optimal dosages for menthol supplementation in livestock production remain unclear. Given menthol's antimicrobial properties, overuse has the potential to detrimentally affect host digestion and metabolic equilibrium. Higher doses of menthol can also cause damage to the eukaryotic cells of the animal. Varying results were reported between studies for most physiological and metabolic parameters. Differences in menthol supplementation dosages and experimental protocols likely contributed to differing results between studies. The varied menthol forms, from pure menthol to peppermint and commercial supplement blends, also confound the search for an ideal dosage. Thus, more standardized supplementation procedures would be ideal for future studies seeking to optimize the dosage of these compounds for different animals.

9. Conclusions

In conclusion, menthol holds promise for modulating behavioral, microbial, and biochemical parameters in ruminant and poultry livestock, just as it has in humans. Physiologically and economically important effects include alterations to feed intake and feeding behavior, improved FCR and animal product quality, increased absorption of ions such as Ca^{2+} and ammonium, decreased pro-inflammatory cytokines and ROS, destruction of harmful arthropods and microorganisms on and within the animal, reduced methane production, and alterations to feed digestibility and various serum nutrient profiles. Beyond these effects, there remain other underexplored applications for livestock, such as managing heat stress and pain response. Further research into optimizing this supplement for use in a wider livestock industry setting could help alleviate growing issues in livestock production, such as heat stress, antimicrobial resistance, and nitrogen and methane pollution.

Author Contributions: B.B. and H.J. wrote the first version of the manuscript with the supervision of P.F. edited the manuscript. All authors have read and agreed to the published version of the manuscript.

Funding: This research was funded by National Institute of Food and Agriculture, U.S. Department of Agriculture, under the award number 2024-67015-42622 to PF, USDA's Agricultural Research Service Internship Program, and Mississippi State University College of Agriculture and Life Science/Mississippi Agricultural and Forestry Experiment Station Undergraduate Research Scholars Program.

Conflicts of Interest: The authors declare no conflicts of interest.

References

1. Kamatou, G.P.P.; Vermaak, I.; Viljoen, A.M.; Lawrence, B.M. Menthol: A Simple Monoterpene with Remarkable Biological Properties. *Phytochemistry* **2013**, *96*, 15–25. [CrossRef] [PubMed]
2. Gholamipourfard, K.; Salehi, M.; Banchio, E. *Mentha piperita* Phytochemicals in Agriculture, Food Industry and Medicine: Features and Applications. *S. Afr. J. Bot.* **2021**, *141*, 183–195. [CrossRef]
3. Dylong, D.; Hausoul, P.J.C.; Palkovits, R.; Eisenacher, M. Synthesis of (−)-menthol: Industrial Synthesis Routes and Recent Development. *Flavour. Fragr. J.* **2022**, *37*, 195–209. [CrossRef]
4. Kotan, R.; Kordali, S.; Cakir, A. Screening of Antibacterial Activities of Twenty-One Oxygenated Monoterpenes. *Z. Naturforschung C* **2007**, *62*, 507–513. [CrossRef] [PubMed]
5. Singh, R.; Shushni, M.A.M.; Belkheir, A. Antibacterial and Antioxidant Activities of *Mentha piperita* L. *Arab. J. Chem.* **2015**, *8*, 322–328. [CrossRef]
6. Azmi, N.A.N.; Elgharbawy, A.; Salleh, H.M.; Hayyan, A. Evaluation of the Antimicrobial Performance of Menthol and Menthol-Based Deep Eutectic Solvents as Potential Future Antibiotic. *E3S Web Conf.* **2021**, *287*, 02010. [CrossRef]
7. Pergolizzi, J.V.; Taylor, R.; LeQuang, J.-A.; Raffa, R.B. The Role and Mechanism of Action of Menthol in Topical Analgesic Products. *J. Clin. Pharm. Ther.* **2018**, *43*, 313–319. [CrossRef]
8. Cheng, H.; An, X. Cold Stimuli, Hot Topic: An Updated Review on the Biological Activity of Menthol in Relation to Inflammation. *Front. Immunol.* **2022**, *13*, 1023746. [CrossRef]
9. Rozza, A.L.; Beserra, F.P.; Vieira, A.J.; Oliveira de Souza, E.; Hussni, C.A.; Martinez, E.R.M.; Nóbrega, R.H.; Pellizzon, C.H. The Use of Menthol in Skin Wound Healing—Anti-Inflammatory Potential, Antioxidant Defense System Stimulation and Increased Epithelialization. *Pharmaceutics* **2021**, *13*, 1902. [CrossRef]
10. Rozza, A.L.; Meira de Faria, F.; Souza Brito, A.R.; Pellizzon, C.H. The Gastroprotective Effect of Menthol: Involvement of Anti-Apoptotic, Antioxidant and Anti-Inflammatory Activities. *PLoS ONE* **2014**, *9*, e86686. [CrossRef]
11. Liu, Z.; Shen, C.; Tao, Y.; Wang, S.; Wei, Z.; Cao, Y.; Wu, H.; Fan, F.; Lin, C.; Shan, Y.; et al. Chemopreventive Efficacy of Menthol on Carcinogen-Induced Cutaneous Carcinoma through Inhibition of Inflammation and Oxidative Stress in Mice. *Food Chem. Toxicol.* **2015**, *82*, 12–18. [CrossRef] [PubMed]

12. Ghasemi-Pirbaluti, M.; Motaghi, E.; Bozorgi, H. The Effect of Menthol on Acute Experimental Colitis in Rats. *Eur. J. Pharmacol.* **2017**, *805*, 101–107. [CrossRef] [PubMed]
13. Willis, D.N.; Liu, B.; Ha, M.A.; Jordt, S.-E.; Morris, J.B. Menthol Attenuates Respiratory Irritation Responses to Multiple Cigarette Smoke Irritants. *FASEB J.* **2011**, *25*, 4434–4444. [CrossRef]
14. Lee, V.; Linden, R. An Olfactory-submandibular Salivary Reflex in Humans. *Exp. Physiol.* **1992**, *77*, 221–224. [CrossRef]
15. Haahr, A.; Bardow, A.; Thomsen, C.; Jensen, S.; Nauntofte, B.; Bakke, M.; Adlernissen, J.; Bredie, W. Release of Peppermint Flavour Compounds from Chewing Gum: Effect of Oral Functions. *Physiol. Behav.* **2004**, *82*, 531–540. [CrossRef]
16. Davies, G.A.; Wantling, E.; Stokes, J.R. The Influence of Beverages on the Stimulation and Viscoelasticity of Saliva: Relationship to Mouthfeel? *Food Hydrocoll.* **2009**, *23*, 2261–2269. [CrossRef]
17. Hutchings, S.C.; Horner, K.M.; Dible, V.A.; Grigor, J.M.V.; O'Riordan, D. Modification of Aftertaste with a Menthol Mouthwash Reduces Food Wanting, Liking, and Ad Libitum Intake of Potato Crisps. *Appetite* **2017**, *108*, 57–67. [CrossRef] [PubMed]
18. Sneeringer, S. Restrictions on Antibiotic Use for Production Purposes in U.S. In *Livestock Industries Likely To Have Small Effects on Prices and Quantities*; Economic Research Service: Washington, DC, USA, 2016. Available online: https://www.ers.usda.gov/data-products/charts-of-note/chart-detail?chartId=78736#:~:text=Modelling%20the%20effect%20of%20production,of%20less%20than%200.5%20percent (accessed on 5 March 2025).
19. He, Y.; Yuan, Q.; Mathieu, J.; Stadler, L.; Senehi, N.; Sun, R.; Alvarez, P.J.J. Antibiotic Resistance Genes from Livestock Waste: Occurrence, Dissemination, and Treatment. *NPJ Clean. Water* **2020**, *3*, 4. [CrossRef]
20. Tseten, T.; Sanjorjo, R.A.; Kwon, M.; Kim, S.-W. Strategies to Mitigate Enteric Methane Emissions from Ruminant Animals. *J. Microbiol. Biotechnol.* **2022**, *32*, 269–277. [CrossRef]
21. Balasubramanian, B.; Liu, W.-C. Editorial: Gut Microbiota: Allied with Livestock Nutrition, Health, and Welfare. *Front. Vet. Sci.* **2024**, *11*, 1413671. [CrossRef]
22. Wasti, S.; Sah, N.; Mishra, B. Impact of Heat Stress on Poultry Health and Performances, and Potential Mitigation Strategies. *Animals* **2020**, *10*, 1266. [CrossRef] [PubMed]
23. Thornton, P.; Nelson, G.; Mayberry, D.; Herrero, M. Impacts of Heat Stress on Global Cattle Production during the 21st Century: A Modelling Study. *Lancet Planet. Health* **2022**, *6*, e192–e201. [CrossRef]
24. Abdelli, N.; Solà-Oriol, D.; Pérez, J.F. Phytogenic Feed Additives in Poultry: Achievements, Prospective and Challenges. *Animals* **2021**, *11*, 3471. [CrossRef] [PubMed]
25. Wells, C.W. Effects of Essential Oils on Economically Important Characteristics of Ruminant Species: A Comprehensive Review. *Anim. Nutr.* **2024**, *16*, 1–10. [CrossRef]
26. Wang, J.; Deng, L.; Chen, M.; Che, Y.; Li, L.; Zhu, L.; Chen, G.; Feng, T. Phytogenic Feed Additives as Natural Antibiotic Alternatives in Animal Health and Production: A Review of the Literature of the Last Decade. *Anim. Nutr.* **2024**, *17*, 244–264. [CrossRef]
27. Tchimene, M.K.; Okunji, C.O.; Iwu, M.M.; Kuete, V. Monoterpenes and Related Compounds from the Medicinal Plants of Africa. In *Medicinal Plant Research in Africa*; Elsevier: Amsterdam, The Netherlands, 2013; pp. 1–32.
28. FDA. *Substances Added to Food (Formerly EAFUS)*; Food and Drug Administration: Silver Spring, MD, USA, 2018. Available online: https://www.hfpappexternal.fda.gov/scripts/fdcc/index.cfm?set=FoodSubstances&id=MENTHOL&sort=Sortterm_ID&order=ASC&startrow=1&type=basic&search=menthol (accessed on 5 March 2025).
29. Silva, H. Current Knowledge on the Vascular Effects of Menthol. *Front. Physiol.* **2020**, *11*, 298. [CrossRef] [PubMed]
30. Limpanuparb, T.; Lorpaiboon, W.; Chinsukserm, K. An in Silico Investigation of Menthol Metabolism. *PLoS ONE* **2019**, *14*, e0216577. [CrossRef]
31. Trombetta, D.; Castelli, F.; Sarpietro, M.G.; Venuti, V.; Cristani, M.; Daniele, C.; Saija, A.; Mazzanti, G.; Bisignano, G. Mechanisms of Antibacterial Action of Three Monoterpenes. *Antimicrob. Agents Chemother.* **2005**, *49*, 2474–2478. [CrossRef] [PubMed]
32. Wu, Z.; Tan, B.; Liu, Y.; Dunn, J.; Martorell Guerola, P.; Tortajada, M.; Cao, Z.; Ji, P. Chemical Composition and Antioxidant Properties of Essential Oils from Peppermint, Native Spearmint and Scotch Spearmint. *Molecules* **2019**, *24*, 2825. [CrossRef]
33. Bautista, D.M.; Siemens, J.; Glazer, J.M.; Tsuruda, P.R.; Basbaum, A.I.; Stucky, C.L.; Jordt, S.-E.; Julius, D. The Menthol Receptor TRPM8 Is the Principal Detector of Environmental Cold. *Nature* **2007**, *448*, 204–208. [CrossRef]
34. Xing, H.; Ling, J.X.; Chen, M.; Johnson, R.D.; Tominaga, M.; Wang, C.-Y.; Gu, J. TRPM8 Mechanism of Autonomic Nerve Response to Cold in Respiratory Airway. *Mol. Pain* **2008**, *4*, 22. [CrossRef]
35. Nealen, M.L.; Gold, M.S.; Thut, P.D.; Caterina, M.J. TRPM8 MRNA Is Expressed in a Subset of Cold-Responsive Trigeminal Neurons From Rat. *J. Neurophysiol.* **2003**, *90*, 515–520. [CrossRef] [PubMed]
36. Abe, J.; Hosokawa, H.; Okazawa, M.; Kandachi, M.; Sawada, Y.; Yamanaka, K.; Matsumura, K.; Kobayashi, S. TRPM8 Protein Localization in Trigeminal Ganglion and Taste Papillae. *Mol. Brain Res.* **2005**, *136*, 91–98. [CrossRef]
37. Liu, B.; Fan, L.; Balakrishna, S.; Sui, A.; Morris, J.B.; Jordt, S.-E. TRPM8 Is the Principal Mediator of Menthol-Induced Analgesia of Acute and Inflammatory Pain. *Pain* **2013**, *154*, 2169–2177. [CrossRef] [PubMed]

38. Li, Z.; Zhang, H.; Wang, Y.; Li, Y.; Li, Q.; Zhang, L. The Distinctive Role of Menthol in Pain and Analgesia: Mechanisms, Practices, and Advances. *Front. Mol. Neurosci.* **2022**, *15*, 1006908. [CrossRef] [PubMed]
39. Behrendt, H.; Germann, T.; Gillen, C.; Hatt, H.; Jostock, R. Characterization of the Mouse Cold—Menthol Receptor TRPM8 and Vanilloid Receptor Type—1 VR1 Using a Fluorometric Imaging Plate Reader (FLIPR) Assay. *Br. J. Pharmacol.* **2004**, *141*, 737–745. [CrossRef]
40. Nazıroğlu, M.; Blum, W.; Jósvay, K.; Çiğ, B.; Henzi, T.; Oláh, Z.; Vizler, C.; Schwaller, B.; Pecze, L. Menthol Evokes Ca^{2+} Signals and Induces Oxidative Stress Independently of the Presence of TRPM8 (Menthol) Receptor in Cancer Cells. *Redox Biol.* **2018**, *14*, 439–449. [CrossRef]
41. Takaishi, M.; Uchida, K.; Suzuki, Y.; Matsui, H.; Shimada, T.; Fujita, F.; Tominaga, M. Reciprocal Effects of Capsaicin and Menthol on Thermosensation through Regulated Activities of TRPV1 and TRPM8. *J. Physiol. Sci.* **2016**, *66*, 143–155. [CrossRef]
42. Nguyen, T.H.D.; Itoh, S.G.; Okumura, H.; Tominaga, M. Structural Basis for Promiscuous Action of Monoterpenes on TRP Channels. *Commun. Biol.* **2021**, *4*, 293. [CrossRef]
43. Zhang, Z.; Wu, X.; Zhang, L.; Mao, A.; Ma, X.; He, D. Menthol Relieves Acid Reflux Inflammation by Regulating TRPV1 in Esophageal Epithelial Cells. *Biochem. Biophys. Res. Commun.* **2020**, *525*, 113–120. [CrossRef]
44. Rosenbaum, T.; Morales-Lázaro, S.L.; Islas, L.D. TRP Channels: A Journey towards a Molecular Understanding of Pain. *Nat. Rev. Neurosci.* **2022**, *23*, 596–610. [CrossRef] [PubMed]
45. Yin, Y.; Park, C.-G.; Zhang, F.; Fedor, J.G.; Feng, S.; Suo, Y.; Im, W.; Lee, S.-Y. Mechanisms of Sensory Adaptation and Inhibition of the Cold and Menthol Receptor TRPM8. *Sci. Adv.* **2024**, *10*, eadp2211. [CrossRef] [PubMed]
46. Castillo-Lopez, E.; Rivera-Chacon, R.; Ricci, S.; Petri, R.M.; Reisinger, N.; Zebeli, Q. Short-Term Screening of Multiple Phytogenic Compounds for Their Potential to Modulate Chewing Behavior, Ruminal Fermentation Profile, and PH in Cattle Fed Grain-Rich Diets. *J. Dairy Sci.* **2021**, *104*, 4271–4289. [CrossRef] [PubMed]
47. Ricci, S.; Rivera-Chacon, R.; Petri, R.M.; Sener-Aydemir, A.; Sharma, S.; Reisinger, N.; Zebeli, Q.; Castillo-Lopez, E. Supplementation With Phytogenic Compounds Modulates Salivation and Salivary Physico-Chemical Composition in Cattle Fed a High-Concentrate Diet. *Front. Physiol.* **2021**, *12*, 645529. [CrossRef]
48. Kholif, A.E.; Hassan, A.A.; El Ashry, G.M.; Bakr, M.H.; El-Zaiat, H.M.; Olafadehan, O.A.; Matloup, O.H.; Sallam, S.M.A. Phytogenic Feed Additives Mixture Enhances the Lactational Performance, Feed Utilization and Ruminal Fermentation of Friesian Cows. *Anim. Biotechnol.* **2021**, *32*, 708–718. [CrossRef]
49. Reza-Yazdi, K.; Fallah, M.; Khodaparast, M.; Kateb, F.; Hosseini-Ghaffari, M. Effects of Specific Essential Oil Compounds on, Feed Intake, Milk Production, and Ruminal Environment in Dairy Cows during Heat Exposure. *Int. J. Biol. Vet. Agric. Food Eng.* **2014**, *8*, 1242–1245.
50. Braun, H.-S.; Schrapers, K.T.; Mahlkow-Nerge, K.; Stumpff, F.; Rosendahl, J. Dietary Supplementation of Essential Oils in Dairy Cows: Evidence for Stimulatory Effects on Nutrient Absorption. *Animal* **2019**, *13*, 518–523. [CrossRef]
51. Kholif, A.E.; Hassan, A.A.; Matloup, O.H.; El Ashry, G.M. Top-Dressing of Chelated Phytogenic Feed Additives in the Diet of Lactating Friesian Cows to Enhance Feed Utilization and Lactational Performance. *Ann. Anim. Sci.* **2021**, *21*, 657–673. [CrossRef]
52. Hosoda, K.; Matsuyama, H.; Park, W.; Nishida, T.; Ishida, M. Supplementary Effect of Peppermint (*Mentha* × *Piperita*) on Dry Matter Intake, Digestibility, Ruminal Fermentation and Milk Production in Early Lactating Dairy Cows. *Anim. Sci. J.* **2006**, *77*, 503–509. [CrossRef]
53. Hosoda, K.; Nishida, T.; Park, W.-Y.; Eruden, B. Influence of *Mentha*×*piperita* L. (*Peppermint*) Supplementation on Nutrient Digestibility and Energy Metabolism in Lactating Dairy Cows. *Asian-Australas. J. Anim. Sci.* **2005**, *18*, 1721–1726. [CrossRef]
54. Hosoda, K.; Kuramoto, K.; Eruden, B.; Nishida, T.; Shioya, S. The Effects of Three Herbs as Feed Supplements on Blood Metabolites, Hormones, Antioxidant Activity, IgG Concentration, and Ruminal Fermentation in Holstein Steers. *Asian-Australas. J. Anim. Sci.* **2005**, *19*, 35–41. [CrossRef]
55. Patra, A.K.; Geiger, S.; Braun, H.-S.; Aschenbach, J.R. Dietary Supplementation of Menthol-Rich Bioactive Lipid Compounds Alters Circadian Eating Behaviour of Sheep. *BMC Vet. Res.* **2019**, *15*, 352. [CrossRef]
56. Patra, A.K.; Geiger, S.; Schrapers, K.T.; Braun, H.-S.; Gehlen, H.; Starke, A.; Pieper, R.; Cieslak, A.; Szumacher-Strabel, M.; Aschenbach, J.R. Effects of Dietary Menthol-Rich Bioactive Lipid Compounds on Zootechnical Traits, Blood Variables and Gastrointestinal Function in Growing Sheep. *J. Anim. Sci. Biotechnol.* **2019**, *10*, 86. [CrossRef] [PubMed]
57. Khamisabadi, H.; Kafilzadeh, F.; Charaien, B. Effect of Thyme (*Thymus vulgaris*) or Peppermint (*Mentha piperita*) on Performance, Digestibility and Blood Metabolites of Fattening Sanjabi Lambs. *Biharean Biol.* **2016**, *10*, 118–122.
58. Verma, V.; Chaudhary, L.C.; Agarwal, N.; Bhar, R.; Kamra, D.N. Effect of Feeding Mixture of Garlic Bulb and Peppermint Oil on Methane Emission, Rumen Fermentation and Microbial Profile in Buffaloes. *Anim. Nutr. Feed Technol.* **2012**, *12*, 157–164.
59. Abdel-Wareth, A.A.A.; Kehraus, S.; Südekum, K.-H. Peppermint and Its Respective Active Component in Diets of Broiler Chickens: Growth Performance, Viability, Economics, Meat Physicochemical Properties, and Carcass Characteristics. *Poult. Sci.* **2019**, *98*, 3850–3859. [CrossRef] [PubMed]

60. Bajagai, Y.S.; Petranyi, F.; Yu, S.J.; Lobo, E.; Batacan, R.; Kayal, A.; Horyanto, D.; Ren, X.; Whitton, M.M.; Stanley, D. Phytogenic Supplement Containing Menthol, Carvacrol and Carvone Ameliorates Gut Microbiota and Production Performance of Commercial Layers. *Sci. Rep.* **2022**, *12*, 11033. [CrossRef]
61. Rashid, Z.; Mirani, Z.A.; Zehra, S.; Gilani, S.M.H.; Ashraf, A.; Azhar, A.; Al-Ghanim, K.A.; Al-Misned, F.; Al-Mulahim, N.; Mahboob, S.; et al. Enhanced Modulation of Gut Microbial Dynamics Affecting Body Weight in Birds Triggered by Natural Growth Promoters Administered in Conventional Feed. *Saudi J. Biol. Sci.* **2020**, *27*, 2747–2755. [CrossRef]
62. Hafeez, A.; Männer, K.; Schieder, C.; Zentek, J. Effect of Supplementation of Phytogenic Feed Additives (Powdered vs. Encapsulated) on Performance and Nutrient Digestibility in Broiler Chickens. *Poult. Sci.* **2016**, *95*, 622–629. [CrossRef]
63. Paraskeuas, V.; Fegeros, K.; Palamidi, I.; Hunger, C.; Mountzouris, K.C. Growth Performance, Nutrient Digestibility, Antioxidant Capacity, Blood Biochemical Biomarkers and Cytokines Expression in Broiler Chickens Fed Different Phytogenic Levels. *Anim. Nutr.* **2017**, *3*, 114–120. [CrossRef]
64. Narimani-Rad, M.; Nobakht, A.; Shahryar, H.A.; Kamani, J.; Lotfi, A. Influence of Dietary Supplemented Medicinal Plants Mixture (*Ziziphora, Oregano* and *Peppermint*) on Performance and Carcass Characterization of Broiler Chickens. *J. Med. Plants Res.* **2011**, *5*, 5626–5629.
65. Abdel-Wareth, A.A.A.; Lohakare, J.D. Effect of Dietary Supplementation of Peppermint on Performance, Egg Quality, and Serum Metabolic Profile of Hy-Line Brown Hens during the Late Laying Period. *Anim. Feed Sci. Technol.* **2014**, *197*, 114–120. [CrossRef]
66. Al-Kassie, G. The Role of Peppermint (*Mentha piperita*) on Performance in Broiler Diets. *Agric. Biol. J. N. Am.* **2010**, *1*, 1009–1013. [CrossRef]
67. Ocak, N.; Erener, G.; Ak, F.B.; Sungu, M.; Altop, A.; Ozmen, A. Performance of Broilers Fed Diets Supplemented with Dry Peppermint (*Mentha piperita* L.) or Thyme (*Thymus vulgaris* L.) Leaves as Growth Promoter Source. *Czech J. Anim. Sci.* **2008**, *53*, 169–175. [CrossRef]
68. Nanekarani, S.; Goodarzi, M.; Heidari, M.; Landy, N. Efficiency of Ethanolic Extract of Peppermint (*Mentha piperita*) as an Antibiotic Growth Promoter Substitution on Performance, and Carcass Characteristics in Broiler Chickens. *Asian Pac. J. Trop. Biomed.* **2012**, *2*, S1611–S1614. [CrossRef]
69. Khodambashi Emami, N.; Samie, A.; Rahmani, H.R.; Ruiz-Feria, C.A. The Effect of Peppermint Essential Oil and Fructooligosaccharides, as Alternatives to Virginiamycin, on Growth Performance, Digestibility, Gut Morphology and Immune Response of Male Broilers. *Anim. Feed Sci. Technol.* **2012**, *175*, 57–64. [CrossRef]
70. Khempaka, S.; Pudpila, U.; Molee, W. Effect of Dried Peppermint (*Mentha cordifolia*) on Growth Performance, Nutrient Digestibility, Carcass Traits, Antioxidant Properties, and Ammonia Production in Broilers. *J. Appl. Poult. Res.* **2013**, *22*, 904–912. [CrossRef]
71. Ameri, S.A.; Samadi, F.; Dastar, B.; Zarehdaran, S. Efficiency of Peppermint (*Mentha piperita*) Powder on Performance, Body Temperature and Carcass Characteristics of Broiler Chickens in Heat Stress Condition. *Iran. J. Appl. Anim. Sci.* **2016**, *6*, 943–950.
72. Rahman, A.; Bayram, I.; Gultepe, E.E. Effect of Mentha on Performance, Haematological and Biochemical Parameters in Laying Hens. *S. Afr. J. Anim. Sci.* **2021**, *51*, 221–230. [CrossRef]
73. Bai, M.; Liu, H.; Zhang, Y.; Wang, S.; Shao, Y.; Xiong, X.; Hu, X.; Yu, R.; Lan, W.; Cui, Y.; et al. Peppermint Extract Improves Egg Production and Quality, Increases Antioxidant Capacity, and Alters Cecal Microbiota in Late-Phase Laying Hens. *Front. Microbiol.* **2023**, *14*, 1252785. [CrossRef]
74. Gurbuz, Y.; Ismael, A. Effect of Peppermint and Basil as Feed Additive on Broiler Performance and Carcass Characteristics. *Iran. J. Appl. Anim. Sci.* **2016**, *6*, 123–126.
75. Toghyani, M.; Toghyani, M.; Gheisari, A.; Ghalamkari, G.; Mohammadrezaei, M. Growth Performance, Serum Biochemistry and Blood Hematology of Broiler Chicks Fed Different Levels of Black Seed (*Nigella sativa*) and Peppermint (*Mentha piperita*). *Livest. Sci.* **2010**, *129*, 173–178. [CrossRef]
76. Barbarestani, S.Y.; Samadi, F.; Hassani, S.; Asadi, S. Effects of Encapsulated Nano- and Microparticles of Peppermint (*Mentha piperita*) Alcoholic Extract on the Growth Performance, Blood Parameters and Immune Function of Broilers under Heat Stress Condition. *Iran. J. Appl. Anim. Sci.* **2017**, *7*, 669–677.
77. Abdel-Wareth, A.A.A.; Lohakare, J.D. Productive Performance, Egg Quality, Nutrients Digestibility, and Physiological Response of Bovans Brown Hens Fed Various Dietary Inclusion Levels of Peppermint Oil. *Anim. Feed Sci. Technol.* **2020**, *267*, 114554. [CrossRef]
78. Akbari, M.; Torki, M.; Kaviani, K. Single and Combined Effects of Peppermint and Thyme Essential Oils on Productive Performance, Egg Quality Traits, and Blood Parameters of Laying Hens Reared under Cold Stress Condition (6.8 ± 3 °C). *Int. J. Biometeorol.* **2016**, *60*, 447–454. [CrossRef]
79. Dilawar, M.A.; Mun, H.S.; Rathnayake, D.; Yang, E.J.; Seo, Y.S.; Park, H.S.; Yang, C.J. Egg Quality Parameters, Production Performance and Immunity of Laying Hens Supplemented with Plant Extracts. *Animals* **2021**, *11*, 975. [CrossRef] [PubMed]
80. Akbari, M.; Torki, M. Effects of Dietary Chromium Picolinate and Peppermint Essential Oil on Growth Performance and Blood Biochemical Parameters of Broiler Chicks Reared under Heat Stress Conditions. *Int. J. Biometeorol.* **2014**, *58*, 1383–1391. [CrossRef]

81. Mehri, M.; Sabaghi, V.; Bagherzadeh-Kasmani, F. *Mentha piperita* (*Peppermint*) in Growing Japanese Quails' Diet: Serum Biochemistry, Meat Quality, Humoral Immunity. *Anim. Feed Sci. Technol.* **2015**, *206*, 57–66. [CrossRef]
82. Lejonklev, J.; Kidmose, U.; Jensen, S.; Petersen, M.A.; Helwing, A.L.F.; Mortensen, G.; Weisbjerg, M.R.; Larsen, M.K. Short Communication: Effect of Oregano and Caraway Essential Oils on the Production and Flavor of Cow Milk. *J. Dairy. Sci.* **2016**, *99*, 7898–7903. [CrossRef]
83. Chen, L.; Deng, H.; Cui, H.; Fang, J.; Zuo, Z.; Deng, J.; Li, Y.; Wang, X.; Zhao, L. Inflammatory Responses and Inflammation-Associated Diseases in Organs. *Oncotarget* **2018**, *9*, 7204–7218. [CrossRef]
84. Tellez-Isaias, G.; Eisenreich, W.; Petrone-Garcia, V.M.; Hernandez-Velasco, X.; Castellanos-Huerta, C.-H.; Tellez, G., Jr.; Latorre, J.D.; Bottje, W.G.; Senas-Cuesta, R.; Coles, M.E.; et al. Effects of Chronic Stress and Intestinal Inflammation on Commercial Poultry Health and Performance: A Review. *Ger. J. Vet. Res.* **2023**, *3*, 38–57. [CrossRef]
85. Bradford, B.J.; Yuan, K.; Farney, J.K.; Mamedova, L.K.; Carpenter, A.J. Invited Review: Inflammation during the Transition to Lactation: New Adventures with an Old Flame. *J. Dairy. Sci.* **2015**, *98*, 6631–6650. [CrossRef]
86. Most, M.S.; Yates, D.T. Inflammatory Mediation of Heat Stress-Induced Growth Deficits in Livestock and Its Potential Role as a Target for Nutritional Interventions: A Review. *Animals* **2021**, *11*, 3539. [CrossRef] [PubMed]
87. Liu, S.; Guo, W.; Jia, Y.; Ye, B.; Liu, S.; Fu, S.; Liu, J.; Hu, G. Menthol Targeting AMPK Alleviates the Inflammatory Response of Bovine Mammary Epithelial Cells and Restores the Synthesis of Milk Fat and Milk Protein. *Front. Immunol.* **2021**, *12*, 782989. [CrossRef]
88. Rivera-Chacon, R.; Castillo-Lopez, E.; Ricci, S.; Petri, R.M.; Reisinger, N.; Zebeli, Q. Supplementing a Phytogenic Feed Additive Modulates the Risk of Subacute Rumen Acidosis, Rumen Fermentation and Systemic Inflammation in Cattle Fed Acidogenic Diets. *Animals* **2022**, *12*, 1201. [CrossRef] [PubMed]
89. Amini Pour, H.; Naserian, A.-A.; Vakili, A.R.; Tahmasbi, A.-M. The Effect of *Mentha piperita* Essential Oil on Biochemical and Haematological Parameters of Rams. *Res. Opin. Anim. Vet. Sci.* **2016**, *6*, 181–184. [CrossRef]
90. Bach, M.; Moon, J.; Moore, R.; Pan, T.; Nelson, J.L.; Lood, C. A Neutrophil Activation Biomarker Panel in Prognosis and Monitoring of Patients With Rheumatoid Arthritis. *Arthritis Rheumatol.* **2020**, *72*, 47–56. [CrossRef]
91. Bhikram, T.; Sandor, P. Neutrophil-Lymphocyte Ratios as Inflammatory Biomarkers in Psychiatric Patients. *Brain Behav. Immun.* **2022**, *105*, 237–246. [CrossRef]
92. Nambooppha, B.; Photichai, K.; Wongsawan, K.; Chuammitri, P. Quercetin Manipulates the Expression of Genes Involved in the Reactive Oxygen Species (ROS) Process in Chicken Heterophils. *J. Vet. Med. Sci.* **2018**, *80*, 1204–1211. [CrossRef]
93. Ruhs, E.C.; Martin, L.B.; Downs, C.J. The Impacts of Body Mass on Immune Cell Concentrations in Birds. *Proc. Biol. Sci.* **2020**, *287*, 20200655. [CrossRef]
94. Gross, W.B.; Siegel, H.S. Evaluation of the Heterophil/Lymphocyte Ratio as a Measure of Stress in Chickens. *Avian Dis.* **1983**, *27*, 972. [CrossRef]
95. Minias, P.; Włodarczyk, R.; Meissner, W. Leukocyte Profiles Are Associated with Longevity and Survival, but Not Migratory Effort: A Comparative Analysis of Shorebirds. *Funct. Ecol.* **2018**, *32*, 369–378. [CrossRef]
96. Minias, P. Evolution of Heterophil/Lymphocyte Ratios in Response to Ecological and Life—History Traits: A Comparative Analysis across the Avian Tree of Life. *J. Anim. Ecol.* **2019**, *88*, 554–565. [CrossRef]
97. Thiam, M.; Wang, Q.; Barreto Sánchez, A.L.; Zhang, J.; Ding, J.; Wang, H.; Zhang, Q.; Zhang, N.; Wang, J.; Li, Q.; et al. Heterophil/Lymphocyte Ratio Level Modulates Salmonella Resistance, Cecal Microbiota Composition and Functional Capacity in Infected Chicken. *Front. Immunol.* **2022**, *13*, 816689. [CrossRef]
98. Fallah, R.; Kiani, A.; Azarfar, A. Effect of Artichoke Leaves Meal and Mentha Extract (*Mentha piperita*) on Immune Cells And Blood Biochemical Parameters of Broilers. *Glob. Vet.* **2013**, *10*, 99–102.
99. Winterbourn, C.C.; Kettle, A.J.; Hampton, M.B. Reactive Oxygen Species and Neutrophil Function. *Annu. Rev. Biochem.* **2016**, *85*, 765–792. [CrossRef] [PubMed]
100. Tavassolifar, M.J.; Vodjgani, M.; Salehi, Z.; Izad, M. The Influence of Reactive Oxygen Species in the Immune System and Pathogenesis of Multiple Sclerosis. *Autoimmune Dis.* **2020**, *2020*, 5793817. [CrossRef]
101. Li, H.; Zhou, X.; Huang, Y.; Liao, B.; Cheng, L.; Ren, B. Reactive Oxygen Species in Pathogen Clearance: The Killing Mechanisms, the Adaption Response, and the Side Effects. *Front. Microbiol.* **2021**, *11*, 622534. [CrossRef]
102. Mittal, M.; Siddiqui, M.R.; Tran, K.; Reddy, S.P.; Malik, A.B. Reactive Oxygen Species in Inflammation and Tissue Injury. *Antioxid. Redox Signal.* **2014**, *20*, 1126–1167. [CrossRef]
103. Su, L.-J.; Zhang, J.-H.; Gomez, H.; Murugan, R.; Hong, X.; Xu, D.; Jiang, F.; Peng, Z.-Y. Reactive Oxygen Species-Induced Lipid Peroxidation in Apoptosis, Autophagy, and Ferroptosis. *Oxid. Med. Cell. Longev.* **2019**, *2019*, 5080843. [CrossRef]
104. Ghimpețeanu, O.M.; Pogurschi, E.N.; Popa, D.C.; Dragomir, N.; Drăgotoiu, T.; Mihai, O.D.; Petcu, C.D. Antibiotic Use in Livestock and Residues in Food-A Public Health Threat: A Review. *Foods* **2022**, *11*, 1430. [CrossRef] [PubMed]
105. Zhou, L.; Li, S.; Li, F. Damage and Elimination of Soil and Water Antibiotic and Heavy Metal Pollution Caused by Livestock Husbandry. *Environ. Res.* **2022**, *215*, 114188. [CrossRef] [PubMed]

106. Allcock, S.; Young, E.H.; Holmes, M.; Gurdasani, D.; Dougan, G.; Sandhu, M.S.; Solomon, L.; Török, M.E. Antimicrobial Resistance in Human Populations: Challenges and Opportunities. *Glob. Health Epidemiol. Genom.* **2017**, *2*, e4. [CrossRef]
107. İşcan, G.; Kirimer, N.; Kürkcüoğlu, M.; Başer, H.C.; Demirci, F. Antimicrobial Screening of *Mentha piperita* Essential Oils. *J. Agric. Food Chem.* **2002**, *50*, 3943–3946. [CrossRef]
108. Patel, T.; Ishiuji, Y.; Yosipovitch, G. Menthol: A Refreshing Look at This Ancient Compound. *J. Am. Acad. Dermatol.* **2007**, *57*, 873–878. [CrossRef] [PubMed]
109. Aperce, C.C.; Amachawadi, R.; Van Bibber-Krueger, C.L.; Nagaraja, T.G.; Scott, H.M.; Vinasco-Torre, J.; Drouillard, J.S. Effects of Menthol Supplementation in Feedlot Cattle Diets on the Fecal Prevalence of Antimicrobial-Resistant Escherichia Coli. *PLoS ONE* **2016**, *11*, e0168983. [CrossRef]
110. Murray, S.A.; Amachawadi, R.G.; Norman, K.N.; Lawhon, S.D.; Nagaraja, T.G.; Drouillard, J.S.; Scott, H.M. Effects of Zinc and Menthol-Based Diets on Co-Selection of Antibiotic Resistance among *E. Coli* and *Enterococcus* Spp. in Beef Cattle. *Animals* **2021**, *11*, 259. [CrossRef]
111. Donnik, I.M.; Krivonogova, A.S.; Isaeva, A.G.; Shkuratova, I.A.; Petropavlovsky, M.V.; Bespamyatnykh, Y.N.; Moiseeva, K.V.; Chentsova, A.E. Comparative Analysis of Phytobiotics Effectiveness for the Correction of Mucous Membranes Dysbiosis in Cattle. *Int. Trans. J. Eng. Manag. Appl. Sci. Technol.* **2021**, *12*, 1213.
112. Krivonogova, A.; Isaeva, A.; Chentsova, A.; Musikhina, N.; Petropavlovsky, M. The Influence of Phytobiotic Based on Essential Oils of Salvia Sclarea, Mentha Canadensis, *Mentha piperita* and Coriandrum Sativum on Pathogenic Microorganisms of Lactating Cow Udder. *E3S Web Conf.* **2021**, *282*, 04013. [CrossRef]
113. Witkowska, D.; Sowińska, J. The Effectiveness of Peppermint and Thyme Essential Oil Mist in Reducing Bacterial Contamination in Broiler Houses. *Poult. Sci.* **2013**, *92*, 2834–2843. [CrossRef]
114. Mehri, M.; Sabaghi, V.; Bagherzadeh-Kasmani, F. *Mentha piperita* (*Peppermint*) in Growing Japanese Quails Diet: Performance, Carcass Attributes, Morphology and Microbial Populations of Intestine. *Anim. Feed Sci. Technol.* **2015**, *207*, 104–111. [CrossRef]
115. Motlagh, M.K.; Yahyaei, M.; Rezaei, M.; Ghorbanpour, M. Study on Antibacterial Effect of Thyme and Peppermint Aqueous Extracts on *Staphylococcus aureus* and *Escherichia coli* Strains Causing Mastitis in Camels. *Int. J. Tradit. Herb. Med.* **2013**, *1*, 112–115.
116. Shahid, M.; Cobo, E.R.; Chen, L.; Cavalcante, P.A.; Barkema, H.W.; Gao, J.; Xu, S.; Liu, Y.; Knight, C.G.; Kastelic, J.P.; et al. Prototheca Zopfii Genotype II Induces Mitochondrial Apoptosis in Models of Bovine Mastitis. *Sci. Rep.* **2020**, *10*, 698. [CrossRef] [PubMed]
117. Cuc, C.; Catoi, C.; Fiţ, N.; Rapuntean, S.; Nadaş, G.; Bolfa, P.; Taulescu, M.; Gal, A.; Tabaran, F.; Nagy, A.; et al. The Inhibitory Effect of Some Natural Essential Oils upon *Prototheca* Algae in Vitro Growth. *Bull. UASVM Vet. Med.* **2010**, *67*, 34–38.
118. Grzesiak, B.; Kołodziej, B.; Głowacka, A.; Krukowski, H. The Effect of Some Natural Essential Oils Against Bovine Mastitis Caused by Prototheca Zopfii Isolates In Vitro. *Mycopathologia* **2018**, *183*, 541–550. [CrossRef]
119. Lopes, T.S.; Fussieger, C.; Theodoro, H.; Silveira, S.; Pauletti, G.F.; Ely, M.R.; Lunge, V.R.; Streck, A.F. Antimicrobial Activity of Essential Oils against Staphylococcus Aureus and Staphylococcus Chromogenes Isolated from Bovine Mastitis. *Braz. J. Microbiol.* **2023**, *54*, 2427–2435. [CrossRef]
120. Kumar, P.; Mishra, S.; Malik, A.; Satya, S. Repellent, Larvicidal and Pupicidal Properties of Essential Oils and Their Formulations against the Housefly, Musca Domestica. *Med. Vet. Entomol.* **2011**, *25*, 302–310. [CrossRef]
121. Lachance, S.; Grange, G. Repellent Effectiveness of Seven Plant Essential Oils, Sunflower Oil and Natural Insecticides against Horn Flies on Pastured Dairy Cows and Heifers. *Med. Vet. Entomol.* **2014**, *28*, 193–200. [CrossRef]
122. Khater, H.F.; Ramadan, M.Y.; El-Madawy, R.S. Lousicidal, Ovicidal and Repellent Efficacy of Some Essential Oils against Lice and Flies Infesting Water Buffaloes in Egypt. *Vet. Parasitol.* **2009**, *164*, 257–266. [CrossRef]
123. Abdel-Shafy, S.; Soliman, M.M.M. Toxicity of Some Essential Oils on Eggs, Larvae and Females of *Boophilus annulatus* (Acari: Ixodida: Amblyommidae) Infesting Cattle in Egypt. *Acarologia* **2004**, *44*, 23–30.
124. Huhtanen, P.; Sveinbjörnsson, J. Evaluation of Methods for Estimating Starch Digestibility and Digestion Kinetics in Ruminants. *Anim. Feed Sci. Technol.* **2006**, *130*, 95–113. [CrossRef]
125. Zhang, F.; Adeola, O. Techniques for Evaluating Digestibility of Energy, Amino Acids, Phosphorus, and Calcium in Feed Ingredients for Pigs. *Anim. Nutr.* **2017**, *3*, 344–352. [CrossRef] [PubMed]
126. Getachew, G.; DePeters, E.J.; Robinson, P.H.; Fadel, J.G. Use of an in Vitro Rumen Gas Production Technique to Evaluate Microbial Fermentation of Ruminant Feeds and Its Impact on Fermentation Products. *Anim. Feed Sci. Technol.* **2005**, *123–124*, 547–559. [CrossRef]
127. Van Bibber-Krueger, C.L.; Miller, K.A.; Aperce, C.C.; Alvarado-Gilis, C.A.; Higgins, J.J.; Drouillard, J.S. Effects of Crystalline Menthol on Blood Metabolites in Holstein Steers and in Vitro Volatile Fatty Acid and Gas Production1. *J. Anim. Sci.* **2016**, *94*, 1170–1178. [CrossRef]
128. Kumar, R.; Kamra, D.N.; Agarwal, N.; Chaudhary, L.C. Effect of Feeding a Mixture of Plants Containing Secondary Metabolites and Peppermint Oil on Rumen Fermentation, Microbial Profile and Nutrient Utilization in Buffaloes. *Indian J. Anim. Sci.* **2011**, *81*, 488–492.

129. Kouazounde, J.B.; Jin, L.; Assogba, F.M.; Ayedoun, M.A.; Wang, Y.; Beauchemin, K.A.; McAllister, T.A.; Gbenou, J.D. Effects of Essential Oils from Medicinal Plants Acclimated to Benin on in Vitro Ruminal Fermentation of *Andropogon gayanus* Grass. *J. Sci. Food Agric.* **2015**, *95*, 1031–1038. [CrossRef]
130. Ando, S.; Nishida, T.; Ishida, M.; Hosoda, K.; Bayaru, E. Effect of Peppermint Feeding on the Digestibility, Ruminal Fermentation and Protozoa. *Livest. Prod. Sci.* **2003**, *82*, 245–248. [CrossRef]
131. Beyzi, S.B. Effect of Lavender and Peppermint Essential Oil on in Vitro Methanogenesis and Fermentation of Feed with Buffalo Rumen Liquor. *Buffalo Bull.* **2020**, *39*, 311–321.
132. Roy, D.; Tomar, S.K.; Kumar, V. Rumen Modulatory Effect of Thyme, Clove and Peppermint Oils in Vitro Using Buffalo Rumen Liquor. *Vet. World* **2015**, *8*, 203–207. [CrossRef]
133. Patra, A.K.; Yu, Z. Effects of Essential Oils on Methane Production and Fermentation by, and Abundance and Diversity of, Rumen Microbial Populations. *Appl. Environ. Microbiol.* **2012**, *78*, 4271–4280. [CrossRef]
134. Ozkan, C.O.; Kamalak, A.; Atalay, A.I.; Tatliyer, A.; Kaya, E. Effect of Peppermint (*Mentha piperita*) Essential Oil on Rumen Microbial Fermentation of Barley Grain. *J. Appl. Anim. Res.* **2015**, *43*, 287–290. [CrossRef]
135. Patra, A.K.; Saxena, J. Dietary Phytochemicals as Rumen Modifiers: A Review of the Effects on Microbial Populations. *Antonie Leeuwenhoek* **2009**, *96*, 363–375. [CrossRef]
136. Cobellis, G.; Trabalza-Marinucci, M.; Yu, Z. Critical Evaluation of Essential Oils as Rumen Modifiers in Ruminant Nutrition: A Review. *Sci. Total Environ.* **2016**, *545–546*, 556–568. [CrossRef]
137. Patra, A.K.; Park, T.; Braun, H.-S.; Geiger, S.; Pieper, R.; Yu, Z.; Aschenbach, J.R. Dietary Bioactive Lipid Compounds Rich in Menthol Alter Interactions Among Members of Ruminal Microbiota in Sheep. *Front. Microbiol.* **2019**, *10*, 2038. [CrossRef]
138. Agarwal, N.; Shekhar, C.; Kumar, R.; Chaudhary, L.C.; Kamra, D.N. Effect of Peppermint (*Mentha piperita*) Oil on In Vitro Methanogenesis and Fermentation of Feed with Buffalo Rumen Liquor. *Anim. Feed Sci. Technol.* **2009**, *148*, 321–327. [CrossRef]
139. Patra, A.K.; Yu, Z. Effects of Vanillin, Quillaja Saponin, and Essential Oils on In Vitro Fermentation and Protein-Degrading Microorganisms of the Rumen. *Appl. Microbiol. Biotechnol.* **2014**, *98*, 897–905. [CrossRef]
140. Arjun, S.; Neha, P.; Mohith Sai, S.R.; Ravi, L. Microbial Symbionts in Ruminants. In *Microbial Symbionts*; Elsevier: Amsterdam, The Netherlands, 2023; pp. 493–509.
141. Wallace, R.J.; McEwan, N.R.; McIntosh, F.M.; Teferedegne, B.; Newbold, C.J. Natural Products as Manipulators of Rumen Fermentation. *Asian-Australas. J. Anim. Sci.* **2002**, *15*, 1458–1468. [CrossRef]
142. Abdela, N. Sub-Acute Ruminal Acidosis (SARA) and Its Consequence in Dairy Cattle: A Review of Past and Recent Research at Global Prospective. *Achiev. Life Sci.* **2016**, *10*, 187–196. [CrossRef]
143. Kleen, J.L.; Hooijer, G.A.; Rehage, J.; Noordhuizen, J.P.T.M. Subacute Ruminal Acidosis (SARA): A Review. *J. Vet. Med. Ser. A* **2003**, *50*, 406–414. [CrossRef]
144. Orzuna-Orzuna, J.F.; Dorantes-Iturbide, G.; Lara-Bueno, A.; Miranda-Romero, L.A.; Mendoza-Martínez, G.D.; Santiago-Figueroa, I. A Meta-Analysis of Essential Oils Use for Beef Cattle Feed: Rumen Fermentation, Blood Metabolites, Meat Quality, Performance and, Environmental and Economic Impact. *Fermentation* **2022**, *8*, 254. [CrossRef]
145. Elmhadi, M.E.; Ali, D.K.; Khogali, M.K.; Wang, H. Subacute Ruminal Acidosis in Dairy Herds: Microbiological and Nutritional Causes, Consequences, and Prevention Strategies. *Anim. Nutr.* **2022**, *10*, 148–155. [CrossRef] [PubMed]
146. Benchaar, C.; Greathead, H. Essential Oils and Opportunities to Mitigate Enteric Methane Emissions from Ruminants. *Anim. Feed Sci. Technol.* **2011**, *166–167*, 338–355. [CrossRef]
147. Russell, J.B. The Importance of PH in the Regulation of Ruminal Acetate to Propionate Ratio and Methane Production In Vitro. *J. Dairy Sci.* **1998**, *81*, 3222–3230. [CrossRef]
148. Wagner, A.O.; Reitschuler, C.; Illmer, P. Effect of Different Acetate:Propionate Ratios on the Methanogenic Community during Thermophilic Anaerobic Digestion in Batch Experiments. *Biochem. Eng. J.* **2014**, *90*, 154–161. [CrossRef]
149. Guliński, P.; Salamończyk, E.; Młynek, K. Improving Nitrogen Use Efficiency of Dairy Cows in Relation to Urea in Milk—A Review. *Anim. Sci. Pap. Rep.* **2016**, *34*, 5–24.
150. Platel, K.; Srinivasan, K. Stimulatory Influence of Select Spices on Bile Secretion in Rats. *Nutr. Res.* **2000**, *20*, 1493–1503. [CrossRef]
151. Goodarzi, M.; Firouzabadi, M.S.S.; Mehrizi, M.M.Z.; Jafarian, M. Evaluation of Effect of Peppermint as a New Preventive Method for Milk Fever and Subclinical Hypocalcaemia in Transition Holstein Cows. *Int. J. Anim. Vet. Adv.* **2012**, *4*, 184–186.
152. Ghaly, M.H.; Elghoneimy, A.A.; Mohamed, H.K.; Ali, M.F. Biochemical and Histopathological Effects of Dietary Supplementation of *Nigella sativa* and *Mentha piperita* Oils to Broilers. *J. Adv. Vet. Res.* **2017**, *7*, 7–15.
153. Ghazaghi, M.; Mehri, M.; Bagherzadeh-Kasmani, F. Effects of Dietary Mentha Spicata on Performance, Blood Metabolites, Meat Quality and Microbial Ecosystem of Small Intestine in Growing Japanese Quail. *Anim. Feed Sci. Technol.* **2014**, *194*, 89–98. [CrossRef]
154. Deignan, J.L.; Cederbaum, S.D.; Grody, W.W. Contrasting Features of Urea Cycle Disorders in Human Patients and Knockout Mouse Models. *Mol. Genet. Metab.* **2008**, *93*, 7–14. [CrossRef]

155. Matsumoto, S.; Haberle, J.; Kido, J.; Mitsubuchi, H.; Endo, F.; Nakamura, K. Urea Cycle Disorders—Update. *J. Hum. Genet.* **2019**, *64*, 833–847. [CrossRef] [PubMed]
156. Peier, A.M.; Moqrich, A.; Hergarden, A.C.; Reeve, A.J.; Andersson, D.A.; Story, G.M.; Earley, T.J.; Dragoni, I.; McIntyre, P.; Bevan, S.; et al. A TRP Channel That Senses Cold Stimuli and Menthol. *Cell* **2002**, *108*, 705–715. [CrossRef]
157. Sevinç, M.; Başoğlu, A.; Güzelbektaş, H.; Boydak, M. Lipid and Lipoprotein Levels in Dairy Cows with Fatty Liver. *J. Vet. Anim. Sci.* **2003**, *27*, 295–299.
158. Tohala, S.H. The Relationship between Blood Lipid Profile and Performance of Broilers Fed Two Types of Finisher Diets. *Iraqi J. Vet. Sci.* **2010**, *24*, 87–91. [CrossRef]
159. Islam, M.A.; Haque, A.; Nishibori, M. Growth Performance, Meat Yield and Blood Lipid Profile of Broiler and Sonali Chickens. *Vet. Anim. Sci.* **2022**, *18*, 100272. [CrossRef] [PubMed]
160. Haines, B.E.; Wiest, O.; Stauffacher, C.V. The Increasingly Complex Mechanism of HMG-CoA Reductase. *Acc. Chem. Res.* **2013**, *46*, 2416–2426. [CrossRef]
161. Clegg, R.J.; Middleton, B.; Bell, G.D.; White, D.A. Inhibition of Hepatic Cholesterol Synthesis and S-3-Hydroxy-3-Methylglutaryl-CoA Reductase by Mono and Bicyclic Monoterpenes Administered in Vivo. *Biochem. Pharmacol.* **1980**, *29*, 2125–2127. [CrossRef] [PubMed]
162. Clegg, R.J.; Middleton, B.; Bell, G.D.; White, D.A. The Mechanism of Cyclic Monoterpene Inhibition of Hepatic 3-Hydroxy-3-Methylglutaryl Coenzyme A Reductase in Vivo in the Rat. *J. Biol. Chem.* **1982**, *257*, 2294–2299. [CrossRef]
163. Peffley, D.M.; Gayen, A.K. Plant-Derived Monoterpenes Suppress Hamster Kidney Cell 3-Hydroxy-3-Methylglutaryl Coenzyme A Reductase Synthesis at the Post-Transcriptional Level. *J. Nutr.* **2003**, *133*, 38–44. [CrossRef]
164. Lee, K.W.; Everts, H.; Beynen, A. Essential Oils in Broiler Nutrition. *Int. J. Poult. Sci.* **2004**, *3*, 738–752. [CrossRef]
165. Khare, A.; Gaur, S. Cholesterol-Lowering Effects of Lactobacillus Species. *Curr. Microbiol.* **2020**, *77*, 638–644. [CrossRef] [PubMed]
166. Goff, J.P. The Monitoring, Prevention, and Treatment of Milk Fever and Subclinical Hypocalcemia in Dairy Cows. *Vet. J.* **2008**, *176*, 50–57. [CrossRef] [PubMed]
167. Seifi, H.A.; Kia, S. Subclinical Hypocalcemia in Dairy Cows: Pathophysiology, Consequences and Monitoring. *Iran. J. Vet. Sci. Technol.* **2017**, *9*, 1–15.
168. Hoenderop, J.G.J.; Nilius, B.; Bindels, R.J.M. Calcium Absorption Across Epithelia. *Physiol. Rev.* **2005**, *85*, 373–422. [CrossRef]
169. Vangeel, L.; Voets, T. Transient Receptor Potential Channels and Calcium Signaling. *Cold Spring Harb. Perspect. Biol.* **2019**, *11*, a035048. [CrossRef]
170. Rosendahl, J.; Braun, H.S.; Schrapers, K.T.; Martens, H.; Stumpff, F. Evidence for the Functional Involvement of Members of the TRP Channel Family in the Uptake of Na^+ and $NH4^+$ by the Ruminal Epithelium. *Pflug. Arch.* **2016**, *468*, 1333–1352. [CrossRef]
171. Schrapers, K.T.; Sponder, G.; Liebe, F.; Liebe, H.; Stumpff, F. The Bovine TRPV3 as a Pathway for the Uptake of Na^+, Ca^{2+}, and NH_4^+. *PLoS ONE* **2018**, *13*, e0193519. [CrossRef]
172. Geiger, S.; Patra, A.K.; Schrapers, K.T.; Braun, H.S.; Aschenbach, J.R. Menthol Stimulates Calcium Absorption in the Rumen but Not in the Jejunum of Sheep. *J. Dairy Sci.* **2021**, *104*, 3067–3081. [CrossRef] [PubMed]
173. Farco, J.A.; Grundmann, O. Menthol—Pharmacology of an Important Naturally Medicinal "Cool". *Mini Rev. Med. Chem.* **2013**, *13*, 124–131. [CrossRef]
174. Bagath, M.; Krishnan, G.; Devaraj, C.; Rashamol, V.P.; Pragna, P.; Lees, A.M.; Sejian, V. The Impact of Heat Stress on the Immune System in Dairy Cattle: A Review. *Res. Vet. Sci.* **2019**, *126*, 94–102. [CrossRef]
175. Keringer, P.; Farkas, N.; Gede, N.; Hegyi, P.; Rumbus, Z.; Lohinai, Z.; Solymar, M.; Ruksakiet, K.; Varga, G.; Garami, A. Menthol Can Be Safely Applied to Improve Thermal Perception during Physical Exercise: A Meta-Analysis of Randomized Controlled Trials. *Sci. Rep.* **2020**, *10*, 13636. [CrossRef] [PubMed]
176. Albishi, F.M.; Albeshi, S.M.; Alotaibi, K.; Alhussain, N.; Kamal, A.; Sultan, A.A.; Aljishi, M.J. The Effect of Menthol on Anxiety and Related Behaviors in Mice. *Bahrain Med. Bull.* **2020**, *42*, 274–279.
177. Gavel, E.H.; Logan-Sprenger, H.M.; Good, J.; Jacobs, I.; Thomas, S.G. Menthol Mouth Rinsing and Cycling Performance in Females Under Heat Stress. *Int. J. Sports Physiol. Perform.* **2021**, *16*, 1014–1020. [CrossRef] [PubMed]
178. Sun, Z.; Wang, H.; Wang, J.; Zhou, L.; Yang, P. Chemical Composition and Anti-Inflammatory, Cytotoxic and Antioxidant Activities of Essential Oil from Leaves of *Mentha piperita* Grown in China. *PLoS ONE* **2014**, *9*, e114767. [CrossRef]
179. Trevisan, S.C.C.; Menezes, A.P.P.; Barbalho, S.M.; Guiguer, É.L. Properties of *Mentha piperita*: A Brief Review. *World J. Pharm. Med. Res.* **2017**, *3*, 309–313.
180. Beigi, M.; Torki-Harchegani, M.; Ghasemi Pirbalouti, A. Quantity and Chemical Composition of Essential Oil of Peppermint (*Mentha* × *piperita* L.) Leaves under Different Drying Methods. *Int. J. Food Prop.* **2018**, *21*, 267–276. [CrossRef]

antioxidants

MDPI

Article

Drug Target Investigation of *N*-*p*-Coumaroyl-*N′*-Caffeoylputrescine, a Naturally-Occurring Alkaloid Derived from *Saxifraga tangutica*

Chuang Liu [1], Jun Dang [2,*] and Minchen Wu [1,*]

[1] School of Biotechnology, Jiangnan University, Wuxi 214122, China; 7210201054@stu.jiangnan.edu.cn
[2] Key Laboratory of Tibetan Medicine Research, Northwest Institute of Plateau Biology, Chinese Academy of Sciences, Xining 810000, China
* Correspondence: dangjun@nwipb.cas.cn (J.D.); wmchen@jiangnan.edu.cn (M.W.)

Abstract: The exploration of drug targets has always been a priority in new drug research, and this work is even more essential for natural active compounds. *Saxifraga tangutica* is a traditional Tibetan medicine with excellent antioxidant properties. In this study, an alkaloid, *N*-*p*-coumaroyl-*N′*-caffeoylputrescine (PCC), was first isolated from the plant, *Saxifraga tangutica*, with a DPPH scavenging rate of 0.936 μg/mL. To further identify its target, the drug affinity responsive target stability technique and multiple public databases were integrated to retrieve a total of 317 common targets from comprehensive screening. A further bioinformatics analysis not only identified 13 hub targets but also indicated PCC as having biological activities against cancer and affecting metabolic diseases. Integrating reverse virtual docking, molecular dynamics simulations, and cellular thermal shift assays ultimately focused on HSP90AA1 as the target of PCC. An in vitro study on liver (HepG2) cells and breast (MCF-7) cancer cells revealed that PCC modulates HSP90AA1, subsequently affecting Mut-p53 expression, triggering a cascade effect that reduced adriamycin-induced drug resistance in cells. Furthermore, a prediction of the absorption, distribution, metabolism, excretion, and toxicity was also applied to evaluate the drug-like properties of PCC. Overall, the integrated strategy used in this study successfully identified the target of PCC, providing a valuable paradigm for future research on the action targets of natural products.

Keywords: *Saxifraga tangutica*; *N*-*p*-coumaroyl-*N′*-caffeoylputrescine; drug affinity responsive target stability; reverse virtual docking; molecular dynamics simulation

1. Introduction

Novel small-molecule compounds found in nature are a vital source of inspiration for new drug development, and the continual advancement in biochemical techniques has significantly improved the ability to identify the drug targets of these compounds [1,2]. Drug affinity responsive target stability (DARTS) is designed to identify protein targets of small-molecule ligands without altering their structure [3]. During this process, the binding affinity between the ligand and its target is a pivotal factor. The formation of ligand-protein complexes alter the original proteolytic susceptibility, and the involvement of nonspecific proteases (e.g., subtilisin, thermolysin, pronase) will maximize the screening of these complexes. Finally, high-sensitivity mass spectrometry enables label-free target identification. Considering the inherent advantages of the low cost and high efficiency of DARTS, it has been widely applied in the study of unknown mechanisms and target identification of bioactive natural products [4,5].

In contrast to the traditional "one molecule-one target-one disease" paradigm, scientists now generally recognize that "drug-target-disease" interactions are a complex regulatory network [6,7]. On the basis of the above concept, several online databases have been established for drug target prediction, and their reliability has been recognized by scientists [8]. These online platforms are primarily based on pharmacophore models and molecular fingerprinting techniques, leveraging large datasets for training and learning to generate a high-confidence potential target database for compounds with unknow activity [9–12]. In addition, the construction of protein-protein interaction (PPI) networks and the analysis of bioinformatics further explains the key targets through which small molecule drugs exert their biological functions, as well as the complex relationships (e.g., pharmaceutical efficacy, side effects, and off-target effects) among them [13].

Currently, combining traditional wet experimental methods with dry experimental means that rely on computers is a more widespread sight in drug research. Owing to the rapid advancements of computer performance, virtual docking has gained widespread acceptance for preliminary drug target discovery, which is more efficient and cost-controlled [14,15]. Under the concept of "one molecule-multiple targets", reverse virtual screening allows the simultaneous docking of multiple proteins with a small molecule to rapidly identify complexes with a high binding affinity to it [16,17]. Through a molecular dynamics simulation, we can further elucidate the binding mode of small molecules and protein targets, as well as the dynamic changes within the complex [18], thereby improving the hit rate of subsequent wet experiments.

Reactive oxygen (ROS) and reactive nitrogen (RNS) are natural byproducts of cellular metabolism. When their production and consumption become imbalanced, oxidative stress occurs. Long-term oxidative stress has been shown to contribute to the onset and progression of numerous diseases [19,20]. HSP90AA1, a highly conserved molecular chaperone protein with hundreds of client proteins, undergoes misfolding, unfolding, and aggregation under stress conditions (e.g., temperature, oxidative stress), disrupting the function of its client proteins. Given the physiological roles of these client proteins, HSP90AA1 is closely linked to various diseases (e.g., cancer, neurodegenerative diseases) [21,22]. Thus, the exploration of HSP90AA1 inhibitors often leads to unexpected comprehensive therapeutic effects.

In this study, *N*-*p*-coumaroyl-*N*′-caffeoylputrescine (PCC), an alkaloid antioxidant, was first isolated from *Saxifraga tangutica* (*S. tangutica*), and a comprehensive strategy of wet and dry experiments was employed to further investigate its bioactivity and protein targets. This approach not only reveals the potential high-value applications of PCC, but also offers a methodological reference for the application of natural products in drug development.

2. Materials and Methods

2.1. Preparation and Characterization of PCC

The whole plants of *S. tangutica* were found in the Guoluo Tibetan Autonomous Prefecture (99°47′35″ E, 34°33′37″ N), Qinghai, China. A voucher specimen (No. 0325734) was deposited at the Qinghai-Tibet Plateau Museum of Biology. Five hundred grams of dried whole plants was extracted three times with 12 L of methanol (Kelon Chemical Reagent Factory, Chengdu, Sichuan, China), concentrated to 500 mL by a rotary evaporator, mixed with 200 g of polyamide, and then transferred to an oven for drying, to obtain 265 g of sample-polyamide mixture. The mixture was pretreated by connecting an MCI column (Mitsubishi, Tokyo, Japan) to an MPLC (Hanbon Science & Technology Co., Ltd., Huaian, Jiangsu, China) system, with the methanol concentration gradually increased from 0 to 100% over 120 min, followed by 30 min of elution with 100% methanol. Six fractions were eventually recovered, and the target fraction 4 (Fr4) was mixed with 20.4 g of polyamide and dried, pending the next procedure.

A Spherical C18 column (SiliCycle, Quebec, QC, Canada) was connected to an MPLC system for the preparation of Fr4. The elution program was as follows: 0–90 min with 18–26% acetonitrile, followed by 20 min with 26% acetonitrile. Five fractions were finally collected, with the target fractions 5 (Fr4-5) dissolved in 12 mL of methanol, awaiting further processing. A Click XIon column (Acchrom Corporation, Beijing, China) was connected to an HPLC system for the preparation of Fr4-5. The isocratic elution with 91% acetonitrile for 30 min yielded the target fraction Fr4-5-1. The fraction was concentrated under reduced pressure and weighed, yielding 678.6 mg.

The ESI-MS data of Fr4-5-1 was recorded with a Waters QDa electrospray ionization mass spectrometer (Waters Instruments Co., Milford, MA, USA), and the NMR data were collected with a Bruker Avance 600 MHz instrument (Bruker, Billerica, MA, USA).

2.2. *Assay of the Antioxidant Capacity*

The antioxidant activity of PCC has been evaluated via the DPPH method, which is based on the literature, with minor modifications [23]. A 0.3 mg/mL DPPH (Merck, Darmstadt, Hesse, Germany) solution was prepared in ethanol for use. Different concentrations (0, 0.1, 1, 5, 10, 25, 50, and 100 μg/mL) of PCC solution (30 μL) were mixed with DPPH solution (70 μL) and incubated for 30 min in the dark. Then, the absorbance of these solutions was read at 517 nm via a microplate reader. To ensure the stability, this experiment was repeated three times. The antioxidant capacity of PCC was calculated via the following equation:

$$\text{DPPH scavenging activity (\%)} = [1 - (A_a - A_b)/A_c] \times 100\%$$

where A_a is the absorbance of the sample solution, A_b is the absorbance of a blank and Ac is the absorbance of the control, respectively.

2.3. *Fishing of Protein Targets*

2.3.1. DARTS Assay

The cell lysates were incubated with or without PCC for 40 min at room temperature, followed by its treatment with pronase (Sigma-Aldrich, St. Louis, MO, USA) for 10 min. Subsequently, the protein information was analyzed via label-free proteomics and bioinformatics. $p < 0.05$ and a fold change >1.5 were used as the screening thresholds for potential protein targets.

2.3.2. Online Database Probing

The 3D structure and SMILES string of PCC were uploaded to the following databases for target probing: TargetNet (http://targetnet.scbdd.com/, accessed on 3 May 2024) [11], Swiss Target Prediction (STP, http://www.swisstargetprediction.ch/, accessed on 3 May 2024) [24], PharmMapper (https://lilab-ecust.cn/pharmmapper/, accessed on 3 May 2024) [10], and Super-PRED (https://prediction.charite.de/, accessed on 3 May 2024) [12]. All the targets retrieved from the four databases were consolidated, and duplicate entries were removed to identify the potential targets of PCC. These targets were then standardized and annotated via the online UniProt database (https://www.uniprot.org/, accessed on 10 May 2024), with *Homo sapiens* selected as the species.

2.3.3. Construction of the PCC Potential Targets Database

The results of the DARTS assay and online database probing were integrated, and a local database of potential PCC targets was constructed after removing duplicates. The

STRING database (https://cn.string-db.org/, accessed on 10 May 2024) was used to analyze the protein-protein interaction (PPI) networks of these targets. The high-confidence interaction scores (0.7) were screened and output as tsv files, which were then visualized via Cytoscape 3.10.2. The hub targets were identified on the basis of the "Degree" values in the Cytohubba plugin, implying that the biological function of PCC is closely related to these targets.

2.4. Bioinformatics Analysis

Gene Ontology (GO) and Kyoto Encyclopedia of Genes and Genomes (KEGG) analyses, which are performed by the DAVID database (https://david.ncifcrf.gov/, accessed on 10 June 2024), are essential for exploring the molecular mechanisms of potential PCC targets [25]. Moreover, the hub targets were uploaded to the Diseases database (https://diseases.jensenlab.org/, accessed on 10 June 2024) [26], and the target-disease association profiles were derived from the text mining module of this database, with high-confidence results selected for visualization.

2.5. Reverse Virtual Docking

The pdb files of these hub targets with 3D coordinates were downloaded from the RCSB Protein Data Bank database (https://www.rcsb.org/, accessed on 3 August 2024), and some operations (e.g., removal of original ligands, charge assignment, and hydrogen addition) were implemented through PyMOL 3.1 and AutoDock 4. ChemBio3D 16.0 was used to map the 3D structure of the PCC and perform the energy minimization procedure. Then, AutoDock was used to further examine the hydrogen atoms, as well as the torsion bonds of PCC. After the AutoGrid program generated docking boxes, at least 100 docking runs were conducted with AutoDock to identify the optimal conformations. Finally, the results were visualized via ChimeraX 1.8 and LigPlot 2.2.

2.6. Molecular Dynamics Simulation

The open-source software GROningen MAchine for Chemical Simulations (GROMACS) 2023.2 was used to perform molecular dynamics simulations on the ligand-protein complex generated from reverse virtual docking. The protein force field was defined as CHARMM36, and the GAFF force field for the PCC was added via Sobtop 1.0 software [27]. A simulation box filled with TIP3P water molecules was constructed to encapsulate the complex. The energy minimization of the system was carried out using the steepest descent method. After minimization, isothermal-isochoric (NVT) and isothermal-isobaric (NPT) ensembles were applied to stabilize the temperature at 300 K and pressure at 1 bar. A 100 ns molecular dynamics simulation was then performed with a time step of 2 femtoseconds (fs), and simulation trajectories were saved every 10 picoseconds (ps) for further analysis. Root mean square deviation (RMSD) is used to measure the degree of deviation between the atomic coordinates and the reference coordinates. Hydrogen bond (H-bond) refers to the number of hydrogen bonds established by the simulated system during the simulation time. The Radius of gyration (Rg) is used to examine the average distance of individual atoms in the simulation system, relative to the center of mass of the molecule, which is an important parameter for measuring the size and compactness of the molecule. Root mean square fluctuation (RMSF) is used to quantify the degree of fluctuation in the positions of the atoms.

2.7. Cellular Thermal Shift Assay (CETSA)

An M-PER lysis buffer (Thermo Fisher, Waltham, MA, USA) was used to extract the total protein from the cells. The protein mixture was incubated with or without PCC for 30 min at room temperature. Next, the samples were evenly divided into 6 aliquots and heat-treated in a water bath at 50, 56, 62, 68, 74, and 80 °C for 3 min. After high-speed centrifugation (12,000 rpm, 3 min), the supernatant was collected for Western blot analysis to evaluate the HSP90AA1 levels.

2.8. In Vitro Experiments

2.8.1. Cell Culture

For the experiment, 293T cells, HepG2 cells, and MCF-7 cells were purchased from Procell Life Science & Technology Co., Ltd. (Wuhan, China). Prior to further processing, the cells were cultured in DMEM, supplemented with 10% fetal bovine serum (Procell, Wuhan, China) and 1% penicillin-streptomycin (Servicebio, Wuhan, China). The conditions of the cell culture incubator were maintained at 37 °C with 5% CO_2. Furthermore, the cell viability was measured according to the instructions of the CCK-8 kit (Vazyme, Nanjing, China).

2.8.2. Western Blot Analysis

HepG2 and MCF-7 cells were inoculated at a density of 25×10^4 cells per well in 6-well plates. After allowing the cells to adhere, they were incubated with varying concentrations of PCC (5, 10, and 30 μM) for 24 h. The total proteins from the different experimental groups were extracted via M-PER lysis buffer, and the protein content of each group was measured via a BCA kit (Vazyme, China).

Equal amounts of protein mixture were separated via 8% SDS-PAGE and transferred onto a PVDF membrane. The membrane was blocked with 5% skim milk for 2 h. After blocking, the PVDF membrane was further incubated with a primary antibody (14 h, 4 °C) and a secondary antibody (2 h, room temperature). Antibodies against HSP90AA1 and β-actin were purchased from Proteintech, Wuhan, China. Upon the completion of all the procedures, the target bands were visualized via an enhanced chemiluminescence (ECL) detection kit (Abbkine, Wuhan, China) and automated chemiluminescence detection equipment (Tanon, Shanghai, China). Furthermore, the semiquantitative analysis was realized via ImageJ software (imagej.net/ij/).

2.8.3. qPCR Assay

HepG2 and MCF-7 cells were inoculated at a density of 25×10^4 cells per well in 6-well plates. After the cells had adhered, they were incubated with adriamycin (ADR, 50 μM) and PCC (10 μM) for 16 h. Total RNA from each experimental group was extracted via RNA-easy isolation reagent (Vazyme, China). After the total RNA was converted to cDNA, it was further processed with 2 × AceQ qPCR SYBR Green Master Mix (Vazyme, China) for subsequent qPCR detection. The *Ct* value of β-actin was used as a benchmark, and the relative expression level of each group of mRNAs was represented by the value of $2^{-\Delta\Delta Ct}$. The detailed information on the primers used in this study is listed in Table 1.

Table 1. Sequences of primers used for qPCR.

Gene	Primer Sequence
β-actin	5′-AAGAGATGGCCACGGCTGCT-3′ 5′-GACTCGTCATACTCCTGCTTG-3′
HSP90AA1	5′-GTCTGGGTATCGGAAAGCAAG-3′ 5′-CTGAGGGGTGGGGATGATGTC-3′
Mut-p53	5′-CCTCAGCATCTTATCCGAGTGG-3′ 5′-TGGATGGTGGTACAGTCAGAGC-3′
MDR1	5′-CCCATCATTGCAATAGCAGG-3′ 5′-GTTCAAACTTCTGCTCCTGA-3′
SP1	5′-GCTATGCCAAACCTACTCC-3′ 5′-CTGTAGCCCACTGACCT-3′

2.9. Pharmacokinetic Profiling

The sdf structure file of PCC was uploaded to the ADMETlab 3.0 online platform (https://admetlab3.scbdd.com/, accessed on 23 August 2024) for predicting the pharmacokinetic properties. The ADMET characteristics primarily include absorption—Caco-2 permeability and human intestinal absorption (HIA); distribution—steady state volume of distribution (VDss) and blood-brain barrier (BBB); metabolism—human liver microsomal (HLM) stability, CYP1A2 inhibitor, CYP1A2 substrate, CYP2D6 inhibitor, CYP2D6 substrate, CYP3A4 inhibitor, and CYP3A4 substrate; excretion—CLplasma; toxicity—drug induced liver injury (DILI), rat oral acute toxicity, carcinogenicity, human hepatotoxicity, hematotoxicity, immunotoxicity, drug-induced nephrotoxicity, and drug-induced neurotoxicity.

2.10. Statistical Analysis

To ensure the reliability of the results in the in vitro experiments, all data were repeated three times. The final results were statistically analyzed and exported via a one-way analysis of variance (ANOVA) or *t*-tests from GraphPad Prism software (version 10, San Diego, CA, USA). Generally, a p-value < 0.05 indicated a statistically significant difference.

3. Results

3.1. Isolation and Characterization of the Compounds

After pretreatment with MCI MPLC, the methanol extract of *S. tangutica* yielded six fractions (Figure 1A), with the target fraction Fr4 weighing 17.5 g. Subsequently, the Spherical C18 MPLC preparation separated five fractions from Fr4 (Figure 1B), with the target fraction Fr4-5 weighing 5.22 g. The 5.22 g sample was dissolved in methanol and subjected to further separation via a ClickXIon column (Figure 1C). After 24 cycles of preparation, Fr4-5-1 (PCC) was finally obtained, and 678.6 mg was weighed following concentration under reduced pressure. The purity verification diagram of PCC is shown in Figure 1D.

The dried PCC appeared as a yellowish solid, and the ESI-MS data for $[M + Na]^+$ indicated a molecular mass of 396.17. In the ^{1}H-NMR spectrum, the signal at δ_H 7.97 corresponds to two protons, suggesting the presence of nitrogen atoms in PCC, whereas other hydrogen proton signals in the low field region (δ_H 7.38, 6.93, 6.83, 6.79, and 6.74) indicate the presence of two aromatic rings. Additionally, signals at δ_H 3.17 and 1.46 revealed the presence of alkyl fragments. In the ^{13}C-NMR spectra, a total of 22 carbons were stacked, with a peak at δ_C 165.3 indicating two carbonyl carbon atoms. In the HMBC spectrum, the correlation between δ_C 129.1 and δ_H 7.32 confirmed the relative position of a para-substituted aromatic ring, whereas the correlations between δ_C 120.3, 113.8, and δ_H 7.23 pinpointed the position of the hydrogen atom at carbon 12. In the HSQC spectrum, the correlations between δ_C 38.3 and δ_H 3.17, as well as between δ_C 26.8 and δ_H 1.46, allowed for the assignment of protons to their respective carbon atoms in the alkyl fragments. Finally, Fr4-5-1 was identified as *N*-*p*-coumaroyl-*N′*-caffeoylputrescine [28]. The detailed NMR signal assignments for PCC are listed in Table 2, with the structure shown in Figure 1E, and the corresponding spectral data provided in the Supporting Information (Figures S1–S5).

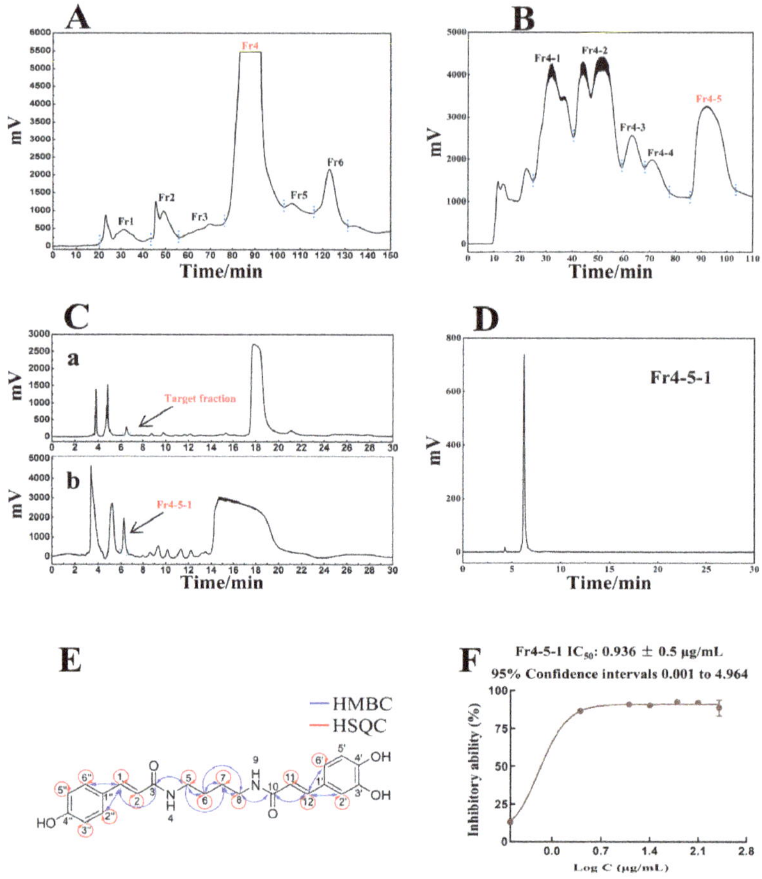

Figure 1. Pretreatment chromatogram of *S. tangutica* on MCI MPLC (**A**); preparation chromatogram of Fr4 on Spherical C18 MPLC (**B**); comparative chromatograms of the analysis (**Ca**) and preparation (**Cb**) of Fr4-5 on a Click XIon column; analytical chromatograms of Fr4-5-1 on a Click XIon column (**D**); chemical structure of PCC and two-dimensional correlation (**E**); and DPPH scavenging assay of PCC (**F**).

Table 2. ^{1}H-NMR and ^{13}C-NMR data of PCC.

Atom Number	^{1}H-NMR	^{13}C-NMR
1	7.32	138.5
2	6.3	118.6
3	-	165.3
4	7.97	-
5	3.17	38.3
6	1.46	26.8
7	1.46	26.8
8	3.17	38.3
9	7.97	-
10	-	165.3
11	6.4	118.8
12	7.23	138.9

Table 2. *Cont.*

Atom Number	^{1}H-NMR	^{13}C-NMR
1′	-	126.4
2′	6.93	113.8
3′	-	145.5
4′	-	147.2
5′	6.74	113.8
6′	6.83	120.3
1″	-	126
2″	7.38	129.1
3″	6.79	115.7
4″	-	158.8
5″	6.79	115.7
6″	7.38	129.1

3.2. DPPH Scavenging Assay of PCC

The DPPH assay was conducted to assess the antioxidant activity of the highly purified PCC, then an inhibition activity curve was generated. As shown in Figure 1F, the concentration at which PCC achieved 50% inhibition (IC_{50}) was determined to be 0.936 μg/mL, suggesting an excellent antioxidant capacity. On the basis of investigation, this is currently the most potent natural small molecule with antioxidant activity isolated by our team.

3.3. Screening Potential Targets of PCC

Label-free proteomics, based on DARTS, was used to screen for potential protein targets that interact with PCC (Figure 2A), resulting in 64 identified targets (Figure 2B). Additionally, 254 potential protein targets that interact with PCC were retrieved from four online network databases (Figure 2C). After normalization and the removal of duplicates, a total of 317 potential PCC targets were identified (Figure 2D), all of which were assumed to have possible interactions with PCC. The detailed information on these targets is presented in the Supporting Information (Table S1).

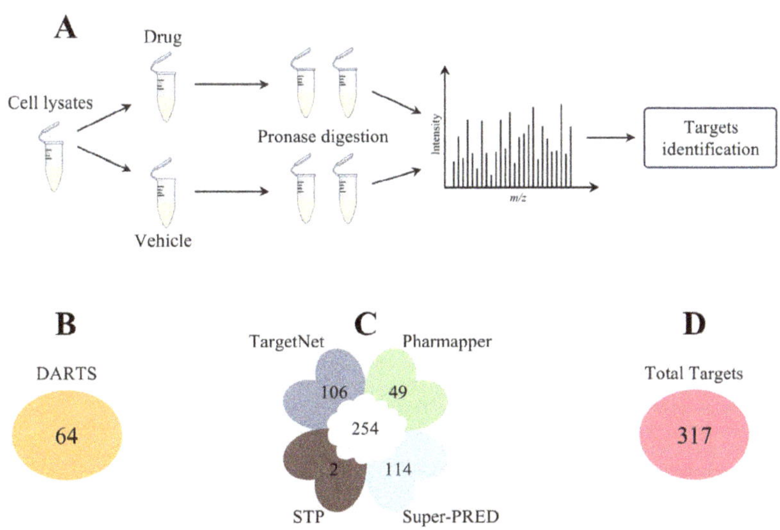

Figure 2. *Cont.*

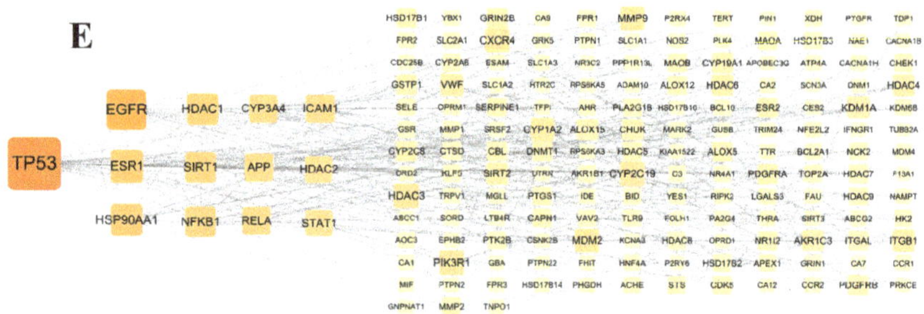

Figure 2. Protein target probing of PCC: flowchart of DARTS (**A**); number of targets identified by DARTS (**B**); number of targets retrieved from 4 open-source databases (**C**); number of potential targets for PCC (**D**); and identification of hub targets via Cytoscape analysis (**E**).

3.4. Hub Targets of PCC

Using the STRING database and Cytoscape software, 13 hub targets were identified from the 317 common targets (Figure 2E), including TP53, EGFR, ESR1, HSP90AA1, NFKB1, SIRT1, HDAC1, CYP3A4, APP, RELA, ICAM1, HDAC1, and STAT1.

3.5. Enrichment Analysis

The enrichment analysis of the 317 common targets was performed via the DAVID database. The GO results revealed that the common targets were associated with 157 molecular function (MF), 78 cellular component (CC), and 404 biological process (BP) terms. The top ten results for each of the GO terms were visualized and are presented in Figure 3A. BP was primarily associated with the inflammatory response, protein phosphorylation, and apoptosis. The CCs were mainly related to the cytoplasm, plasma membrane, and nucleoplasm. The MFs were associated with protein binding and kinase activity.

The KEGG pathway enrichment analysis identified a total of 104 signaling pathways, and the top 30 pathways, after *p*-value ranking, were visualized and output (Figure 3B). As a result, many genes were enriched in metabolic pathways (hsa01100) and cancer pathways (hsa05200). Furthermore, on the basis of text mining of biomedical literature, an in-depth retrieval of the diseases associated with the 13 hub targets was conducted (Figure 4), which also supports the further investigation of the positive role that PCC plays in cancer (liver cancer and lung cancer) and metabolic diseases (diabetes mellitus and obesity).

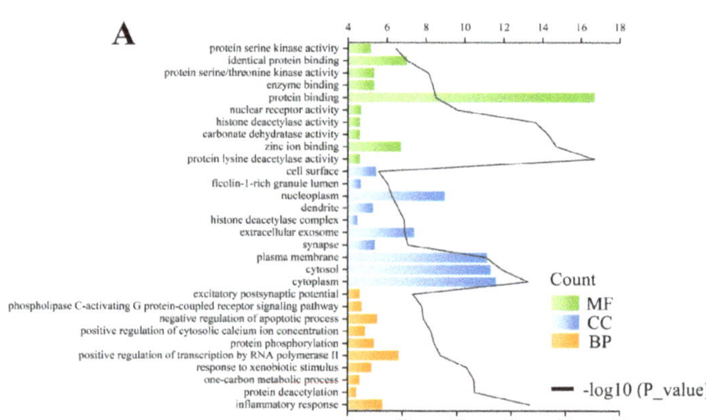

Figure 3. *Cont.*

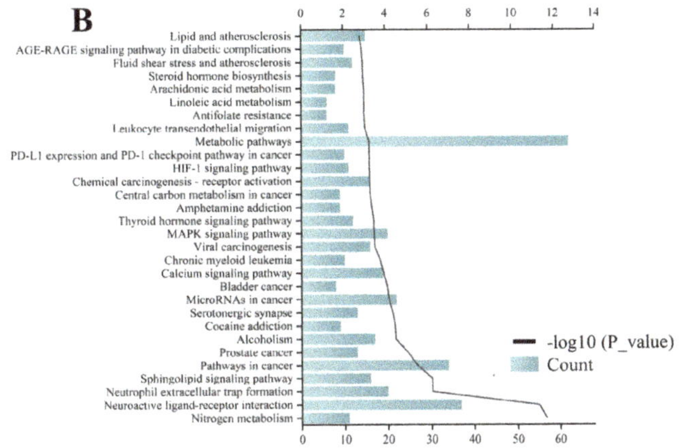

Figure 3. Result of the GO enrichment analysis of common targets (**A**); and KEGG enrichment analysis results of common targets (**B**).

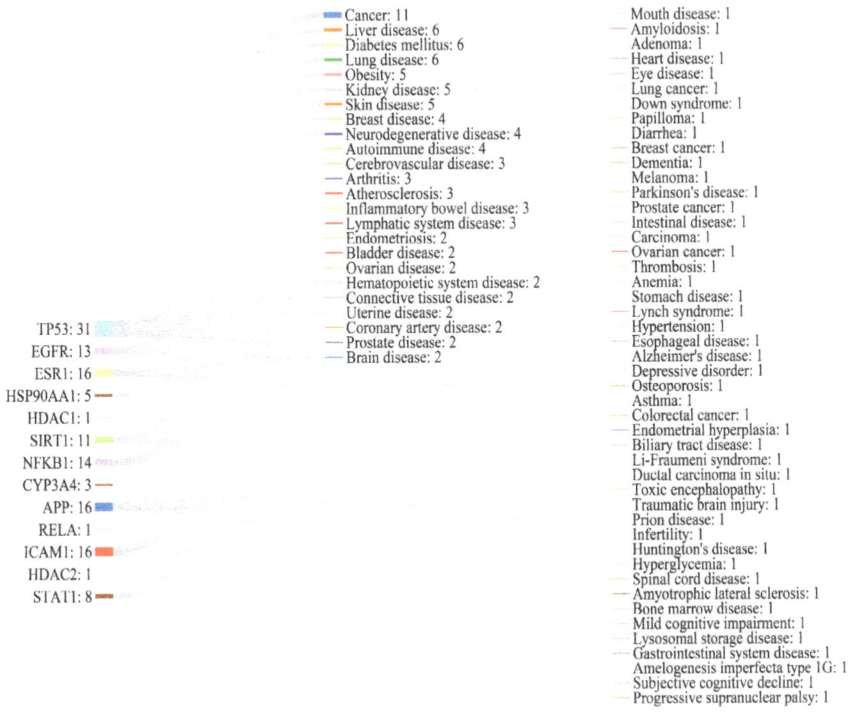

Figure 4. Text mining for disease research on hub targets.

3.6. Reverse Virtual Docking

To clarify the binding affinity of PCC for 13 hub targets, a reverse virtual docking procedure was implemented via AutoDock. The parameters of the reverse virtual docking, as well as the ligand-receptor binding energies, are shown in Table 3. The interactions between the PCC and each potential target are shown in Figure 5. In this study, the greatest binding energy (−10.74 kcal/mol) was attributed to the complex formed by PCC with

HSP90AA1, in which Gln23, Asp93, Gly97, and Ile104 of the N-terminal domain (NTD) perform critical actions (Figure 5M).

Table 3. Reverse virtual docking parameters and results.

Protein	Number of Points	Center Grid Box	Spacing	Binding Energy
TP53 ID: 2XWR	X_dimension = 88 Y_dimension = 108 Z_dimension = 76	X_center = −42.03 Y_center = 10.36 Z_center = −53.92	0.408	−9.41 kcal/mol
EGFR ID: 4G5J	X_dimension = 90 Y_dimension = 92 Z_dimension = 72	X_center = 63.19 Y_center = 8.73 Z_center = −22.84	0.614	−6.94 kcal/mol
ESR1 ID: 7UJW	X_dimension = 118 Y_dimension = 102 Z_dimension = 120	X_center = −4.09 Y_center = 19.58 Z_center = 71.2	0.375	−8.96 kcal/mol
HSP90AA1 ID: 3O0I	X_dimension = 82 Y_dimension = 70 Z_dimension = 92	X_center = −0.48 Y_center = −11.34 Z_center = −30.30	0.51	−10.74 kcal/mol
HDAC1 ID: 4BKX	X_dimension = 90 Y_dimension = 90 Z_dimension = 74	X_center = −61.35 Y_center = −16.19 Z_center = −5.84	0.68	−7.14 kcal/mol
SIRT1 ID: 5BTR	X_dimension = 92 Y_dimension = 82 Z_dimension = 106	X_center = −16.77 Y_center = 66.21 Z_center = 4.02	0.653	−8.21 kcal/mol
NFKB1 ID: 3GUT	X_dimension =102 Y_dimension = 64 Z_dimension = 100	X_center = 45.02 Y_center = −22.83 Z_center = 47.6	0.808	−5.67 kcal/mol
CYP3A4 ID: 1TQN	X_dimension = 58 Y_dimension = 106 Z_dimension = 94	X_center = −18.93 Y_center = −25.25 Z_center = −13.91	0.61	−9.61 kcal/mol
APP ID: 1AAP	X_dimension = 80 Y_dimension = 84 Z_dimension = 98	X_center = 16.73 Y_center = 19.36 Z_center = 36.51	0.375	−5.92 kcal/mol
RELA ID: 6POZ	X_dimension = 80 Y_dimension = 76 Z_dimension = 98	X_center = 102.83 Y_center = −14.07 Z_center = −21.91	0.669	−9.12 kcal/mol
ICAM1 ID: 1P53	X_dimension = 119 Y_dimension = 94 Z_dimension = 54	X_center = 9.35 Y_center = 150.7 Z_center = 46.94	0.831	−5.54 kcal/mol
HDAC2 ID: 3MAX	X_dimension = 78 Y_dimension = 92 Z_dimension = 88	X_center = 90.83 Y_center = 40.31 Z_center = −41.94	0.525	−9.11 kcal/mol
STAT1 ID: 1YVL	X_dimension = 104 Y_dimension = 60 Z_dimension = 108	X_center = −12.28 Y_center = −44.74 Z_center = 84.37	0.986	−4.85 kcal/mol

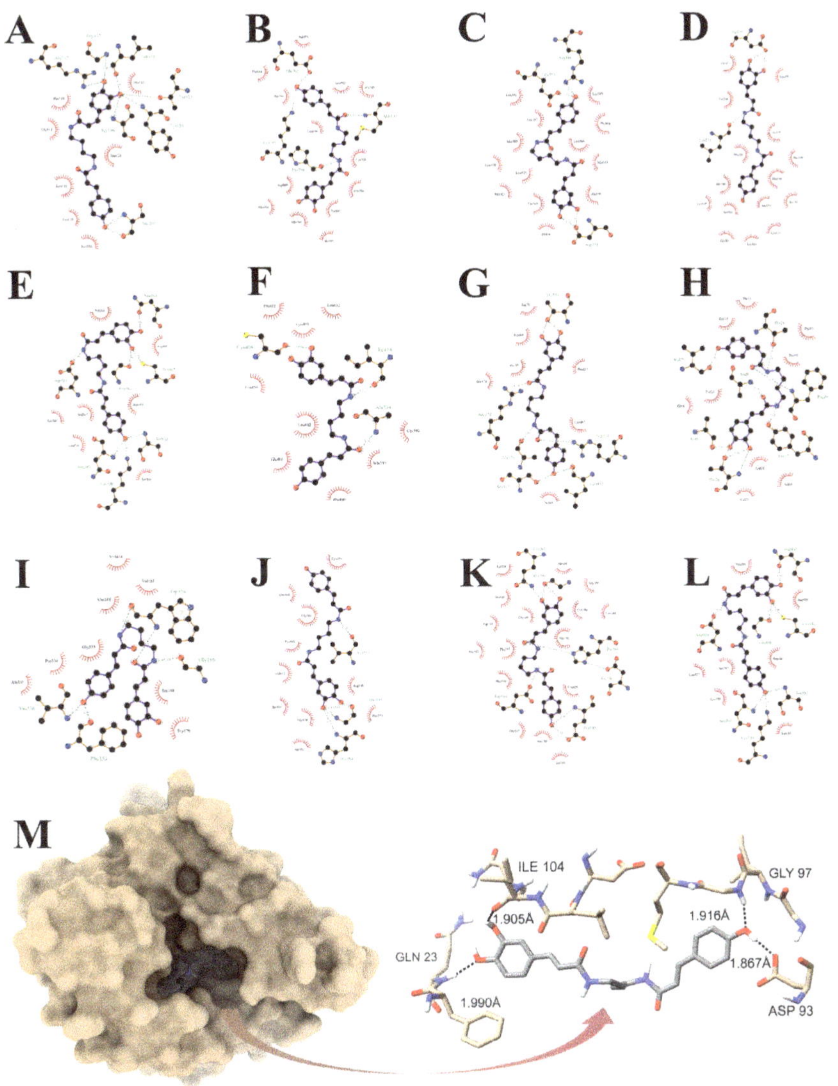

Figure 5. Reverse virtual docking: 2D interaction diagram of PCC and TP53 (**A**); 2D interaction diagram of PCC and EGFR (**B**); 2D interaction diagram of PCC and ESR1 (**C**); 2D interaction diagram of PCC and HDAC1 (**D**); 2D interaction diagram of PCC and SIRT1 (**E**); 2D interaction diagram of PCC and ICAM1 (**F**); 2D interaction diagram of PCC and CYP3A4 (**G**); 2D interaction diagram of PCC and APP (**H**); 2D interaction diagram of PCC and RELA (**I**); 2D interaction diagram of PCC and NFKB1 (**J**); 2D interaction diagram of PCC and HDAC2 (**K**); 2D interaction diagram of PCC and STAT1 (**L**); 2D and 3D interaction diagram of PCC and HSP90AA1 (**M**).

3.7. Molecular Dynamics Simulations

The result was analyzed after the completion of the 100 ns molecular dynamics simulation. Figure 6A shows that the RMSD values of the ligand-receptor complex stabilized after 15 ns, with fluctuations consistently being within 0.1 nm (Figure 6A). The H-bond analysis revealed that PCC could provide at least one hydrogen bond to advance its binding to HSP90AA1 during the 100 ns simulation (Figure 6B). Additionally, the RG analysis implied that the fluctuation range of the complex remained under 0.1 nm over the 100 ns simulation (Figure 6C), whereas the RMSF analysis revealed some flexible residue fragments in the receptor that may interact with the ligand (Figure 6D). Taken together, these results support the fact that PCC can form a stable complex structure with HSP90AA1 and thus, perform its biological functions.

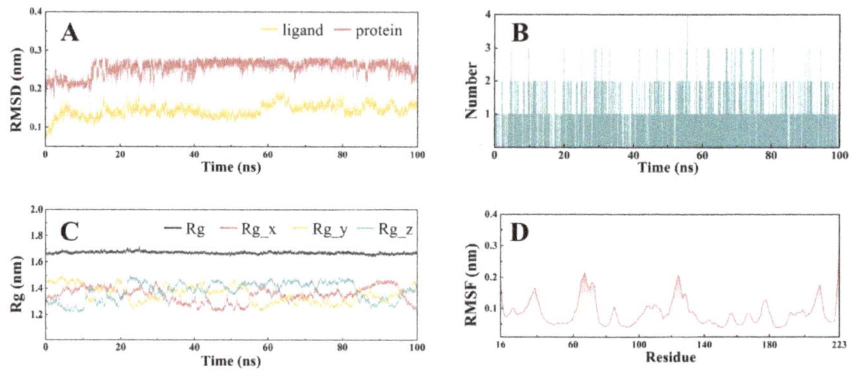

Figure 6. Molecular dynamics simulation: RMSD analysis of the PCC-HSP90AA1 complex (**A**); H-bond analysis of the PCC-HSP90AA1 complex (**B**); Rg analysis of the PCC-HSP90AA1 complex (**C**); and RMSF analysis of the PCC-HSP90AA1 complex (**D**).

3.8. PCC Bound to HSP90AA1

CETSA results indicated that the complex formed by PCC binding to HSP90AA1 reduced the temperature sensitivity of HSP90AA1 (Figure 7). Within the temperature range of 50–80 °C, although the relative band intensity of HSP90AA1 in PCC-treated cell lysates gradually decreased with increasing temperature, the stability of this protein significantly improved, compared with that of the control group at the same temperature.

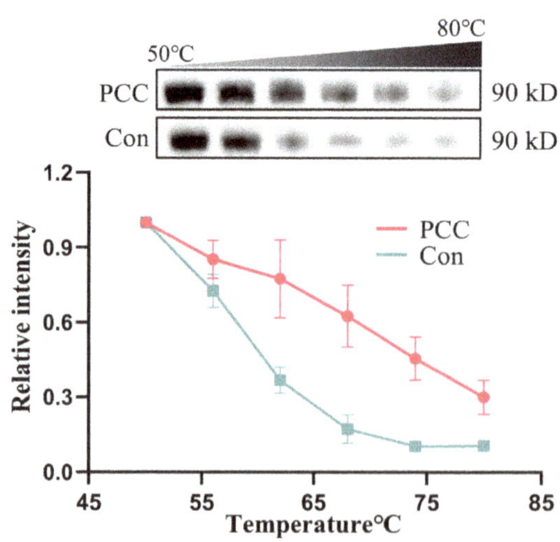

Figure 7. Identification of PCC binding to target protein HSP90AA1 via CETSA.

3.9. In Vitro Evaluation

After co-culturing with different concentrations of PCC for 24 h, the results showed that PCC dose-dependently decreased HSP90AA1 expression in both HepG2 and MCF-7 cells

(Figure 8Aa,Ba). The cell viability was assessed via the CCK-8 assay (Figure S6). In HepG2 cells, PCC in the concentration range of 0–120 μM did not show significant cytotoxicity. In contrast, its treatment with 50 μM ADR resulted in a significant decrease in cell viability, with a reduction of 38.3%, compared with that of the control group. When 50 μM ADR was co-treated with 5 μM PCC, the cell viability was reduced by 50.5%, compared with that of the control group. In MCF-7 cells, the cell viability was reduced by 41.7% after treating with 50 μM ADR for 24 h. When 5 μM PCC was combined with 50 μM ADR, the cell viability decreased by 45.7%. These results suggested that PCC promoted apoptosis when in combination with ADR. Through the use of a fixed concentration of ADR (50 μM) with PCC (10 μM) to treat HepG2 cells and MCF-7 cells, it was found that PCC reduced the high transcription levels of the *SP1* and *MDR1* genes induced by ADR, while also inhibiting the transcription of *HSP90AA1* and *Mut-p53* (Figure 8Ab,Bb). In summary, in vitro experiments demonstrated that PCC acts as an HSP90AA1 inhibitor, promoting ADR efficacy and exerting anticancer activity by influencing the Mut-p53/SP1/MDR1 pathway. Notably, the effects of PCC are slightly more pronounced in HepG2 cells, compared to MCF-7 cells.

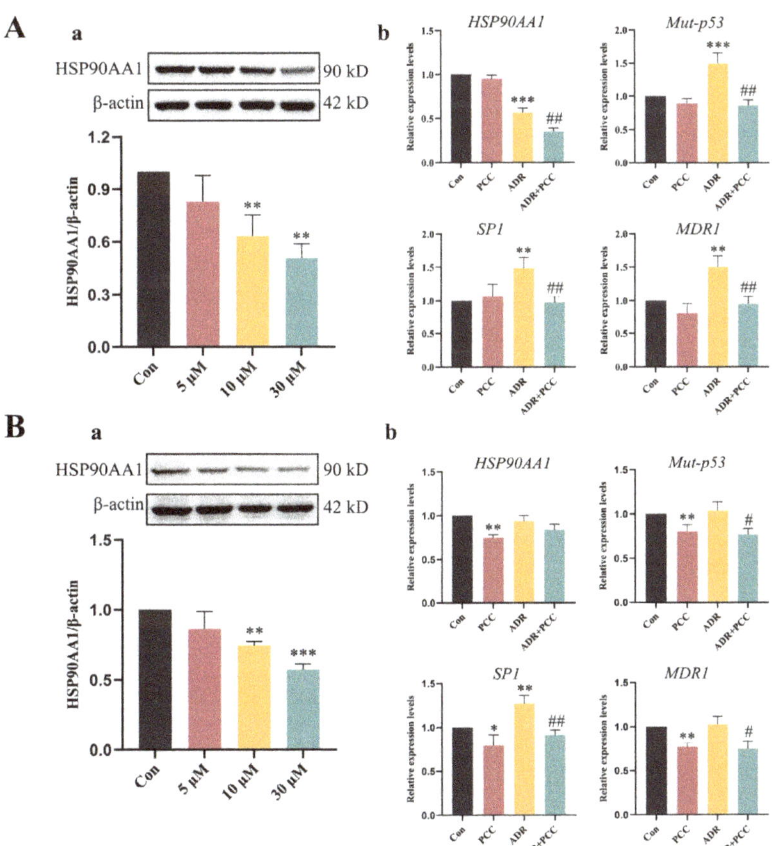

Figure 8. Semiquantitative analysis of HSP90AA1 via Western blot of HepG2 cells (**Aa**). Effect of PCC on the expression levels of *HSP90AA1*, *Mut-p53*, *SP1* and *MDR1* mRNAs in HepG2/ADR cells (**Ab**). Semiquantitative analysis of HSP90AA1 via Western blot of MCF-7 cells (**Ba**). Effect of PCC on the expression levels of *HSP90AA1*, *Mut-p53*, *SP1* and *MDR1* mRNAs in MCF-7/ADR cells (**Bb**). Compared to the Con group, * represents $p < 0.05$, ** represents $p < 0.01$, *** represents $p < 0.001$. Compared to the ADR group, # represents $p < 0.05$, ## represents $p < 0.01$.

3.10. ADMET and Physicochemical Properties of PCC

The physicochemical properties of PCC were analyzed according to the Lipinski rule of five (Table 4). The appropriate molecular weight, number of hydrogen bond donors and acceptors, and LogP value all suggest that PCC has great potential as a pharmaceutical candidate. The results of the ADMET prediction are enumerated in Table 5. The PCC showed acceptable absorption, with a Caco-2 permeability value of −5.052. The cytochrome P450 (CYP) enzyme family, which catalyzes the oxidative metabolism of various endogenous and exogenous substances, was analyzed in terms of substrate and inhibitor predictions, providing insights for future targeted therapies involving PCC. Furthermore, the toxicity analysis of PCC revealed no significant toxicity, including DILI, rat oral acute toxicity, human hepatotoxicity, and immunotoxicity.

Table 4. Physicochemical properties of PCC.

Property	Value	Optimal Value
MW	396.17	100~600
nHD	5	0~7
nHA	7	0~12
nRot	11	0~11
nRing	2	0~6
MaxRing	6	0~18
nHet	7	1~15
TPSA	118.89	0~140
LogS	−3.064	-
LogP	1.643	-
LogD	1.954	-
Synth	2	<6

Table 5. ADMET prediction of PCC.

Property	Value	Optimal Value
Caco-2 Permeability	−5.052	>−5.15
HIA	0.961	-
BBB	0	-
VDss	−0.715	0.04~20
HLM stability	0.002	0
CYP1A2 inhibitor	1	0
CYP1A2 substrate	0	0
CYP2D6 inhibitor	0.018	0
CYP2D6 substrate	0.281	0
CYP3A4 inhibitor	0	0
CYP3A4 substrate	0	0
CLplasma	12.563	>15
DILI	0.612	<1
Rat Oral Acute Toxicity	0.025	<1
Carcinogenicity	0.055	<1
Human Hepatotoxicity	0.588	<1
Drug-induced Nephrotoxicity	0.041	<1
Drug-induced Neurotoxicity	0.596	<1
Hematotoxicity	0.005	<1
Immunotoxicity	0.023	<1

4. Discussion

Thousands of years of continuous evolution have led to the production of a diverse array of secondary metabolites in plants. These secondary metabolites have acquired various biological functions through their interactions with biological systems [29]. Consequently, in the face of considerable challenges in drug development, researchers often tend to look for countermeasures from the secondary metabolites of plants. *S. tangutica* is a Tibetan medicinal herb with a long medicinal history, which has been characterized by its excellent antioxidant, anti-inflammatory, anti-hepatic injury and antitumor properties in modern pharmacology [30,31]. In this study, a natural alkaloid, named *N-p*-coumaroyl-*N'*-caffeoylputrescine (PCC), was isolated from the Tibetan medicinal plant *S. tangutica* using a combined medium-pressure and high-performance chromatography approach. A literature search revealed that the structure and spectral information of PCC were first recorded in 2011 from the ethyl acetate fraction of *Exochorda racemosa* [28]. However, in the subsequent decade, no further reports have identified PCC from natural products, and its bioactivity and molecular targets remain entirely unexplored.

The biological activity and targets of small molecular compounds are often the primary challenges to be addressed in the drug development process. DARTS allows for the identification of binding targets of small molecules in biological systems without altering their structure or activity. In addition, as far as online databases are concerned, the PharmMapper database, which is based on pharmacophore matching; the STP and SuperNet databases, which are based on structure-activity relationships; and the Super-Pred database, which is based on machine learning, retrieve the potential targets of small molecule compounds from different dimensions, and the organic integration of these databases can mine the potential targets of small molecules as much as possible and characterize the complex interactions between them [32,33]. Our research confirmed that such a comprehensive strategy is applicable to PCC. The 317 common targets identified by the combination of multiple databases and DARTS were further screened (PPI network and reverse virtual docking), and HSP90AA1 was finally targeted as PCC's target, which was also validated by subsequent experiments.

Heat shock protein 90 (HSP90) is a highly conserved ATP-dependent molecular chaperone in eukaryotes, which is important for maintaining cellular homeostasis and regulating the cell cycle. The expression levels of HSP90 under stress conditions are 2–6 times higher than those under normal conditions [34], which may be attributed to the overexpression of HSP90α (a subtype of HSP90). In contrast to HSP90β, HSP90α is encoded by the *HSP90AA1* gene and is often abnormally expressed in various diseases [35,36]. Oxidative stress is an essential trigger for the aberrant expression of HSP90AA1, and some antioxidants regulate the oxidative homeostasis of the body while driving HSP90AA1 back to the normal level or interfering with the function of client proteins by targeting HSP90AA1 [37]. Our work, firstly, clarified that PCC has an excellent antioxidant activity, and further target validation experiments found that the thermal stability of HSP90AA1 was improved after binding to PCC, implying that HSP90AA1 is the molecular target of PCC. The N-terminal domain (NTD) of HSP90AA1 contains an ATP-binding site (Bergerat fold) [38]. Molecular docking and dynamics simulation revealed that PCC interacts with residues Gln23, Asp93, Gly97, and Ile104 within the ATP-binding site, causing steric hindrance that disrupts ATPase activity and prevents transient dimerization. This misfolded conformation ultimately leads to the degradation and functional loss of its client proteins. Bioinformatics analyses and data mining suggest that PCC has promising applications in cancer by affecting the activity and expression of HSP90AA1, subsequently interacting with TP53, EGFR, and ESR1 (client proteins of HSP90AA1), triggering a cascade reaction.

For cancer, pharmacologic interventions remain the primary approach for its treatment; however, the resistance generated in this process is rapidly attracting the attention of scientists [39]. Moreover, the resistance generated by one anticancer drug is extremely likely to reduce the sensitivity of other drugs, and this manifestation of multidrug resistance (MDR) is one of the major reasons for the failure of cancer treatment [40,41]. Multi-drug resistance gene-1 (MDR1) is the crux in addressing drug resistance in many malignant tumors, and its encoded P-pg (P-glycoprotein) is able to pump intracellular drugs out of the cytoplasm by hydrolyzing ATP for its own energy supply [42]. In addition, previous studies have also reported excessive HSP90AA1 stature in studies of MDR [43], whose client protein mutant p53 (Mut-p53) in malignant tumors reduces drug efficacy (off-target), and it can also activate the transcription factor SP1 (specificity protein 1), which promotes the transcription and expression of MDR1 [44,45]. In this study, PCC was able to reduce the expression of HSP90AA1 and had no significant impact on the viability of HepG2 and MCF-7 cells, suggesting that the anticancer activity of PCC may not be directly related to apoptosis. However, PCC, in combination with ADR, reduced the viability of tumor cells more than ADR alone did; reversed the high transcript levels of *Mut-p53, SP1* and *MDR1* caused by ADR and increased the cell sensitivity to drugs. As a prominent tumor suppressor gene, TP53 is also one of the hub targets of PCC, and its encoded protein P53 is often present in its mutant form in malignant tumors [46]. PCC was shown to reduce the transcriptional levels of Mut-p53, which implies that the synergistic effect with other targets while PCC exerts its biological function through HSP90AA1 is also an important factor to consider. Overall, these findings imply that PCC, as a small-molecule inhibitor of the chaperone protein HSP90AA1, is able to further expand the potency of ADR for antitumor purposes through the Mut-p53/SP1/MDR1 pathway, demonstrating a significant therapeutic potential.

In conclusion, this study integrated network pharmacology and DARTS into a reproducible strategy to clarify HSP90AA1 as the target of the natural alkaloid PCC, with Gln23, Asp93, Gly97, and Ile104 being key residues. In future work, crystallography and site-directed mutagenesis will be emphasized in the exploration of the interaction mechanism and structure-activity relationship between HSP90AA1 and PCC. Additionally, taking the biological function of HSP90AA1 as an entry point, the potential of PCC in cancer therapy was explored in this work. Given that PCC is an effective HSP90AA1 inhibitor, a more comprehensive in vitro and in vivo experimental design will be worth considering to further explore its medicinal potential and evaluate its pharmacokinetics.

5. Conclusions

This study utilized DARTS technology, combined with online databases, to fish for the protein targets of PCC, a natural alkaloid from *S. tangutica*. A total of 317 common targets were identified, which were further analyzed using bioinformatics and reverse virtual screening. Ultimately, HSP90AA1 was confirmed as the target of PCC, with a binding energy as low as −10.74 kcal/mol. Our findings suggested that PCC acts as a potent antioxidant, along with being a promising candidate for cancer treatment. Follow-up in vitro experiments showed that the combination of PCC with ADR significantly reduces the expression of genes associated with drug resistance. In conclusion, this study offers valuable insights into the development of PCC as a lead compound; meanwhile, such a strategy also provides robust assistance for future bioactivity and protein target studies of natural products.

Supplementary Materials: The following supporting information can be downloaded at: https://www.mdpi.com/article/10.3390/antiox14010012/s1, Figure S1: ESI-MS spectrum data of Fr4-5-1; Figure S2: ^{1}H-NMR data of Fr4-5-1 (DMSO-d6); Figure S3: ^{13}C-NMR data of Fr4-5-1 (DMSO-d6); Figure S4: HSQC data of Fr4-5-1; Figure S5: HMBC data of Fr4-5-1; Figure S6: Cell viability assay of HepG2 (A) and MCF-7cells (B); Table S1: Potential target of PCC; Original data S1: Darts; Original data S2: molecular dynamics simulation.

Author Contributions: Conceptualization, J.D. and M.W.; methodology, C.L. and J.D.; software, C.L.; validation, C.L.; data curation, C.L.; writing—original draft preparation, C.L.; writing—review and editing, J.D. and M.W.; visualization, C.L. and M.W.; supervision, J.D. and M.W.; project administration, J.D.; funding acquisition, J.D. All authors have read and agreed to the published version of the manuscript.

Funding: This work was supported by the Applied Basic Research Project of Qinghai Province (2021-ZJ-720).

Institutional Review Board Statement: Not applicable.

Data Availability Statement: Data are contained within the article and Supplementary Materials.

Conflicts of Interest: The authors declare no conflicts of interest.

References

1. Du, J.; Guo, J.; Kang, D.; Li, Z.; Wang, G.; Wu, J.; Zhang, Z.; Fang, H.; Hou, X.; Huang, Z.; et al. New Techniques and Strategies in Drug Discovery. *Chin. Chem. Lett.* **2020**, *31*, 1695–1708. [CrossRef]
2. Yang, L.; Bui, L.; Hanjaya-Putra, D.; Bruening, M.L. Membrane-Based Affinity Purification to Identify Target Proteins of a Small-Molecule Drug. *Anal. Chem.* **2020**, *92*, 11912–11920. [CrossRef] [PubMed]
3. Lomenick, B.; Hao, R.; Jonai, N.; Chin, R.M.; Aghajan, M.; Warburton, S.; Wang, J.; Wu, R.P.; Gomez, F.; Loo, J.A.; et al. Target Identification Using Drug Affinity Responsive Target Stability (DARTS). *Proc. Natl. Acad. Sci. USA* **2009**, *106*, 21984–21989. [CrossRef]
4. Ha, J.; Park, H.; Park, J.; Park, S.B. Recent Advances in Identifying Protein Targets in Drug Discovery. *Cell Chem. Biol.* **2021**, *28*, 394–423. [CrossRef]
5. Ren, Y.-S.; Li, H.-L.; Piao, X.-H.; Yang, Z.-Y.; Wang, S.-M.; Ge, Y.-W. Drug Affinity Responsive Target Stability (DARTS) Accelerated Small Molecules Target Discovery: Principles and Application. *Biochem. Pharmacol.* **2021**, *194*, 114798. [CrossRef]
6. Mao, X.; Xu, H.; Li, S.; Su, J.; Li, W.; Guo, Q.; Wang, P.; Guo, R.; Xiao, X.; Zhang, Y.; et al. Exploring Pharmacological Mechanisms of Xueshuan-Xinmai-Ning Tablets Acting on Coronary Heart Disease Based on Drug Target-Disease Gene Interaction Network. *Phytomedicine* **2019**, *54*, 159–168. [CrossRef]
7. Drakontaeidi, A.; Papanotas, I.; Pontiki, E. Multitarget Pharmacology of Sulfur–Nitrogen Heterocycles: Anticancer and Antioxidant Perspectives. *Antioxidants* **2024**, *13*, 898. [CrossRef]
8. Agamah, F.E.; Mazandu, G.K.; Hassan, R.; Bope, C.D.; Thomford, N.E.; Ghansah, A.; Chimusa, E.R. Computational/in Silico Methods in Drug Target and Lead Prediction. *Brief. Bioinform.* **2020**, *21*, 1663–1675. [CrossRef] [PubMed]
9. Masoudi-Sobhanzadeh, Y.; Omidi, Y.; Amanlou, M.; Masoudi-Nejad, A. Drug Databases and Their Contributions to Drug Repurposing. *Genomics* **2020**, *112*, 1087–1095. [CrossRef] [PubMed]
10. Wang, X.; Shen, Y.; Wang, S.; Li, S.; Zhang, W.; Liu, X.; Lai, L.; Pei, J.; Li, H. PharmMapper 2017 Update: A Web Server for Potential Drug Target Identification with a Comprehensive Target Pharmacophore Database. *Nucleic Acids Res.* **2017**, *45*, W356–W360. [CrossRef]
11. Yao, Z.-J.; Dong, J.; Che, Y.-J.; Zhu, M.-F.; Wen, M.; Wang, N.-N.; Wang, S.; Lu, A.-P.; Cao, D.-S. TargetNet: A Web Service for Predicting Potential Drug–Target Interaction Profiling via Multi-Target SAR Models. *J. Comput. Aided Mol. Des.* **2016**, *30*, 413–424. [CrossRef]
12. Nickel, J.; Gohlke, B.-O.; Erehman, J.; Banerjee, P.; Rong, W.W.; Goede, A.; Dunkel, M.; Preissner, R. SuperPred: Update on Drug Classification and Target Prediction. *Nucleic Acids Res.* **2014**, *42*, W26–W31. [CrossRef] [PubMed]
13. Szklarczyk, D.; Kirsch, R.; Koutrouli, M.; Nastou, K.; Mehryary, F.; Hachilif, R.; Gable, A.L.; Fang, T.; Doncheva, N.T.; Pyysalo, S.; et al. The STRING Database in 2023: Protein–Protein Association Networks and Functional Enrichment Analyses for Any Sequenced Genome of Interest. *Nucleic Acids Res.* **2023**, *51*, D638–D646. [CrossRef]
14. Avilés-Alía, A.I.; Zulaica, J.; Perez, J.J.; Rubio-Martínez, J.; Geller, R.; Granadino-Roldán, J.M. The Discovery of Inhibitors of the SARS-CoV-2 S Protein through Computational Drug Repurposing. *Comput. Biol. Med.* **2024**, *171*, 108163. [CrossRef]
15. Sabe, V.T.; Ntombela, T.; Jhamba, L.A.; Maguire, G.E.M.; Govender, T.; Naicker, T.; Kruger, H.G. Current Trends in Computer Aided Drug Design and a Highlight of Drugs Discovered via Computational Techniques: A Review. *Eur. J. Med. Chem.* **2021**, *224*, 113705. [CrossRef]
16. Caballero, J. The Latest Automated Docking Technologies for Novel Drug Discovery. *Expert Opin. Drug Discov.* **2021**, *16*, 625–645. [CrossRef] [PubMed]
17. Westermaier, Y.; Barril, X.; Scapozza, L. Virtual Screening: An in Silico Tool for Interlacing the Chemical Universe with the Proteome. *Methods* **2015**, *71*, 44–57. [CrossRef] [PubMed]
18. Xu, J.; Zhang, S.; Wu, T.; Fang, X.; Zhao, L. Discovery of TGFBR1 (ALK5) as a Potential Drug Target of Quercetin Glycoside Derivatives (QGDs) by Reverse Molecular Docking and Molecular Dynamics Simulation. *Biophys. Chem.* **2022**, *281*, 106731. [CrossRef]
19. Pisoschi, A.M.; Pop, A.; Iordache, F.; Stanca, L.; Predoi, G.; Serban, A.I. Oxidative Stress Mitigation by Antioxidants—An Overview on Their Chemistry and Influences on Health Status. *Eur. J. Med. Chem.* **2021**, *209*, 112891. [CrossRef] [PubMed]

20. Seiva, F.R.F.; Agneis, M.L.G.; de Almeida, M.R.; Caputo, W.L.; de Souza, M.C.; das Neves, K.A.; Oliveira, É.N.; Justulin, L.A.; Chuffa, L.G. de A. In Silico Analysis of Non-Conventional Oxidative Stress-Related Enzymes and Their Potential Relationship with Carcinogenesis. *Antioxidants* **2024**, *13*, 1279. [CrossRef]
21. Yang, S.; Nie, T.; She, H.; Tao, K.; Lu, F.; Hu, Y.; Huang, L.; Zhu, L.; Feng, D.; He, D.; et al. Regulation of TFEB Nuclear Localization by HSP90AA1 Promotes Autophagy and Longevity. *Autophagy* **2023**, *19*, 822–838. [CrossRef]
22. Chen, Q.; Zhou, R.; Yang, C.; Jiang, Q.; Yuan, H.; Qiu, X.; Tian, H.; Zhou, J.; Liu, C. Ergothioneine Attenuates Varicocele-Induced Testicular Damage by Upregulating HSP90AA1 in Rats. *J. Biochem. Mol. Toxicol.* **2023**, *37*, e23301. [CrossRef]
23. Liu, C.; Lei, Y.; Liu, Y.; Guo, J.; Chen, X.; Tang, Y.; Dang, J.; Wu, M. An Integrated Strategy for Investigating Antioxidants from Ribes Himalense Royle Ex Decne and Their Potential Target Proteins. *Antioxidants* **2023**, *12*, 835. [CrossRef]
24. Daina, A.; Zoete, V. Testing the Predictive Power of Reverse Screening to Infer Drug Targets, with the Help of Machine Learning. *Commun. Chem.* **2024**, *7*, 105. [CrossRef] [PubMed]
25. Sherman, B.T.; Hao, M.; Qiu, J.; Jiao, X.; Baseler, M.W.; Lane, H.C.; Imamichi, T.; Chang, W. DAVID: A Web Server for Functional Enrichment Analysis and Functional Annotation of Gene Lists (2021 Update). *Nucleic Acids Res.* **2022**, *50*, W216–W221. [CrossRef]
26. Pletscher-Frankild, S.; Pallejà, A.; Tsafou, K.; Binder, J.X.; Jensen, L.J. DISEASES: Text Mining and Data Integration of Disease–Gene Associations. *Methods* **2015**, *74*, 83–89. [CrossRef] [PubMed]
27. Lu, T. Sobtop, 1.0 (dev5). Available online: http://sobereva.com/soft/Sobtop/ (accessed on 25 August 2024).
28. Zhang, J.; Li, X.; Ren, L.; Fang, C.; Wang, F. Chemical constituents from Exochorda racemosa. *China J. Chin. Mater. Medica.* **2011**, *36*, 1198–1201.
29. Twilley, D.; Rademan, S.; Lall, N. A Review on Traditionally Used South African Medicinal Plants, Their Secondary Metabolites and Their Potential Development into Anticancer Agents. *J. Ethnopharmacol.* **2020**, *261*, 113101. [CrossRef] [PubMed]
30. Tong, Y.; Li, G.; Shi, X.; Wang, L.; Zhou, J.; Chu, M.; Wang, Z.; El-Aty, A.M.A.; Dang, J. Protection against Myocardial Ischemia/Reperfusion Injury in Mice by 3-Caffeoylquinic Acid Isomers Isolated from Saxifraga Tangutica. *RSC Adv.* **2024**, *14*, 6642–6655. [CrossRef]
31. Dang, J.; Wang, Q.; Wang, Q.; Yuan, C.; Li, G.; Ji, T. Preparative Isolation of Antioxidative Gallic Acid Derivatives from Saxifraga Tangutica Using a Class Separation Method Based on Medium-Pressure Liquid Chromatography and Reversed-Phase Liquid Chromatography. *J. Sep. Sci.* **2021**, *44*, 3734–3746. [CrossRef] [PubMed]
32. Meissner, F.; Geddes-McAlister, J.; Mann, M.; Bantscheff, M. The Emerging Role of Mass Spectrometry-Based Proteomics in Drug Discovery. *Nat. Rev. Drug Discov.* **2022**, *21*, 637–654. [CrossRef] [PubMed]
33. Nogales, C.; Mamdouh, Z.M.; List, M.; Kiel, C.; Casas, A.I.; Schmidt, H.H.H.W. Network Pharmacology: Curing Causal Mechanisms Instead of Treating Symptoms. *Trends Pharmacol. Sci.* **2022**, *43*, 136–150. [CrossRef] [PubMed]
34. van Oosten-Hawle, P. Organismal Roles of Hsp90. *Biomolecules* **2023**, *13*, 251. [CrossRef] [PubMed]
35. Zhang, M.; Peng, Y.; Yang, Z.; Zhang, H.; Xu, C.; Liu, L.; Zhao, Q.; Wu, J.; Wang, H.; Liu, J. DAB2IP Down-Regulates HSP90AA1 to Inhibit the Malignant Biological Behaviors of Colorectal Cancer. *BMC Cancer* **2022**, *22*, 561. [CrossRef]
36. Shi, W.; Feng, L.; Dong, S.; Ning, Z.; Hua, Y.; Liu, L.; Chen, Z.; Meng, Z. FBXL6 Governs C-MYC to Promote Hepatocellular Carcinoma through Ubiquitination and Stabilization of HSP90AA1. *Cell Commun Signal* **2020**, *18*, 100. [CrossRef]
37. Deng, S.-L.; Sun, T.-C.; Yu, K.; Wang, Z.-P.; Zhang, B.-L.; Zhang, Y.; Wang, X.-X.; Lian, Z.-X.; Liu, Y.-X. Melatonin Reduces Oxidative Damage and Upregulates Heat Shock Protein 90 Expression in Cryopreserved Human Semen. *Free Radic. Biol. Med.* **2017**, *113*, 347–354. [CrossRef]
38. Peng, C.; Zhao, F.; Li, H.; Li, L.; Yang, Y.; Liu, F. HSP90 Mediates the Connection of Multiple Programmed Cell Death in Diseases. *Cell Death Dis.* **2022**, *13*, 929. [CrossRef]
39. Davodabadi, F.; Sajjadi, S.F.; Sarhadi, M.; Mirghasemi, S.; Nadali Hezaveh, M.; Khosravi, S.; Kamali Andani, M.; Cordani, M.; Basiri, M.; Ghavami, S. Cancer Chemotherapy Resistance: Mechanisms and Recent Breakthrough in Targeted Drug Delivery. *Eur. J. Pharmacol.* **2023**, *958*, 176013. [CrossRef] [PubMed]
40. Muriithi, W.; Macharia, L.W.; Heming, C.P.; Echevarria, J.L.; Nyachieo, A.; Filho, P.N.; Neto, V.M. ABC Transporters and the Hallmarks of Cancer: Roles in Cancer Aggressiveness beyond Multidrug Resistance. *Cancer Biol. Med.* **2020**, *17*, 253–269. [CrossRef]
41. Kopecka, J.; Trouillas, P.; Gašparović, A.Č.; Gazzano, E.; Assaraf, Y.G.; Riganti, C. Phospholipids and Cholesterol: Inducers of Cancer Multidrug Resistance and Therapeutic Targets. *Drug Resist. Updat.* **2020**, *49*, 100670. [CrossRef] [PubMed]
42. Dong, J.; Yuan, L.; Hu, C.; Cheng, X.; Qin, J.-J. Strategies to Overcome Cancer Multidrug Resistance (MDR) through Targeting P-Glycoprotein (ABCB1): An Updated Review. *Pharmacol. Ther.* **2023**, *249*, 108488. [CrossRef] [PubMed]
43. Park, M.; Jung, E.; Park, J.M.; Park, S.; Ko, D.; Seo, J.; Kim, S.; Nam, K.D.; Kang, Y.K.; Farrand, L.; et al. The HSP90 Inhibitor HVH-2930 Exhibits Potent Efficacy against Trastuzumab-Resistant HER2-Positive Breast Cancer. *Theranostics* **2024**, *14*, 2442–2463. [CrossRef] [PubMed]

44. Alhaj-Suliman, S.O.; Naguib, Y.W.; Wafa, E.I.; Saha, S.; Ebeid, K.; Meng, X.; Mohammed, H.H.; Abuo-Rahma, G.E.-D.A.; Yang, S.; Salem, A.K. A Ciprofloxacin Derivative with Four Mechanisms of Action Overcomes Paclitaxel Resistance in P53-Mutant and MDR1 Gene-Expressing Type II Human Endometrial Cancer. *Biomaterials* **2023**, *296*, 122093. [CrossRef]
45. Reynolds, T.S.; Blagg, B.S.J. Extracellular Heat Shock Protein 90 Alpha (eHsp90α)'s Role in Cancer Progression and the Development of Therapeutic Strategies. *Eur. J. Med. Chem.* **2024**, *277*, 116736. [CrossRef]
46. Cordani, M.; Garufi, A.; Benedetti, R.; Tafani, M.; Aventaggiato, M.; D'Orazi, G.; Cirone, M. Recent Advances on Mutant P53: Unveiling Novel Oncogenic Roles, Degradation Pathways, and Therapeutic Interventions. *Biomolecules* **2024**, *14*, 649. [CrossRef] [PubMed]

analytica

MDPI

Article

Chemical Characterization and Biological Activity of *Varronia curassavica* Jacq. Essential Oil (Boraginaceae) and In Silico Testing of α-Pinene

José Thyálisson da Costa Silva [1], Viviane Bezerra da Silva [2], Sabrina Bezerra da Silva [3], Maria Ivaneide Rocha [3], Adrielle Rodrigues Costa [3], Jailson Renato de Lima Silva [3], Marcos Aurélio Figueirêdo dos Santos [4], Maria Elizete Machado Generino [4], Jeovane Henrique de Souza [3], Maraiza Gregorio de Oliveira [3], Clara Mariana Gonçalves Lima [5,*], Raimundo Luiz Silva Pereira [5], Renata Ferreira Santana [6], Isaac Moura Araujo [5], Maria Flaviana Bezerra Morais-Braga [1], Talha Bin Emran [7,8,9], Henrique Douglas Melo Coutinho [5,*] and José Weverton Almeida-Bezerra [1]

1 Cariri Applied Mycology Laboratory, Regional University of Cariri, Crato 63105-000, CE, Brazil
2 Applied Ecology and Phytochemistry Laboratory, Federal University of Pernambuco, Recife 50740-600, PE, Brazil
3 Plant Ecophysiology Laboratory, Regional University of Cariri, Crato 63105-000, CE, Brazil
4 Applied Botany Laboratory, Regional University of Cariri, Crato 63105-000, CE, Brazil
5 Laboratory of Microbiology and Molecular Biology, Regional University of Cariri, Crato 63105-000, CE, Brazil
6 Department of Food Science and Engineering, Southwestern Bahia State University, Itapetinga 45083-900, BA, Brazil
7 Department of Pathology and Laboratory Medicine, Warren Alpert Medical School, Brown University, Providence, RI 02912, USA; talha_bin_emran@brown.edu
8 Legorreta Cancer Center, Brown University, Providence, RI 02912, USA
9 Department of Pharmacy, Faculty of Allied Health Sciences, Daffodil International University, Dhaka 1207, Bangladesh
* Correspondence: claramarianalima@gmail.com (C.M.G.L.); hdmcoutinho@gmail.com (H.D.M.C.)

Abstract: Multidrug-resistant bacteria have complicated the treatment of gastrointestinal diseases; their microbial resistance stems from the indiscriminate use of medications and the transfer of resistance genes. *Varronia curassavica* Jacq., a plant traditionally used to treat rheumatic and gastrointestinal diseases in underserved populations, has sparked interest as a potential source of antimicrobial compounds. This study aimed to investigate the chemical composition and antibacterial effects of *V. curassavica* essential oil and to evaluate its toxicity in *Drosophila melanogaster*. The essential oil was extracted through hydrodistillation and its chemical composition was determined using GC-MS. Antibacterial tests were performed with microdilution. The results showed the presence of major compounds including α-pinene and β-caryophyllene. The essential oil did not show relevant MIC, but it enhanced the effects of the antibiotics, gentamicin, norfloxacin, and oxacillin. It exhibited no toxicity and did not affect geotaxis, even at high concentrations. The in silico analysis of α-pinene revealed low toxicity; however, its permeability to the BBB shows that caution is needed in its application. These results indicate that the essential oil of *V. curassavica* shows promising potential in enhancing pharmaceuticals to prevent increased bacterial resistance. In addition, it demonstrated safe aspects when tested on *D. melanogaster*.

Keywords: erva-baleeira; *Cordia verbenacea*; α-humulene; secondary metabolites

1. Introduction

Multidrug-resistant bacteria (MDR) pose a significant threat to public health, as the increasing resistance of these bacteria renders antibiotics ineffective in eliminating them or preventing their multiplication in the human body. This results in various serious health complications for individuals, potentially leading to death and, consequently, increasing the number of fatalities caused by bacterial infections. In recent decades, several factors have contributed to the evolution of bacteria, culminating in the emergence of super-resistant strains. These changes occurred due to mutations, recombinations, and various genetic modifications, including the presence of efflux pumps, in addition to inadequate and uncontrolled exposure to antibiotics [1–5].

MDR bacterial strains are common, especially in hospital settings, where infections frequently occur due to the presence of many microorganisms, affecting people with compromised immune systems and spreading rapidly. Bacterial strains such as *Staphylococcus aureus*, *Escherichia coli*, and *Pseudomonas aeruginosa* are of particular relevance due to their potent resistance mechanisms [6–9]. Thus, the use of medicinal plants as treatments for diseases has been a practice advocated by traditional populations throughout history, becoming more common in regions with limited access to healthcare services and scarce medications because of their easy accessibility and low cost [10,11].

The therapeutic activities of medicinal and aromatic plants are considered an effective complement to treatments and health maintenance, especially when associated with essential oils that are extracted from plant materials. As an alternative in combating bacterial infections, the use of essential oils has attracted more attention in research due to their complex composition (derived from plants' secondary metabolites) and diverse biological activities, such as antiparasitic, antioxidant, anti-inflammatory, antibacterial, and antifungal [12–15].

Notably, the Boraginaceae family possesses various important medicinal properties that are of clinical relevance, with promising applications as therapeutic supplements [16–18]. *Varronia curassavica* Jacq. is one of the standout species, valued both pharmaceutically for its medicinal activities and economically due to the essential oil extracted from its leaves. It is popularly used in various forms, such as teas, extracts, decoctions, ointments, and tinctures, and is especially recognized for its anti-inflammatory effects, as well as for treating rheumatic diseases, myalgia, arthritis, and stomach ulcers [19,20].

Research on the ethnopharmacological application of *V. curassavica* has highlighted the plant's potential biological effects as an antimicrobial, demonstrating efficacy in controlling pathogenic microorganisms. Additionally, the essential oil of this plant does not exhibit toxicity. Thus, this study aimed to quantify the chemical composition of the essential oil of *V. curassavica*, evaluate its antibacterial efficacy and drug-enhancing potential, examine its in vivo toxicity levels in the model organism *Drosophila melanogaster*, and perform an in silico analysis of the major phytochemical.

2. Materials and Methods

2.1. Botanical Material Collection

The botanical material, the leaves of *V. curassavica*, was collected in the municipality of Jardim, Ceará, Brazil, at coordinates latitude −7.554917 W and longitude −39.306611 S, during January/2022. A voucher specimen of the collected plant material was deposited in the Herbarium Caririense Dárdano de Andrade Lima—HCDAL, at the Universidade Regional do Cariri—URCA, under voucher number 15.291. Additionally, the research was registered in the Sistema Nacional de Gestão do Patrimônio Genético e do Conhecimento Tradicional Associado (SisGen), with code AEFC723, and in the Sistema de Autorização e Informação em Biodiversidade (SisBio), with permit number 82789-1.

2.2. Essential Oil Extraction

For the extraction of the essential oil, the collected leaves of *V. curassavica* were naturally dried and manually crushed to increase the surface area for solvent contact. Subsequently, they were placed in a 5 L volumetric flask with 2 L of distilled water and subjected to constant boiling for 2 h, coupled with the Clevenger system. Each extraction utilized 200 g of leaves. After each extraction, the resulting oil was stored in an amber-colored bottle, at a refrigeration temperature of 4 °C.

2.3. *Phytochemical Analysis of Essential Oil by Gas Chromatography*

The gas chromatography (GC) analysis was conducted using an Agilent Technologies 6890N GC-FID system (Agilent Technologies, Santa Clara, CA, USA), which was equipped with a DB-5 capillary column (30 m × 0.32 mm; 0.50 mm) and linked to an FID detector. The temperature program involved initial heating to 60 °C (1 min), followed by an increase to 180 °C, at a rate of 3 °C per minute. The injector and detector were both maintained at 220 °C, with a split ratio of 1:10. Helium served as the carrier gas, at a flow rate of 1.0 mL/min. The injected volume of *V. curassavica* essential oil was 1 μL, diluted in chloroform (1:10). Two replicates of the samples were processed using the same method. Component relative concentrations were calculated based on GC peak areas, without the utilization of correction factors.

Constituent identification relied on several methods, including retention index (RI) determination, using a reference set of n-alkanes (C7–C30) under the same experimental conditions. This identification was further validated through comparison with mass spectra library searches (NIST and Wiley) and referenced mass spectra literature [21]. The relative quantities of individual components were then calculated based on their respective gas chromatography (GC) peak areas, as measured by the flame ionization detector (FID) response.

2.4. *Antibacterial Activity*

2.4.1. Strains, Culture Media, and Drugs

To assess antibacterial activity and minimum inhibitory concentration (MIC), standard and multidrug-resistant bacterial strains were employed. Standard strains included *Escherichia coli* ATCC 25922, *Pseudomonas aeruginosa* ATCC 25853, and *Staphylococcus aureus* ATCC 25923, while the multidrug-resistant strains encompassed *E. coli* 06, *P. aeruginosa* 24, and *S. aureus* 10 (Table 1) [22]. Brain Heart Infusion (BHI, Merck KGaA, Darmstadt, Germany) culture medium was utilized in accordance with the manufacturer's recommendations.

Table 1. Multidrug-resistant strains and drug resistance profile.

Multi-Resistant Bacterial Strains	Origin/Source	Resistance Profile	Reference
Escherichia coli 06	Urine	Cephalexin, cefoxitin, cefadroxil, ceftriaxone, cefepime, and ampicillin/sulbactam.	
Pseudomonas aeruginosa 24	Urine culture	Amikacin, imipenem, ciprofloxacin, levofloxacin, piperacillin/tazobactam, ceftazidime, merpenem, and cefepime.	[23]
Staphylococcus aureus 10	Rectal swab culture	Cefadroxil, cephalexin, cephalothin, oxacillin, penicillin, ampicillin, amoxicillin, moxifloxacin, ciprofloxacin, levofloxacin, ampicillin/sulbactam, amoxilin/clavulanic acid, erythromycin, clarithromycin, azithromycin, and clindamycin.	

After the bacterial strains had grown, the samples were diluted in test tubes containing 3 mL of sterile saline solution (0.9% NaCl) and agitated using a vortex device. Turbidity was then compared to the McFarland standard of 0.5 scale (equivalent to 1.5×10^8 colony-forming units/mL) [23]. The antibiotics used for biological testing and to assess the potential enhancing activity of EOVC were gentamicin, oxacillin and norfloxacin, all diluted in distilled water.

2.4.2. Minimum Inhibitory Concentration (MIC)

To determine the minimum inhibitory concentration (MIC) of the essential oil responsible for inhibiting the complete growth of bacterial strains, the methodology used in [24] was adopted. A 1000 μL solution was prepared, consisting of 100 μL of inoculum and 900 μL of liquid BHI culture medium, mixed in Eppendorf tubes and then applied to a 96-well plate, with 100 μL of the solution added to each well. Subsequently, EOVC was added, with a range of concentrations, from 0.5 to 512 μg/mL. The plates were numbered and incubated for 24 h, at 37° C.

After the 24 h incubation period, 20 μL of liquid resazurin was added to each well. Resazurin undergoes a redox reaction in the presence of bacterial growth. Following a 1 h reaction period, the plates were analyzed based on the bioindicator coloration. The persistence of violet coloration indicated no bacterial growth, while a change to light pink coloration indicated bacterial growth.

2.4.3. Activity Modifying the Action of Antibiotics

To evaluate the modifying effect of the essential oil, the MIC results of multidrug-resistant bacteria were utilized to determine the sub-inhibitory concentration (MIC/8). This concentration was then combined with antibiotics in different proportions, ranging from 0.1 to 512 μg/mL. For the tests, 1162 μL of 10% BHI and 150 μL of inoculum were used. The control tube, on the other hand, consisted of 1350 μL of BHI and 150 μL of bacterial suspension [25]. The tests followed the microdilution methodology in wells, with antibiotic concentrations (0.5 to 512 μg/mL) dissolved in 100 μL in each well, up to the penultimate well. The plates were then incubated for 24 h at 37 °C and conducted in triplicate.

2.5. Toxicity Test with Drosophila melanogaster

2.5.1. Breeding and Storage of *D. melanogaster*

The species *D. melanogaster* was maintained in cornmeal composed of 1% *w*/*v* brewer's yeast, 2% *w*/*v* sucrose, 1% *w*/*v* powdered milk, and 0.08% *w*/*v* methylparabenonipage. The flies remained at room temperature (25 °C) and relative humidity (60–70%) over a 12 h light/dark photoperiod [26].

2.5.2. Toxicological Tests

The groups received different dosages of 100, 500, and 1000 μg/mL of the oil, which was dissolved in ethanol (1%) and mixed with the fly diet over a 5-day exposure period. The test was conducted in triplicate, and every 24 h period, the count of dead flies was recorded until the end of the experiment [26].

2.5.3. Negative Geotaxis Assessment

To assess changes in the locomotor activity of the flies, the Negative Geotaxis test was performed. This test evaluated whether the essential oil was effective in reducing the flight height to no more than 6 cm in a vertical vial within a 5 s period. The tests were conducted five times, with each vial containing 20 adult flies, and these were compared to the control group [26].

2.6. In Silico Prediction of ADMET

To perform the in silico prediction of the major compound, identified as α-Pinene (42.26%), pkCSM, which was developed by the Biosig Lab at the University of Melbourne (Victoria, Australia), was used. This server was used for ADMET predictions of the compound, predicting the pharmacokinetic properties of ADMET (absorption, distribution, metabolism, and toxicity), which was the main focus [27].

2.7. Statistical Analysis

All assays were conducted in triplicate. The results were analyzed using GraphPad Prism version 6 (Graph Pad Software Inc., San Diego, CA, USA), employing a one-way analysis of variance (ANOVA), followed by Tukey's post-hoc test. Significance was considered at $p < 0.05$.

3. Results

3.1. Chemical Composition

Based on the results obtained from the GC-MS analysis, it was possible to analyze the chemical composition of the essential oil that was extracted from the leaves of *Varronia curassavica*, as presented in Table 2. The investigation identified 11 chemical components, representing 94.66% of the oil's composition. Most of its composition consisted of oxygenated monoterpenes (45.08%) and oxygenated sesquiterpenes (43.25%). The main component among the monoterpenes was α-pinene (42.26%), while the main sesquiterpene identified was β-caryophyllene (22.08%).

Table 2. Chemical composition (%) of *Varronia curassavica* essential oil.

Components	RI	(%)
α-Pinene	976	42.26
β-Pinene	980	2.82
β-Elemene	1375	1.13
β-Caryophyllene	1428	22.08
α-humulene	1460	2.77
Zingiberene	1492	1.16
Biciclogermacrene	1496	13.24
cis-α-Bisabolene	1778	2.87
Nerolidol	1961	3.26
Caryophyllene oxide	2023	1.92
Juniper Camphor	2205	1.15
Hydrocarbon Monoterpene		45.08
Oxygenated Monoterpene		1.15
Hydrocarbon Sesquiterpene		43.25
Oxygenated Sesquiterpene		5.18
Total (%)		94.66%

RI—retention index.

3.2. Antibacterial Activity

The evaluation of the antibacterial activity, which was conducted on the essential oil of the *V. curassavica* leaves, against standard strains of *E. coli*, *P. aeruginosa*, and *S. aureus* did not exhibit significant antimicrobial activity. When assessing the minimum inhibitory concentration (MIC), the results obtained exceeded 512 μg/mL, a concentration considered clinically irrelevant. Similar results were observed against multidrug-resistant strains of these bacteria (*E. coli* 06, *P. aeruginosa* 24, and *S. aureus* 10), with MIC values also exceeding 512 μg/mL, indicating no antibacterial activity.

3.3. Activity Modifying the Action of Antibiotics

As shown in Figure 1, the EOVC results showed a potential enhancing effect when combined with the antibiotics, demonstrating efficient modification potential. There was a significant decrease in the MIC of the referenced antibiotics (gentamicin, norfloxacin, and oxacillin) against the bacterial strains. Gentamicin, when combined with EOVC, significantly reduced the MIC against all bacteria, including *P. aeruginosa* 24 (MIC = 8 μg/mL); *E. coli* 06 (MIC = 1.58 μg/mL); and *S. aureus* 10 (MIC = 3.17 μg/mL). EOVC positively influenced this action.

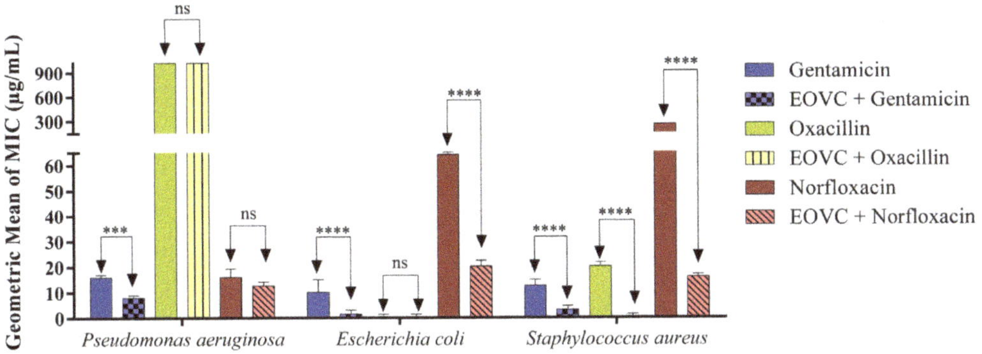

Figure 1. Minimum inhibitory concentration activity to enhance the action of antibiotics against multidrug-resistant strains. Ns—not significant; ****—$p < 0.0001$; and ***—$p < 0.001$.

The combination of EOVC with oxacillin did not exhibit a positive modifying action against *P. aeruginosa* 24 (MIC = 1024 µg/mL) or *E. coli* 06 (Figure 1), which are both classified as Gram-negative bacteria. However, it reduced the cell viability of *S. aureus* 10 (MIC = 0.5 µg/mL), classified as Gram-positive, indicating that the enhanced action directly affected its bactericidal action.

Additionally, norfloxacin showed significant reductions when combined with the essential oil, significantly lowering the MIC against both *E. coli* 06 (MIC = 20.15 µg/mL) and *S. aureus* 10 (MIC = 16 µg/mL). However, the effect on *P. aeruginosa* 24 was not significant and it depended on the dose, as it exhibited a synergistic effect at higher concentrations compared to the others.

3.4. Toxicity against Drosophila melanogaster

As shown in Figure 2, the results of the toxicity tests after the ingestion of the essential oil through the diet of the model organism, *Drosophila melanogaster,* demonstrated that there were no significant changes in mortality when compared to the control test. The test results indicated very low or even no changes, suggesting that these organisms were not affected in a way that would increase their mortality, even at higher concentrations, such as 1000 µg/g, over the course of 5 days of exposure, highlighting low toxicity in the in vivo tests.

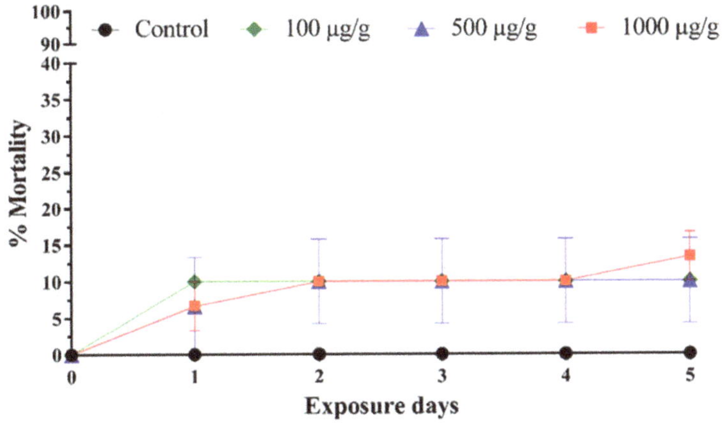

Figure 2. Toxic effect of the *V. curassavica* essential oil against *D. melanogaster*.

Furthermore, as depicted in Figure 3, it was investigated whether EOVC affected the locomotor system of these flies by observing if there were significant changes in the negative geotaxis of *D. melanogaster*. The results obtained indicated that there were no alterations in the basic functioning of the locomotor system. This indicated that the essential oil has low levels of toxicity regarding the mobility of *D. melanogaster*; however, it is necessary to consider the possible cytotoxicity and genotoxicity action.

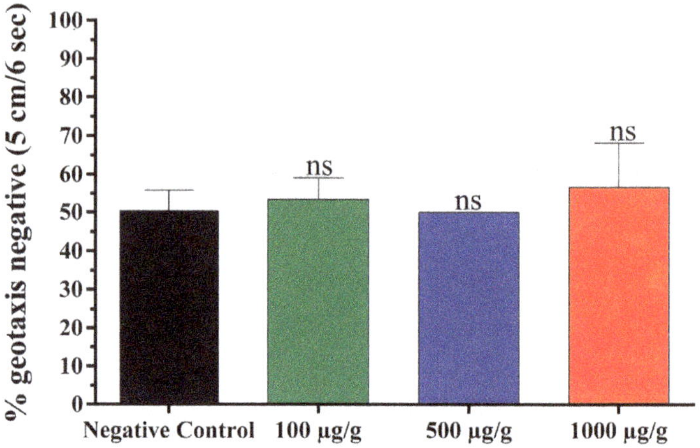

Figure 3. Results of the assessment of negative geotaxis in *Drosophila melanogaster*. ns—not significant.

3.5. *In Silico Analysis (pkCMS)*

The molecular analysis of α-Pinene (Table 3) revealed significant properties related to this molecule. The number of rotatable bonds in the molecule indicated a low molecular flexibility in this compound. Additionally, the aqueous partition coefficient (logP) showed characteristics associated with lipophilicity, falling within the recommended parameters for drugs.

Table 3. Molecular properties of the major compound in the essential oil, α-Pinene.

Descriptor	Value
Molecular formula	$C_{10}H_{16}$
Molecular weight	136.238
LogP	2.9987
Number of rotatable bonds	0
Number of hydrogen acceptors	0
Number of hydrogen donors	0
Surface area	63.322

LogP—octanol/water partition coefficient.

Table 4 displays the ADMET (absorption, distribution, metabolism, and toxicity) properties of α-Pinene. In terms of absorption and distribution, intestinal absorption showed favorable results, as well as permeability across the blood–brain barrier (BBB), which can also be seen positively. Additionally, α-Pinene is neither a substrate nor an inhibitor of permeability glycoproteins (P-gp), which are associated with active efflux from cells.

Table 4. ADMET properties (absorption, distribution, metabolism, and toxicity) of the compound α-Pinene.

Property	Model Name	Predicted Value
Absorption	Water solubility	−3.733 mol/L
	Caco2 permeability	1.38×10^{-6} cm/s
	Intestinal absorption (human)	96.041
	Skin permeability (log Kp)	−1.827
	P-glycoprotein substrate	No
	P-glycoprotein I inhibitor	No
	P-glycoprotein II inhibitor	No
Distribution	VDss (human)	0.667 L/kg
	Fraction unbound (human)	0.425
	BBB permeability	0.791
	CNS permeability	−2.201
Metabolism	CYP2D6 substrate	No
	CYP3A4 substrate	No
	CYP1A2 inhibitor	No
	CYP2C19 inhibitor	No
	CYP2C9 inhibitor	No
	CYP2D6 inhibitor	No
	CYP3A4 inhibitor	No
Excretion	Total clearance	0.043 mL/min/kg
	Renal OCT2 substrate	No
Toxicity	AMES toxicity	No
	Max. tolerated dose (human)	0.48 mg/kg/day
	hERG I inhibitor	No
	hERG II inhibitor	No
	Oral rat acute toxicity (LD50)	1.77 mol/kg
	Oral rat chronic toxicity (LOAEL)	2.262
	Hepatotoxicity	No
	Skin sensitization	No
	T.Pyriformis toxicity	0.45 ug/L
	Minnow toxicity	1.159 mM

BBB—blood–brain barrier; CYP—Cytochrome-P; hERG—human ether-go-go gene.

A positive aspect regarding the metabolism of the compound is that it does not inhibit cytochrome P450 (CYP) enzymes, which play a crucial role in drug metabolism. Therefore, the inhibition of these enzymes can result in side effects or drug interactions. Furthermore, α-Pinene does not present toxicological concerns, as shown in the table, suggesting that it has a good application when used in isolation.

4. Discussion

Various ethnopharmacological uses and applications of *V. curassavica* are employed in the treatment of gastrointestinal diseases, in addition to its promising anti-inflammatory and antimicrobial activity, which is influenced by terpenoids [19,28]. Phytochemical studies have identified α-pinene and β-caryophyllene as the main components, with variations of 56.69–25.32% and 21.78–12.52%, respectively [20,29–32]. However, other studies have found discrepancies, identifying sesquiterpenes as predominant, with β-caryophyllene comprising 25.4–23.26% [33,34] and shyobunol representing 27.46–24.24% of the total [35].

The observed percentage change can be affected by seasonal variations; environmental conditions and the specific plant parts used [36]. Collecting and extracting essential oil at different times of the year; and changes in abiotic factors [37], such as soil and seasonality, can influence the variation of some of the chemically active compounds present [38,39]. Other factors that can cause variations include plant age [32]; photosynthetically active radiation; the choice of drying process [40]; variations caused by air, high temperatures, parasitic herbivory [41]; and changes in light and different seasons [19].

Studies have shown that EOVC exhibits varied antibacterial activities, which may be positive or insignificant. The efficacy of the oil against different bacterial strains is directly influenced by the phytochemicals present. In previous experiments, ß-caryophyllene, which was identified as the major compound (25.4%), presented a MIC of 64 µg/mL against *S. aureus*, *Bacillus cereus*, and *E. coli* [33]. Another study found that Tricyclene (23.9%) has a MIC of 170 µg/mL against *S. aureus* 6538 [42]. Furthermore, sabinene (31.99%) was shown to be effective against *E. coli* and *S. aureus* [43], highlighting the need for caution regarding phytochemistry.

Essential oils can affect electron transport, DNA, and protein synthesis, and can influence the absorption and inhibition of essential enzymes, culminating in cell death [44,45]. This effect can be attributed to the ability of oils to cross the outer membranes of bacterial cells and the inner cytoplasmic membranes, resulting in the disintegration of cellular structures and increased permeability to other compounds [46]. However, essential oils can also have a bacteriostatic effect, temporarily inhibiting the reproduction of bacteria, such as *V. curassavica*, which has bacteriostatic action against Gram-positive bacteria [28].

The use of EOVC in conjunction with antibiotics may enhance the therapeutic effect of the latter. Research indicates that the compound responsible for this synergistic action may be partially linked to α-pinene [47], as this compound presents promising biological activities, such as antibacterial activity against *E. coli* and *S. aureus* [48,49]. Specifically, *E. coli* is sensitive to α-pinene at concentrations ranging from 98 to 512 µg/mL (MIC) [50,51] and *S. aureus* with 68.6 ± 7.9 µg/mL (IC50) [52]. Furthermore, analyses of isolated α-pinene have shown that it can damage membrane proteins [53].

The prediction made in this study suggests a high probability of distribution beyond the blood–brain barrier (BBB), which has been confirmed by in vivo tests performed by Satou et al. [54], in which α-pinene demonstrated significant transport to the brain. This is considered positive due to the neuroprotective effect of the compound, which modulates anti-inflammatory gene expression and reduces neuroinflammation, in addition to potentially restoring the BBB function in tested rats [55,56]. By effectively modulating the NF-κB pathway, which results in a promising anti-inflammatory effect, α-pinene can also act through the Nrf2/HO-1 regulatory pathway, exhibiting antioxidant action; this pathway is crucial in defending against damage caused by oxidative stress, increasing the activity of antioxidant enzymes [57–59].

The sesquiterpene compound, β-caryophyllene, has been shown to have significant antimicrobial activity and was effective against bacterial resistance, particularly against *S. aureus*, with a minimum inhibitory concentration (MIC) of 32 µg/mL. Furthermore, β-caryophyllene potentiates the effect of norfloxacin on other pathogenic strains [60,61]. Studies have indicated that it acts as an antibiofilm agent against *Streptococcus mutans* [62] and may cause changes in the cell membrane, such as the formation of pores that lead to the leakage of intracellular contents, as previously observed in *Bacillus cereus* [63].

The cytotoxic and genotoxic evaluation is of great importance, since the absence of toxicity in *D. melanogaster* exposed to EOVC can be compared with the results of tests on herbivorous insects, such as *Tetranychus urticae* and *Myzus persicae*, which also did not show toxicity [34]. However, the cytotoxic analysis of fibroblasts revealed the need for caution in its application, since a mean lethal concentration (LC_{50}) of 138.1 µg/mL was demonstrated [31], which may increase with the age of the plant [32].

5. Conclusions

The results of this study indicate that the essential oil of *Varronia curassavica* is predominantly composed of monoterpenes, with an emphasis on α-Pinene, followed by sesquiterpenes, such as β-Caryophyllene. In vitro tests revealed that the essential oil of *V. curassavica* does not have antibacterial activity on its own, but it did demonstrate potential to increase the efficacy of drugs such as gentamicin, oxacillin, and norfloxacin. In addition, the toxicity tests did not indicate harmful effects on *Drosophila melanogaster*.

The presence of α-Pinene suggests the need for caution in applications due to its metabolic interactions and ability to cross the blood–brain barrier (BBB). Despite this, the study had limitations: it highlighted the need to investigate potential cytotoxic and genotoxic actions and for a detailed analysis of the molecular interactions between phytochemicals and drugs, including how these interactions can affect biological activity, especially in relation to antibacterial action.

Author Contributions: Conceptualization, J.W.A.-B., C.M.G.L. and J.T.d.C.S.; methodology, V.B.d.S., J.R.d.L.S. and R.L.S.P.; formal analysis, V.B.d.S., A.R.C., C.M.G.L. and H.D.M.C.; investigation, M.F.B.M.-B., M.G.d.O., I.M.A., R.F.S. and M.A.F.d.S.; resources, S.B.d.S., M.F.B.M.-B. and I.M.A.; data curation, M.I.R., M.A.F.d.S. and M.E.M.G.; writing—original draft preparation, S.B.d.S., M.I.R., A.R.C., M.E.M.G., J.H.d.S., M.G.d.O., R.L.S.P. and J.W.A.-B.; writing—review and editing, J.T.d.C.S., R.F.S. and T.B.E.; visualization, J.R.d.L.S., J.H.d.S., R.F.S., H.D.M.C. and T.B.E.; supervision, A.R.C.; project administration, J.T.d.C.S. and T.B.E. All authors have read and agreed to the published version of the manuscript.

Funding: This study did not receive funding for its implementation.

Data Availability Statement: Data are contained within the article.

Acknowledgments: The authors extend their appreciation to the Researchers Supporting Project, number (RSPD2024R620), King Saud University, Riyadh, Saudi Arabia. The authors would like to thank the Laboratório de Micologia Aplicada do Cariri (LMAC), Laboratório de Microbiologia e Biologia Molecular (LMBM), and Universidade Regional do Cariri (URCA).

Conflicts of Interest: The authors declare no conflicts of interest.

References

1. Freires, M.S.; Junior, O.M.R. Bacterial Resistance to Indiscriminate Use of Azithromycin versus COVID-19: An Integrative Review. *Res. Soc. Dev.* **2022**, *11*, e31611125035. [CrossRef]
2. Makabenta, J.M.V.; Nabawy, A.; Li, C.H.; Schmidt-Malan, S.; Patel, R.; Rotello, V.M. Nanomaterial-based therapeutics for antibiotic-resistant bacterial infections. *Nat. Rev. Microbiol.* **2021**, *19*, 23–36. [CrossRef]
3. EFSA (European Food Safety Authority); ECDC (European Centre for Disease Prevention and Control). The European Union Summary Report on Antimicrobial Resistance in zoonotic and indicator bacteria from humans, animals and food in 2018/2019. *EFSA J.* **2021**, *19*, 1–179. [CrossRef]
4. Arbab, S.; Iqbal, M.K.; Hussain, T.; Yasmeen, R.; Bano, R.; Abbas, G. Antimicrobial drug resistance against *Escherichia coli* and its harmful effect on animal health. *Vet. Med. Sci.* **2022**, *8*, 1780–1786. [CrossRef] [PubMed]
5. Huemer, M.; Mairpady Shambat, S.; Brugger, S.D.; Zinkernagel, A.S. Antibiotic resistance and persistence—Implications for human health and treatment perspectives. *EMBO Rep.* **2020**, *21*, e51034. [CrossRef] [PubMed]
6. Avershina, E.; Shapovalova, V.; Shipulin, G. Fighting antibiotic resistance in hospital-acquired infections: Current state and emerging technologies in disease prevention, diagnostics and therapy. *Front. Microbiol.* **2021**, *12*, 707330. [CrossRef]
7. Teixeira, A.R.; Figueiredo, A.F.C.; França, R.F. Resistência bacteriana relacionada ao uso indiscriminado de antibióticos. *Rev. Saúde Foco* **2019**, *11*, 853–875.
8. Christaki, E.; Marcou, M.; Tofarides, A. Antimicrobial resistance in bacteria: Mechanisms, evolution, and persistence. *J. Mol. Evol.* **2020**, *88*, 26–40. [CrossRef]
9. Jian, Z.; Li, Y.; Xiao, X.; Zhang, S.; Zhao, Y.; Zhang, L.; Dong, L.; Wang, Y. Antibiotic resistance genes in bacteria: Occurrence, spread, and control. *J. Basic Microbiol.* **2021**, *61*, 1049–1070. [CrossRef]
10. Ribeiro, D.A.; Macedo, D.G.; Oliveira, L.G.S.; Santos, M.O.; Almeida, B.V.; Macedo, J.G.F.; Macêdo, M.J.F.; Souza, R.K.D.; Araújo, T.M.S.; Almeida-Souza, M.M. Conservation priorities for medicinal woody species in a cerrado area in the Chapada do Araripe, northeastern Brazil. *J. Environ. Sustain.* **2019**, *21*, 61–77. [CrossRef]
11. Rodrigues, F.C.; Santos, A.T.L.; Machado, A.J.T.; Bezerra, C.F.; Freitas, T.S.; Coutinho, H.D.M.; Morais-Braga, M.F.B.; Almeida-Bezerra, J.W.; Duarte, A.E.; Kamdem, J.P.; et al. Chemical composition and anti-*Candida* potencial of the extracts of *Tarenaya spinosa* (Jacq.) Raf. (Cleomaceae). *Comp. Immunol. Microbiol. Infect. Dis.* **2019**, *64*, 14–19. [CrossRef] [PubMed]
12. Bortoluzzi, M.M.; Schmitt, V.; Mazur, C.E. Effect of herbal medical plants on anxiety: A brief review. *Res. Soc. Dev.* **2020**, *9*, e02911504. [CrossRef]
13. Nuță, D.C.; Limban, C.; Chiriță, C.; Chifiriuc, M.C.; Costea, T.; Ioniță, P.; Nicolau, L.; Zarafu, I. Contribution of essential oils to the fight against microbial biofilms—A review. *Processes* **2021**, *9*, 537. [CrossRef]
14. Alves, N.V.; Peres, M.M.; Lopes, L.A.; Rodrigues, T.G.L. Potencial farmacológico dos óleos essenciais: Uma atualização. In Práticas Integrativas e Complementares: Visão Holística e Multidisciplinar. *Ed. Científica Digit.* **2022**, *13*, 144–160. [CrossRef]

15. Tariq, S.; Wani, S.; Rasool, W.; Shafi, K.; Bhat, M.A.; Prabhakar, A.; Shalla, A.H.; Rather, M.A. A comprehensive review of the antibacterial, antifungal and antiviral potential of essential oils and their chemical constituents against drug-resistant microbial pathogens. *Microb. Pathog.* **2019**, *134*, 103580. [CrossRef]
16. Martim, J.K.; Maranho, L.T.; Costa-Casagrande, T.A. Role of the chemical compounds present in the essential oil and in the extract of *Cordia verbenacea* DC as an anti-inflammatory, antimicrobial and healing product. *J. Ethnopharmacol.* **2021**, *265*, 113300. [CrossRef]
17. Jabbar, A.A.; Abdullah, F.O.; Hassan, A.O.; Galali, Y.; Hassan, R.R.; Rashid, E.Q.; Salih, M.I.; Aziz, K.F. Ethnobotanical, Phytochemistry, and Pharmacological Activity of *Onosma* (Boraginaceae): An Updated Review. *Molecules* **2022**, *27*, 8687. [CrossRef]
18. Nigussie, G.; Ibrahim, F.; Neway, S. A Phytopharmacological Review on a Medicinal Plant: *Cordia africana* Lam. *J. Trop. Pharm. Chem.* **2021**, *5*, 254–263. [CrossRef]
19. Toghlobi, G.S.S.; Arantes, R.A.; Knudsen, B.G.; Tabach, R.; Pereira, M.A.A.; Carvalho, R.G.; Ferraz, R.R.N.; Rodrigues, F.S.M. Usos clínicos do fitoterápico da erva-baleeira (*Varronia curassavica* jacq.): Revisão da literatura. *Int. J. Health Manag. Rev.* **2022**, *8*, 1–10. [CrossRef]
20. Marques, A.P.S.; Bonfim, F.P.G.; Dantas, W.F.C.; Puppi, R.J.; Marques, M.O.M. Chemical composition of essential oil from *Varronia curassavica* Jacq. accessions in different seasons of the year. *Ind. Crops Prod.* **2019**, *140*, 111656. [CrossRef]
21. Adams, R.P. *Identification of Essential Oil Components by Gas Chromatography/Mass Spectrometry*, 5th ed.; Texensis Publishing: Gruver, TX, USA, 2017.
22. Almeida, R.S.; Freitas, P.R.; Araújo, A.C.J.; Alencar Menezes, I.R.; Santos, E.L.; Tintino, S.R.; Moura, T.F.; Ribeiro-Filho, J.; Ferreira, V.A.; Silva, A.C.A.; et al. GC-MS profile and enhancement of antibiotic activity by the essential oil of *Ocotea odorífera* and safrole: Inhibition of *Staphylococcus aureus* efflux pumps. *Antibiotics* **2020**, *9*, 247. [CrossRef] [PubMed]
23. Fernandes, P.A.D.S.; Pereira, R.L.S.; Santos, A.T.L.D.; Coutinho, H.D.M.; Morais-Braga, M.F.B.; Silva, V.B.; Costa, A.R.; Generino, M.E.M.; Oliveira, M.G.; Menezes, S.A.; et al. Phytochemical analysis, antibacterial activity and modulating effect of essential oil from *Syzygium cumini* (L.) skeels. *Molecules* **2022**, *27*, 3281. [CrossRef]
24. Almeida-Bezerra, J.W.; Cruz, R.P.; Pereira, R.L.S.; Silva, V.B.; Sousa, D.D.O.B.; Neto, J.X.D.S.; Souza, L.A.L.; Araújo, N.M.S.; Silva, R.G.G.; Lucetti, D.L.; et al. *Caryocar coriaceum* fruits as a potential alternative to combat fungal and bacterial infections: In vitro evaluation of methanolic extracts. *Microb. Pathog.* **2023**, *181*, 106203. [CrossRef] [PubMed]
25. Coutinho, H.D.; Costa, J.G.; Lima, E.O.; Falcão-Silva, V.S.; Siqueira-Júnior, J.P. Enhancement of the antibiotic activity against a multiresistant *Escherichia coli* by *Mentha arvensis* L. and chlorpromazine. *Chemotherapy* **2008**, *54*, 328–330. [CrossRef] [PubMed]
26. Costa, A.R.; Lima-Silva, J.R.; Oliveira, T.J.S.; Silva, T.G.; Pereira, P.S.; Oliveira-Borba, E.F.; Brito, E.S.; Ribeiro, P.R.V.; Almeida-Bezerra, J.W.; Júnior, J.T.C.; et al. Phytochemical profile of *Anacardium occidentale* L. (cashew tree) and the cytotoxic and toxicological evaluation of its bark and leaf extracts. *S. Afr. J.* **2020**, *135*, 355–364. [CrossRef]
27. Azzam, K.A.L. SwissADME and pkCSM webservers predictors: An integrated online platform for accurate and comprehensive predictions for in silico ADME/T properties of artemisinin and its derivatives. *Complex Use Miner. Resour.* **2023**, *325*, 14–21. [CrossRef]
28. Bristot, S.F.; Della-Colle, M.P.; Rossato, A.E.; Citadini-Zanette, V. Uso medicinal de *Varronia curassavica* Jacq. "erva-baleeira"(Boraginaceae): Estudo de caso no sul do Brasil. *Braz. J. Anim. Environ. Res.* **2021**, *4*, 170–182. [CrossRef]
29. Sciarrone, D.; Rigano, F.; Carnovale, C.; Cimino, F.; Dugo, P. Quali-quantitative characterization of the volatile constituents in *Cordia verbenacea* DC essential oil exploiting advanced chromatographic approaches and nuclear magnetic resonance analysis. *J. Chromatogr. A* **2017**, *1524*, 246–253. [CrossRef]
30. Silva, K.P.; de Carvalho Santos, T.A.; Moutinho, B.L.; da Silva, R.S.; dos Santos Pinto, V.; Blank, A.F.; Corrêa, C.B.; Scher, R.; Fernandes, R.P.M. Using *Varronia curassavica* (Cordiaceae) essential oil for the biocontrol of *Phytomonas serpens*. *Ind. Crops Prod.* **2019**, *139*, 111523. [CrossRef]
31. Pereira, P.S.; de Oliveira, L.G.; de Lima, V.F.; da Silva, M.A.F.; Rodrigues, I.A.; Almeida, E.M. Cytotoxicity of essential oil *Cordia verbenaceae* against *Leishmania brasiliensis* and *Trypanosoma cruzi*. *Molecules* **2021**, *26*, 4485. [CrossRef]
32. Farias, J.P.; Barros, A.L.A.N.; Araújo-Nobre, A.R.; Sobrinho-Júnior, E.P.C.; Alves, M.M.D.M.; Carvalho, F.A.D.A.; Rodrigues, K.A.F.; Andrade, I.M.; Silva-Filho, F.A.; Moreira, D.C.; et al. Influence of Plant Age on Chemical Composition, Antimicrobial Activity and Cytotoxicity of *Varronia curassavica* Jacq. Essential Oil Produced on an Industrial Scale. *Agriculture* **2023**, *13*, 373. [CrossRef]
33. Rodrigues, F.F.G.; Costa, J.G.M.; Rios, K.A.; Carvalho, M.G.; Carvalho, F.A.A. Chemical composition, antibacterial and antifungal activities of essential oil from *Cordia verbenacea* DC leaves. *Pharmacogn. Res.* **2012**, *4*, 161–165. [CrossRef] [PubMed]
34. Andrade, F.P.; Venzon, M.; Dôres, R.G.R.; Franzin, M.L.; Martins, E.F.; Araújo, G.J.; Fonseca, M.C.M. Toxicity of *Varronia curassavica* Jacq. essential oil to two arthropod pests and their natural enemy. *Neotrop. Entomol.* **2021**, *50*, 835–845. [CrossRef] [PubMed]
35. Castro-Nizio, D.A.; Blank, A.F.; de Andrade Brito, F.; Gagliardi, P.R.; Alves, E.; Arrigoni-Blank, M.D.F. A comparative study of the antifungal activity of essential oils of *Varronia curassavica* Jacq. obtained by different distillation methods. *Biosci. Res.* **2020**, *36*, 1856–1865. [CrossRef]
36. Rodrigues, F.A.F.; Silva, G.C.D.; Santana, M.F.; Bazzolli, D.M.S.; Rossi, C.C.; Diaz, M.A.N. Essential oils isolated from popular medicinal plants and spices as alternative antimicrobial and antibiofilm compounds against the pig pathogen *Actinobacilluspleuro pneumoniae*. *Ciência Rural* **2023**, *53*, 1–10. [CrossRef]

37. Li, Y.; Kong, D.; Fu, Y.; Sussman, M.R.; Wu, H. The effect of developmental and environmental factors on secondary metabolites in medicinal plants. *Plant Physiol. Biochem.* **2020**, *148*, 80–89. [CrossRef]
38. Oliveira, B.M.; Melo, C.R.; Santos, A.C.; Nascimento, L.F.; Nízio, D.A.; Cristaldo, P.F.; Blank, A.F.; Bacci, L. Essential oils from *Varronia curassavica* (Cordiaceae) accessions and their compounds (E)-caryophyllene and α-humulene as an alternative to control *Dorymyrmex thoracius* (Formicidae: Dolichoderinae). *Environ. Sci. Pollut. Res. Int.* **2019**, *26*, 6602–6612. [CrossRef]
39. Matias, E.F.F.; Santos, K.K.A.; Almeida, T.S.; Costa, J.G.M.; Coutinho, H.D.M. Seasonal variation, chemical composition and biological activity of the essential oil of *Cordia verbenacea* DC (Boraginaceae) and the sabinene. *Ind. Crops Prod.* **2016**, *87*, 45–53. [CrossRef]
40. Tonial, C.H.; Rodrigues, M.F.; Bosse, M.A.; Sousa, I.M.; Lima, J.D.; Cunha, M.A.A.; Foglio, M.A.; Marques, M.O.M.; Marchese, J.A. Technical and economic evaluation of cultivation and obtaining of *Varronia curassavica* Jacq. essential oil. *Ind. Crops Prod.* **2020**, *154*, 112650. [CrossRef]
41. Lima, F.J.A.; Sousa, R.O.; Artur, F.; Araújo-Mendes, M.R.; Val, A.D.B. Characterization of the growth and production of essential oil from "erva baleeira" (*Varronia curassavica* Jaqc). *Res. Soc. Dev.* **2021**, *10*, e5810716204. [CrossRef]
42. Meccia, G.; López, S.; Gutiérrez, J.; Echeverría, J.; Suárez, L.; Porras, N.; Delgado, G.; Stashenko, E.; Bazzocchi, I.L. Chemical composition and antibacterial activity of the essential oil of *Cordia verbenacea* from the Venezuelan Andes. *Nat. Prod. Commun.* **2009**, *4*, 1119–1122. [CrossRef] [PubMed]
43. Carvalho, V.R.A.; Freitas, P.R.; Alencar Menezes, I.R.; Tintino, S.R.; Santos, E.L.; Lima, M.A.; Coutinho, H.D.M.; Junior, W.J.F.L. Antibiotic-Modifying Activity and Chemical Profile of the Essential Oil from the Leaves of *Cordia verbenacea* DC. *J. Essent. Oil Bear. Plants* **2017**, *20*, 337–345. [CrossRef]
44. Bhavaniramya, S.; Vishnupriya, S.; Al-Aboody, M.S.; Vijayakumar, R.; Baskaran, D. Role of essential oils in food safety: Antimicrobial and antioxidant applications. *Grain Oil Sci. Technol.* **2019**, *2*, 49–55. [CrossRef]
45. Mutlu-Ingok, A.; Tasir, S.; Seven, A.; Akgun, N.; Karbancioglu-Guler, F. Evaluation of the single and combined antibacterial efficiency of essential oils for controlling *Campylobacter coli, Campylobacter jejuni, Escherichia coli, Staphylococcus aureus*, and mixed cultures. *Flavour Fragr. J.* **2019**, *34*, 280–287. [CrossRef]
46. Rao, J.; Chen, B.; McClements, D.J. Improving the efficacy of essential oils as antimicrobials in foods: Mechanisms of action. *Annu. Rev. Food Sci. Technol.* **2019**, *10*, 365–387. [CrossRef] [PubMed]
47. Freitas, P.R.; Araújo, A.C.J.; Santos-Barbosa, C.R.; Muniz, D.F.; Silva, A.C.A.; Rocha, J.E.; Oliveira-Tintino, C.D.M.; Ribeiro-Filho, J.; Silva, L.E.; Confortin, C.; et al. GC-MS-FID and potentiation of the antibiotic activity of the essential oil of *Baccharis reticulata* (ruiz & pav.) pers. and α-pinene. *Ind. Crops Prod.* **2020**, *145*, 112106. [CrossRef]
48. Allenspach, M.; Steuer, C. α-Pinene: A never-ending story. *Phytochemistry* **2021**, *190*, 112857. [CrossRef]
49. Eduardo, L.S.; Silva, R.O.; Silva, K.M.; Moreira, G.O.; Costa, J.G.M.; Coutinho, H.D.M.; Almeida, V.M.; Menezes, I.R.A.; Tintino, S.R. Antibacterial activity and time-kill kinetics of positive enantiomer of α-pinene against strains of *Staphylococcus aureus* and *Escherichia coli*. *Curr. Top. Med. Chem.* **2018**, *18*, 917–924. [CrossRef]
50. Yang, C.; Hu, D.-H.; Feng, Y. Antibacterial activity and mode of action of the *Artemisia capillaris* essential oil and its constituents against respiratory tract infection-causing pathogens. *Mol. Med. Rep.* **2015**, *11*, 2852–2860. [CrossRef]
51. Leite-Sampaio, N.F.; Nogueira, C.E.S.; Silva, A.F.M.; Sampaio, B.L.; Andrade, L.N.; Fernandes, P.C.; Rocha, J.E.; Oliveira, M.R.; Quintans-Júnior, L.J.; Coutinho, H.D.M.; et al. Potentiation of the Activity of Antibiotics against ATCC and MDR Bacterial Strains with (+)-α-Pinene and (-)-Borneol. *BioMed Res. Int.* **2022**, *2022*, 8217380. [CrossRef]
52. Utegenova, G.A.; Pallavi, R.; Fukin, A.M.; Kondratenko, E.; Bagryanskaya, I.Y.; Atazhanova, G.A.; Adekenov, S.M.; Zibareva, L.N.; Desenko, S.M.; Sharma, R.; et al. Chemical composition and antibacterial activity of essential oils from *Ferula* L. species against methicillin-resistant *Staphylococcus aureus*. *Molecules* **2018**, *23*, 1679. [CrossRef] [PubMed]
53. Melkina, O.E.; Plyuta, V.A.; Khmel, I.A.; Zavilgelsky, G.B. The mode of action of cyclic monoterpenes (−)-limonene and (+)-α-pinene on bacterial cells. *Biomolecules* **2021**, *11*, 806. [CrossRef] [PubMed]
54. Satou, T.; Murakami, S.; Hayashi, S.; Koike, K.; Sengoku, T. Mouse brain concentrations of α-pinene, limonene, linalool, and 1,8-cineole following inhalation. *Flavour Fragr. J.* **2016**, *32*, 36–39. [CrossRef]
55. Khoshnazar, M.; Parvardeh, S.; Bigdeli, M.R. Alpha-pinene exerts neuroprotective effects via anti-inflammatory and anti-apoptotic mechanisms in a rat model of focal cerebral ischemia-reperfusion. *J. Stroke Cerebrovasc. Dis.* **2020**, *29*, 104977. [CrossRef] [PubMed]
56. Rahayu, M.; Mahardika, A.M.; Fattah, F.A.; Krisnadi, D. Alpha-pinene attenuates microglial NF-κB activation and iNOS expression in gp120-induced neuroinflammation. *Malang Neurol. J.* **2021**, *7*, 80–84. [CrossRef]
57. Rahimi, K.; Ghanbari, A.; Badi, H.N.; Asadi, F.; Sadeghi, S.; Azadi, H. The effects of alpha-pinene on the Nrf2-HO1 signaling pathway in gastric damage in rats. *Mol. Biol. Rep.* **2023**, *50*, 8615–8622. [CrossRef]
58. Zhou, J.-Y.; Tang, F.-D.; Mao, G.-G.; Bian, R.-L. Effect of alpha-pinene on nuclear translocation of NF-kappa B in THP-1 cells. *Acta Pharmacol. Sin.* **2004**, *25*, 480–484.
59. Yanaka, A. Role of NRF2 in protection of the gastrointestinal tract against oxidative stress. *J. Clin. Biochem. Nutr.* **2018**, *63*, 18–25. [CrossRef]
60. Santos, E.L.; de Lima, M.A.; de Almeida, R.S.; de Menezes, I.R.A.; Tintino, S.R.; Rodrigues, M.A.V.; Rocha, J.E.; Júnior, W.J.F.L. Phytochemical characterization and antibiotic potentiating effects of the essential oil of *Aloysia gratissima* (Gillies & Hook.) and beta-caryophyllene. *S. Afr. J. Bot.* **2021**, *143*, 1–6. [CrossRef]

61. Santos, E.L.; de Lima, M.A.; de Almeida, R.S.; de Menezes, I.R.A.; Tintino, S.R.; Rodrigues, M.A.V.; Rocha, J.E.; Júnior, W.J.F.L. Enhanced antibacterial effect of antibiotics by the essential oil of *Aloysia gratissima* (Gillies & Hook.) Tronc. and its major constituent beta-caryophyllene. *Phytomed. Plus* **2021**, *1*, 100100. [CrossRef]
62. Yoo, H.-J.; Jwa, S.-K. Inhibitory effects of β-caryophyllene on *Streptococcus mutans* biofilm. *Arch. Oral Biol.* **2018**, *88*, 42–46. [CrossRef] [PubMed]
63. Moo, C.L.; Yang, S.K.; Osman, M.A.; Yuswan, M.H.; Loh, J.Y.; Lim, W.M.; Lim, S.H.E.; Lai, K.S. Antibacterial Activity and Mode of Action of β-caryophyllene on *Bacillus cereus*. *Pol. J. Microbiol.* **2020**, *69*, 49–54. [CrossRef] [PubMed]

analytica

Article

ADME/Tox Study, Phytochemical Analysis and In Vitro Antifungal Activity of Essential Oil from *Varronia curassavica* Jacq. (Boraginaceae)

José Thyálisson da Costa Silva [1], Saulo Almeida Menezes [2], Viviane Bezerra da Silva [3], Maria Hellena Garcia Novais [4], Emílio Sousa Albuquerque [4], Rafael Albuquerque Franco [5], Naiza Saraiva Farias [4], Nathallia Correia da Silva [1], Dieferson Leandro de Souza [1], Elaine Cristina Conceição de Oliveira [1], Damiana Gonçalves de Sousa Freitas [1], Clara Mariana Gonçalves Lima [1,*], Severino Denicio Gonçalves de Sousa [6], Maria Flaviana Bezerra Morais Braga [1], Henrique Douglas Melo Coutinho [4,*] and José Weverton Almeida-Bezerra [4]

1 Department of Biological Sciences, Cariri Regional University—URCA, Crato 63105-000, Brazil; nathallia.silva@urca.br (N.C.d.S.)
2 Biotechnology Center, Federal University of Rio Grande do Sul—UFRGS, Porto Alegre 91501-970, Brazil
3 Department of Botany, Federal University of Pernambuco—UFPE, Recife 50670-901, Brazil
4 Department of Biological Chemistry, Cariri Regional University—URCA, Crato 63105-000, Brazil
5 Department of Medicine, Christus University Center—Unichristus, Fortaleza 60160-230, Brazil
6 Department of Basic Life Sciences, Juiz de Fora Federal University—UFJF, Governador Valadares 35010-180, Brazil
* Correspondence: claramarianalima@gmail.com (C.M.G.L.); hdmcoutinho@gmail.com (H.D.M.C.)

Abstract: *Varronia curassavica* Jacq. is an aromatic species appertaining to the Boraginaceae family and has been mentioned for its numerous traditional uses and pharmacological properties, especially its antimicrobial and anti-inflammatory effects. The aim of the present study was to investigate the phytochemical profile and antifungal activities of the essential oils of *V. curassavica*, in addition to analyzing the ADMET properties of the majority components. The GC-MS analysis of *V. curassavica* essential oil (EOVC) comprised 97.36% of total composition, with α-pinene, β-caryophyllene, and bicyclogermacrene (44.46%, 22.87%, and 13.05%, respectively) as the main constituents among other minor/trace constituents. The antifungal activity of EOVC was evaluated against three *Candida* species and was observed with IC_{50} > 200 μg/mL. Remarkably, the combination of EOVC with fluconazole significantly reduced the IC_{50} required for the drug to inhibit *C. tropicalis* (0.003 μg/mL), *C. albicans* (0.7996 μg/mL), and *C. krusei* (17.73 μg/mL). In addition, ADME/Tox studies using α-pinene revealed that the compound poses no toxicity threats but requires caution due to its high permeability to the blood–brain barrier (BBB). Overall, the obtained results suggest that *Varronia curassavica* essential oil is a potentially good antifungal agent for combating fungal resistance.

Keywords: *Cordia verbenacea*; fungal resistance; α-pinene; antifungal; ethnopharmacology

1. Introduction

Invasive fungal diseases caused by opportunistic pathogenic fungi represent a significant public health concern due to the high mortality rate among individuals with compromised immune systems [1]. The most common organisms that cause clinical manifestations, such as cutaneous, mucosal, or organ-disseminated candidiasis, belong to the *Candida* genus, especially *C. albicans* (responsible for more than 50% of cases), *C. glabrata*, *C. parapsilosis*, and *C. tropicalis* [2,3]. The main challenges are related to the resistance of these organisms to conventional therapy. Fungal resistance can be influenced by factors such as repetitive therapy and the limited availability of antifungal drugs [4,5].

In recent years, alternative treatment approaches have been investigated based on the therapeutic use of medicinal plants, searching for new bioactive agents with antifungal action. The use of products of natural origin is considered effective in maintaining health, as well as being easily accessible to the population and having mild adverse effects [6,7]. Antioxidant and antimicrobial activities have clinical relevance and can be attributed to the bioactive compounds present in medicinal plants [8], in addition to medicinal plants being seen as a promising solution for treating conditions such as fungal infections [9].

Medicinal plants are widely used to extract secondary metabolites with pharmacological applications, such as essential oils. Essential oils are volatile and lipophilic components that have been the subject of research due to their promising antimicrobial action, which acts through different mechanisms [10]. In addition, they have diverse biological activities, including antioxidant, antiparasitic, antibacterial, and antifungal properties. These properties represent effective alternatives against microbial resistance, including an efficient action against biofilms [11–13].

The medicinal species *Varronia curassavica* Jacq. (Synonyms *Cordia verbenacea* A. DC. and *C. curassavica* (Jacq) Roemer & Schultes) stands out widely in the field of natural medicine due to its use as an anti-inflammatory, anti-rheumatic, and analgesic agent [14,15]. Current research underscores the therapeutic value of the essential oil, whose chemical composition has been extensively investigated due to the presence of relevant phytochemicals, such as terpenes previously reported as α-pinene and β-caryophyllene, which exhibit diverse activities, including anti-inflammatory, analgesic, antimicrobial, larvicidal, and antiparasitic properties [16–19]. The presence of compounds such as flavonoids contributes to its antibacterial properties, which can influence the biological activity of antibiotics belonging to the class of aminoglycosides, with the absence of substances such as alkaloids [20,21].

Therefore, research into the ethnopharmacological application of *V. curassavica* highlights its antimicrobial action and shows that this plant is effective in combating pathogenic microorganisms, particularly fungal strains. The efficacy of this species and the use of its essential oil do not show any possible toxic effects. The present study reports the phytochemical profile and in vitro antifungal and fluconazole modulatory activity of the essential oil from leaves of *V. curassavica*, in addition to the ADME/Tox studies of its major compound.

2. Materials and Methods

2.1. Plant Material

The leaves of *V. curassavica* (Figure 1) were collected in the municipality of Jardim, Ceará, Brazil, at coordinates: −7.554917 W and −39.306611 S, in the period of January (2022). The sample collected was stored in the Herbário Caririense Dárdano de Andrade-Lima (HCDAL) of the Universidade Regional do Cariri (URCA) under voucher number 15.291. The research was registered in the National System for the Management of Genetic Heritage and Associated Traditional Knowledge (SisGen) under the code AEFC723 and in the Biodiversity Authorization and Information System (SisBio) under the number 82789-1.

Figure 1. *Varronia curassavica* identified in the municipality of Jardim, Ceará, Brazil.

2.2. *Essential Oil Extraction*

To extract the essential oil of *V. curassavica* (EOVC), the collected leaves were dried, crushed, and added to a 5 L volumetric flask with 2 L of distilled water and subjected to constant boiling for 2 h using a Clevenger-type system. Each extraction used 200 g of leaves, obtaining a yield of 0.83%. After extraction, the oil obtained was stored in amber bottles and refrigerated at 4 °C.

2.3. *Gas Chromatography-Mass Spectrometry Analysis*

Gas chromatography-mass spectrometry (GC-MS) was used for the phytochemical analysis of EOVC. The analysis was carried out using an Agilent Technologies AutoSystem XL GC-MS system, operating in EI mode at 70 eV. Two capillary columns were used: an HP 5MS (30 m × 0.35 mm; film thickness 0.50 μm) and an HP Innowax (30 m × 0.32 mm; film thickness 0.50 μm). The system was equipped with a split/splitless injector (220 °C) and coupled to an FID detector. The thermal programmer was set from 60 °C (1 min) to 180 °C at a rate of 3 °C/min; the detector temperature was 220 °C. Helium was used as the carrier gas with a flow rate of 1.0 mL/min. The injected volume of EOVC was 1 μL, diluted in chloroform (1:10). Two replicate samples were processed in the same way, and the relative concentrations of the components were calculated based on the GC peak areas, without the use of correction factors.

2.4. *Antifungal Activity*

The antifungal activity of EOVC was tested against *Candida albicans* INCQS 40006, *Candida krusei* INCQS 40095, and *Candida tropicalis* INCQS 40042 obtained from the Collection of Reference Microorganisms in Health Surveillance (CMRVS) of the National Institute for Quality Control in Health (FIOCRUZ-INCQS). The *Candida* strains were grown in Petri dishes containing Sabouraud Dextrose Agar (SDA, Kasvi) and incubated at 37 °C for 24 h. Aliquots were then transferred to test tubes containing 4 mL of saline solution (0.9%) and adjusted to a turbidity of 0.5 McFarland (1.5×10^8 CFU/mL). The EOVC (0.0191 g) was diluted in 0.5% DMSO. It was then diluted in Sabouraud Dextrose Broth (SDB) until it reached the stock concentration (1.024 μg/mL) [22]. Fluconazole (capsule—FLUCOMED) was used as a positive control.

The broth microdilution technique with 96-well plates was used to determine the IC_{50}. EOVC and fluconazole were diluted in SDB (90 μL) (1:1 *v*/*v*) at concentrations ranging from 2 to 1.024 μg/mL, each in quadruplicate. Then, 10 μL of the fungal inoculum was added. Fungal growth and sterility controls were included. The plates were incubated at 37 °C for 24 h, and absorbance was measured at 630 nm using an ELISA reader (Termoplate® Kasuaki, Beijing, China) [23].

2.5. *Fluconazole Potentiating Action*

In the fluconazole potentiating evaluation, OEVC was tested using the Sub-inhibitory Matrix Concentration (CM/8). Flat-bottomed 96-well plates containing SDB medium with OEVC at its sub-inhibitory concentrations were used. Fluconazole was used in a range of concentrations between 2 and 1.024 μg/mL, following the method described by Coutinho et al. [24] with modifications. The plates prepared for the broth microdilution and serial dilution technique were incubated at 37 °C for 24 h, and the analysis was carried out using an ELISA spectrophotometer (Termoplate® Kasuaki, China) [23].

2.6. *In Silico Prediction*

The in silico prediction of the major compound (α-pinene, >30%) was evaluated using the ADMETlab 2.0 platform. This platform, recognized for its enhanced functionalities for the analysis of ADME (absorption, distribution, metabolism, excretion), toxicity, physicochemical properties, and medicinal chemistry, is based on more accurate and efficient predictions, relying on general analysis tools such as the toxicological interaction radar [25].

2.7. Statistical Analysis

The means of the data and their respective standard errors of the mean (SEM) were calculated and subjected to a one-way Analysis of Variance (ANOVA). Subsequently, the data were subjected to a reliability test using the Tukey test at 95% reliability. The results were considered statistically significant when $p < 0.05$. The data were analyzed using GraphPad Prism software version 6 (GraphPad Software Inc., San Diego, CA, USA).

3. Results

3.1. Phytochemical Composition

The phytochemical analysis of EOVC using GC-MS identified 11 chemical components which represent 97.36% of the oil's total composition. The EOVC is mainly composed of hydrocarbon monoterpenes (47.25%), followed by hydrocarbon sesquiterpenes (43.72%). The major compounds identified were α-pinene (44.46%), β-caryophyllene (22.87%), and bicyclogermacrene (13.05%). As shown in Table 1, α-pinene was identified as the major constituent (>30%) and was therefore selected for the in silico prediction analysis.

Table 1. Chemical composition (%) of the essential oil of *Varronia curassavica*.

Components	RI		(%)
α-pinene	976		44.46
β-Pinene	980		2.79
β-Elemene	1375		1.14
β-Caryophyllene	1428		22.87
α-humulene	1460		2.91
Zingiberene	1492		1.01
Bicyclogermacrene	1496		13.05
cis-α-Bisabolene	1778		2.74
Nerolidol	1961		3.32
Caryophyllene oxide	2023		1.89
Juniper camphor	2205		1.18
Hydrocarbon Monoterpene		47.25	
Oxygenated Monoterpene		1.18	
Hydrocarbon Sesquiterpene		43.72	
Oxygenated Sesquiterpene		5.21	
Total		97.36	

RI: Retention index.

3.2. Antifungal Activity and Fluconazole Potentiating Effect

The results of EOVC antifungal activity are shown in Table 2. Different *Candida* strains exhibited varying levels of susceptibility to EOVC. *Candida albicans* showed the greatest sensitivity to the essential oil, as demonstrated by IC_{50} values reaching concentrations of 254.3 μg/mL, considered clinically relevant. *Candida tropicalis* (IC_{50} = 649.2 μg/mL) showed the second lowest inhibition value, suggesting the potential use of EOVC in antifungal applications against *C. albicans* strains according to their susceptibility.

Table 2. Half-maximal inhibitory concentration (IC_{50}) of *Varronia curassavica* essential oil (EOVC) tested against *Candida* strains and fluconazole (FCZ) potentiating action.

IC50	μg/mL		
	C. albicans	*C. krusei*	*C. tropicalis*
EOVC	254.3	>1024	649.2
FCZ	16.14	52.41	4.775
FCZ + EOVC	0.7996	17.73	0.003

Regarding *C. krusei*, no significant inhibitory action was observed. However, when combined with the drug fluconazole, there was a significant reduction in IC_{50} values to 17.73 μg/mL, representing a decrease of approximately 65% in the concentration of fluconazole required to inhibit fungal growth. The synergistic activity of EOVC with fluconazole was also noted against strains of *C. albicans* and *C. tropicalis* (Figure 2), with concentration reductions of ~95% and 98%, respectively. These results suggest the potential use of EOVC as a complementary agent in antifungal therapies.

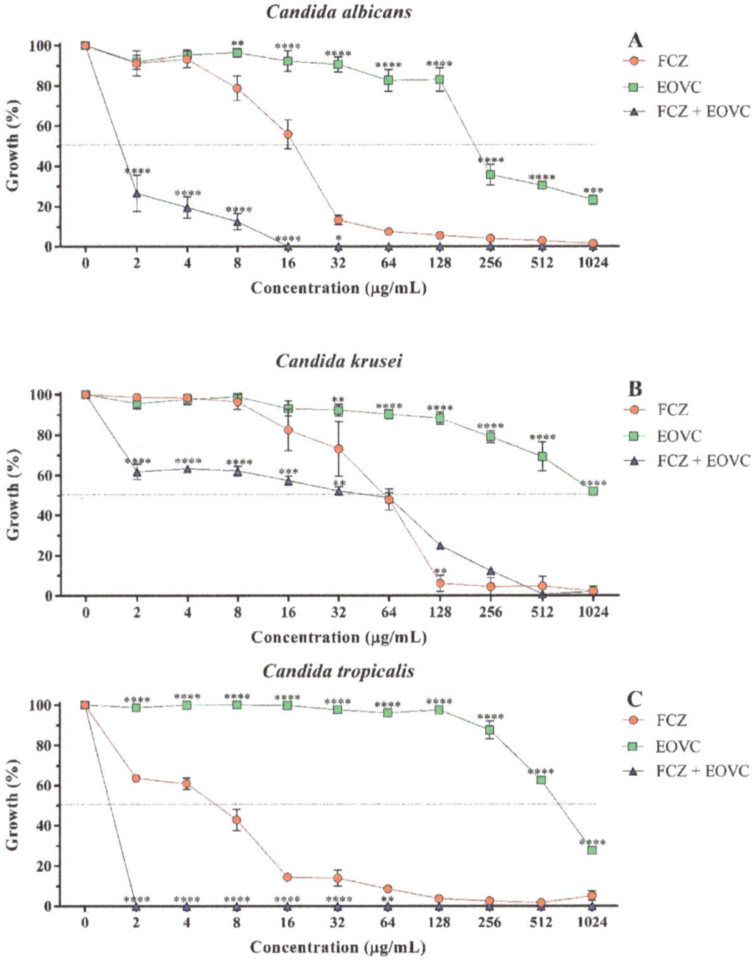

Figure 2. Potentiating activity of fluconazole (FCZ) combined with *V. curassavica* essential oil (EOVC), tested against *C. albicans* (**A**), *C. krusei* (**B**), and *C. tropicalis* (**C**). * = $p < 0.05$, ** = $p < 0.01$, *** = $p < 0.001$, **** = $p < 0.0001$. The bars represent the standard error of the mean (n = 3).

3.3. ADME/Tox Prediction with α-Pinene

According to the in silico analysis, the radar of the physicochemical properties of the α-pinene (Figure 3) indicates divergences regarding its application as a drug, since the aqueous partitioning capacity (logP < 3) and the influence on physiological pH (logD < 3) are above the maximum desired limit, for which reason the Pfizer, GSK, and Golden Triangle drug-like rules do not apply (Table 3). However, positive aspects are observed in the solubility (logS) and flexibility (Flexibility = nRot/nRig) parameters.

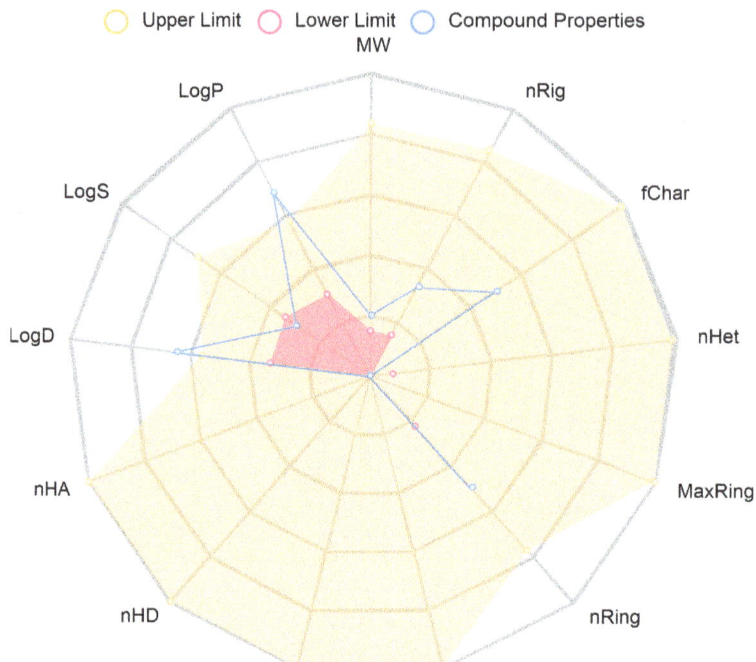

Figure 3. Radar of physicochemical behavior of the compound α-pinene, comparison of minimum (lower) and maximum (upper) desirable measurements.

Table 3. Performance of physicochemical properties and similarity to drugs using α-pinene as a model.

Category	Property	Value
Physicochemical Property	MF	$C_{10}H_{16}$
	MW	136.13 g/mol
	NHA	0
	NHD	0
	NRB	0
	TPSA	0.0
	logS	−4.662
Medicinal Chemistry	Lipinski Rule	Accepted
	Pfizer Rule	Rejected
	GSK Rule	Rejected
	Golden Triangle	Rejected

MF: molecular formula; MW: molecular weight; NRB: number of rotatable bonds; NHA: number of hydrogen acceptors; NHD: number of hydrogen donors; TPSA: Topological Polar Surface Area; LogS: Log of the aqueous solubility.

The ADME/Tox properties of α-pinene are summarized in Table 4, highlighting important data of pharmacological relevance. Absorption is considered promising, since human intestinal absorption activity (HIA) does not present problems, and the compound does not inhibit the permeability glycoprotein (Pgp) responsible for active efflux. However, the distribution of α-pinene and its permeability to the blood–brain barrier (BBB) warns of possible toxic activity. As for the metabolization and toxicity of the compound, there are no significant concerns, except for ophthalmic and pulmonary applications. In addition, Table 5 shows possible routes of toxicity for α-pinene, indicating promising safe aspects.

Table 4. ADME/Tox performance (absorption, distribution, metabolism, excretion, and toxicity) of α-pinene.

Category	Property	Value	Decision
Absorption	Caco-2 Permeability	−4.303	•
	MDCK Permeability	1.8×10^{-5}	•
	Pgp-inhibitor	---	•
	Pgp-substrate	---	•
	HIA	---	•
Distribution	BBB Penetration	++	•
Metabolism	CYP1A2 inhibitor	-	•
	CYP2C19 inhibitor	--	•
	CYP2C9 inhibitor	-	•
	CYP2D6 inhibitor	---	•
	CYP3A4 inhibitor	---	•
Excretion	CL	15.022	•
	$T_{1/2}$	0.114	-
Toxicity	Human Hepatotoxicity	--	•
	Drug-Induced Liver Injury	---	•
	AMES Toxicity	---	•
	Rat Oral Acute Toxicity	---	•
	Skin Sensitization	--	•
	Carcinogenicity	---	•
	Eye Corrosion	+++	•
	Eye Irritation	+++	•
	Respiratory Toxicity	++	•

P-gp; p glycoprotein; HIA: Human intestinal absorption; BBB: Blood–Brain Barrier; CYP: Cytochrome-P; CL: Clearance; $T_{1/2}$: Half-life time. Symbols means 0–0.1 (---), 0.1–0.3 (--), 0.3–0.5 (-),0.7–0.9 (++) e 0.9–1.0 (+++); •: Non-toxic; •: high possibility of toxic activity.

Table 5. Possible routes of α-pinene toxicity.

Property	Value	Decision
Androgen receptor	---	•
Androgen receptor ligand-binding domain	---	•
Aryl hydrocarbon receptor	---	•
NR-Aromatase	---	•
Estrogen receptor	---	•
Estrogen receptor ligand-binding domain	+	•
Peroxisome proliferator-activated receptor gamma	---	•
Antioxidant response element	---	•
ATPase family AAA domain-containing protein 5	---	•
Heat shock factor response element	0.032	•
Mitochondrial membrane potential	0.082	•

• and (---): Non-toxic feature; • and (+): Not very relevant value.

4. Discussion

The chemical composition results are supported by several scientific studies that analyzed the essential oil of *V. curassavica*. It was identified that α-pinene and β-caryophyllene are the major phytochemicals in this oil, with percentages ranging from 56.69–25.32% and 21.78–12.52%, respectively [16,19,26–28]. However, different results were observed in which sesquiterpenes are predominant, with β-caryophyllene comprising 25.4–23.26% [29,30] and shyobunol with 27.46–24.24% of the total oil percentage [31].

Variations in the quantity and volatile components of essential oils can be explained by multiple biotic and abiotic factors, such as plant age [28], season and location [27], herbivory [32], and collection during different seasons [14]. Additionally, alterations in phytochemicals may occur due to different essential oil extraction techniques, as observed in hydrodistillation and microwave extraction methods [31,33]. Changes in phytoconstituents can directly influence the biological activity of the essential oil.

Previous studies indicate that EOVC exhibits antimicrobial activity against parasites that cause human diseases, with the potential to disrupt cell membrane integrity [16,19]. The antifungal activity of EOVC against *C. albicans* can be partially confirmed, since Farias et al. [28] demonstrated an MIC of 1000 μg/mL. Rodrigues et al. [29] also identified the MIC of 512 μg/mL for standard strains of *C. albicans* 40006 and *C. krusei* 653, concluding that EOVC exhibits fungistatic activity.

Terpenoid compounds such as α-pinene have been shown to possess antibacterial, antifungal, anti-*Leishmania*, anti-inflammatory, antioxidant, neuroprotective, and antitumor properties [34–37]. In tests against fungi, α-pinene has been demonstrated to cause organelle damage, induce oxidative stress [38], interrupt enzyme production and biofilm formation, and interfere with fungal membranes [39], specifically by disrupting permeability through binding to ergosterol [40].

Multiple studies demonstrate the anti-*Candida* potential of α-pinene. The Minimum Fungicidal Concentration (MFC) values range from 2 to 4 mg/mL for different strains of *C. albicans* [41], and the MIC ranges from 64 to 128 μg/mL. Additionally, α-pinene can be combined with other antifungal agents, such as boric acid and polyene compounds [42,43]. When tested on 15 strains of *C. albicans*, the MIC values reach 268.13 mg/L [44].

β-caryophyllene is another interesting compound due to its biological activities, including antimicrobial action and the ability to disrupt biofilms by penetrating this protective resistance mechanism [3,45]. Its potential as an antifungal agent has also been evaluated, showing low MIC values [46,47]. When tested against *Candida* strains, β-caryophyllene affects fungal virulence mechanisms [48]. It can be suggested that β-caryophyllene might contribute to synergism with fluconazole, like the synergism observed with other drugs such as ketoconazole [49].

Considering the biological activities of α-pinene, it is also important to investigate its toxic potential. Cytotoxic analyses of α-pinene in fibroblasts [50] and human keratinocytes [42] did not identify any toxic effects. Similarly, toxicity studies using the Zebrafish (*Danio rerio*, Hamilton) model indicated a median lethal concentration (LC_{50}) of 441.360 mg/L [51], which is considered non-toxic as high concentrations are required to achieve toxicity. These results corroborate previous in silico analyses of α-pinene, which indicated milder toxicological effects allowing safer applications [52].

Furthermore, in silico predictions indicate that α-pinene exhibits high rates of BBB penetration. In vivo assays in mice show that inhalation of α-pinene results in significant transport to the brain [53]. Conversely, it has been demonstrated to have a neuroprotective effect by modulating the expression of anti-inflammatory genes, thereby attenuating neuroinflammation, and potentially restoring BBB function in rats [54,55]. Additionally, in vivo models reveal that α-pinene is not a substrate for permeability glycoprotein (Pgp) [56].

5. Conclusions

The essential oil of *Varronia curassavica* leaves is mainly composed of monoterpene and sesquiterpene hydrocarbons, mainly α-pinene and β-caryophyllene. Assays carried out with the essential oil showed the presence of significant antifungal activity against strains of *Candida albicans* and *Candida tropicalis*, revealing potential for possible applications. In addition, a remarkably potentiation of the antifungal action of fluconazole against different strains of *Candida* was observed, indicating possible use as an adjuvant in the treatment of fungal infections. The in silico prediction shows that α-pinene has safe characteristics for relevant clinical applications as an anti-*Candida* agent. However, further research is needed to evaluate the synergistic antifungal action of the major constituents, α-pinene and β-caryophyllene, as well as in vivo toxicity evaluation, in order to establish the safety of using this natural product.

Author Contributions: Conceptualization, methodology, M.F.B.M.B., D.G.d.S.F. and S.D.G.d.S.; validation, formal analysis, investigation, M.H.G.N., E.S.A., N.S.F. and D.L.d.S.; resources, data curation, N.C.d.S. and E.C.C.d.O.; writing—original draft preparation, J.T.d.C.S. and C.M.G.L.; writing—review and editing, S.A.M. and R.A.F.; visualization, V.B.d.S. and S.A.M.; supervision, project administration, J.W.A.-B. and H.D.M.C. All authors have read and agreed to the published version of the manuscript.

Funding: This research received no external funding.

Institutional Review Board Statement: Not applicable.

Informed Consent Statement: Not applicable.

Data Availability Statement: Data are contained within the article.

Acknowledgments: The authors thank the Universidade Regional do Cariri (URCA—Brazil).

Conflicts of Interest: The authors declare no conflicts of interest.

References

1. Perfect, J.R.; Ghannoum, M. Emerging issues in antifungal resistance. *Infect. Dis. Clin. N. Am.* **2020**, *34*, 921–943. [CrossRef] [PubMed]
2. Köhler, J.R.; Hube, B.; Puccia, R.; Casadevall, A.; Perfect, J.R. Fungi that infect humans. *Microbiol. Spectr.* **2017**, *5*, 1–29. [CrossRef] [PubMed]
3. Bhattacharya, S.; Sae-Tia, S.; Fries, B.C. Candidiasis and mechanisms of antifungal resistance. *Antibiotics* **2020**, *9*, 312. [CrossRef]
4. Perlin, D.S.; Rautemaa-Richardson, R.; Alastruey-Izquierdo, A. The global problem of antifungal resistance: Prevalence, mechanisms, and management. *Lancet Infect. Dis.* **2017**, *17*, 383–392. [CrossRef] [PubMed]
5. Fisher, M.C.; Alastruey-Izquierdo, A.; Berman, J.; Bicanic, T.; Bignell, E.M.; Bowyer, P.; Bromley, M.; Brüggemann, R.; Garber, G.; Cornely, O.A.; et al. Tackling the emerging threat of antifungal resistance to human health. *Nat. Rev. Microbiol.* **2022**, *20*, 557–571. [CrossRef]
6. Bortoluzzi, M.M.; Schmitt, V.; Mazur, C.E. Efeito fitoterápico de plantas medicinais sobre a ansiedade: Uma breve revisão. *Res. Soc. Dev.* **2020**, *9*, 47. [CrossRef]
7. Uma, K.; Huang, X.; Kumar, B.A. Antifungal effect of plant extract and essential oil. *Chin. J. Integr. Med.* **2016**, *23*, 233–239. [CrossRef]
8. Jain, C.; Khatana, S.; Vijayvergia, R. Bioactivity of secondary metabolites of various plants: A review. *Int. J. Pharm. Sci. Res.* **2019**, *10*, 494–504. [CrossRef]
9. Muftah, H.; Oezcelik, B.; Oyardi, O.; Orhan, D.D. Comparative Evaluation of Medicinal Plant Extracts and Antimicrobial Magistrals. *New Microbiol.* **2024**, *46*, 361–366.
10. Rao, J.; Chen, B.; McClements, D.J. Improving the efficacy of essential oils as antimicrobials in foods: Mechanisms of action. *Annu. Rev. Food Sci. Technol.* **2019**, *10*, 365–387. [CrossRef]
11. Ashokkumar, K.; Murugan, M.; Dhanya, M.K.; Pandian, A.; Warkentin, T.D. Phytochemistry and therapeutic potential of black pepper [*Piper nigrum* (L.)] essential oil and piperine: A review. *Clin. Phytosci.* **2021**, *7*, 1–11. [CrossRef]
12. Kowalczyk, A.; Przychodna, M.; Sopata, S.; Bodalska, A.; Fecka, I. Thymol and thyme essential oil—New insights into selected therapeutic applications. *Molecules* **2020**, *25*, 4125. [CrossRef] [PubMed]
13. Nuță, D.C.; Limban, C.; Chiriță, C.; Chifiriuc, M.C.; Costea, T.; Ionită, P.; Nicolau, I.; Zarafu, I. Contribution of essential oils to the fight against microbial biofilms—A review. *Processes* **2021**, *9*, 537. [CrossRef]
14. Toghlobi, G.S.S.; Arantes, R.A.; Knudsen, B.G.; Tabach, R.; Pereira, M.A.A.; de Carvalho, R.G.; Ferraz, R.R.; Rodrigues, F.S. Usos clínicos do fitoterápico da erva-baleeira (*Varronia curassavica* Jacq.): Revisão da literatura. *Int. J. Health Manag. Rev.* **2022**, *8*, 1–10. [CrossRef]
15. Andrade, K.C.R.; Martins, D.H.N.; Barros, D.D.A.; Souza, P.M.D.; Silveira, D.; Bazzo, Y.M.F.; Magalhães, P.D.O. Essential oils of *Cordia* species, compounds and applications: A systematic review. *Bol. Latinoam. Caribe Plant. Med. Aromat.* **2021**, *21*, 156–175. [CrossRef]
16. Silva, K.P.; de Carvalho Santos, T.A.; Moutinho, B.L.; da Silva, R.S.; dos Santos Pinto, V.; Blank, A.F.; Corrêa, C.B.; Scher, R.; Fernandes, R.P.M. Using *Varronia curassavica* (Cordiaceae) essential oil for the biocontrol of Phytomonas serpens. *Ind. Crops Prod.* **2019**, *139*, 1–7. [CrossRef]
17. Santos, R.P.; Nunes, E.P.; Nascimento, R.F.; Santiago, G.M.P.; Menezes, G.H.A.; Silveira, E.R.; Pessoa, O.D.L. Chemical composition and larvicidal activity of the essential oils of *Cordia leucomalloides* and *Cordia curassavica* from the Northeast of Brazil. *J. Braz. Chem. Soc.* **2006**, *17*, 1027–1030. [CrossRef]
18. Martim, J.K.P.; Maranho, L.T.; Costa-Casagrande, T.A. Role of the chemical compounds present in the essential oil and in the extract of *Cordia verbenacea* DC as an anti-inflammatory, antimicrobial and healing product. *J. Ethnopharmacol.* **2021**, *265*, 1–8. [CrossRef]
19. Pereira, P.S.; de Oliveira, L.G.; de Lima, V.F.; da Silva, M.A.F.; Rodrigues, I.A.; Almeida, E.M. Cytotoxicity of essential oil *Cordia verbenaceae* against *Leishmania brasiliensis* and *Trypanosoma cruzi*. *Molecules* **2021**, *26*, 4485. [CrossRef]

20. Hernandez, T.; Canales, M.; Avila, J.G.; García, A.M.; Martínez, A.; Caballero, J.; Romo de Vivar, A. Antimicrobial activity of the essential oil and extracts of *Cordia curassavica* (Boraginaceae). *J. Ethnopharmacol.* **2007**, *111*, 137–141. [CrossRef]
21. Matias, E.F.F.; Alves, R.R.; Silva, M.K.N.; da Costa, J.G.M.; Coutinho, H.D.M. Biological activities and chemical characterization of *Cordia verbenacea* DC. as tool to validate the ethnobiological usage. *Evid.-Based Complement. Altern. Med.* **2013**, *2013*, 1–7. [CrossRef] [PubMed]
22. Stoppa, M.A.; Casemiro, L.A.; Vinholis, A.H.C.; Cunha, W.R.; Silva, M.L.A.; Martins, C.H.G.; Furtado, N.A.J.C. Comparative study of the recommended methodologies by Clsi and Eucast for activity evaluation antifungal. *Quim. Nova* **2009**, *32*, 498–502. [CrossRef]
23. Morais-Braga, M.F.B.; Sales, D.L.; Carneiro, J.N.P.; Machado, A.J.T.; Dos Santos, A.T.L.; de Freitas, M.A.; Martins, G.M.d.A.B.; Leite, N.F.; de Matos, Y.M.L.; Tintino, S.R.; et al. *Psidium guajava* L. and *Psidium brownianum* Mart ex DC.: Chemical composition and anti–Candida effect in association with fluconazole. *Microb. Pathog.* **2016**, *95*, 200–207. [CrossRef]
24. Coutinho, H.D.; Costa, J.G.; Lima, E.O.; Falcão-Silva, V.S.; Siqueira-Júnior, J.P. Enhancement of the antibiotic activity against a multiresistant *Escherichia coli* by *Mentha arvensis* L. and chlorpromazine. *Chemotherapy* **2008**, *54*, 328–330. [CrossRef] [PubMed]
25. Xiong, G.; Wu, Z.; Yi, J.; Fu, L.; Yang, Z.; Hsieh, C.; Yin, M.; Zeng, X.; Wu, C.; Lu, A.; et al. ADMETlab 2.0: An integrated online platform for accurate and comprehensive predictions of ADMET properties. *Nucleic Acids Res.* **2021**, *49*, 5–14. [CrossRef]
26. Sciarrone, D.; Rigano, F.; Carnovale, C.; Cimino, F.; Dugo, P. Quali-quantitative characterization of the volatile constituents in *Cordia verbenacea* DC essential oil exploiting advanced chromatographic approaches and nuclear magnetic resonance analysis. *J. Chromatogr. A* **2017**, *1524*, 246–253. [CrossRef]
27. Marques, A.P.S.; de Andrade, M.A.; Reis, J.D.; de Castro, F.D.; de Oliveira, F.L.; Costa, J.G.M. Chemical composition of essential oil from *Varronia curassavica* Jacq. accessions in different seasons of the year. *Ind. Crops Prod.* **2019**, *140*, 1–10. [CrossRef]
28. Farias, J.P.; Lima, F.A.; Lins, P.M.P.; Nogueira, P.M.; Rocha, S.K.S.; Soares, F.L. Influence of plant age on chemical composition, antimicrobial activity and cytotoxicity of *Varronia curassavica* Jacq. essential oil produced on an industrial scale. *Agriculture* **2023**, *13*, 373. [CrossRef]
29. Rodrigues, F.F.G.; Silva, D.A.; Menezes, I.R.A.; Coutinho, H.D.M.; Morais, E.C.; Rocha, M.F.G. Chemical composition, antibacterial and antifungal activities of essential oil from *Cordia verbenacea* DC leaves. *Pharmacogn. Res.* **2012**, *4*, 161–165. [CrossRef]
30. Andrade, F.P.; Braga, L.S.; Soares, R.A.; Fernandes, R.P.M. Toxicity of *Varronia curassavica* Jacq. essential oil to two arthropod pests and their natural enemy. *Neotrop. Entomol.* **2021**, *50*, 835–845. [CrossRef]
31. Castro-Nizio, D.A.; Blank, A.F.; de Andrade Brito, F.; Gagliardi, P.R.; Alves, E.; Arrigoni-Blank, M.D.F. A comparative study of the antifungal activity of essential oils of *Varronia curassavica* Jacq. obtained by different distillation methods. *Biosci. J.* **2020**, *36*, 1856–1865. [CrossRef]
32. Lima, F.J.A.; Leite, K.R.B.; Silva, T.M.; Oliveira, F.S.A.; Nascimento, D.M.; Santana, A.S. Caracterização do crescimento e produção de óleo essencial da erva baleeira (*Varronia curassavica* Jaqc). *Res. Soc. Dev.* **2021**, *10*, 1–10. [CrossRef]
33. Chemat, F.; Abert-Vian, M.; Ravi, H.K.; Khan, M.K.; Périno-Issartier, S. Review of alternative solvents for green extraction of food and natural products: Panorama, principles, applications and prospects. *Molecules* **2019**, *24*, 3007. [CrossRef] [PubMed]
34. Allenspach, M.; Steuer, C. α-Pinene: A never-ending story. *Phytochemistry* **2021**, *190*, 112857. [CrossRef] [PubMed]
35. Salehi, B.; Upadhyay, S.; Erdogan Orhan, I.; Kumar Jugran, A.; Jayaweera, L.D.; Dias, D.A.; Sharopov, F.; Taheri, Y.; Martins, N.; Baghalpour, N.; et al. Therapeutic potential of α-and β-pinene: A miracle gift of nature. *Biomolecules* **2019**, *9*, 738. [CrossRef] [PubMed]
36. Rahimi, K.; Rezvani, M.E.; Ghoreishi, A.; Soukhtanloo, M. The effects of alpha-pinene on inflammatory responses and oxidative stress in the formalin test. *Brain Res. Bull.* **2023**, *203*, 110774. [CrossRef]
37. Abe, M.; Haga, Y.; Endo, Y.; Suzuki, Y. Antitumor activity of α-pinene in T-cell tumors. *Cancer Sci.* **2024**, *115*, 1317–1332. [CrossRef]
38. Shahina, Z.; Hanif, M.; Gulzar, T.; Gilani, S. Rosemary essential oil and its components 1, 8-cineole and α-pinene induce ROS-dependent lethality and ROS-independent virulence inhibition in *Candida albicans*. *PLoS ONE* **2022**, *17*, e0277097. [CrossRef]
39. Barros, D.B.; Sousa, L.R.; Silva, M.A.; Santos, M.G.; Lima, E.O.; Campos, L.M. Antifungal activity of terpenes isolated from the Brazilian Caatinga: A review. *Braz. J. Biol.* **2023**, *83*, e270966. [CrossRef]
40. Barros, D.B.; Sousa, L.R.; Silva, M.A.; Santos, M.G.; Lima, E.O.; Campos, L.M. α-Pinene: Docking study, cytotoxicity, mechanism of action, and anti-biofilm effect against *Candida albicans*. *Antibiotics* **2023**, *12*, 345. [CrossRef]
41. Rivera-Yañez, C.R.; Rivero-Cruz, J.F.; Pedraza-Chaverri, J.; Sanchez-Salgado, J.C.; Nogueda-Torres, B.; Ortega-Cervantes, L. Anti-*Candida* activity of *Bursera morelensis* Ramirez essential oil and two compounds, α-pinene and γ-terpinene—An in vitro study. *Molecules* **2017**, *22*, 2095. [CrossRef] [PubMed]
42. Nóbrega, J.R.; Lima, E.O.; Silva, S.S.; Santos, J.B. Antifungal action of α-pinene against *Candida* spp. isolated from patients with otomycosis and effects of its association with boric acid. *Nat. Prod. Res* **2021**, *35*, 6190–6193. [CrossRef] [PubMed]
43. Barros, D.B.; Sousa, L.R.; Silva, M.A.; Santos, M.G.; Lima, E.O.; Campos, L.M. Efeito antifúngico de α-pineno isolado e em associação com antifúngicos frente às cepas de *Candida albicans*. *Res. Soc. Dev.* **2022**, *11*, 1–8. [CrossRef]
44. Saracino, I.M.; Foschi, C.; Pavoni, M.; Spigarelli, R.; Valerii, M.C.; Spisni, E. Antifungal activity of natural compounds vs. *Candida* spp.: A mixture of cinnamaldehyde and eugenol shows promising in vitro results. *Antibiotics* **2022**, *11*, 73. [CrossRef] [PubMed]
45. Francomano, F.; Caruso, A.; Salzano, G.; Fresta, M.; Cosco, D. β-Caryophyllene: A sesquiterpene with countless biological properties. *Appl. Sci.* **2019**, *9*, 5420. [CrossRef]

46. Alighiri, D. Isolation and antifungal activity of caryophyllene from clove leaf oil (*Syzygium aromaticum* L.) on mahogany leaf composites. *Sci. Community Pharm. J.* **2022**, *1*, 17–25.
47. Dahham, S.S.; Tabana, Y.M.; Iqbal, M.A.; Ahamed, M.B.; Ezzat, S.M.; Majid, A.S. The anticancer, antioxidant and antimicrobial properties of the sesquiterpene β-caryophyllene from the essential oil of *Aquilaria crassna*. *Molecules* **2015**, *20*, 11808–11829. [CrossRef]
48. Bezerra, C.F.; Pereira, A.C.; Lima, E.O.; Almeida, J.R. Antifungal effect of the liposome encapsulation of the trans-caryophylene and its association with fluconazole. *Chem. Biol. Interact.* **2023**, *373*, 1–10. [CrossRef]
49. Sobrinho, A.C.N.; Silva, M.L.; Oliveira, R.R.; Sousa, E.P.; Soares, M.B. Antifungal and antioxidant activities of *Vernonia chalybaea* Mart. ex DC. essential oil and their major constituent β-caryophyllene. *Braz. Arch. Biol. Technol.* **2020**, *63*, 1–11. [CrossRef]
50. Salas-Oropeza, J.; Gonzalez-Trujano, M.E.; Reyes-Ramirez, A.; Estrada-Soto, S.; Soto-Rios, R. Wound healing activity of α-pinene and α-phellandrene. *Molecules* **2021**, *26*, 2488. [CrossRef]
51. Şişman, T.; Ceylan, Z. The embryotoxicity of alpha-pinene to the early life stages of zebrafish (*Danio rerio* Hamilton, 1822). *Nat. Life Sci. Commun.* **2023**, *22*, 1–11. [CrossRef]
52. Silva, J.T.d.C.; Moreira, F.C.; Bezerra, J.J.L.; Farias, N.S.; Menêses, A.V.S.; Santos, A.G.d.; Santana, M.d.S.; Silva, M.E.P.d.; Fonseca, V.J.A.; Costa, A.R.; et al. In Vitro and In Silico Biological Evaluation of the Essential Oil from *Syzigium cumini* Leaves as a Source of Novel Antifungal and Trichomonacidal Agents. *Future Pharmacol.* **2024**, *4*, 380–394. [CrossRef]
53. Satou, T.; Murakami, S.; Hayashi, S.; Koike, K.; Sengoku, T. Mouse brain concentrations of α-pinene, limonene, linalool, and 1,8-cineole following inhalation. *Flavour Fragr. J.* **2016**, *32*, 36–39. [CrossRef]
54. Khoshnazar, M.; Parvardeh, S.; Bigdeli, M.R. Alpha-pinene exerts neuroprotective effects via anti-inflammatory and anti-apoptotic mechanisms in a rat model of focal cerebral ischemia-reperfusion. *J. Stroke Cerebrovasc. Dis.* **2020**, *29*, 1–10. [CrossRef]
55. Rahayu, M.; Mahardika, A.M.; Fattah, F.A.; Krisnadi, D. Alpha-pinene attenuates microglial NF-κB activation and iNOS expression in gp120-induced neuroinflammation. *MNJ (Malang Neurol. J.)* **2021**, *7*, 80–84. [CrossRef]
56. Green, A.K.; Morgan, J.A.; Vogt, P.F.; Harlow, H.J.; Barnes, B.M.; Levenson, J.W. Is alpha-pinene a substrate for permeability-glycoprotein in wood rats? *J. Chem. Ecol.* **2006**, *32*, 1197–1211. [CrossRef]

antioxidants

MDPI

Article

Identification and Validation of the miR/RAS/RUNX2 Autophagy Regulatory Network in AngII-Induced Hypertensive Nephropathy in MPC5 Cells Treated with Hydrogen Sulfide Donors

Qing Ye [1,†], Mi Ren [2,†], Di Fan [1], Yicheng Mao [1,*] and Yi-Zhun Zhu [1,3,*]

1 Shanghai Key Laboratory of Bioactive Small Molecules, School of Pharmacy, Fudan University, Shanghai 201203, China
2 The Department of Hepatobiliary Surgery and Liver Transplantation, Shanghai General Hospital, Shanghai Jiaotong University School of Medicine, Shanghai 200080, China
3 State Key Laboratory of Quality Research in Chinese Medicines, (R & D Center) Lab. for Drug Discovery from Natural Resource, School of Pharmacy, Macau University of Science and Technology, Macau 999078, China
* Correspondence: maoyc@fudan.edu.cn (Y.M.); yzzhu@must.edu.mo (Y.-Z.Z.)
† These authors contributed equally to this work.

Abstract: The balanced crosstalk between miRNAs and autophagy is essential in hypertensive nephropathy. Hydrogen sulfide donors have been reported to attenuate renal injury, but the mechanism is unclear. We aimed to identify and verify the miRNAs and autophagy regulatory networks in hypertensive nephropathy treated with hydrogen sulfide donors through bioinformatics analysis and experimental verification. From the miRNA dataset, autophagy was considerably enriched in mice kidney after angiotensin II (AngII) and combined hydrogen sulfide treatment (H_2S_AngII), among which there were 109 differentially expressed miRNAs (DEMs) and 21 hub ADEGs (autophagy-related differentially expressed genes) in the AngII group and 70 DEMs and 13 ADEGs in the H_2S_AngII group. A miRNA–mRNA–transcription factors (TFs) autophagy regulatory network was then constructed and verified in human hypertensive nephropathy samples and podocyte models. In the network, two DEMs (miR-98-5p, miR-669b-5p), some hub ADEGs (*KRAS*, *NRAS*), and one TF (*RUNX2*) were altered, accompanied by a reduction in autophagy flux. However, significant recovery occurred after treatment with endogenous or exogenous H_2S donors, as well as an overexpression of miR-98-5p and miR-669b-5p. The miR/RAS/RUNX2 autophagy network driven by H_2S donors was related to hypertensive nephropathy. H_2S donors or miRNAs increased autophagic flux and reduced renal cell injury, which could be a potentially effective medical therapy.

Keywords: hypertensive nephropathy; hydrogen sulfide donors; miRNA; autophagy; bioinformatics analysis

1. Introduction

Hypertension is recognized as one of the leading causes linked to the development of cardiovascular and renal disease [1,2], and it also promotes the progression of chronic kidney disease towards end-stage renal disease [3]. Hypertensive nephropathy is mainly manifested as renal structural and functional damage caused by essential hypertension, among which renal inflammation is an important pathological feature [4,5]. In essential hypertension, the renin–angiotensin–aldosterone system (RAAS) is extensively activated, and the expression of its main effector angiotensin II (AngII) is upregulated. These subsequently lead to the dysfunction of renal endothelial cells, the release of various inflammatory factors, and the proliferation of mesangial cells, thereby inducing vascular remodeling, promoting renal inflammation and fibrosis, and ultimately leading to a decreased glomerular filtration rate, glomerular ischemia, sclerosis, and nephron atrophy [6,7]. Therefore, AngII is an important mediator of hypertensive nephropathy, and it is also the modeling condition chosen by many studies [8]. In addition, many studies have shown that damage to and structural changes in podocytes are very important in renal injury [9]. Here, we employed AngII-induced podocytes as a cell model. Autophagy is an important and highly conserved pathway, which acts as an essential role in maintaining the homeostasis of physiological and pathological processes, such as immunity, inflammation, aging and metabolism, etc. [10]. Accumulating evidence suggests that hypertensive nephropathy may be associated with the imbalance of autophagy regulation, and targeting the autophagy pathway may alleviate hypertension-induced kidney damage [9,11].

Hydrogen sulfide (H_2S) is an important physiological gas molecule, and it along with nitric oxide (NO) and carbon monoxide (CO) are considered as the three major gas signaling molecules in the body [12]. Endogenous hydrogen sulfide is synthesized by cystathionine-γ-lyase (CSE), cystathionine-β-synthase (CBS), and 3-mercaptopiruvate sulfurtransferase (MST) enzymes [13]. Previous studies have shown that hydrogen sulfide is involved in the regulation of various physiological and pathological conditions, including the cardiovascular, renal, respiratory, central nervous, and digestive systems [14]. In common kidney diseases, such as CKD and acute kidney injury, hydrogen sulfide production is reduced, and the expression of CBS, CSE, or MST is also downregulated to varying degrees [15–17]. Treatment with hydrogen sulfide donors not only restores hydrogen sulfide levels but also ameliorates kidney function [18]. Multiple studies have shown that hydrogen sulfide donors alleviate renal damage by regulating autophagy, oxidative stress, inflammation, and cell injury through various signaling pathways [19]. However, few studies have focused on the epigenetic regulation of hydrogen sulfide donors in the treatment of hypertensive nephropathy, especially on microRNA regulation.

MicroRNAs (miRNAs, miRs) are a group of single-stranded non-coding RNAs with a length of 19–22 nucleotides, which are important regulators of gene post-transcriptional expression [20]. By specifically binding to the 3′UTR sequences of mRNA, miRNAs lead to the degradation or post-transcriptional inhibition of target genes and then participate in the regulation of different biological processes [21]. The dysregulation of miRNAs is important in the occurrence and development of various kidney diseases [22]. In hypertensive nephropathy, many miRNAs, such as miR-200a, miR-200b, miR-141, miR-429, miR-205 and miR-192, have increased expression [23]. Studies have shown that angiotensin-converting enzyme inhibitors downregulate the expression of miR-324-3p in glomeruli and tubules, thereby reducing renal fibrosis [24]. However, few studies have addressed miRNAs regulating autophagy pathways in hypertensive nephropathy. In addition, a growing number of studies have shown that hydrogen sulfide can also regulate miRNAs to improve cardiac and renal dysfunction [25,26]. Since the role of miRNAs in hypertensive nephropathy is emerging, the functional miRNAs and corresponding key mRNAs that regulate the autophagy pathway in hypertensive nephropathy and hydrogen sulfide donor therapy are explored to construct the miRNA-mRNA regulatory network, which is helpful for elucidating the molecular mechanism of hydrogen sulfide donors in the treatment of hypertensive nephropathy.

Herein, we screened out differentially expressed miRNAs (DEMs) after AngII or a combination of AngII and hydrogen sulfide treatment using the Gene Expression Omnibus (GEO) database. Then, their target mRNAs were predicted by the validation and prediction databases, the top 5% hub mRNAs were identified using the protein–protein interaction (PPI) network and CytoHubba, and potential autophagy-related differentially expressed genes (ADEGs) were identified by the autophagy-related gene set. Subsequently, functional annotation and pathway enrichment analysis were conducted and a miRNA-ADEGs-TF (transcription factor) regulatory network was constructed and validated to better understand the underlying mechanism of the hydrogen sulfide treatment of hypertensive nephropathy.

2. Materials and Methods

2.1. Data Acquisition

In order to obtain genetic analysis data for hypertensive nephropathy and hydrogen sulfide treatment, we used "hypertension", "kidney", and "hydrogen sulfide" as keywords to search for genome-wide expression studies in the GEO database (https://www.ncbi.nlm.nih.gov/geo/, accessed on 1 October 2022). The non-coding RNA expression profiling dataset GSE92857 was screened out and downloaded using the R package "GEO query" (v 2.62.2). The GSE92857 dataset, containing 12 kidney tissues each from normal control (Ctrl), AngII-treated (AngII), hydrogen-sulfide-treated, and a combination of AngII and hydrogen sulfide (AngII_H_2S)-treated mice, was compiled on the GPL19117 ([miRNA-4] Affymetrix Multispecies miRNA-4 Array) platform [26]. This dataset was normalized with the RMA (robust multiarray analysis) algorithm using the Partek Genomics Suite software (Partek v6.6, St. Louis, MO, USA), and the independent GSE37455 and GSE37460 datasets containing human hypertensive nephropathy samples were utilized for validation. The workflow chart of the methodology used in this study is shown in Figure 2.1.

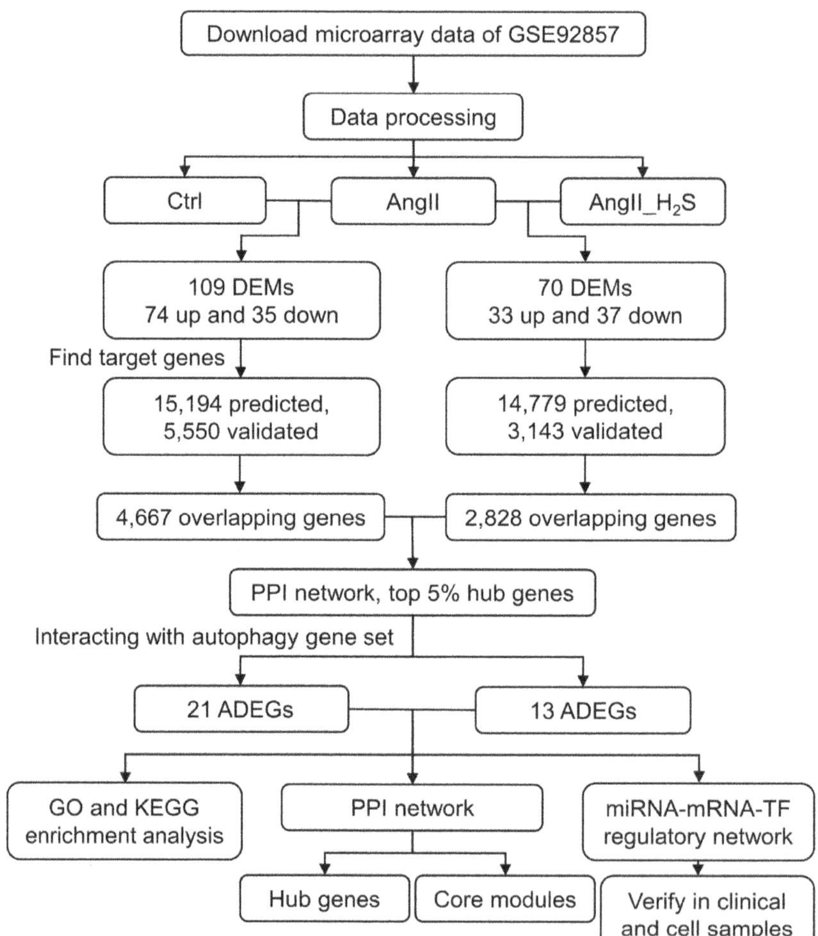

Figure 1. The flowchart of screening strategy. Ctrl, control kidney at 28 days. AngII, mice treated with AngII via mini osmotic pump for 28 days. AngII_H_2S, mice treated with AngII via mini osmotic

pump and hydrogen sulfide donor via i.p. injection for 28 days. DEMs, differentially expressed miRNAs. ADEGs, potential autophagy differentially expressed genes. GO, Gene Ontology. KEGG, Kyoto Encyclopedia of Genes and Genomes. PPI, protein–protein interaction. TF, transcription factor.

2.2. Analysis of Differentially Expressed miRNAs

The normalized data matrix of the miRNA profiling dataset was acquired and represented as boxplot and density plot. The probes in the dataset were then annotated with the annotation file from the GPL19117 platform, and only probes interrogating M. Muculus transcripts were included. We screened out DEMs comparing the AngII and Ctrl groups and the AngII_H_2S and AngII groups using the "limma" package (v 3.50.3) of the R software (v 4.1.2) [27]. MiRNAs with a p value less than 0.05 and an absolute fold change (FC) greater than 1.5 were considered as DEMs. Box line, density, and volcano plots of DEMs were generated using the "ggplot2" package (v 3.3.6) [28], and the circular heatmap of the DEMs was illustrate through the TBtools software (v 1.098769).

2.3. Prediction and Identification of Hub Target Genes

The multiMiR package is a database of miRNAs and target genes, disease, and drug interactions, including 8 prediction databases (DIANA-microT-CDS, ElMMo, MicroCosm, miRanda, miRDB, PicTar, PITA, and TargetScan), 3 experimentally validated databases (miRecords, miRTarBase, and TarBase), and 3 databases containing drug-/disease-related information (miR2Disease, Pharmaco-miR, and PhenomiR) [29]. The predicted and validated target genes of the DEMs were selected by multiMiR package (v 2.3) analysis, and the intersection of the two sets was selected as the target genes of DEMs. The PPI network of these intersecting target genes was then constructed using the Cytoscape software (v 3.9.1), followed by the Cytohubba (v 0.1) plug-in's Degree algorithm to take the top 5% genes as hub target genes [30,31].

2.4. Selection of Autophagy-Related Genes

The autophagy-related gene set in Mus musculus was collected from the entries mmu04140 and mmu04136 in the Kyoto Encyclopedia of Genes and Genomes (KEGG) pathway database (https://www.genome.jp/entry/mmu04140, https://www.genome.jp/entry/mmu04136, accessed on 1 November 2022). The autophagy-related gene set is provided in Table S1. In addition, we identified potential ADEGs via the Venn diagram package (v 1.7.3).

2.5. Functional and Pathway Enrichment Analysis of ADEGs

To evaluate the biological functions of the DEMs targeting ADEGs, Gene Ontology (GO) enrichment analysis and KEGG pathway analysis were performed using the "ClusterProfiler" package (v 4.2.2) in the R software. Among them, the species was set to Mus musculus, and the Benjamini–Hochberg method was used to adjust the p value. Finally, the enrichments or pathways with adjusted p values of less than 0.05 were screened out for analysis and plot display.

2.6. PPI Network and Recognition of Hub ADEGs and Core Modules

The PPI network of ADEGs was visualized using the STRING database (https://string-db.org/, v 11.5, accessed on 8 November 2022), with the interaction score setting at a high confidence (0.700) [32]. Afterward, the analysis data of the PPI network was imported into the Cytoscape software (v 3.9.1), and the CytoHubba plug-in (v 0.1) was used to assign values to each gene through the topological network algorithm, and then the top 10 genes of the "Degree" attribute were regarded as hub ADEGs [31]. In addition, the Molecular Complex Detection (MCODE, v 2.0.2) plug-in was utilized to analyze the core modules [33].

2.7. Construction of miRNA-mRNA-TF Regulatory Network

Based on the results of the screened DEMs and targeted ADEGs, an autophagy-related miRNA-mRNA regulatory network was constructed using the Cytoscape software (v 3.9.1). Transcription factors (TFs) and miRNAs are two important regulators of gene expression, often controlling gene regulatory networks in a dependent or independent manner [34,35]. In order to further study the molecular mechanism of hydrogen sulfide regulation of autophagy, we used the iRegulon plug-in (v 1.3) to predict potential transcription factors associated with ADEGs [36]. Ultimately, transcription factors enriched in the top 5 fractions, miRNAs co-regulated by AngII and hydrogen sulfide, and corresponding ADEGs were selected to construct an autophagy-related miRNA-mRNA-TF regulatory network.

2.8. Drugs and Reagents

S-Propargyl-cysteine (SPRC), a substrate donor for H_2S synthesis, was synthesized and purified as described in our previous study [37,38]. NaHS, interferon-γ, DL-Propargylglycine (PAG), and angiotensin II (AngII) were purchased form Sigma-Aldrich (St. Louis, MO, USA). Losartan was obtained from MCE (Shanghai, China). RPMI 1640 medium, fetal bovine serum (FBS), penicillin/streptomycin solution, and 0.25% trypsin were purchased from Gibco (New York, NY, USA). RNAiso Plus and RNAiso for small RNA reagents were obtained from TaKaRa (Shiga, Japan). A Hifair III 1st Strand cDNA Synthesis Kit (gDNA digester plus) and Hieff miRNA Universal qPCR SYBR Master Mix were obtained from Yeasen(Shanghai, China). ABScript III RT Master Mix for qPCR and 2X Universal SYBR Green Fast qPCR Mix were obtained from ABclonal (Wuhan, China). The miR-98-5p mimic (micrON mmu-miR-98-5p mimic), miR-669b-5p (micrON mmu-miR-669b-5p mimic), miR-NC (micrON mimic NC), and ribo*FECT*™ CP were obtained from RiboBio (Guangzhou, China).

2.9. Cell Culture

Conditionally immortalized mouse podocyte MPC5 cells were purchased from ATCC (USA). The MPC5 cells were cultured and differentiated as previously described [39]. The MPC5 cells were first cultured at 33 °C in RPMI 1640 medium containing 10% FBS, 1% penicillin/streptomycin, and 30 U/mL recombinant mouse interferon-γ. Then, the MPC5 cells were placed at 37 °C and cultured in complete RPMI 1640 medium without interferon for 10–14 days, and further experiments were performed after differentiation and maturity. When the MPC5 cells reached 80% confluence, they were digested with 0.25% trypsin and passaged into new culture dishes at a ratio of 1:3 to continue culturing.

For miRNAs mimic transfection, MPC5 cells were seeded into a 6-well plate containing complete culture medium the day before transfection, allowing the cell density to be about 40% at the time of transfection. Then, according to the manufacturer's instructions, the transfection mixture was prepared and added dropwise to the cells in complete medium without penicillin/streptomycin, and the culture was continued in a 37 °C incubator for 48 h for subsequent AngII treatment and other operations.

For the H_2S donor treatment, MPC5 cells were treated in the following groupings: Ctrl group (vehicle), AngII group (1 μM AngII treatment), NaHS or SPRC group (pre-treated with 50 μM NaHS or 50 μM SPRC for 1 h before exposure to 1 μM AngII), and SPRC + PAG group (pre-incubated with 2 mM PAG for 30 min and then pre-treated with 50 μM SPRC for 1 h before exposure to 1 μM AngII). For quantitative PCR and WB, AngII was stimulated for 24 or 72 h, respectively. NaHS, SPRC, and PAG were freshly prepared before each experiment.

2.10. Quantitative PCR

The total RNA and miRNA were extracted using RNAiso Plus and RNAiso for small RNA reagents according to the manufacturer's protocol. For the mRNA targets, total RNA was reversed into cDNA using ABScript III RT Master Mix. Subsequent quantitative PCR (qPCR) experiments were performed in a Bio-Rad CFX96 PCR instrument using 2X Universal SYBR Green Fast qPCR Mix. For miRNAs, complementary DNA (cDNA) was synthesized using specific stem–loop primers for miR-98-5p and miR-669b-5p through a Hifair III 1st Strand cDNA Synthesis Kit. Then, qPCR analyses were run in triplicate to calculate miRNAs expression using Hieff miRNA Universal qPCR SYBR Master Mix. U6 snRNA and Gapdh were used as a reference for miRNAs and mRNAs. All the primers used are shown in Table S2.

2.11. Western Blot

Western blot (WB) analysis was performed as previously reported [40]. Briefly, proteins in MPC5 cells were lysed and extracted with RIPA buffer (Yeasen, China) and then boiled in 5× loading buffer (Yeasen, China). Subsequently, the protein concentration in each sample was determined using a BCA kit (Yeasen, China). Samples with the same amount of protein were subjected to SDS-PAGE (sodium dodecyl sulfate–polyacrylamide gel electrophoresis) and transferred to polyvinylidene fluoride (PVDF, Millipore, Burlington, MA, USA) membranes. The membranes were then blocked with 5% nonfat dry milk (Cell Signaling, Danvers, MA, USA) and incubated with the following primary antibodies: anti-PTEN, anti-KRAS, anti-NRAS, anti-RUNX2, anti-CSE, anti-MST (1:1000, Abclonal, Wuhan, China), anti-MAPK1 (Erk1/2), anti-LC3B (1:1000, Cell Signaling, Danvers, MA, USA), anti-P62 (SQSTM1, 1:5000), anti-nephrin, anti-podocin, anti-CBS (1:1000, Proteintech, Rosemont, IL, USA), and anti-GAPDH (1:10,000, ABclonal, Wuhan, China). After washing with 1X TBST (Tris-buffered saline with tween 20), secondary HRP goat anti-rabbit or anti-mouse antibodies (1:10,000, Abclonal, Wuhan, China) combined with immobilon Western chemiluminescent HRP substrate (Millipore) were used to visualize bands under a ChemiDoc XRS+ system (BIO-RAD, Hercules, CA, USA). The grey value of each band was calculated using the Image J software (v1.54f, NIH, Bethesda, MA, USA), and the relative expression of the target protein was determined using the internal reference protein GADPH.

2.12. H_2S Content Assay

H_2S content was measured as per the manufacturer's instructions (H_2S content assay kit, Solarbio, Beijing, China). In brief, a certain number of cells were collected using the extraction solution, and they were then subjected to ultrasound and centrifugation. The reaction reagents were added and incubated at room temperature for 10 min. Subsequently, the absorbance of the solution at 665 nm was detected using a microplate reader (Varioskan Flash, Thermo Scientific, Waltham, MA, USA), and the corresponding H_2S concentration was obtained by substituting it into the standard curve of the standard solution concentration.

For fluorescence detection, a WSP-1 fluorescent probe (MCE, Shanghai, China) for H_2S was used. After stimulation, 10 μM WSP-1 was added and incubated at 37 degrees for 60 min. After a quick wash with PBS twice, 10 μg/mL Hoechst 33342 staining solution (Yeasen, Shanghai, China) was added and incubated for 10 min. Finally, observations and recordings were made under an Olympus CKX53 inverted fluorescence microscope (Tokyo, Japan).

2.13. Statistics

In addition to the above-mentioned R package, the GraphPad Prism 9 (v. 9.0.0, Boston, MA, USA) software was used for graphing and statistical analysis. For pairwise comparisons between more than two group sets, one-way ANOVA was performed, and Tukey's multiple comparison post hoc test was utilized to correct the p value. Statistical significance was considered when the resulting p value was less than 0.05. All experiments were repeated at least three times independently, and data are shown as mean ± SD.

3. Results

3.1. MiRNAs Were Dysregulated in Mouse Kidney after AngII Induction and H_2S Donor Treatment

A dataset of miRNA expression in kidneys from AngII- and/or H_2S-treated mice was downloaded from the GEO database. The distribution trend in the boxplot of this dataset was basically a straight line (Figure S1A), and the density plots of the values in the different groups were basically coincident (Figure S1B). The results showed that the data quality was good and had good repeatability.

We revealed a total of 109 DEMs between the AngII and Ctrl groups, with 74 miRNAs upregulated and 35 miRNAs downregulated according to the principle of absolute FC > 1.5 and p value < 0.05 (Figure 2A,C). After the AngII and H_2S donor treatment, a total of 70 DEMs were screened out in comparison with the AngII alone group, with 33 miRNAs upregulated and 37 miRNAs downregulated (Figure 2B,D). The hierarchical clustering analysis and volcano plots were used to assess the variation between the different groups (Figure 2). All the DEMs are listed in Supplementary Tables S3 and S4. These results showed the presence of abundant altered miRNAs in mouse kidneys after treatment with AngII alone or in combination with hydrogen sulfide donors.

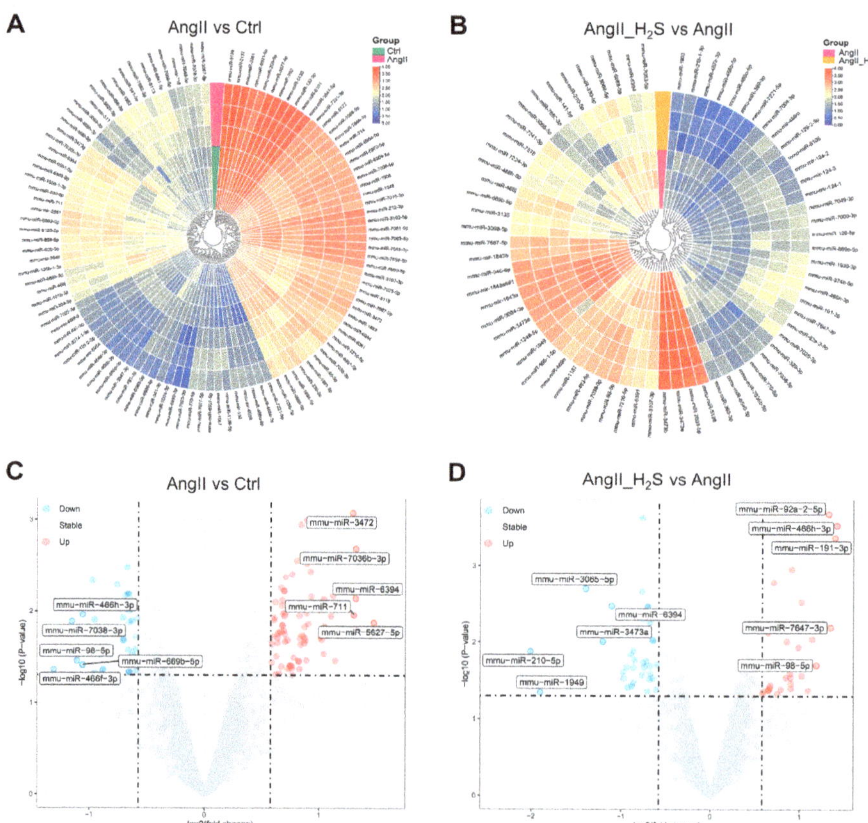

Figure 2. Screening of DEMs in AngII- or H_2S-treated mouse kidney. Clustered heatmap of DEMs between AngII and Ctrl groups (**A**) as well as comparison of AngII and H_2S donor treatments (AngII_H_2S) and AngII alone group (**B**). Green label represents Ctrl group, fuchsia represents AngII group, and khaki represents AngII_H_2S group. The miRNA expression values were processed by

log base 2 and are represented from blue to red in ascending order. (**C**) The volcano plot of DEMs between AngII and Ctrl groups. (**D**) The volcano plot of DEMs between AngII_H_2S and AngII groups. Each of the top five miRNAs with the largest difference in forward and reverse changes are marked. Down means downregulated miRNAs, and these are shown as blue dots. Up, presented as red dots, means upregulated miRNAs. The gray dots show the not significantly changed miRNAs. The criteria were absolute FC > 1.5 and p value < 0.05.

3.2. The Target Genes of These Dysregulated miRNAs Were Mainly Concentrated in the Autophagy Pathway

In order to identify the potential functions of these DEMs, we used eight prediction databases and three validation databases in the multiMiR database to find the target genes of these DEMs. In total, 5550 validated and 15,194 predicted target genes and 3143 validated and 14,779 predicated target genes were found in the AngII vs. Ctrl and AngII_H_2S vs. AngII groups, respectively. Next, overlapping genes among the predicted and validated genes were selected as candidate target genes by crossover analysis. A total of 4667 and 2828 candidate target genes were selected accordingly (Figure 3A,B). To further screen hub target genes, candidate genes were imported into the STRING database and Cytoscape software, and the genes with the top 5% of the PPI scores were marked as hub target genes according to the Cytohubba plug-in. A total of 233 and 141 hub target genes were marked in the AngII vs. Ctrl and AngII_H_2S vs. AngII groups, respectively, and these were displayed with the PPI network (Figure 3C,D). Afterwards, these hub target genes were interacted with the autophagy-related gene set to obtain 21 and 13 potential ADEGs, respectively (Figure 3E,F and Supplementary Table S5).

In an effort to gain insight into the functions and mechanisms of these ADEGs, the GO and KEGG databases were used to enrich GO terms, including biological process (BP), cellular component (CC), and molecular function (MF), as well as the KEGG pathway via the ClusterProfiler package. In the comparison between the AngII and Ctrl groups, the enrichment analysis of the top 30 GO terms is shown in Figure 4A. In the biological process category, AngII mainly affected the phosphorylation and activation of proteins such as protein kinase B signaling, protein phosphorylation, and peptidyl-threonine phosphorylation the mouse kidney. In addition, in terms of cellular components, AngII mainly altered aspects such as the phosphatidylinositol 3-kinase complex and mitochondria, while the major molecular functions affected were protein binding and enzymatic activity (Figure 4A). In contrast, after treatment with hydrogen sulfide donors, protein phosphorylation in biological processes was also enriched, in addition to the positive regulation of gene expression and the JNK cascade (Figure 4B). In the cellular component and molecular function categories, hydrogen sulfide donor treatment also altered the phosphatidylinositol 3-kinase complex as well as protein binding and kinase activation (Figure 4B).

The enrichment results of the top 20 KEGG pathways of ADEGs from the two comparison groups are shown in Figure 4C,D. In the KEGG enrichment analysis, AngII mainly regulated autophagy, the mTOR signaling pathway, and the FoxO signaling pathway in kidney (Figure 4C). Similarly, the H_2S donor treatment also modulated autophagy, the FoxO signaling pathway, and the ErbB signaling pathway (Figure 4D). These enriched GO terms and KEGG signaling pathways may be the main mechanism involved in the H_2S treatment of hypertensive renal injury caused by AngII.

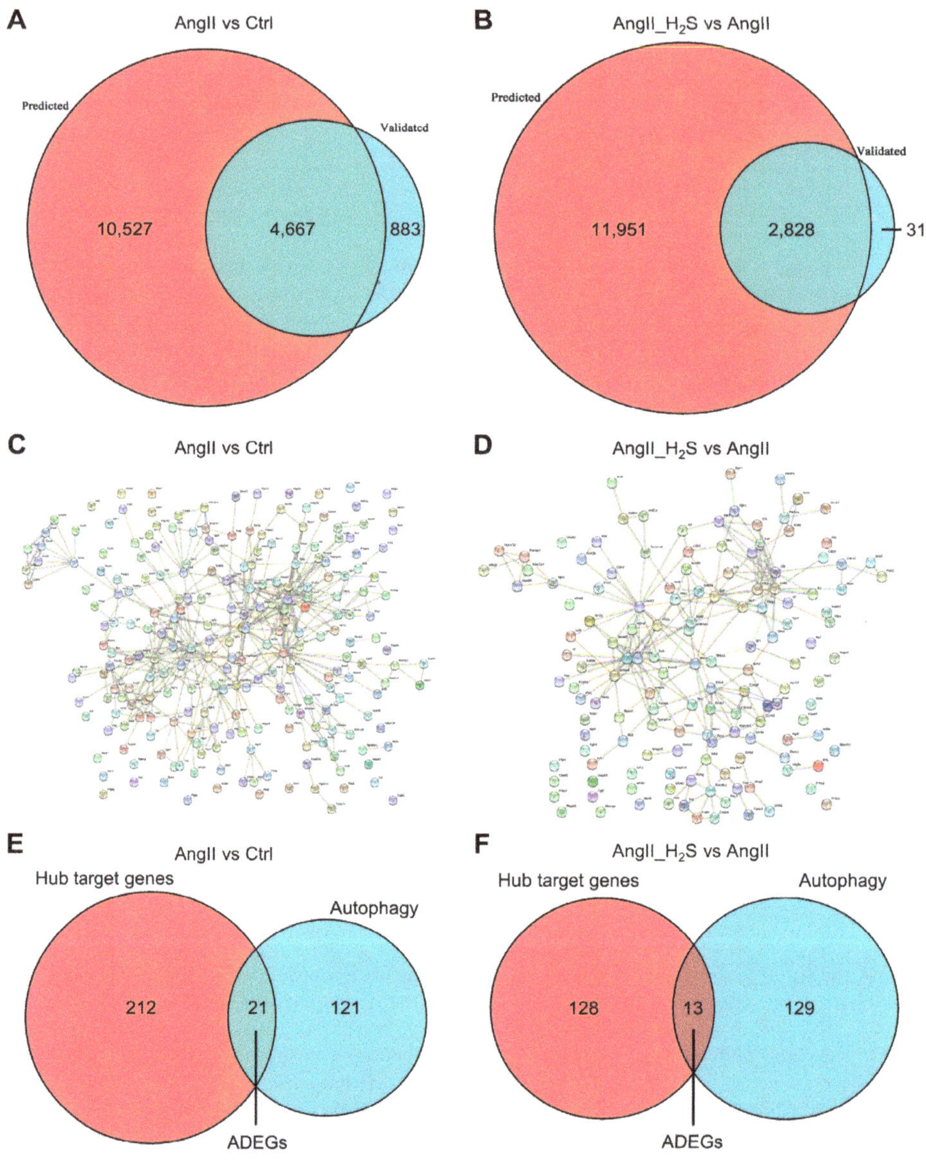

Figure 3. Hub target genes and ADEGs were selected for DEMs associated with AngII alone or AngII plus H_2S donor treatment. Venn diagrams showing predicted target genes (red) and validated target genes (sky blue) corresponding to DEMs in comparison between AngII vs. Ctrl (**A**) and AngII_H_2S vs. AngII (**B**). PPI network displaying the interaction of hub target genes from comparison between AngII vs. Ctrl (**C**), and AngII_H_2S vs. AngII (**D**). The interacting genes between hub target genes and autophagy-related gene set in AngII vs. Ctrl (**E**) and AngII_H_2S vs. AngII (**F**) comparison.

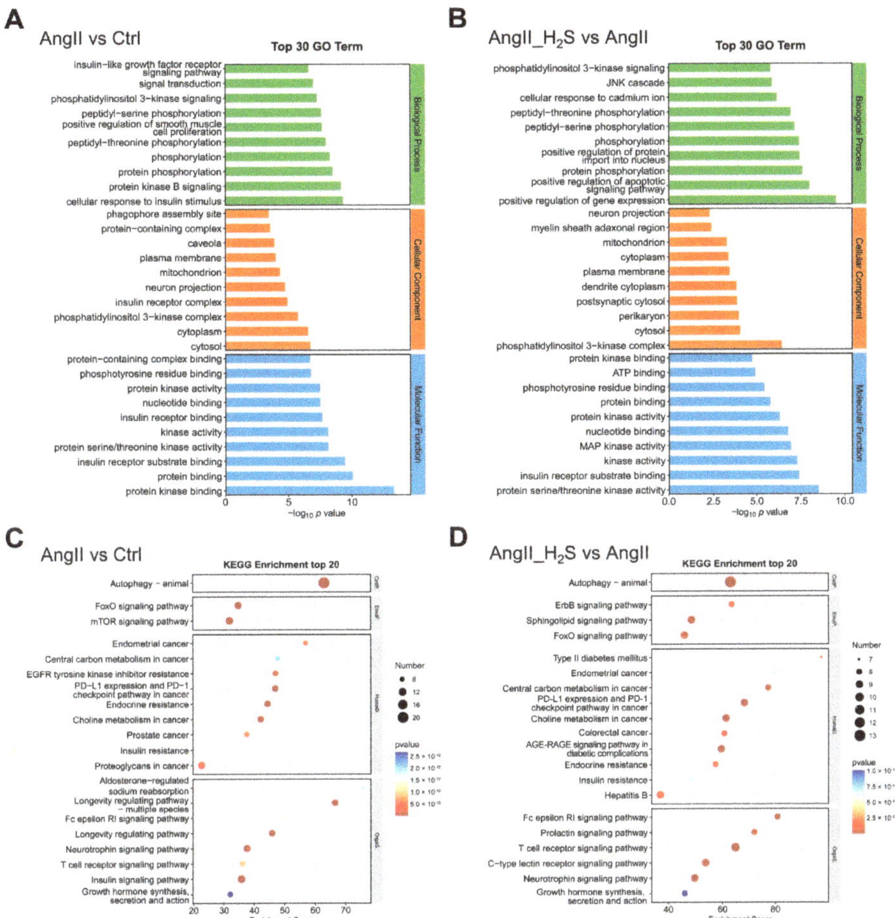

Figure 4. Enrichment plots from GO and KEGG functional analysis of targeted ADEGs. Barplots of the enrichment analysis for each of the top 10 biological processes (green), cellular component (orange-red), and molecular function (blue) from AngII vs. Ctrl (**A**) and AngII_H$_2$S vs. AngII (**B**). In addition, the barplots are arranged from smallest to largest according to the negative logarithm of the adjusted *p* value. The KEGG pathway enrichment analysis results of AngII vs. Ctrl (**C**) and AngII_H$_2$S vs. AngII (**D**) are shown as dotplots. Among them, the size of the dots represents the number of ADEGs hitting the corresponding pathway, and the adjusted *p* value of each pathway is displayed from red to blue in ascending order. CellP., cellular processes; EnvIP., environmental information processing; HumaD., human diseases; OrgaS., organismal systems.

3.3. The Hub ADEGs of These Dysregulated miRNAs Were Analyzed

To further investigate the function of the targeted ADEGs at the protein level and reveal the core interactions affected by hydrogen sulfide donor treatment, we constructed PPI networks from the Ctrl vs. AngII and AngII vs. AngII_H$_2$S groups using the STRING database (Figure 5A,B). The PPI networks of Ctrl vs. AngII with 21 nodes and 196 interaction relationships and AngII vs. AngII_H$_2$S with 13 nodes and 94 edges are shown in Figure 5A and B, respectively. Then, the top 10 hub ADEGs were determined based on the cytoHubba Degree algorithm using the Cytoscape software. After the AngII treatment, the hub ADEGs identified were Kras, Irs1, Igf1r, Pik3ca, Mapk1, Pten, Pik3r1, Rps6kb1, Pdpk1, and Prkcd. (Figure 5C). As for the H$_2$S donor treatment, Kras, Nras, Mapk1, Prkcd,

Mapk8, Pten, Pik3ca, Mapk9, Prkcq, and Pik3r3 were found to be hub ADEGs (Figure 5D). Meanwhile, the core modules in these PPI networks were analyzed using MCODE with the k-score set to 2.0. A sub-network consisting of 9 nodes and 32 edges was considered as a core cluster in Ctrl vs. AngII, and Pik3ca, Pten, Kras, and Igf1r occupied the center of the module (Figure 5E). In addition, the core module of AngII vs. AngII_H_2S contained 10 nodes and 27 edges, and its center was Kras (Figure 5F). The hub ADEGs and core modules revealed by these results may be important mechanisms by which hydrogen sulfide donors and AngII regulate the renal autophagy network.

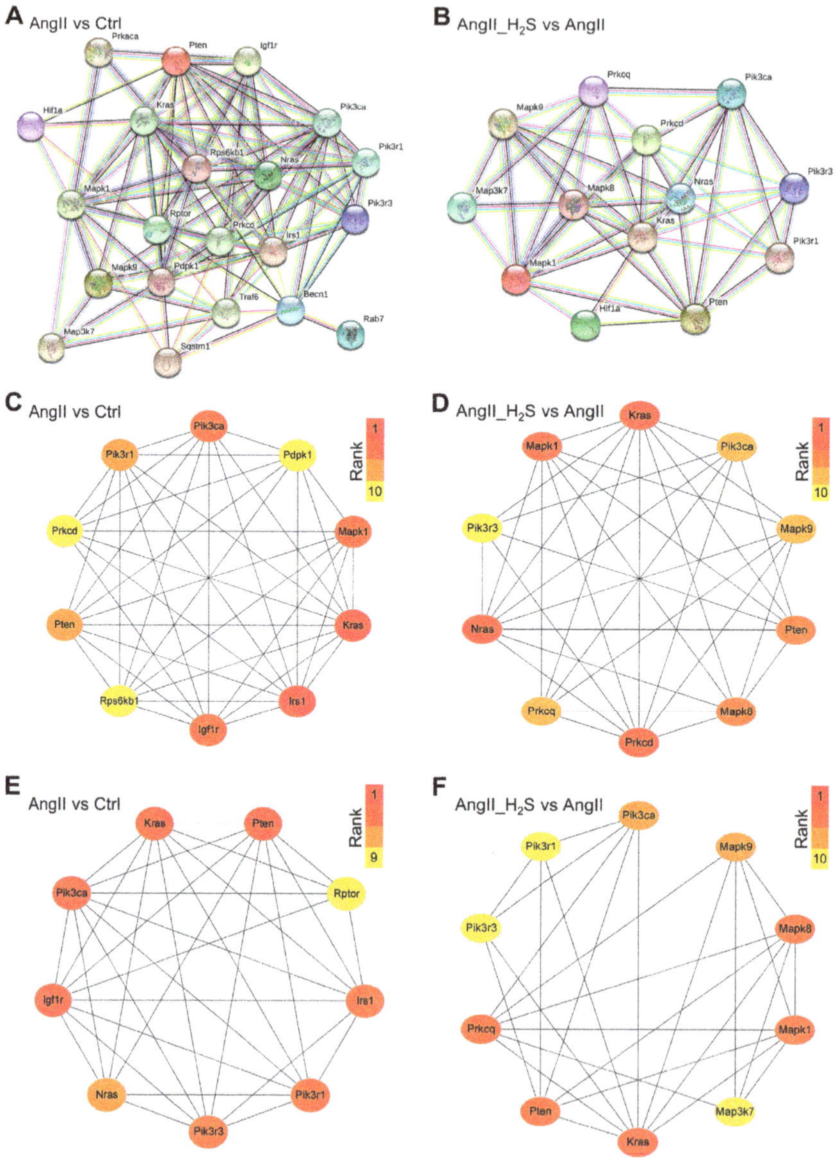

Figure 5. Protein–protein interaction networks and core modules of ADEGs constructed by STRING and Cytoscape. PPI analysis of targeted ADEGs from AngII vs. Ctrl (**A**) and AngII_H_2S vs. AngII (**B**).

The network illustration of top 10 hub ADEGs explored by CytoHubba in comparison between AngII vs. Ctrl (**C**) and AngII_H_2S vs. AngII (**D**). Hub ADEGs are ranked by Degree value from dark red to orange red. Core modules analyzed by molecular complex detection network clustering analysis in AngII vs. Ctrl (**E**) and AngII_H_2S vs. AngII (**F**).

3.4. Construction of the miRNA-mRNA-TF Autophagy Regulatory Network for H_2S Donor and/or AngII Treatment

Finally, the DEMs and corresponding potential hub ADEGs of the two comparison groups were summarized and visualized using Cytoscape. This miRNA-mRNA regulatory network consisted of two main factors, namely AngII-induced hypertensive nephropathy and hydrogen sulfide donor treatment, as well as 21 differentially expressed miRNAs and 23 key ADEGs (Figure 6A). To further elucidate the functions of these miRNAs and highlight the key processes of the transcriptional control of key ADEGs, regulatory networks of common miRNA–mRNA–transcription factors were constructed, respectively. The top five transcription factors in the enrichment score were selected to map the regulatory network of miR-98-5p and miR-669b-5p. The regulatory network of miR-98-5p contained 12 target genes and 5 transcription factors, of which the target gene *Hif1a* was also one of the enriched transcription factors (Figure 6B). For miR-669b-5p, the network contained eight target genes and the top five transcription factors (Figure 6C). *Runx2* and *Zfp219* are common transcription factors of miR-98-5p and miR-669b-5p targeted ADEGs.

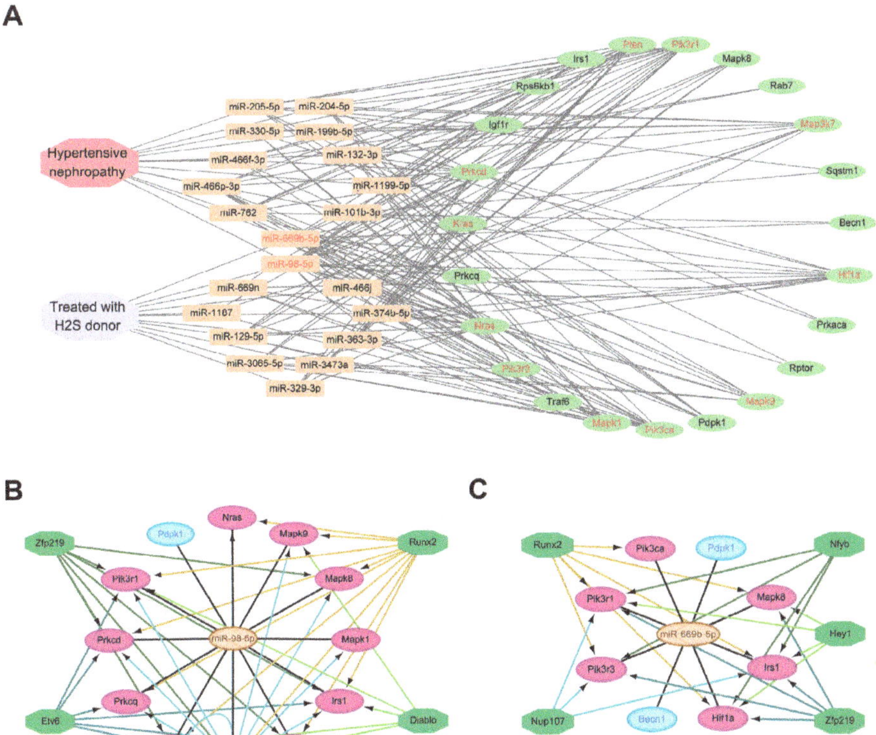

Figure 6. Regulatory networks of the DEMs, target hub ADEGs, and transcription factors. (**A**) The miRNA-mRNA autophagy regulatory network in AngII-induced hypertensive nephropathy and hydrogen sulfide donor drug therapy. Octagons, rectangles, and ovals represent diseases/drugs,

DEMs, and target hub ADEGs, respectively. The red fonts represent miRNAs and mRNAs co-regulated by AngII and H_2S donors. The miRNA-mRNA-TF autophagy regulatory network of miR-98-5p (**B**) and miR-669b-5p (**C**). Green octagons represent transcription factors, blue ovals indicate target genes regulated by miRNAs, and purple ovals show target genes regulated by both miRNAs and transcription factors.

3.5. In AngII-Treated MPC5 Cells, the Hydrogen Sulfide Pathway Is Dysregulated

Furthermore, we used mouse podocyte MPC5 cells to evaluate the therapeutic molecular mechanism of H_2S donors in hypertensive nephropathy. AngII stimulation of MPC5 cells was used to mimic the pathological state of hypertensive nephropathy. AngII significantly reduced the podocyte-specific markers of nephrin and podocin (Figure 7A). In addition, we used NaHS and SPRC, a substrate donor for H_2S synthesis, as endogenous and exogenous H_2S generators [41,42]. NaHS and SPRC alleviated AngII-induced podocyte injury (Figure 7A). Similar to hypertensive renal injury in vivo, AngII significantly increased the transcription levels of intracellular *Tnf-α*, *il-1β*, and *il-6*, while NaHS and SPRC alleviated this inflammatory state (Figure 7B). This indicated that AngII puts cells in a state of damage and inflammation. Moreover, we also examined changes in H_2S levels and synthases in this cellular state. The H_2S content and fluorescent probe intensity in the MPC5 cells were significantly reduced under AngII stimulation, while SPRC partially restored the H_2S level (Figure 7C,D). Furthermore, we monitored the changes in H_2S synthase CBS, CSE, and MST. In the MPC5 cells stimulated by AngII, CSE was significantly downregulated, while the other two enzymes, CBS and MST, did not change (Figure 7E,F). This implicates the dysregulation of H_2S pathway in AngII-treated MPC5 cells.

3.6. Changes in miR-98/669b, Related ADEGs, and Transcription Factors Were Observed in the Autophagy Regulatory Network

To validate the reliability of the regulatory network, the co-regulated DEMs, ADEGs, and TFs were further verified in human hypertensive nephropathy renal samples and AngII-treated MPC5 cells. Co-regulated gene expression data were extracted from datasets GSE37455 and GSE37460 as previously described. The expression of *KRAS*, *MAPK1*, *NRAS*, and *PTEN* was significantly upregulated in the tubulointerstitial region of patients with hypertensive nephropathy compared with healthy living donors (Figure 8A, left panel). Similarly, the expression of *MAPK1*, *NRAS*, and *PTEN* was also significantly upregulated in the glomeruli of patients with hypertensive nephropathy (Figure 8A, right panel). Next, we detected co-regulated miRNAs and mRNAs by AngII and H_2S donors in MPC5 cells using qPCR. In addition, PAG, an inhibitor of the CSE enzyme, was used to block SPRC for verification [37,43]. Similar to the results of the miRNA dataset, the AngII treatment decreased the expression levels of miR-98-5p and miR-669b-5p, but both endogenous and exogenous H_2S donors reversed these changes in MPC5 cells (Figure 8B). To confirm the reliability of AngII's regulation of these miRNAs, losartan was used here to bind to angiotensin receptors to block the effect of AngII. As shown in Figure 8C, losartan almost restored the expression of miR-98-5p and miR-669b-5p to the control level.

Moreover, the RNA expression of miRNA hub target genes and TFs were further detected. In the MPC5 cells, *Mapk1*, *Nras*, *Pten*, *Mapk9*, and *Runx2* were upregulated by AngII and downregulated by the H_2S donors. In addition to the changes in the above genes, *Pik3ca* and *Pik3r3* were downregulated by AngII, which could be reversed by H_2S donor treatment (Figure 8D). For the expression of *Kras*, AngII treatment increased its expression, with no statistical significance. However, both endogenous and exogenous hydrogen sulfide caused it to decrease. In addition, the regulatory role of SPRC on DEMs, ADEGs, and TFs was partially inhibited by PAG (Figure 8B,D).

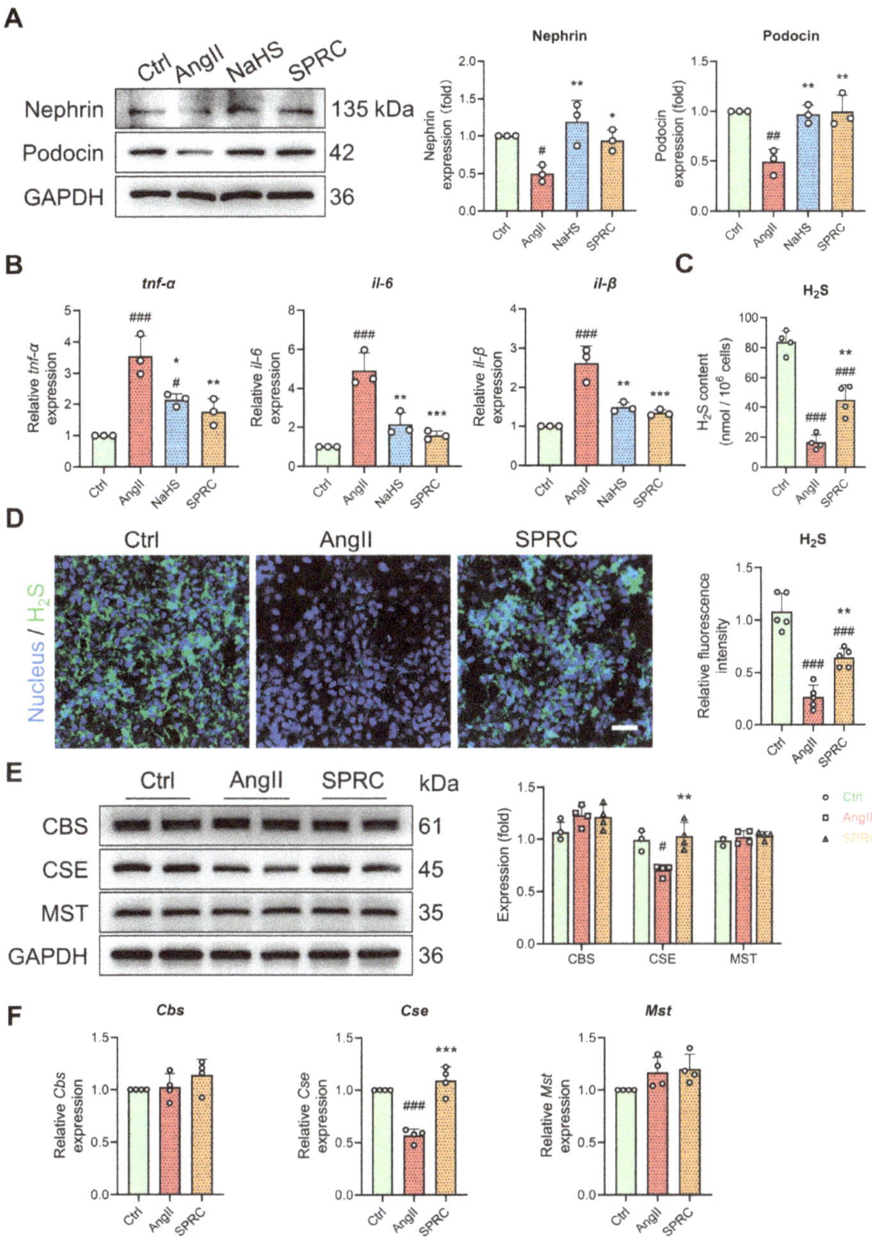

Figure 7. H_2S pathway in AngII-treated MPC5 cells. (**A**) Western blot analysis of nephrin, podocin, and GAPDH in MPC5 cells under different stimuli. $n = 3$. (**B**) Normalized mRNA expression of Tnf-α, il-1β, and il-6. $n = 3$. (**C**) H_2S content using spectrophotometer; $n = 4$. (**D**) H_2S levels using fluorescent probe WSP-1. Bar = 50 μm; $n = 5$. (**E**) Western blot analysis of CBS, CSE, MST, and GAPDH in MPC5 cells under indicated stimuli; $n = 3$. (**F**) Normalized mRNA expression of *Cbs*, *Cse*, and *Mst*; $n = 4$. # $p < 0.05$, ## $p < 0.01$, ### $p < 0.001$ vs. AngII group, * $p < 0.05$, ** $p < 0.01$, *** $p < 0.001$ vs. Ctrl group.

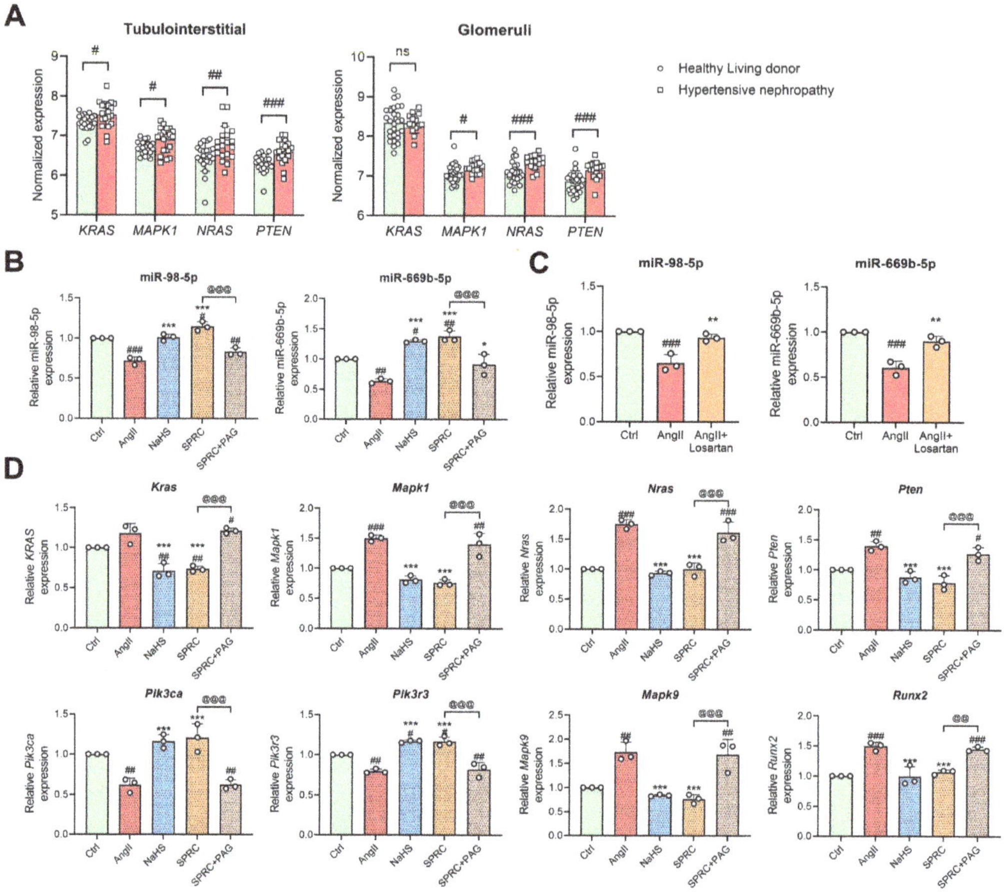

Figure 8. Validation of co-regulated DEMs, ADEGs, and TFs in hypertensive nephropathy clinical samples and AngII-treated MPC5 cells. (**A**) Normalized mRNA expression of *KRAS*, *MAPK1*, *NRAS*, and *PTEN* in the tubulointerstitial region (left) and glomeruli (right) of human renal biopsies. Data were extracted from GSE37455 and GSE37460. # $p < 0.05$, ## $p < 0.01$, ### $p < 0.001$ vs. healthy living donor group using two-sided unpaired *t*-test; $n = 21$ and 20 (**left**) or 27 and 15 (**right**) in the healthy and hypertensive group. (**B**,**C**) RNA expression of miR-98-5p and miR-669b-5p were measured in MPC5 cells by qPCR. (**D**) The mRNA levels of *Kras*, *Mapk1*, *Nras*, *Pten*, *Pik3ca*, *Pik3r3*, *Mapk9*, and *Runx2* in MPC5 cells were calculated using qPCR. For (**B**,**D**), the MPC5 cells were pre-incubated with or without 2mM PAG for 30 min and then pre-treated with NaHS (50 μM) or SPRC (50 μM) for 1 h before exposure to AngII (1 μM) treatment. NaHS, SPRC, and SPRC + PAG groups were all treated with AngII. # $p < 0.05$, ## $p < 0.01$, ### $p < 0.001$ vs. Ctrl group, * $p < 0.05$, ** $p < 0.01$, *** $p < 0.001$ vs. AngII group, and @@ $p < 0.01$, @@@ $p < 0.001$ vs. SPRC group. For (**C**), MPC5 cells were pre-stimulated with or without losartan (300 μM) for 12 h and then co-incubated with or without AngII (1 μM). ### $p < 0.001$ vs. Ctrl group, ** $p < 0.01$ vs. AngII group. One-way ANOVA coupled with Tukey's multiple comparison post hoc test was used. Data are shown as mean ± SD, $n = 3$. ns, not significant.

Furthermore, miRNAs mimics were used to overexpress miR-98-5p and miR-669b-5p to find their genuine targets in the presence of AngII. The miR-98-5p mimic significantly increased the expression of miR-98-5p by about 6-fold, and the miR-669b-5p mimic increased the expression of miR-669b-5p by 5-fold, indicating successful overexpression

(Figure 9A). In the case of co-treatment with AngII, the miR-98-5p mimic significantly reduced AngII-induced elevations in *Kras*, *Mapk1*, *Nras*, *Pten*, *Mapk9*, and *Runx2*, and the miR-669b-5p mimic decreased the expression of *Nras*, *Pik3ca*, *Pik3r3*, and *Runx2* changed by AngII (Figure 9B).

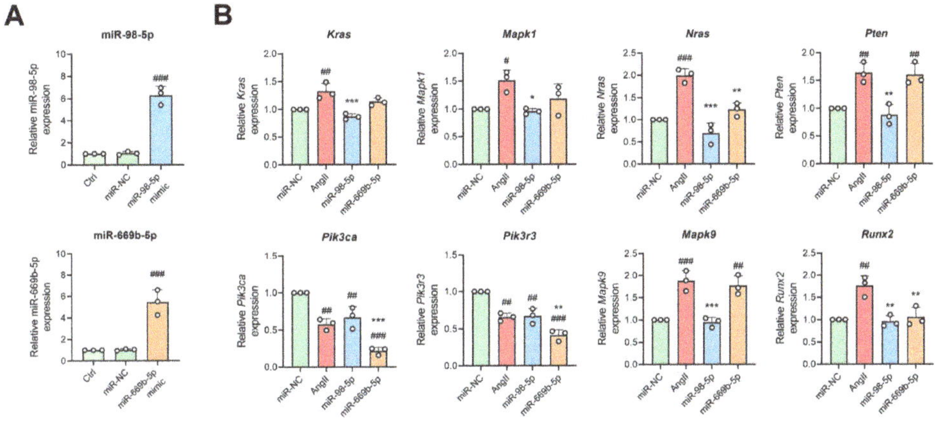

Figure 9. Overexpression of miR-98 and miR-669b. (**A**) RNA expression of miR-98-5p and miR-669b-5p were measured in MPC5 cells by qPCR. (**B**) The mRNA levels of *Kras*, *Mapk1*, *Nras*, *Pten*, *Pik3ca*, *Pik3r3*, *Mapk9*, and *Runx2* in MPC5 were calculated using qPCR. MPC5 cells were transfected with miR-NC, miR-98-5p mimic, and miR-669b-5p mimic. Forty-eight hours after infection, cells were incubated with or without AngII (1 μM) to detect RNA expression. Both miR-98-5p and miR-669b-5p mimic groups were incubated with AngII. # $p < 0.05$, ## $p < 0.01$, ### $p < 0.001$ vs. miR-NC group, * $p < 0.05$, ** $p < 0.01$, *** $p < 0.001$ vs. AngII group. One-way ANOVA coupled with Tukey's multiple-comparison post hoc test was used. Data are shown as mean ± SD, $n = 3$.

3.7. H_2S Donors and miR-98/669b Overexpression Reversed Target Gene Changes, Restored Autophagy Flux, and Reduced Cell Damage

To further investigate the protein-level changes in this regulatory network, we investigated the protein expression of these co-regulated DEMs and TFs in MPC5 cells. As shown in Figure 10A, AngII stimulation significantly increased the expression of autophagy substrate P62 (SQSTM1) in the MPC5 cells, which implies a decrease in autophagic flux [44]. However, both the exogenous and endogenous hydrogen sulfide donors NaHS and SPRC restored the P62 expression to some extent. At the same time, similar to the gene-level changes, AngII significantly increased the levels of NRAS and RUNX2 in the MPC5 cells, and these changes were reversed by NaHS and SPRC. Furthermore, the alterations in KRAS, NRAS, RUNX2, and P62 induced by SPRC were partially offset by PAG (Figure 10A). In addition, we found small changes in PTEN and MAPK1, but most of them were not statistically significant. Subsequently, miRNA mimics were used to overexpress miR-98-5p and miR-669b-5p in the presence or absence of AngII to detect changes in autophagy markers and kidney injury markers. The AngII stimulation significantly increased P62 and decreased LC3B expression, implying a decrease in autophagy flux. However, the overexpression of miR-98-5p and miR-669b-5p significantly restored the expression of P62 and LC3B and improved intracellular autophagy (Figure 10B). In terms of kidney injury indicators, AngII reduced the expression of the podocyte markers nephrin and podocin, but the overexpression of miR-98-5p and miR-669b-5p restored the AngII-induced reduction in these two proteins (Figure 10C). Finally, WB analysis was conducted to check which hub target genes and TFs were altered in response to miR-98-5p and miR-669b-5p overexpression as well as AngII stimulation. As shown in Figure 10D, the miR-98-5p mimic reduced the AngII-induced increases in KRAS, NRAS, and RUNX2. Meanwhile, the miR-669b-5p mimic partially restored the AngII-induced changes in NRAS and RUNX2.

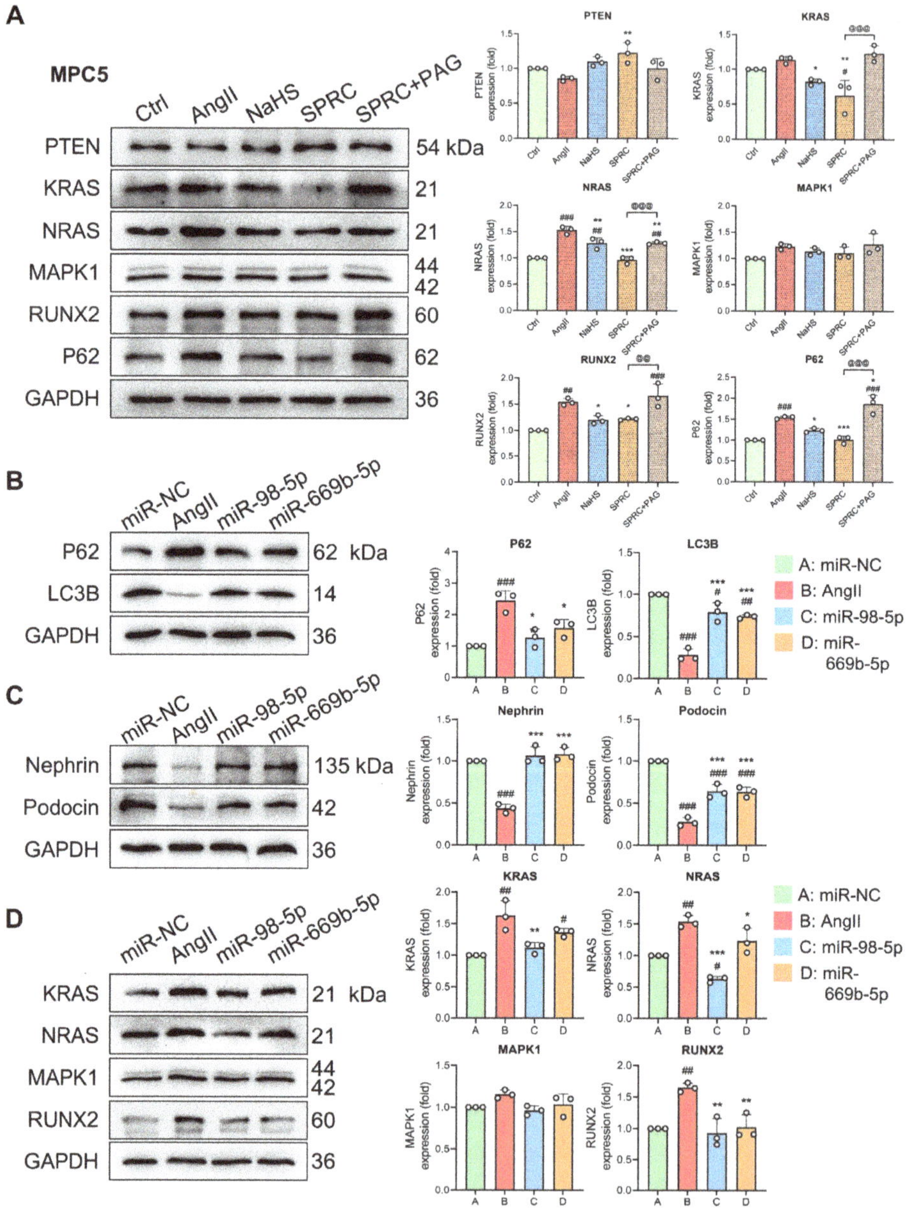

Figure 10. Validation of co-regulated DEMs, ADEGs, and TFs in protein levels. (**A**) Western blot analysis of PTEN, KRAS, NRAS, MAPK1, RUNX2, P62, and GAPDH protein expression levels in MPC5 cells under different stimuli. Cells were pre-incubated with or without PAG and then pre-treated with NaHS or SPRC for 1 h before exposure to AngII treatment. NaHS, SPRC, and SPRC + PAG groups were all treated with AngII. Expression levels were calculated by densitometric analysis and normalized to GAPDH. Protein quantification is shown in bar charts.

# $p < 0.05$, ## $p < 0.01$, ### $p < 0.001$ vs. Ctrl group, * $p < 0.05$, ** $p < 0.01$, *** $p < 0.001$ vs. AngII group, and @@ $p < 0.01$, @@@ $p < 0.001$ vs. SPRC group. For (**B–D**), MPC5 cells were transfected with miR-NC, miR-98-5p mimic, and miR-669b-5p mimic and then incubated with AngII to detect the expression of autophagy markers P62 and LC3B (**B**), renal injury markers nephrin and podocin (**C**), and hub targets such as KRAS, NRAS, and MAPK1 as well as the TF RUNX2 (**D**) by Western blot analysis. Both miR-98-5p and miR-669b-5p mimic groups were incubated with AngII. With GAPDH as a normalized reference, protein quantification is shown in bar charts. Dark green, red, blue, and orange represent miR-NC, AngII, miR-98-5p, and miR-669b-5p mimic groups, respectively. # $p < 0.05$, ## $p < 0.01$, ### $p < 0.001$ vs. miR-NC group, * $p < 0.05$, ** $p < 0.01$, *** $p < 0.001$ vs. AngII group. One-way ANOVA coupled with Tukey's multiple comparison post hoc test was used. Data are shown as mean ± SD, $n = 3$.

Collectively, in the hypertensive nephropathy samples and AngII-induced podocyte models, the renal injury markers were increased, autophagic flux was decreased, and differential miRNAs (miR-98-5p and miR-669b-5p), hub target genes (*KRAS* and *NRAS*), and transcription factor (*RUNX2*) were dysregulated. The endogenous and exogenous H_2S donors restored the expression of miR-98-5p and miR-669b-5p as well as other hub genes in the regulatory network. The overexpression of miR-98-5p and miR-669b-5p increased autophagic flux, reduced markers of kidney injury, and also restored the abnormal expression of KRAS, NRAS, and RUNX2. This may be the mechanism by which H_2S donors alleviate hypertensive nephropathy.

4. Discussion

Hypertensive nephropathy is one of the major causes of chronic kidney disease and end-stage renal disease [45]. Recently, emerging evidence has shown that autophagy plays a crucial role in the maintenance of kidney function and kidney diseases [46,47]. Targeting the autophagy pathway may have therapeutic benefits in the treatment of kidney diseases [48]. In acute kidney injury, autophagy is induced in the proximal tubule as a protective mechanism [47]. The deletion of key autophagy proteins increases P62 levels and oxidative stress, which impairs renal function [49]. In diabetic nephropathy, the dysregulation of autophagy in podocytes, glomerular endothelial cells, and proximal tubules is thought to contribute to disease progression [50]. Dysregulated autophagy has also been reported in many kidney diseases, such as tubulointerstitial fibrosis, focal segmental glomerulosclerosis, and polycystic kidney disease [48,51]. However, the role of autophagy in hypertensive nephropathy or kidney injury caused by hypertension has not yet been elucidated. Here, we have demonstrated that autophagy may be involved in AngII-induced hypertensive nephropathy. We screened out 109 differentially expressed miRNAs and the corresponding 4667 target genes after AngII treatment. Then, 21 of the 233 hub genes, selected from the top 5% CytoHubba algorithm, were related to autophagy. If hub genes are not counted, the 57 of the 4667 target genes were also associated with autophagy. This indicates that autophagy-related genes accounted for a large proportion of the hub target genes of DEMs after the AngII treatment.

Studies have shown that hydrogen sulfide play a therapeutic role by regulating the autophagy pathway [52]. In renal disease, exogenous H_2S treatment can protect the kidney from ROS-induced autophagy and renal injury by inhibiting the ROS-AMPK pathway [53]. However, there are few reports on the relationship between hydrogen sulfide and autophagy in hypertensive nephropathy. Our study has demonstrated that hydrogen sulfide donor treatment may affect the autophagy pathway altered by AngII. We identified 70 DEMs and the corresponding 2828 target genes in the AngII_H_2S vs. AngII group, 44 of which were associated with autophagy, and 13 of the 141 key target genes were associated with autophagy. To our knowledge, this is the first bioinformatic report describing the regulation of autophagy pathways by hydrogen sulfide donors in hypertensive nephropathy.

miRNA dysregulation is an important component of epigenetic regulation, and studies have identified a large number of miRNAs that play a role in hypertensive nephropathy [54], and the role of hydrogen sulfide and microRNA crosstalk has also gradually emerged in kidney diseases [25,55]. In the present study, 12 miRNAs targeting key ADEGs were altered upon AngII treatment, and correspondingly, 11 miRNAs were altered upon co-treatment with AngII and hydrogen sulfide. Among them, miR-98-5p and miR-669b-5p were co-altered miRNAs, and AngII caused their decrease, while the hydrogen sulfide donors significantly increased the expression of both. Studies have shown that miR-98-5p is decreased in the kidney tissue of diabetic mice and in high-glucose-treated human podocytes (HPCs) and HK2 cells, and the overexpression of miR-98-5p inhibits apoptosis, proteinuria, and the renal fibrosis process [56,57]. In cardiovascular diseases, the overexpression of miR-98-5p can also protect cardiomyocytes from apoptosis [58,59]. These all indicate the protective effect of miR-98-5p. For miR-669b-5p, it was only found in mus musculus, and there are few reports on its function. But for its family, miR-669c was protective in a mouse model of ischemic stroke, and long-term miR-669a treatment attenuated chronic dilated cardiomyopathy in dystrophic mice [60,61]. These studies have suggested a possible protective role of the miR-669 family in cardiovascular diseases.

This study focused on changes in miR-98-5p and miR-669b-5p, but the remaining DEMs may also play a role in the progression of hypertensive nephropathy. Among the other AngII-upregulated miRNAs, previous studies have shown that silencing microRNA-132 reduced renal fibrosis by selectively inhibiting myofibroblast proliferation [62]. The miR-132 family also directly targets the pro-autophagy FoxO3 transcription factor [63]. miR-762 is significantly upregulated in septic acute kidney injury [64]. For other miRNAs downregulated by AngII, the most studied is miR-204-5p. miR-204-5p is downregulated in renal biopsy specimens from patients with hypertensive nephrosclerosis, diabetic nephropathy, and in the kidneys of rats fed with a high-salt diet [65,66]. Furthermore, the knockdown or knockout of miR-204-5p results in substantial pathological changes in the kidneys as well as proteinuria [66], and the protective role of miR-204 in chronic kidney disease is related to SHP2 and STAT3 [67]. For the downregulated DEMs in the hydrogen sulfide group, miRNA-363-3p promotes apoptosis in response to heavy-metal-induced kidney injury by downregulating phosphoinositide 3-kinase expression [68]. In H_2S-upregulated DEMs, miR-129-5p attenuates LPS-induced podocyte injury and acute kidney injury, and this kind of protection is related to the regulation of the NF-κB signaling pathway [69]. In short, these altered miRNAs may be the underlying mechanism behind AngII-induced hypertensive nephropathy and the therapeutic effect of hydrogen sulfide.

A total of 21 and 13 ADEGs were screened out, and their potential biological functions were identified by GO and KEGG enrichment analysis. Interestingly, these ADEGs collectively affect protein phosphorylation, phosphatidylinositol 3-kinase complex, protein binding, and protein kinase activity. These aspects are all related to autophagy. Protein kinases are integral to autophagy. Both autophagy initiation and autophagy signaling utilize kinase mechanisms [70]. Among them, kinase-catalyzed phosphorylation is an important part of the most-studied post-translational modification of autophagy [71]. For example, phosphatidylinositol 3-kinase (PI3K) interacts with various regulatory proteins to form multiple complexes that selectively participate in different stages of autophagy. A complex of PI3K and ATG14 is involved in the formation of autophagic vesicles [72]. In addition, the ADEGs that affect these biological functions may be genes such as PTEN, AMPK1, KRAS, and NRAS. In the enrichment study of signaling pathways, autophagy and FoxO signal transduction are commonly enriched signaling pathways. This further illustrates that AngII and H_2S donors affect the autophagy pathway in the kidney. The role of the FoxO transcription factor family in autophagy has been widely reported. For example, FoxO1 and FoxO3 enhance autophagic flux by increasing the expression of autophagy genes, such as Ulk2, Becn1, Lc3b, Atg12, and GabarapL1 [73]. Furthermore, SNAI2 is transcriptionally activated by FoxO3 and interacts with FoxO3 to form a feed-forward regulatory loop to enhance the expression of autophagy genes [74]. In addition to general autophagy, FoxO3 is also involved in the regulation of mitophagy [75]. Among the other AngII-enriched signaling pathways, mTOR signal transduction is closely related to autophagy, and mTORC1 in the signaling pathway is also a promising pharmacological target for regulating autophagy [76]. Future experiments will be necessary to explore the potential biological functions of these ADEGs regulated by AngII and hydrogen sulfide donors.

After the PPI analysis, we validated co-regulated DEMs, ADEGs, and TFs using clinical patient databases as well as several cell experiments. In the kidney cell experiments, AngII stimulation significantly increased the expression of the autophagy substrate P62, implying a decrease in autophagic flux. Previous studies have shown that P62, a substrate of the autophagy–lysosomal degradation pathway, was observed to accumulate in the kidneys of STZ-induced diabetic mice, Wistar obese rat bodies, and kidney biopsies of patients with type 2 diabetes, suggesting that autophagy is impaired [77]. Targeting the autophagy pathway to activate and restore autophagic activity may be renoprotective. For example, the endogenous calpain inhibitor calpastatin can maintain autophagy to alleviate AngII-mediated podocyte injury [9]. In addition, AngII can also induce the activation of TLR4 to inhibit autophagy and induce apoptosis and kidney injury [78]. At the same time, changes in KRAS and NRAS were also observed. On the one hand, the inhibition of KRAS increases autophagic flux, and the inhibition of KRAS/RAF/MEK/ERK signaling triggers autophagy [79,80]. On the other hand, for NRAS, there are not many corresponding reports. In the MPC5 cells, we found that both endogenous and exogenous hydrogen sulfide reversed AngII-induced KRAS and NRAS changes to some extent, which may partially restore autophagy in cells. Changes in PTEN and MAPK1 were found in the clinical samples and kidney cells. Published findings suggest that PTEN activates autophagy through the AKT/mTOR pathway [81]. Furthermore, autophagic flux and ATG7 (autophagy-related 7) levels were increased by the activation of MAPK1/3 [82]. We found that PTEN and MAPK1 were increased at the gene level, which may be related to the positive feedback regulation of autophagy in the early stage of disease. In cervical cancer cells, the overexpression of miR-98-5p significantly increased the expression of the PTEN protein, and silencing miR-98-5p had the opposite result [83]. In the future, more experiments are needed to explore the effect of timing of AngII regulation on PTEN and autophagy.

The synergistic effect of transcription factors and miRNAs has not yet been fully elucidated, and this study is also the first attempt to reveal the interactions between DEMs, hub target genes, and transcription factors in the treatment of AngII-induced hypertensive kidney injury with hydrogen sulfide donors. We identified and validated one transcription factor, Runx2, that co-regulates miR-98-5p and miR-669b-5p target hub genes. Runx2 is a well-known transcription factor for skeletal development, but its role in non-bone tissues is gradually being reported. Studies have shown that AngII can significantly increase the level of Runx2 in aortic tissue and human aortic smooth muscle cells, which is similar to our validation results [84,85]. In addition, the activation of Runx2 promotes aortic valve fibrosis as well as aortic fibrosis and stiffness in patients with type 2 diabetes [86,87]. In chronic kidney disease, Runx2 is deacetylated by SIRT6 to inhibit osteogenic trans differentiation of vascular smooth muscle cells [88]. Runx2 is also regulated by miRNAs. The downregulation of miR-204 promoted hyperproliferation and calcified lesions of pulmonary artery smooth muscle cells by increasing the expression of the transcription factor Runx2 [89]. Increased miR-204-5p also suppressed Runx2 expression, thereby inhibiting aortic valve calcification [90]. Interestingly, studies have shown that Runx2 also promoted autophagy by enhancing the trafficking of LC3B vesicles [91]. In this study, the transcription factor Runx2 was upregulated by AngII, and this upregulation was reversed by endogenous and exogenous hydrogen sulfide donors. These results suggest that the transcription factor Runx2 may be a good therapeutic target for hydrogen sulfide donors to treat the pathological process of renal fibrosis in hypertensive nephropathy. The detailed functions and underlying mechanistic pathways of Runx2 require further investigation. More in vitro and in vivo studies and validations are needed in the future to elucidate the role of these new markers, including DEMs, hub ADEGs, and TFs in hypertensive nephropathy and hydrogen sulfide therapy.

5. Conclusions

By using bioinformatics analysis, 109 DEMs in mouse kidney tissue after treatment with AngII alone and 70 DEMs after treatment with a combined treatment of AngII and H_2S donors were identified. Through the regulatory network and validation study, the H_2S donor treatment increased autophagic flux, reduced renal cell injury, and restored the two identified and co-regulated miRNAs, miR-98-5p and miR-669b-5p, attenuated the dysregulation of ADEGs (*KRAS, NRAS*) and a key transcription factor (*RUNX2*). These findings help to define the pathophysiological mechanism of AngII-induced hypertensive nephropathy and shed new light on the therapeutic effects of hydrogen sulfide donors.

Supplementary Materials: The following supporting information can be downloaded at: https://www.mdpi.com/article/10.3390/antiox13080958/s1. Figure S1: Profiles of the non-coding RNA expression profile dataset GSE92857, Table S1: Autophagy-related gene set in mouse, Table S2: Primer sequences, Table S3: Differentially expressed miRNAs between AngII and Ctrl group, Table S4: Differentially expressed miRNAs between AngII_H_2S and AngII group, Table S5: DEMs and their target ADEGs in AngII vs Ctrl and AngII_H_2S vs AngII comparison.

Author Contributions: Conceptualization, Q.Y., Y.M. and Y.-Z.Z.; data curation, Q.Y., M.R., Y.M. and Y.-Z.Z.; formal analysis, Q.Y. and M.R.; funding acquisition, Y.-Z.Z.; investigation, Q.Y. and D.F.; methodology, Q.Y. and M.R.; project administration, Q.Y. and Y.-Z.Z.; resources, Q.Y. and Y.M.; software, Q.Y. and M.R.; supervision, Y.M. and Y.-Z.Z.; validation, Q.Y., M.R. and D.F.; visualization, Q.Y.; writing—original draft, Q.Y. and M.R.; writing—review and editing, Q.Y., Y.M. and Y.-Z.Z. All authors have read and agreed to the published version of the manuscript.

Funding: This work was funded by Macau Science and Technology Development fund (FDCT (0012/2021/AMJ, 003/2022/ALC, 0092/2022/A2, 0144/2022/A3)), Shenzhen-Hong Kong-Macao Science and Technology Fund (Category C: SGDX20220530111203020), and Shanghai Committee of Science and Technology (No. 23ZR1413200).

Institutional Review Board Statement: Not applicable.

Informed Consent Statement: Not applicable.

Data Availability Statement: All data generated or analyzed during this study are included in this published article, it's supplementary information files, and publicly available repositories. The datasets GSE92857, GSE37455, and GSE37460 were downloaded from the GEO database.

Conflicts of Interest: The authors declare no conflicts of interest.

References

1. Burnier, M.; Damianaki, A. Hypertension as Cardiovascular Risk Factor in Chronic Kidney Disease. *Circ. Res.* **2023**, *132*, 1050–1063. [CrossRef] [PubMed]
2. Tian, Z.; Liang, M. Renal metabolism and hypertension. *Nat. Commun.* **2021**, *12*, 963. [CrossRef] [PubMed]
3. Ku, E.; Lee, B.J.; Wei, J.; Weir, M.R. Hypertension in CKD: Core Curriculum 2019. *Am. J. Kidney Dis.* **2019**, *74*, 120–131. [CrossRef] [PubMed]
4. Bidani, A.K.; Griffin, K.A. Pathophysiology of hypertensive renal damage: Implications for therapy. *Hypertension* **2004**, *44*, 595–601. [CrossRef] [PubMed]
5. Rucker, A.J.; Rudemiller, N.P.; Crowley, S.D. Salt, Hypertension, and Immunity. *Annu. Rev. Physiol.* **2018**, *80*, 283–307. [CrossRef] [PubMed]
6. Zhuo, J.L.; Ferrao, F.M.; Zheng, Y.; Li, X.C. New frontiers in the intrarenal Renin-Angiotensin system: A critical review of classical and new paradigms. *Front. Endocrinol.* **2013**, *4*, 166. [CrossRef] [PubMed]
7. Laffer, C.L.; Elijovich, F.; Sahinoz, M.; Pitzer, A.; Kirabo, A. New Insights into the Renin-Angiotensin System in Chronic Kidney Disease. *Circ. Res.* **2020**, *127*, 607–609. [CrossRef] [PubMed]
8. Liu, Z.; Huang, X.R.; Lan, H.Y. Smad3 mediates ANG II-induced hypertensive kidney disease in mice. *Am. J. Physiol. Ren. Physiol.* **2012**, *302*, F986–F997. [CrossRef] [PubMed]

9. Bensaada, I.; Robin, B.; Perez, J.; Salemkour, Y.; Chipont, A.; Camus, M.; Lemoine, M.; Guyonnet, L.; Lazareth, H.; Letavernier, E.; et al. Calpastatin prevents Angiotensin II-mediated podocyte injury through maintenance of autophagy. *Kidney Int.* **2021**, *100*, 90–106. [CrossRef]
10. Levine, B.; Kroemer, G. Biological Functions of Autophagy Genes: A Disease Perspective. *Cell* **2019**, *176*, 11–42. [CrossRef]
11. Ding, Y.; Choi, M.E. Autophagy in diabetic nephropathy. *J. Endocrinol.* **2015**, *224*, R15–R30. [CrossRef]
12. Wang, B.; Huang, C.; Chen, L.; Xu, D.; Zheng, G.; Zhou, Y.; Wang, X.; Zhang, X. The Emerging Roles of the Gaseous Signaling Molecules NO, H_2S, and CO in the Regulation of Stem Cells. *ACS Biomater. Sci. Eng.* **2020**, *6*, 798–812. [CrossRef]
13. Wang, D.; Yang, H.; Zhang, Y.; Hu, R.; Hu, D.; Wang, Q.; Liu, Y.; Liu, M.; Meng, Z.; Zhou, W.; et al. Inhibition of cystathionine β-synthase promotes apoptosis and reduces cell proliferation in chronic myeloid leukemia. *Signal Transduct. Target. Ther.* **2021**, *6*, 52. [CrossRef]
14. Cao, X.; Ding, L.; Xie, Z.Z.; Yang, Y.; Whiteman, M.; Moore, P.K.; Bian, J.S. A Review of Hydrogen Sulfide Synthesis, Metabolism, and Measurement: Is Modulation of Hydrogen Sulfide a Novel Therapeutic for Cancer? *Antioxid. Redox Signal.* **2019**, *31*, 1–38. [CrossRef]
15. Aminzadeh, M.A.; Vaziri, N.D. Downregulation of the renal and hepatic hydrogen sulfide (H_2S)-producing enzymes and capacity in chronic kidney disease. *Nephrol. Dial. Transplant.* **2012**, *27*, 498–504. [CrossRef]
16. Han, S.J.; Noh, M.R.; Jung, J.M.; Ishii, I.; Yoo, J.; Kim, J.I.; Park, K.M. Hydrogen sulfide-producing cystathionine γ-lyase is critical in the progression of kidney fibrosis. *Free Radic. Biol. Med.* **2017**, *112*, 423–432. [CrossRef]
17. Yuan, X.; Zhang, J.; Xie, F.; Tan, W.; Wang, S.; Huang, L.; Tao, L.; Xing, Q.; Yuan, Q. Loss of the Protein Cystathionine β-Synthase during Kidney Injury Promotes Renal Tubulointerstitial Fibrosis. *Kidney Blood Press. Res.* **2017**, *42*, 428–443. [CrossRef]
18. Feng, J.; Lu, X.; Li, H.; Wang, S. The roles of hydrogen sulfide in renal physiology and disease states. *Ren. Fail.* **2022**, *44*, 1289–1308. [CrossRef]
19. Ngowi, E.E.; Sarfraz, M.; Afzal, A.; Khan, N.H.; Khattak, S.; Zhang, X.; Li, T.; Duan, S.F.; Ji, X.Y.; Wu, D.D. Roles of Hydrogen Sulfide Donors in Common Kidney Diseases. *Front. Pharmacol.* **2020**, *11*, 564281. [CrossRef] [PubMed]
20. Laggerbauer, B.; Engelhardt, S. MicroRNAs as therapeutic targets in cardiovascular disease. *J. Clin. Investig.* **2022**, *132*, e159179. [CrossRef] [PubMed]
21. Bartel, D.P. MicroRNAs: Genomics, biogenesis, mechanism, and function. *Cell* **2004**, *116*, 281–297. [CrossRef] [PubMed]
22. Mahtal, N.; Lenoir, O.; Tinel, C.; Anglicheau, D.; Tharaux, P.L. MicroRNAs in kidney injury and disease. *Nat. Rev. Nephrol.* **2022**, *18*, 643–662. [CrossRef] [PubMed]
23. Wang, G.; Kwan, B.C.; Lai, F.M.; Choi, P.C.; Chow, K.M.; Li, P.K.; Szeto, C.C. Intrarenal expression of miRNAs in patients with hypertensive nephrosclerosis. *Am. J. Hypertens.* **2010**, *23*, 78–84. [CrossRef] [PubMed]
24. Macconi, D.; Tomasoni, S.; Romagnani, P.; Trionfini, P.; Sangalli, F.; Mazzinghi, B.; Rizzo, P.; Lazzeri, E.; Abbate, M.; Remuzzi, G.; et al. MicroRNA-324-3p promotes renal fibrosis and is a target of ACE inhibition. *J. Am. Soc. Nephrol.* **2012**, *23*, 1496–1505. [CrossRef] [PubMed]
25. Hackfort, B.T.; Mishra, P.K. Emerging role of hydrogen sulfide-microRNA crosstalk in cardiovascular diseases. *Am. J. Physiol. Heart Circ. Physiol.* **2016**, *310*, H802–H812. [CrossRef] [PubMed]
26. Weber, G.J.; Pushpakumar, S.B.; Sen, U. Hydrogen sulfide alleviates hypertensive kidney dysfunction through an epigenetic mechanism. *Am. J. Physiol. Heart Circ. Physiol.* **2017**, *312*, H874–H885. [CrossRef] [PubMed]
27. Davis, S.; Meltzer, P.S. GEOquery: A bridge between the Gene Expression Omnibus (GEO) and BioConductor. *Bioinformatics* **2007**, *23*, 1846–1847. [CrossRef] [PubMed]
28. Wickham, H. Data analysis. In *ggplot2*; Springer: Berlin, Germany, 2016; pp. 189–201.
29. Ru, Y.; Kechris, K.J.; Tabakoff, B.; Hoffman, P.; Radcliffe, R.A.; Bowler, R.; Mahaffey, S.; Rossi, S.; Calin, G.A.; Bemis, L.; et al. The multiMiR R package and database: Integration of microRNA-target interactions along with their disease and drug associations. *Nucleic Acids Res.* **2014**, *42*, e133. [CrossRef] [PubMed]
30. Shannon, P.; Markiel, A.; Ozier, O.; Baliga, N.S.; Wang, J.T.; Ramage, D.; Amin, N.; Schwikowski, B.; Ideker, T. Cytoscape: A software environment for integrated models of biomolecular interaction networks. *Genome Res.* **2003**, *13*, 2498–2504. [CrossRef]
31. Chin, C.H.; Chen, S.H.; Wu, H.H.; Ho, C.W.; Ko, M.T.; Lin, C.Y. *cytoHubba*: Identifying hub objects and sub-networks from complex interactome. *BMC Syst. Biol.* **2014**, *8*, S11. [CrossRef]
32. Szklarczyk, D.; Franceschini, A.; Wyder, S.; Forslund, K.; Heller, D.; Huerta-Cepas, J.; Simonovic, M.; Roth, A.; Santos, A.; Tsafou, K.P.; et al. STRING v10: Protein-protein interaction networks, integrated over the tree of life. *Nucleic Acids Res.* **2015**, *43*, D447–D452. [CrossRef]
33. Bader, G.D.; Hogue, C.W. An automated method for finding molecular complexes in large protein interaction networks. *BMC Bioinform.* **2003**, *4*, 2. [CrossRef]
34. Zhao, Q.; Liu, H.; Yao, C.; Shuai, J.; Sun, X. Effect of Dynamic Interaction between microRNA and Transcription Factor on Gene Expression. *BioMed. Res. Int.* **2016**, *2016*, 2676282. [CrossRef] [PubMed]
35. Martinez, N.J.; Walhout, A.J. The interplay between transcription factors and microRNAs in genome-scale regulatory networks. *Bioessays* **2009**, *31*, 435–445. [CrossRef]
36. Janky, R.; Verfaillie, A.; Imrichová, H.; Van de Sande, B.; Standaert, L.; Christiaens, V.; Hulselmans, G.; Herten, K.; Naval Sanchez, M.; Potier, D.; et al. iRegulon: From a gene list to a gene regulatory network using large motif and track collections. *PLoS Comput. Biol.* **2014**, *10*, e1003731. [CrossRef] [PubMed]

37. Wu, W.J.; Jia, W.W.; Liu, X.H.; Pan, L.L.; Zhang, Q.Y.; Yang, D.; Shen, X.Y.; Liu, L.; Zhu, Y.Z. S-propargyl-cysteine attenuates inflammatory response in rheumatoid arthritis by modulating the Nrf2-ARE signaling pathway. *Redox Biol.* **2016**, *10*, 157–167. [CrossRef] [PubMed]
38. Wang, Q.; Liu, H.R.; Mu, Q.; Rose, P.; Zhu, Y.Z. S-propargyl-cysteine protects both adult rat hearts and neonatal cardiomyocytes from ischemia/hypoxia injury: The contribution of the hydrogen sulfide-mediated pathway. *J. Cardiovasc. Pharmacol.* **2009**, *54*, 139–146. [CrossRef]
39. Mundel, P.; Reiser, J.; Zúñiga Mejía Borja, A.; Pavenstädt, H.; Davidson, G.R.; Kriz, W.; Zeller, R. Rearrangements of the cytoskeleton and cell contacts induce process formation during differentiation of conditionally immortalized mouse podocyte cell lines. *Exp. Cell Res.* **1997**, *236*, 248–258. [CrossRef]
40. Ye, Q.; Zhang, J.; Zhang, C.; Yi, B.; Kazama, K.; Liu, W.; Sun, X.; Liu, Y.; Sun, J. Endothelial PRMT5 plays a crucial role in angiogenesis after acute ischemic injury. *JCI Insight* **2022**, *7*, e152481. [CrossRef]
41. Johansen, D.; Ytrehus, K.; Baxter, G.F. Exogenous hydrogen sulfide (H_2S) protects against regional myocardial ischemia-reperfusion injury—Evidence for a role of K ATP channels. *Basic Res. Cardiol.* **2006**, *101*, 53–60. [CrossRef]
42. Rose, P.; Whiteman, M.; Moore, P.K.; Zhu, Y.Z. Bioactive S-alk(en)yl cysteine sulfoxide metabolites in the genus Allium: The chemistry of potential therapeutic agents. *Nat. Prod. Rep.* **2005**, *22*, 351–368. [CrossRef]
43. Tsikas, D.; Cooper, A.J. Letter by Tsikas and Cooper regarding article, "dysregulation of hydrogen sulfide (H_2S) producing enzyme cystathionine γ-lyase (CSE) contributes to maternal hypertension and placental abnormalities in preeclampsia". *Circulation* **2014**, *129*, e516. [CrossRef]
44. Vargas, J.N.S.; Hamasaki, M.; Kawabata, T.; Youle, R.J.; Yoshimori, T. The mechanisms and roles of selective autophagy in mammals. *Nat. Rev. Mol. Cell Biol.* **2022**, *24*, 167–185. [CrossRef]
45. Wang, L.; Xu, X.; Zhang, M.; Hu, C.; Zhang, X.; Li, C.; Nie, S.; Huang, Z.; Zhao, Z.; Hou, F.F.; et al. Prevalence of Chronic Kidney Disease in China: Results from the Sixth China Chronic Disease and Risk Factor Surveillance. *JAMA Intern. Med.* **2023**, *183*, 298–310. [CrossRef]
46. Livingston, M.J.; Shu, S.; Fan, Y.; Li, Z.; Jiao, Q.; Yin, X.M.; Venkatachalam, M.A.; Dong, Z. Tubular cells produce FGF2 via autophagy after acute kidney injury leading to fibroblast activation and renal fibrosis. *Autophagy* **2023**, *19*, 256–277. [CrossRef]
47. Tang, C.; Livingston, M.J.; Liu, Z.; Dong, Z. Autophagy in kidney homeostasis and disease. *Nat. Rev. Nephrol.* **2020**, *16*, 489–508. [CrossRef]
48. Choi, M.E. Autophagy in Kidney Disease. *Annu. Rev. Physiol.* **2020**, *82*, 297–322. [CrossRef]
49. Kaushal, G.P.; Shah, S.V. Autophagy in acute kidney injury. *Kidney Int.* **2016**, *89*, 779–791. [CrossRef]
50. Yang, D.; Livingston, M.J.; Liu, Z.; Dong, G.; Zhang, M.; Chen, J.K.; Dong, Z. Autophagy in diabetic kidney disease: Regulation, pathological role and therapeutic potential. *Cell. Mol. Life Sci.* **2018**, *75*, 669–688. [CrossRef]
51. Nowak, K.L.; Edelstein, C.L. Apoptosis and autophagy in polycystic kidney disease (PKD). *Cell. Signal.* **2020**, *68*, 109518. [CrossRef]
52. Aroca, A.; Gotor, C. Hydrogen Sulfide: A Key Role in Autophagy Regulation from Plants to Mammalians. *Antioxidants* **2022**, *11*, 327. [CrossRef]
53. Chen, Q.; Yu, S.; Zhang, K.; Zhang, Z.; Li, C.; Gao, B.; Zhang, W.; Wang, Y. Exogenous H_2S Inhibits Autophagy in Unilateral Ureteral Obstruction Mouse Renal Tubule Cells by Regulating the ROS-AMPK Signaling Pathway. *Cell. Physiol. Biochem.* **2018**, *49*, 2200–2213. [CrossRef]
54. Peters, L.J.F.; Floege, J.; Biessen, E.A.L.; Jankowski, J.; van der Vorst, E.P.C. MicroRNAs in Chronic Kidney Disease: Four Candidates for Clinical Application. *Int. J. Mol. Sci.* **2020**, *21*, 6547. [CrossRef]
55. Hsu, C.N.; Tain, Y.L. Hydrogen Sulfide in Hypertension and Kidney Disease of Developmental Origins. *Int. J. Mol. Sci.* **2018**, *19*, 1438. [CrossRef]
56. Zhu, Y.; Xu, J.; Liang, W.; Li, J.; Feng, L.; Zheng, P.; Ji, T.; Bai, S. miR-98-5p Alleviated Epithelial-to-Mesenchymal Transition and Renal Fibrosis via Targeting Hmga2 in Diabetic Nephropathy. *Int. J. Endocrinol.* **2019**, *2019*, 4946181. [CrossRef]
57. Xiao, M.; Bai, S.; Chen, J.; Li, Y.; Zhang, S.; Hu, Z. CDKN2B-AS1 participates in high glucose-induced apoptosis and fibrosis via NOTCH2 through functioning as a miR-98-5p decoy in human podocytes and renal tubular cells. *Diabetol. Metab. Syndr.* **2021**, *13*, 107. [CrossRef]
58. Sun, C.; Liu, H.; Guo, J.; Yu, Y.; Yang, D.; He, F.; Du, Z. MicroRNA-98 negatively regulates myocardial infarction-induced apoptosis by down-regulating Fas and caspase-3. *Sci. Rep.* **2017**, *7*, 7460. [CrossRef]
59. Neiburga, K.D.; Vilne, B.; Bauer, S.; Bongiovanni, D.; Ziegler, T.; Lachmann, M.; Wengert, S.; Hawe, J.S.; Güldener, U.; Westerlund, A.M.; et al. Vascular Tissue Specific miRNA Profiles Reveal Novel Correlations with Risk Factors in Coronary Artery Disease. *Biomolecules* **2021**, *11*, 1683. [CrossRef]
60. Kolosowska, N.; Gotkiewicz, M.; Dhungana, H.; Giudice, L.; Giugno, R.; Box, D.; Huuskonen, M.T.; Korhonen, P.; Scoyni, F.; Kanninen, K.M.; et al. Intracerebral overexpression of miR-669c is protective in mouse ischemic stroke model by targeting MyD88 and inducing alternative microglial/macrophage activation. *J. Neuroinflamm.* **2020**, *17*, 194. [CrossRef] [PubMed]
61. Quattrocelli, M.; Crippa, S.; Montecchiani, C.; Camps, J.; Cornaglia, A.I.; Boldrin, L.; Morgan, J.; Calligaro, A.; Casasco, A.; Orlacchio, A.; et al. Long-term miR-669a therapy alleviates chronic dilated cardiomyopathy in dystrophic mice. *J. Am. Heart Assoc.* **2013**, *2*, e000284. [CrossRef] [PubMed]

62. Bijkerk, R.; de Bruin, R.G.; van Solingen, C.; van Gils, J.M.; Duijs, J.M.; van der Veer, E.P.; Rabelink, T.J.; Humphreys, B.D.; van Zonneveld, A.J. Silencing of microRNA-132 reduces renal fibrosis by selectively inhibiting myofibroblast proliferation. *Kidney Int.* **2016**, *89*, 1268–1280. [CrossRef]
63. Ucar, A.; Gupta, S.K.; Fiedler, J.; Erikci, E.; Kardasinski, M.; Batkai, S.; Dangwal, S.; Kumarswamy, R.; Bang, C.; Holzmann, A.; et al. The miRNA-212/132 family regulates both cardiac hypertrophy and cardiomyocyte autophagy. *Nat. Commun.* **2012**, *3*, 1078. [CrossRef]
64. Tod, P.; Róka, B.; Kaucsár, T.; Szatmári, K.; Vizovišek, M.; Vidmar, R.; Fonovič, M.; Szénási, G.; Hamar, P. Time-Dependent miRNA Profile during Septic Acute Kidney Injury in Mice. *Int. J. Mol. Sci.* **2020**, *21*, 5316. [CrossRef]
65. Liu, Y.; Usa, K.; Wang, F.; Liu, P.; Geurts, A.M.; Li, J.; Williams, A.M.; Regner, K.R.; Kong, Y.; Liu, H.; et al. MicroRNA-214-3p in the Kidney Contributes to the Development of Hypertension. *J. Am. Soc. Nephrol.* **2018**, *29*, 2518–2528. [CrossRef]
66. Cheng, Y.; Wang, D.; Wang, F.; Liu, J.; Huang, B.; Baker, M.A.; Yin, J.; Wu, R.; Liu, X.; Regner, K.R.; et al. Endogenous miR-204 Protects the Kidney against Chronic Injury in Hypertension and Diabetes. *J. Am. Soc. Nephrol.* **2020**, *31*, 1539–1554. [CrossRef]
67. Liu, J.; Liu, Y.; Wang, F.; Liang, M. miR-204: Molecular Regulation and Role in Cardiovascular and Renal Diseases. *Hypertension* **2021**, *78*, 270–281. [CrossRef]
68. Chen, J.; Lai, W.; Deng, Y.; Liu, M.; Dong, M.; Liu, Z.; Wang, T.; Li, X.; Zhao, Z.; Yin, X.; et al. MicroRNA-363-3p promotes apoptosis in response to cadmium-induced renal injury by down-regulating phosphoinositide 3-kinase expression. *Toxicol. Lett.* **2021**, *345*, 12–23. [CrossRef]
69. Huang, X.; Hou, X.; Chuan, L.; Wei, S.; Wang, J.; Yang, X.; Ru, J. miR-129-5p alleviates LPS-induced acute kidney injury via targeting HMGB1/TLRs/NF-kappaB pathway. *Int. Immunopharmacol.* **2020**, *89*, 107016. [CrossRef]
70. Xiang, H.; Zhang, J.; Lin, C.; Zhang, L.; Liu, B.; Ouyang, L. Targeting autophagy-related protein kinases for potential therapeutic purpose. *Acta Pharm. Sin. B* **2020**, *10*, 569–581. [CrossRef] [PubMed]
71. Wani, W.Y.; Boyer-Guittaut, M.; Dodson, M.; Chatham, J.; Darley-Usmar, V.; Zhang, J. Regulation of autophagy by protein post-translational modification. *Lab. Investig.* **2015**, *95*, 14–25. [CrossRef] [PubMed]
72. Liu, F.; Hu, W.; Li, F.; Marshall, R.S.; Zarza, X.; Munnik, T.; Vierstra, R.D. AUTOPHAGY-RELATED14 and Its Associated Phosphatidylinositol 3-Kinase Complex Promote Autophagy in Arabidopsis. *Plant Cell* **2020**, *32*, 3939–3960. [CrossRef]
73. Du, S.; Zheng, H. Role of FoxO transcription factors in aging and age-related metabolic and neurodegenerative diseases. *Cell Biosci.* **2021**, *11*, 188. [CrossRef]
74. Guo, X.; Li, Z.; Zhu, X.; Zhan, M.; Wu, C.; Ding, X.; Peng, K.; Li, W.; Ma, X.; Lv, Z.; et al. A coherent FOXO3-SNAI2 feed-forward loop in autophagy. *Proc. Natl. Acad. Sci. USA* **2022**, *119*, e2118285119. [CrossRef]
75. Yao, J.; Wang, J.; Xu, Y.; Guo, Q.; Sun, Y.; Liu, J.; Li, S.; Guo, Y.; Wei, L. CDK9 inhibition blocks the initiation of PINK1-PRKN-mediated mitophagy by regulating the SIRT1-FOXO3-BNIP3 axis and enhances the therapeutic effects involving mitochondrial dysfunction in hepatocellular carcinoma. *Autophagy* **2022**, *18*, 1879–1897. [CrossRef]
76. Dossou, A.S.; Basu, A. The Emerging Roles of mTORC1 in Macromanaging Autophagy. *Cancers* **2019**, *11*, 1422. [CrossRef]
77. Gonzalez, C.D.; Carro Negueruela, M.P.; Nicora Santamarina, C.; Resnik, R.; Vaccaro, M.I. Autophagy Dysregulation in Diabetic Kidney Disease: From Pathophysiology to Pharmacological Interventions. *Cells* **2021**, *10*, 2497. [CrossRef]
78. Majumder, S.; Pushpakumar, S.; Juin, S.K.; Jala, V.R.; Sen, U. Toll-like receptor 4 mutation protects the kidney from Ang-II-induced hypertensive injury. *Pharmacol. Res.* **2022**, *175*, 106030. [CrossRef]
79. Bryant, K.L.; Stalnecker, C.A.; Zeitouni, D.; Klomp, J.E.; Peng, S.; Tikunov, A.P.; Gunda, V.; Pierobon, M.; Waters, A.M.; George, S.D.; et al. Combination of ERK and autophagy inhibition as a treatment approach for pancreatic cancer. *Nat. Med.* **2019**, *25*, 628–640. [CrossRef]
80. Kinsey, C.G.; Camolotto, S.A.; Boespflug, A.M.; Guillen, K.P.; Foth, M.; Truong, A.; Schuman, S.S.; Shea, J.E.; Seipp, M.T.; Yap, J.T.; et al. Protective autophagy elicited by RAF→MEK→ERK inhibition suggests a treatment strategy for RAS-driven cancers. *Nat. Med.* **2019**, *25*, 620–627. [CrossRef] [PubMed]
81. Tian, D.; Xiang, Y.; Tang, Y.; Ge, Z.; Li, Q.; Zhang, Y. Circ-ADAM9 targeting PTEN and ATG7 promotes autophagy and apoptosis of diabetic endothelial progenitor cells by sponging mir-20a-5p. *Cell Death Dis.* **2020**, *11*, 526. [CrossRef] [PubMed]
82. Xiao, Y.; Liu, H.; Yu, J.; Zhao, Z.; Xiao, F.; Xia, T.; Wang, C.; Li, K.; Deng, J.; Guo, Y.; et al. MAPK1/3 regulate hepatic lipid metabolism via ATG7-dependent autophagy. *Autophagy* **2016**, *12*, 592–593. [CrossRef] [PubMed]
83. Xiao, R.; Wang, H.; Yang, B. MicroRNA-98-5p modulates cervical cancer progression via controlling PI3K/AKT pathway. *Bioengineered* **2021**, *12*, 10596–10607. [CrossRef] [PubMed]
84. Li, Z.; Zhao, Z.; Cai, Z.; Sun, Y.; Li, L.; Yao, F.; Yang, L.; Zhou, Y.; Zhu, H.; Fu, Y.; et al. Runx2 (Runt-Related Transcription Factor 2)-Mediated Microcalcification Is a Novel Pathological Characteristic and Potential Mediator of Abdominal Aortic Aneurysm. *Arterioscler. Thromb. Vasc. Biol.* **2020**, *40*, 1352–1369. [CrossRef] [PubMed]
85. Tsai, H.Y.; Wang, J.C.; Hsu, Y.J.; Chiu, Y.L.; Lin, C.Y.; Lu, C.Y.; Tsai, S.H. miR-424/322 protects against abdominal aortic aneurysm formation by modulating the Smad2/3/runt-related transcription factor 2 axis. *Mol. Ther. Nucleic Acids* **2022**, *27*, 656–669. [CrossRef] [PubMed]
86. Chen, J.; Lin, Y.; Sun, Z. Deficiency in the anti-aging gene Klotho promotes aortic valve fibrosis through AMPKα-mediated activation of RUNX2. *Aging Cell* **2016**, *15*, 853–860. [CrossRef] [PubMed]

87. Raaz, U.; Schellinger, I.N.; Chernogubova, E.; Warnecke, C.; Kayama, Y.; Penov, K.; Hennigs, J.K.; Salomons, F.; Eken, S.; Emrich, F.C.; et al. Transcription Factor Runx2 Promotes Aortic Fibrosis and Stiffness in Type 2 Diabetes Mellitus. *Circ. Res.* **2015**, *117*, 513–524. [CrossRef] [PubMed]
88. Li, W.; Feng, W.; Su, X.; Luo, D.; Li, Z.; Zhou, Y.; Zhu, Y.; Zhang, M.; Chen, J.; Liu, B.; et al. SIRT6 protects vascular smooth muscle cells from osteogenic transdifferentiation via Runx2 in chronic kidney disease. *J. Clin. Investig.* **2022**, *132*, e150051. [CrossRef] [PubMed]
89. Ruffenach, G.; Chabot, S.; Tanguay, V.F.; Courboulin, A.; Boucherat, O.; Potus, F.; Meloche, J.; Pflieger, A.; Breuils-Bonnet, S.; Nadeau, V.; et al. Role for Runt-related Transcription Factor 2 in Proliferative and Calcified Vascular Lesions in Pulmonary Arterial Hypertension. *Am. J. Respir. Crit. Care Med.* **2016**, *194*, 1273–1285. [CrossRef] [PubMed]
90. Yu, C.; Li, L.; Xie, F.; Guo, S.; Liu, F.; Dong, N.; Wang, Y. LncRNA TUG1 sponges miR-204-5p to promote osteoblast differentiation through upregulating Runx2 in aortic valve calcification. *Cardiovasc. Res.* **2018**, *114*, 168–179. [CrossRef]
91. Tandon, M.; Othman, A.H.; Ashok, V.; Stein, G.S.; Pratap, J. The role of Runx2 in facilitating autophagy in metastatic breast cancer cells. *J. Cell. Physiol.* **2018**, *233*, 559–571. [CrossRef]

nutrients

Article

The Anti-Obesogenic Effects of Muscadine Grapes through Ciliary Neurotrophic Factor Receptor (Cntfr) and Histamine Receptor H1 (Hrh1) Genes in 3T3-L1 Differentiated Mouse Cells

Samia S. Messeha [1,2,†], Meenakshi Agarwal [3,†], Sherif G. Gendy [4], Sheikh B. Mehboob [3,*] and Karam F. A. Soliman [2,*]

1 College of Science and Technology, Florida A&M University, Tallahassee, FL 32307, USA; samia.messeha@famu.edu
2 College of Pharmacy and Pharmaceutical Sciences, Institute of Public Health, Florida A&M University, New Pharmacy Building, 1415 ML King Blvd., Tallahassee, FL 32307, USA
3 Center for Viticulture & Small Fruit Research, Florida A&M University, Tallahassee, FL 32317, USA; meenakshi.agarawal@famu.edu
4 School of Allied Health Sciences, Florida A&M University, Tallahassee, FL 32307, USA; sherif.gendy@famu.edu
* Correspondence: mehboob.sheikh@famu.edu (S.B.M.); karam.soliman@famu.edu (K.F.A.S.); Tel.: +1-850-412-5189 (S.B.M.); +1-850-599-3306 (K.F.A.S.)
† These authors contributed equally to this work.

Abstract: Obesity and type 2 diabetes are prevalent metabolic diseases that have significant links to several chronic diseases, including cancer, diabetes, hypertension, and cardiovascular disease. Muscadine grape extracts have shown the potential to reduce adiposity and improve insulin sensitivity and glucose control. Thus, this study was designed to determine the potential of muscadine grape berries extract (Pineapple and Southern Home) for its antiobesity properties in 3T3-L1 cells as a model for obesity research. The current study's data indicated the total phenolic content (TPC) and 2,2-diphenyl-1-picrylhydraziyl (DPPH) activity were higher in cultivar (CV) Southern Home, meanwhile, elevated the total flavonoid content (TFC) in Pineapple. Both extracts were safe across the tested range (0–5 mg/mL). A noticeable reduction in lipid accumulation was also found in extract-treated cells. In preadipocytes and adipocytes, the tested extracts showed significant alterations in various genes involved in glucose homeostasis and obesity. The most remarkable findings of the current study are the upregulation of two genes, Cntfr (+712.715-fold) and Hrh1 (+270.11-fold) in CV Pineapple extract-treated adipocytes 3T3-L1 and the high fold increase in Ramp3 induced by both Pineapple and Southern Home in pre-adipose cells. Furthermore, the tested extracts showed a potential to alter the mRNA of various genes, including Zfp91, B2m, Nr3c1, Insr, Atrn, Il6ra, Hsp90ab1, Sort1, and Npy1r. In conclusion, the data generated from the current study suggested that the two extracts under investigation are considered potential candidates for controlling insulin levels and managing obesity.

Keywords: muscadine grape extract; 3T3-L1; Preadipocytes; adipocytes; obesity; gene expression

1. Introduction

Obesity is classified as either a multifaceted disease or a non-communicable condition. This condition is characterized by excessive fat accumulation in adipocytes, leading to high lipids (triglycerides) levels in the plasma and tissues such as the liver and muscles. Various subsets of neurons interact with peripheral nutrients and hormones to control an organism's energy balance and body weight. Obesity occurs when energy intake and expenditure are out of balance, resulting in a variety of physiological abnormalities and chronic diseases such as hypertension, heart disease, osteoarthritis, cardiovascular disease, type II diabetes mellitus, malignancies, reproductive hormone abnormalities, and respiratory problems, among others [1–4].

Multiple environmental variables, including a sedentary lifestyle and genetic vulnerability, contribute to the increased risk of obesity [5,6]. Due to its alarming pace of expansion, it has garnered significant attention as a possible global health threat [7–10]. As a result, it is critical to address the consequences of obesity and take initiative-taking measures to prevent it. A variety of public health intervention programs and initiatives have been proposed as solutions to the growing obesity epidemic. These include changes to dietary habits, exercise levels, lifestyle choices, pharmacological treatment, surgical weight loss, etc. [11,12]. Despite this, the outcomes of these initiatives have not been very fruitful in addressing the increasing incidence of obesity and type 2 diabetes [13].

Furthermore, there are certain disadvantages associated with the use of anti-obesity medications, including the potential for encountering side effects and the likelihood of weight regain after discontinuing the prescription [14]. Therefore, it is vital to delve into new research studies on healthy meals or pharmaceuticals without damaging side effects or undesirable consequences and comprehend their influence on controlling obesity. 3T3-L1 preadipocytes are often employed in in vitro lipid metabolism and adipogenesis investigations. Under certain conditions, these cells can transform into a phenotype similar to adipocytes by changing gene expression. [15–17]. Various dietary polyphenols from plant sources rich in bioactive compounds have been reported to reduce obesity through different mechanisms. These include preventing adipocyte hypertrophy, inhibiting preadipocyte differentiation, increasing lipolysis, or induction of fat cell apoptosis [18,19]. For example, a previous study by Song et al. showed treating 3T3-L1 cells with blueberry peel extract could lower the lipid accumulation and adipocyte differentiation of 3T3-L1 cells [20]. Another study by Kubota et al. showed that *Blumea balsamifera*, a medicinal plant extract, causes a significant decrease in the activity of glycerol-3-phosphate dehydrogenase in 3T3-L1 preadipocytes suggesting its potential role in inhibiting adipogenesis [21].

From this perspective, fruits like grapes are regarded as a rich source of phytochemicals that contain vitamins, minerals, fibers, phenolic acids, flavanols, etc. Muscadine grapes (*Vitis rotundifolia*), which are commonly grown in the southeastern United States, are exceptionally high in polyphenolic compounds such as ellagic acid, gallic acid, procyanidin B2, catechin, and catechin gallate, quercetin, cyanidin, and delphinidin, among others [22–24]. Muscadine grapes exhibit a variety of hues, including bronze, red, purple, and black. In addition, Muscadine grapes differ from bunch grapes (*Vitis vinifera*) in terms of phytochemical composition, with more antioxidant compounds, the presence of anthocyanin 3,5-glucosides in purple cultivar skin, a high concentration of ellagitannins and ellagic acids in seeds and skin [23,25]. To date, no research has been conducted to examine the impact of muscadine grape phytochemicals on the differentiation of adipocytes from 3T3-L1 cells. A couple of studies have shown that muscadine grape may help reduce adiposity. One research group found that phytochemicals from muscadine cultivar (CV) Noble improved insulin sensitivity and glucose control in C57BL/6J mice [26]. Another recent study found that adding muscadine grape extract and probiotics to a Western diet lowered obesity in adult female C57BL/6 mice [27]. However, the molecular process remains unknown, including how phytochemicals from muscadine grape lower adiposity and how transcription changes occur in preadipocyte cells.

This study investigates the potential of Muscadine grape berry extract (MGE) from phytochemical-rich muscadine grapes in regulating obesity. We utilized whole berry extract from bronze- and purple-colored berries of muscadine cultivars to investigate the impact on 3T3-L1 preadipocyte cells and adipocyte cell differentiation at the molecular and cellular levels. Our research would help to build vital nutraceutical food supplements to broaden their application beyond fresh fruit and wine.

2. Materials and Methods

2.1. Berry Sample Collection

Berries from two separate muscadine grape cultivars having bronze and deep purple-black berries were harvested from the vineyard at the Center for Viticulture and Small Fruit Research, Florida Agriculture and Mechanical University, Tallahassee, FL, USA, during the September 2021 vintage. Berries were immediately preserved on ice before being transported to the laboratory and processed for extraction.

2.2. Muscadine Grape Extract Preparation

Ten grams of berries were crushed, mixed with 7 mL of methanol, and homogenized for 10 min. The suspension was spun at 14,000 rpm for 15 min. As stated above, the supernatant was carefully removed, and the remaining residues were extracted again with 3 mL of methanol. The combined organic solvent extracts were vacuum-dried in a concentrator at room temperature in the dark. The dried materials were then redissolved in dimethyl sulfoxide (DMSO) at 150 mg/mL concentration level for bioactivity assessment.

2.3. Total Phenolic Content (TPC) Measurement

The TPC of each extract was measured using the Folin–Ciocalteu (FC) assay, following the method reported by Singleton and Rossi with certain modifications [28]. In summary, a 100 μL sample of grape berry methanolic extract (diluted 1:5) was combined with 150 μL of the FC reagent (diluted 1:1) and incubated for 5 min at room temperature. Afterward, 0.5 mL of a solution containing 20% sodium carbonate was added. The suspension was then kept in a dark and incubated for an additional 40 min at 37 °C. The absorbance was measured at a wavelength of 765 nm. TPC was quantified as milligrams per gram of dry weight of the original sample. Gallic acid was used as the phenolic standard, with 10 to 100 μg/mL concentrations. Analysis was done in triplicates.

2.4. Flavonoid Measurement

Flavonoid measurements were performed as previously described with some modifications [28]. Briefly, 300 μL of extract was mixed with 300 μL of 5% sodium nitrite solution and incubated for 5 min. After that, 3 mL of 10% aluminum chloride was added and incubated for 6 min. The suspension was mixed well with 2 mL of 1 M sodium hydroxide and 3.3 mL of distilled water. Absorbance was measured at 510 nm using a blank as a reference. Catechin was used as a standard for the calibration curve. The total flavonoid content of the extract was expressed as mg catechin equivalents per gram of sample (mg/g).

2.5. DPPH Activity

The antioxidant capacity of the berry extracts was determined by measuring their ability to scavenge free radicals using the 2,2-diphenyl-1-picrylhydraziyl (DPPH) compound, as described in a previous study [29]. Briefly, 50 μL of the extract was mixed with 2 mL of freshly prepared DPPH methanolic solution (60 μM). The mixture was then incubated for 30 min in the dark at room temperature. The absorbance was measured at 515 nm. DMSO was used as a control instead of as a sample. The blank was prepared with the methanolic dilution of DPPH. Data were calculated as the percentage scavenging of DPPH radical and calculated using the following equation: DPPH%= [1 − (A sample − A blank)/(A control − A blank)] × 100.

2.6. Cell Culture and Adipocyte Differentiation

The 3T3-L1 cells were acquired from the ATCC and subjected to differentiation using a previously established protocol [29] with some modifications. The cells were incubated in Dulbecco's modified eagle medium (DMEM) supplemented with 10% fetal bovine serum (FBS) and 100 μg/mL penicillin-streptomycin at a temperature of 37 °C in a 5% CO_2 for 2 days or until they reached 70% confluency. The media was substituted with a differentiation medium comprising 90% DMEM, 10% FBS, 1.0 μM dexamethasone, 0.5 mM

3-isobutyl-1-methylxanthine (IBMX), and 1.0 μg/mL insulin. After 2 days, the medium was substituted with DMEM solution containing 1.0 μg/mL insulin every 2 days and left to incubate for 8 days or until the development of lipid droplets occurred.

2.7. Oil Red O Staining

The oil red O stain kit (Sigma, St. Louis, MO, USA) was used following the manufacturer's instructions. In short, the medium was gently removed and rinsed twice with phosphate-buffered saline. The cells were fixed with 10% formalin for 40 min. Cells were rinsed twice with water, then 60% isopropanol was added and incubated for 5 min. Isopropanol was discarded and replaced with Oil Red O solution to cover the cell surface and incubate for 10 min. The cells were rinsed four times with sterile water before Hematoxylin was added and incubated for one minute. The cells were rinsed four times with distilled water. The cell surface was coated with water and examined under a microscope. The microscopic images were captured using an inverted EVOS M5000 microscope (Thermo Fisher Scientific, Carlsbad, CA, USA) with a 20× objective lens as described previously [30]. The images were processed using Fiji ImageJ software 2.1.0.

2.8. Cytotoxicity Assay

The cytotoxic effect of the two extracts under investigation (Southern Home and Pineapple) in 3T3-L1 cells was determined using Alamar Blue®. Cells were first plated in 96-well plates at a density of 5 × 105 cells/well and placed in the CCI under the previously mentioned settings. Next, cells were treated with the extracts at 0 to 5 mg/mL concentrations. Control cells were exposed to DMSO, and Blank wells with only media/media with extracts were used. The experiments were performed in triplicates. After 24 h exposure period, 20 μL Alamar Blue® (0.5 mg/mL) was added to each well, and the plates kept in CCI for 4 h. Lastly, we read the plates at 530/590 nm (excitation/emission wavelength) using a Synergy H.T.X. multi-mode microplate reader (BioTek Instruments, Inc., Winooski, VT, USA). Data were analyzed using Excel software(Microsoft 365, 2019) and GraphPad Prism 6.2 software (GraphPad Software Inc., San Diego, CA, USA).

2.9. Gene Expression Analysis

2.9.1. Treating Cells

According to the data obtained from the cytotoxicity study, we first selected the safe concentration of 2.4 mg/mL that does not interfere with the cell viability. The impact of Southern Home and Pineapple extracts on different genes mediating obesity was established in a T-25 flask loaded with 5×10^5 cells. We treated 3T3-L1 cells in the pre-adipose stage and during the differentiation period. By the end of each experiment, cells were collected and centrifuged to obtain the pellets.

2.9.2. RNA Extraction and Complementary DNA (cDNA) Synthesis

Extracting the total RNA from 3T3-L1 cell pellets was established as follows: homogenize the pellets with TRIzol reagent (Life Technologies, Paisley, UK), separating the RNA-rich layer using chloroform, pellet the RNA with isopropyl alcohol, then wash the RNA pellets in 75% ethanol solution before dissolving it in the nuclease-free water. The concentration of RNA was measured in each sample. We followed the manufacture protocol for the DNA-free™ kit (Thermo Fisher Scientific) to eliminate the genomic DNA contamination. In contrast, the iScript™ cDNA Synthesis kit (Bio-Rad Laboratories, Hercules, CA, USA) was used to convert 1 μg of RNA into cDNA. The R.T. reaction started at 46 °C for 20 min, followed by 1 min. inactivation at 95 °C, using the CFX96 Touch Real-Time PCR Detection System (Bio-Rad). The obtained cDNAs were stored in a −80 °C freezer.

2.9.3. Quantitative Reverse Transcription Polymerase Chain Reaction (qRT PCR) Obesity Array

A 96-well human obesity array (SAB Target List, cat # 10034386, Bio-Rad) was loaded with diluted cDNA (2.3 ng) and Sso Advanced™ Universal SYBR® Green Supermix (Bio-Rad) for a final volume of 20 µL/well. The fluorescence quantification was accomplished using the Bio-Rad CFX96 Real-Time System (Bio-Rad). cDNA was amplified by 39 cycles: activation, denaturation, and annealing [31,32]. The qRT-PCR data were confirmed using at least three independent experiments.

2.10. Statistical Analysis

Data obtained from this study were analyzed using GraphPad Prism 6.2 software. Data are expressed as mean ± S.E.M. from three biological replicates. One-way analysis of variance was used to compare more than two groups (control vs. treated). CFX 3.1 Manager software (Bio-Rad Laboratories, Hercules, CA, USA) was used to quantify gene expression in the obesity arrays. The significance of differences was generated by analysis of variance (ANOVA) followed by Bonferroni's multiple comparison test. Unpaired Student's t-test was used to analyze two datasets. Differences were considered significant at $p < 0.05$ (as mentioned in the figures and legends).

3. Results

3.1. Total Phenolic, Flavonoid, and Antioxidant Capacity of MGEs

An analysis was conducted on the ripe berries of muscadine cultivars, Southern Home and Pineapple, to determine their total phenolic content (TPC), total flavonoid content (TFC), and antioxidant levels. Figure 1 demonstrates that the TPC and DPPH activities of CV Southern Home were higher than in Pineapple, whereas the flavonoid content was lower in CV Southern Home as compared to CV Pineapple.

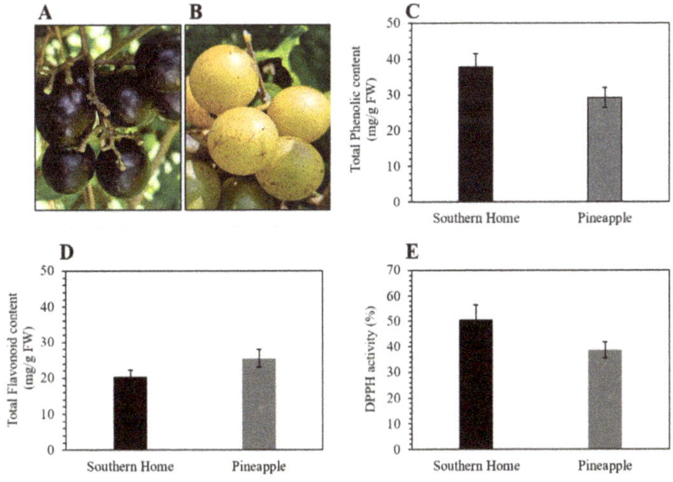

Figure 1. Characteristics of muscadine grapes. (**A**) Images of Berries from Southern Home. (**B**) Berries from Pineapple. (**C**) Assessment of TPC. (**D**) Assessment of TFC. (**E**) Assessment of DPPH activity. The error bar indicates the standard deviation from three triplicates.

3.2. Cytotoxic Effects of Southern Home and Pineapple Extracts

The cytotoxic effects of the extracts in the 3T3-L1 model cell were examined using AB® assays to detect metabolically active cells. Figure 2A,B showed a non-significant effect between control and cells treated at different concentrations (0–5 mg/mL) following 24-h exposure to the tested extracts.

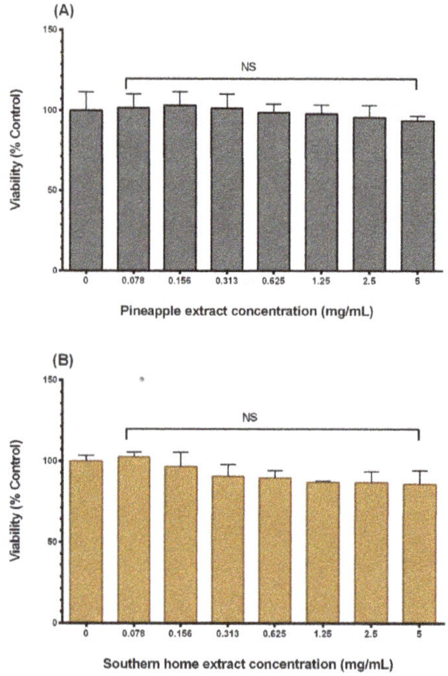

Figure 2. Cytotoxic effect of the examined extracts on 3T3-L1 cells. (**A**) Pineapple extract and (**B**) Southern Home extract. The cells under investigation were seeded in 96-well plates (5×10^5 cells/well) and placed overnight in the cell culture incubator. They were exposed to different concentrations of each extract (0–5 mg/mL) and re-incubated for 24 h. The figures demonstrated the cell viability as a percentage of living cells compared to the control. The presented data were generated from three independent studies. The data were analyzed using one-way ANOVA followed by Bonferroni's multiple comparisons test. N.S., nonsignificant.

3.3. MGEs Reduce Lipid Accumulation in Adipocyte Cells

To assess the impact of MGEs on lipid accumulation in differentiated adipocytes, oil red staining was conducted at eight days following the induction of differentiation. The control cells (absence of MGE treatment) showed the accumulation of lipid droplets upon differentiation into adipocytes, as shown in Figure 3A. In contrast, cells exposed to MGEs derived from Southern Home and Pineapple cultivars at a concentration of 2.4 mg/mL exhibited a significantly diminished accumulation of lipids (Figure 3B,C).

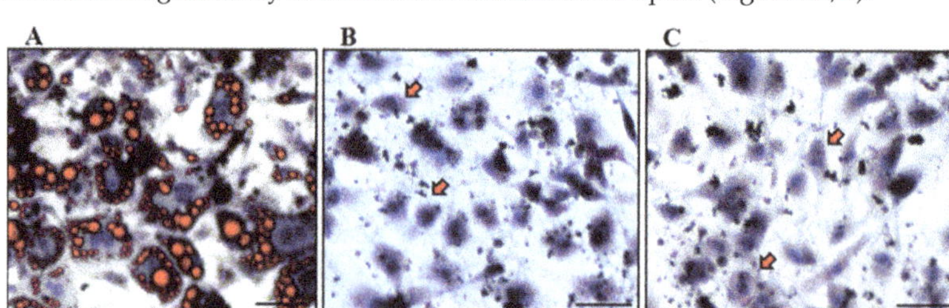

Figure 3. Analysis of lipid accumulation using oil red O staining. (**A**) Control cells without any treatment of MGE. (**B**) Treatment with MGE, Southern Home. (**C**) Treatment with MGE, Pineapple. Red stain indicates lipid droplets, whereas blue stain indicates the nuclei. The red arrows indicate the absence of lipid droplets in treated cells. Images were obtained using an inverted microscope at 60× magnification. Scale bar—100 µm.

3.4. Impact of Extracts on the Expression of Obesity-Associated Genes

RT-PCR was performed to test the underlying molecular mechanisms impacted by Pineapple and Southern Home in 3T3-L1 mouse cells. A list of obesity-linked genes was investigated using the 96-well plate obesity array. Following a previously described protocol, cells were treated for 24 h with a specific dose of the extracts equal to 2.4 mg/mL. An overview of the normalized obesity-related gene expression provided insight into the impact of both extracts on various genes involved in obesity. In Figure 4A,B, the red dots indicate the upregulated genes in both cell lines, whereas the green-colored dots represent the downregulated genes. The black dot in the middle panel indicates unchanged gene expression in both cell lines.

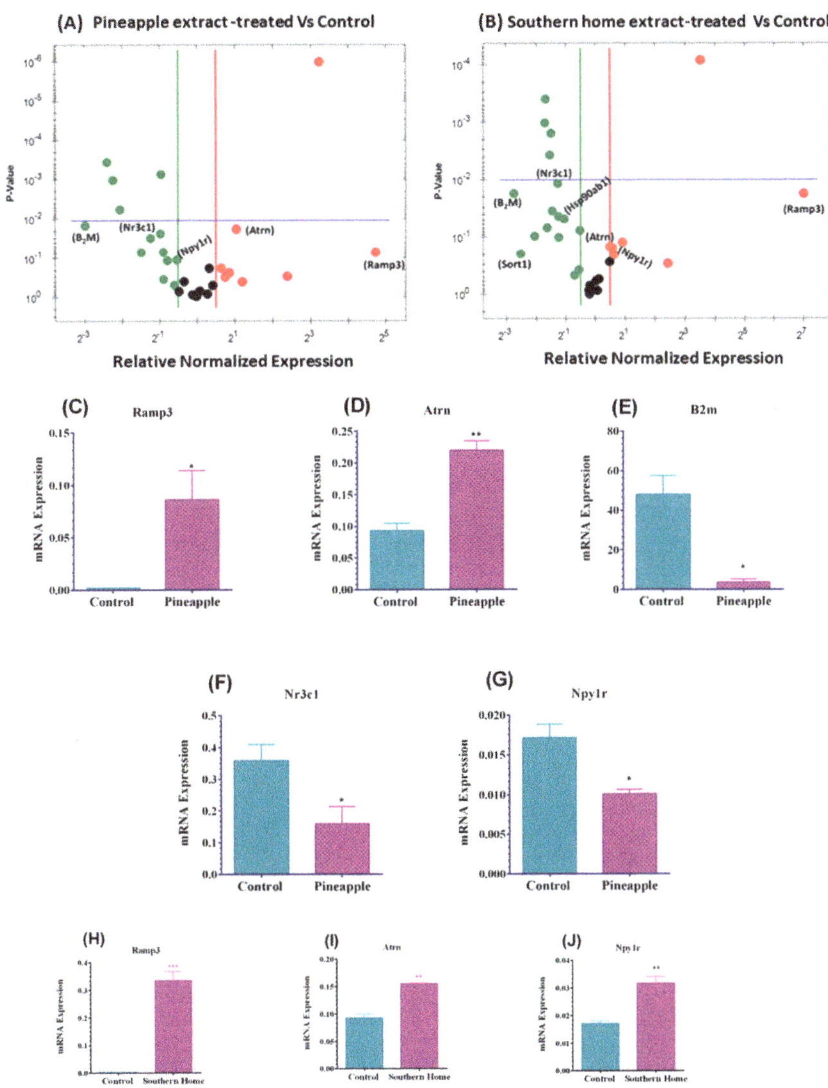

Figure 4. *Cont.*

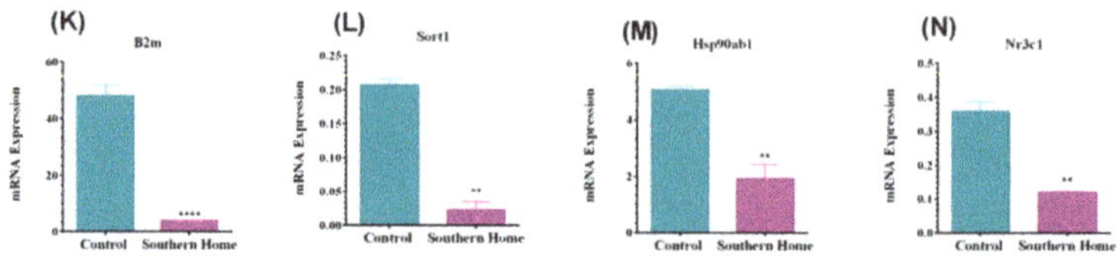

Figure 4. Categorization of obesity-related gene expression induced by Pineapple and Southern Home in pre-adipose 3T3-L1 cells. A volcano plot elucidates the altered genes in pre-adipose 3T3-L1 cells following 24-h exposure to 2.4 mg/mL of Pineapple (**A**) and Southern Home (**B**) extracts. The red dots refer to upregulated mRNAs, green dots for the inhibited genes, and black dots for unchanged. (**C–G**) the altered genes in Pineapple-treated cells. (**H–N**) the altered genes in Southern Home-treated cells. * $p < 0.05$, ** $p < 0.01$, *** $p < 0.001$, **** $p < 0.0001$.

Interestingly, some genes were expressed in extremely low concentrations and were not shown in the generated data. Treating pre-adipose 3T3-L1 cells with the two extracts under investigation showed a significant alteration in crucial genes controlling insulin level and glucose homeostasis, as shown in Figure 4C–G for Pineapple-treated, Figure 4H–N for Southern Home-treated cells, as well as in Table 1. In brief, the obtained data showed a similar response pattern in 3T3-L1 cells. However, the most valuable finding is the outstanding upregulation of Receptor activity modifying proteins (Ramp3) in Southern Home-treated cells (+174.24-fold, Figure 4H) vs. +44.87-fold in Pineapple-treated cells (Figure 4C). An almost 2-fold increase in Attractin (Atrn) was induced by both extracts (Figure 4D,I and Table 1). On the other hand, significant inhibition of two genes, Beta-2-microglobulin; B2m (−13.59 vs. −12.20, Figure 4E,K, and Table 1) and the glucocorticoid receptor nuclear receptor subfamily 3, group C, member 1; Nr3c1 (−2.25 vs. −2.98, Figure 4F,N, and Table 1) was induced by Pineapple and Southern Home, respectively. An exclusive downregulation in sortilin1; Sort1 (−9.00-fold, Figure 4L and Table 1) and Heat shock protein 90kDa alpha family Class B member 1; Hsp90ab1 (−2.62-fold, Figure 4M and Table 1) was induced by Southern Home extract. Interestingly, an inverted alteration was found in the Neuropeptide Y1 receptor, Npy1r mRNA. Meanwhile, a significant attenuation was detected in Pineapple-treated cells (−1.70-fold, Figure 4G and Table 1), and an almost 2-fold increase in the genes was measured in Southern Home-treated cells (Figure 4J and Table 1).

Table 1. A comparative illustration of Pineapple and Southern Home extracts impacts mRNA gene regulation in pre-adipose 3T3-L1 mouse cells.

Impacted Genes	Pineapple		Southern Home	
	Fold Change	p-Value	Fold Change	p-Value
Ramp3	+44.87	0.0107	+174.24	0.0009
Atrn	+2.36	0.0019	+1.67	0.0067
B2m	−13.59	0.0228	−12.20	0.0226
Sort1			−9.00	0.0067
Hsp90ab1			−2.62	0.0047
Nr3c1	−2.25	0.0248	−2.98	0.0084
Npy1r	−1.70	0.0127	+1.85	0.0076

On the other hand, incubating 3T3-L1 cells with the extracts during the differentiation phase showed an alteration in many genes other than Nr3c1 and Hsp90ab1 (Figure 5A–N and Table 2). At first glance, the Pineapple extract augmented the expression of three genes (Figure 5A), giving the remarkable upregulation in the ciliary neurotrophic factor receptor; Cntfr (+712.72-fold), followed by Histamine Receptor H1; Hrh1 (+270.11-fold), and Zinc Finger Protein 91; Zfp91 was the least (8-fold) as indicated in Figure 5C–E, respectively and Table 2. In contrast, we did not detect any gene upregulation in Southern Home-treated cells (Figure 5B).

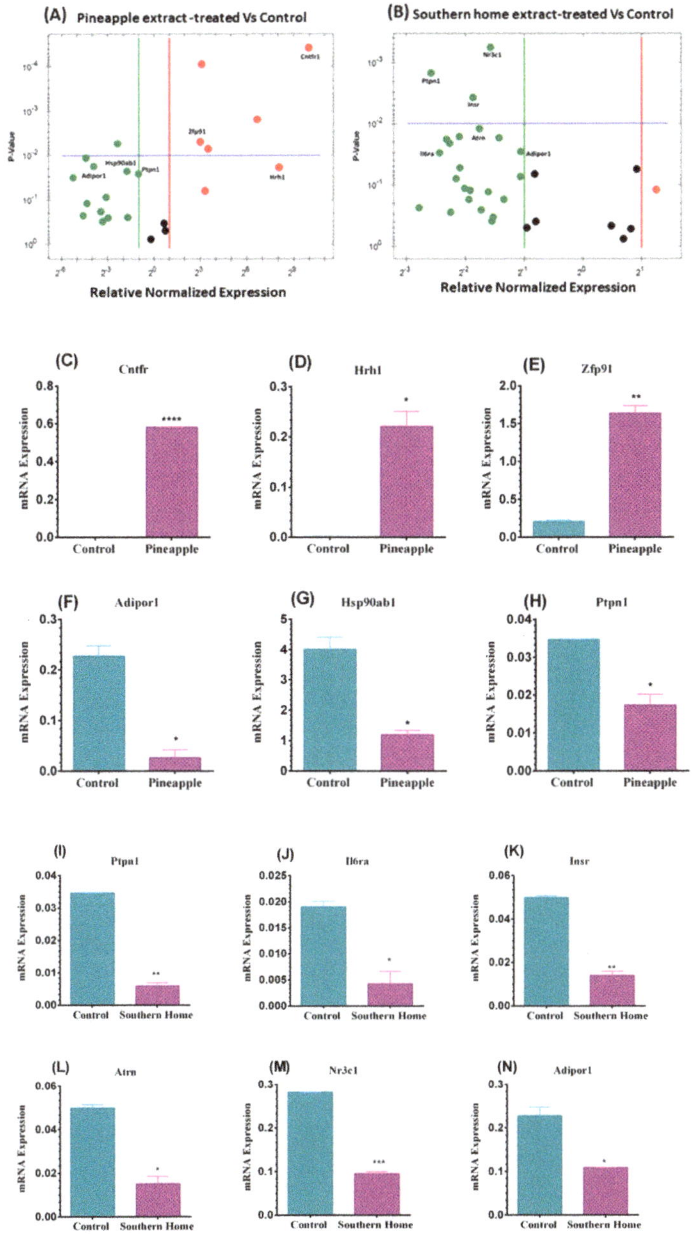

Figure 5. Categorization of obesity-related gene expression induced by Pineapple and Southern Home in differentiated 3T3-L1 cells. A volcano plot elucidates the altered genes in differentiated 3T3-L1 cells following exposure to 2.4 mg/mL of Pineapple (**A**) and Southern Home (**B**) extracts. The red dots refer to upregulated mRNAs, green dots for the inhibited genes, and black dots for unchanged. (**C–H**) the altered genes in Pineapple-treated cells. (**I–N**) the altered genes in Southern Home-treated cells. * $p < 0.05$, ** $p < 0.01$, *** $p < 0.001$, **** $p < 0.0001$.

Table 2. A comparative illustration of Pineapple and Southern Home extracts' impacts on mRNA gene regulation in differentiated 3T3-L1 mouse cells.

Impacted Genes	Pineapple		Southern Home	
	Fold Change	*p*-Value	Fold Change	*p*-Value
Cntfr	+712.715	<0.0001		
Hrh1	+270.11	0.0187		
Zfp91	+7.90	0.0050		
Adipor1	−9.58	0.0163	−2.10	0.0287
Hsp90ab1	−3.40	0.0228		
Insr			−3.61	0.0037
Nr3c1			−2.97	0.0006
Ptpn1	−2.01	0.0261	−5.90	0.0015
Atrn			−3.30	0.0121
Il6ra			−4.50	0.0300

Consistent with preadipose, the Southern Home extract showed the exact fold change in Nr3c1 (~−3-fold, Figure 5M and Table 2). Meanwhile, Hsp90ab1 was inhibited only by Pineapple extract (−3.40-fold, Figure 5G and Table 2). Furthermore, a significant downregulation in two more genes; adiponectin receptor protein 1; Adipor1 (−9.58-fold vs. −2.10-fold, Figures 5F and 5N, respectively and Table 2), and the protein tyrosine phosphatase non-receptor type 1; Ptpn1 (−2.01-fold vs. −5.90-fold, Figures 5H and 5I, respectively and Table 2) was measured in Pineapple and Southern Home extracts-treated cells, respectively.

Compared with preadipocytes, Southern Home extract showed an inverted effect in adipocytes 3T3-L1, inducing more than 3-fold inhibition in the Atrn gene. Furthermore, the mRNAs were also attenuated for two more genes, Interleukin 6 (Il-6) receptor alpha (Il6ra) and the insulin receptor (Insr), by Southern Home extract (Figure 5J,K, and Table 2), giving the highest fold change (−4.50-fold) in Il6ra (Figure 5J and Table 2).

4. Discussion

Muscadine grapes are valued for their bioactive metabolites and are reported to contain antioxidant, anti-inflammatory, and anticancer activities. In this study, we aim to explore the potential of muscadine grape extracts in regulating obesity by monitoring its impact on 3T3-L1 cells. We employed two muscadine cultivars: Pineapple, which has bronze berries, and Southern Home, which has purple berries. Since metabolites are essential for the nutritional value of grapes, we measured the TPC, TFC, and antioxidant activity of whole muscadine berry extracts. We found a higher level of TPC and antioxidants in CV Southern Home compared to the Pineapple. At the same time, the TFC was found to be higher in CV Pineapple. These results align with past findings that different muscadine cultivars had varying metabolite contents [33,34].

The TPC, TFC, and antioxidant activity results in our study are consistent with the range reported in previous research on different muscadine grape genotypes [35]. Molecules with antioxidant properties can neutralize ROS and mitigate oxidative stress, counteracting its deleterious effects associated with obesity [36]. A recent review [37] highlights that oxidative stress can be both a primary cause and a secondary effect of various disorders, including those related to obesity.

Our study elucidates the phenolic and flavonoid properties, drawing from insights from prior investigations. Extensive literature underscores the pivotal role of (poly)phenols and flavonoids in mitigating the risk of obesity and conferring beneficial effects under obese conditions [38]. These compounds have been associated with modulating various cellular responses, including alleviating intracellular oxidative stress, attenuating chronic low-grade inflammation, inhibiting adipogenesis and lipogenesis, and suppressing preadipocyte differentiation into mature adipocytes [39]. We selected muscadine cultivars, known for their elevated total stilbene content, including t-Piceid, t-Resveratrol, ε-Viniferin, and t-Pterostilbene, as demonstrated in our previous investigation [40,41]. The extraction method employed in our study has been tailored to efficiently capture the predominant phenolic and flavonoid constituents present in muscadine grape berries. Additionally, our previous study showed more stilbene in Southern Home than in Pineapple [40]. While both MGEs exhibited variations in their TPC, TFC, and antioxidant activity, no significant difference was observed in the lipid accumulation in 3T3-L1 cells following treatment, as observed by Oil red staining (Figure 3). This finding suggests that the phytochemical content found in each cultivar may be adequate to inhibit lipid accumulation at the measured concentration.

It is important to highlight that this is our first investigation utilizing whole muscadine grape berry extract and examining its impact on the 3T3-L1 cell. The utilization of the entire berry dilutes the total phytochemical content compared to extracts obtained from specific tissue or parts. The protocol used for preparing the extract is also a determinant factor for the concentration used. In the preliminary viability study, we began with low extract concentrations. However, we observed no effect on either cell viability in preadipocytes or lipid accumulation in adipocytes at these lower concentrations. Consequently, we tested a range of extract concentrations until we observed an effect on cell viability in preadipocyte cells. We selected a concentration from this range that maintained more than 80% cell viability, as depicted in Figure 3, while ensuring that it contained sufficient phytochemicals to exert its effect.

Emphasizing the molecular basis of obesity is an important tool in developing promising therapeutic agents against increased body weight. Therefore, in the current study, profiling the mRNA of various genes-mediating obesity was established for two sets (pre-adipose and differentiated 3T3-L1 mouse cells), following treatment with safe concentrations of the extracts under investigation (Figure 2A,B). Collectively, treating the 3T3-L1 cells at different phases showed interesting data. Meanwhile, a consistent alteration in some genes was measured at both phases, and each extract also induced an exclusive response. These genes directly regulate energy homeostasis or encode the hormones and receptors of anorectic and orexigenic peptides.

The most valuable outcome of this study is the outstanding upregulation of two genes, Cntfr and Hrh1, in Pineapple extract-treated differentiated 3T3-L1 cells, in addition to the high fold increase in Ramp3 that was induced by both extracts in pre-adipose cells. Indeed, a highly significant upregulation (+712.715) of Cntfr was measured in pineapple-treated -adipocyte cells. This receptor is a crucial activator of Cntfr, a member of the interleukin (IL)-6 type cytokine family [42,43]. Individuals with multiple sclerosis and amyotrophic lateral sclerosis experienced a marked decrease in weight when they received Cntfr [44]. Activation of leptin-independent or leptin-like intracellular signaling pathways is employed by Cntfr, as indicated by previous studies [45–47]. Also, a +270.11-fold increase in the Hrh1 gene was exhibited by pineapple-treated adipocyte cells. Hrh1 is one of the genes that influence both second-generation antipsychotics (SGAP) and mood stabilizers (MS) weight gain [48]. A previous study has demonstrated a significant association between the Hrh1 gene variants rs346070 and rs346074 and B.M.I. in Caucasian patients with a psychotic disorder [49]. The upregulated level of Zfp91 suggests the promising effect of Pineapple extract in managing obesity. The obtained data agree with previous studies that revealed the negative correlation between Zfp91 mRNA expression levels and body mass index (B.M.I.) [50].

Both CV Pineapple and Southern Home induced an outstanding upregulation of the gene Ramp3 in pre-adipose cells. This finding highlighted the importance of these extracts as a preventive approach, particularly the Southern Home extract that induced +174.24-fold vs. + 44.87-fold in Pineapple-treated cells. Ramps are an important family of G protein-coupled receptors (Gpcrs) accessory proteins [51,52] that initiate intracellular signaling [53]. The Ramps family contains three distinct transmembrane-spanning proteins; one is Ramp3, and the other is a receptor (G protein-coupled) activity-modifying protein 3. Postmenopausal obesity is linked to estrogen deficiency, which is accompanied by the accumulation of abdominal fat and decreased energy expenditure [54]. A previous study highlighted the relationship between estrogen and Ramp3 [55]. Knockout of Ramp3 in ovariectomized mice showed elevated serum insulin levels accompanied by exacerbation in obesity, adipocyte hypertrophy, and adipose tissue weight gain [55]. In pre-adipose cells, Pineapple and Southern Home extracts also showed an almost 2-fold increase in Atrn mRNA, whereas the same gene was inhibited in Southern Home-treated adipocytes. A previous in vitro study demonstrated that the absence of Atrn suppresses agouti (Agrp)-induced obesity [56]. Reduced body weight and adiposity, as well as partial suppression of diet-induced obesity, was also found in Atrn- mutant mice [57,58]. The obtained reduction of Atrn expression in Southern Home extract-treated adipocyte cells suggested that targeting Atrn could be a promising mechanism for managing obesity. Treating pre-adipose cells with either Pineapple or Southern Home extracts showed a reduction in Adipor1 and Ptpn1 gene expression. Downregulating Adipor1 demonstrated the value of these extracts in managing obesity, particularly Pineapple, which inhibited the gene by 10-fold vs. −2.10-fold in Southern Home-treated adipocyte cells. Adipor1 is involved in glucose and lipid metabolism. Indeed, an upregulated level of Adipor1 was found in obese subjects that could be related to metabolic disorders [59]. Furthermore, Adipor1 gene expression in chondrocytes positively correlates with a patient's body mass index (B.M.I.) [60].

On the other hand, Ptpn1is expressed in multiple tissues and engages in numerous signal transduction pathways [61,62]. Ptpn1 contributes significantly to insulin signaling by dephosphorylating the insulin receptor and the insulin receptor substrate (IRS-1). A previous finding using knockout mice revealed the link of Ptpn1 to adiposity. Hence, Ptpn1 deletion appears to confer resistance against weight gain [61,63]. In pre-adipose cells, an almost similar reduction in B2m expression (~12-fold) was induced by both extracts. Meanwhile, Southern Home extract inhibited Sort1. B2m, the crucial gene is considered a biomarker in different diseases. According to the previously established study, an elevated level of serum B2m is associated with various adverse health effects, including overweight/obesity [64]. The gene Sort1was significantly attenuated (−9-fold). This gene is crucial in managing the metabolic phenotype, as revealed by a previous in-vivo study [65]. However, when they received the same diet, mice with diminished levels of Sort1 showed an overall lower body weight change and less visceral fat compared to their counterpart W.T.-type mice. Furthermore, insulin tolerance tests highlighted the boosted glucose uptake [65,66].

Interestingly, the impact of the two extracts under investigation on Hsp90ab1 expression was differently shown. This gene was downregulated in Southern Home-treated pre-adipose cells. Meanwhile, a similar reduction was measured in pineapple-treated adipocyte cells. Hsp90ab1 plays an essential role in the metabolic pathway [67]. Knock-down Hsp90ab1 in the mouse model of diabetes demonstrated the key role of this gene in controlling diabetes-mediated signaling pathways such as glucose metabolism and insulin signaling [68]. In parallel, both extracts inhibited the expression of Nr3c1 in pre-adipose cells by ~2–3-fold. However, the same reduction was exclusively found in Southern Home extract-treated adipocyte cells. Obesity, hyperinsulinemia, and abdominal visceral fat are associated with Nr3c1. Treatment of bipolar disorder with MS and SGAP is associated with significant side effects, including weight gain.

Furthermore, Nr3c1 is significantly associated with abdominal obesity [69–71]. In adipocyte cells, the Southern Home extracts inhibited the expression of two glucose homeostasis regulators: Insr and Il6ra. Insr is expressed mainly in insulin-sensitive tissues [72]. Skeletal muscle incorporates high expression of the Insr-b variant that is closely associated with insulin resistance and type 2 diabetes [73]. Consistently, an upregulated level of Insr-B was also found in adipocytes in people with type 2 diabetes compared with those with normoglycemic [74]. Upon binding, Il6ra is a crucial factor in Il-6 release [75]. In rodents and humans, a positive correlation was revealed between Il-6 levels and increased fat mass [76], with levels decreasing in weight loss [77]. The downregulated levels obtained in this study support the role of Southern Home extract in managing obesity. The data also showed an inverse effect of the two extracts under investigation. In pre-adipose 3T3-L1 cells, Pineapple induced a significant downregulation of Npy1r. In contrast, the same genes were upregulated in Southern Home-treated cells. Upregulated expression of Npy1r [78] was previously found in different cell models, such as human adipose cells, preadipocytes, and adipocytes 3T3-L1 cells [79–81]. Consistent with this observation, elevated levels of Npy1r were also measured in obese patients [82]. Having Npy1r downregulated by Pineapple extract suggests its potential role in managing obesity.

5. Conclusions

The current research provides insights into the mechanism underlying the anti-obesity potential of the Muscadine grape berry extracts (Pineapple and Southern Home) in both preadipocytes and adipocytes 3T3-L1. Our finding demonstrated the potential of the extracts under investigation to alter the expression of various genes regulating insulin and energy homeostasis. The most noteworthy finding of the current study is the outstanding upregulation of two genes, Cntfr and Hrh1, that were measured in Pineapple extract-treated adipocytes, in addition to the high fold-increase in Ramp3 induced by both Pineapple and Southern Home in preadipose cells. Both extracts showed a similar pattern of gene alteration, including the downregulation of B2m and Nr3c1 in preadipose cells and the inhibition of Ptpn1 and Adipore1 in adipocytes. Southern Home extract also showed a potential to inhibit other genes, including Sort1 in preadipose cells, Insr, and Il6ra in adipocytes. A downregulation of Hsp90ab1 was also shown in Southern Home-treated preadipose cells, and Pineapple-treated differentiated cells. In preadipocytes, the two extracts showed an inverted regulation of Npy1r, giving a mild fold increase in Southern Home treated and downregulation in Pineapple-treated cells.

Interestingly, pre-adipocyte-treated cells exhibited an increase in Atrn. However, the same gene was exclusively inhibited in Southern Home-treated adipocytes. Indeed, the obtained data suggested the antiobesity potential of Muscadine grape berry extracts (Pineapple and Southern Home). However, we plan to investigate these extracts further using an in-vivo model and fractionated extracts to identify the active components and fulfill the current research's limitations.

Author Contributions: M.A. established a berries collection and conducted phytochemical studies. Cell culture and staining studies were performed by S.S.M. and M.A. Cytotoxicity studies and gene expression analysis were done by S.S.M. and S.G.G. Conceptualization: S.B.M., M.A.; Methodology: S.S.M., M.A.; Formal analysis: S.S.M., M.A., S.G.G.; Funding acquisition: K.F.A.S., S.B.M.; Project administration: K.F.A.S., S.B.M.; Resources: K.F.A.S., S.B.M.; Software: S.S.M., M.A.; Supervision: M.A., S.S.M.; Writing—original draft: S.S.M., M.A.; Writing—review & editing: S.S.M., M.A., S.G.G., S.B.M., K.F.A.S. All authors have read and agreed to the published version of the manuscript.

Funding: This research was funded by N.I.H. grants from the National Institute on Minority Health and Health Disparities (NIMHD), grant number U54 MD007582 and USDA/NIFA Capacity Building Grants # 2020-38821-31120, 2021-38821-34711.

Institutional Review Board Statement: Not applicable.

Informed Consent Statement: Not applicable.

Data Availability Statement: The original contributions presented in the study are included in the article, further inquiries can be directed to the corresponding authors.

Conflicts of Interest: The authors declare no conflicts of interest.

References

1. Grundy, S.M. Multifactorial causation of obesity: Implications for prevention. *Am. J. Clin. Nutr.* **1998**, *67*, 563s–572s. [CrossRef] [PubMed]
2. Hursting, S.D.; Dunlap, S.M. Obesity, metabolic dysregulation, and cancer: A growing concern and an inflammatory (and microenvironmental) issue. *Ann. N. Y. Acad. Sci.* **2012**, *1271*, 82–87. [CrossRef] [PubMed]
3. Kopelman, P.G. Obesity as a medical problem. *Nature* **2000**, *404*, 635–643. [CrossRef] [PubMed]

4. Yoo, S. Dynamic Energy Balance and Obesity Prevention. *J. Obes. Metab. Syndr.* **2018**, *27*, 203–212. [CrossRef] [PubMed]
5. Bouchard, C. Defining the genetic architecture of the predisposition to obesity: A challenging but not insurmountable task. *Am. J. Clin. Nutr.* **2010**, *91*, 5–6. [CrossRef] [PubMed]
6. Heber, D. An integrative view of obesity. *Am. J. Clin. Nutr.* **2010**, *91*, 280s–283s. [CrossRef] [PubMed]
7. Flegal, K.M.; Carroll, M.D.; Ogden, C.L.; Curtin, L.R. Prevalence and trends in obesity among US adults, 1999–2008. *JAMA* **2010**, *303*, 235–241. [CrossRef]
8. Mokdad, A.H.; Serdula, M.K.; Dietz, W.H.; Bowman, B.A.; Marks, J.S.; Koplan, J.P. The spread of the obesity epidemic in the United States, 1991–1998. *JAMA* **1999**, *282*, 1519–1522. [CrossRef]
9. Swinburn, B.A.; Sacks, G.; Hall, K.D.; McPherson, K.; Finegood, D.T.; Moodie, M.L.; Gortmaker, S.L. The global obesity pandemic: Shaped by global drivers and local environments. *Lancet* **2011**, *378*, 804–814. [CrossRef]
10. Wang, Y.C.; McPherson, K.; Marsh, T.; Gortmaker, S.L.; Brown, M. Health and economic burden of the projected obesity trends in the USA and the UK. *Lancet* **2011**, *378*, 815–825. [CrossRef]
11. Baker, J.S.; Supriya, R.; Dutheil, F.; Gao, Y. Obesity: Treatments, Conceptualizations, and Future Directions for a Growing Problem. *Biology* **2022**, *11*, 160. [CrossRef] [PubMed]
12. Sacks, F.M.; Bray, G.A.; Carey, V.J.; Smith, S.R.; Ryan, D.H.; Anton, S.D.; McManus, K.; Champagne, C.M.; Bishop, L.M.; Laranjo, N.; et al. Comparison of weight-loss diets with different compositions of fat, protein, and carbohydrates. *N. Engl. J. Med.* **2009**, *360*, 859–873. [CrossRef] [PubMed]
13. Chan, R.S.; Woo, J. Prevention of overweight and obesity: How effective is the current public health approach. *Int. J. Environ. Res. Public Health* **2010**, *7*, 765–783. [CrossRef] [PubMed]
14. Kang, J.G.; Park, C.Y. Anti-Obesity Drugs: A Review about Their Effects and Safety. *Diabetes Metab. J.* **2012**, *36*, 13–25. [CrossRef] [PubMed]
15. Li, P.; Carter, G.; Romero, J.; Gower, K.M.; Watson, J.; Patel, N.A.; Cooper, D.R. Clk/STY (cdc2-like kinase 1) and Akt regulate alternative splicing and adipogenesis in 3T3-L1 pre-adipocytes. *PLoS ONE* **2013**, *8*, e53268. [CrossRef] [PubMed]
16. Poulos, S.P.; Dodson, M.V.; Hausman, G.J. Cell line models for differentiation: Preadipocytes and adipocytes. *Exp. Biol. Med.* **2010**, *235*, 1185–1193. [CrossRef] [PubMed]
17. Rizzatti, V.; Boschi, F.; Pedrotti, M.; Zoico, E.; Sbarbati, A.; Zamboni, M. Lipid droplets characterization in adipocyte differentiated 3T3-L1 cells: Size and optical density distribution. *Eur. J. Histochem.* **2013**, *57*, e24. [CrossRef] [PubMed]
18. Ramírez-Moreno, E.; Arias-Rico, J.; Jiménez-Sánchez, R.C.; Estrada-Luna, D.; Jiménez-Osorio, A.S.; Zafra-Rojas, Q.Y.; Ariza-Ortega, J.A.; Flores-Chávez, O.R.; Morales-Castillejos, L.; Sandoval-Gallegos, E.M. Role of Bioactive Compounds in Obesity: Metabolic Mechanism Focused on Inflammation. *Foods* **2022**, *11*, 1232. [CrossRef] [PubMed]
19. Wang, S.; Moustaid-Moussa, N.; Chen, L.; Mo, H.; Shastri, A.; Su, R.; Bapat, P.; Kwun, I.; Shen, C.L. Novel insights of dietary polyphenols and obesity. *J. Nutr. Biochem.* **2014**, *25*, 1–18. [CrossRef]
20. Song, Y.; Park, H.J.; Kang, S.N.; Jang, S.H.; Lee, S.J.; Ko, Y.G.; Kim, G.S.; Cho, J.H. Blueberry peel extracts inhibit adipogenesis in 3T3-L1 cells and reduce high-fat diet-induced obesity. *PLoS ONE* **2013**, *8*, e69925. [CrossRef]
21. Kubota, H.; Kojima-Yuasa, A.; Morii, R.; Huang, X.; Norikura, T.; Rho, S.N.; Matsui-Yuasa, I. Anti-obesity effect of Blumea balsamifera extract in 3T3-L1 preadipocytes and adipocytes. *Am. J. Chin. Med.* **2009**, *37*, 843–854. [CrossRef] [PubMed]
22. Chappell, M.C.; Duncan, A.V.; Melo, A.C.; Schaich, C.L.; Pirro, N.T.; Diz, D.I.; Tallant, E.A.; Gallagher, P.E. Targeted UHPLC-MS Analysis Reveals Disparate Polyphenol Composition and Concentration in Muscadine Grape Supplements with Proportional Antioxidant Activity. *Antioxidants* **2022**, *11*, 2117. [CrossRef] [PubMed]
23. Lee, J.H.; Johnson, J.V.; Talcott, S.T. Identification of ellagic acid conjugates and other polyphenolics in muscadine grapes by HPLC-ESI-MS. *J. Agric. Food Chem.* **2005**, *53*, 6003–6010. [CrossRef] [PubMed]
24. Sandhu, A.K.; Gu, L. Antioxidant capacity, phenolic content, and profiling of phenolic compounds in the seeds, skin, and pulp of Vitis rotundifolia (*Muscadine* Grapes) As determined by HPLC-DAD-ESI-MS(n). *J. Agric. Food Chem.* **2010**, *58*, 4681–4692. [CrossRef] [PubMed]
25. Pastrana-Bonilla, E.; Akoh, C.C.; Sellappan, S.; Krewer, G. Phenolic content and antioxidant capacity of muscadine grapes. *J. Agric. Food Chem.* **2003**, *51*, 5497–5503. [CrossRef] [PubMed]
26. Gourineni, V.; Shay, N.F.; Chung, S.; Sandhu, A.K.; Gu, L. Muscadine grape (*Vitis rotundifolia*) and wine phytochemicals prevented obesity-associated metabolic complications in C57BL/6J mice. *J. Agric. Food Chem.* **2012**, *60*, 7674–7681. [CrossRef] [PubMed]
27. Newman, T.M.; Wilson, A.S.; Clear, K.Y.J.; Tallant, E.A.; Gallagher, P.E.; Cook, K.L. Probiotic and Muscadine Grape Extract Interventions Shift the Gut Microbiome and Improve Metabolic Parameters in Female C57BL/6 Mice. *Cells* **2023**, *12*, 2599. [CrossRef] [PubMed]
28. Singleton, V.L.; Rossi, J.A. Colorimetry of total phenolics with phosphomolybdic-phosphotungstic acid reagents. *Am. J. Enol. Vitic.* **1965**, *16*, 144–158. [CrossRef]
29. Von Gadow, A.; Joubert, E.; Hansmann, C. Comparison of the antioxidant activity of rooibos tea (*Aspalathus linearis*) with green, oolong and black tea. *Food Chem.* **1997**, *60*, 73–77. [CrossRef]
30. Agarwal, M.; Rathore, R.S.; Jagoe, C.; Chauhan, A. Multiple lines of evidences reveal mechanisms underpinning mercury resistance and volatilization by Stenotrophomonas sp. MA5 isolated from the Savannah River Site (SRS), USA. *Cells* **2019**, *8*, 309. [CrossRef]

31. Messeha, S.S.; Noel, S.; Zarmouh, N.O.; Womble, T.; Latinwo, L.M.; Soliman, K.F.A. Involvement of AKT/PI3K Pathway in Sanguinarine's Induced Apoptosis and Cell Cycle Arrest in Triple-negative Breast Cancer Cells. *Cancer Genom. Proteom.* **2023**, *20*, 323–342. [CrossRef] [PubMed]
32. Messeha, S.S.; Zarmouh, N.O.; Antonie, L.; Soliman, K.F.A. Sanguinarine Inhibition of TNF-α-Induced CCL2, IKBKE/NF-κB/ERK1/2 Signaling Pathway, and Cell Migration in Human Triple-Negative Breast Cancer Cells. *Int. J. Mol. Sci.* **2022**, *23*, 8329. [CrossRef] [PubMed]
33. Marshall, D.A.; Stringer, S.J.; Spiers, D.; Stilbene, J. Ellagic acid, flavonol, and phenolic content of muscadine grape (*Vitis rotundifolia* Michx.) cultivars. *Pharm. Crops* **2012**, *3*, 69–77. [CrossRef]
34. Xu, C.; Yagiz, Y.; Zhao, L.; Simonne, A.; Lu, J.; Marshall, M.R. Fruit quality, nutraceutical and antimicrobial properties of 58 muscadine grape varieties (*Vitis rotundifolia* Michx.) grown in United States. *Food Chem.* **2017**, *215*, 149–156. [CrossRef] [PubMed]
35. Mendonca, P.; Darwish, A.G.; Tsolova, V.; El-Sharkawy, I.; Soliman, K.F. The anticancer and antioxidant effects of muscadine grape extracts on racially different triple-negative breast cancer cells. *Anticancer Res.* **2019**, *39*, 4043–4053. [CrossRef]
36. Houstis, N.; Rosen, E.D.; Lander, E.S. Reactive oxygen species have a causal role in multiple forms of insulin resistance. *Nature* **2006**, *440*, 944–948. [CrossRef] [PubMed]
37. Bonomini, F. Antioxidants and Obesity. *Int. J. Mol. Sci.* **2023**, *24*, 12832. [CrossRef]
38. Oliveira, A.K.d.S.; de Oliveira e Silva, A.M.; Pereira, R.O.; Santos, A.S.; Barbosa Junior, E.V.; Bezerra, M.T.; Barreto, R.S.; Quintans-Junior, L.J.; Quintans, J.S. Anti-obesity properties and mechanism of action of flavonoids: A review. *Crit. Rev. Food Sci. Nutr.* **2022**, *62*, 7827–7848. [CrossRef]
39. Mompeo, O.; Spector, T.D.; Matey Hernandez, M.; Le Roy, C.; Istas, G.; Le Sayec, M.; Mangino, M.; Jennings, A.; Rodriguez-Mateos, A.; Valdes, A.M. Consumption of stilbenes and flavonoids is linked to reduced risk of obesity independently of fiber intake. *Nutrients* **2020**, *12*, 1871. [CrossRef]
40. Balasubramani, S.P.; Rahman, M.A.; Basha, S.M. Synergistic Action of Stilbenes in Muscadine Grape Berry Extract Shows Better Cytotoxic Potential Against Cancer Cells Than Resveratrol Alone. *Biomedicines* **2019**, *7*, 96. [CrossRef]
41. Ismail, A.; Gajjar, P.; Park, M.; Mahboob, A.; Tsolova, V.; Subramanian, J.; Darwish, A.G.; El-Sharkawy, I. A recessive mutation in muscadine grapes causes berry color loss without influencing the anthocyanin pathway. *Commun. Biol.* **2022**, *5*, 1012. [CrossRef] [PubMed]
42. Lin, L.F.; Mismer, D.; Lile, J.D.; Armes, L.G.; Butler, E.T., 3rd; Vannice, J.L.; Collins, F. Purification, cloning, and expression of ciliary neurotrophic factor (CNTF). *Science* **1989**, *246*, 1023–1025. [CrossRef] [PubMed]
43. Rose-John, S. Interleukin-6 Family Cytokines. *Cold Spring Harb. Perspect. Biol.* **2018**, *10*, a028415. [CrossRef] [PubMed]
44. ALS CNTF Treatment Study Group. A double-blind placebo-controlled clinical trial of subcutaneous recombinant human ciliary neurotrophic factor (rHCNTF) in amyotrophic lateral sclerosis. ALS CNTF Treatment Study Group. *Neurology* **1996**, *46*, 1244–1249. [CrossRef] [PubMed]
45. Gloaguen, I.; Costa, P.; Demartis, A.; Lazzaro, D.; Di Marco, A.; Graziani, R.; Paonessa, G.; Chen, F.; Rosenblum, C.I.; Van der Ploeg, L.H.; et al. Ciliary neurotrophic factor corrects obesity and diabetes associated with leptin deficiency and resistance. *Proc. Natl. Acad. Sci. USA* **1997**, *94*, 6456–6461. [CrossRef] [PubMed]
46. Lambert, P.D.; Anderson, K.D.; Sleeman, M.W.; Wong, V.; Tan, J.; Hijarunguru, A.; Corcoran, T.L.; Murray, J.D.; Thabet, K.E.; Yancopoulos, G.D.; et al. Ciliary neurotrophic factor activates leptin-like pathways and reduces body fat, without cachexia or rebound weight gain, even in leptin-resistant obesity. *Proc. Natl. Acad. Sci. USA* **2001**, *98*, 4652–4657. [CrossRef] [PubMed]
47. Xu, J.; Forger, N.G. Expression and androgen regulation of the ciliary neurotrophic factor receptor (CNTFRalpha) in muscles and spinal cord. *J. Neurobiol.* **1998**, *35*, 217–225. [CrossRef]
48. Creta, E.; Fabbri, C.; Serretti, A. Genetics of second-generation antipsychotic and mood stabilizer-induced weight gain in bipolar disorder: Common and specific effects of key regulators of fat-mass homoeostasis genes. *Pharmacogenet Genom.* **2015**, *25*, 354–362. [CrossRef] [PubMed]
49. Vehof, J.; Risselada, A.J.; Al Hadithy, A.F.; Burger, H.; Snieder, H.; Wilffert, B.; Arends, J.; Wunderink, L.; Knegtering, H.; Wiersma, D.; et al. Association of genetic variants of the histamine H1 and muscarinic M3 receptors with BMI and HbA1c values in patients on antipsychotic medication. *Psychopharmacology* **2011**, *216*, 257–265. [CrossRef]
50. Mehta, R.; Birerdinc, A.; Wang, L.; Younoszai, Z.; Moazzez, A.; Elariny, H.; Goodman, Z.; Chandhoke, V.; Baranova, A.; Younossi, Z.M. Expression of energy metabolism related genes in the gastric tissue of obese individuals with non-alcoholic fatty liver disease. *BMC Gastroenterol.* **2014**, *14*, 72. [CrossRef]
51. Shao, L.; Chen, Y.; Zhang, S.; Zhang, Z.; Cao, Y.; Yang, D.; Wang, M.W. Modulating effects of RAMPs on signaling profiles of the glucagon receptor family. *Acta Pharm. Sin. B* **2022**, *12*, 637–650. [CrossRef] [PubMed]
52. Wang, M.; Lyu, J.; Zhang, C. Single transmembrane GPCR modulating proteins: Neither single nor simple. *Protein Cell* **2023**, *15*, 395–402. [CrossRef] [PubMed]
53. Ellis, C.; Nature Reviews Drug Discovery GPCR Questionnaire Participants. The state of GPCR research in 2004. *Nat. Rev. Drug Discov.* **2004**, *3*, 577–626. [CrossRef]
54. Lovejoy, J.C.; Champagne, C.M.; de Jonge, L.; Xie, H.; Smith, S.R. Increased visceral fat and decreased energy expenditure during the menopausal transition. *Int. J. Obes.* **2008**, *32*, 949–958. [CrossRef]
55. Liu, T.; Kamiyoshi, A.; Tanaka, M.; Iida, S.; Sakurai, T.; Ichikawa-Shindo, Y.; Kawate, H.; Hirabayashi, K.; Dai, K.; Cui, N.; et al. RAMP3 deficiency enhances postmenopausal obesity and metabolic disorders. *Peptides* **2018**, *110*, 10–18. [CrossRef] [PubMed]

56. He, L.; Gunn, T.M.; Bouley, D.M.; Lu, X.Y.; Watson, S.J.; Schlossman, S.F.; Duke-Cohan, J.S.; Barsh, G.S. A biochemical function for attractin in agouti-induced pigmentation and obesity. *Nat. Genet.* **2001**, *27*, 40–47. [CrossRef]
57. Klebig, M.L.; Wilkinson, J.E.; Geisler, J.G.; Woychik, R.P. Ectopic expression of the agouti gene in transgenic mice causes obesity, features of type II diabetes, and yellow fur. *Proc. Natl. Acad. Sci. USA* **1995**, *92*, 4728–4732. [CrossRef]
58. Walker, W.P.; Aradhya, S.; Hu, C.L.; Shen, S.; Zhang, W.; Azarani, A.; Lu, X.; Barsh, G.S.; Gunn, T.M. Genetic analysis of attractin homologs. *Genesis* **2007**, *45*, 744–756. [CrossRef]
59. de Luis, D.A.; Almansa, R.; Aller, R.; Izaola, O.; Romero, E. Gene expression analysis identify a metabolic and cell function alterations as a hallmark of obesity without metabolic syndrome in peripheral blood, a pilot study. *Clin. Nutr.* **2018**, *37*, 1348–1353. [CrossRef] [PubMed]
60. Harasymowicz, N.S.; Azfer, A.; Burnett, R.; Simpson, H.; Salter, D.M. Chondrocytes from osteoarthritic cartilage of obese patients show altered adiponectin receptors expression and response to adiponectin. *J. Orthop. Res.* **2021**, *39*, 2333–2339. [CrossRef]
61. Elchebly, M.; Payette, P.; Michaliszyn, E.; Cromlish, W.; Collins, S.; Loy, A.L.; Normandin, D.; Cheng, A.; Himms-Hagen, J.; Chan, C.C.; et al. Increased insulin sensitivity and obesity resistance in mice lacking the protein tyrosine phosphatase-1B gene. *Science* **1999**, *283*, 1544–1548. [CrossRef] [PubMed]
62. Zabolotny, J.M.; Bence-Hanulec, K.K.; Stricker-Krongrad, A.; Haj, F.; Wang, Y.; Minokoshi, Y.; Kim, Y.B.; Elmquist, J.K.; Tartaglia, L.A.; Kahn, B.B.; et al. PTP1B regulates leptin signal transduction in vivo. *Dev. Cell* **2002**, *2*, 489–495. [CrossRef] [PubMed]
63. Klaman, L.D.; Boss, O.; Peroni, O.D.; Kim, J.K.; Martino, J.L.; Zabolotny, J.M.; Moghal, N.; Lubkin, M.; Kim, Y.B.; Sharpe, A.H.; et al. Increased energy expenditure, decreased adiposity, and tissue-specific insulin sensitivity in protein-tyrosine phosphatase 1B-deficient mice. *Mol. Cell. Biol.* **2000**, *20*, 5479–5489. [CrossRef]
64. Zhen, J.; Liu, S.; Kam, R.Y.L.; Zhao, G.; Peng, H.; Liang, J.; Xu, A.; Li, C.; Ren, L.; Wu, J.; et al. Association of beta-2-microglobulin, cystatin C and lipocalin-2 with stroke risk in the general Chinese population. *Ann. Med.* **2023**, *55*, 2203516. [CrossRef]
65. Rabinowich, L.; Fishman, S.; Hubel, E.; Thurm, T.; Park, W.J.; Pewzner-Jung, Y.; Saroha, A.; Erez, N.; Halpern, Z.; Futerman, A.H.; et al. Sortilin deficiency improves the metabolic phenotype and reduces hepatic steatosis of mice subjected to diet-induced obesity. *J. Hepatol.* **2015**, *62*, 175–181. [CrossRef]
66. Goettsch, C.; Kjolby, M.; Aikawa, E. Sortilin and Its Multiple Roles in Cardiovascular and Metabolic Diseases. *Arterioscler. Thromb. Vasc. Biol.* **2018**, *38*, 19–25. [CrossRef] [PubMed]
67. Lee, J.H.; Gao, J.; Kosinski, P.A.; Elliman, S.J.; Hughes, T.E.; Gromada, J.; Kemp, D.M. Heat shock protein 90 (HSP90) inhibitors activate the heat shock factor 1 (HSF1) stress response pathway and improve glucose regulation in diabetic mice. *Biochem. Biophys. Res. Commun.* **2013**, *430*, 1109–1113. [CrossRef]
68. Jing, E.; Sundararajan, P.; Majumdar, I.D.; Hazarika, S.; Fowler, S.; Szeto, A.; Gesta, S.; Mendez, A.J.; Vishnudas, V.K.; Sarangarajan, R.; et al. Hsp90β knockdown in DIO mice reverses insulin resistance and improves glucose tolerance. *Nutr. Metab.* **2018**, *15*, 11. [CrossRef]
69. John, K.; Marino, J.S.; Sanchez, E.R.; Hinds, T.D., Jr. The glucocorticoid receptor: Cause of or cure for obesity? *Am. J. Physiol. Endocrinol. Metab.* **2016**, *310*, E249–E257. [CrossRef]
70. Lin, R.C.; Wang, X.L.; Dalziel, B.; Caterson, I.D.; Morris, B.J. Association of obesity, but not diabetes or hypertension, with glucocorticoid receptor N363S variant. *Obes. Res.* **2003**, *11*, 802–808. [CrossRef]
71. Rosmond, R.; Chagnon, Y.C.; Holm, G.; Chagnon, M.; Pérusse, L.; Lindell, K.; Carlsson, B.; Bouchard, C.; Björntorp, P. A glucocorticoid receptor gene marker is associated with abdominal obesity, leptin, and dysregulation of the hypothalamic-pituitary-adrenal axis. *Obes. Res.* **2000**, *8*, 211–218. [CrossRef] [PubMed]
72. Kaminska, D.; Hämäläinen, M.; Cederberg, H.; Käkelä, P.; Venesmaa, S.; Miettinen, P.; Ilves, I.; Herzig, K.H.; Kolehmainen, M.; Karhunen, L.; et al. Adipose tissue INSR splicing in humans associates with fasting insulin level and is regulated by weight loss. *Diabetologia* **2014**, *57*, 347–351. [CrossRef] [PubMed]
73. Belfiore, A.; Frasca, F.; Pandini, G.; Sciacca, L.; Vigneri, R. Insulin receptor isoforms and insulin receptor/insulin-like growth factor receptor hybrids in physiology and disease. *Endocr. Rev.* **2009**, *30*, 586–623. [CrossRef] [PubMed]
74. Sesti, G.; Marini, M.A.; Tullio, A.N.; Montemurro, A.; Borboni, P.; Fusco, A.; Accili, D.; Lauro, R. Altered expression of the two naturally occurring human insulin receptor variants in isolated adipocytes of non-insulin-dependent diabetes mellitus patients. *Biochem. Biophys. Res. Commun.* **1991**, *181*, 1419–1424. [CrossRef] [PubMed]
75. Wu, O.; Yuan, C.; Leng, J.; Zhang, X.; Liu, W.; Yang, F.; Zhang, H.; Li, J.; Khederzadeh, S.; Jiang, Z.; et al. Colorable role of interleukin (IL)-6 in obesity hypertension: A hint from a Chinese adult case-control study. *Cytokine* **2023**, *168*, 156226. [CrossRef]
76. Roytblat, L.; Rachinsky, M.; Fisher, A.; Greemberg, L.; Shapira, Y.; Douvdevani, A.; Gelman, S. Raised interleukin-6 levels in obese patients. *Obes. Res.* **2000**, *8*, 673–675. [CrossRef] [PubMed]
77. Bastard, J.P.; Jardel, C.; Bruckert, E.; Blondy, P.; Capeau, J.; Laville, M.; Vidal, H.; Hainque, B. Elevated levels of interleukin 6 are reduced in serum and subcutaneous adipose tissue of obese women after weight loss. *J. Clin. Endocrinol. Metab.* **2000**, *85*, 3338–3342. [CrossRef] [PubMed]
78. Kuo, L.E.; Kitlinska, J.B.; Tilan, J.U.; Li, L.; Baker, S.B.; Johnson, M.D.; Lee, E.W.; Burnett, M.S.; Fricke, S.T.; Kvetnansky, R.; et al. Neuropeptide Y acts directly in the periphery on fat tissue and mediates stress-induced obesity and metabolic syndrome. *Nat. Med.* **2007**, *13*, 803–811. [CrossRef] [PubMed]
79. Amisten, S.; Neville, M.; Hawkes, R.; Persaud, S.J.; Karpe, F.; Salehi, A. An atlas of G-protein coupled receptor expression and function in human subcutaneous adipose tissue. *Pharmacol. Ther.* **2015**, *146*, 61–93. [CrossRef]

80. Gericke, M.T.; Kosacka, J.; Koch, D.; Nowicki, M.; Schröder, T.; Ricken, A.M.; Nieber, K.; Spanel-Borowski, K. Receptors for NPY and PACAP differ in expression and activity during adipogenesis in the murine 3T3-L1 fibroblast cell line. *Br. J. Pharmacol.* **2009**, *157*, 620–632. [CrossRef]
81. Serradeil-Le Gal, C.; Lafontan, M.; Raufaste, D.; Marchand, J.; Pouzet, B.; Casellas, P.; Pascal, M.; Maffrand, J.P.; Le Fur, G. Characterization of NPY receptors controlling lipolysis and leptin secretion in human adipocytes. *FEBS Lett.* **2000**, *475*, 150–156. [CrossRef] [PubMed]
82. Sitticharoon, C.; Chatree, S.; Churintaraphan, M. Expressions of neuropeptide Y and Y1 receptor in subcutaneous and visceral fat tissues in normal weight and obese humans and their correlations with clinical parameters and peripheral metabolic factors. *Regul. Pept.* **2013**, *185*, 65–72. [CrossRef] [PubMed]

separations

MDPI

Article

Ultrasonic Pretreatment Combined with Microwave-Assisted Hydrodistillation for Extraction of Essential Oil from *Melaleuca bracteata* 'Revolution Gold' Leaves Scales Induced by Cellulase-Inorganic Salt and Its Anti-Fungal Activity

Yan Huang [1], Xiaonan Zhang [1,2,*], Fajian Zeng [1], Jinmei Chang [1,2,*] and Zhiwei Liu [1,2,*]

[1] Life Science College, Jiaying University, Meizhou 514015, China; yanhuang@jyu.edu.cn (Y.H.); fajianzeng@163.com (F.Z.)

[2] Guangdong Provincial Key Laboratory of Conservation and Precision Utilization of Characteristic Agricultural Resources in Mountainous Areas, Meizhou 514015, China

* Correspondence: xiaonanzhang@neau.edu.cn (X.Z.); cjm231@126.com (J.C.); zhweiliu@jyu.edu.cn (Z.L.); Tel.: +86-07-5321-86713 (X.Z.); Fax: +86-07-5321-86877 (X.Z.)

Abstract: In order to further develop the commercial use of *Melaleuca bracteata* (F. Muell), this report studied the extraction of essential oil from *Melaleuca bracteata* (F. Muell) leaves using ultrasonic pretreatment, cellulase-inorganic salt soaked and combined with microwave-assisted hydrodistillation. To optimize the primary contributing parameters, the Box–Behnken design (BBD) was applied. The optimum yield of essential oil was 9.61 mL/kg DW at a microwave power of 510.77 W, lithium chloride dose of 63.56 μmol, and microwave irradiation period of 46.97 min. The essential oil included a total of 41 compounds, and methyl eugenol (76.53%) and methyl cinnamate (12.62%) were the main compounds. The inhibitory impact was notable when the essential oil concentration was 1.6 mg/mL. Therefore, it has the potential to replace chemical pesticides. When the concentration of the essential oil solution was 1.6 mg/mL, the three pathogenic species of fungus (*Pseudocercospora psidii*, *Colletotrichum eriobotryae*, and *Colletotrichum siamense*) were greatly affected; at this dose, the fungus was unable to develop and its growth diameter was 0 mm. Additionally, the fungus's inhibition rate reached 100%.

Keywords: microwave-assisted hydrodistillation; leaves of *Melaleuca bracteata*; cellulase-inorganic salt; fungal inhibition effects

1. Introduction

Fungal diseases are frequent in agricultural production and continue to affect the healthy growth of plants and products. *Pseudocercospora psidii* is an asexual ascomyces fungus [1] that has been found to cause serious harm to crops and fruits such as eggplants [2], guavas [3], and bananas [4], causing leaf browning [5]. Anthrax is mainly caused by *Colletotrichum eriobotryae* and *Colletotrichum siamense*, which are difficult to remove [6,7]. They frequently parasitize *Ziziphus jujuba* Mill [8], chili [9], avocado [10], and other plant leaves and fruit surfaces.

With the growth of new plants, illnesses continue to be propagated and spread by rain, insects, and other means, culminating in an irreversible condition [11] and causing widespread sores and infections. Eventually, the fruit wilts, and the leaves wither, resulting in significant economic waste [12]. The most efficient technique to manage illnesses is to spray pesticides to kill hazardous germs. However, according to studies, these chemical synthetic pesticides promote fungal disease resistance [13], and pesticide residues and environmental pollution are major concerns caused by pesticide usage [14]. The primary drawbacks of synthetic pesticides include increased hidden hazards, unexpected effects, and incapacity to deal with disease outbreaks [15,16].

Natural plant essential oils (EOs) are hydrophobic and consist of a range of volatile chemicals [17]. The chemical makeup of essential oils is heavily influenced by geographical region, plant location, soil type, plant water content, and even extraction methods. Because essential oils are diverse, their fungal inhibition effect does not rely on a single mechanism but rather on a number of various routes and processes [18]. The synergistic effect of the chemicals in essential oils can cause leaking of the fungus's cell membranes, cytoplasmic material, and ions, causing the fungus to die. *Melaleuca bracteata* is an aromatic plant of the genus *Myrtle* native to Australia and is now widely dispersed around the world [19], including Indonesia, South Asia, and southern China [20,21].

There is a distinct perfume emanating from the branches and leaves of *Melaleuca bracteata*, and prior research has indicated that certain parts of the plant are abundant in fragrant essential oils. In addition to being utilized as a premium plant scent, *Melaleuca bracteata*'s branches and leaves are used to extract essential oils, which are today one of the most widely used and very valuable ingredients in Europe for the production of perfumes. Furthermore, it has recently been demonstrated that *Melaleuca bracteata* possesses a wide range of pharmacological activities both in vivo and in vitro, including effects on tumor inhibition [22], antibacterial [23], anti-inflammatory [24], skin disease, stroke, wound infection, and antiulcer [25]. Aromatic agents and fungal inhibition agents [24] are widely distributed in the leaves of *Melaleuca bracteata* (LMB). Martina B et al. researched the ecology and biology of essential oils and their fungal inhibition activity and found that essential oils have potential antifungal and antibacterial effects on organisms that harm plant or human health [26].

An energy-wasting traditional method for extracting essential oils is steam distillation; the stability and content of essential oils will also be impacted to differing degrees by the prolonged exposure to high temperatures. Research focus is currently being paid to a number of challenges, including energy conservation, environmental pollution, and global ecological warming (carbon emissions). Therefore, there is an urgent need for an extraction process with reduced resource consumption and higher ecological sustainability in order to ensure the production, composition, and activity of essential oils.

The plant cell wall is a low-permeability tissue. To improve the extraction impact of essential oils, the salting-out method is frequently employed as a pretreatment method for fresh raw materials. This approach will break the plant cell wall in the leaves and then increase the release of volatile chemicals [27]. Avelina Franco-Vega et al. used a salt-out method to pretreat leaves [28], which had the effect of destroying the plant cell wall, thus increasing the essential oil extraction rate. Zaizhi Liu et al. used a solvent-free microwave-assisted method to pretreat fresh leaves, which had the effect of increasing extraction efficiency [29]. The "cavitation effect", tissue fragmentation, solvent shuttle, and deoxidation are the mechanisms behind ultrasonic action. Using ultrasonic can increase essential oil yield quickly.

In order to pretreat raw materials collaboratively, green ultrasonic pretreatment and the addition of a cellulase-inorganic salt mixed aqueous solution can hasten the release of active ingredients in plant tissues, lower liquid surface tension, enhance the osmotic pressure of active ingredients in cells, and increase the dispersion of substances in the solution. The above method can be used to more correctly assess essential oil yield while preventing hydrosol production in high-temperature water, which can lead to loss of essential oil and water contamination. The solution containing metal ions may effectively decrease the boiling time, minimize the heating gradient, and accomplish the boiling effect in a quick period during the microwave radiation process. Although lithium chloride is a good extraction catalyst, it is rarely cited or employed [30]. We speculate that microwave irradiation of an aqueous solution containing inorganic salt can rapidly absorb microwave energy and hence decrease the extraction time. Furthermore, cellulase pretreatment may efficiently degrade the cell wall in plant leaves, increasing the degree of cell wall damage. HeLa Mahmoudi et al. employed enzymatic pretreatment to boost essential oil output [31].

The application of cellulase-inorganic salt solution for raw material treatment, as well as in LMB essential oil extraction, has not yet been documented. We believe that combining the exceedingly effective salting-out method with the selective enzyme catalysis method may yield unexpected results. Additionally, we used three distinct fungi (*Pseudocercospora psidii*, *Colletotrichum eriobotryae*, and *Colletotrichum siamense*) as research subjects and verified the LMB essential oil's inherent inhibitory impact on fungi, in the hopes of offering a useful guide for real applications.

2. Material and Method

2.1. Materials

The fresh raw materials were gathered from Jiying University (Meizhou, China), and the collected leaves are dried in a dry and ventilated place to remove moisture. We purchased anhydrous versions of dimethyl sulfoxone, anhydrous sodium sulfate, anhydrous sodium chloride, and anhydrous ethanol from Shandong Aowei Chemical Co., Ltd. in Jinan, China (purity $\geq$ 98%). Tianjin Kemiou Chemical Reagent Co., Ltd. (Tianjin, China) supplied the chromatographically pure N-hexane that was used. *Pseudocercospora fungus*, *Colletotrichum siamense*, and *Colletotrichum eriobotryae* were obtained from the China Fungus Preservation Center.

2.2. Essential Oil Extraction

A desktop numerical control ultrasonic cleaner (KQ-100DE, Kunshan, China; 300 mm $\times$ 150 mm $\times$ 100 mm) was employed for the ultrasonic preprocessing. This apparatus had two Centro symmetric transducers with a 45 kHz operating frequency, 40–100 W of programmable power, and 20–100 °C of operating temperature. To determine the water content, we first dried fresh LMB for 24 h at a steady temperature and calculated water content. At the beginning, 100 g of fresh LMB was first ground into a 20-mesh powder and then placed in a flask with a round bottom. The raw material was then soaked in catalyst solution (with a liquid–solid ratio range of 3–12) between 0–75 µmol (the ratio of cellulase to lithium chloride was 1:1); the aforementioned solution is treated in an ultrasonic environment with 100 W of power and 50 °C of temperature for 5 h. The essential oil was separated using microwave-assisted distillation under the following conditions: the microwave-assisted distillation device for extracting essential oil consisted of a P70D20N1P-G5 microwave oven (Galanz, Zhongshan, China), a reflux condenser, and a Clevenger extraction tube (Figure 1). The microwave radiation frequency of the oven was 2450 MHz, and its microwave irradiation power was continuously adjustable between 120–700 W. The reactor, a 1000 mL round-bottom flask placed in the inner chamber of the microwave oven, needed the Clevenger tube to pass through the top of the appliance and connect, with a solid–liquid ratio of 4–12 mL/g, extraction period of 10–60 min, and microwave irradiation power of 144–720 W.

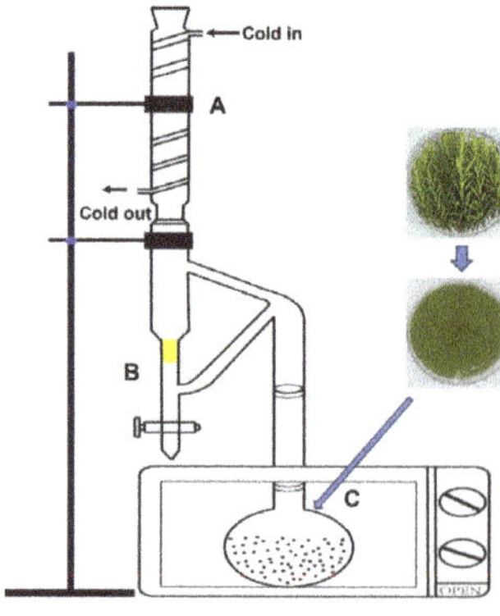

Figure 1. Microwave-assisted extraction of essential oils (A: Circulating water condenser, B: Essential oil collector, and C: Round bottom flask-1000 mL).

2.3. Box–Behnken Design Optimizes the Extraction Rate of Essential Oils

To statistically optimize the essential oil yield, we use response surface methodology (Design-Expert 10) to examine the effects of each variable and level on the yield as well as the correlation between variable values and response values, including analysis of variance and fitting of quadratic regression equations.

2.4. Essential Oil Composition and Analysis

Gas chromatography–mass spectrometry was performed (Agilent-7000 GC/MS, Santa Clara, CA, USA), using a capillary column type, with a nonpolar capillary column (30 m × 0.25 mm × 320 μm) made of fused silica with dimethyl polysiloxane (containing 5% phenyl). A carrier gas of hydrogen was used to identify essential oil components, OV-101 0.1 mL of EO was dissolved in 500 times the volume of n-hexane, and the sample was injected at a column temperature range of 40–200 °C, a heating rate of 10 °C/min, and a column pressure of 0.8 kg/cm^2, among other conditions. The temperature of gasification is 250 °C, and the electron energy is 70 eV. The compound identification was carried out through the library database and chemical composition analysis method for EO components, and data were analyzed and counted through hierarchical data packet inspection tools of chiplot [32].

2.5. Fungal Inhibition Activity

2.5.1. Activation of Strains

To create the suspensions, we used a 6 mm diameter cake that was drilled into the center of the medium at a dense and uniform growth location. We then cultured the cake for 7 days at 28 °C in a constant temperature incubator, inoculated the activated fungal material into sterile PDB medium, and incubated the mixture for 48 h on a rotating shaking table at 28 °C (150 r/min).

2.5.2. Fungal Inhibition of Essential Oil

In a 200 mL triangle bottle, sterilized PDA (89.5 mL) medium was added. The essential oil with the corresponding gradient (the essential oil's concentration range was 0.1–1.6 mg, dissolved in 0.5 mL DMSO) was then added to the PDA, mixed thoroughly, and poured into a petri dish with a diameter of 90 mm. PDA without essential oil was used as the negative control. The medium containing essential oil was created with a specific range of concentrations (the concentration range of essential oil in PDA: 0.1–1.6 mg/mL).

The 6 mm drug-sensitive paper was placed in the center of the sample plate (concentration: 0.1, 0.4, 0.8, 1.6, unit: mg/mL), and 10 μL fungal suspension was added to a tablet, which was sealed and cultivated in a 28 ± 1 °C electric thermostatic incubator. The procedure took 3 days. Tablets with varying amounts of essential oils served as experimental groups, while tablets without essential oils served as negative controls. The colony diameter was measured using the cross-crossing method, and the experiment was performed three times for each group, with the average value taken. The calculation method of the inhibition index:

$$II(\%) = (1 - \frac{Da}{Db}) \times 100\% \quad (1)$$

II: Inhibition index, *Da*: Fungal growth during treatment (mm), *Db*: Fungal growth in the control group (mm).

3. Results and Discussion

3.1. Influence of Various Factors on Extraction Rate

As indicated in Figure 2, raw materials were soaked and pretreated with a lithium chloride inorganic salt solution, cellulase solution, and cellulase-lithium chloride (1:1) combination solution (treatment temperature 50 °C, solution concentration range 5–75 μmol). The essential oil yield of all treated samples increased in a positive relationship with the concentration of catalyst. As demonstrated in Figure 2C, the yield of essential oil following cellulase-inorganic salt treatment was the highest of all samples, at 12.09 mL/kg DW (dry weight). The combined catalyst showed a stronger extraction effect than the other two samples, which had the greatest essential oil yields of 9.01 mL/kgDW and 9.35 mL/kgDW, respectively.

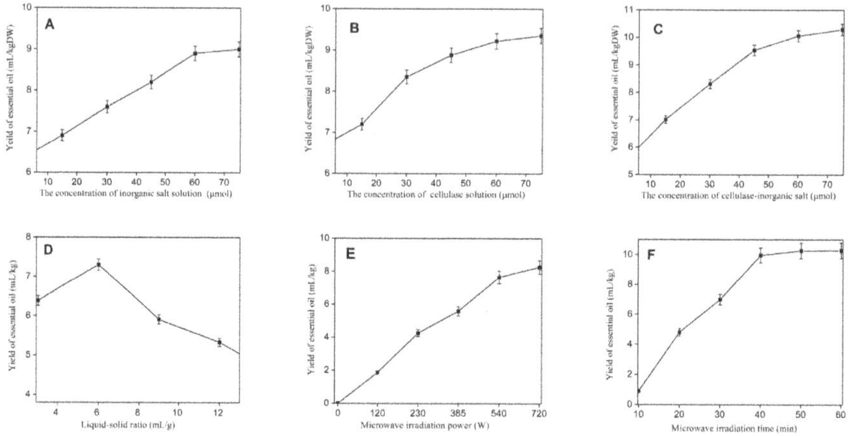

Figure 2. Effect of factors on the yield of essential oil. The above subgraphs show the effects of (**A**) inorganic salt concentration, (**B**) concentration of cellulase solution, (**C**) cellulase-inorganic salt concentration, (**D**) liquid-solid ratio, (**E**) microwave irradiation power and (**F**) microwave irradiation time on yield of essential oil.

We hypothesized that since cellulase and lithium chloride ions synergistically increased the damaging impact on the plant cell wall, essential oil components escaped, resulting in an increase in essential oil output. Lithium chloride is a metal catalyst that may improve the activity of cellulase. Chen et al. investigated the synergistic impact of metal ions and enzymes on cell wall flocculation [33]. A modest combination of cellulase and inorganic salts can act together to boost yields by raising the boiling point of water in plant cells and removing fiber networks in plant cell walls. Ultrasonic technology and combined water bath container-ultrasonic device approaches are the two forms of ultrasound-assisted surgery. To save energy, the ultrasonic probe can be positioned in close contact with the substance. There aren't many reports of combining normal ultrasound-assisted extraction technology with microwave technology to extract essential oils, despite the fact that this method is frequently employed in the process of essential oil separation.

We evaluated the effect of the liquid–solid ratio, microwave irradiation power, and microwave duration on essential oil production. Figure 2D depicts the impact of several liquid–solid ratios (3–12 mL/g) on the yield of three EOs. The essential oil output was 6.38 mL/kg DW when the liquid–solid ratio was 3. The essential oil yield was maximum when the liquid–solid ratio reached 6, reaching 7.30 mL/kg DW, and subsequently dropped as the liquid–solid ratio increased. As a result, a liquid–solid ratio of 6 is chosen as the ideal. It has been found that increasing the liquid–solid ratio decreases the mass transfer resistance and boosts the essential oil yield; however, increasing the liquid–solid ratio causes the forced loss of chemical components in essential oils. We assume that the increased liquid–solid ratio caused some of the essential oil to dissolve in the water, causing the extraction rate to vanish.

Figure 2E depicts the effect of various power ranges (230–700 W) on the experiment. The maximum essential oil obtained when the microwave power exceeds 700 W is 8.27 mL/kgDW. We chose the yield of essential oil produced at 540 W (7.65 mL/kg DW) as the level for the following experiment based on the regular connection between the cost and yield of essential oil. Microwave irradiation at specific levels can accelerate the extraction process and enhance the release of essential oils [34], but utilizing too much power might result in fast temperature fluctuations that impact the yield and quality of essential oils. Figure 2F depicts the influence of the microwave irradiation time on the extraction rate. The increasing rate of essential oil yield is roughly the same once the extraction duration approaches 50 min. This phenomenon might be induced by uneven internal heating of the material over a short period of time. Long-term microwave irradiation causes osmotic pressure inside the material, and high-frequency vibration is produced as a result of water conduction between the materials during microwave irradiation. As a consequence of additional experimental adjustment, 50 min (10.27 mL/kgDW) was chosen. Since the yield in the trials is mostly unaffected by the liquid–solid ratio, we decided to base future optimization on the microwave power and time.

3.2. The Extraction Rate of Essential Oil Was Optimized by Response Surface

To create and refine the statistical analysis of EO yield, we investigated the ideal process parameters for each element in the test range. Through the optimized outcomes, we discovered that $p = 0.0011$ was a significant value. The response surface data are in good agreement with the experimental results, and the C, AB, and BC items have no significant influence ($p > 0.05$). The lack of fit term is 0.0917, R^2 is 0.9466, CV is 5.45%, unknown factors had little impact on the experiment, the error was within the acceptable range, and the response surface data were in good agreement with the experimental results (Table 1). As a result, the examination of the response surface model yields the following theoretically optimum conclusion: the greatest production of essential oil was 9.73 mL/kg DW when all the indices achieved the optimal values, which occurred when the microwave irradiation power was 488.54 W, the microwave irradiation period was 48.21 min, and the lithium salt addition was 64.51 μmol.

Table 1. Box–Behnken design with experimental value for total yield of EO, and analysis of variance (ANOVA) for response surface quadratic model.

Run	BBD Experiments				ANOVA							
	A (W)	B (min)	C (μmol)	Y_{EO} (mL/kg)	Source of Variation	Sum of Squares	Degree of Freedom	Mean Square	*F* Value	*p* Value		
1	576	50	60	9.31	Model	24.59	9	2.73	13.78	0.0011 *		
2	576	50	60	9.82	A	1.44	1	1.44	7.29	0.0306		
3	576	50	60	9.73	B	3.51	1	3.51	17.71	0.0040		
4	720	60	60	6.98	C	0.061	1	0.06	0.31	0.5956		
5	720	40	60	7.92	AB	0	1	0.00	0.00	1.0000		
6	720	50	75	6.00	AC	4.41	1	4.41	22.25	0.0022		
7	576	40	45	8.11	BC	0.20	1	0.20	1.02	0.3458		
8	720	50	45	8.22	A^2	2.78	1	2.78	14.02	0.0072		
9	432	50	45	7.63	B^2	6.98	1	6.98	35.21	0.0006		
10	576	60	75	6.21	C^2	3.70	1	3.70	18.67	0.0035		
11	576	50	60	9.90	Residual	1.39	7	0.19				
12	432	50	75	9.60	Lack of fit	1.07	3	0.36	4.45	0.0917		
13	576	60	45	6.90	Pure error	0.32	4	0.08				
14	432	60	60	7.16	Cor total	25.98	16					
15	576	40	75	8.36	Credibility analysis of the regression equations							
16	432	40	60	8.18	Index mark	SD	Mean	C.V.%	R^2	Adjust R^2	Predicted R^2	AP
17	576	50	60	9.32	Y	0.4452	8.17	5.45	0.9466	0.8779	0.3232	9.7009

SD: standard deviation; AP: adequacy precision. *: Significant.

The regression equation of the response surface analysis fitted data is as follows:

$$Y = 9.6 - 0.425A - 0.6625B - 0.088C - 1.05AC - 0.225BC - 0.8125A^2 - 1.29B^2 - 0.9375C^2 \quad (2)$$

The 3D response surface, also known as the 3D fitting surface, is the response surface of the microwave irradiation duration, microwave irradiation power, and EO yield of the catalyst addition. In general, there was a favorable link between the yield of essential oil and the expansion of the microwave irradiation power and duration as well as the inclusion of the catalyst. The yield of EO steadily increased as the microwave power and duration increased; however, as time increased, the yield of EO displayed a curve.

The maximum EO extraction rate (8.9 mL/kgDW), as shown in Figure 3A, occurs when the microwave period is 47 min and the microwave power is 480 W. The yield of EOs was influenced quadratically by the strength of the microwave irradiation and the quantity of catalyst supplied, as shown in Figure 3B. The EO yield was maximum (9.41 mL/kgDW) when the catalyst addition was 60 µmol and the microwave power was 650 W. The interaction effects of catalyst addition quantity and microwave irradiation period on EO yield are shown in Figure 3C. The yield of EOs rose as the catalyst concentration increased between 46–60 µmol; however, when the catalyst concentration grew as a percentage, the liquid–solid ratio continued to rise after reaching its ideal level. The essential oil extraction technique maintains a high temperature in the microwave oven by increasing the microwave power or microwave duration.

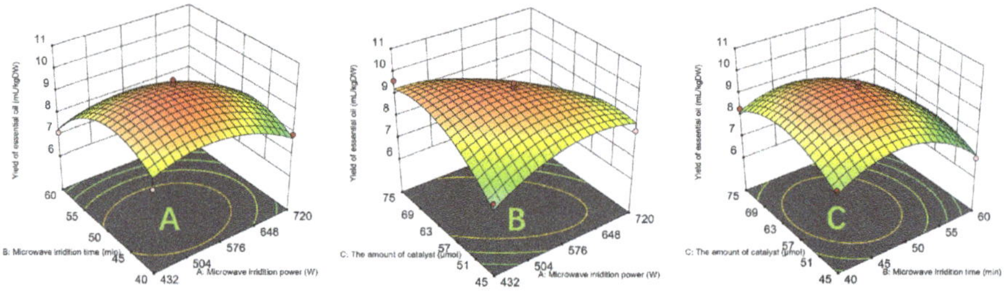

Figure 3. The essential oil was optimized by Box–Behnken design. (**A**) The interaction effects of microwave power and time on the yield of essential oil, (**B**) the interaction effects of catalyst addition amount and microwave power on the yield of essential oil, and (**C**) the interaction of catalyst addition amount and microwave irradiation time on essential oil yield).

3.3. Analysis of Essential Oil by Gas Chromatography–Mass Spectrometry

Forty-one compounds were discovered when the acquired essential oils were first dried and analyzed using GC–MS (Table 2). Methyleugenol (76.53%) makes up most of the essential oil's composition, followed by methyl cinnamate (12.62%). The compounds together make up the entire composition of 97.82%. Methyl eugenol, the primary ingredient in a spice recipe, is the principal component of essential oil. It is also a crucial raw material for the synthesis of chemical compounds. As a result, using GC–MS detection, the essential oil of LMB has the potential to be useful in food safety and clinical treatment [35].

We made a phylogenetic tree map for the classification of different components in essential oils (as is shown in Figure 4), which was categorized based on the composition of various chemical components through cluster analysis, in order to have a more thorough understanding of the composition classification of these compounds; it is easy to observe that alcohols, monoterpenoids, sesquiterpenoids, aldehydes, ketones, and esters make up essential oils. An amount of 13 sesquiterpenoids make up 2.49% of the overall composition of essential oils. Eight different types of alcohol made up 3.71% of the total. The overall oil content was made up of four ketones, which made up 76.63% of the oil content, and five aldehydes, which made up 0.16%. There are two monoterpenoids (0.04%), and three ester compounds (13.1%) were also present. Sesquiterpenoids and alcohols comprised the greatest number of species among all the components that were extracted (Table 2). Ketones (76.63%) and esters (13.1%) had the highest concentrations. Methyleugenol is a significant natural flavoring ingredient with a variety of applications in the food and medicine field. In addition to having biological activities such as antioxidant and antibacterial properties, it also has a spicy and warm scent that is frequently utilized in flavoring agents and perfumes [36]. Methyl cinnamate is an ester molecule that is a typical food flavoring and perfume addition that provides a fresh fruit scent [37].

Table 2. Chemical composition of the essential oil from LMB identified by GC–MS.

Number	Retention Time (min)	Compound Name [A]	RI [B]	Cas #	Similarity (%)	Area Percentage (%) [C]
1	3.81	2-Hexenal, (E)-	848	006728-26-3	98	0.02
2	7.69	O-Cymene	1017	000527-84-4	97	0.03
3	7.80	D-Limonene	1024	005989-27-5	99	0.02
4	7.89	Benzyl alcohol	1033	000100-51-6	95	0.03
5	9.46	Terpinolene	1083	000586-62-9	95	0.02
6	9.76	Linalool	1097	000078-70-6	97	0.76
7	11.18	Isopulegol	1146	000089-79-2	98	0.03
8	11.44	Citronellal	1153	000106-23-0	96	0.02
9	12.34	Terpinen-4-ol	1171	000562-74-3	90	0.19
10	12.65	P-cymenol	1181	001197-01-9	91	0.15
11	12.89	α-Terpineol	1187	010482-56-1	87	0.90
12	13.23	Estragole	1196	000140-67-0	98	0.65
13	14.64	Citronellol	1212	000106-22-9	98	0.71
14	15.34	β-Citral	1236	000106-26-3	87	0.03
15	16.13	P-Chavicol	1254	000501-92-8	95	0.03
16	16.86	Citral	1276	005392-40-5	96	0.06
17	19.41	Methyl geranate	1326	002349-14-6	83	0.21
18	20.51	α-Cubebene	1339	017699-14-8	98	0.02
19	20.74	2,6-Octadiene, 2,6-dimethyl-	1351	002792-39-4	95	0.15
20	20.85	Chavibetol	1362	000501-19-9	98	0.79
21	21.60	α-Copaene	1376	1000360-33-0	99	0.11
22	21.97	Methyl cinnamate	1388	000103-26-4	95	12.62
23	23.14	Methyleugenol	1408	000093-15-2	98	76.53
24	23.39	Caryophyllene	1420	000087-44-5	96	0.55
25	23.80	β-Cubebene	1425	013744-15-5	93	0.06
26	24.16	10 s,11 s-Himachala-3(12),4-diene	1437	060909-28-6	86	0.02
27	24.97	Alloaromadendrene	1463	025246-27-9	99	0.08
28	25.48	γ-Cadinene	1470	039029-41-9	83	0.03
29	25.60	γ-Muurolene	1477	030021-74-0	98	0.08
30	25.76	D-Germacrene	1487	023986-74-5	98	0.66
31	26.45	Methylisoeugenol	1492	000093-16-3	96	0.08
32	26.56	α-Muurolene	1493	031983-22-9	99	0.06
33	27.15	α-Amorphene	1495	000483-75-0	97	0.06
34	27.57	Calamenene	1511	000483-77-2	96	0.66
35	27.98	Cadinadiene-1,4	1524	016728-99-7	98	0.10
36	29.31	Elemicin	1558	000487-11-6	97	0.35
37	30.26	Espatulenol	1566	006750-60-3	99	0.27
38	31.57	Ledol	1580	000577-27-5	98	0.05
39	33.99	α-Cadinol	1651	000481-34-5	99	0.18
40	36.91	Methyl tri-O-methylgallate	1669	001916-07-0	98	0.42
41	38.27	Benzyl Benzoate	1753	000120-51-4	93	0.03
	Total					97.82

[A]: Compounds listed in order of elution from the HP-5MS capillary column; [B]: Retention indices relative to C11–C21 n-alkanes on the HP-5MS capillary column; [C]: Relative area percentage (peak area relative to the total peak area, %).

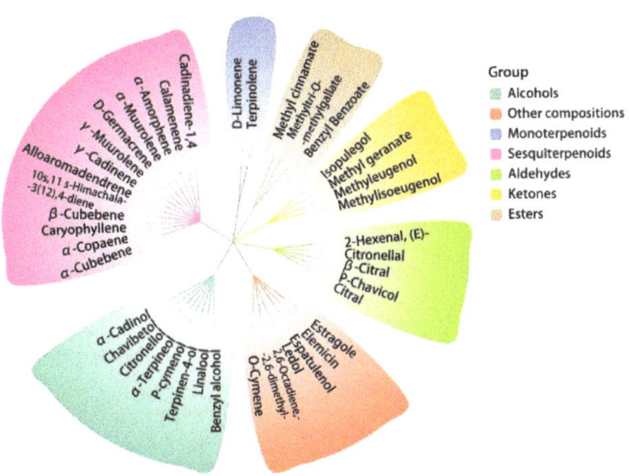

Figure 4. Phylogenetic tree characterization of different compounds in essential oil.

3.4. Comparison with Reference Techniques

The conventional approach for extracting essential oil from water using microwave-assisted hydrodistillation involves directly irradiating the material with a microwave; however, this method is not successful for homogenizing the material due to the absence of an ultrasonic device. By using a high-frequency microwave field instead of the conventional microwave heating extraction method, we are able to fully collide the material within the molecule under the action of the microwave, allowing electromagnetic energy to enter as heat energy. This improves the ability to extract material, speeds up temperature, and yields excellent extra essential oil. The extraction efficiency of this study is much greater than that of the conventional approach when compared to the two experimental procedures mentioned above.

3.5. Study on Antifungal Activity of Essential Oils

Methyl cinnamate also possesses anti-bacterial, anti-inflammatory, and other biological properties. Due to its distinct scent and specific biological activity, the essential oil of LMB has several potential uses in the culinary, taste, and medical industries, among other disciplines [38]. Figure 5 illustrates the impact of LMB essential oil on the development of fungal fluids. The essential oil clearly inhibited the growth of three different types of fungal fluids. The growing area of *Pseudocercospora psidii* increased with culture and growth time expansion. After 72 h of cultivation, *Pseudocercospora psidii* exposed to 0.1 mg/mL essential oil showed some inhibition compared to the blank control, with an inhibitory rate of 75.7%. Under the same conditions, the inhibitory activity of essential oil on *Colletotrichum* was the best, reaching 95.26%. The activity of inhibiting *Colletotrichum* reached 80.51%. The three fungi were significantly affected by the essential oil solution when the concentration was 1.6 mg/mL; at this dosage, the fungus could not live, and the inhibition rate reached 100%. The growth of the pathogens *Colletotrichum eriobotryae* and *Colletotrichum siamense* was considerably suppressed by the LMB essential oils and were more susceptible than *Pseudocercospora psidii*.

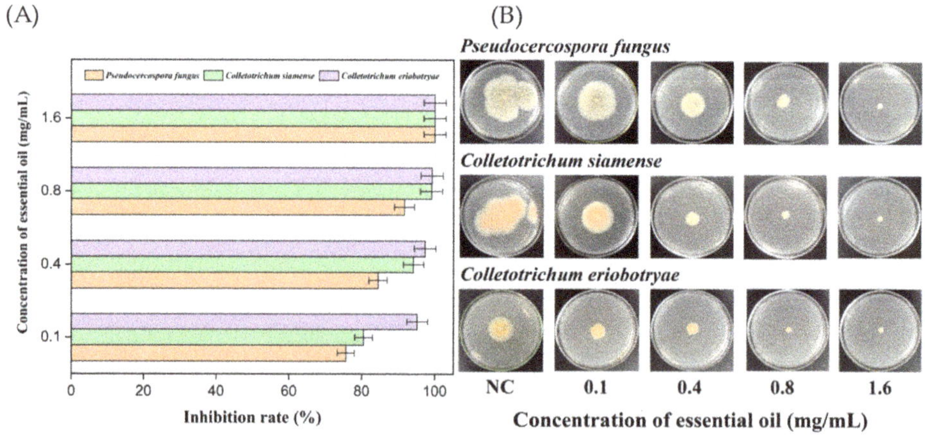

Figure 5. Inhibitory effect of essential oils on fungi. (**A**) Rate of inhibition; and (**B**) vary concentration of essential on the inhibit effects of fungi.

Methyleugenol has been shown to have potent fungal inhibition action in earlier research hence, it is hypothesized that these highly lipophilic compounds are the primary cause of inhibition activity in this work. The lipophilic characteristics of these aliphatic chemicals are sufficient to split and alter the structure of lipophilic lipids in mitochondria and the cell plasma membrane, causing leakage of the contents of fungal cells. This is how this inhibition mechanism works. The results of the inhibition studies indicate that the essential oil has tremendous potential for preventing plant infection and preserving fruits and vegetables, as well as for use as a natural pesticide. In addition to variations in EO components, variations in fungal test procedures may affect the findings of essential oil inhibition activities in diverse research. After the fungal culture experiment, the fungus in the negative control (NC) environment expanded rapidly, and the inhibitory impact on the fungi gradually became stronger as the essential oil content increased (Figure 5B). The fungus entirely vanished at a dosage of 10 mg/mL essential oil. This capability can be connected to the quantity of hydrophobic chemical groups in the oil, which prevent fungal cells from retaining water and cause their demise. Additionally, the primary component of EO, methylleugenol, may also be the key factor contributing to fungal mortality. EOs are frequently used to enhance the flavor and quality of food. This further suggests that EOs are regarded as safe by the US Food and Drug Administration when used as food additives. According to preliminary tests of antimicrobial activity and a study of the literature on ecological and biological features by Martina B et al., essential oils (EOs) may have antifungal effects on a range of organisms that may affect plants or human health substances. Numerous studies have demonstrated that applying plant components can lessen the severity of illnesses in a variety of crops, and using essential oils (EOs) is a useful strategy for managing bacteria and fungi.

4. Conclusions

In this work, we described the ultrasonic pretreatment combined with microwave-assisted hydrodistillation for extraction of essential oil from LMB; three representative fungi were used as references to verify the functionality of EO. The response surface BBD test was used to optimize the extraction rate. The greatest production of essential oil was 9.73 mL/kg DW when all the indices achieved the optimal values, which occurred when the microwave irradiation power was 488.54 W, the microwave irradiation period was 48.21 min, and the lithium salt addition was 64.51 μmol. Methylleugenol, methyl cinnamate, α-terpineol, etc., are the principal substances discovered by GC–MS. *Pseudocercospora psidii*, *Colletotrichum eriobotryae*, and *Colletotrichum siamense* were significantly inhibited by a 1.6 mg/mL essential oil solution, according to the researchers. This suggests that EO is a promising substitute for synthetic pesticides; however, toxicological testing is needed before using these natural products as a natural antibiotic to ensure that they do not harm humans or plants and to better understand the mechanisms by which essential oils affect organisms.

Author Contributions: Conceptualization, X.Z. and Y.H.; methodology, Y.H.; software, Y.H.; validation, X.Z., Y.H. and Z.L.; investigation, J.C.; resources, J.C.; data curation, F.Z.; writing—original draft preparation, X.Z. and F.Z.; writing—review and editing. All authors have read and agreed to the published version of the manuscript.

Funding: Guangdong Province Key Areas of Universities (2023ZDZX4058), Guangdong University Innovation Team Project (2023KCXTD034), Guangdong Province Key Construction Discipline Promotion Project (2022ZDJS087), Research Project of Jiaying College (2023KJY05, 2022KJY09), and Educational Reform Project (PX-29231980).

Data Availability Statement: The publication of such data does not compromise the anonymity of the participants or breach local data protection laws.

Conflicts of Interest: The authors declare no conflict of interest.

References

1. Carlier, J.; Robert, S.; Roussel, V.; Chilin-Charles, Y.; Lubin-Adjanoh, N.; Gilabert, A.; Abadie, C. Central American and Caribbean population history of the *Pseudocercospora fijiensis* fungus responsible for the latest worldwide pandemics on banana. *Fungal Genet. Biol.* **2021**, *148*, 103528. [CrossRef]
2. Gebhardt, C. The historical role of species from the Solanaceae plant family in genetic research. *Theor. Appl. Genet.* **2016**, *129*, 2281–2294. [CrossRef] [PubMed]

3. Seshadri, V.D.; Balasubramanian, B.; Al-Dhabi, N.A.; Esmail, G.A.; Arasu, M.V. Essential oils of *Cinnamomum loureirii* and *Evolvulus alsinoides* protect guava fruits from spoilage bacteria, fungi and insect (*Pseudococcus longispinus*). *Ind. Crops Prod.* **2020**, *154*, 112629. [CrossRef]
4. Alakonya, A.E.; Kimunye, J.; Mahuku, G.; Amah, D.; Uwimana, B.; Brown, A.; Swennen, R. Progress in understanding *Pseudocercospora* banana pathogens and the development of resistant *Musa* germplasm. *Plant Pathol.* **2018**, *67*, 759–770. [CrossRef]
5. Gaikwad, S.S.; Rumma, S.S.; Hangarge, M. *Classification of Fungi Effected Psidium Guajava Leaves Using ML and DL Techniques BT—Computer Vision and Machine Intelligence Paradigms for SDGs*; Kannan, R.J., Thampi, S.M., Wang, S.-H., Eds.; Springer Nature: Singapore, 2023; pp. 69–81.
6. Damm, U.; Sun, Y.-C.; Huang, C.-J. *Colletotrichum eriobotryae* sp. nov. and *C. nymphaeae*, the anthracnose pathogens of loquat fruit in central Taiwan, and their sensitivity to azoxystrobin. *Mycol. Prog.* **2020**, *19*, 367–380. [CrossRef]
7. Li, M.; Feng, W.; Yang, J.; Gao, Z.; Zhang, Z.; Zhang, W.; Wang, S.; Wang, W.; Gong, D.; Hu, M. First report of anthracnose caused by *Colletotrichum siamense* on avocado fruits in China. *Crop Prot.* **2022**, *155*, 105922. [CrossRef]
8. Han, F.; Qi, Y.-K.; Zhang, Y.; Qi, J.-H.; Wang, J.-W.; Liu, W.; Zhang, L.W.; Ji, Y.-P.; Wang, Q.-H. First report of jujube anthracnose caused by *Colletotrichum siamense* in China. *Plant Dis.* **2023**, *107*, 2538. [CrossRef]
9. Krishnan, S.; Kaari, M.; Sawhney, S.; Sheoran, N.; Gautam, R.K.; Mohan Das, M.; Kumar, A. First report of *Colletotrichum siamense* from Andaman and Nicobar Islands causing anthracnose in chilli. *J. Plant Pathol.* **2019**, *101*, 767. [CrossRef]
10. Fuentes-Aragón, D.; Silva-Rojas, H.V.; Guarnaccia, V.; Mora-Aguilera, J.A.; Aranda-Ocampo, S.; Bautista-Martínez, N.; Téliz-Ortíz, D. *Colletotrichum* species causing anthracnose on avocado fruit in Mexico: Current status. *Plant Pathol.* **2020**, *69*, 1513–1528. [CrossRef]
11. Aliya, S.S.S.; Nusaibah, S.A.; Mahyudin, M.M.; Yun, W.M.; Yusop, M.R. *Colletotrichum siamense* and *Pestalotiopsis jesteri* as potential pathogens of new rubber leaf spot disease via detached leaf assay. *J. Rubber Res.* **2022**, *25*, 195–212. [CrossRef]
12. Eh Teet, S.; Hashim, N. Recent advances of application of optical imaging techniques for disease detection in fruits and vegetables: A review. *Food Control.* **2023**, *152*, 109849. [CrossRef]
13. Duhan, J.S.; Kumar, R.; Kumar, N.; Kaur, P.; Nehra, K.; Duhan, S. Nanotechnology: The new perspective in precision agriculture. *Biotechnol. Rep.* **2017**, *15*, 11–23. [CrossRef]
14. Tudi, M.; Daniel Ruan, H.; Wang, L.; Lyu, J.; Sadler, R.; Connell, D.; Chu, C.; Phung, D.T. Agriculture Development, Pesticide Application and Its Impact on the Environment. *Int. J. Environ. Res. Public Health* **2021**, *18*, 1112. [CrossRef]
15. Garrigou, A.; Laurent, C.; Berthet, A.; Colosio, C.; Jas, N.; Daubas-Letourneux, V.; Jackson Filho, J.-M.; Jouzel, J.-N.; Samuel, O.; Baldi, I.; et al. Critical review of the role of PPE in the prevention of risks related to agricultural pesticide use. *Saf. Sci.* **2020**, *123*, 104527. [CrossRef]
16. Luo, L.; Dong, L.; Huang, Q.; Ma, S.; Fantke, P.; Li, J.; Jiang, J.; Fitzgerald, M.; Yang, J.; Jia, Z.; et al. Detection and risk assessments of multi-pesticides in 1771 cultivated herbal medicines by LC/MS-MS and GC/MS-MS. *Chemosphere* **2021**, *262*, 127477. [CrossRef] [PubMed]
17. Hou, T.; Sana, S.S.; Li, H.; Xing, Y.; Nanda, A.; Netala, V.R.; Zhang, Z. Essential oils and its antibacterial, antifungal and anti-oxidant activity applications: A review. *Food Biosci.* **2022**, *47*, 101716. [CrossRef]
18. Álvarez-Martínez, F.J.; Barrajón-Catalán, E.; Herranz-López, M.; Micol, V. Antibacterial plant compounds, extracts and essential oils: An updated review on their effects and putative mechanisms of action. *Phytomedicine* **2021**, *90*, 153626. [CrossRef] [PubMed]
19. Yang, C.; Lin, Y.; Qiu, Z.; Xiang, X.; Shao, D.; Li, Y.; Wu, S. Reference gene selection for qRT-PCR normalization of gene expression analysis in *Melaleuca bracteata* F. Muell. under abiotic stresses and hormonal stimuli. *Sci. Hortic.* **2023**, *319*, 112184. [CrossRef]
20. Padalia, R.C.; Verma, R.S.; Chauhan, A.; Goswami, P.; Verma, S.K.; Darokar, M.P. Chemical composition of *Melaleuca linarrifolia* Sm. from India: A potential source of 1,8-cineole. *Ind. Crops Prod.* **2015**, *63*, 264–268. [CrossRef]
21. Zhang, J.; Wang, Y.; Feng, Y.; Du, S.; Jia, L. Contact Toxicity and Repellent Efficacy of Essential Oil from Aerial Parts of *Melaleuca bracteata* and its Major Compositions against Three Kinds of Insects. *J. Essent. Oil Bear. Plants* **2021**, *24*, 349–359. [CrossRef]
22. Yasin, M.; Younis, A.; Javed, T.; Akram, A.; Ahsan, M.; Shabbir, R.; Ali, M.M.; Tahir, A.; El-Ballat, E.M.; Sheteiwy, M.S.; et al. River Tea Tree Oil: Composition, Antimicrobial and Antioxidant Activities, and Potential Applications in Agriculture. *Plants* **2021**, *10*, 2105. [CrossRef]
23. Bottoni, M.; Milani, F.; Mozzo, M.; Radice Kolloffel, D.A.; Papini, A.; Fratini, F.; Maggi, F.; Santagostini, L. Sub-Tissue Localization of Phytochemicals in *Cinnamomum camphora* (L.) J. Presl. Growing in Northern Italy. *Plants* **2021**, *10*, 1008. [CrossRef] [PubMed]
24. Raman, G.; Gaikar, V.G. Microwave-Assisted Extraction of Piperine from *Piper nigrum*. *Ind. Eng. Chem. Res.* **2002**, *41*, 2521–2528. [CrossRef]
25. Franco-Vega, A.; López-Malo, A.; Palou, E.; Ramírez-Corona, N. Effect of imidazolium ionic liquids as microwave absorption media for the intensification of microwave-assisted extraction of Citrus sinensis peel essential oils. *Chem. Eng. Process. Process Intensif.* **2021**, *160*, 108277. [CrossRef]
26. Liu, Z.; Li, H.; Zhu, Z.; Huang, D.; Qi, Y.; Ma, C.; Zou, Z.; Ni, H. *Cinnamomum camphora* fruit peel as a source of essential oil extracted using the solvent-free microwave-assisted method compared with conventional hydrodistillation. *LWT* **2022**, *153*, 112549. [CrossRef]
27. Hou, K.; Bao, M.; Wang, L.; Zhang, H.; Yang, L.; Zhao, H.; Wang, Z. Aqueous enzymatic pretreatment ionic liquid–lithium salt based microwave–assisted extraction of essential oil and procyanidins from pinecones of *Pinus koraiensis*. *J. Clean. Prod.* **2019**, *236*, 117581. [CrossRef]

28. Mahmoudi, H.; Marzouki, M.; M'Rabet, Y.; Mezni, M.; Ait Ouazzou, A.; Hosni, K. Enzyme pretreatment improves the recovery of bioactive phytochemicals from sweet basil (*Ocimum basilicum* L.) leaves and their hydrodistilled residue by-products, and potentiates their biological activities. *Arab. J. Chem.* **2020**, *13*, 6451–6460. [CrossRef]
29. Xie, J.; Chen, Y.; Cai, G.; Cai, R.; Hu, Z.; Wang, H. Tree Visualization by One Table (tvBOT): A web application for visualizing, modifying and annotating phylogenetic trees. *Nucleic Acids Res.* **2023**, *51*, W587–W592. [CrossRef]
30. Chen, F.; Su, X.; Gao, J.; Liu, Y.; Zhang, Q.; Luo, D. A modified strategy to improve the dissolution of flavonoids from Artemisiae Argyi Folium using ultrasonic-assisted enzyme-deep eutectic solvent system. *J. Chromatogr. A* **2023**, *1707*, 464282. [CrossRef] [PubMed]
31. Kapadiya, S.M.; Parikh, J.; Desai, M.A. A greener approach towards isolating clove oil from buds of *Syzygium aromaticum* using microwave radiation. *Ind. Crops Prod.* **2018**, *112*, 626–632. [CrossRef]
32. Gao, H.; Zhao, R.; Fan, C.; Yang, Y.; Wang, Z.; Gu, H.; Yang, L.; Tian, H.; Zhang, Q.; Zhang, X. An efficient approach to obtain essential oil, oleanoic acid, 3-O-acetyloleanolic acid and betulinic acid from fresh leaves of *Melaleuca bracteata* F. Muell. "Revolution Gold" using microwave and gravity-assisted solvent-free distillation followed by extra. *Ind. Crops Prod.* **2023**, *203*, 117178. [CrossRef]
33. Gooderham, N.J.; Cohen, S.M.; Eisenbrand, G.; Fukushima, S.; Guengerich, F.P.; Hecht, S.S.; Rietjens, I.M.C.M.; Rosol, T.J.; Davidsen, J.M.; Harman, C.L.; et al. FEMA GRAS assessment of natural flavor complexes: Clove, cinnamon leaf and West Indian bay leaf-derived flavoring ingredients. *Food Chem. Toxicol.* **2020**, *145*, 111585. [CrossRef] [PubMed]
34. Guo, D.; Wu, S.; Fu, X.; Pan, H. De Novo Biosynthesis of Methyl Cinnamate in Engineered *Escherichia coli*. *J. Agric. Food Chem.* **2022**, *70*, 7736–7741. [CrossRef] [PubMed]
35. Sosa, L.; Espinoza, L.C.; Valarezo, E.; Bozal, N.; Calpena, A.; Fábrega, M.-J.; Baldomà, L.; Rincón, M.; Mallandrich, M. Therapeutic Applications of Essential Oils from Native and Cultivated Ecuadorian Plants: Cutaneous Candidiasis and Dermal Anti-Inflammatory Activity. *Molecules* **2023**, *28*, 5903. [CrossRef] [PubMed]
36. Xiao, Y.; Liu, Z.; Gu, H.; Yang, L.; Liu, T.; Tian, H. Preparation and characterization of a modified Canna starch as a wall material for the encapsulation of methyleugenol improves its antifungal activity against *Fusarium trichothecioides*. *Food Chem.* **2023**, *433*, 137324. [CrossRef] [PubMed]
37. Liu, X.; Cai, J.; Chen, H.; Zhong, Q.; Hou, Y.; Chen, W.; Chen, W. Antibacterial activity and mechanism of linalool against *Pseudomonas aeruginosa*. *Microb. Pathog.* **2020**, *141*, 103980. [CrossRef]
38. Tomazoni, E.Z.; Pauletti, G.F.; da Silva Ribeiro, R.T.; Moura, S.; Schwambach, J. In vitro and in vivo activity of essential oils extracted from *Eucalyptus staigeriana*, *Eucalyptus globulus* and *Cinnamomum camphora* against *Alternaria solani* Sorauer causing early blight in tomato. *Sci. Hortic.* **2017**, *223*, 72–77. [CrossRef]

antioxidants

MDPI

Article

Norcantharidin Sensitizes Colorectal Cancer Cells to Radiotherapy via Reactive Oxygen Species–DRP1-Mediated Mitochondrial Damage

Qiong Xu [1,2,3], Heng Zhang [1], Haoren Qin [2], Huaqing Wang [1] and Hui Wang [1,*]

[1] Department of Oncology, Tianjin Union Medical Center, Nankai University, Tianjin 300350, China; ezxxuqiong02@163.com (Q.X.); zhangheng@umc.net.cn (H.Z.); wanghuaqing@umc.net.cn (H.W.)
[2] School of Medicine, Nankai University, Tianjin 300350, China; qinhaoren@umc.net.cn
[3] School of Integrative Medicine, Tianjin University of Traditional Chinese Medicine, Tianjin 301600, China
* Correspondence: wanghui2@umc.net.cn

Abstract: Norcantharidin (NCTD), a cantharidin derivative, induces ROS generation and is widely used to treat CRC. In this study, we clarified the role and mechanism of action of norcantharidin in increasing CRC sensitivity to radiotherapy. We treated the CRC cell lines LoVo and DLD-1 with NCTD (10 or 50 μmol/L), ionizing radiation (IR, 6 Gy), and a combination of the two and found that NCTD significantly inhibited the proliferation of CRC cells and enhanced their sensitivity to radiotherapy. NCTD induced ROS generation by decreasing the mitochondrial membrane potential, increasing mitochondrial membrane permeability, and promoting cytochrome C release from mitochondria into the cytoplasm. IR combined with NCTD induced ROS production, which activated the mitochondrial fission protein DRP1, leading to increased mitochondrial fission and CRC sensitivity to radiotherapy. NCTD also reduced CRC cell resistance to radiotherapy by blocking the cell cycle at the G2/M phase and decreasing p-CHK2, cyclin B1, and p-CDC2 expression. NCTD and IR also inhibited radiation resistance by causing DNA damage. Our findings provide evidence for the potential therapeutic use of NCTD and IR against CRC. Moreover, this study elucidates whether NCTD can overcome CRC radiation tolerance and provides insights into the underlying mechanisms.

Keywords: ROS; NCTD; colorectal cancer; mitochondria; DRP1

1. Introduction

Colorectal cancer (CRC) is the third most aggressive cancer worldwide and represents a serious threat to human health [1]. In 2022, approximately 592,232 new CRC cases and 309,114 CRC-related deaths were reported in China [2]. Current treatments for CRC are based on surgical resection, chemoradiotherapy, and molecular targeted therapy, with neoadjuvant chemoradiotherapy combined with surgery being the standard care for patients with locally advanced CRC [3]. Despite improvements in the treatment of CRC through early screening, radical surgery, and comprehensive CRC treatment guideline optimization, the overall outcome for CRC patients remains unfavorable, with a 5-year survival rate of approximately 65% [1]. Radiotherapy (RT) plays an important role in the treatment of CRC. However, patients with CRC are less sensitive to adjuvant RT. Therefore, studying radiation tolerance mechanisms and enhancing RT are of great significance.

Cancer cells generate reactive oxygen species (ROS) for survival, proliferation, angiogenesis, and metastasis [4]. Studies have revealed that a lower level of intracellular ROS following radiation leads to malignant tumor tolerance to RT [5,6]. The regulation of intracellular ROS levels is critical for cellular homeostasis because cells respond differently to different levels of ROS [7]. Low ROS levels in cancer cells can modulate energy production efficiency and promote cell proliferation. IR substantially increases ROS levels [8]. ROS are critical mediators of the lethal effects of ionizing radiation (IR) [4]. High levels of ROS can induce cell senescence and death through oxidative damage to intracellular biomacromolecules (e.g., proteins, lipids, RNA, and DNA). NADPH oxidase, another important source of ROS, is activated by radiation exposure, thus leading to persistent oxidative stress [9]. Cancer cells must combat high ROS levels, especially during the early stages of tumor development, and their high antioxidant capacity regulates ROS to levels compatible with cellular functions [10]. Therefore, enhancing ROS production after exposure to IR and maintaining oxidative stress in tumor cells may be the keys to overcoming radiation tolerance and enhancing tumor radiosensitivity.

The structural and functional integrity of mitochondria are essential for maintaining cellular energy and metabolic homeostasis. The mitochondria-dependent apoptotic pathway is the main mode of radiation-induced cell death, and it is initiated by excessive ROS production [11]. High ROS levels can disrupt mitochondrial function and lead to dysfunctional mitochondrial oxidative phosphorylation, which results in the release of large amounts of ROS from mitochondria, further exacerbating the intracellular ROS load [12]. When cells undergo metabolic or environmental stress, mitochondrial fission and fusion maintain mitochondrial function by regulating mitochondrial morphology and structure. Because IR induces ROS generation, it leads to impaired mitochondrial fusion and fission kinetics, which further lead to a loss of mitochondrial integrity and function. Dynamin-related protein 1 (DRP1) plays a key role in mitochondrial division. DRP1-Ser616 activation-driven excessive mitochondrial fission exacerbates oxidative stress and apoptosis [13–15]. During early apoptosis, DRP1 is recruited from the cytoplasm to the outer mitochondrial membrane, which triggers mitochondrial division. The inhibition of DRP1 has been shown to inhibit mitochondrial division as well as caspase activation and cell death [16]. Taken together, mitochondria are both the main target of intracellular ROS after IR and the main source of radiation-induced ROS. Radiation increases ROS production, which promotes DRP1 protein phosphorylation, leading to impaired mitochondrial dynamics and aggravated mitochondrial damage, which promote each other to form a cycle that ultimately leads to cell death. Therefore, enhancing ROS-mediated mitochondrial damage may increase the sensitivity of malignant tumors to IR.

Cantharidin is a traditional Chinese medicine extracted from the dried bodies of the insect *Mylabris phalerata*. Norcantharidin (NCTD) is synthesized by removing the methyl group at the 1,2 position from cantharidin, and it has stronger anti-tumor properties and fewer side effects than cantharidin [17]. Several studies have shown that NCTD can induce apoptosis in prostate, gastric, breast, and other tumor cells, mainly by increasing ROS production via a mechanism similar to that of radiation-induced cell death. For example, Shen et al. showed that NCTD induces mitochondrial membrane potential (MMP) reduction and mitochondrial dysfunction and revealed that the accumulation of intercellular ROS can eventually induce apoptosis by causing DNA damage [18–20]. In addition, NCTD can directly affect the expression of Bax, Bcl-2, and caspase-3 and -9. Specifically, NCTD significantly increases the expression of caspase-3, -8, and -9, decreases the expression of caspase-4 and -12 and the anti-apoptotic proteins Bcl-XL and Mcl-1, and increases the expression of the pro-apoptotic protein Bak. However, studies on the increased radiation sensitivity of CRC due to NCTD are limited; therefore, exploring the role of NCTD in CRC radiation tolerance is of great clinical significance.

Therefore, this study clarified the role and mechanism of action of norcantharidin in increasing the sensitivity of CRC to radiotherapy. CRC cell lines were treated with NCTD, ionizing radiation (IR), or a combination of the two. In addition, to elucidate the underlying molecular pathway, we investigated DRP1, a protein central to mitochondrial fission, and treated cells with the mitochondrial division inhibitor Mdivi-1. Moreover, in vivo experiments were performed to further validate the safety and efficacy of this treatment strategy.

2. Materials and Methods

2.1. Cell Culture

The human colon cancer cell line DLD-1 was purchased from Procell Life Science & Technology Co., Ltd. (Wuhan, China) and the LoVo cell line was gifted by the Laboratory of Translational Medicine, Tianjin People's Hospital, Tianjin, China. All cells were incubated in RPMI 1640 medium (Gibco, Thermo, Waltham, MA, USA) containing 10% fetal bovine serum (FBS) (Gibco, Thermo, Waltham, MA, USA), 1% penicillin, and 0.1% streptomycin (Thermo, Waltham, MA, USA) at 5% CO_2 and 37 °C.

2.2. Cell Irradiation and Treatment

Sealed sterile cell culture plates or dishes were placed in the center of the irradiation chamber and exposed to a radioactive source using 6 MeV high-energy X-rays generated by a linear accelerator (Varian Clinic 21ES, Palo Alto, CA, USA) at a dose rate of 3 Gy/min. NCTD was purchased from Yuanye Biotechnology Co., Ltd. (Shanghai, China). NCTD powder was dissolved in dimethylsulfoxide (DMSO) to make a stock solution of 100 mmol/L and kept at −20 °C. Depending on the purpose of the experiment, the stock solution was diluted in complete 1640 medium to obtain the desired concentration. Working solutions were freshly prepared from standard solutions and used for cell culture.

2.3. Cell Viability Assays

The viabilities of the LoVo and DLD-1 cells were measured using a CCK8 assay (Solarbio, Beijing, China) according to the manufacturer's instructions. Briefly, the cells were plated in 96-well plates at a density of 5000 (DLD-1) or 7000 (LoVo) cells/well. After the cells adhered to the walls, they were exposed to 100 μL of culture medium containing various concentrations of NCTD (10, 20, 40, 80, 120, or 160 μM). For the inhibitor experiment, pretreatment with the inhibitor (5 mM N-Acetyl Cysteine (NAC) and 5 μM Mdivi-1) (MCE, Monmouth juncyion, NJ, USA) was performed for 2 h before the NCTD (10 or 50 μM) treatment. Then, 10 μL of CCK-8 reagent was added to each well after culturing for 24, 48, and 72 h. Absorbance values were measured at 450 nm using an enzyme-labeled instrument (Bio-Rad, Hercules, CA, USA).

2.4. Single-Cell Gel Electrophoresis Assay

The CRC cells were subjected to an alkaline comet assay (ELK Biotechnology, Wuhan, China). Briefly, cells suspended in PBS were collected at a density of 1×10^6 cells/mL and then mixed with low-melting-point agarose gel, spread onto chamber slides, and allowed to cool. The slides were immersed in a lysis solution and incubated at 4 °C for 2 h. The slides were incubated for 20 min at room temperature (22–26 °C) in an alkaline electrophoresis buffer (200 mM NaOH and 1 mM EDTA). The slides were left at room temperature for 60 min to maintain the DNA under alkaline conditions, followed by electrophoresis at 25 V and 300 mA for 30 min. Subsequently, the slides were washed at least three times with 0.4 mM Tris–HCl (pH = 7.5) before they were stained with propidium iodide (PI) (10 μL) for 10 min. Comet tails were observed using a fluorescence microscope.

2.5. Flow Cytometric Analysis

A cell cycle assay kit (Yeasen, Shanghai, China) was used to determine the effects of IR and NCTD on the cycle of CRC cells. Briefly, CRC cells were cultured in 6-well plates, NCTD was added 2 h before irradiation, and the IR and combined groups were irradiated with 6 Gy X-rays. The cells were then cultured in an incubator for 24 h and digested with trypsin, and the cell precipitates were fixed with pre-cooled 70% ethanol at 4 °C overnight. The next day, 10 μL of PI and 10 μL of RNase A were added, and the cells were protected from light for 30 min.

An Annexin V/PI (Abbkine, Wuhan, China) apoptosis detection kit was used to determine the effects of IR and NCTD on the percentage of apoptotic cells. Briefly, cells were treated with NCTD (10 and 50 μM) and/or IR (6 Gy) for 48 h or pretreated with 5 mM

NAC and 5 μM Mdivi-1 for 2 h, followed by the addition of NCTD and/or IR for 48 h. Finally, the cells were harvested and washed with PBS. Each sample was stained with 200 μL of 1× binding buffer containing 5 μL of Annexin V-FITC and 2 μL of PI, and then flow cytometry (BD Biosciences, San Jose, CA, USA) was performed. The above data was analyzed using Flow Jo software version 10.8.1.

2.6. Western Blot Analysis

Cells were resuspended in a RIPA buffer (Solarbio, Beijing, China) containing 1% PMSF (Solarbio, Beijing, China) and a 1% protease inhibitor cocktail (Thermo, Waltham, MA, USA), lysed on ice for 10 min, broken using an ultrasonic crusher, and then centrifuged at 12,000× *g* for 15 min at 4 °C. The supernatant was collected, and a BCA assay kit (Beyotime, Shanghai, China) was used to determine the total protein concentration. The samples were then supplemented with 5× SDS-PAGE loading buffer (Solarbio, Beijing, China) and denatured in a Thermo shaker at 95 °C for 10 min. Western blotting was performed as described previously [21]. Briefly, proteins (30 μg/well) were separated by SDS-PAGE and transferred onto PVDF membranes, and then the membranes were blocked with 5% non-fat dry milk and incubated with the diluted antibody (Supplementary Material Table S2) overnight on a shaker at 4 °C. The next day, the primary antibody was recovered, and the PVDF membrane was washed three times with TBST. The membrane was then incubated with horseradish peroxidase-labeled secondary antibodies (CST, Danvers, MA, USA) for 1 h at room temperature and visualized using an enhanced chemiluminescence reagent (Millipore, Darmstadt, Germany), and chemiluminescence was detected using a gel imaging system (Tanon, Shanghai, China).

2.7. Detection of ROS

ROS were detected using a DCFH-DA kit (Beyotime, Shang hai, China) according to the manufacturer's instructions. Briefly, cells were treated with IR and/or NCTD for 24 h and stained with DCFH-DA (10 μM) for 30 min. Green fluorescence was analyzed using flow cytometry. To detect mitochondrial ROS, the cells were incubated with a 5 μM MitoSOX™ (Yeasen, Shanghai, China) working solution for 10 min at 37 °C and visualized under a fluorescence microscope.

2.8. MitoTracker® Red CMXRos

To prepare a 1 mM stock solution, we added 94.1 μL of DMSO to 50 μg of lyophilized solid for dissolution and then diluted the solution to a working concentration of 200 nM using 1640 complete medium. The cells were treated with the MitoTracker® Red CMXRos (CST, Danvers, MA, USA) working solution and incubated for 30 min at 37 °C in the dark. If no other staining was performed, the staining solution was aspirated, washed with PBS three times (for 5 min each), blocked, and observed under a confocal microscope. If other staining was performed, the cells were fixed with cold methanol at −20 °C for 15 min and then washed with PBS three times (for 5 min each).

2.9. Colony Formation Assay

LoVo and DLD-1 cells were inoculated in 35 mm dishes, and the number of inoculated cells was adjusted according to the different radiation doses as follows: 200 (0 Gy), 400 (2 Gy), 1500 (4 Gy), 6000 (6 Gy), and 12,000 (8 Gy) cells. The cells were then pretreated with NCTD for 2 h and exposed to the indicated doses of X-radiation (Gy/min). When colonies were visible in the dishes, they were fixed, stained, and counted using ImageJ software version win64. Clone formation and cell survival rates were calculated, and a single-hit multitarget model was used to fit the cell survival curve and calculate the sensitization enhancement ratio (SER).

2.10. Immunocytofluorescence Assay

Cells were cultured in 6-well plates with or without IR/NCTD treatment. Depending on the experimental design, cells were collected at 1.5 h or 48 h after irradiation, washed three times with PBS, and fixed with 4% paraformaldehyde for 30 min. Cells were then penetrated using 0.5% Triton X-100 for 30 min and blocked with 5% BSA at room temperature for 60 min. Next, the primary antibodies γ-H2AX (CST, 1:200, #80312) and DRP1 (CST, 1:50, #8570) were incubated overnight at 4 °C. Then, the cells were incubated with Alexa Fluor 488-labeled secondary antibodies (CST, 1:1000) in the dark for 60 min. After washing the cells, the nuclei were stained with 10 μg/mL DAPI for 10 min. Finally, images were obtained using a confocal microscope (Leica Stellaris 8, Mannheim, Germany).

2.11. Measurement of Mitochondrial Membrane Potential (JC-1 Fluorescent Probe Experiment)

The mitochondrial membrane potential assay kit (Yeasen, Shanghai, China) uses JC-1 as a fluorescent probe to rapidly and sensitively detect changes in the mitochondrial membrane potential in cells, tissues, or purified mitochondria. It can be used to detect mitochondrial health and early apoptosis. Briefly, CRC cells were seeded in 24-well plates at a suitable density and treated with NCTD (10, 50 μM), IR (6 Gy), NAC, or Mdivi-1. The culture medium was removed after 24 h, the JC-1 working solution was added, and the cells were incubated for 15 min at 37 °C. Subsequently, the cells were washed with pre-warmed PBS two times. Finally, a fluorescence microscope (Nikon, Tokyo, Japan) was used to observe changes in $\Delta\Psi m$. In healthy cells, JC-1 monomers aggregate to form polymers, and mitochondria show strong red fluorescence (excitation at 550 nm; emission at 600 nm). In apoptotic or necrotic cells, JC-1 exists as a monomer, and mitochondria show strong green fluorescence (excitation wavelength: 485 nm; emission wavelength: 535 nm). The ratio of the red fluorescence signal to the green fluorescence signal was then calculated and used to determine cell health.

2.12. RNA Isolation and Quantitative Real-Time PCR

Total RNA was extracted using TRIzol (Invitrogen, Carlsbad, CA, USA) and used for cDNA synthesis, using a Hifair II 1st Strand cDNA Synthesis Kit (Yeasen, Shanghai, China). A qRT-PCR was performed using the qPCR SYBR Green Master Mix kit (Yeasen, Shanghai, China). Gene expression was normalized to GADPH. The PCR primers (Sangon Biotech, Shanghai, China) are shown in Supplementary Material, Table S1.

2.13. Hematoxylin and Eosin Staining and Immunohistochemistry Assay

Tumor tissues were dehydrated, embedded, cut into slices, and stained with a hematoxylin and eosin (H&E) solution for 10–20 min. The slices were placed in 1% alcohol hydrochloric acid for differentiation for 1–3 s, and then the color changed back to blue. Neutral gum was used for sealing, and the slices were observed under a microscope (Nikon, Tokyo, Japan).

Paraffin sections were deparaffinized for 2 h at 65 °C, followed by rehydration in an alcohol series and sodium citrate buffer. The sections were covered with endogenous peroxidase and blocked with 5% normal goat or mouse serum. Sections were incubated with anti-Ki67 antibodies (1:400), anti-8OHDG antibodies (1:2400), anti-Y-H2AX antibodies (1:800), and anti-cleaved caspase-3 (1:1800) at 4 °C overnight. Immunohistochemical (IHC) staining was performed using HRP conjugates and diaminobenzidine. IHC images were captured using a microscope. Three independent random fields were selected for a semi-quantitative analysis using ImageJ software version win64, and the average optical density (AOD) was measured using the following formula: AOD = integrated optical density (IOD)/area.

2.14. Animals

Four-week-old male BALB/c nude mice were purchased from Beijing Vital River Laboratory Animal Technology (Beijing, China). All animal experiments were performed according to National Institutes of Health guidelines and Tianjin University of TCM protocol. The animals were housed in a temperature-controlled room (22 ± 2 °C) with a 12 h light/dark cycle and free access to standard mouse chow and water. The feeding conditions (food and water) were monitored daily. After 1 week of acclimatization, the mice were subcutaneously inoculated with 1×10^7 DLD-1 cells in the left inguinal area. Approximately 10 days later, when the size of the tumor reached approximately 5 mm, the mice were randomly divided into four groups (5–6 mice) according to the experimental design. Tumor-burdened mice in the IR and combination groups were administered 10 Gy of X-ray irradiation at a time. Then, the combined group was continuously intraperitoneally injected with NCTD (5 mg/kg) for 14 days. The body weight of the mice was measured every 2 days, and tumor size was also measured every 2 days using digital calipers. At the end of the treatment, tumor tissues, livers, lungs, and kidneys were harvested for further study. Tumor volumes were calculated according to the following formula: volume = $0.5 \times \text{length} \times \text{width}^2$.

2.15. TUNEL Assay

Experiments were performed according to the manufacturer's instructions (Yeasen, Shang hai, China). Tissue sections were routinely dewaxed and rehydrated in an alcohol series. Then, the tissue sections were covered with Proteinase K solution and incubated for 20 min at room temperature. The tissues were washed three times with PBS and incubated with the TUNEL reaction mixture for 60 min at 37 °C in a damp and dark place. Finally, the samples were observed under a fluorescence microscope.

2.16. Statistical Analyses

All experiments were performed in triplicate. The results are shown as mean ± standard deviation (SD) values. GraphPad Prism statistical software (V9) was used for data analysis. Data were analyzed using a one-way analysis of variance (ANOVA). The significance of the parameters was set at $p < 0.05$.

3. Results

3.1. NCTD Inhibits the Proliferation of CRC Cells and Enhances Their Radiosensitivity In Vitro

To test the anti-tumor effects of NCTD on CRC cells, we first examined cell viability after treatment with different concentrations of NCTD. The viability of the LoVo and DLD-1 cells was significantly inhibited at 24, 48, and 72 h after NCTD treatment in a dose- and time-dependent manner (Figure 1A–E). We used GraphPad Prism statistical software (V9) to calculate the IC20 values, which were 9.455 μM and 50.467 μM for LoVo and DLD-1, respectively. For the convenience of calculation and dosing, we used 10 and 50 μM as the subsequent drug concentrations. To investigate the effect of NCTD on CRC cell radiosensitivity, the cells were treated with NCTD at 10 and 50 μM, followed by IR at different doses. The inhibitory effect on colony formation was significantly enhanced in the combined group, and the survival fraction was significantly lower than that in the radiotherapy-only group. A SER > 1 suggests that a drug has a sensitizing effect. We calculated the SERs of the LoVo and DLD-1 cells using the single-hit multitarget model, and the values were 1.75 and 1.04, respectively (Figure 1F,G). To evaluate the inhibitory effect of NCTD in combination with IR on CRC cells, the two cell lines were subjected to different treatments, and colony formation was observed. The IR/NCTD groups effectively inhibited colony formation in CRC cells (Figure 1H–K).

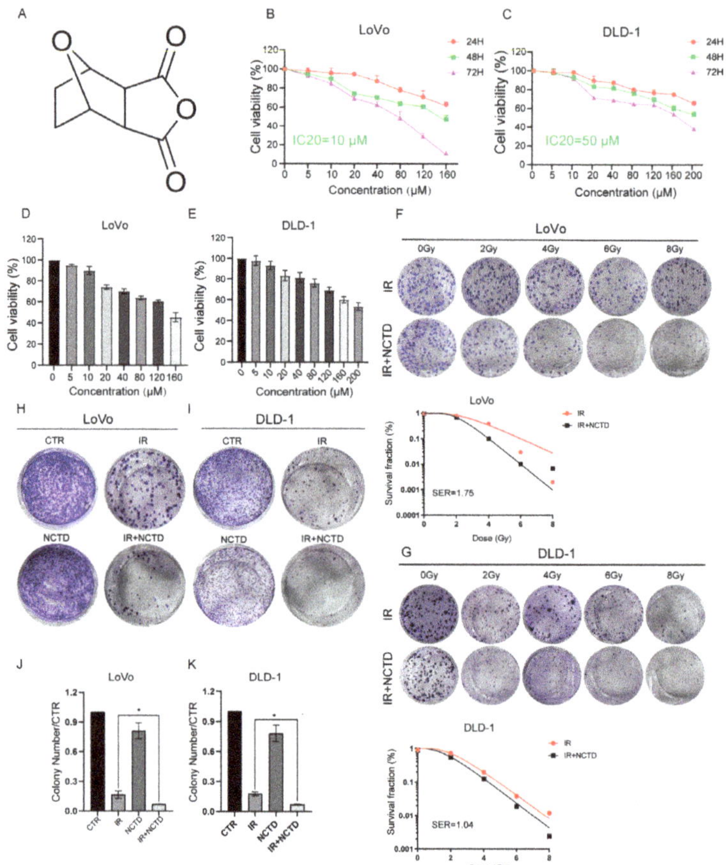

Figure 1. Norcantharidin (NCTD) enhances colorectal cancer (CRC) cell radiosensitivity in vitro. (**A**) The chemical structure of NCTD. (**B**,**C**) The viability of LoVo and DLD-1 cells treated with NCTD. (**D**,**E**) CRC cell viability and IC20 values after 48 h of treatment with different concentrations of NCTD. (**F**,**G**) Colony formation assay showing the enhanced radiosensitivity of CRC cells in vitro, as evaluated by the radiation multi-target single-hit model, after NCTD (10 and 50 μM) treatment. (**H**–**K**) CRC cells were treated with ionizing radiation (IR, 6 Gy) alone or in combination with NCTD (10 and 50 μM) for cell clone formation, *, $p < 0.5$.

3.2. NCTD Induces DNA Damage and Mitochondria-Dependent Apoptosis in CRC Cells

Damage to DNA double strands by energetic particle beams is the main cause of cell death by IR and a direct cause of radiosensitization. We explored whether IR combined with NCTD affects DNA damage induced by IR. To this end, we assessed phosphorylated H2AX (γ-H2AX) levels in CRC cells using immunofluorescence. In cells treated with NCTD alone, the level of γ-H2AX was remarkably higher than in the control cells, while in cells treated with IR/NCTD, the level of γ-H2AX was significantly higher than that in cells treated with IR alone (Figure 2A,B,D). These results were further confirmed by Western blotting (Figure 2C). In addition to the immunofluorescence assay, single-cell gel assays were used to detect DNA damage. An analysis of the percentage of tail moments revealed negligible comet tail formation in cells treated with NCTD alone compared to cells in the control group. As predicted, the combined treatment led to a higher percent of tail DNA and longer tail length than IR alone, further exacerbating DNA damage (Figure 2E–G).

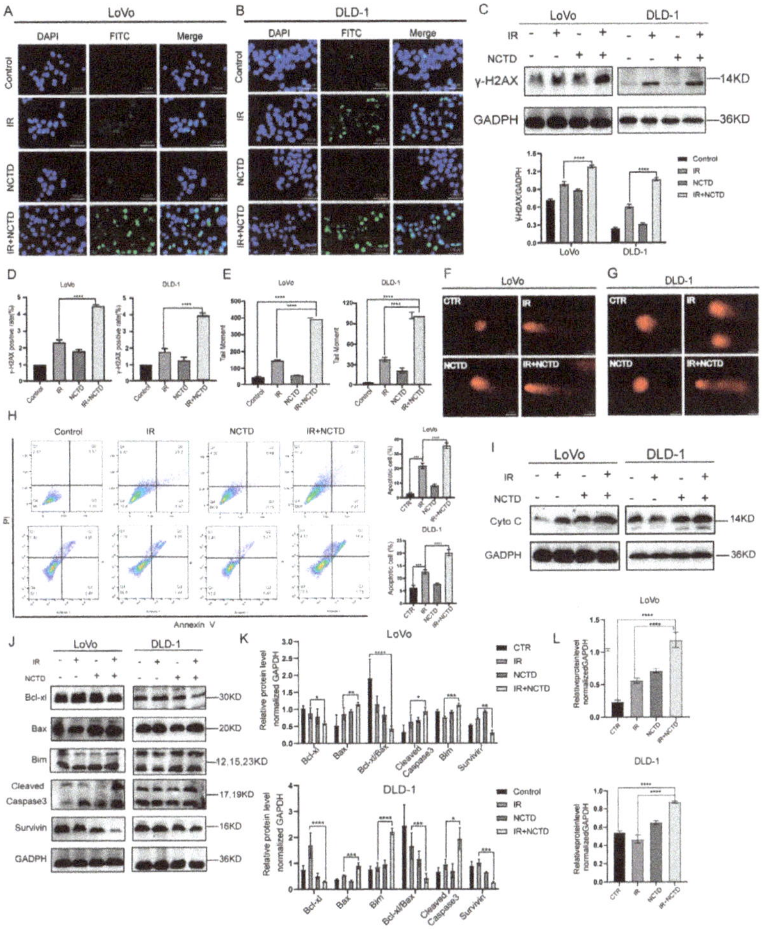

Figure 2. NCTD induces DNA damage and mitochondria-dependent apoptosis in CRC cells. (**A**,**B**) Fluorescence microscopy images showing increased DNA fracture (Υ-H2AX, green) after the combination treatment of IR (6 Gy) and NCTD (10 and 50 μM). (**C**) Representative immunoblotting of DNA damage (Υ-H2AX) in CRC cells. ****, $p < 0.0001$. (**D**) Histogram of intracellular Υ-H2AX-positive cytometry after IR combined with NCTD treatment. ****, $p < 0.0001$. (**E**) Casplab software version 1.2.3 b1 was applied to process and analyze the comet images, and the lengths of the tail moments of the four groups of comets after different interventions were analyzed. ****, $p < 0.0001$. (**F**,**G**) Detection of DNA damage using the comet assay. Scale bar = 100 μm. (**H**) NCTD increased apoptosis at 48 h post IR in CRC cells. ***, $p < 0.001$, ****, $p < 0.0001$ (**I**) NCTD increased the expression of Cyt C 48 h post IR. (**L**) Histogram of Cyt C protein expression after different treatments. ****, $p < 0.0001$. (**J**,**K**) Expression of Bcl-xl, Bax, Bim, cleaved caspase-3, and survivin was detected by Western blotting 48 h post IR in CRC cells. *, $p < 0.05$; **, $p < 0.01$, ***, $p < 0.001$, ****, $p < 0.0001$.

To determine whether the radiosensitizing effect of NCTD was related to apoptosis, the apoptosis rate of the cells was measured using flow cytometry after double staining with Annexin V-FITC and PI. In addition, the expression of Bcl-xl, Bax, Bim, survivin, and cleaved caspase-3 was detected by Western blotting. After 48 h, the apoptosis rate was significantly increased in the IR/NCTD group compared to the IR alone group (Figure 2H). As shown in Figure 2H, the total apoptosis rate increased from 23.77% to 31.91% in LoVo cells after treatment with 10 μM NCTD for 48 h compared with that of the IR groups. The same results were obtained for the DLD-1 cell line. Moreover, in the IR/NCTD group, the expression of Bcl-xl and survivin was decreased while that of Bax, Bim, and cleaved caspase-3 was increased (Figure 2J–K). Cytochrome C (Cyto C) release is a key step in the mitochondrial apoptotic pathway, and the expression of Cyto C was increased in the IR/NCTD group compared to the IR alone group (Figure 2I,L).

3.3. NCTD Induces CRC Cell Senescence and Blocks the Cell Cycle

In addition to apoptosis, cellular senescence is an effective mechanism of inhibiting tumor cell proliferation and survival. We used a senescence β-galactosidase staining kit and found that compared to the IR group, the IR/NCTD combination group produced significantly more dark blue products (catalyzed by senescence-specific β-galactosidase) and that the activity level of senescence-associated β-galactosidase (SA-β-gal) was elevated (Figure 3A–C). In addition, cells treated with IR/NCTD showed significantly higher levels of expression of P21 and P16 than IR alone (Figure 3D–F).

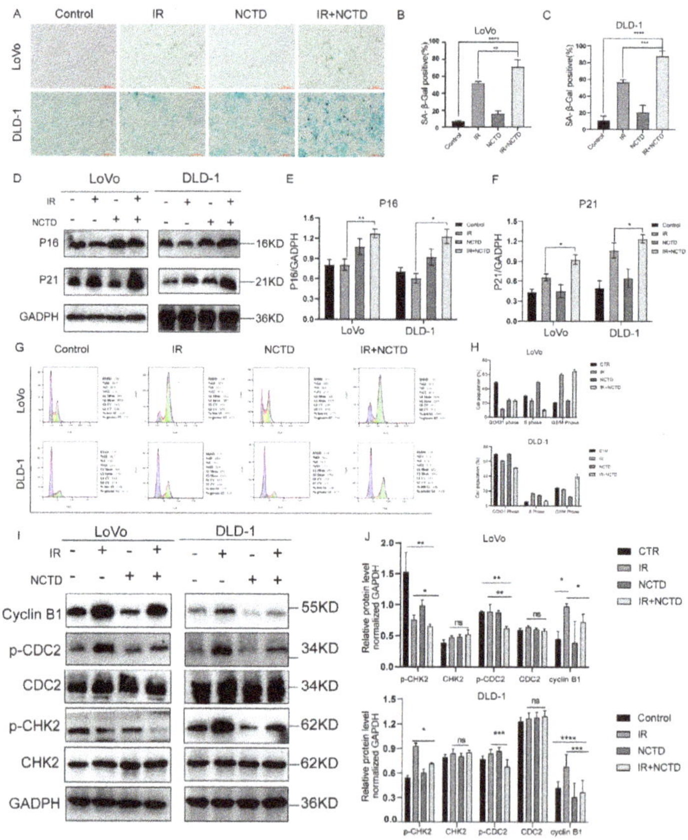

Figure 3. NCTD induces CRC cell senescence and blocks the cell cycle post IR. LoVo and DLD-1 cells were treated with NCTD for 24 or 48 h. (**A–C**) NCTD increased the expression of senescence-associated β-galactosidase (SA-β-gal) after IR in CRC cells. **, $p < 0.01$, ***, $p < 0.001$, ****, $p < 0.0001$. Scale bar = 100 μm. (**D–F**) Western blotting analyses of p21 and p16 in irradiated LoVo and DLD-1 cells. *, $p < 0.05$; **, $p < 0.01$. (**G,H**) The CRC cell cycle was assessed using flow cytometry. (**I**) Representative immunoblotting of the cell-cycle proteins cyclin B1, CDC2, p-CDC2, CHK2, and p-CHK2. (**J**). Histogram of p21 and p16 proteins in gray values. *, $p < 0.05$; **, $p < 0.01$, ***, $p < 0.001$, ****, $p < 0.0001$, ns, $p > 0.05$.

The proportion of cells in the G2/M phase significantly increased in the IR/NCTD combination group (Figure 3G,H). The cell-cycle-related proteins cyclin B1, p-CDC2, and p-CHK2 were significantly decreased in the IR/NCTD combination group compared with the IR group (Figure 3I,J).

3.4. NCTD Combined with IR Impairs Mitochondrial Morphology and Function, Leading to Increased Mitochondrial Division

We further investigated the potential mechanisms by which NCTD sensitizes CRC cells to IR. Because apoptosis is induced through the mitochondrial pathway, we examined the effects of IR combined with NCTD on mitochondrial morphology and function. We used MitoTracker® to specifically label the IR group, NCTD group, and IR/NTCD combination group. The results revealed that in the control group, the mitochondria were mostly "rod-like", while in the combined group, mitochondrial fragmentation was markedly increased and punctate compared to that in the IR group (Figure 4A).

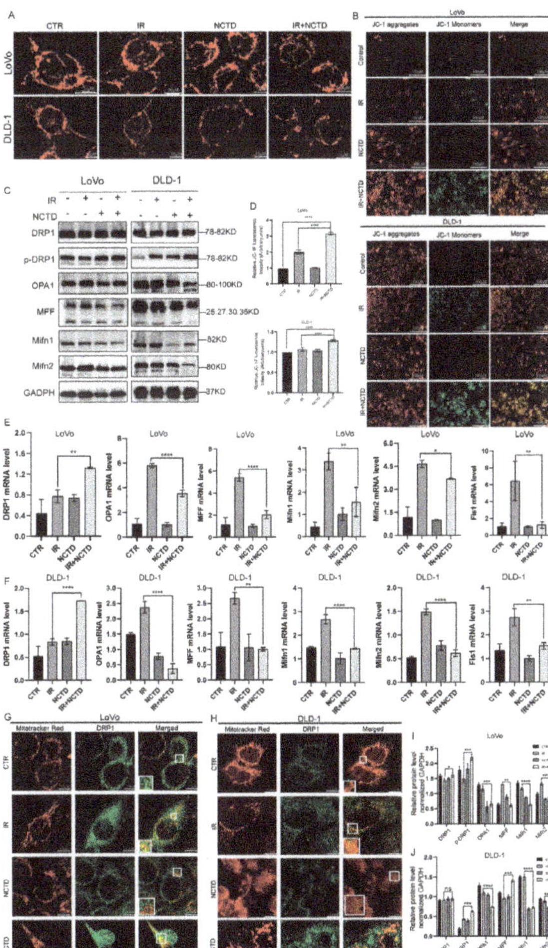

Figure 4. Effect of IR combined with NCTD on mitochondrial damage and mitochondrial division in CRC cells. (**A**) Morphology of mitochondria in CRC cells treated with IR and/or NCTD, as determined

by confocal microscopy. Scale bar = 10 μm. (**B**) JC-1 in CRC cells. Scale bar = 100 μm. (**C**) Representative Western blot results and the quantification of mitochondrial fusion- and fission-associated proteins. (**D**) JC-1 fluorescent probe bar chart, ****, $p < 0.0001$. (**E**,**F**) Statistical analysis of the mRNA levels of mitochondrial fission- and fusion-associated proteins in CRC cells. *, $p < 0.05$, **, $p < 0.01$, ****, $p < 0.0001$. (**G**,**H**) Representative confocal images showing DRP1 immunofluorescence and mitochondria stained with MitoTracker®. Nuclei were stained with DAPI. Scale bar = 10 μm. (**I**,**J**) The quantification of mitochondrial fusion- and fission-associated proteins. *, $p < 0.05$, **, $p < 0.01$; ***, $p < 0.001$, ****, $p < 0.0001$, ns, $p > 0.05$.

Since mitochondria show significant morphological changes in response to treatment with IR and NCTD, we sought to determine whether mitochondrial functions were also impaired. The loss of MMP is an important indicator of mitochondrial dysfunction. Therefore, we used JC-1 to measure MMP. In apoptotic cells, JC-1 cannot cross the mitochondrial membrane and therefore cannot form JC-1 aggregates, thus maintaining its original green fluorescence. Consistent with the expected results, green fluorescence was significantly increased in the IR/NCTD group compared to the IR group (Figure 4B).

In a further study, we found that IR combined with NCTD resulted in the activation of DRP1, a key regulator of mitochondrial division [22]. DRP1 is the most important protein involved in mitochondrial fission because it provides the energy necessary for fission [23]. The phosphorylation of DRP1 at serine 616 and activation induce additional mitochondrial division [24]. Here, we found that the level of phosphorylated DRP1 was significantly increased in the IR/NCTD group (Figure 4C). Similarly, the mRNA level of DRP1 was increased (Figure 4E,F).

To further investigate changes in mitochondrial dynamics, we evaluated the expression levels of mitochondrial fission- and fusion-related proteins. In the IR/NTCD group, the expression of MFF, Mifn1, Mifn2, and OPA1 was reduced in both LoVo and DLD-1 cells (Figure 4C,D), suggesting that NCTD combined with IR disrupts mitochondrial fission and fusion. DRP1 is a cytoplasmic protein that can induce division upon its transfer to mitochondria. IR causes DRP1 to transfer from the cytoplasm to the mitochondria and colocalize with the mitochondria, while NCTD combined with IR increases the translocation of DRP1 into mitochondria (Figure 4G,H).

3.5. NCTD Increased CRC Cell Apoptosis via Upregulating ROS Levels

Next, we investigated the potential mechanisms by which NCTD sensitizes CRC cells to IR. Radiobiological studies have shown that conventional doses of X-rays do not directly kill tumor cells but cause persistent damage to DNA by ROS stimulation, resulting in single- or double-stranded breaks in cancer cells. They may also cause ROS-induced lipid peroxidation, as well as ROS damage to mitochondria and the endoplasmic reticulum, leading to tumor cell death [10]. To determine whether NCTD induces an increase in ROS levels after IR, we measured intracellular and mitochondrial ROS levels using the fluorescent indicator DCFH-DA. The IR/NCTD combination group showed significantly increased intracellular (Figure 5A,C) and mitochondrial (Figure 5B,D) ROS levels. We further used NAC, a ROS scavenger, to identify whether ROS mediate the anticancer properties of NCTD and found that NAC rescued the inhibition of clone formation caused by combination therapy (Figure 5E) and inhibited intracellular (Figure 5F,G) and mitochondrial (Figure 5H–J) ROS generation. We then investigated the effect of NAC on apoptosis and showed that NAC reversed IR- and NCTD-induced apoptosis, resulting in a significant decrease in the apoptosis rate (Figure 5K–N), which was verified by Western blotting (Figure 5O,P).

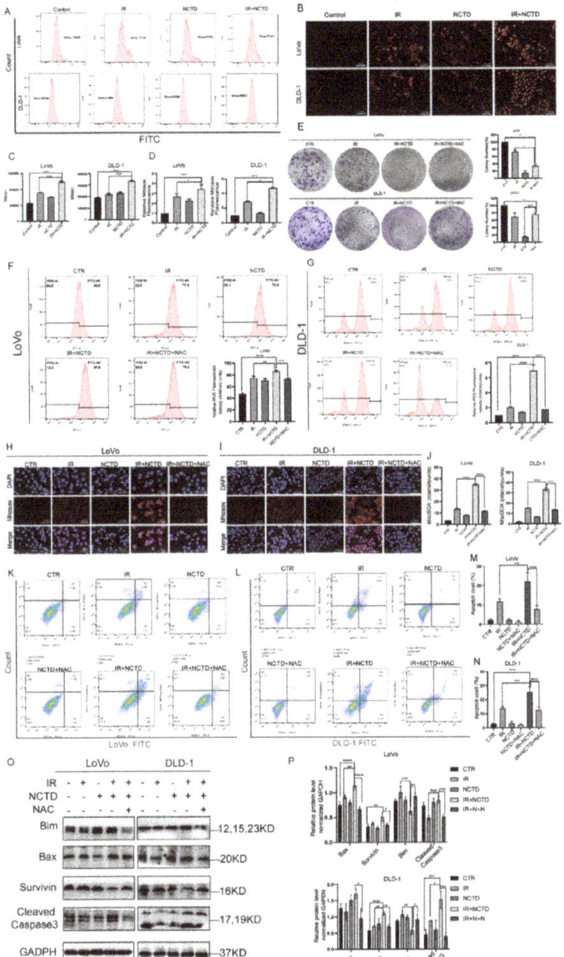

Figure 5. NCTD increased CRC cell apoptosis by upregulating ROS levels. (**A–D**) Combination therapy increased intracellular and mitochondrial ROS levels. *, $p < 0.05$, ****, $p < 0.0001$. (**E**) Images of clone formation in the groups after the addition of NAC. *, $p < 0.05$; **, $p < 0.01$, ****, $p < 0.0001$. (**F,G**) NAC decreased intracellular ROS levels in CRC cells. **, $p < 0.01$, ***, $p < 0.01$, ****, $p < 0.0001$. (**H–J**) NAC also inhibited ROS generation in mitochondria. ****, $p < 0.0001$. (**K,L**) Detection of apoptosis by flow cytometry after Annexin V–propidium iodide (PI) staining. (**M,N**) Annexin V−PI staining histograms. ***, $p < 0.01$, ****, $p < 0.0001$. (**O,P**) Representative immunoblotting of related apoptosis proteins and statistical histograms. *, $p < 0.05$; **, $p < 0.01$, ***, $p < 0.01$, ****, $p < 0.0001$.

3.6. ROS Lead to Excessive Mitochondrial Division by Increasing Mitochondrial Damage in CRC Cells

ROS production and mitochondrial damage are mutually inducing and represent common mechanisms for many apoptosis-inducing factors. Therefore, to explore the role of ROS in mitochondrial damage, mitochondrial changes were examined in NAC-treated CRC cells. We found that NAC pretreatment significantly reversed the combination-treatment-mediated decrease in $\Delta\Psi$m, with a significant decrease in green fluorescence and an increase in red fluorescence after NAC treatment (Figure 6A,B). We also observed changes in mitochondrial morphology, which was more punctate and fragmented in the combined treatment group and reversed by NAC, with a more rod-like distribution (Figure 6C).

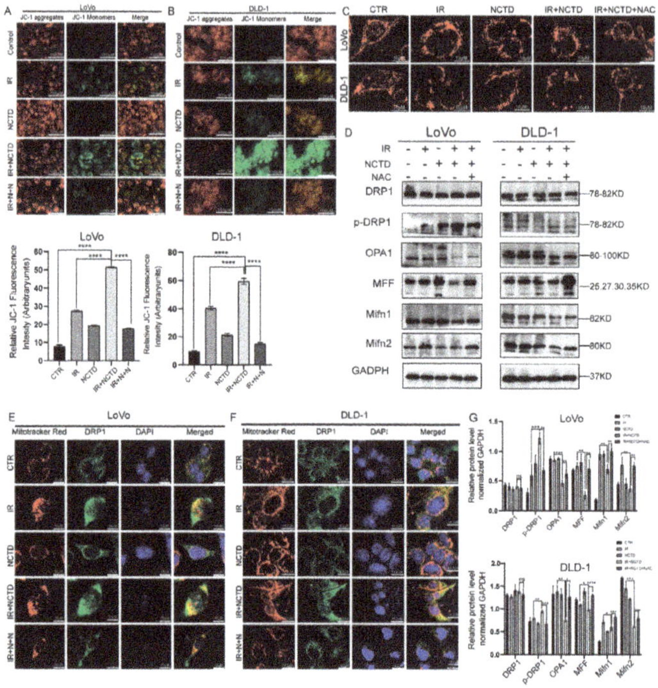

Figure 6. Reactive oxygen species (ROS) lead to excessive mitochondrial division by increasing mitochondrial damage in CRC cells. (**A**,**B**) Mitochondrial membrane potential in CRC cells. **** $p < 0.0001$. (**C**) Mitochondrial morphology, as observed using confocal microscopy. NAC reverses mitochondrial fragmentation caused by combination therapy. Scale bar = 10 μm. (**D**) Representative immunoblotting of mitochondrial fusion– and fission–associated proteins after NAC treatment in CRC cells. (**E**,**F**) Immunofluorescence of DRP1 and mitochondria after NAC treatment in CRC cells. Scale bar = 10 μm. (**G**) Statistical bar graph of mitochondrial division and fusion. *, $p < 0.05$; **, $p < 0.01$, ***, $p < 0.001$, ****, $p < 0.0001$, ns > 0.05.

DRP1 activation can be attributed to mitochondrial ROS accumulation [25,26]. To further explore the role of ROS in mitochondrial fission and fusion, we pretreated cells with NAC (an ROS inhibitor) and found that the NAC scavenging of mitochondrial ROS led to a decrease in DRP1 activation, the inhibition of mitochondrial fission, and an increase in the expression of the mitochondrial fusion proteins Mifn1, Mifn2, and OPA1 (Figure 6D). In addition, confocal microscopy showed that NCTD combined with IR induced the co-localization of DRP1 with mitochondria, which was reversed in the NAC-treated group (Figure 6E). The scavenging of ROS by NAC resulted in reduced DRP1 activation and a concomitant inhibition of mitochondrial fission.

3.7. DRP1 Mediates IR/NCTD-Induced Mitochondrial Division and Inhibition of DRP1 Expression Rescues Mitochondria-Dependent Apoptosis and Decreases ROS

DRP1 plays a key role in mitochondrial division and may mediate mitochondrial fusion and division [23,27]. To further confirm the role of DRP1 in mitochondrial division, we pretreated cells with Mdivi-1 and observed the role of DRP1 in mitochondrial damage. First, we used confocal microscopy to observe the mitochondrial morphology and found that the mitochondria were swollen and fragmentation was increased after co-treatment;

however, these changes were reversed by Mdivi-1. In addition, Mdivi-1 inhibited mitochondrial division and reduced mitochondrial damage, ultimately alleviating mitochondrial dysfunction (Supplementary Material, Figure S1). Mdivi-1 did not significantly alter the expression of total DRP1 but effectively alleviated the expression of phosphorylated DRP1 and reversed the reductions in OPA1, MFF, Mifn1, and Mifn2 in CRC cells induced by the combined IR and NCTD treatment (Figure 7C–E). The latter induced the translocation of cytoplasmic DRP1 to the mitochondria; however, no translocation occurred in CRC cells treated with Mdivi-1 (Figure 7A,B).

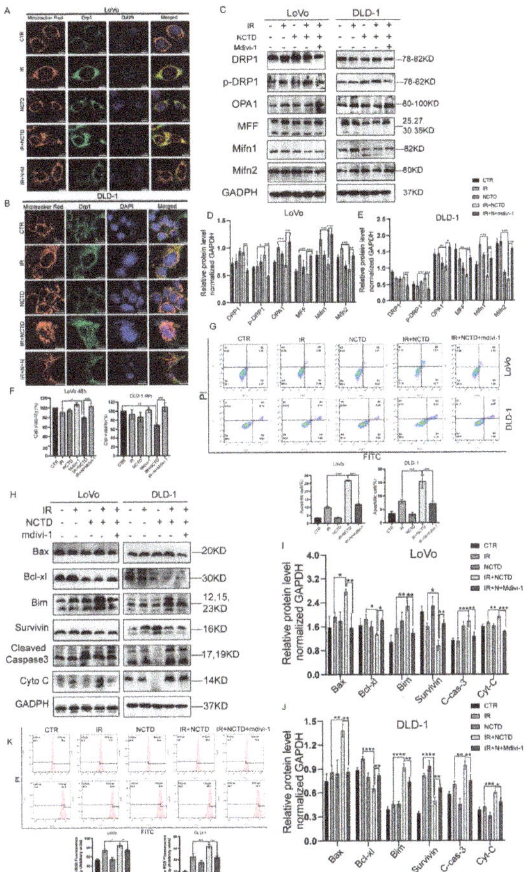

Figure 7. Mdivi-1 rescues mitochondria-dependent apoptosis and decreases ROS. (**A**,**B**) Immunofluorescence of DRP1 and mitochondria after Mdivi-1 (5 μmol/L) treatment in CRC cells. Scale bar = 10 μm. (**C**) Representative immunoblotting of mitochondrial fusion- and fission-associated proteins after Mdivi-1 treatment in CRC cells. (**D**,**E**) Statistical histogram of the relative expression of proteins associated with mitochondrial division and fusion after pretreatment with Mdivi-1. *, $p < 0.05$; **, $p < 0.01$, ***, $p < 0.001$. (**F**) Changes in cell viability after treatment with Mdivi-1 in CRC cells. *, $p < 0.05$; **, $p < 0.01$, ***, $p < 0.001$. (**G**) Apoptosis rate of CRC cells after Mdivi-1 treatment. ***, $p < 0.001$, ****, $p < 0.0001$. (**H**) Western blotting for Bax, Bim, Bcl-xl, survivin, cleaved caspase-3, and Cyt-C expression in CRC cells. (**I**,**J**) Histogram of relative expression of apoptotic proteins after Mdivi-1 pretreatment. *, $p < 0.05$; **, $p < 0.01$, ***, $p < 0.001$, **** $p < 0.0001$. (**K**) Changes in ROS after Mdivi-1 treatment in CRC cells. *, $p < 0.05$; **, $p < 0.01$, ***, $p < 0.001$.

To elucidate the relationship between mitochondrial fission and apoptosis, we pretreated the cells with Mdivi-1. Numerous studies have shown that the inhibition of DRP1 delays Cyto C release and inhibits apoptosis in vivo [28–30]. We investigated whether mitochondrial division promotes apoptosis and found that cells pretreated with Mdivi-1 showed a significant decrease in apoptosis (Figure 7G), a decrease in the expression of the pro-apoptotic proteins Bax and cleaved caspase-3, an increase in the expression of Bcl-xl (Figure 7H–J), and a significant increase in cell viability (Figure 7F). We then examined changes in ROS levels after Mdivi-1 treatment and found that ROS production was inhibited (Figure 7K). The results of previous studies have shown that NAC reverses the expression of DRP1, suggesting that ROS and DRP1 promote each other's expression.

3.8. NCTD Increased the Radiosensitivity of CRC Cells In Vivo

Tumor size and number were significantly reduced in mice treated with NCTD and IR compared with those treated with either modality alone (Figure 8A–E). None of the mice showed mortality or significant weight loss during the treatment period (Figure 8F,G), and H&E staining results showed no apparent toxicity to the heart, liver, or kidney in mice treated with NCTD and IR, suggesting the safety of this combination (Figure 8J). The TUNEL assay results showed that NCTD combined with IR resulted in increased apoptosis compared with the other treatment groups (Figure 8H). IHC staining showed a significant decrease in the Ki67-positive cell population, an increase in cleaved caspase-3 expression, and a significant increase in the expression of 8-OHDG and γ-H2AX in tumors co-treated with IR and NCTD (Figure 8I,K). This suggests that the tumor tissues were in a state of oxidative stress after the co-treatment and thus showed a reduced proliferative capacity and increased apoptosis rate.

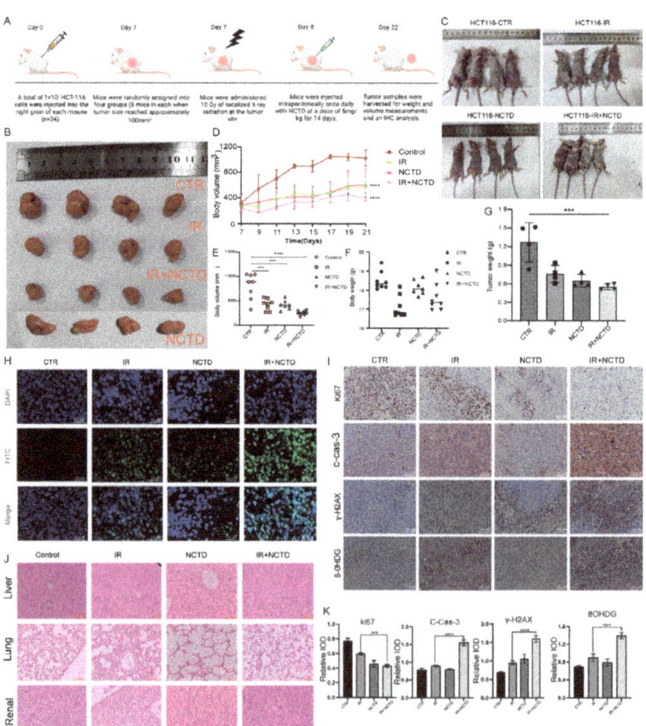

Figure 8. NCTD enhances CRC cell radiosensitivity in vivo. (**A–E**) Tumor growth curves and images of tumors in each group (n = 6 and 4 tumors were observed) (***, $p < 0.001$, **** $p < 0.0001$). (**F**) Body

weight of mice in each group. (**G**) Quality of tumors in each group (*** $p < 0.001$). (**H**) Detection of apoptosis in mouse tumor tissues by TUNEL staining. (**I,K**) Immunohistochemical staining to test the expression of Ki67, cleaved caspase-3, γ-H2AX, and 8-OHDG in tumor sections from all study groups, ***, $p < 0.001$, **** $p < 0.0001$. (**J**) Hematoxylin and eosin staining of tumor sections from all groups to detect the effects of NCTD on the liver, lungs, and kidneys of mice.

4. Discussion

Adjuvant radiotherapy has obvious advantages in reducing tumor downstaging, increasing the anal preservation rate, and prolonging tumor-free survival, thereby greatly improving the quality of life of patients with rectal cancer. Therefore, the NCCN treatment guidelines in the United States have proposed adjuvant RT combined with surgical treatment as the recommended treatment for locally advanced rectal cancer [3,31]. However, sensitivity to adjuvant RT is generally low in patients with rectal cancer. The results of the German CAO/ARO/AIO-94 trial showed that the rate of complete regression after preoperative RT for rectal cancer was only 8% [31], indicating that a large proportion of patients do not benefit from adjuvant RT. Consequently, numerous studies have been conducted to develop effective treatment strategies for patients with CRC to improve survival rates and reduce mortality.

Recently, the role of intracellular ROS levels in resistance to RT has received increasing attention. Radiobiology has shown that conventional doses of high-energy X-rays do not directly kill tumor cells but rather stimulate ROS-sustained damage to DNA, thereby destroying single- or double-stranded DNA. Moreover, ROS causes protein and lipid peroxidation and the destruction of mitochondria and the endoplasmic reticulum, which together lead to tumor cell death [10].

NCTD is widely used for the clinical treatment of CRC and other malignant tumors and acts as a chemosensitizer in various cancer cell lines [19,20]. NCTD has been shown to inhibit the expression of Ki-67 and Bcl-2, induce S-phase cell-cycle arrest, and directly or indirectly downregulate the VEGF-A,-C,-D/VEGFR-2,-3 signaling pathways, thereby inhibiting the proliferation of CRC cells [32]. Qiu et al. showed that NCTD inhibits cell growth by inhibiting the expression and phosphorylation of EGFR and c-Met in human colon cancer cells. Another study showed that NCTD inhibits tumor angiogenesis by blocking the VEGFR2/MEK/ERK signaling pathway [33]. In addition, NCTD inhibits the epithelial–mesenchymal transition in colon cancer cells by inhibiting the alphavbeta6-ERK-Ets1 signaling pathway [34]. However, few studies have focused on the increased sensitivity of NCTD to radiotherapy in rectal cancer, and the mechanism underlying the ability of NCTD to overcome radiation tolerance in rectal cancer has not been reported. Therefore, we sought to determine whether NCTD could increase CRC radiotherapy sensitization by increasing ROS production.

Ataxia-telangiectasia mutated (ATM) protein, a member of the phosphatidylinositol 3-kinase-related kinases family, induces a break in the cellular DNA double-strand. In addition, ATR (ATM and RAD 3-related) and other proteins phosphorylate and modify serine 139 on H2AX to form phosphorylated H2AX (γ-H2AX) [35]. In response to double-stranded breaks, the histone H2AX is phosphorylated at serine 139 in a region of several mega-base pairs, thus forming discrete nuclear foci that can be detected using a fluorescence microscope. Our results showed that the level of γ-H2AX was significantly elevated in the combined group in both cell lines, as evidenced by enhanced fluorescence in the cell nuclei. The involvement of cell-cycle blocking and senescence in IR tolerance and tumor metastasis has been previously reported [36]. Our results indicate that NCTD inhibits tumor cell survival by inducing cell-cycle arrest and senescence. This phenomenon indicates that NCTD could reverse the RT-tolerant state of CRC cells.

Our study showed that NCTD increases the sensitivity of CRC cells to RT by inducing apoptosis via ROS-DRP1-mediated mitochondrial damage. Mitochondria are the main sources and targets of intracellular ROS after exposure to radiation. IR induces ROS production and disrupts mitochondrial fusion and fission, leading to a loss of mitochondrial integrity and function. An NCTD-induced MMP reduction was reversed by ROS removal, suggesting that ROS contribute to NCTD-induced mitochondrial damage. Further experiments revealed that ROS-induced mitochondria-dependent apoptosis showed an increase in the expression of Cyto C, a decrease in the expression of the anti-apoptotic proteins Bcl-xl and survivin, and an increase in the expression of the pro-apoptotic proteins Bax, Bim, and cleaved caspase-3, and these changes were partially reversed by NAC, a typical antioxidant [37]. These results confirm that ROS are important mediators of radiation-induced damage.

ROS impair mitochondrial dynamics, leading to imbalances in mitochondrial fusion and division. Therefore, we further explored mitochondrial fission and fusion in ROS-promoted mitochondrial injury and found that IR combined with NCTD increased the expression of the mitochondrial fission protein DRP1 and decreased that of mitochondrial fusion proteins (mifn1, mifn2, and OPA1). NAC partially restored the expression of the mitochondrial fusion and fission proteins, implying that ROS play an important role in mitochondrial fusion and division. To elucidate the underlying molecular pathway, we investigated DRP1, a protein central to mitochondrial fission, and found that IR combined with NCTD significantly upregulated DRP1 phosphorylation, leading to its activation, and subsequently increased mitochondrial division [23]. Studies have shown that mitochondrial division promotes apoptosis [38]. Moreover, the inhibition of mitochondrial fusion has been shown to promote apoptosis [27–29]. To further elucidate the relationship between apoptosis and mitochondrial division, we treated cells with the mitochondrial division inhibitor Mdivi-1, which led to a significant decrease in apoptosis and mitochondrial damage, suggesting that increased mitochondrial division induces apoptosis.

To further elucidate the relationship between ROS generation and mitochondrial division, we pretreated the cells with Mdivi-1 and measured intracellular ROS levels. Mdivi-1 partially inhibited the expression of ROS. Early in apoptosis, DRP1 is recruited from the cytoplasm to the outer mitochondrial membrane to trigger mitochondrial fission [39]. DRP1 induces apoptosis by stimulating Bax oligomerization and massive Cyto C efflux to activate the apoptotic protease activator (Apaf-1), thereby irreversibly altering mitochondrial function [39]. Considering that NAC inhibited the expression of DRP1, these results suggest that ROS and DRP1 jointly promote apoptosis. However, in this study, IR directly led to ROS generation, which initiated mitochondrial damage-induced apoptosis. Previous studies have shown that NCTD facilitates the accumulation of ROS and activates the mitochondrial pathway to induce tumor cell apoptosis [40,41]. Consistent with previous findings, our results suggest that IR in combination with NCTD induces mitochondrial damage by increasing ROS production, thereby promoting apoptosis. Thus, these results reveal a potential mechanism for the radiosensitivity enhancement effect of NCTD, Figure 9 shows the mechanism of action of NCTD to improve the sensitivity of colorectal cancer radiotherapy.

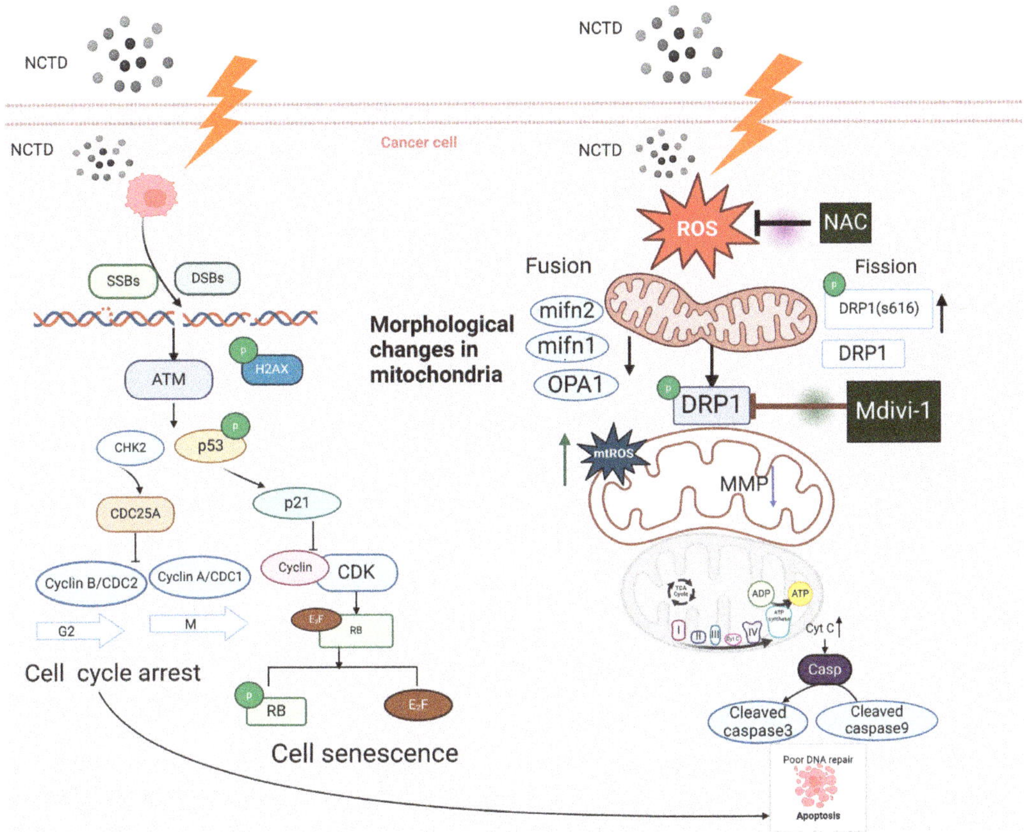

Figure 9. Mechanism of action of NCTD in increasing sensitivity to radiotherapy in colorectal cancer.

5. Conclusions

NCTD combined with IR increased the sensitivity of CRC cells to RT by mediating the ROS-driven activation of DRP1 and inducing mitochondrial division and apoptosis. In vivo experiments further validated the safety and efficacy of this treatment strategy.

Supplementary Materials: The following supporting information can be downloaded at: https://www.mdpi.com/article/10.3390/antiox13030347/s1, Figure S1: DRP1 mediates IR combined with NCTD-induced mitochondrial damage; Table S1: shRNA and main primer sequences; Table S2: List of primary antibodies and their sources.

Author Contributions: Conceptualization, Q.X. and H.W. (Hui Wang); methodology, Q.X.; validation, Q.X. and H.W. (Hui Wang).; formal analysis, H.Q.; investigation, Q.X.; resources, H.W. (Hui Wang); data curation, Q.X.; writing—original draft preparation, Q.X.; writing—review and editing, Q.X.; visualization, Q.X.; supervision, H.Z.; project administration, H.Q.; funding acquisition, H.W. (Huaqing Wang). All authors have read and agreed to the published version of the manuscript.

Funding: This study is supported by the Tianjin Science and Technology Planning Project (21JC-QNJC01900), the Tianjin Key Medical Discipline (Specialty) Construction Project (TJYXZDXK-053B), National Natural Science Foundation of China (81573089,81972847), and Natural Science Foundation of Tianjin Municipal Science and Technology Commission (21 JCYBJC01830).

Institutional Review Board Statement: Not applicable.

Informed Consent Statement: Not applicable.

Data Availability Statement: All data generated in this study are included in this article and its Supplementary Materials.

Acknowledgments: We thank the Instrumental Analysis and Research Center of Tianjin University of Traditional Chinese medicine for providing confocal microscopy and flow cytometry support.

Conflicts of Interest: The authors declare no conflicts of interest. The funders had no role in the design of the study; in the collection, analyses, or interpretation of data; in the writing of the manuscript; or in the decision to publish the results.

Abbreviations

NCTD	Norcantharidin
RT	Radiotherapy
ROS	Reactive oxygen species
CRC	Colorectal cancer
IR	Ionizing radiation
DRP1	Dynamin-related protein 1
MMP	Mitochondrial membrane potential
AOD	Average optical density
IOD	Integrated optical density
IHC	Immunohistochemistry
SER	Sensitization enhancement ratio
Apaf-1	Apoptotic protease activator
SA-β-gal	Senescence-associated β-galactosidase activity
Cyt C	Cytochrome C
CHK2	Checkpoint kinase 2
NCCN	National Comprehensive Cancer Network

References

1. Siegel, R.L.; Miller, K.D.; Wagle, N.S.; Jemal, A. Cancer statistics, 2023. *CA Cancer J. Clin.* **2023**, *73*, 17–48. [CrossRef] [PubMed]
2. Xia, C.; Dong, X.; Li, H.; Cao, M.; Sun, D.; He, S.; Yang, F.; Yan, X.; Zhang, S.; Li, N.; et al. Cancer statistics in China and United States, 2022: Profiles, trends, and determinants. *Chin. Med. J.* **2022**, *135*, 584–590. [CrossRef]
3. Petrelli, F.; Trevisan, F.; Cabiddu, M.; Sgroi, G.; Bruschieri, L.; Rausa, E.; Ghidini, M.; Turati, L. Total neoadjuvant therapy in rectal cancer: A systematic review and meta-analysis of treatment outcomes. *Ann. Surg.* **2020**, *271*, 440–448. [CrossRef] [PubMed]
4. Gorrini, C.; Harris, I.S.; Mak, T.W. Modulation of oxidative stress as an anticancer strategy. *Nat. Rev. Drug Discov.* **2013**, *12*, 931–947. [CrossRef]
5. Chen, Y.; Li, Y.; Huang, L.; Du, Y.; Gan, F.; Li, Y. Antioxidative Stress: Inhibiting Reactive Oxygen Species Production as a Cause of Radioresistance and Chemoresistance. *Oxid. Med. Cell Longev.* **2021**, *66*, 20306. [CrossRef] [PubMed]
6. Nguyen, L.; Dobiasch, S.; Schneider, G.; Schmid, R.M.; Azimzadeh, O.; Kanev, K. Impact of DNA repair and reactive oxygen species levels on radioresistance in pancreatic cancer. *Radiother. Oncol.* **2021**, *159*, 265–276. [CrossRef]
7. Hayes, J.D.; Dinkova-Kostova, A.T.; Tew, K.D. Oxidative Stress in Cancer. *Cancer Cell* **2020**, *38*, 167–197. [CrossRef]
8. Yoshida, T.; Goto, S.; Kawakatsu, M.; Urata, Y.; Li, T.S. Mitochondrial dysfunction, a probable cause of persistent oxidative stress after exposure to ionizing radiation. *Free Radic. Res.* **2012**, *46*, 147–153. [CrossRef]
9. Wang, Y.; Liu, L.; Pazhanisamy, S.K.; Li, H.; Meng, A.; Zhou, D. Total body irradiation causes residual bone marrow injury by induction of persistent oxidative stress in murine hematopoietic stem cells. *Free Radic. Biol. Med.* **2010**, *48*, 348–356. [CrossRef]
10. Zou, Z.; Chang, H.; Li, H.; Wang, S. Induction of reactive oxygen species: An emerging approach for cancer therapy. *Apoptosis* **2017**, *22*, 1321–1335. [CrossRef]
11. McCann, E.; O'Sullivan, J.; Marcone, S. Targeting cancer-cell mitochondria and metabolism to improve radiotherapy response. *Transl. Oncol.* **2021**, *14*, 100905. [CrossRef]
12. Kawamura, K.; Qi, F.; Kobayashi, J. Potential relationship between the biological effects of low-dose irradiation and mitochondrial ROS production. *J. Radiat. Res.* **2018**, *59*, i91–i97. [CrossRef]
13. Wang, Y.; Kong, L.; Wu, T.; Tang, M. Urban particulate matter disturbs the equilibrium of mitochondrial dynamics and biogenesis in human vascular endothelial cells. *Environ. Pollut.* **2020**, *264*, 114639. [CrossRef]
14. Jiang, J.; Liang, S.; Zhang, J.; Du, Z.; Xu, Q.; Duan, J.; Sun, Z. Melatonin ameliorates PM2.5-induced cardiac perivascular fibrosis through regulating mitochondrial redox homeostasis. *J. Pineal. Res.* **2021**, *70*, e12686. [CrossRef] [PubMed]
15. Wu, D.; Lu, J.; Ma, Y.; Cao, Y.; Zhang, T. Mitochondrial dynamics and mitophagy involved in MPA-capped CdTe quantum dots-induced toxicity in the human liver carcinoma (HepG2) cell line. *Environ. Pollut.* **2021**, *274*, 115681. [CrossRef] [PubMed]
16. Suen, D.F.; Norris, K.L.; Youle, R.J. Mitochondrial dynamics and apoptosis. *Gene Dev.* **2008**, *22*, 1577–1590. [CrossRef] [PubMed]

17. Zhou, J.; Ren, Y.; Tan, L.; Song, X.; Wang, M.; Li, Y.; Cao, Z.; Guo, C. Norcantharidin: Research advances in pharmaceutical activities and derivatives in recent years. *Biomed. Pharmacother.* **2020**, *131*, 110755. [CrossRef] [PubMed]
18. Shen, B.; He, P.J.; Shao, C.L. Norcantharidin induced DU145 cell apoptosis through ROS-mediated mitochondrial dysfunction and energy depletion. *PLoS ONE* **2013**, *8*, e84610. [CrossRef] [PubMed]
19. Lin, C.L.; Chen, C.M.; Lin, C.L.; Cheng, C.W.; Lee, C.H.; Hsieh, Y.H. Norcantharidin induces mitochondrial-dependent apoptosis through Mcl-1 inhibition in human prostate cancer cells. *Biochim. Biophys. Acta Mol. Cell Res.* **2017**, *1864*, 1867–1876. [CrossRef] [PubMed]
20. Zheng, L.-C.; Yang, M.-D.; Kuo, C.-L.; Lin, C.-H.; Fan, M.-J.; Chou, Y.-C.; Lu, H.-F.; Huang, W.-W.; Peng, S.-F.; Chung, J.-G. Norcantharidin-induced apoptosis of AGS human gastric cancer cells through reactive oxygen species production, and caspase- and mitochondria-dependent signaling pathways. *Anticancer Res.* **2016**, *36*, 6031–6042. [CrossRef]
21. Qin, H.; Zhang, H.; Zhang, X.; Zhang, S.; Zhu, S.; Wang, H. Resveratrol protects intestinal epithelial cells against radiation-induced damage by promoting autophagy and inhibiting apoptosis through SIRT1 activation. *J. Radiat. Res.* **2021**, *62*, 574–581. [CrossRef]
22. Kitamura, S.; Yanagi, T.; Imafuku, K.; Hata, H.; Abe, R.; Shimizu, H. Drp1 regulates mitochondrial morphology and cell proliferation in cutaneous squamous cell carcinoma. *J. Derrmatol. Sci.* **2017**, *88*, 298–307. [CrossRef]
23. Bleazard, W.; McCaffery, J.M.; King, E.J.; Bale, S.; Mozdy, A.; Tieu, Q.; Nunnari, J.; Shaw, J.M. The dynamin-related GTPase Dnm1 regulates mitochondrial fission in yeast. *Nat. Cell Biol.* **1999**, *1*, 298–304. [CrossRef] [PubMed]
24. Labrousse, A.M.; Zappaterra, M.D.; Rube, D.A.; van der Bliek, A.M.C. Elegans dynamin-related protein DRP-1 controls severing of the mitochondrial outer membrane. *Mol. Cell* **1999**, *4*, 815–826. [CrossRef] [PubMed]
25. Tsushima, K.; Bugger, H.; Wende, A.R.; Soto, J.; Jenson, G.A.; Tor, A.R.; McGlauflin, R.; Kenny, H.C.; Zhang, Y.; Souvenir, R.; et al. Mitochondrial reactive oxygen species in lipotoxic hearts induce post-translational modifications of AKAP121, DRP1, and OPA1 that promote mitochondrial fission. *Circ. Res.* **2018**, *122*, 58–73. [CrossRef] [PubMed]
26. Yan, T.; Zhao, Y. Acetaldehyde induces phosphorylation of dynamin-related protein 1 and mitochondrial dysfunction via elevating intracellular ROS and Ca2+ levels. *Redox Biol.* **2020**, *28*, 101381. [CrossRef] [PubMed]
27. Brooks, C.; Wei, Q.; Feng, L.; Dong, G.; Tao, Y.; Mei, L.; Xie, Z.-J.; Dong, Z. Bak regulates mitochondrial morphology and pathology during apoptosis by interacting with mitofusins. *Proc. Natl. Acad. Sci. USA* **2007**, *104*, 11649–11654. [CrossRef] [PubMed]
28. Frank, S.; Gaume, B.; Bergmann-Leitner, E.S.; Leitner, W.W.; Robert, E.G.; Catez, F.; Smith, C.L.; Youle, R.J. The role of dynamin-related protein 1, a mediator of mitochondrial fission, in apoptosis. *Dev. Cell* **2001**, *1*, 515–525. [CrossRef]
29. Germain, M.; Mathai, J.P.; McBride, H.M.; Shore, G.C. Endoplasmic reticulum BIK initiates DRP1-regulated remodelling of mitochondrial cristae during apoptosis. *Embo J.* **2005**, *24*, 1546–1556. [CrossRef]
30. Ludmir, E.B.; Palta, M.; Willett, C.G.; Czito, B.G. Total neoadjuvant therapy for rectal cancer: An emerging option. *Cancer* **2017**, *123*, 1497–1506. [CrossRef]
31. Sauer, R.; Liersch, T.; Merkel, S.; Fietkau, R.; Hohenberger, W.; Hess, C.; Becker, H.; Raab, H.-R.; Villanueva, M.-T.; Witzigmann, H.; et al. Preoperative versus postoperative chemoradiotherapy for locally advanced rectal cancer: Results of the German CAO/ARO/AIO-94 randomized phase III trial after a median follow-up of 11 years. *J. Clin. Oncol.* **2012**, *30*, 1926–1933. [CrossRef] [PubMed]
32. Li, X.-P.; Jing, W.; Sun, J.-J.; Liu, Z.-Y.; Zhang, J.-T.; Sun, W.; Zhu, W.; Fan, Y.-Z. A potential small-molecule synthetic anti-lymphangiogenic agent norcantharidin inhibits tumor growth and lymphangiogenesis of human colonic adenocarcinomas through blocking VEGF-A,-C,-D/VEGFR-2,-3 "multi-points priming" mechanisms in vitro and in vivo. *BMC Cancer* **2015**, *15*, 527. [CrossRef]
33. Qiu, P.; Wang, S.; Liu, M.; Ma, H.; Zeng, X.; Zhang, M.; Xu, L.; Cui, Y.; Xu, H.; Tang, Y.; et al. Norcantharidin Inhibits cell growth by suppressing the expression and phosphorylation of both EGFR and c-Met in human colon cancer cells. *BMC Cancer* **2017**, *17*, 55. [CrossRef] [PubMed]
34. Peng, C.; Li, Z.; Niu, Z.; Niu, W.; Xu, Z.; Gao, H.; Niu, W.; Wang, J.; He, Z.; Gao, C.; et al. Norcantharidin Suppresses Colon Cancer Cell Epithelial-Mesenchymal Transition by Inhibiting the $\alpha v\beta 6$-ERK-Ets1 Signaling Pathway. *Sci. Rep.* **2016**, *6*, 20500. [CrossRef]
35. Hanley, R.; Pagliari, F.; Garcia-Calderón, D.; Guerreiro, J.F.; Genard, G.; Jansen, J.; Nisticò, C.; Marafioti, M.G.; Tirinato, L.; Seco, J. Radio-resistance of hypoxic tumors: Exploring the effects of oxygen and x-ray radiation on non-small lung cancer cell lines. *Radiat. Oncol.* **2023**, *18*, 81. [CrossRef]
36. Patel, P.; Sun, L.; Robbins, Y.; Clavijo, P.E.; Friedman, J.; Silvin, C.; Van Waes, C.; Cook, J.; Mitchell, J.; Allen, C. Enhancing direct cytotoxicity and response to immune checkpoint blockade following ionizing radiation with Weel kinase inhibition. *Oncoimmunology* **2019**, *8*, e1638207. [CrossRef] [PubMed]
37. Sun, S.Y. N-acetylcysteine, reactive oxygen species and beyond. *Cancer Biol. Ther.* **2010**, *9*, 109–110. [CrossRef]
38. Wasiak, S.; Zunino, R.; McBride, H.M. Bax/Bak promote sumoylation of DRP1 and its stable association with mitochondria during apoptotic cell death. *J. Cell Biol.* **2007**, *177*, 439–450. [CrossRef]
39. Prudent, J.; Zunino, R.; Sugiura, A.; Mattie, S.; Shore, G.C.; McBride, H.M. MAPL SUMOylation of Drp1 stabilizes an ER/mitochondrial platform required for cell death. *Mol. Cell* **2015**, *59*, 941–955. [CrossRef]

40. Ishihara, N.; Nomura, M.; Jofuku, A.; Kato, H.; Suzuki, S.O.; Masuda, K.; Otera, H.; Nakanishi, Y.; Nonaka, I.; Goto, Y.-I.; et al. Mitochondrial fission factor Drp1 is essential for embryonic development and synapse formation in mice. *Nat. Cell Biol.* **2009**, *11*, 958–966. [CrossRef]
41. Lee, Y.J.; Jeong, S.Y.; Karbowski, M.; Smith, C.L.; Youle, R.J. Roles of the mammalian mitochondrial fission and fusion mediators Fis1, Drp1, and Opa1 in apoptosis. *Mol. Biol. Cell* **2004**, *15*, 5001–5011. [CrossRef] [PubMed]

biomedicines

MDPI

Article

A Brain-Protective Sterol from Soft Coral Inhibits Lipopolysaccharide-Induced Matrix Metalloproteinase-9-Mediated Astrocytic Migration

Tsong-Hai Lee [1,†], Jiun-Liang Chen [2], Chuan-Hsin Chang [3,†], Ming-Ming Tsai [3], Hui-Ching Tseng [3], Yu-Chia Chang [3], Velayuthaprabhu Shanmugam [4] and Hsi-Lung Hsieh [3,5,6,*]

1 Stroke Center and Stroke Section, Department of Neurology, Chang Gung Memorial Hospital, College of Medicine, Chang Gung University, Taoyuan 333, Taiwan; thlee@cgmh.org.tw
2 Division of Chinese Internal Medicine, Center for Traditional Chinese Medicine, Chang Gung Memorial Hospital, School of Traditional Chinese Medicine, College of Medicine, Chang Gung University, Taoyuan 333, Taiwan; a12015@cgmh.org.tw
3 Division of Basic Medical Sciences, Department of Nursing, Research Center for Chinese Herbal Medicine, Graduate Institute of Health Industry Technology, Chang Gung University of Science and Technology, Taoyuan 333, Taiwan; chuanhsin@mail.cgust.edu.tw (C.-H.C.); mmtsai@mail.cgust.edu.tw (M.-M.T.); hctseng@mail.cgust.edu.tw (H.-C.T.); ycchang03@mail.cgust.edu.tw (Y.-C.C.)
4 Department of Biotechnology, Bharathiar University, Coimbatore 641046, India; velayuthaprabhu@buc.edu.in
5 Department of Neurology, Chang Gung Memorial Hospital, Taoyuan 333, Taiwan
6 Department of Chemical Engineering, Ming Chi University of Technology, R&D Center of Biochemical Engineering Technology, New Taipei City 301, Taiwan
* Correspondence: hlhsieh@mail.cgust.edu.tw; Tel.: +886-3-2118999 (ext. 5421)
† These authors contributed equally to this work.

Abstract: Matrix metalloproteinases (MMPs), which are proteolytic enzymes, promote blood–brain barrier (BBB) disruption, leading to neuronal damage and neuroinflammation. Among them, MMP-9 upregulation serves as an inflammatory biomarker in the central nervous system (CNS). Currently, the development of marine organism-derived bioactive compounds or metabolites as anti-inflammatory drugs has received considerable attention. The 9,11-secosteroid, 3β,11-dihydroxy-9,11-secogorgost-5-en-9-one (4p3f), is a novel sterol compound extracted from the soft coral *Sinularia leptoclado* with potential anti-inflammatory activity. However, the effect of and potential for brain protection of 4p3f on brain astrocytes remain unclear. Herein, we used rat brain astrocytes (RBAs) to investigate the effects and signaling mechanisms of 4p3f on lipopolysaccharide (LPS)-induced MMP-9 expression via zymographic, quantitative reverse transcription–polymerase chain reaction (qRT-PCR), Western blot, immunofluorescence staining, promoter–reporter, and cell migration analyses. We first found that 4p3f blocked LPS-induced MMP-9 expression in RBAs. Next, we demonstrated that LPS induced MMP-9 expression via the activation of ERK1/2, p38 MAPK, and JNK1/2, which is linked to the STAT3-mediated NF-κB signaling pathway. Finally, 4p3f effectively inhibited LPS-induced upregulation of MMP-9-triggered RBA cell migration. These data suggest that a novel sterol from soft coral, 4p3f, may have anti-inflammatory and brain-protective effects by attenuating these signaling pathways of MMP-9-mediated events in brain astrocytes. Accordingly, the soft coral-derived sterol 4p3f may emerge as a potential candidate for drug development or as a natural compound with neuroprotective properties.

Keywords: soft coral; lipopolysaccharide; matrix metalloproteinase-9; cell migration; brain astrocytes; anti-inflammation

1. Introduction

Astrocytes are one type of glial cells and the most abundant non-neuronal cell type in the central nervous system (CNS), comprising 19–40% of glial cells in the brain [1].

They exert a wide range of functions in the brain, including homeostatic maintenance and post-injury repair of the blood–brain barrier (BBB) in the CNS [2–5], as well as regulation of synapse formation and pruning, lactate levels, glutamate levels, and neuroinflammation in the brain [6]. However, the chronic inflammatory response of astrocytes triggers the migration of peripheral immune cells to the site of inflammation in the CNS, which further aggravates the inflammatory response and causes brain injury [7]. Astrocytes undergo reactive changes in morphology and molecular profile known as astrogliosis, leading to the release of proinflammatory molecules (including extracellular matrix, cytokines, and growth factors), which exacerbates the severity of brain injury [8].

Matrix metalloproteinases (MMPs), which comprise a family of calcium-dependent zinc-containing endopeptidases, play a role in the pathological processes of neuroinflammatory and neurodegenerative diseases [9]. MMP-9 serves as a potential disease biomarker in response to various physiological stimuli and pathological insults; the upregulation of MMP-9 enzymatic activity and expression contributes to a wide range of brain disorders, including BBB breakdown, epilepsy, schizophrenia, autism spectrum disorder, brain injury, stroke, neurodegeneration, pain, and brain tumors, among others [10,11].

Lipopolysaccharide (LPS) is a constituent found in the outer membrane of Gram-negative bacteria, and it is widely used as a potent proinflammatory agent in neuroinflammation studies [12]. Previous research has demonstrated that LPS induces the expression of MMP-9 in brain astrocytes and causes astrocyte migration via various signaling pathways, including phosphatidylinositol 3′-kinase (PI3K)/Akt, extracellular signal-regulated kinases (ERKs), and c-Jun N-terminal protein kinases (JNKs) [13], as well as nuclear factor kappa B (NF-κB) activation [14]. In addition to LPS, we previously reported that bradykinin (BK), a common proinflammatory mediator, upregulates MMP-9 protein expression through signal transducer and activator of transcription 3 (STAT3) activation in brain astrocytes [15].

Marine natural products (MNPs) are potent and promising sources of biologically active agents, which are extracted from marine organisms, such as tunicates, soft corals, and sponges [16]. Recently, research topics on MNPs and their potential in medicine have gradually attracted attention. The 9,11-secosteroid, 3β,11-dihydroxy-9,11-secogorgost-5-en-9-one (4p3f), which is isolated from the soft coral *Sinularia leptoclados*, can be structurally characterized by the C-9/11 oxidative cleavage of the C-ring [17–19]. Several studies have demonstrated that steroids from the genus *Sinularia* exhibit cytotoxicity and anti-proliferative effects against various cancer cells, including lung cancer cells, cervical adenocarcinoma, pancreatic epithelioid carcinoma, and promyelocytic leukemia cells [20–22]. Two novel 9,11-secosteroids, named sinleptosterols A and B, from the Taiwan soft coral *Sinularia leptoclados* have been reported to be compounds that have anti-inflammatory effects by inhibiting superoxide anion generation and elastase release in active human neutrophils [18]. Therefore, we believe that marine compounds have the potential to be developed as therapeutic drugs for inflammation-related pathologies. Herein, we investigated whether 9,11-secosteroid (i.e., 4p3f) exerts anti-inflammatory action in the CNS. In this study, the effect of 4p3f on LPS-induced MMP-9 expression in rat brain astrocytes and the underlying mechanism of action were examined.

In the current study, we demonstrated that 4p3f significantly inhibited LPS-induced MMP-9 expression in rat brain astrocytes (RBAs). Moreover, LPS-induced MMP-9 expression was mediated through phosphorylation of MAPKs (including ERK1/2, P38 MAPK, and JNK1/2), leading to the activation of STAT3-dependent NF-κB, which could be inhibited by pretreatment with 4p3f. Furthermore, pretreatment with 4p3f attenuated LPS-induced MMP-9-mediated RBA cell migration. These results suggest that the anti-inflammatory action of 4p3f (9,11-secosteroid) might be a potential therapeutic agent for brain inflammatory disorders.

2. Materials and Methods

2.1. Materials

Dulbecco's modified Eagle's medium (DMEM)/F-12 medium, fetal bovine serum (FBS), and TRIzol were purchased from Invitrogen (Carlsbad, CA, USA). Polyvinylidene fluoride (PVDF) membranes, enhanced chemiluminescence (ECL), and Western blot detection systems were obtained from GE Healthcare Biosciences (Chalfont St Giles, Buckinghamshire, UK). Anti-phospho-ERK1/2 (Cat#4377), anti-phospho-p38 MAPK (Cat#9211), anti-phospho-p65 NF-κB (Cat#3033), and anti-glyceraldehyde-3-phosphate dehydrogenase (GAPDH) (Cat#2118) antibodies were purchased from Cell Signaling Technology (Danvers, MA, USA). Anti-phospho-JNK1/2 and anti-STAT3 (Cat#sc-482) antibodies were purchased from Santa Cruz Biotechnology (Santa Cruz, CA, USA). Anti-mouse (Cat#7056) and anti-rabbit (Cat#5054) horseradish peroxidase-conjugated secondary antibodies were purchased from Santa Cruz Biotechnology (Santa Cruz, CA, USA). The iScript cDNA Synthesis Kit, SsoFast EvaGreen Supermix, and CFX Connect Real-Time Polymerase Chain Reaction (PCR) detection system were obtained from Bio-Rad Laboratories, Inc. (Hercules, CA, USA). A dual-luciferase reporter system was obtained from Promega (Madison, WI, USA). The inhibitors, including U0126, SB202190, SP600126, and Bay 11-7082, were purchased from Santa Cruz Biotechnology, and STAT3 inhibitor V (STAT3I) was obtained from Sigma-Aldrich Chemical, Co. (St Louis, MO, USA). All other enzymes, reagents, chemicals, and lipopolysaccharide (LPS) were obtained from Sigma-Aldrich (St. Louis, MO, USA).

2.2. Coral Material

The soft coral *Sinularia leptoclados* samples were collected from the coast of Pingtung, Taiwan. The samples were stored in a freezer at −20 °C until extraction. A specimen voucher was deposited at the Research Center for Chinese Herbal Medicine, Chang Gung University of Science and Technology, Taiwan (specimen No.: CGUST-C004-20.18-NOV).

2.3. Extraction and Isolation

The frozen samples were minced and extracted via maceration in ethyl acetate (EA) until exhaustion. The EA extract was subjected to repeated column chromatography on silica gel, and preparative RP-HPLC was used to obtain compounds of a steroidal nature. The structure of 9,11-secosteroids was deduced from a general spectroscopic analysis, including an examination of NMR spectra, and via comparison with data of related compounds [18].

2.4. Cell Culture and Treatment

The rat brain astrocytic cell line (RBA, CTX TNA2) was purchased from BCRC (Hsinchu, Taiwan). The cells were cultured in a DMEM/F12 medium containing 5% FBS, 100 IU/mL penicillin G, 100 mg/mL streptomycin sulfate, and nonessential amino acids at 37 °C under a humidified atmosphere with 5% CO_2 according to a previously described standard protocol [15]. The cells were either untreated or treated with 4p3f or inhibitors of ERK1/2 (U0126), p38 MAPK (SB202190), JNK1/2 (SP600125), NF-κB (Bay11-7082), or STAT3 (STAT3I). These substances were added to the cell culture 1 h before the treatment of LPS (10 μg/mL) in all experiments. Treatment of RBAs with 4p3f, these inhibitors alone, or LPS stimulation had no significant effect on cell viability, as determined by an XTT assay. The cell passage numbers we used were from P10 to P15.

2.5. MMP Gelatin Zymography

Growth-arrested cells were incubated with different treatments for the indicated time intervals [15]. The cells were either untreated or treated with 4p3f or inhibitors of ERK1/2 (U0126), p38 MAPK (SB202190), JNK1/2 (SP600125), NF-κB (Bay11-7082), or STAT3 (STAT3I). After the treatments, the conditioned media were collected and analyzed by means of gelatin zymography, as previously described [15]. In briefly, the collected conditioned media were mixed with a 5× nonreducing sample buffer and analyzed on a

10% gel containing 0.15% gelatin. After electrophoresis, the gel was washed, incubated, stained, and then destained. The gelatinolytic activity appeared as parallel white bands on a blue background.

2.6. Total RNA Extraction and Real-Time RT-PCR Analysis

Total RNA was extracted from RBAs using the TRIzol reagent (Thermo Fisher Scientific, Waltham, MA, USA), and the concentration of total RNA was measured using a Nano100 Micro-Spectrophotometer (CLUBIO; Taipei, Taiwan) [15]. Then, cDNA was synthesized using an iScript cDNA Synthesis Kit and amplified on a spectrofluorometric thermal cycler (iCycler; Bio-Rad Laboratories). Real-time PCR was performed with the TaqMan gene expression assay system, using the primers and probe mixes for *COX-2* and endogenous *GAPDH* control genes. PCRs were performed using SYBR Green PCR reagents (Applied Biosystems, Branchburg, NJ, USA). The relative gene expression was determined based on the ΔΔCt method, where Ct denotes the threshold cycle. All experiments were performed in triplicate ($n = 3$).

2.7. Western Blot Analysis

Growth-arrested cells were incubated with different treatments for the indicated time intervals. After the treatments, the cells were washed with ice-cold phosphate-buffered saline (PBS), scraped, lysed in a lysis buffer, and centrifuged at 45,000× g for 1 h at 4 °C to yield a whole-cell extract, as previously described [15]. The samples were analyzed by means of Western blot, transferred to nitrocellulose membranes, and then incubated overnight with anti-phospho-ERK1/2, phospho-p38, phospho-JNK1/2, phospho-p65 NF-κB, phospho-STAT3, or GAPDH antibodies. The membranes were washed four times with TTBS for 5 min each and incubated with an anti-rabbit horseradish peroxidase antibody (1:2000) for 1 h. The immunoreactive bands were detected using ECL reagents and captured using a UVP BioSpectrum 500 Imaging System (Upland, CA, USA). The images were quantified and analyzed using the UN-SCAN-IT gel 6.1 software (Orem, UT, USA).

2.8. Immunofluorescence Stain

Cells were either untreated or pretreated with the inhibitors or 4p3f and then stimulated with LPS for 30 min, washed twice with ice-cold PBS, fixed with 4% (w/v) paraformaldehyde in PBS for 30 min, and then permeabilized with 0.3% Triton X-100 in PBS for 15 min. The cells were stained by incubating with 10% normal goat serum in PBS for 30 min, followed by incubating with an anti-NF-κB (p65) antibody (1:200 dilution (Cat#sc-372)) in PBS with 1% BSA at 4 °C overnight. On the following day, the cells were washed three times with PBS and incubated with a FITC-conjugated goat anti-rabbit antibody (1:150 dilution) in PBS with 1% BSA for 1 h. After three additional washes with PBS, the cells were mounted using an aqueous mounting medium. Images were acquired under a fluorescence microscope (Axiovert 200 M, ZEISS, Göttingen, Germany).

2.9. Promoter-Luciferase Reporter Gene Assay

The κB binding sites were cloned to the pGL4.32 (luc2P/NF-κB-RE/Hygro) vector containing a luciferase reporter system. All plasmids were prepared by using QIAGEN plasmid DNA preparation kits. These constructs were transfected into RBA cells by using a Lipofectamine reagent according to the instructions of the manufacturer. The transfection efficiency (~60%) was determined based on transfection with enhanced GFP. After incubation with LPS, the cells were collected and disrupted via sonication in a lysis buffer (25 mM Tris, pH 7.8, 2 mM EDTA, 1% Triton X-100, and 10% glycerol). After centrifugation, aliquots of the supernatants were tested for promoter activity using a Dual-Luciferase® Reporter Assay System (Promega, Madison, WI, USA). Firefly luciferase activity was standardized for Renilla luciferase activity.

2.10. Cell Migration Assay

RBA cells were cultured to confluence in 6-well culture plates and starved with a serum-free DMEM/F-12 medium for 24 h. The monolayer cells were manually scratched using a pipette blue tip to create extended and definite scratches in the center of the dishes with a bright and clear field (~2 mm). The detached cells were removed, and a serum-free DMEM/F-12 medium was added with or without LPS after pretreatment with the inhibitors for 1 h, which contained a DNA synthesis inhibitor, hydroxyurea (10 μM), during the experimental period [15]. Cell migration was observed under a microscope and quantified by counting the number of cells from the resulting four-phase images for each point, as well as averaged for each experimental condition. The presented data are summarized from three independent assays.

2.11. Statistical Analysis

All data were analyzed using the GraphPad Prism Program (GraphPad, San Diego, CA, USA). Quantitative data were analyzed by means of one-way ANOVA, followed by Tukey's honestly significant difference tests between individual groups. Data were expressed as mean ± SEM. A value of $p < 0.05$ was considered significant.

3. Results

3.1. The Effect of Soft Coral-Derived Sterol Extract on LPS-Induced MMP-9 Expression in Brain Astrocytes

An upregulation of MMP-9 is associated with a disruption of the blood–brain barrier (BBB) and neuroinflammation, which is a risk factor for brain inflammatory disorders, neurodegenerative diseases, cardiovascular diseases, and diabetes [23–26]. In this study, we first investigated whether LPS can induce MMP-9 expression in rat brain astrocytes (RBAs). Cells were treated with 10 μg/mL LPS for the indicated time intervals (0~24 h), and MMP-9 protein and mRNA levels were measured via zymographic and real time-PCR analyses. The results showed that LPS induced MMP-9 expression in a time-dependent manner, but not MMP-2 expression, with a significantly increased MMP-9 expression at 16 and 24 h (Figure 1A). Moreover, qRT-PCR was used to determine the effect of LPS on MMP-9 mRNA regulation. As shown in Figure 1B, LPS induced a significant increase in *MMP-9* mRNA expression after 6~24 h of incubation. The data revealed that LPS could induce MMP-9 expression in RBAs by upregulating the transcriptional and translational levels.

Previously, a study indicated that sterol extracts from soft coral have an anti-inflammatory ability [18]. Therefore, we further evaluated the effect of a soft coral-derived sterol extract of 4p3f on LPS-induced MMP-9 expression in RBAs. These cells were pretreated with 4p3f (1 μM) for 1 h, and then incubated with 10 μg/mL LPS for the indicated times (0, 16, and 24 h). The data showed that pretreatment with 4p3f significantly repressed LPS-induced MMP-9 expression in RBAs (Figure 1C). Moreover, LPS-induced MMP-9 mRNA expression was also inhibited after pretreatment with 4p3f in these cells (Figure 1D). These results suggested that the coral sterol extract of 4p3f may have a preventive effect against brain inflammation by attenuating LPS-induced MMP-9 expression in brain astrocytes.

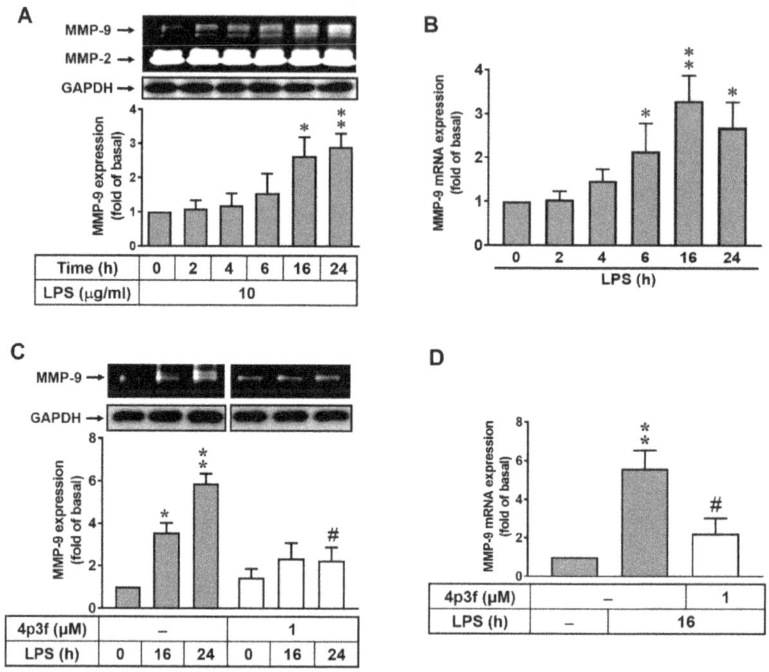

Figure 1. The effect of a soft coral-derived sterol extract on LPS-induced MMP-9 expression in brain astrocytes. (**A**,**B**) Cells were treated with LPS (10 μg/mL) for the indicated time intervals. (**A**) For MMP-9 expression, the conditioned media were collected and analyzed via gelatin zymography. And the glyceraldehyde-3-phosphate dehydrogenase (GAPDH) level of cell lysates (as an internal control) was assayed by means of Western blot analysis. (**B**) Total RNA was prepared and then *MMP-9* mRNA expression was analyzed via real-time RT-PCR. (**C**,**D**) Cells were pretreated with 4p3f (1 μM) for 1 h and then incubated with LPS for the indicated times. (**C**) The conditioned media were collected and analyzed for MMP-9 expression via gelatin zymography. (**D**) *MMP-9* mRNA expression was analyzed by means of real-time RT-PCR. Data are expressed as mean ± SEM (n = 3). * $p < 0.05$ and ** $p < 0.01$, as compared with the untreated control; # $p < 0.05$, as compared with LPS-treated cells only. The images represent one of three individual experiments.

3.2. 4p3f Attenuates LPS-Induced MMP-9 Expression by Blocking the MAPK Signaling Pathways

Activation of MAPKs regulates various functions of brain cells [27]. In addition, many reports have indicated that LPS induces MMP-9 expression via MAPK-dependent pathways in several cell types, including brain astrocytes [28,29]. Thus, to determine whether MAPKs also participated in LPS-induced MMP-9 expression in RBAs, cells were pretreated with inhibitors of MAPKs, including ERK1/2 inhibitor U0126 (0.1 μM), p38 MAPK inhibitor SB202190 (1 μM), and JNK1/2 inhibitor SP600125 (0.1 μM), for 1 h and then incubated with LPS (10 μg/mL) for 0, 16, or 24 h. As shown in Figure 2A, pretreatment with U0126, SB202190, or SP600125 significantly reduced LPS-induced MMP-9 protein expression in the cells. Moreover, LPS-induced *MMP-9* mRNA expression was also inhibited by pretreatment with U0126, SB202190, or SP600125 (Figure 2B). These data demonstrate that ERK1/2, p38 MAPK, and JNK1/2 signals are involved in LPS-induced MMP-9 expression in RBAs. To further investigate the effect of 4p3f on MAPK signaling pathways, a Western blot analysis was performed to examine the phosphorylation of ERK1/2, p38 MAPK, and JNK1/2 in cells exposed to LPS for 0, 30, or 60 min. The results showed that LPS could stimulate phosphorylation of ERK1/2 (upper panel), p38 MAPK (middle panel), and JNK1/2 (lower panel) in a time-dependent manner in RBAs, with a significant increase at 30 min

(Figure 2C). Pretreatment with U0126, SB202190, and SP202190 significantly inhibited LPS-stimulated phosphorylation of ERK1/2, p38 MAPK, and JNK1/2, respectively. Moreover, LPS-stimulated phosphorylation of MAPKs was attenuated by pretreatment with 4p3f (Figure 2C). These results indicated that 4p3f could inhibit LPS-induced MMP-9 expression by attenuating activation of MAPK (i.e., ERK1/2, p38, and JNK1/2) signaling pathways.

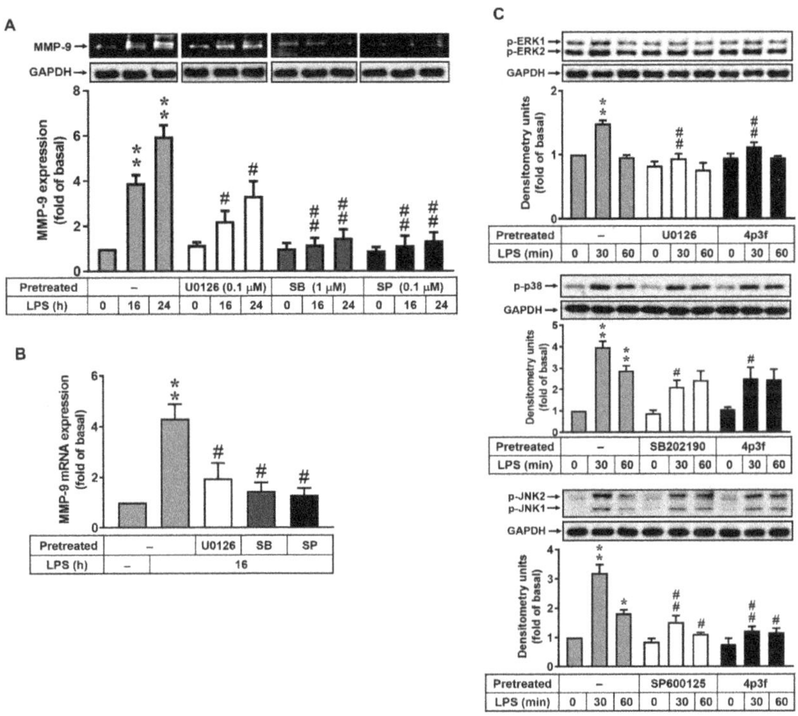

Figure 2. 4p3f attenuates LPS-induced MMP-9 expression by blocking MAPK signaling pathways. Cells were pretreated with U0126 (0.1 μM), SB202190 (1 μM), or SP600125 (0.1 μM) for 1 h and then incubated with LPS (10 μg/mL) for the indicated time intervals. (**A**) For MMP-9 expression, the conditioned media were collected and analyzed via gelatin zymography. The GAPDH level of cell lysates was assayed by means of Western blot. (**B**) For *MMP-9* mRNA expression, total RNA was prepared and analyzed via real-time PCR. (**C**) Cells were pretreated with U0126 (0.1 μM), SB202190 (1 μM), SP600125 (0.1 μM), or 4p3f (1 μM) for 1 h and then incubated with LPS (10 μg/mL) for the indicated times. After treatment, cell lysates were collected and analyzed via Western blot for phosphorylation of ERK1/2 (p-ERK1/2), p38 MAPK (p-p38), JNK1/2 (p-JNK1/2), and GAPDH (as an internal control). Data are expressed as mean ± SEM (n = 3). * $p < 0.05$ and ** $p < 0.01$, as compared with the untreated control; # $p < 0.05$ and ## $p < 0.01$, as compared with LPS-treated cells only. The images represent one of three individual experiments.

3.3. *4p3f Inhibits LPS-Induced MMP-9 Expression by Reducing NF-κB Activation*

In the LPS signaling pathway, NF-κB binds to the promoter region of MMP-9 gene and modulates its expression [30]. To examine the role of NF-κB in LPS-induced MMP-9 expression in RBAs, cells were treated with or without the NF-κB inhibitor Bay11-7082 (Bay) for 1 h and then incubated with LPS (10 μg/mL) for 0, 16, or 24 h. The results showed that pretreatment with Bay (0.1 μM) significantly attenuated LPS-induced MMP-9 expression (Figure 3A). Additionally, pretreatment with 4p3f (1 μM) also suppressed LPS-induced *MMP-9* mRNA expression based on the real time-PCR analysis (Figure 3B). We further explored the effects of 4p3f on LPS-stimulated activation of NF-κB in RBAs, and the phosphorylation of p65 NF-κB (a subunit of NF-κB) was detected via Western blot. As shown in Figure 3C, LPS stimulated the phosphorylation of p65 NF-κB (p-p65) in a time-dependent manner, with a maximum increase at 30 min. We further found that LPS-stimulated p65 NF-κB phosphorylation was reduced by pretreatment with either Bay or 4p3f (Figure 3C). Hence, we further used immunofluorescence staining to assess the effect of 4p3f on LPS-stimulated NF-κB translocation from the cytoplasm into the nucleus in RBAs. The data showed that LPS could stimulate NF-κB translocation, and pretreatment with Bay or 4p3f both attenuated LPS-stimulated NF-κB translocation (Figure 3D). Next, to demonstrate whether LPS enhances NF-κB transcriptional activity, a promoter (containing κB binding sites)–luciferase reporter gene assay was used. The data showed that LPS increased NF-κB transcriptional activity in a time-dependent manner, with a maximum response after 4 h of incubation (Figure 3E). The transcriptional activity was attenuated by pretreatment with either Bay or 4p3f in RBAs. These results indicated that LPS-induced MMP-9 expression is mediated via the NF-κB-dependent pathway in brain astrocytes, and 4p3f can inhibit this response.

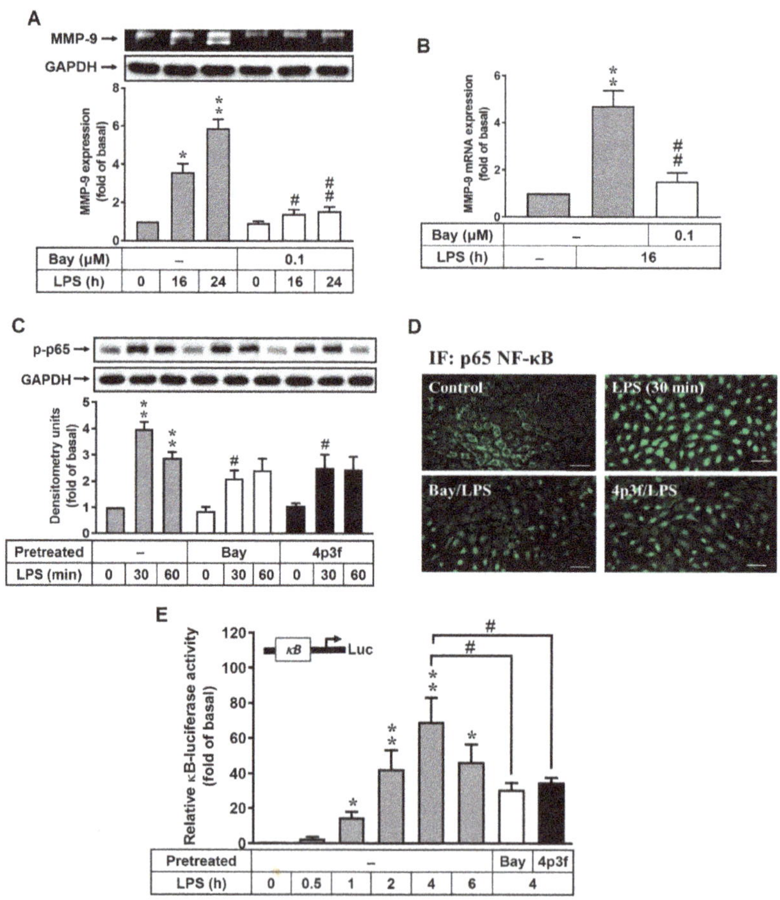

Figure 3. 4p3f inhibits LPS-induced MMP-9 expression by reducing NF-κB activation. Cells were pretreated with Bay11-7082 (Bay, 0.1 μM) for 1 h and then incubated with LPS (10 μg/mL) for the indicated time intervals. (**A**) For MMP-9 expression, the conditioned media were collected and analyzed via gelatin zymography. The GAPDH level of cell lysates was assayed via Western blot. (**B**) For *MMP-9* mRNA expression, total RNA was prepared and analyzed using real-time PCR.

(**C**) Cells were pretreated with Bay (0.1 μM) or 4p3f (1 μM) for 1 h and then incubated with LPS (10 μg/mL) for the indicated times. After treatment, cell lysates were collected and analyzed using Western blot for phosphorylation of p65 NF-κB (p-p65) and GAPDH (as an internal control). (**D**) The translocation of p65 NF-κB was determined by means of immunofluorescence staining in RBAs. Cells were pretreated with Bay or 4p3f for 1 h, and then stimulated with LPS for 30 min. Cells were fixed and labeled with an anti-p65 NF-κB antibody and a FITC-conjugated secondary antibody. Individual cells were imaged (scale bar = 50 μm) as described in Section 2. (**E**) Cells were transiently transfected with a promoter–reporter construct (pGL4.32-containing κB binding sites), pretreated with Bay (0.1 μM) or 4p3f (1 μM) for 1 h, and then stimulated with LPS (10 μg/mL) for the indicated times. After stimulation, the firefly luciferase activity of the promoter (κB) construct was measured as relative promoter activity to that of Renilla luciferase activity. Data are expressed as mean ± SEM (n = 3). * $p < 0.05$ and ** $p < 0.01$, as compared with the untreated control; # $p < 0.05$ and ## $p < 0.01$, as compared with LPS-treated cells only. The images represent one of three individual experiments.

3.4. Effects of 4p3f on LPS-Induced STAT3-Mediated MMP-9 Expression in RBAs

In addition to NF-κB, STAT3 is known to regulate the induction of MMP-9 expression following stimulation by many factors in different types of cells [15,31,32]. Moreover, LPS-induced MMP-9 expression occurs via the STAT3 pathway in macrophages [31]. To investigate whether LPS-induced MMP-9 expression is mediated via a STAT3-dependent pathway, a STAT3 inhibitor (STAT3I) was used. As shown in Figure 4, cells were pretreated with STAT3I (1 μM) and then incubated with LPS (10 μg/mL) for the indicated time intervals. The data showed that pretreatment with STAT3I markedly attenuated LPS-induced upregulation of MMP-9 protein (Figure 4A) and *MMP-9* mRNA (Figure 4B). Furthermore, we observed whether LPS could stimulate STAT3 activation in RBAs, and the phosphorylation of STAT3 was detected using Western blot. The results showed that LPS could stimulate STAT3 phosphorylation, with a significant increase at 60 min (Figure 4C). Pretreatment with either STAT3I or 4p3f significantly inhibited LPS-stimulated phosphorylation of STAT3 in RBAs (Figure 4C). These results suggested that 4p3f attenuated LPS-induced MMP-9 expression by decreasing the activation of STAT3 in brain astrocytes.

3.5. MAPK-STAT3 Signaling Axis Is Crucial for LPS-Stimulated NF-κB Transcriptional Activity in RBAs

In human monocytes, LPS triggers the activation of NF-κB through ERK1/2, JNK1/2, and p38 MAPKs [33]. In dendritic cells, LPS activates the STAT3 signaling pathway, which results in the recruitment of NF-κB and the expression of proinflammatory cytokine genes [34]. Thus, we explored the relationships between these signals. For the activation of MAPKs and NF-κB, cells were pretreated with U0126 (0.1 μM), SB202190 (1 μM), or SP600125 (0.1 μM) for 1 h and then incubated with LPS (10 μg/mL) for 0, 30, or 60 min. The phosphorylation of p65 NF-κB was detected using Western blot. As shown in Figure 5A, pretreatment with U0126, SB202190, or SP600125 significantly attenuated LPS-stimulated p65 NF-κB phosphorylation (p-p65), suggesting that LPS-stimulated activation of NF-κB is mediated in an MAPK (i.e., ERK1/2, p38, and JNK1/2)-dependent manner in RBAs. We further studied the relationships between MAPKs and STAT3. The results showed that pretreatment with U0126, SB202190, and SP600125 significantly decreased LPS-stimulated STAT3 phosphorylation (Figure 5B), suggesting that MAPKs (i.e., ERK1/2, p38, and JNK1/2) are also involved in LPS-stimulated STAT3 phosphorylation in RBAs. Moreover, we investigated the effects of the MAPK-STAT3 signaling axis on LPS-stimulated transcriptional activity of NF-κB in RBAs. As shown in Figure 5C, pretreatment with U0126, SB202190, SP600125, or STAT3I all markedly reduced κB-dependent promoter–reporter activity. Accordingly, these results demonstrated that LPS stimulated NF-κB transcriptional activity via an MAPK-mediated STAT3 signaling pathway in RBAs.

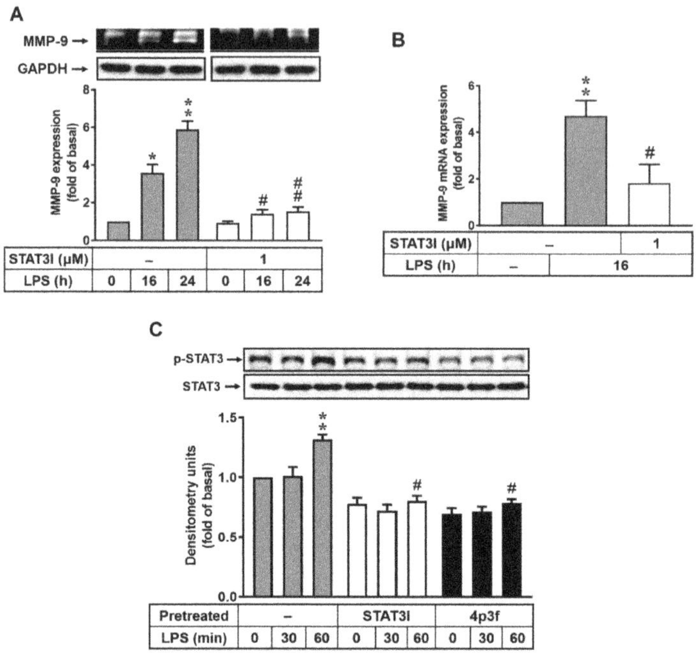

Figure 4. Effects of 4p3f on LPS-induced STAT3-mediated MMP-9 expression in RBAs. Cells were pretreated with or without STAT3I (1 μM) for 1 h and then incubated with LPS (10 μg/mL) for the indicated time intervals. (**A**) For MMP-9 expression, the conditioned media were collected and analyzed via gelatin zymography. The GAPDH level of cell lysates (as an internal control) was assayed by means of Western blot. (**B**) For *MMP-9* mRNA expression, total RNA was prepared and analyzed via real-time PCR. (**C**) Cells were pretreated with STAT3I (1 μM) or 4p3f (1 μM) for 1 h and then incubated with LPS (10 μg/mL) for the indicated times. After treatment, cell lysates were collected and analyzed via Western blot for phosphorylation of STAT3 (p-STAT3) and total STAT3. Data are expressed as mean ± SEM (n = 3). * $p < 0.05$ and ** $p < 0.01$, as compared with the untreated control; # $p < 0.05$ and ## $p < 0.01$, as compared with LPS-treated cells only. The images represent one of three individual experiments.

3.6. 4p3f Inhibits LPS-Induced MMP-9-Mediated Astrocytic Migration

In brain astrocytes, we previously demonstrated that upregulation of MMP-9 participates in cell migration [35]. A recent study indicated that LPS induces MMP-9 expression and enhances cell migration, thereby contributing to the development of neuroinflammation [36]. Here, we further evaluated the effect of 4p3f on LPS-induced MMP-9-dependent RBA migration and its underlying mechanisms. Images of RBA migration were taken at 24 h after treatment with LPS (10 μg/mL) and observed. As shown in Figure 6A, LPS significantly triggered RBA migration, which was blocked by pretreatment with U0126 (0.1 μM), SB202190 (1 μM), SP600125 (0.1 μM), STAT3I (1 μM), or Bay (0.1 μM), indicating that LPS induces RBA migration via the MAPK (i.e., ERK1/2, p38, and JNK1/2), STAT3, and NF-κB cascade (Figure 6B). Furthermore, pretreatment with 4p3f also markedly inhibited LPS-induced RBA migration, demonstrating that 4p3f has an inhibitory effect on LPS-induced MMP-9-mediated RBA migration. These results confirmed that 4p3f have a protective effect on LPS-induced MMP-9-mediated brain inflammation by blocking the MAPK-STAT3-dependent NF-κB pathway in brain astrocytes.

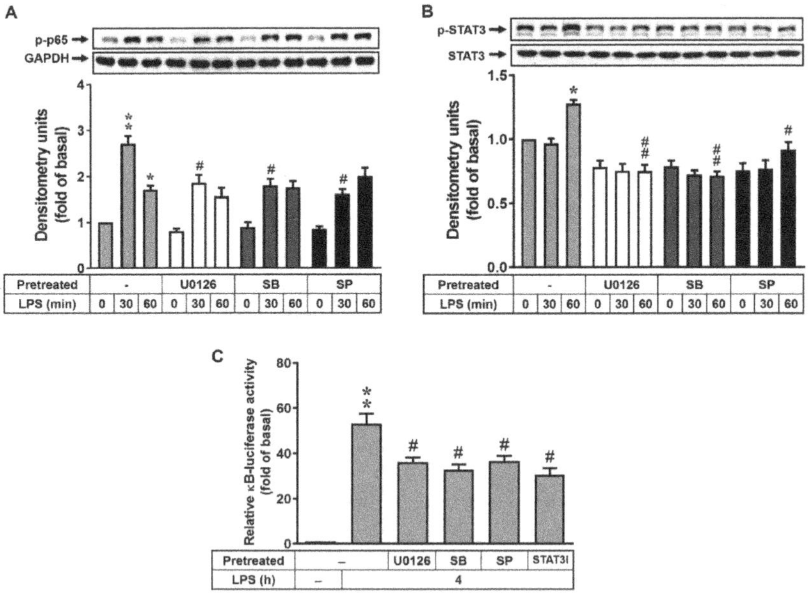

Figure 5. MAPK-STAT3 signaling axis is crucial for LPS-stimulated NF-κB transcriptional activity in RBAs. Cells were pretreated with U0126 (0.1 μM), SB202190 (1 μM), or SP600125 (0.1 μM) for 1 h and then incubated with LPS (10 μg/mL) for the indicated times. After treatment, cell lysates were collected and analyzed via Western blot for phosphorylation of p65 NF-κB (p-p65) (**A**) and STAT3 (p-STAT3 and total STAT3) (**B**), as well as GAPDH (an internal control). (**C**) Cells were transiently transfected with a κB-Luc reporter construct (pGL4.32). After transfection, cells were pretreated with U0126 (0.1 μM), SB202190 (1 μM), SP600125 (0.1 μM), or STAT3I (1 μM) for 1 h and then incubated with LPS (10 μg/mL) for 4 h. Cell lysates were collected and detected using a Dual-Luciferase® Reporter Assay System. Data are expressed as mean ± SEM (n = 3). * $p < 0.05$ and ** $p < 0.01$, as compared with the untreated control; # $p < 0.05$ and ## $p < 0.01$, as compared with LPS-treated cells only. The images represent one of three individual experiments.

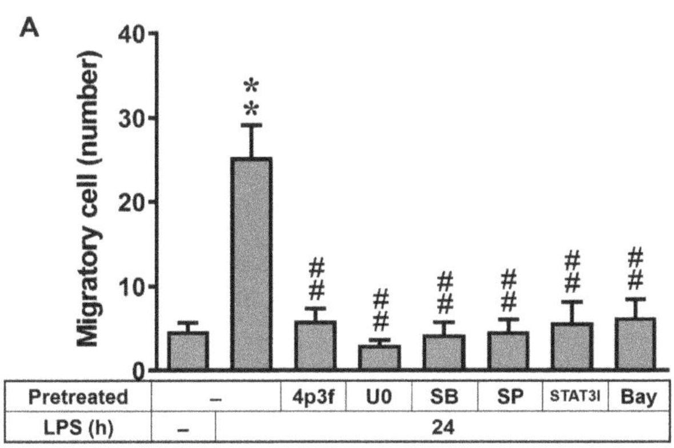

Figure 6. *Cont.*

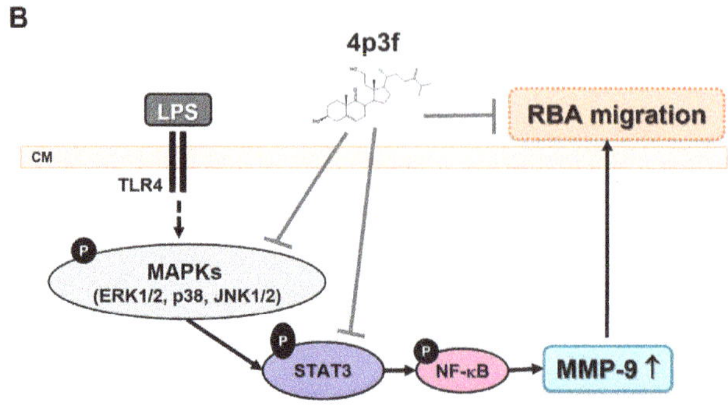

Figure 6. 4p3f inhibits LPS-induced MMP-9-mediated astrocytic migration. (**A**) Cells were plated on 6-well culture plates, grew to confluence, and starved with a serum-free medium for 24 h. Cells were pretreated with U0126 (0.1 μM), SB202190 (1 μM), SP600125 (0.1 μM), STAT3I (1 μM), Bay (0.1 μM), or 4p3f (1 μM) for 1 h, and monolayer cells were manually scratched using a blue tip, as described in Section 2, and then incubated with LPS (10 μg/mL) for 24 h. Phase-contrast images of cells were taken at 24 h, and the number of cells that migrated was counted, as described in Section 2. Data are expressed as mean ± SEM (n = 3). ** $p < 0.01$, as compared with the untreated control; ## $p < 0.01$, as compared with LPS-treated cells only. (**B**) Schematic presentation of the effects of 4p3f on LPS-induced MMP-9 expression and astrocytic migration. In brain astrocytes (RBAs), LPS induces STAT3 activation through MAPK (i.e., ERK1/2, p38, and JNK1/2) signals, resulting in NF-κB-dependent MMP-9 expression. The increased MMP-9 expression leads to RBA migration. 4p3f inhibits these LPS-induced MMP-9-mediated events (brain astrocytic migration) by suppressing the activation of MAPKs, STAT3, and NF-κB signaling pathways.

4. Discussion

In the CNS, MMPs play a critical role in neurogenesis, neuronal network remodeling, and blood–brain barrier integrity [37,38]. And MMPs, especially MMP-9, are involved in the pathological processes of neuroinflammation, epilepsy, schizophrenia, autism spectrum disorder, multiple sclerosis, cerebral aneurysm, stroke, subarachnoid hemorrhage, Alzheimer's disease, and Parkinson's disease. The inhibition of MMP-9 has been proposed as a possible therapeutic strategy for the treatment of many CNS diseases [11,23,37–40]. Neuroinflammatory processes are critically involved in neurodegenerative conditions [41,42], with significant implications for the role of astrocytes. As the key cell type in the CNS, astrocytes actively participate in inflammatory and neuro-immunomodulatory responses [6,43]. The use of LPS as a potent proinflammatory agent is a well-established model of neuroinflammation in both in vitro and in vivo studies [12,36,44]. Previous studies have shown that LPS induces MMP-9 expression through various signaling mechanisms, including AP-1, FoxO1, and Nox/ROS-dependent NF-κB expression in brain astrocytes [13,14,36]. The RBA cell line, derived from dissociated cultures of normal neonatal rat brain tissues, is a widely recognized model of rat astroglial cells; it exhibits properties that closely resemble those of normal astrocytes, making it a valuable tool in research studies [12,36,44,45]. There are several steroids obtained from the genus *Sinularia* with anti-inflammatory ability and cytotoxicity on cancer cells [46–49]. In this study, we first report that a 9,11-secosteroid (4p3f), isolated from the Taiwan soft coral *Sinularia leptoclados*, exhibits inhibitory effects on LPS-induced MMP-9-mediated neuroinflammatory responses in rat brain astrocytes (RBAs). Notably, these responses include the regulation of MMP-9 expression and cell migration, and the underlying mechanism responsible for these effects involves the modulation of MAPK and STAT3 signaling pathways, as well as NF-κB activation. These results shed light on the potential therapeutic implications of 4p3f in several neuroinflammation-related brain disorders.

MMP-9 plays a significant role in CNS inflammation, and the development of an MMP-9 inhibitor holds promise as a therapeutic agent for both acute and chronic neuroinflammation [50]. The data from this study demonstrate that *MMP-9* gene expression in RBAs is induced by LPS in a time-dependent manner (Figure 1A,B). In Figure 1C,D, the marine sterol, 4p3f, exhibits anti-inflammatory activity in brain astrocytes by effectively inhibiting LPS-induced MMP-9 expression.

MAPKs, a family of serine/threonine protein kinases, play a pivotal role in inducing cellular responses to cytokines and external stress signals and regulating the production of inflammation mediators [27,51]. An increased MAPK activity in activated astrocytes leads to inflammatory and immune responses within the brain [52,53]. The MAPK family consists of serially activated kinases and the effector kinases ERK, JNK, and p38 MAPK [27,54]. Previous studies have shown that LPS stimulates MAPK activation [55–57], and activation of ERK1/2, JNK1/2, and p38 MAPK regulates MMP-9 expression and enzymatic activity in various types of cells [28,29,36,58]. Therefore, we investigated the role of MAPKs in LPS-induced MMP-9 expression in RBA cells. Our results demonstrate that ERK1/2, p38 MAPK, and JNK1/2 play a role in LPS-induced MMP-9 expression in brain astrocytes (Figure 2A,B). In addition, pretreatment of RBAs with 4p3f could attenuate LPS-induced phosphorylation of ERK1/2, p38 MAPK, and JNK1/2 (Figure 2C). However, the detailed mechanism underlying the attenuation of MAPK phosphorylation by 4p3f is challenging to delineate. We further used molecular docking analysis, and the data show that 4p3f binds to ERK1/2 directly (Figure S1A). All of these results are compatible with previous studies indicating that MMP-9 induction is mediated through the activation of MAPKs [29,36,58], and 4p3f may attenuate LPS-induced MMP-9 expression by interfering with MAPK signaling. However, the mechanism underlying the decreased LPS-induced phosphorylation of p38 MAPK and JNK1/2 by 4p3f pretreatment still needs to be elucidated.

Several studies have indicated that MMP-9 is induced in an NF-κB-dependent manner [59,60], and the NF-κB binding sites of the MMP-9 gene contribute to its expression upon LPS stimulation [30]. The data reveal that pretreatment with an NF-κB inhibitor significantly suppresses LPS-induced MMP-9 expression in RBA cells (Figure 3A,B). Additionally, both pretreatment with 4p3f and pretreatment with the NF-κB inhibitor effectively eliminate LPS-stimulated NF-κB phosphorylation (Figure 3C, p-p65) and translocation (Figure 3D), and reduce its transcriptional activity in the κB-promoter–reporter assay (Figure 3E). These findings suggest that the inhibitory effect of 4p3f on LPS-induced MMP-9 expression is likely attributed to the suppression of NF-κB activation in RBA cells.

STAT3 plays a critical role in the pathogenesis of neuroinflammation and Alzheimer's disease [61]. Moreover, it has been reported that the activation of STAT3 regulates MMP-9 production [31,32]. Here, we further observed the role of STAT3 in LPS-induced MMP-9 expression in RBA cells. As shown in Figure 4, pretreatment with a STAT3 inhibitor (STAT3I) significantly attenuated the LPS-induced MMP-9 increase and STAT3 phosphorylation in RBA cells. Additionally, pretreatment with 4p3f also inhibited LPS-stimulated phosphorylation of STAT3 in RBA cells (Figure 4C). Furthermore, 4p3f could directly bind to STAT3, as shown in the molecular docking analysis (Figure S1B). These results suggest that the STAT3 signaling pathway may play a critical role in the regulation of *MMP-9* gene expression during inflammatory responses, whereby 4p3f attenuates MMP-9 expression by inhibiting the STAT3 pathway.

TLR4 acts as a receptor for LPS, and TLR signaling activates the downstream of MAPKs, NF-κB [62], and STAT3 [63]. Moreover, LPS stimulation triggers the activation of NF-κB through the MAPK signaling pathway [33] and the STAT3 signaling pathway [34]. Herein, we further investigated the crosstalk between the MAPK, NF-κB, and STAT3 signaling pathways in LPS-activated RBA cells. The data indicate that MAPKs (ERK1/2, p38, and JNK1/2) are involved in LPS-stimulated NF-κB and STAT3 activation (Figure 5A,B). Furthermore, our findings suggest that LPS-enhanced NF-κB transcriptional activity may occur through MAPK (ERK1/2, p38, and JNK1/2) and STAT3 signals (Figure 5C). These results provide evidence for the complex interplay between these signaling pathways and their roles in regulating the inflammatory responses in RBA cells upon LPS stimulation.

Finally, the upregulation of MMP-9 expression in brain astrocytes and its consequent enhancement of cell migration contribute to the development of neuroinflammation and neurodegenerative diseases [33,64,65], such as AD. AD is a progressive neurodegenerative disorder with synaptic loss as an early event in disease development. Synaptic loss and dysfunction contribute to the cognitive deficits seen in AD patients. Cerebrovascular disruption of the BBB leads to neuronal damage and inflammation. At an early time point of BBB dysfunctions, MMP-9 is actively engaged in response to a neuronal injury with astrocytic activation. Although MMP-9-induced astrocyte migration plays a role in forming a glial scar and lesion repair [8], the activated MMP-9 may also disrupt the neurovascular unit by altering synaptic plasticity and leading to cognitive decline. As shown in Figure 6A, we observed that LPS-triggered RBA cell migration was effectively blocked by pretreatment with 4p3f, as well as by pretreatment with inhibitors of MAPKs (ERK1/2, p38, and JNK1/2), STAT3, or NF-κB. These results collectively indicate that 4p3f exhibits both anti-inflammatory and antimetastatic activities in LPS-induced MMP-9-mediated events in RBA cells. The findings suggest that the marine sterol 4p3f may be a potential therapeutic agent for the treatment of neuroinflammatory and neurodegenerative disorders.

In conclusion, we investigated the in vitro effects of 4p3f, a sterol isolated from the soft coral *Sinularia leptoclados*, on anti-inflammatory and anti-metastatic activities in brain astrocytes. 4p3f protects against LPS-induced damage by attenuating the signaling pathway involved in MMP-9 expression and cell migration in rat brain astrocytes (RBA cells). We further used various signaling inhibitors to demonstrate that 4p3f protects against LPS-induced MMP-9-mediated RBA cell migration by inhibiting the MAPK (ERK1/2, p38, and JNK1/2), STAT3, and NF-κB cascade (Figure 6B). Pharmacological approaches suggest that research on 4p3f may yield useful therapeutic targets for the treatment of brain inflammatory diseases. In the future, in vivo experiments, such as animal or organoid models, should be tested to explore the protective effects of 4p3f on neuroinflammatory events.

Supplementary Materials: The following supporting information can be downloaded at: https://www.mdpi.com/article/10.3390/biomedicines12010226/s1, Figure S1: Molecular docking about 4p3f and the proteins of ERK1/2 (A) or STAT3 (B). Two-dimensional binding modes and three-dimensional H-binding modes showing the interactions between 4p3f and ERK1/2 or STAT3 protein.

Author Contributions: Conceptualization, H.-L.H.; methodology, H.-L.H., H.-C.T. and M.-M.T.; software, T.-H.L., J.-L.C. and H.-L.H.; validation, H.-L.H. and C.-H.C.; formal analysis, H.-L.H., H.-C.T. and C.-H.C.; investigation, T.-H.L., J.-L.C., H.-C.T., Y.-C.C., V.S. and M.-M.T.; resources, H.-L.H. and Y.-C.C.; data curation, H.-L.H. and C.-H.C.; writing—original draft preparation, H.-L.H. and C.-H.C.; writing—review and editing, T.-H.L., J.-L.C. and H.-L.H.; visualization, H.-L.H. and H.-C.T.; supervision, H.-L.H.; project administration, H.-L.H.; funding acquisition, H.-L.H. and M.-M.T. All authors have read and agreed to the published version of the manuscript.

Funding: This research was funded by the Ministry of Science and Technology, Taiwan, grant number MOST111-2320-B-255-004-MY3; the Chang Gung Medical Research Foundation, grant numbers CMRPF1M0071~2, CMRPF1M0111~2, CMRPF1M0171~172, CMRPF1L0081, and CMRPF1N0011~2; and Chang Gung University of Science and Technology, grant numbers ZRRPF3M0091 and ZRRPF3N0101.

Institutional Review Board Statement: Not applicable.

Informed Consent Statement: Not applicable.

Data Availability Statement: The data obtained from this study are available in this article.

Acknowledgments: We thank Jia-Ci Chang, Ssu-Yu Chen, Yin-Chen Chen, Shu-Ching Hsu, and Yi-Hsuan Wu for their technical assistance.

Conflicts of Interest: The authors declare no conflicts of interest.

References

1. von Bartheld, C.S.; Bahney, J.; Herculano-Houzel, S. The search for true numbers of neurons and glial cells in the human brain: A review of 150 years of cell counting. *J. Comp. Neurol.* **2016**, *524*, 3865–3895. [CrossRef] [PubMed]
2. Vivinetto, A.L.; Kim, I.D.; Goldberg, D.C.; Fones, L.; Brown, E.; Tarabykin, V.S.; Hill, C.E.; Cho, S.; Cave, J.W. Zeb2 Is a Regulator of Astrogliosis and Functional Recovery after CNS Injury. *Cell Rep.* **2020**, *31*, 107834. [CrossRef] [PubMed]
3. Heithoff, B.P.; George, K.K.; Phares, A.N.; Zuidhoek, I.A.; Munoz-Ballester, C.; Robel, S. Astrocytes are necessary for blood-brain barrier maintenance in the adult mouse brain. *Glia* **2021**, *69*, 436–472. [CrossRef] [PubMed]
4. Faulkner, J.R.; Herrmann, J.E.; Woo, M.J.; Tansey, K.E.; Doan, N.B.; Sofroniew, M.V. Reactive astrocytes protect tissue and preserve function after spinal cord injury. *J. Neurosci.* **2004**, *24*, 2143–2155. [CrossRef] [PubMed]
5. Bush, T.G.; Puvanachandra, N.; Horner, C.H.; Polito, A.; Ostenfeld, T.; Svendsen, C.N.; Mucke, L.; Johnson, M.H.; Sofroniew, M.V. Leukocyte infiltration, neuronal degeneration, and neurite outgrowth after ablation of scar-forming, reactive astrocytes in adult transgenic mice. *Neuron* **1999**, *23*, 297–308. [CrossRef] [PubMed]
6. Elston, G.N.; Oga, T.; Fujita, I. Spinogenesis and pruning scales across functional hierarchies. *J. Neurosci.* **2009**, *29*, 3271–3275. [CrossRef] [PubMed]
7. Rezai-Zadeh, K.; Gate, D.; Town, T. CNS infiltration of peripheral immune cells: D-Day for neurodegenerative disease? *J. Neuroimmune Pharmacol.* **2009**, *4*, 462–475. [CrossRef] [PubMed]
8. Lagos-Cabré, R.; Burgos-Bravo, F.; Avalos, A.M.; Leyton, L. Connexins in Astrocyte Migration. *Front. Pharmacol.* **2019**, *10*, 1546. [CrossRef]
9. Behl, T.; Kaur, G.; Sehgal, A.; Bhardwaj, S.; Singh, S.; Buhas, C.; Judea-Pusta, C.; Uivarosan, D.; Munteanu, M.A.; Bungau, S. Multifaceted Role of Matrix Metalloproteinases in Neurodegenerative Diseases: Pathophysiological and Therapeutic Perspectives. *Int. J. Mol. Sci.* **2021**, *22*, 1413. [CrossRef]
10. Vafadari, B.; Salamian, A.; Kaczmarek, L. MMP-9 in translation: From molecule to brain physiology, pathology, and therapy. *J. Neurochem.* **2016**, *139* (Suppl. S2), 91–114. [CrossRef]
11. Ji, Y.; Gao, Q.; Ma, Y.; Wang, F.; Tan, X.; Song, D.; Hoo, R.L.; Wang, Z.; Ge, X.; Han, H.; et al. An MMP-9 exclusive neutralizing antibody attenuates blood-brain barrier breakdown in mice with stroke and reduces stroke patient-derived MMP-9 activity. *Pharmacol. Res.* **2023**, *190*, 106720. [CrossRef] [PubMed]
12. Skrzypczak-Wiercioch, A.; Sałat, K. Lipopolysaccharide-Induced Model of Neuroinflammation: Mechanisms of Action, Research Application and Future Directions for Its Use. *Molecules* **2022**, *27*, 5481. [CrossRef] [PubMed]
13. Yang, C.C.; Hsiao, L.D.; Yang, C.M. Galangin Inhibits LPS-Induced MMP-9 Expression via Suppressing Protein Kinase-Dependent AP-1 and FoxO1 Activation in Rat Brain Astrocytes. *J. Inflamm. Res.* **2020**, *13*, 945–960. [CrossRef] [PubMed]
14. Yang, C.C.; Hsiao, L.D.; Tseng, H.C.; Kuo, C.M.; Yang, C.M. Pristimerin Inhibits MMP-9 Expression and Cell Migration Through Attenuating NOX/ROS-Dependent NF-κB Activation in Rat Brain Astrocytes Challenged with LPS. *J. Inflamm. Res.* **2020**, *13*, 325–341. [CrossRef] [PubMed]
15. Lee, T.H.; Liu, P.S.; Tsai, M.M.; Chen, J.L.; Wang, S.J.; Hsieh, H.L. The COX-2-derived PGE(2) autocrine contributes to bradykinin-induced matrix metalloproteinase-9 expression and astrocytic migration via STAT3 signaling. *Cell Commun. Signal* **2020**, *18*, 185. [CrossRef]
16. Molinski, T.F.; Dalisay, D.S.; Lievens, S.L.; Saludes, J.P. Drug development from marine natural products. *Nat. Rev. Drug Discov.* **2009**, *8*, 69–85. [CrossRef]
17. Sica, D.; Musumeci, D. Secosteroids of marine origin. *Steroids* **2004**, *69*, 743–756. [CrossRef]
18. Chang, Y.C.; Lai, K.H.; Kumar, S.; Chen, P.J.; Wu, Y.H.; Lai, C.L.; Hsieh, H.L.; Sung, P.J.; Hwang, T.L. (1)H NMR-Based Isolation of Anti-Inflammatory 9,11-Secosteroids from the Octocoral *Sinularia leptoclados*. *Mar. Drugs* **2020**, *18*, 271. [CrossRef]
19. Tsai, C.R.; Huang, C.Y.; Chen, B.W.; Tsai, Y.Y.; Shih, S.P.; Hwang, T.L.; Dai, C.F.; Wang, S.Y.; Sheu, J.H. New bioactive steroids from the soft coral *Klyxum flaccidum*. *RSC Adv.* **2015**, *5*, 12546–12554. [CrossRef]
20. Ngoc, N.T.; Hanh, T.T.H.; Thanh, N.V.; Thao, D.T.; Cuong, N.X.; Nam, N.H.; Thung, D.C.; Kiem, P.V.; Minh, C.V. Cytotoxic Steroids from the Vietnamese Soft Coral Sinularia leptoclados. *Chem. Pharm. Bull.* **2017**, *65*, 593–597. [CrossRef]
21. Camacho, C.V.; Choudhari, R.; Gadad, S.S. Long noncoding RNAs and cancer, an overview. *Steroids* **2018**, *133*, 93–95. [CrossRef] [PubMed]
22. Jiang, C.S.; Ru, T.; Huan, X.J.; Miao, Z.H.; Guo, Y.W. New cytotoxic ergostane-type sterols from the Chinese soft coral *Sinularia* sp. *Steroids* **2019**, *149*, 108425. [CrossRef] [PubMed]
23. Turner, R.J.; Sharp, F.R. Implications of MMP9 for Blood Brain Barrier Disruption and Hemorrhagic Transformation Following Ischemic Stroke. *Front. Cell Neurosci.* **2016**, *10*, 56. [CrossRef] [PubMed]
24. Rosenberg, G.A. Matrix metalloproteinases and their multiple roles in neurodegenerative diseases. *Lancet Neurol.* **2009**, *8*, 205–216. [CrossRef] [PubMed]
25. Kaminari, A.; Tsilibary, E.C.; Tzinia, A. A New Perspective in Utilizing MMP-9 as a Therapeutic Target for Alzheimer's Disease and Type 2 Diabetes Mellitus. *J. Alzheimers Dis.* **2018**, *64*, 1–16. [CrossRef]
26. Hsieh, H.L.; Wu, C.Y.; Yang, C.M. Bradykinin induces matrix metalloproteinase-9 expression and cell migration through a PKC-delta-dependent ERK/Elk-1 pathway in astrocytes. *Glia* **2008**, *56*, 619–632. [CrossRef] [PubMed]
27. Kaminska, B.; Gozdz, A.; Zawadzka, M.; Ellert-Miklaszewska, A.; Lipko, M. MAPK signal transduction underlying brain inflammation and gliosis as therapeutic target. *Anat. Rec.* **2009**, *292*, 1902–1913. [CrossRef]

28. Hsieh, C.C.; Papaconstantinou, J. Akt/PKB and p38 MAPK signaling, translational initiation and longevity in Snell dwarf mouse livers. *Mech. Ageing Dev.* **2004**, *125*, 785–798. [CrossRef]
29. Wu, C.Y.; Hsieh, H.L.; Jou, M.J.; Yang, C.M. Involvement of p42/p44 MAPK, p38 MAPK, JNK and nuclear factor-kappa B in interleukin-1beta-induced matrix metalloproteinase-9 expression in rat brain astrocytes. *J. Neurochem.* **2004**, *90*, 1477–1488. [CrossRef]
30. Rhee, J.W.; Lee, K.W.; Kim, D.; Lee, Y.; Jeon, O.H.; Kwon, H.J.; Kim, D.S. NF-kappaB-dependent regulation of matrix metalloproteinase-9 gene expression by lipopolysaccharide in a macrophage cell line RAW 264.7. *J. Biochem. Mol. Biol.* **2007**, *40*, 88–94. [CrossRef]
31. Yang, Y.H.; Li, D.L.; Bi, X.Y.; Sun, L.; Yu, X.J.; Fang, H.L.; Miao, Y.; Zhao, M.; He, X.; Liu, J.J.; et al. Acetylcholine Inhibits LPS-Induced MMP-9 Production and Cell Migration via the α7 nAChR-JAK2/STAT3 Pathway in RAW264.7 Cells. *Cell Physiol. Biochem.* **2015**, *36*, 2025–2038. [CrossRef] [PubMed]
32. Jia, Z.H.; Jia, Y.; Guo, F.J.; Chen, J.; Zhang, X.W.; Cui, M.H. Phosphorylation of STAT3 at Tyr705 regulates MMP-9 production in epithelial ovarian cancer. *PLoS ONE* **2017**, *12*, e0183622. [CrossRef] [PubMed]
33. Guha, M.; Mackman, N. LPS induction of gene expression in human monocytes. *Cell Signal.* **2001**, *13*, 85–94. [CrossRef] [PubMed]
34. Hoentjen, F.; Sartor, R.B.; Ozaki, M.; Jobin, C. STAT3 regulates NF-kappaB recruitment to the IL-12p40 promoter in dendritic cells. *Blood* **2005**, *105*, 689–696. [CrossRef] [PubMed]
35. Lee, T.H.; Chen, J.L.; Liu, P.S.; Tsai, M.M.; Wang, S.J.; Hsieh, H.L. Rottlerin, a natural polyphenol compound, inhibits upregulation of matrix metalloproteinase-9 and brain astrocytic migration by reducing PKC-δ-dependent ROS signal. *J. Neuroinflammation* **2020**, *17*, 177. [CrossRef] [PubMed]
36. Yang, C.C.; Lin, C.C.; Hsiao, L.D.; Kuo, J.M.; Tseng, H.C.; Yang, C.M. Lipopolysaccharide-Induced Matrix Metalloproteinase-9 Expression Associated with Cell Migration in Rat Brain Astrocytes. *Int. J. Mol. Sci.* **2019**, *21*, 259. [CrossRef] [PubMed]
37. Rempe, R.G.; Hartz, A.M.S.; Bauer, B. Matrix metalloproteinases in the brain and blood-brain barrier: Versatile breakers and makers. *J. Cereb. Blood Flow. Metab.* **2016**, *36*, 1481–1507. [CrossRef]
38. Cabral-Pacheco, G.A.; Garza-Veloz, I.; Castruita-De la Rosa, C.; Ramirez-Acuña, J.M.; Perez-Romero, B.A.; Guerrero-Rodriguez, J.F.; Martinez-Avila, N.; Martinez-Fierro, M.L. The Roles of Matrix Metalloproteinases and Their Inhibitors in Human Diseases. *Int. J. Mol. Sci.* **2020**, *21*, 9739. [CrossRef]
39. Tan, Z.; Lucke-Wold, B.P.; Logsdon, A.F.; Turner, R.C.; Tan, C.; Li, X.; Hongpaison, J.; Alkon, D.L.; Simpkins, J.W.; Rosen, C.L.; et al. Bryostatin extends tPA time window to 6 h following middle cerebral artery occlusion in aged female rats. *Eur. J. Pharmacol.* **2015**, *764*, 404–412. [CrossRef]
40. Panther, E.J.; Lucke-Wold, B. Subarachnoid hemorrhage: Management considerations for COVID-19. *Explor. Neuroprotective Ther.* **2022**, *2*, 65–73. [CrossRef]
41. Kempuraj, D.; Thangavel, R.; Natteru, P.A.; Selvakumar, G.P.; Saeed, D.; Zahoor, H.; Zaheer, S.; Iyer, S.S.; Zaheer, A. Neuroinflammation Induces Neurodegeneration. *J. Neurol. Neurosurg. Spine* **2016**, *1*, 1003. [PubMed]
42. Chen, W.W.; Zhang, X.; Huang, W.J. Role of neuroinflammation in neurodegenerative diseases (Review). *Mol. Med. Rep.* **2016**, *13*, 3391–3396. [CrossRef] [PubMed]
43. Guzman-Martinez, L.; Maccioni, R.B.; Andrade, V.; Navarrete, L.P.; Pastor, M.G.; Ramos-Escobar, N. Neuroinflammation as a Common Feature of Neurodegenerative Disorders. *Front. Pharmacol.* **2019**, *10*, 1008. [CrossRef] [PubMed]
44. Catorce, M.N.; Gevorkian, G. LPS-induced Murine Neuroinflammation Model: Main Features and Suitability for Pre-clinical Assessment of Nutraceuticals. *Curr. Neuropharmacol.* **2016**, *14*, 155–164. [CrossRef] [PubMed]
45. Jou, T.C.; Jou, M.J.; Chen, J.Y.; Lee, S.Y. Properties of rat brain astrocytes in long-term culture. *Taiwan Yi Xue Hui Za Zhi* **1985**, *84*, 865–881. [PubMed]
46. Huang, C.Y.; Liaw, C.C.; Chen, B.W.; Chen, P.C.; Su, J.H.; Sung, P.J.; Dai, C.F.; Chiang, M.Y.; Sheu, J.H. Withanolide-based steroids from the cultured soft coral Sinularia brassica. *J. Nat. Prod.* **2013**, *76*, 1902–1908. [CrossRef]
47. Li, S.W.; Chen, W.T.; Yao, L.G.; Guo, Y.W. Two new cytotoxic steroids from the Chinese soft coral *Sinularia* sp. *Steroids* **2018**, *136*, 17–21. [CrossRef]
48. Huang, C.Y.; Su, J.H.; Liaw, C.C.; Sung, P.J.; Chiang, P.L.; Hwang, T.L.; Dai, C.F.; Sheu, J.H. Bioactive Steroids with Methyl Ester Group in the Side Chain from a Reef Soft Coral Sinularia brassica Cultured in a Tank. *Mar. Drugs* **2017**, *15*, 280. [CrossRef]
49. Zhang, N.X.; Tang, X.L.; van Ofwegen, L.; Xue, L.; Song, W.J.; Li, P.L.; Li, G.Q. Cyclopentenone derivatives and polyhydroxylated steroids from the soft coral *Sinularia acuta*. *Chem. Biodivers.* **2015**, *12*, 273–283. [CrossRef]
50. Vandooren, J.; Van Damme, J.; Opdenakker, G. On the structure and functions of gelatinase B/matrix metalloproteinase-9 in neuroinflammation. *Prog. Brain Res.* **2014**, *214*, 193–206. [CrossRef]
51. Sun, Y.; Liu, W.Z.; Liu, T.; Feng, X.; Yang, N.; Zhou, H.F. Signaling pathway of MAPK/ERK in cell proliferation, differentiation, migration, senescence and apoptosis. *J. Recept. Signal Transduct. Res.* **2015**, *35*, 600–604. [CrossRef] [PubMed]
52. Benveniste, E.N. Cytokine actions in the central nervous system. *Cytokine Growth Factor Rev.* **1998**, *9*, 259–275. [CrossRef] [PubMed]
53. Farina, C.; Aloisi, F.; Meinl, E. Astrocytes are active players in cerebral innate immunity. *Trends Immunol.* **2007**, *28*, 138–145. [CrossRef] [PubMed]
54. Chang, L.; Karin, M. Mammalian MAP kinase signalling cascades. *Nature* **2001**, *410*, 37–40. [CrossRef] [PubMed]

55. Ahn, S.; Siddiqi, M.H.; Aceituno, V.C.; Simu, S.Y.; Yang, D.C. Suppression of MAPKs/NF-κB Activation Induces Intestinal Anti-Inflammatory Action of Ginsenoside Rf in HT-29 and RAW264.7 Cells. *Immunol. Investig.* **2016**, *45*, 439–449. [CrossRef]
56. Ahn, S.C.; Kim, G.Y.; Kim, J.H.; Baik, S.W.; Han, M.K.; Lee, H.J.; Moon, D.O.; Lee, C.M.; Kang, J.H.; Kim, B.H.; et al. Epigallocatechin-3-gallate, constituent of green tea, suppresses the LPS-induced phenotypic and functional maturation of murine dendritic cells through inhibition of mitogen-activated protein kinases and NF-kappaB. *Biochem. Biophys. Res. Commun.* **2004**, *313*, 148–155. [CrossRef]
57. Li, Y.C.; Kuo, P.C.; Yang, M.L.; Chen, T.Y.; Hwang, T.L.; Chiang, C.C.; Thang, T.D.; Tuan, N.N.; Tzen, J.T.C. Chemical Constituents of the Leaves of Peltophorum pterocarpum and Their Bioactivity. *Molecules* **2019**, *24*, 240. [CrossRef]
58. Hsieh, H.L.; Yu, M.C.; Cheng, L.C.; Chu, M.Y.; Huang, T.H.; Yeh, T.S.; Tsai, M.M. Quercetin exerts anti-inflammatory effects via inhibiting tumor necrosis factor-α-induced matrix metalloproteinase-9 expression in normal human gastric epithelial cells. *World J. Gastroenterol.* **2022**, *28*, 1139–1158. [CrossRef]
59. Lin, Y.; Ukaji, T.; Koide, N.; Umezawa, K. Inhibition of Late and Early Phases of Cancer Metastasis by the NF-κB Inhibitor DHMEQ Derived from Microbial Bioactive Metabolite Epoxyquinomicin: A Review. *Int. J. Mol. Sci.* **2018**, *19*, 729. [CrossRef]
60. Lambrou, G.I.; Hatziagapiou, K.; Vlahopoulos, S. Inflammation and tissue homeostasis: The NF-κB system in physiology and malignant progression. *Mol. Biol. Rep.* **2020**, *47*, 4047–4063. [CrossRef]
61. Millot, P.; San, C.; Bennana, E.; Porte, B.; Vignal, N.; Hugon, J.; Paquet, C.; Hosten, B.; Mouton-Liger, F. STAT3 inhibition protects against neuroinflammation and BACE1 upregulation induced by systemic inflammation. *Immunol. Lett.* **2020**, *228*, 129–134. [CrossRef]
62. Fan, Y.; Mao, R.; Yang, J. NF-κB and STAT3 signaling pathways collaboratively link inflammation to cancer. *Protein Cell* **2013**, *4*, 176–185. [CrossRef] [PubMed]
63. Nakano, Y.; Furube, E.; Morita, S.; Wanaka, A.; Nakashima, T.; Miyata, S. Astrocytic TLR4 expression and LPS-induced nuclear translocation of STAT3 in the sensory circumventricular organs of adult mouse brain. *J. Neuroimmunol.* **2015**, *278*, 144–158. [CrossRef] [PubMed]
64. Kamat, P.K.; Swarnkar, S.; Rai, S.; Kumar, V.; Tyagi, N. Astrocyte mediated MMP-9 activation in the synapse dysfunction: An implication in Alzheimer disease. *Ther. Targets Neurol. Dis.* **2014**, *1*, e243. [CrossRef] [PubMed]
65. Singh, A.V.; Chandrasekar, V.; Laux, P.; Luch, A.; Dakua, S.P.; Zamboni, P.; Shelar, A.; Yang, Y.; Pandit, V.; Tisato, V.; et al. Micropatterned Neurovascular Interface to Mimic the Blood-Brain Barrier's Neurophysiology and Micromechanical Function: A BBB-on-CHIP Model. *Cells* **2022**, *11*, 2801. [CrossRef]

nutrients

Article

Agaricus blazei Polysaccharide Alleviates DSS-Induced Colitis in Mice by Modulating Intestinal Barrier and Remodeling Metabolism

Zhong-Hao Ji [1,2,†], Song He [1,†], Wen-Yin Xie [1], Pei-Sen Zhao [1], Wen-Zhi Ren [1], Wei Gao [1,*] and Bao Yuan [1,*]

[1] Department of Laboratory Animals, College of Animal Sciences, Jilin University, Changchun 130062, China
[2] Department of Basic Medicine, Changzhi Medical College, Changzhi 046000, China
* Correspondence: gaowei81@jlu.edu.cn (W.G.); yuan_bao@jlu.edu.cn (B.Y.)
† These authors contributed equally to this work.

Abstract: Ulcerative colitis (UC) is a chronic noninfectious intestinal disease that severely affects patients' quality of life. *Agaricus blazei* Murrill polysaccharide (ABP) is an effective active ingredient extracted from *Agaricus blazei* Murrill (ABM). It has good efficacy in inhibiting tumor cell growth, lowering blood pressure, and improving atherosclerosis. However, its effect on colitis is unclear. The aim of this study was to analyze the protective effects and potential mechanisms of ABP against dextran sulfate sodium (DSS)-induced acute colitis in mice. The results showed that dietary supplementation with ABP significantly alleviated DSS-induced colitis symptoms, inflammatory responses, and oxidative stress. Meanwhile, ABP intervention was able to maintain the integrity of the intestinal mechanical barrier by promoting the expression of ZO-1 and Occludin tight junction proteins and facilitating mucus secretion. Moreover, 16S rRNA sequencing results suggested that ABP intervention was able to alleviate DSS-induced gut microbiota disruption, and nontargeted metabolomics results indicated that ABP was able to remodel metabolism. In conclusion, these results demonstrate that dietary supplementation with ABP alleviated DSS-induced acute colitis by maintaining intestinal barrier integrity and remodeling metabolism. These results improve our understanding of ABP function and provide a theoretical basis for the use of dietary supplementation with ABP for the prevention of ulcerative colitis.

Keywords: *Agaricus blazei* polysaccharide (ABP); ulcerative colitis (UC); oxidative stress; gut microbiota

1. Introduction

Inflammatory bowel disease (IBD), a group of chronic, noncommunicable gastrointestinal disorders, primarily encompasses ulcerative colitis (UC) and Crohn's disease (CD) [1]. Characteristic symptoms include abdominal discomfort, diarrhea, and hematochezia, which over an extended period can lead to malnutrition and a substantial reduction in the quality of life for patients [2,3]. Furthermore, IBD may heighten the risk of cardiovascular and neurological diseases, adding to its burden [4,5]. Recently, the global incidence of IBD has been increasing, and it is estimated that by 2030, there will be more than seven million people living with IBD in Europe and the United States. Its prevalence in countries such as those in North America, Oceania, and Europe will exceed 0.3% [6] The etiology of UC remains partially unclear, but indications point toward a complex interplay between genetic factors, environmental influences, and immune system dysregulation [3]. Presently, the primary therapeutic modalities include pharmacological interventions (such as glucocorticoids, immunosuppressants, and biological agents) and surgical procedures, although long-term drug use may yield adverse reactions, posing an additional challenge [7].

Polysaccharides are complex carbohydrates formed by the condensation and dehydration of more than ten monosaccharide molecules [8]. They are one of the fundamental substances that constitute living organisms and are widely present in nature. Research has found that natural polysaccharides exhibit various biological effects, such as antioxidant, anti-tumor, and immunomodulatory activities [9–11]. *Ganoderma lucidum* polysaccharide and Huangshan *Floral Mushroom* polysaccharide have been shown to possess prebiotic properties, which can increase the abundance of probiotics and alleviate DSS-induced gut microbiota disorders [12,13]. According to their sources and synthesis, gut microbial metabolites can be divided into three categories: metabolites produced from dietary components by gut bacteria, host-derived metabolites modified by gut bacteria, and metabolites resynthesized by gut bacteria [14,15]. Studies have shown that gut microbial metabolites also play an important regulatory role in the pathogenesis of UC. Polysaccharides have shown some benefits for DSS-induced intestinal metabolic disorders, for example, *Gastrodia elata* polysaccharides are able to regulate metabolic processes, such as tryptophan, cysteine, and vitamin B6 [16]; *Bergamot* polysaccharides have a beneficial effect on tyrosine and phenylalanine metabolism, the synthetic pathways of phenylalanine, tyrosine, and tryptophan organisms are widely regulated, in which the concentration of intestinal L-phenylalanine is significantly increased after Bergamot polysaccharide treatment, and in vitro experiments have shown that L-phenylalanine has anti-inflammatory activity [17]; fucoidan, on the other hand, mainly affects bile acid metabolism, which in turn acts through activation of the Farnesoid X Receptor [18].

Agaricus blazei Murrill (ABM) is a medicinal mushroom native to Brazil, whose fruiting bodies and mycelia contain abundant polysaccharides [19,20]. *Agaricus blazei* polysaccharide (ABP) refers to an active component extracted from ABM, primarily consisting of β-glucans [20,21]. Studies have demonstrated that ABP possesses a wide range of biological activities, including antitumor [22,23], antimicrobial [24,25], anti-inflammatory [26,27], antioxidant [28], hypoglycemic, and hypolipidemic effects [29,30]. Li Y et al. [20] reported that ABP had a regulatory effect on dyslipidemia in hyperlipidemic rats, and that the mechanism may be through the modulation of high-fat diet-induced intestinal dysbiosis in rats. Whether ABP is also able to regulate the intestinal flora and intestinal microbial metabolites, thereby influencing the development of UC, has not been reported.

In this study, we assessed the preventive effect of dietary supplementation with ABP using a mouse model of DSS-induced acute colitis and analyzed the effects of ABP on the gut microbiota and metabolic pathways through 16S rRNA sequencing and untargeted metabolomics. The results of the study will deepen our understanding of the function of ABP and lay a theoretical foundation for its further use.

2. Materials and Methods

2.1. Materials

Dextran sulfate sodium salt (DSS) (molecular weight 36–50 kDa) (MP Biomedicals, Santa Ana, CA, USA) and *Agaricus blazei* polysaccharide (ABP) were purchased from Shanxi Rongling Biotechnology Co. (Xi'an, China). Streptomycin, ampicillin, gentamicin, and vancomycin were purchased from Dalian Meilun Biotechnology Co. (Dalian, China). Anti-Muc2, anti-Claudin 1, anti-ZO-1, and anti-Occludin antibodies were purchased from Affinity Biosciences (Cincinnati, OH, USA). Anti-GAPDH and anti-rabbit IgG antibodies were purchased from Cell Signaling Technology (Danvers, MA, USA).

2.2. Animal Experiments

Twenty-four six- to seven-week-old specific pathogen free male BALB/c mice were purchased from Liaoning Changsheng Biotechnology Co., Ltd. (Shenyang, China) (SCXK (Liao) 2020-0001). Twenty-four mice were acclimated for 1 week prior to randomization into 3 groups of 8 mice each: the negative control group (NC), the model group (DSS), and the ABP intervention group (DSS + ABP). This study was approved by the Animal Ethics and Welfare Committee of Jilin University (License No. SY202305009). All experimental procedures were conducted in strict compliance with animal welfare ethics and animal welfare laws and regulations.

The experimental design is shown in Figure 1A. During the initial 14 days, all mice received sterile water, whereas the DSS + ABP group received ABP (200 mg/kg, intragastrically (i.g.) (after referencing the literature, 50, 100, and 200 mg/kg/d were utilized in the initial tests, and 200 mg/kg/d was finally selected for the formal experiment)) [18,31,32]. For the next 7 days, both the DSS and DSS + ABP groups were treated with 3% DSS, whereas the DSS + ABP group continued with ABP treatment. The NC group received daily treatment with distilled water. On day 22, the mice were sacrificed under anesthesia for the collection of colon tissues and blood samples.

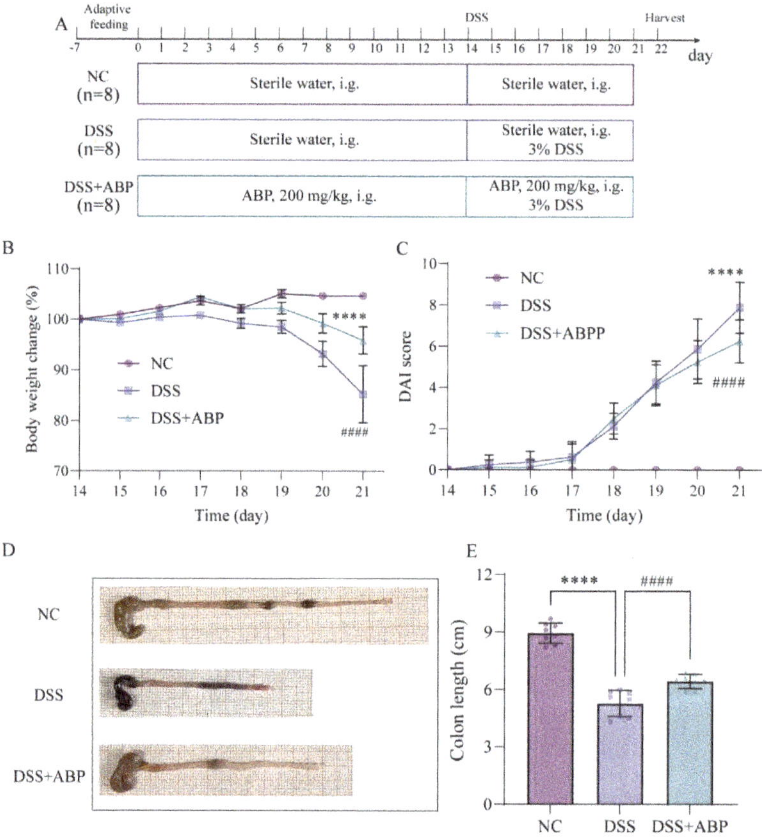

Figure 1. *Agaricus blazei* Murrill polysaccharide (ABP) attenuates dextran sulfate sodium (DSS)-induced colitis symptoms. (**A**) Experimental flow chart; (**B**) the change in body weight in these three groups; (**C**) the disease activity index (DAI) score between these three groups; (**D**) representative images of the colon in the three groups; and (**E**) the colon length in these three groups. Data are presented as mean ± SD, (n = 8). **** $p < 0.0001$; #### $p < 0.0001$ (**** indicates comparison with the NC group and #### indicates comparison with the DSS group).

2.3. Disease Activity Index (DAI) Scoring

To assess the disease activity index, body weight, stool consistency, and stool blood were measured and scored following a previously published grading system [33].

2.4. Enzyme-Linked Immunosorbent (ELISA) Assay

The colon tissue was added to 9 times the volume of PBS at the ratio of weight (g):volume (mL) = 1:9 and homogenized using a tissue grinder (JingXin, Shanghai, China). Tissue homogenates and blood samples were centrifuged at 4 °C and 3000 rpm for 15 min and then the supernatant was taken for determination. Changes in the levels of inflammatory and oxidation-related factors were detected using a mouse ELISA kit (SINOBEST-BIO, Shanghai, China) according to the manufacturer's protocol. The optical density (OD) was detected with a microplate reader and the concentration of individual samples was calculated.

2.5. Tissue Section and Immunohistochemistry (IHC) Staining

The obtained mouse tissue samples were fixed by soaking in 4% paraformaldehyde overnight, embedded in paraffin, and cut into 4 μm thick sections. According to the manufacturer's protocol, the sections were stained with hematoxylin and eosin (HE), Alcian blue (AB), and periodic acid–Schiff (PAS). The HE staining results were scored in terms of four areas: inflammatory cell infiltration, mucosal edema, crypt swelling disruption, and epithelial cell damage. Positive areas of AB staining and PAS staining were analyzed using the IHC-Toolbox plugin in ImajeJ.

The sections were incubated overnight at 4 °C with a primary antibody against Muc2 (1:200). After washing with PBS, the sections were incubated with HRP antibody at 37 °C for 30 min. Then, the sections were stained with a DAB kit for 10 min and visualized under a light microscope. Positive areas of IHC results were analyzed using the IHC-Toolbox plugin in ImajeJ.

2.6. Western Blotting

Tissue proteins were extracted with RIPA buffer and quantified. Samples were separated by SDS-PAGE and transferred to polyvinylidene fluoride membranes, and the membranes were incubated with the primary antibody (1:1000) overnight at 4 °C. The membranes were washed with Tris-buffered saline containing Tween-20 (TBST) and incubated with HRP-conjugated secondary antibody for 1 h at room temperature. Protein bands were visualized using enhanced chemiluminescence (ECL) substrate and captured on a fully automated chemiluminescence imaging system.

2.7. 16S rRNA Sequencing

Microorganisms were collected from mouse fecal samples, and a DNA extraction kit was used to extract DNA according to the manufacturer's instructions. The extracted DNA was used as a template for PCR amplification of the V3–V4 region using the 338F-806R primer pair. PCR amplification products were gel recovered, purified, and evaluated using an Agilent 2100 Bioanalyzer (Agilent, Santa Clara, CA, USA). Qualified libraries were bipartite sequenced at 2 × 250 bp using an Illumina NovaSeq 6000 sequencer (Illumina, Woburn, MA, USA). Data were filtered and spliced using cutadapt (v1.9), FLASH (v1.2.8), fqtrim, and Vsearch software (v2.3.4). The feature sequence table was obtained after DADA2 noise reduction. Follow-up Bioinformatic analysis was performed using the OmicStudio tools at https://www.omicstudio.cn/ (accessed on 22 September 2023).

2.8. Nontargeted Metabolomics Analysis

A total of 100 mg of cecum contents were weighed, ground in liquid nitrogen, and placed in eppendorf tubes. A total of 500 μL of pre-cooled 80% methanol was added and vortexed to mix. The samples were cooled on ice for 5 min and subsequently subjected to centrifugation at 15,000× g and 4 °C for a duration of 20 min. A portion of the supernatant was diluted with LC-MS grade water to reach a final concentration of 53% methanol. Next, the samples were transferred to a fresh Eppendorf tube and centrifuged again at 15,000× g and 4 °C for 20 min. Finally, a Liquid chromatography tandem mass spectrometry (LC-MS) system analysis was performed by injecting the supernatant. The detection and analysis of non-targeted metabolomics was conducted by Lianchuan Biotechnology (Suzhou, China). A partial least squares discriminant analysis (PLS-DA) was used for supervised classification. Differentially abundant metabolites were identified based on variable importance projection (VIP) [34]. The thresholds for defining differentially abundant metabolites between the groups were as follows: multiplicity of differences $\geq$1.5 or $\leq$1/1.5, p value < 0.05, and VIP value $\geq$ 1.

2.9. Correlation Analysis

Multiomics data, including 16S rRNA sequencing, metabolomics, and physiological/biochemical indices, were collected. Spearman's correlation analysis was performed to calculate the correlation coefficients between all the indicators. The ggplot2 and heatmap packages in R were then used to generate visualizations of the correlation matrix and heatmaps.

2.10. Statistical Analyses

The experimental data are presented as the mean $\pm$ standard deviation (SD). One-way ANOVA followed by Dunnet post-testing was used to compare multiple groups. The data were analyzed and plotted using GraphPad Prism 9.5 (La Jolla, CA, USA). $p < 0.05$ was considered to indicate a significant difference.

3. Results

3.1. ABP Attenuates DSS-Induced UC in Mice

The in vivo experimental results demonstrated significant differences in multiple parameters between the NC group and the DSS group. Specifically, the DSS group exhibited decreased mouse body weight ($p < 0.0001$) (Figure 1B), elevated DAI scores ($p < 0.0001$) (Figure 1C), and shortened colon length compared to controls ($p < 0.0001$) (Figure 1D,E). Following ABP treatment, all parameters were improved: mouse body weight increased, DAI scores decreased, and colon length increased. These results suggest that ABP has a therapeutic effect in relieving DSS-induced UC, but the intrinsic mechanism through which it occurs needs to be further explored.

3.2. ABP Reduces Inflammation and Oxidative Damage

Fruchon S et al. [35,36] reported that ABP is significant in regulating the relationship between inflammatory and oxidative factor expression. ELISA results showed that DSS induction significantly increased the serum levels of LPS, IL-1β, IL-6, and TNF-α in mice compared to the NC group ($p < 0.0001$). However, ABP treatment markedly reduced the expression of these factors (Figure 2A–D). At the same time, the levels of IL-1β, IL-6, and TNF-α in colon tissues were also measured and were consistent with the serum results (Figure 2F–H). DSS was found to increase MPO and MDA expression and decrease SOD and T-AOC levels, whereas ABP reversed these changes (Figure 2E,I–K). These results suggest that ABP intervention can significantly inhibit DSS-induced inflammation and oxidative stress.

3.3. ABP Enhanced Intestinal Physical and Chemical Barrier Protection

Colonic histopathological changes and mucus secretion were observed using HE, AB, and PAS staining. The HE staining results showed that DSS treatment disrupted the colonic mucosal structure, with disorganized gland arrangement and disappearance, as well as a decrease in the ratio of villus height to crypt height (Figure 3A). AB staining and PAS staining showed the loss of cup cells and decreased mucus secretion after DSS induction (Figure 3B,C). Immunohistochemistry findings demonstrated markedly down-regulated Muc2 expression in the DSS group (Figure 3D). However, ABP intervention significantly alleviated the DSS-induced changes and repaired colonic mucosal structures, decreased inflammatory cell infiltration, increased mucus secretion, and increased Muc2 expression. In addition, the Western blotting results showed that DSS treatment significantly reduced the levels of ZO-1, Occludin, and Claudin proteins compared to those in the NC group ($p < 0.05$). However, the expression of ZO-1 and Occludin was markedly up-regulated in the ABP treatment group compared to the DSS group ($p < 0.05$), with no significant change in Claudin levels ($p > 0.05$) (Figure 3E–H). These results suggest that ABP is able to alleviate DSS-induced intestinal damage and maintain intestinal barrier integrity.

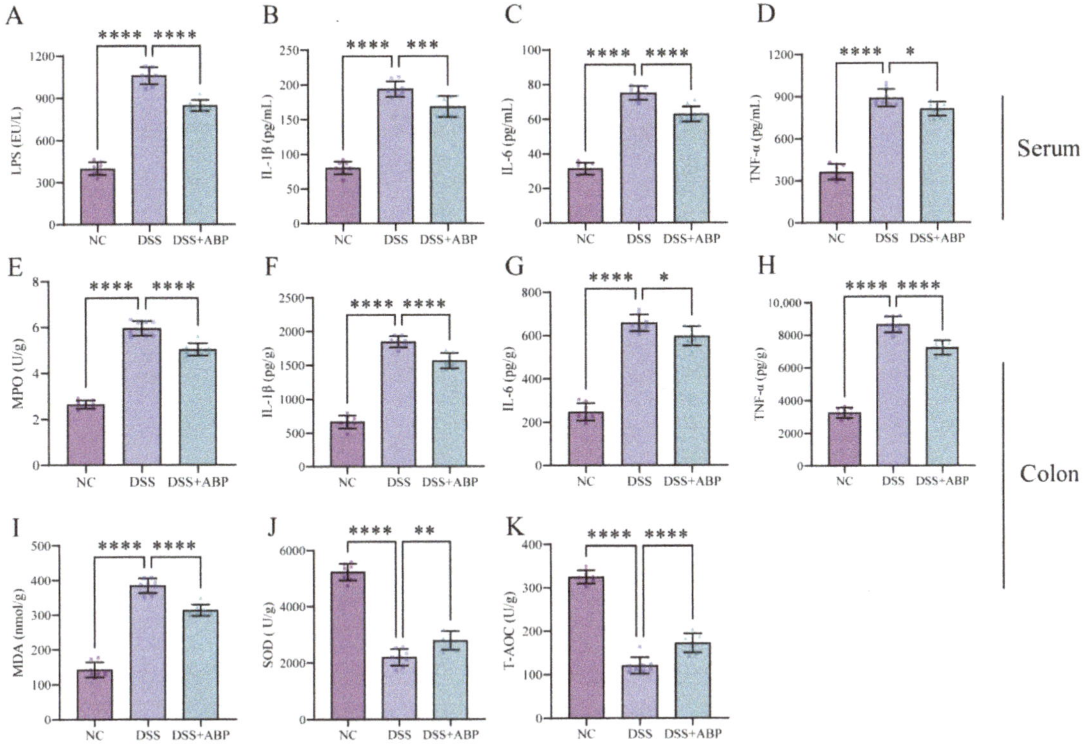

Figure 2. *Agaricus blazei* Murrill polysaccharide (ABP) reduces inflammation and oxidative damage. (**A–D**) Cytokine levels in serum for each group. (**A**) Lipopolysaccharide levels; (**B**) IL-1β levels; (**C**) IL-6 levels; and (**D**) TNF-α levels. (**E–K**) Colon cytokine levels in each group. (**E**) MDA levels; (**F**) IL-1β levels; (**G**) IL-6 levels; (**H**) TNF-α levels; (**I**) MDA levels; (**J**) SOD levels; and (**K**) T-AOC levels. Data are presented as mean ± SD, (n = 8). * $p < 0.05$, ** $p < 0.01$, *** $p < 0.001$, and **** $p < 0.0001$.

3.4. 16S rRNA Analysis of the Effect of ABP on Gut Microbiota

The alpha diversity of the gut microbiota was assessed using the Chao1 and Shannon indices. The results showed that the Chao1 and Shannon indices were significantly lower after DSS treatment ($p < 0.001$), whereas the Chao1 and Shannon indices were significantly higher after ABP intervention ($p < 0.05$) compared to the DSS group (Figure 4A,B). PCA and PCoA analyses were used to assess the beta diversity of gut microorganisms. The results of the downscaling analysis showed that there was a significant separation between the DSS and NC groups, indicating that the composition of their gut microbiota was significantly altered after DSS treatment, whereas the ABP intervention group showed a tendency to regress toward NC (Figure 4C,D). We further analyzed the composition of bacteria at the family and phylum levels among the three groups and identified the top 10 most abundant taxa (Figure 4E,F). However, the ratio of Firmicutes/Bacteroidetes was not significantly different between groups. Indicator species for each group at the genus level are also shown using a bubble chart (Figure 4G). The expression levels of four bacterial genera across three groups at the genus level are also shown. The abundance of *Bacteroides* and *Escherichia-Shigella* was significantly increased ($p < 0.05$), and the abundance of *Ruminococcaceae_unclassified* and *Oscillibacter* did not significantly change ($p > 0.05$) after DSS treatment, whereas the abundance of the above four bacterial genera was significantly higher in the ABP intervention group than in the DSS group ($p < 0.05$) (Figure 4H–K). The above results suggest that ABP intervention can alleviate DSS-induced gut microbiota disruption.

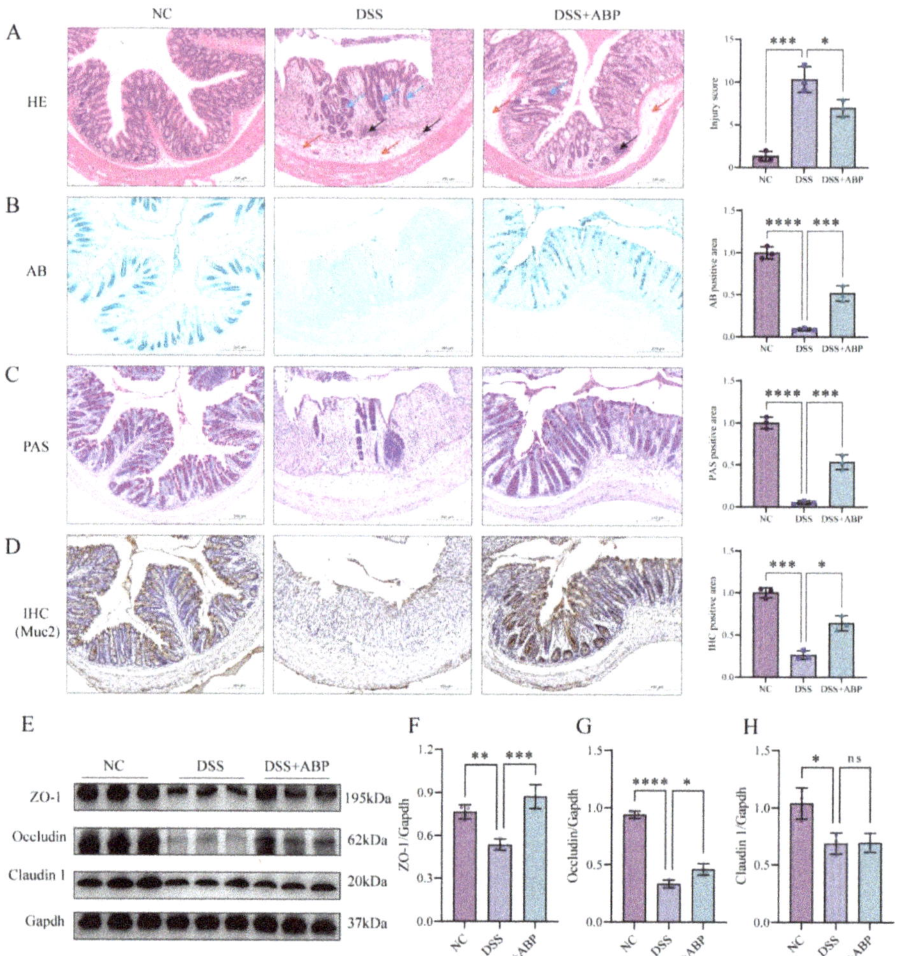

Figure 3. *Agaricus blazei* Murrill polysaccharide (ABP) alleviates dextran sulfate sodium (DSS)-induced intestinal barrier damage. (**A**) Hematoxylin and eosin (HE) staining of colon tissue, red arrows indicate mucosal edema, black arrows indicate inflammatory cell infiltration, and blue arrows indicate crypt damage; (**B**) Alcian blue (AB) staining of colon tissue; (**C**) periodic acid–Schiff (PAS) staining of colon tissue; (**D**) immunohistochemistry detection of Muc2 expression in colonic tissues; (**E**) Western blot strips of tight junction markers; and (**F–H**) protein expression analysis of ZO-1, Occludin, and Claudin1. Data are presented as mean ± SD, (n = 3). ns $p > 0.05$, * $p < 0.05$, ** $p < 0.01$, *** $p < 0.001$, and **** $p < 0.0001$.

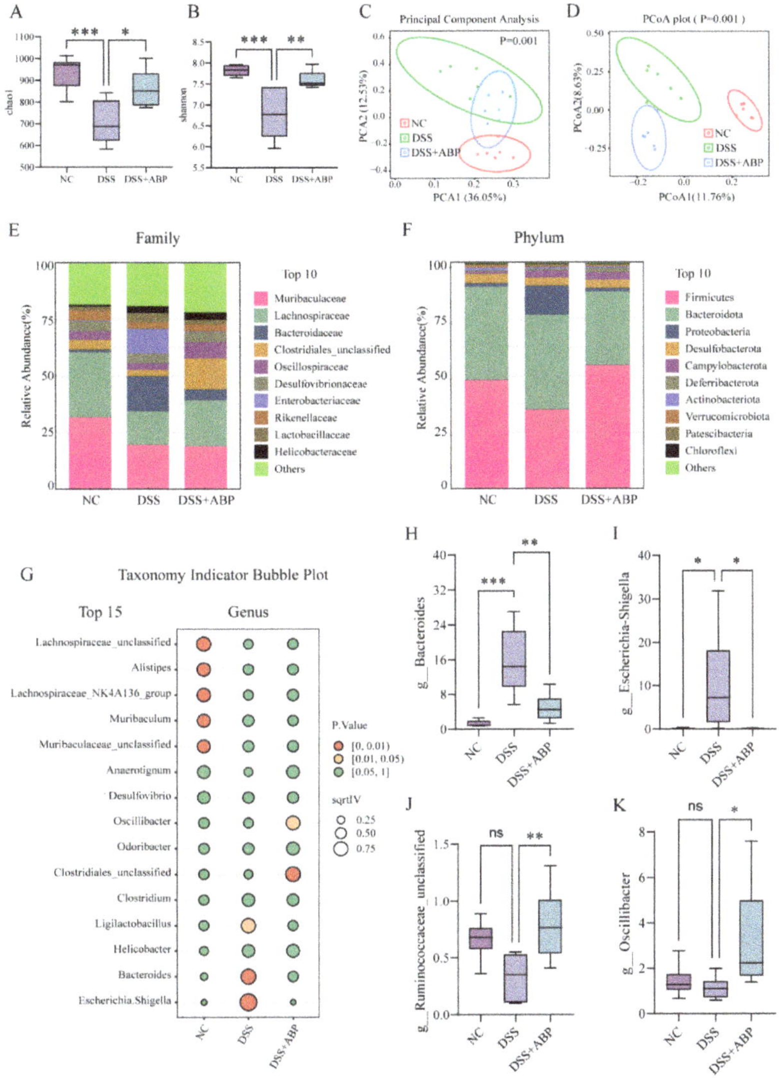

Figure 4. 16S rRNA analysis of the effect of *Agaricus blazei* Murrill polysaccharide (ABP) on gut microbiota. (**A**) Chao1 index; (**B**) Shannon index; (**C**,**D**) PCA and PCoA analysis; (**E**,**F**) top 10 display charts of species composition at the family level and phylum level; (**G**) top 15 displays of taxonomy indicators at the genus level; and (**H**–**K**) abundance of four bacterial genera (*Bacteroides*, *Escherichia-Shigella*, *Ruminococcaceae*_unclassified, and *Oscillibacter*) in different groups. Data are presented as mean ± SD, (n = 6). ns $p > 0.05$, * $p < 0.05$, ** $p < 0.01$, and *** $p < 0.001$.

3.5. Untargeted Metabolomics Analysis of the Effects of ABP on Metabolites

To further elucidate the effects of ABP in mice, we analyzed the metabolic composition of cecum contents in three groups of mice using untargeted metabolomics. With the threshold of fold change $\geq$1.5 or $\leq$2/3, $p < 0.05$, and a VIP value $\geq$1, in the negative ion mode, there were 2019 metabolites down-regulated and 1699 metabolites up-regulated in the DSS group compared with the NC group. A total of 903 metabolites were down-regulated and 906 metabolites were up-regulated in the DSS + ABP group compared with the DSS group. In the positive ion mode, 1411 metabolites were down-regulated and 1272 metabolites were up-regulated in the DSS group compared with the NC group. A total of 753 metabolites were down-regulated and 729 metabolites were up-regulated in the DSS + ABP group compared with the DSS group (Figure 5A). The results of the PLS-DA analysis suggest that the three groups of samples had different metabolic profiles, and the permutation test results suggest that the PLS-DA downscaling model was not overfitted (Figure 5B,C). The classification of differentially abundant metabolites in each group is shown in Figure 5D, and the overall metabolic profiles and clustering of the three groups are shown in Figure 5E. A heatmap showing the top 30 metabolites in the order of fold change with a VIP value >1.5 is shown in Figure 6A. Among them, the levels of tryptophan metabolites Indole and Indole-3-carboxyaldehyde were significantly higher in the intestine after ABP intervention compared to the DSS group (Figure 6A). Further, the contents of six metabolites (3-hydroxybenzaldehyde, 3-hydrpxubutyric acid, caffeic acid, hexafluoroisopropanol, sulfanilamide, and zapotin) in the intestinal contents of the three groups of mice were shown in the form of bar graphs. The results showed that the content of the six metabolites was significantly reduced ($p < 0.05$) after DSS induction, whereas the intervention of ABP resulted in a significant recovery of the content of these six metabolites ($p < 0.05$) (Figure 6B–G). The above results suggest that ABP can remodel DSS-induced metabolic disorders.

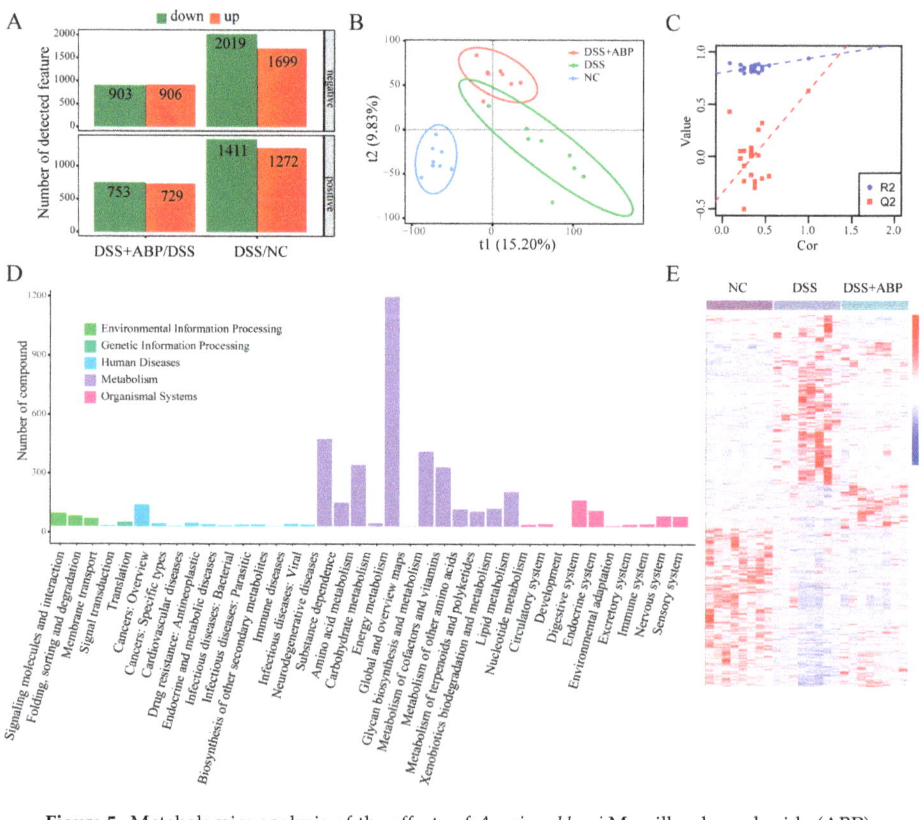

Figure 5. Metabolomics analysis of the effects of *Agaricus blazei* Murrill polysaccharide (ABP) on metabolites. (**A**) Differentially abundant metabolites between groups in positive and negative ionization modes; (**B**) results of PLS−DA analysis; (**C**) replacement test results; (**D**) categorization of differentially abundant metabolites; (**E**) overall metabolite abundance profiles and clustering of groups, (n = 8).

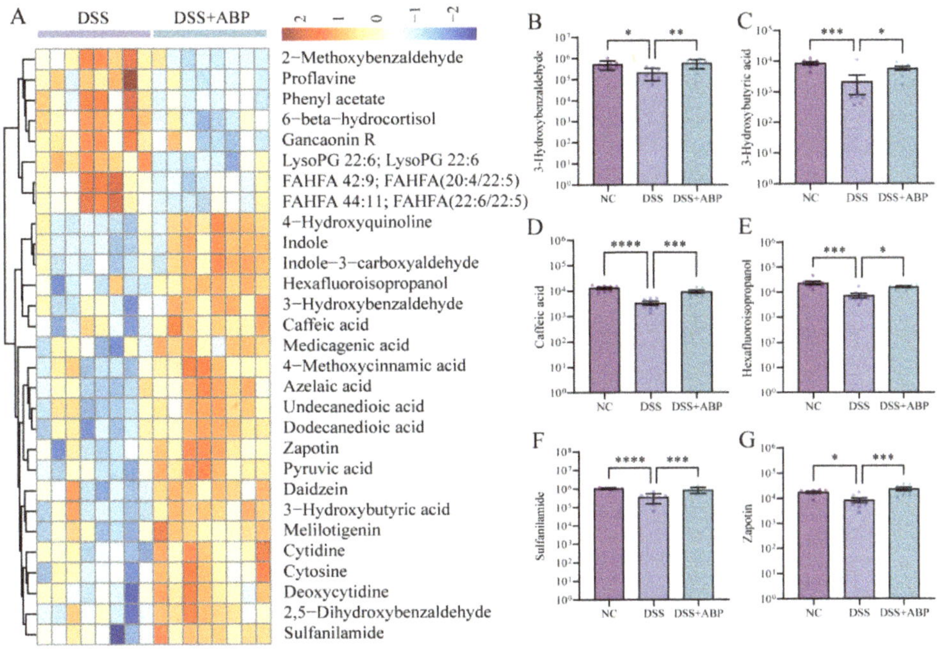

Figure 6. Differentially abundant metabolites. (**A**) Heatmap showing the top 30 metabolites in the order of fold change with a VIP value >1.5; and (**B–G**) the abundance of six metabolites (3-hydroxybenzaldehyde, 3-hydrpxubutyric acid, caffeic acid, hexafluoroisopropanol, sulfanilamide, and zapotin) in different groups. Data are presented as mean ± SD, (n = 8). * $p < 0.05$, ** $p < 0.01$, *** $p < 0.001$, and **** $p < 0.0001$.

3.6. Correlation Analysis of Differential Bacteria, Differentially Abundant Metabolites, and Physiological and Biochemical Indicators

We performed a correlation analysis on the four key bacteria, the six differentially abundant metabolites, and the physiological biochemical indicators previously detected. A heatmap was used to demonstrate the correlation relationships among these factors (Figure 7). The correlation analysis showed that *Bacteroides* and *Escherichia-Shigella* were positively correlated with the levels of pro-inflammatory factors, pro-oxidant factors, and DAI scores, and negatively correlated with the levels of antioxidant factors and the six metabolites. *Ruminococcaceae*_unclassified and *Oscillibacter* were negatively correlated with pro-inflammatory factor levels, pro-oxidant factor levels, and DAI scores, and positively correlated with antioxidant factors and the levels of the six metabolites. The correlation heatmap and network diagram provided insights into the mechanism through which ABP alleviates DSS-induced colitis, but the underlying mechanisms need to be further verified with additional studies.

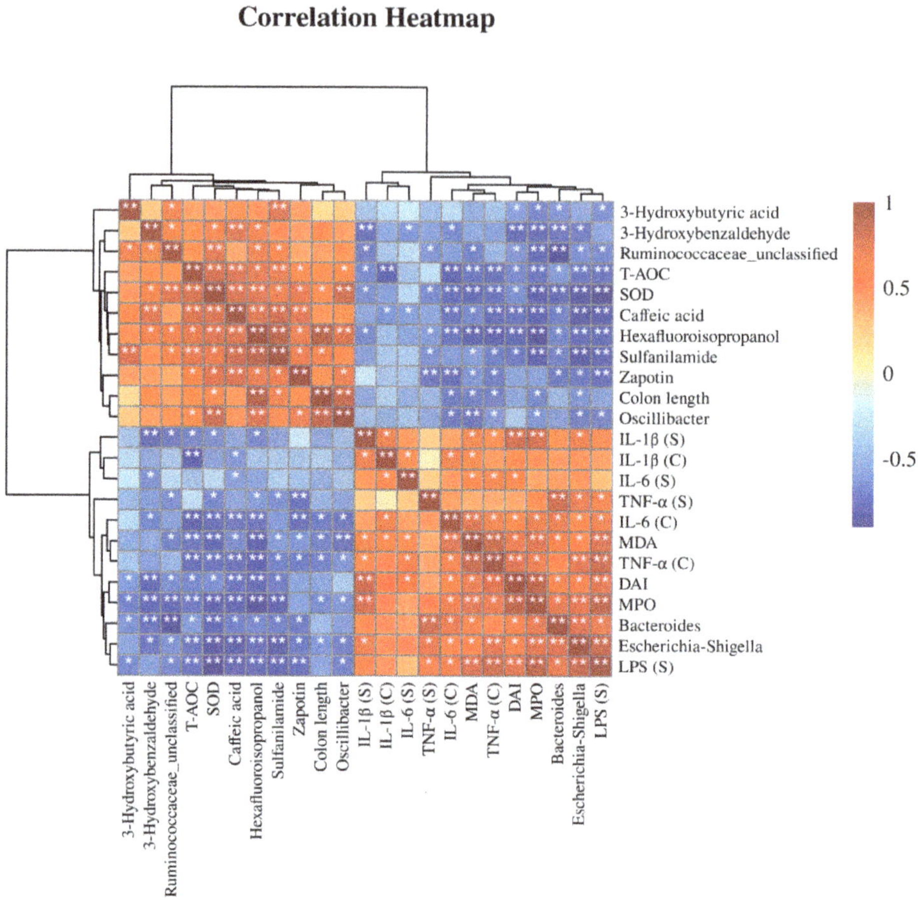

Figure 7. Spearman correlation analysis. A heatmap construction for the correlation analysis of gut microbiota, metabolites, and physiological and biochemical indicators. White star indicates significance analysis, * $p < 0.05$ and ** $p < 0.01$.

4. Discussion

ABP has potent antitumor effects through regulating immune cell differentiation and/or function, inhibiting proliferation, and inducing apoptosis in cancer cells [37–39]. Additionally, ABP exerts anti-inflammatory, antioxidant, and hypoglycemic activities by reducing oxidative stress and blood glucose and lipids levels [40–42]. In the present study, we evaluated the protective effect of dietary supplementation with ABP using a mouse model of DSS-induced acute colitis. The results showed that ABP intervention significantly improved DSS-induced colitis symptoms. It has been reported that damage to the intestinal epithelial barrier can increase the permeability and infiltration of pathogens, induce barrier dysfunction, and manifest as cellular apoptosis, erosion, and ulceration, representing a key pathological change in UC [43,44]. Epithelial tight junctions are key structures that regulate the transport of macromolecules across cells. Dysregulation of the expression of tight-junction-related proteins is closely related to UC progression [45,46]. In addition, inflammation-related cytokines can influence the expression of tight junction proteins and change the permeability of the intestinal epithelium by affecting tight junction proteins, thereby participating in and altering UC developmental processes [47,48]. Therefore, we further explored the expression levels of inflammatory and oxidative factors, as well as three tight junction proteins (ZO-1, Occludin, and Claudin1).

In the DSS-induced UC model, we clearly observed significant up-regulation in the expression of inflammatory factors, such as TNF-α and IL-1β, in serum and colon tissues. Meanwhile, the significant increase in MPO and MDA oxidative stress markers and the significant decrease in SOD and T-AOC antioxidant markers were consistent with the expected outcomes. ABP exhibited excellent counteracting effects on DSS-induced inflammation and oxidative responses, aligning with previous reports [49–51]. In this experiment, DSS induced damage to the intestinal barrier in mice, and the expression levels of three tight junction proteins, ZO-1, Occludin, and Claudin1, were significantly reduced, as evidenced by mucosal disruption, ulceration, and the disappearance of glands in the tissue sections. The expression levels of tight junction proteins were increased, and damage to the intestinal barrier was reduced by ABP treatment. Therefore, in this DSS-induced UC mouse model, ABP treatment attenuated DSS-induced intestinal inflammation and oxidative stress, thereby protecting intestinal barrier function possibly through up-regulating tight junction protein expression.

Existing research provides evidence that gut microbiota dysbiosis, intestinal hypersensitivity, and aberrant mucosal immune responses collectively contribute to UC development. A complex interplay between perturbations in these components is believed to drive uncontrolled intestinal inflammation in genetically susceptible individuals [52,53]. In addition, gut microbiota dysbiosis can also trigger inflammatory spillover to other organs, such as joints, the oral cavity, and eyes, leading to inflammation or even cancer [54]. We performed 16S rRNA sequencing to analyze the changes in the gut microbiota of mice. The top 15 genera with the most significant differential expression were selected from the sequencing results. As shown in Figure 4G, the levels of *Ligilactobacillus*, *Bacteroides*, and *Escherichia-Shigella* were markedly elevated in the DSS group. Four bacterial strains were subsequently screened for further detection and validation.

Bacteroides are a type of gut microbiota that play crucial roles in human gut nutrition, metabolism, immune response, and overall health [55]. Dysbiosis of *Bacteroides* has been associated with various gastrointestinal disorders, including UC, and metabolic diseases, such as diabetes and obesity [56–58]. *Escherichia* and *Shigella* are both Gram-negative bacilli that commonly inhabit the gastrointestinal tract as commensal organisms in the human gut [59]. However, under certain conditions, virulent strains have the potential to breach the intestinal epithelium and induce intestinal disorders [60,61]. It has also been reported that *Ruminococcaceae*_unclassified, as part of the gut microbiota, possesses strong metabolic capabilities for carbohydrates and can perform normal food digestion and absorption functions in the gut [62]. *Oscillibacter* is able to maintain gut pH balance by producing substances such as propionate and butyrate, thus promoting the health and stability of the intestinal mucosa [63,64]. Therefore, these two types of bacteria are generally considered beneficial, but their imbalance or depletion has been closely associated with inflammatory bowel disease, obesity, and other related conditions [65]. The results of the present study showed that the relative abundance of *Lactobacillus* and *Shigella* was significantly increased in DSS-induced UC, which is also consistent with the findings of Schirmer M [66]. Interestingly, treatment with ABP was effective in alleviating DSS-induced intestinal dysbiosis because the levels of *Bacteroides* and *Escherichia-Shigella* were significantly reduced after treatment, and the relative abundance of *Ruminococcaceae*_unclassified and *Oscillibacter* was significantly increased. The increase in these beneficial bacteria leads to improved preventive and protective effects on the intestinal tract, which is also the role of ABP.

Changes in the gut microbiota affect the composition of gut metabolites, including short-chain fatty acids, amino acid metabolites, bioactive peptides, and vitamins. These metabolites have the ability to regulate the immune system, influence energy metabolism, and modulate the intestinal mucosal barrier function [67–69]. Thus, the gut microbiota and gut metabolites interact closely with each other and together influence the health and disease states of the body.

In order to assess the effect of ABP intervention on gut metabolism, we performed an untargeted metabolomic analysis of cecum contents based on LC-MS technology. The results showed that the abundance of several metabolites, including 4-hydroxyquinoline, was up-regulated or decreased in DSS-induced UC mice after ABP treatment. The expression levels of 3-hydroxybenzaldehyde, 3-hydroxybutyric acid, caffeic acid, and zapotin have been reported to be closely associated with the inflammatory response and oxidative stress and have therapeutic potential for UC [70–73]. Subsequently, we examined the abundance of six metabolites (3-hydroxybenzaldehyde, 3-hydroxybutyric acid, caffeic acid, hexafluoroisopropanol, sulfanilamide, and zapotin) identified in the sequencing analysis. As expected, the abundance of these metabolites significantly decreased in DSS-induced UC and significantly increased after ABP treatment.

In summary, we discovered that ABP is able to reduce inflammation and oxidative stress, as well as repair damaged gut barriers, and may also exert its effects through modulation of the gut microbiota and metabolites.

However, our experimental results have certain limitations. Although our study demonstrated significant improvement of DSS-induced UC by ABP, as validated by multi-dimensional analysis, the recommended intake and potential toxic side effects of ABP in human subjects remain unknown. Furthermore, this study did not directly explore and validate the key bacterial and metabolite changes in the gut microbiota during the treatment of UC with ABP, as well as their respective regulatory roles. These aspects require further investigation. Nevertheless, it is undeniable that our study enhances our understanding of the functionality of ABP and provides a theoretical basis for the use of ABP dietary supplements in the prevention of UC.

Author Contributions: Z.-H.J., W.G. and B.Y. contributed to the conception of the manuscript. Z.-H.J. and W.-Y.X. wrote the manuscript. Z.-H.J., S.H. and P.-S.Z. conducted the experiments. S.H. and P.-S.Z. edited the figures and tables. B.Y., W.G. and W.-Z.R. examined the entire manuscript. All authors have read and agreed to the published version of the manuscript.

Funding: This work was supported by the China Agriculture Research System (CARS-37) and the Changchun Science and Technology Bureau (21ZY19).

Institutional Review Board Statement: This study was approved by the Animal Ethics and Welfare Committee of Jilin University (License No. SY202305009, approval date: 11 May 2023). All experimental procedures were conducted in strict compliance with animal welfare ethics and animal welfare laws and regulations.

Informed Consent Statement: Not applicable.

Data Availability Statement: Data will be made available on request.

Conflicts of Interest: The authors declare no conflict of interest.

References

1. Bisgaard, T.H.; Allin, K.H.; Keefer, L.; Ananthakrishnan, A.N.; Jess, T. Depression and anxiety in inflammatory bowel disease: Epidemiology, mechanisms and treatment. *Nat. Rev. Gastroenterol. Hepatol.* **2022**, *19*, 717–726. [CrossRef] [PubMed]
2. Bruner, L.P.; White, A.M.; Proksell, S. Inflammatory Bowel Disease. *Prim. Care* **2023**, *50*, 411–427. [CrossRef] [PubMed]
3. Massironi, S.; Viganò, C.; Palermo, A.; Pirola, L.; Mulinacci, G.; Allocca, M.; Peyrin-Biroulet, L.; Danese, S. Inflammation and malnutrition in inflammatory bowel disease. *Lancet Gastroenterol. Hepatol.* **2023**, *8*, 579–590. [CrossRef] [PubMed]
4. Chen, B.; Collen, L.V.; Mowat, C.; Isaacs, K.L.; Singh, S.; Kane, S.V.; Farraye, F.A.; Snapper, S.; Jneid, H.; Lavie, C.J.; et al. Inflammatory Bowel Disease and Cardiovascular Diseases. *Am. J. Med.* **2022**, *135*, 1453–1460. [CrossRef]
5. Wang, D.; Zhang, X.; Du, H. Inflammatory bowel disease: A potential pathogenic factor of Alzheimer's disease. *Prog. Neuro-Psychopharmacol. Biol. Psychiatry* **2022**, *119*, 110610. [CrossRef]
6. Mak, J.W.Y.; Sun, Y.; Limsrivilai, J.; Abdullah, M.; Kaibullayeva, J.; Balderramo, D.; Vergara, B.I.; Paudel, M.S.; Banerjee, R.; Hilmi, I.; et al. Development of the global inflammatory bowel disease visualization of epidemiology studies in the 21(st) century (GIVES-21). *BMC Med. Res. Methodol.* **2023**, *23*, 129. [CrossRef]
7. Gordon, H.; Biancone, L.; Fiorino, G.; Katsanos, K.H.; Kopylov, U.; Al Sulais, E.; Axelrad, J.E.; Balendran, K.; Burisch, J.; de Ridder, L.; et al. ECCO Guidelines on Inflammatory Bowel Disease and Malignancies. *J. Crohn's Colitis* **2023**, *17*, 827–854. [CrossRef]

8. Huang, Q.; Zhang, Y.; Chu, Q.; Song, H. The Influence of Polysaccharides on Lipid Metabolism: Insights from Gut Microbiota. *Mol. Nutr. Food Res.* **2023**, e2300522. [CrossRef]
9. Tang, Q.; Huang, G. Preparation and antioxidant activities of cuaurbit polysaccharide. *Int. J. Biol. Macromol.* **2018**, *117*, 362–365. [CrossRef]
10. Ren, L.; Perera, C.; Hemar, Y. Antitumor activity of mushroom polysaccharides: A review. *Food Funct.* **2012**, *3*, 1118–1130. [CrossRef]
11. Roszczyk, A.; Turło, J.; Zagożdżon, R.; Kaleta, B. Immunomodulatory Properties of Polysaccharides from Lentinula edodes. *Int. J. Mol. Sci.* **2022**, *2*, 8980. [CrossRef] [PubMed]
12. Guo, C.; Guo, D.; Fang, L.; Sang, T.; Wu, J.; Guo, C.; Wang, Y.; Wang, Y.; Chen, C.; Chen, J.; et al. Ganoderma lucidum polysaccharide modulates gut microbiota and immune cell function to inhibit inflammation and tumorigenesis in colon. *Carbohydr. Polym.* **2021**, *267*, 118231. [CrossRef] [PubMed]
13. Zou, M.Y.; Wang, Y.J.; Liu, Y.; Xiong, S.Q.; Zhang, L.; Wang, J.H. Huangshan Floral Mushroom Polysaccharide Ameliorates Dextran Sulfate Sodium-Induced Colitis in Mice by Modulating Th17/Treg Balance in a Gut Microbiota-Dependent Manner. *Mol. Nutr. Food Res.* **2023**, *67*, e2200408. [CrossRef] [PubMed]
14. Yang, W.; Cong, Y. Gut microbiota-derived metabolites in the regulation of host immune responses and immune-related inflammatory diseases. *Cell. Mol. Immunol.* **2021**, *18*, 866–877. [CrossRef] [PubMed]
15. Yntema, T.; Koonen, D.P.Y.; Kuipers, F. Emerging Roles of Gut Microbial Modulation of Bile Acid Composition in the Etiology of Cardiovascular Diseases. *Nutrients* **2023**, *15*, 1850. [CrossRef]
16. Xu, D.; Wu, Q.; Liu, W.; Hu, G.; Meng, H.; Wang, J. Therapeutic efficacy and underlying mechanisms of Gastrodia elata polysaccharides on dextran sulfate sodium-induced inflammatory bowel disease in mice: Modulation of the gut microbiota and improvement of metabolic disorders. *Int. J. Biol. Macromol.* **2023**, *248*, 125919. [CrossRef]
17. Yang, Y.; Zhang, Y.; Song, J.; Li, Y.; Zhou, L.; Xu, H.; Wu, K.; Gao, J.; Zhao, M.; Zheng, Y. Bergamot polysaccharides relieve DSS-induced ulcerative colitis via regulating the gut microbiota and metabolites. *Int. J. Biol. Macromol.* **2023**, *253*, 127335. [CrossRef]
18. Liu, X.; Zhang, Y.; Li, W.; Zhang, B.; Yin, J.; Liuqi, S.; Wang, J.; Peng, B.; Wang, S. Fucoidan Ameliorated Dextran Sulfate Sodium-Induced Ulcerative Colitis by Modulating Gut Microbiota and Bile Acid Metabolism. *J. Agric. Food Chem.* **2022**, *70*, 14864–14876. [CrossRef]
19. Firenzuoli, F.; Gori, L.; Lombardo, G. The Medicinal Mushroom *Agaricus blazei* Murrill: Review of Literature and Pharmaco-Toxicological Problems. *Evid.-Based Complement. Altern. Med. ECAM* **2008**, *5*, 3–15. [CrossRef] [PubMed]
20. Li, Y.; Lu, X.; Li, X.; Guo, X.; Sheng, Y.; Li, Y.; Xu, G.; Han, X.; An, L.; Du, P. Effects of *Agaricus blazei* Murrill polysaccharides on hyperlipidemic rats by regulation of intestinal microflora. *Food Sci. Nutr.* **2020**, *8*, 2758–2772. [CrossRef]
21. da Silva Campelo, M.; Neto, J.F.C.; Lima, A.B.N.; das Chagas Neto, F.C.; da Costa Gonzaga, M.L.; de Aguiar Soares, S.; Leal, L.; Ribeiro, M.; Ricardo, N. Polysaccharides and extracts from *Agaricus brasiliensis* Murill—A comprehensive review. *Int. J. Biol. Macromol.* **2021**, *183*, 1697–1714. [CrossRef] [PubMed]
22. Mizuno, M.; Minato, K.; Ito, H.; Kawade, M.; Terai, H.; Tsuchida, H. Anti-tumor polysaccharide from the mycelium of liquid-cultured *Agaricus blazei* mill. *Biochem. Mol. Biol. Int.* **1999**, *47*, 707–714. [CrossRef] [PubMed]
23. Wu, B.; Cui, J.; Zhang, C.; Li, Z. A polysaccharide from *Agaricus blazei* inhibits proliferation and promotes apoptosis of osteosarcoma cells. *Int. J. Biol. Macromol.* **2012**, *50*, 1116–1120. [CrossRef] [PubMed]
24. Angeli, J.P.; Ribeiro, L.R.; Gonzaga, M.L.; Soares Sde, A.; Ricardo, M.P.; Tsuboy, M.S.; Stidl, R.; Knasmueller, S.; Linhares, R.E.; Mantovani, M.S. Protective effects of beta-glucan extracted from *Agaricus brasiliensis* against chemically induced DNA damage in human lymphocytes. *Cell Biol. Toxicol.* **2006**, *22*, 285–291. [CrossRef] [PubMed]
25. Zhao, Y.; Tian, N.; Wang, H.; Yan, H. Chemically Sulfated Polysaccharides from *Agaricus blazei* Murill: Synthesis, Characterization and Anti-HIV Activity. *Chem. Biodivers.* **2021**, *18*, e2100338. [CrossRef]
26. Jiang, L.; Yu, Z.; Lin, Y.; Cui, L.; Yao, S.; Lv, L.; Liu, J. Low-molecular-weight polysaccharides from *Agaricus blazei* Murrill modulate the Th1 response in cancer immunity. *Oncol. Lett.* **2018**, *15*, 3429–3436. [CrossRef]
27. Yuan, W.; Huang, M.; Wu, Y.; Liu, J.; Zhou, X.; Wang, J.; Liu, J. *Agaricus blazei* Murrill Polysaccharide Attenuates Periodontitis via H(2) S/NRF2 Axis-Boosted Appropriate Level of Autophagy in PDLCs. *Mol. Nutr. Food Res.* **2023**, e2300112. [CrossRef]
28. Saraiva, M.M.; Campelo, M.D.S.; Câmara Neto, J.F.; Gonzaga, M.; Bastos, M.; Soares, S.A.; Ricardo, N.; Cerqueira, G.S.; Leitão, R.F.C.; Ribeiro, M. *Agaricus blazei* Murill polysaccharides/alginate/poly(vinyl alcohol) blend as dressings for wound healing. *Int. J. Biol. Macromol.* **2023**, *244*, 125278. [CrossRef]
29. Kim, Y.W.; Kim, K.H.; Choi, H.J.; Lee, D.S. Anti-diabetic activity of beta-glucans and their enzymatically hydrolyzed oligosaccharides from *Agaricus blazei*. *Biotechnol. Lett.* **2005**, *27*, 483–487. [CrossRef]
30. Li, Y.; Sheng, Y.; Lu, X.; Guo, X.; Xu, G.; Han, X.; An, L.; Du, P. Isolation and purification of acidic polysaccharides from *Agaricus blazei* Murill and evaluation of their lipid-lowering mechanism. *Int. J. Biol. Macromol.* **2020**, *157*, 276–287. [CrossRef]
31. Xiao, H.; Li, H.; Wen, Y.; Jiang, D.; Zhu, S.; He, X.; Xiong, Q.; Gao, J.; Hou, S.; Huang, S.; et al. Tremella fuciformis polysaccharides ameliorated ulcerative colitis via inhibiting inflammation and enhancing intestinal epithelial barrier function. *Int. J. Biol. Macromol.* **2021**, *180*, 633–642. [CrossRef]

32. Yang, W.; Ren, D.; Shao, H.; Zhang, X.; Li, T.; Zhang, L.; Liu, L.; Zhao, Y.; Niu, P.; Yang, X. Theabrownin from Fu Brick Tea Improves Ulcerative Colitis by Shaping the Gut Microbiota and Modulating the Tryptophan Metabolism. *J. Agric. Food Chem.* **2023**, *71*, 2898–2913. [CrossRef] [PubMed]
33. Egger, B.; Bajaj-Elliott, M.; MacDonald, T.T.; Inglin, R.; Eysselein, V.E.; Büchler, M.W. Characterisation of acute murine dextran sodium sulphate colitis: Cytokine profile and dose dependency. *Digestion* **2000**, *62*, 240–248. [CrossRef] [PubMed]
34. Hou, Y.C.; Yu, H.C.; Martin, R.; Cirulli, E.T.; Schenker-Ahmed, N.M.; Hicks, M.; Cohen, I.V.; Jönsson, T.J.; Heister, R.; Napier, L.; et al. Precision medicine integrating whole-genome sequencing, comprehensive metabolomics, and advanced imaging. *Proc. Natl. Acad. Sci. USA* **2020**, *117*, 3053–3062. [CrossRef]
35. Fruchon, S.; Poupot, R. The ABP Dendrimer, a Drug-Candidate against Inflammatory Diseases That Triggers the Activation of Interleukin-10 Producing Immune Cells. *Molecules* **2018**, *23*, 1272. [CrossRef] [PubMed]
36. Wang, S.; Sugamori, K.S.; Tung, A.; McPherson, J.P.; Grant, D.M. N-hydroxylation of 4-aminobiphenyl by CYP2E1 produces oxidative stress in a mouse model of chemically induced liver cancer. *Toxicol. Sci. Off. J. Soc. Toxicol.* **2015**, *144*, 393–405. [CrossRef] [PubMed]
37. Li, X.; Zhao, X.; Wang, H.; Han, J.; Liu, L. A polysaccharide from the fruiting bodies of *Agaricus blazei* Murill induces caspase-dependent apoptosis in human leukemia HL-60 cells. *Tumour Biol. J. Int. Soc. Oncodev. Biol. Med.* **2014**, *35*, 8963–8968. [CrossRef]
38. Fujimiya, Y.; Suzuki, Y.; Oshiman, K.; Kobori, H.; Moriguchi, K.; Nakashima, H.; Matumoto, Y.; Takahara, S.; Ebina, T.; Katakura, R. Selective tumoricidal effect of soluble proteoglucan extracted from the basidiomycete, *Agaricus blazei* Murill, mediated via natural killer cell activation and apoptosis. *Cancer Immunol. Immunother. CII* **1998**, *46*, 147–159. [CrossRef]
39. Niu, Y.C.; Liu, J.C.; Zhao, X.M.; Cao, J. A low molecular weight polysaccharide isolated from *Agaricus blazei* Murill (LMPAB) exhibits its anti-metastatic effect by down-regulating metalloproteinase-9 and up-regulating Nm23-H1. *Am. J. Chin. Med.* **2009**, *37*, 909–921. [CrossRef]
40. Xie, W.; Lv, A.; Li, R.; Tang, Z.; Ma, D.; Huang, X.; Zhang, R.; Ge, M. *Agaricus blazei* Murill Polysaccharides Protect Against Cadmium-Induced Oxidative Stress and Inflammatory Damage in Chicken Spleens. *Biol. Trace Elem. Res.* **2018**, *184*, 247–258. [CrossRef]
41. Song, Y.; Zhang, R.; Wang, H.; Yan, Y.; Ming, G. Protective Effect of *Agaricus blazei* Polysaccharide Against Cadmium-Induced Damage on the Testis of Chicken. *Biol. Trace Elem. Res.* **2018**, *184*, 491–500. [CrossRef] [PubMed]
42. Liu, Y.; Zhang, L.; Zhu, X.; Wang, Y.; Liu, W.; Gong, W. Polysaccharide *Agaricus blazei* Murill stimulates myeloid derived suppressor cell differentiation from M2 to M1 type, which mediates inhibition of tumour immune-evasion via the Toll-like receptor 2 pathway. *Immunology* **2015**, *146*, 379–391. [CrossRef] [PubMed]
43. Teshima, C.W.; Dieleman, L.A.; Meddings, J.B. Abnormal intestinal permeability in Crohn's disease pathogenesis. *Ann. N. Y. Acad. Sci.* **2012**, *1258*, 159–165. [CrossRef] [PubMed]
44. Heller, F.; Florian, P.; Bojarski, C.; Richter, J.; Christ, M.; Hillenbrand, B.; Mankertz, J.; Gitter, A.H.; Bürgel, N.; Fromm, M.; et al. Interleukin-13 is the key effector Th2 cytokine in ulcerative colitis that affects epithelial tight junctions, apoptosis, and cell restitution. *Gastroenterology* **2005**, *129*, 550–564. [CrossRef]
45. Lee, S.H. Intestinal permeability regulation by tight junction: Implication on inflammatory bowel diseases. *Intest. Res.* **2015**, *13*, 11–18. [CrossRef]
46. Lu, F.; Li, Y.; Zhou, B.; Guo, Q.; Zhang, Y. Early-life supplementation of grape polyphenol extract promotes polyphenol absorption and modulates the intestinal microbiota in association with the increase in mRNA expression of the key intestinal barrier genes. *Food Funct.* **2021**, *12*, 602–613. [CrossRef]
47. Arrieta, M.C.; Madsen, K.; Doyle, J.; Meddings, J. Reducing small intestinal permeability attenuates colitis in the IL10 gene-deficient mouse. *Gut* **2009**, *58*, 41–48. [CrossRef]
48. Landy, J.; Ronde, E.; English, N.; Clark, S.K.; Hart, A.L.; Knight, S.C.; Ciclitira, P.J.; Al-Hassi, H.O. Tight junctions in inflammatory bowel diseases and inflammatory bowel disease associated colorectal cancer. *World J. Gastroenterol.* **2016**, *22*, 3117–3126. [CrossRef]
49. Hetland, G.; Johnson, E.; Lyberg, T.; Kvalheim, G. The Mushroom *Agaricus blazei* Murill Elicits Medicinal Effects on Tumor, Infection, Allergy, and Inflammation through Its Modulation of Innate Immunity and Amelioration of Th1/Th2 Imbalance and Inflammation. *Adv. Pharmacol. Sci.* **2011**, *2011*, 157015. [CrossRef]
50. Wang, W.; Liu, M.; Zhang, M.; Sun, W.; Zhang, J.; Jia, L. *Agaricus blazei* Murill polysaccharides alleviate oxidative stress and inflammatory responses against liver and lung injury. *Food Biosci.* **2022**, *47*, 101645. [CrossRef]
51. Zhang, Y.; Lu, F.; Zhang, H.; Ye, Y.; Liu, P.; Lin, D.; Zhou, H.; Li, M.; Yang, B. Polysaccharides from *Agaricus blazei* Murrill ameliorate dextran sulfate sodium-induced colitis via attenuating intestinal barrier dysfunction. *J. Funct. Food.* **2022**, *92*, 105072. [CrossRef]
52. Hold, G.L.; Smith, M.; Grange, C.; Watt, E.R.; El-Omar, E.M.; Mukhopadhya, I. Role of the gut microbiota in inflammatory bowel disease pathogenesis: What have we learnt in the past 10 years? *World J. Gastroenterol.* **2014**, *20*, 1192–1210. [CrossRef] [PubMed]
53. Juste, C.; Kreil, D.P.; Beauvallet, C.; Guillot, A.; Vaca, S.; Carapito, C.; Mondot, S.; Sykacek, P.; Sokol, H.; Blon, F.; et al. Bacterial protein signals are associated with Crohn's disease. *Gut* **2014**, *63*, 1566–1577. [CrossRef]
54. Tarris, G.; de Rougemont, A.; Charkaoui, M.; Michiels, C.; Martin, L.; Belliot, G. Enteric Viruses and Inflammatory Bowel Disease. *Viruses* **2021**, *13*, 104. [CrossRef]

55. Brown, E.M.; Ke, X.; Hitchcock, D.; Jeanfavre, S.; Avila-Pacheco, J.; Nakata, T.; Arthur, T.D.; Fornelos, N.; Heim, C.; Franzosa, E.A.; et al. Bacteroides-Derived Sphingolipids Are Critical for Maintaining Intestinal Homeostasis and Symbiosis. *Cell Host Microbe* **2019**, *25*, 668–680.e7. [CrossRef]
56. Wang, C.; Zhao, J.; Zhang, H.; Lee, Y.K.; Zhai, Q.; Chen, W. Roles of intestinal bacteroides in human health and diseases. *Crit. Rev. Food Sci. Nutr.* **2021**, *61*, 3518–3536. [CrossRef] [PubMed]
57. Gurung, M.; Li, Z.; You, H.; Rodrigues, R.; Jump, D.B.; Morgun, A.; Shulzhenko, N. Role of gut microbiota in type 2 diabetes pathophysiology. *EBioMedicine* **2020**, *51*, 102590. [CrossRef]
58. Yoshida, N.; Yamashita, T.; Osone, T.; Hosooka, T.; Shinohara, M.; Kitahama, S.; Sasaki, K.; Sasaki, D.; Yoneshiro, T.; Suzuki, T.; et al. *Bacteroides* spp. promotes branched-chain amino acid catabolism in brown fat and inhibits obesity. *iScience* **2021**, *24*, 103342. [CrossRef]
59. Sanchez-Garrido, J.; Ruano-Gallego, D.; Choudhary, J.S.; Frankel, G. The type III secretion system effector network hypothesis. *Trends Microbiol.* **2022**, *30*, 524–533. [CrossRef]
60. Carter, M.Q.; Quiñones, B.; Laniohan, N.; Carychao, D.; Pham, A.; He, X.; Cooley, M. Pathogenicity assessment of Shiga toxin-producing Escherichia coli strains isolated from wild birds in a major agricultural region in California. *Front. Microbiol.* **2023**, *14*, 1214081. [CrossRef]
61. Baker, S.; The, H.C. Recent insights into Shigella. *Curr. Opin. Infect. Dis.* **2018**, *31*, 449–454. [CrossRef] [PubMed]
62. Lam, Y.Y.; Ha, C.W.; Hoffmann, J.M.; Oscarsson, J.; Dinudom, A.; Mather, T.J.; Cook, D.I.; Hunt, N.H.; Caterson, I.D.; Holmes, A.J.; et al. Effects of dietary fat profile on gut permeability and microbiota and their relationships with metabolic changes in mice. *Obesity* **2015**, *23*, 1429–1439. [CrossRef] [PubMed]
63. Jo, J.K.; Seo, S.H.; Park, S.E.; Kim, H.W.; Kim, E.J.; Kim, J.S.; Pyo, J.Y.; Cho, K.M.; Kwon, S.J.; Park, D.H.; et al. Gut Microbiome and Metabolome Profiles Associated with High-Fat Diet in Mice. *Metabolites* **2021**, *11*, 482. [CrossRef] [PubMed]
64. Huang, P.; Jiang, A.; Wang, X.; Zhou, Y.; Tang, W.; Ren, C.; Qian, X.; Zhou, Z.; Gong, A. NMN Maintains Intestinal Homeostasis by Regulating the Gut Microbiota. *Front. Nutr.* **2021**, *8*, 714604. [CrossRef]
65. Zhang, F.; Xiong, Y.; Zhang, Y.; Wu, K.; Zhang, B. Genetically proxied intestinal microbiota and risk of erectile dysfunction. *Andrology* **2023**. [CrossRef]
66. Schirmer, M.; Garner, A.; Vlamakis, H.; Xavier, R.J. Microbial genes and pathways in inflammatory bowel disease. *Nat. Rev. Microbiol.* **2019**, *17*, 497–511. [CrossRef]
67. Qu, R.; Zhang, Y.; Ma, Y.; Zhou, X.; Sun, L.; Jiang, C.; Zhang, Z.; Fu, W. Role of the Gut Microbiota and Its Metabolites in Tumorigenesis or Development of Colorectal Cancer. *Adv. Sci. (Weinh. Baden-Wurtt. Ger.)* **2023**, *10*, e2205563. [CrossRef]
68. Rooks, M.G.; Garrett, W.S. Gut microbiota, metabolites and host immunity. *Nat. Rev. Immunol.* **2016**, *16*, 341–352. [CrossRef]
69. Wieërs, G.; Belkhir, L.; Enaud, R.; Leclercq, S.; Philippart de Foy, J.M.; Dequenne, I.; de Timary, P.; Cani, P.D. How Probiotics Affect the Microbiota. *Front. Cell. Infect. Microbiol.* **2019**, *9*, 454. [CrossRef]
70. Xu, X.; Luo, A.; Lu, X.; Liu, M.; Wang, H.; Song, H.; Wei, C.; Wang, Y.; Duan, X. p-Hydroxybenzoic acid alleviates inflammatory responses and intestinal mucosal damage in DSS-induced colitis by activating ERβ signaling. *J. Funct. Food.* **2021**, *87*, 104835. [CrossRef]
71. Suzuki, R.; Mishima, M.; Nagane, M.; Mizugaki, H.; Suzuki, T.; Komuro, M.; Shimizu, T.; Fukuyama, T.; Takeda, S.; Ogata, M.; et al. The novel sustained 3-hydroxybutyrate donor poly-D-3-hydroxybutyric acid prevents inflammatory bowel disease through upregulation of regulatory T-cells. *FASEB J.* **2023**, *37*, e22708. [CrossRef] [PubMed]
72. Mei, Y.; Wang, Z.; Zhang, Y.; Wan, T.; Xue, J.; He, W.; Luo, Y.; Xu, Y.; Bai, X.; Wang, Q.; et al. FA-97, a New Synthetic Caffeic Acid Phenethyl Ester Derivative, Ameliorates DSS-Induced Colitis Against Oxidative Stress by Activating Nrf2/HO-1 Pathway. *Front. Immunol.* **2019**, *10*, 2969. [CrossRef] [PubMed]
73. Strawa, J.W.; Jakimiuk, K.; Tomczyk, M. Zapotin, a Polymethoxyflavone, with Potential Therapeutic Attributes. *Int. J. Mol. Sci.* **2021**, *22*, 13227. [CrossRef] [PubMed]

nutrients

MDPI

Article

Unraveling the Therapeutic Mechanism of *Saussurea involucrata* against Rheumatoid Arthritis: A Network Pharmacology and Molecular Modeling-Based Investigation

Jinghua Chen [1,2,3], Xiaoke Wu [1,2,3] and Ruitao Yu [1,3,*]

[1] Qinghai Provincial Key Laboratory of Tibetan Medicine Research, Northwest Institute of Plateau Biology, Chinese Academy of Sciences, Xining 810001, China; chenjinghua@nwipb.cas.cn (J.C.)
[2] University of Chinese Academy of Sciences, Beijing 100049, China
[3] Key Laboratory of Tibetan Medicine Research, Chinese Academy of Sciences, Xining 810001, China
* Correspondence: yuruitao@nwipb.cas.cn; Tel.: +86-0971-6143530

Abstract: Rheumatoid arthritis (RA) is a chronic autoimmune disease with a global prevalence of approximately 0.46%, causing significant impairments in patients' quality of life and an economic burden. *Saussurea involucrata* (SI) has long been used in traditional medicine to treat RA, but its underlying mechanism remains unclear. This study utilized network pharmacology and molecular docking to explore the potential pharmacological effects of bioactive compounds in SI on RA. A total of 27 active compounds were identified, along with 665 corresponding targets. Additionally, 593 disease-related targets were obtained from multiple databases, with 119 common targets shared with SI. The high-ranking targets mainly belong to the MAPK family and NF-κB pathway, including MAPK14, MAPK1, RELA, TNF, and MAPK8, all of which are associated with inflammation and joint destruction in RA. Gene Ontology (GO) and Kyoto Encyclopedia of Genes and Genomes (KEGG) analysis revealed significant pathways related to IL-17 signaling, Th17 cell differentiation, and osteoclast differentiation. Molecular docking and dynamic simulations demonstrated strong interactions between several flavonoids and RA-related targets. Xuelianlactone, Involucratin, and Flazin exhibit outstanding binding efficacy with targets such as MAPK1, MAPK8, and TNF. These findings provide valuable insights into the therapeutic potential of SI for RA and offer directions for further drug development.

Keywords: *Saussurea involucrata*; rheumatoid arthritis; network pharmacology; molecular docking; molecular dynamic simulation

1. Introduction

Rheumatoid arthritis (RA), a chronic autoimmune disease, exhibited a global prevalence of 0.46% between 1980 and 2018, with significant regional and country-specific variations [1]. In mainland China, where the prevalence of RA was 0.42%, similar to the world average [2], the number of RA patients reached 5 million, with an average onset age of 45 years. Among all patients, 82% experienced moderate to severe disease, and patients often have complications [3], highlighting an ongoing and concerning situation. With a female-to-male ratio of about 4:1 in China [4], RA is more prevalent among women, and this overrepresentation is likely influenced by genetic (X-linked) factors and hormonal aspects, even though the exact reasons remain unclear [5]. The occurrence of RA is influenced by a combination of genetic and environmental factors, including smoking, infection, alcohol intake, gender, and age [6–8]. RA patients may suffer from various symptoms, including joint destruction, deformity, disability, and even death. In some cases, organs or systems such as the heart, kidneys, lungs, eyes, skin, digestive system, and nervous system may also be affected, leading to the development of various syndromes [9]. RA causes physical and emotional pain to patients and shortens their life expectancy. Additionally, the teratogenic and disabling effects of RA contribute to a loss of labor capacity within the population, resulting in substantial economic losses [10].

There is no cure for RA at present, but there are some pharmacological and non-pharmacological treatments that can relieve symptoms, delay disease progression, and improve quality of life [11]. The main purpose of drug treatment is to reduce inflammation, suppress excessive immune system response, and reduce joint damage. The currently used drugs include non-steroidal anti-inflammatory drugs (NSAIDs), disease-modifying anti-rheumatic drugs (DMARDs), glucocorticoids (GC), TNF inhibitors, and polymer colloids [12,13]. These drugs may cause gastrointestinal side effects such as nausea, vomiting, or abdominal pain, and adverse reactions like stomatitis or mouth sores. Moreover, they can lead to liver toxicity (hepatic dysfunction), hematological disorders, bone density reduction, insomnia, and depression. In more severe cases, patients may experience infections, cardiovascular events, cancer, or even death [14,15]. Therefore, the development of alternative drugs for RA treatment is necessary. Traditional Chinese Medicine and other ethnic medicines have a long history of clinical application and are considered valuable sources for natural drug development. These medicines offer higher safety profiles and have recently garnered significant attention in the field of RA drug research.

Saussurea, a medicinal plant, was first documented in the ancient Tibetan book Sman-dpyad Zla-ba'i-rgyal-po [16] in China. Among its species, *Saussurea involucrata* (SI), grown in Xinjiang, China, is particularly noteworthy and widely used in Uyghur Medicine, known as "Tage leylishi" [17]. According to the first part of the Chinese Pharmacopoeia (2020 edition), this herb is utilized in both Traditional Chinese Medicine and Uyghur Medicine to address conditions such as RA, joint pain, irregular menstruation, and excessive leucorrhea [18]. According to the current literature, SI is found to contain a variety of compounds, including phenolic acids, flavonoids, lignans, phenylpropanoids, steroids, coumarins, sesquiterpenes, ceramides, glycosides, and polysaccharides [19,20]. Ongoing studies primarily concentrate on exploring the potential therapeutic effects of its flavonoids [21,22].

In China, *Saussurea* has found extensive clinical use in the treatment of RA, available in various dosage forms such as injections, capsules, and more [23]. However, limited pharmacological studies have been conducted, with the majority of existing research focused on clinical efficacy verification. This study aims to employ network pharmacology methods to analyze the mechanism of SI in treating RA and verify the binding between its bioactive components and target proteins through molecular modeling. The findings will serve as a basis for subsequent drug development endeavors.

2. Materials and Methods

2.1. Bioactive Components of SI and Prediction of Target Genes

To ensure a comprehensive collection of the bioactive components of SI, this study conducted searches across multiple databases. The databases used included the Traditional Chinese Medicine Systems Pharmacology Database (TCMSP, tcmspw.com/tcmsp.php, accessed on 27 February 2023) [24], the Chinese Medicine and Bioactive components Database of the Shanghai Institute of Organic Chemistry (organchem.csdb.cn/scdb/default.htm, accessed on 5 April 2023) [25], and SymMap (www.symmap.org, accessed on 12 April 2023) [26]. The keyword "*Saussurea involucrata*" was employed for these searches, yielding relevant results. Furthermore, additional active ingredients were supplemented by searching the literature in the China National Knowledge Infrastructure(CNKI) [19,27,28].

The obtained components were screened based on parameters such as oral bioavailability and drug-likeness to ensure their potential for metabolism within the human body. For the query results from the SymMap database, components with an oral bioavailability (OB) threshold of $\geq$30% were selected [26]. These selected components, along with the components obtained from literature searches, were used to query the PubChem database (pubchem.ncbi.nlm.nih.gov, accessed on 12 April 2023) using the pubchempy Python toolkit, acquiring the Simplified Molecular Input Line Entry System (SMILES) notations.

These notations were then imported into the SwissADME database (www.swissadme.ch, accessed on 16 April 2023) and subjected to screening based on criteria such as a gastrointestinal absorption (GI) rating of "High" and drug-likeness having two or more items marked as "Yes" [29]. Subsequently, the screened components were combined with the components directly obtained from the TCMSP database and underwent a further screening within TCMSP according to the standards of an oral bioavailability (OB) threshold of $\geq$30%, a drug-likeness (DL) threshold of $\geq$0.18, and a Caco-2 permeability threshold of ≥ -0.4 [30,31]. Finally, all the screened components were compiled, and any duplicate entries were removed.

For the components queried from the TCMSP, their targets were also obtained from this database, and their gene names were queried from the Uniprot database (www.uniprot.org, accessed on 27 February 2023). For other components, their SMILES were input into SwissTargetPrediction (swisstargetprediction.ch, accessed on 16 April 2023) with the species attribute set to "Homo sapiens" for target prediction, and targets with a probability greater than 0 were collected [32]. Finally, all component targets were summarized and deduplicated.

2.2. Target Genes of RA

Disease targets were collected through searches across multiple databases. The DisGeNet database (www.disgenet.org, accessed on 6 April 2023) was queried using the keyword "rheumatoid arthritis", and disease-related target genes were obtained by applying a screening criterion of Score $\geq$ 0.3 [33]. Similarly, the GeneCards database (www.genecards.org, accessed on 27 February 2023) was queried, and data with a Relevance score > 10 were selected [34]. Furthermore, the OMIM database (Online Mendelian Inheritance in Man, www.omim.org/search/advanced/geneMap, accessed on 13 April 2023) and the TTD database (Therapeutic Target Database, db.idrblab.net/ttd, accessed on 14 April 2023) were employed to query targets associated with RA [35]. Subsequently, all the retrieved results were compiled, summarized, and deduplicated to create the disease target library.

2.3. Protein–Protein Interaction (PPI) Network Analysis

Components exert their effects on the disease by targeting specific genes. The target genes for both the components and the disease were inputted into the Bioinformatics website (www.bioinformatics.com.cn, accessed on 17 May 2023) to generate a Venn diagram [36], obtaining the intersection of targets.

In order to elucidate the relationships among target proteins and further refine key targets, the intersecting target genes were inputted into the STRING database (string-db.org, accessed on 17 May 2023) with a confidence level set at >0.9, and the species selected as H. sapiens (human) [37]. Based on this, the PPI network was constructed. The results were then imported into Cytoscape 3.9.1 software, of which, the CytoNCA plugin was utilized to calculate various centrality metrics for each node, including betweenness centrality (BC), closeness centrality (CC), degree centrality (DC), eigenvector centrality (EC), local average connectivity-based method centrality (LAC), and network centrality (NC) [38]. The median values of each centrality metric were employed as the screening criteria, and target proteins surpassing or equaling these median values across all indicators were identified as key targets for this study.

2.4. Gene Ontology and Pathway Analysis

The key targets were uploaded to the Bioinformatics website for Gene Ontology (GO) and Kyoto Encyclopedia of Genes and Genomes (KEGG) analysis. The results were subjected to screening based on the criterion of *p.adjust* < 0.05 [39], and subsequently plotted using the Count, *p.adjust*, and GeneRatio values. As for the GO analysis results, they were sorted and visualized separately for the cellular component (CC), molecular function (MF), and biological process (BP) categories.

2.5. Network Visualization

Information such as component–target, disease–target, drug–component, pathway–target, function–target, etc., were summarized and imported into Cytoscape for network visualization, to construct their relationship network. Then, network analysis was performed using the network analysis function [37], and according to the obtained degree, 10 components and 10 targets with a higher ranking were selected as core components and core targets.

2.6. Molecular Docking

The core targets were searched in the RCSB PDB database (RCSB Protein Data Bank, www.rcsb.org, accessed on 18 May 2023) to retrieve structures with species as H. sapiens and a resolution of less than or equal to 2.5 Å. The structures were selected based on parameters such as Gene Name, Resolution (Å), ligand, R-Value, pH, Experimental Method, Publication Year, etc. [40]. Priority was given to structures containing similar ligands, with particular attention paid to structures with higher resolution, pH conditions closely resembling the human body environment, and more recent publication years. For each target, one structure was chosen and downloaded.

The downloaded protein structure was refined using Swiss-PdbViewer 4.1.0 [41], remove water and ligands with Pymol, and then imported into AutoDockTools for receptor preparation [42], which involved operations such as hydrogen addition and charge assignment. The structures of the core components were obtained from the PubChem database, and initial conformations for each compound were established by energy minimization using the MM2 force field in Chem3D 14.0 software [42]. After converting these files into appropriate formats, they were imported into AutoDockTools for ligand preparation.

To determine the position and size of the Grid Box, priority was given to the original ligand positions within the structures, taking into account the target position descriptions from the Uniprot database. In the case of structures without their own ligands, the Deepsite tool (www.playmolecule.com/deepsite, accessed on 28 May 2023) [43] on the PlayMolecule website was utilized for docking pocket prediction. The position and size of the grid box were determined based on the pocket scores and the 3D structure observations. Finally, AutoDock Vina 1.1.2 [42] was employed to perform molecular docking on a total of 100 receptor–ligand combinations. Each combination yielded 10 conformations along with binding energy results.

2.7. Molecular Dynamics (MD) Simulation

The well-combined target protein–ligand complex was selected from the molecular docking results, and MD simulations were performed using Gromacs 2023.2. For protein molecules, Charmm36 force field and TIP3P water model were chosen for processing [44]. Ligand conformations with good docking affinity were imported into Avogadro 1.2.0 to add hydrogens and format conversion. Then, the Sobtop tool (Tian Lu, Sobtop, Version 1.0 (dev3.1), http://sobereva.com/soft/Sobtop, accessed on 4 September 2023) was used to generate topology files with the GAFF force field. The receptor–ligand complex was subjected to solvation, ion balance and energy minimization. In order to simulate the human body environment, the ion concentration was set at 0.145 M when adding ions, and the MD simulation of the system was carried out at a temperature of 310 K and a pressure of 1 bar for 50 ns. The cut-off value of the non-bonded interaction was set to 1.2 nm, and the long-distance electrostatic interaction was calculated [45]. Energy calculations were carried out on complexes that exhibit favorable results in MD simulations using the gmx_mmpbsa.py [46] and gmx_mmpbsa script of gmxtool (Jicun Li, gmx_mmpbsa.bsh, DOI 10.5281/zenodo.6408973, accessed 15 September 2023).

3. Results

3.1. Bioactive Components and Key Targets

After the above component-mining, a total of 27 components of SI were obtained (Table 1), corresponding to 665 non-redundant targets. For disease targets, a total of 593 disease-related targets were obtained from four databases. By analyzing the Venn diagram, 119 intersection targets were identified, representing the overlapping targets between the component targets and the disease targets (Figure 1).

Table 1. Bioactive components of SI.

No.	Name	Molecular Formula	Molecular Weight	PubChem CID
1	Dinatin	$C_{16}H_{12}O_6$	300.26	5281628
2	Alloisoimperatorin	$C_{16}H_{14}O_4$	270.28	5317436
3	Beta-Sitosterol	$C_{29}H_{50}O$	414.70	222284
4	Kaempferol	$C_{15}H_{10}O_6$	286.24	5280863
5	Luteolin	$C_{15}H_{10}O_6$	286.24	5280445
6	Flazin	$C_{17}H_{12}N_2O_4$	308.29	5377686
7	Quercetin	$C_{15}H_{10}O_7$	302.23	5280343
8	Involucratin	$C_{20}H_{27}NO_4$	345.40	15628146
9	Guaianolide	$C_{14}H_{20}O_3$	236.31	-
10	Eriodictyol	$C_{15}H_{12}O_6$	288.25	440735
11	Hispidulin	$C_{16}H_{12}O_6$	300.26	5281628
12	Methyl Caffeate Acid	$C_{10}H_{10}O_4$	194.18	689075
13	Cinnamic Acid	$C_9H_8O_2$	148.16	444539
14	Hexadecanoic Acid	$C_{16}H_{32}O_2$	256.42	985
15	1-Monolinolein	$C_{21}H_{38}O_4$	354.50	6256628
16	(2S,3S,4R)-2-Aminoicosane-1,3,4-Triol	$C_{20}H_{43}NO_3$	345.60	12302752
17	Moslosooflavone	$C_{17}H_{14}O_5$	298.29	188316
18	Mosloflavone	$C_{17}H_{14}O_5$	298.29	471722
19	5,6-Dihydroxy-7,8-Dimethoxyflavone	$C_{17}H_{14}O_6$	314.29	821356
20	D-3-Phenyllactic Acid	$C_9H_{10}O_3$	166.17	643327
21	Alisol C	$C_{30}H_{46}O_5$	486.70	101306923
22	Alisol C Monoacetate	$C_{32}H_{48}O_6$	528.70	14036813
23	(E)-P-Coumaroylagmatine(1+)	$C_{14}H_{21}N_4O_2^+$	277.34	25245514
24	Alisol B	$C_{30}H_{48}O_4$	472.70	15558620
25	Acacetin	$C_{16}H_{12}O_5$	284.26	5280442
26	Oroselol	$C_{14}H_{12}O_4$	244.24	160600
27	Xuelianlactone	$C_{15}H_{20}O_3$	248.32	147111

3.2. PPI Network Analysis

Figure 2 presents the results of PPI analysis, revealing the interactions between target proteins. The significance of a target protein is determined by the number of interactions it has with other proteins. Based on the network analysis conducted in Cytoscape, a total of 33 key targets were identified (Table 2). These key targets play crucial roles in the network and are considered important in this study.

3.3. KEGG Pathway Enrichment Analysis

The key targets were input into the Bioinformatics website and, after screening, a total of 131 pathways with *p.adjust* < 0.05 were obtained. Among these pathways, the top 20 pathways with the smallest *p.adjust* values were selected and presented in Figure 3. The color in the plot transitions from green to red, indicating an increasing level of significance. Furthermore, the size of each circle corresponds to the number of genes enriched within the respective pathway. Larger circles signify a higher gene enrichment count.

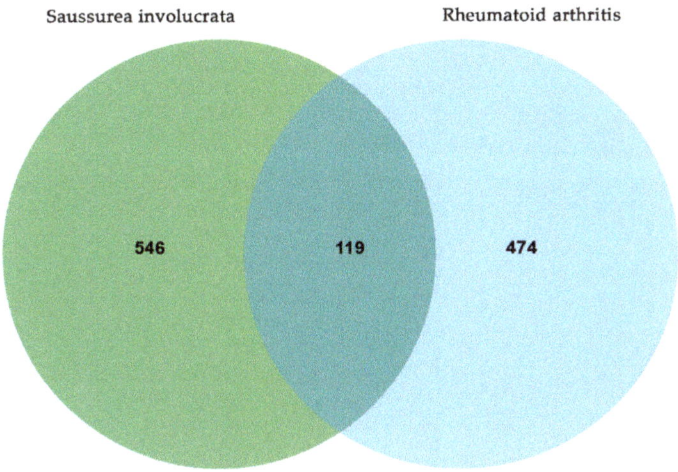

Figure 1. Common targets of SI and RA.

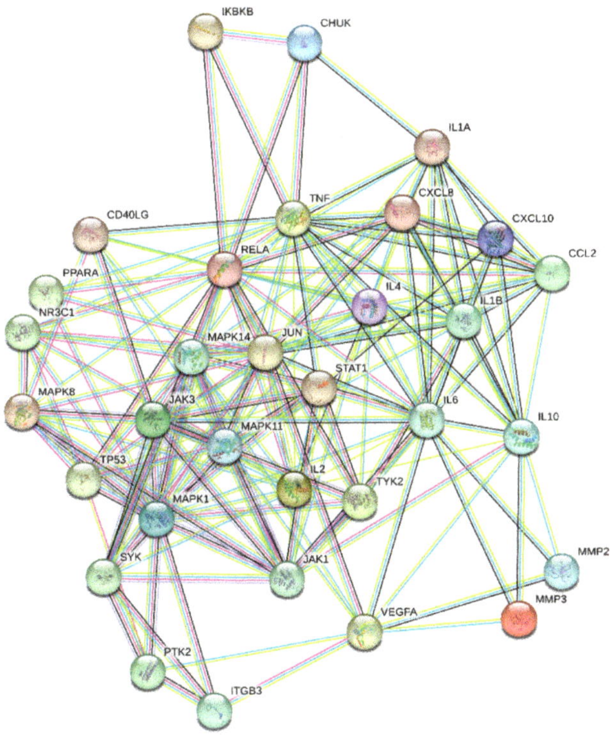

Figure 2. Protein–Protein Interaction Network.

Table 2. List of Key Targets.

No.	Gene Symbol	Gene ID	Gene Name
1	TNF	7124	Tumor necrosis factor
2	RELA	5970	Transcription factor p65
3	IL6	3569	Interleukin-6
4	JUN	3725	Proto-oncogene c-JUN
5	MAPK1	5594	Mitogen-activated protein kinase 1
6	MAPK14	1432	MAP kinase p38 alpha
7	IL10	3586	Interleukin-10
8	IL1B	3553	Interleukin-1 beta
9	CCL2	6347	C-C motif chemokine 2
10	IL4	3565	Interleukin-4
11	IL2	3558	Interleukin-2
12	STAT1	6772	Signal transducer and activator of transcription 1-alpha/beta
13	CXCL8	3576	Interleukin-8
14	IL1A	3552	Interleukin-1 alpha
15	JAK1	3716	Tyrosine-protein kinase JAK1
16	CXCL10	3627	C-X-C motif chemokine 10
17	NFKBIA	4792	NF-kappa-B inhibitor alpha
18	JAK3	3718	Tyrosine-protein kinase JAK3
19	TP53	7157	Cellular tumor antigen p53
20	VEGFA	7422	Vascular endothelial growth factor A
21	MAPK11	5600	MAP kinase p38 beta
22	TYK2	7297	Tyrosine-protein kinase TYK2
23	MAPK8	5599	Mitogen-activated protein kinase 8
24	ITGB3	3690	Integrin alpha-2/beta-3
25	NR3C1	2908	Glucocorticoid receptor
26	PPARA	5465	Peroxisome proliferator-activated receptor alpha
27	PTK2	5747	Focal adhesion kinase 1
28	CHUK	1147	Inhibitor of nuclear factor kappa-B kinase subunit alpha
29	IKBKB	3551	Inhibitor of nuclear factor kappa-B kinase subunit beta
30	MMP3	4314	Stromelysin-1
31	MMP2	4313	72 kDa type IV collagenase
32	CD40LG	959	CD40 ligand
33	SYK	6850	Tyrosine-protein kinase SYK

3.4. GO Enrichment Analysis

Based on the output results from the Bioinformatics website, the findings were categorized into three groups, as shown in Figure 4. In both the MF and BP analyses, multiple results met the criteria of *p.adjust* < 0.05. The top 10 results with the smallest *p.adjust* values were selected for plotting. As for the CC analysis, only four results met the requirements, and all of them were included in the plot. The plot exhibits a color gradient shifting from blue to red, indicating an increasing level of significance. Additionally, the length of each bar corresponds to the number of genes enriched within the specific category, with longer bars signifying a higher gene enrichment count.

3.5. Network Constructions and Analysis

Information such as bioactive components, key targets, related pathways, and the functions obtained above was formatted in a network diagram using Cytoscape software (Figure 5). In the diagram, green circles represent the bioactive components present in SI, which intersect with RA-related targets. The intersection results are depicted by blue squares. Among them, the inner two circles represent the 33 key targets identified through network analysis, while the innermost circle represents the 10 core targets selected for molecular docking. Yellow hexagons represent the top 20 pathways obtained from the key target analysis. At the bottom of the diagram, three distinct groups illustrate the results of the GO analysis. Purple, orange, and red represent the BP, CC, and MF analysis results, respectively. This comprehensive analysis unveils the intrinsic correlation between the bioactive components of SI and their potential in treating RA.

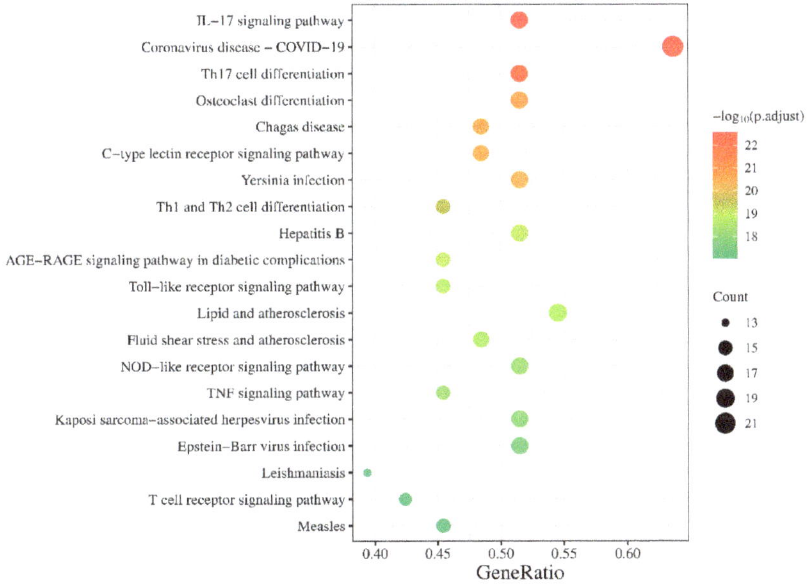

Figure 3. KEGG pathway enrichment analysis.

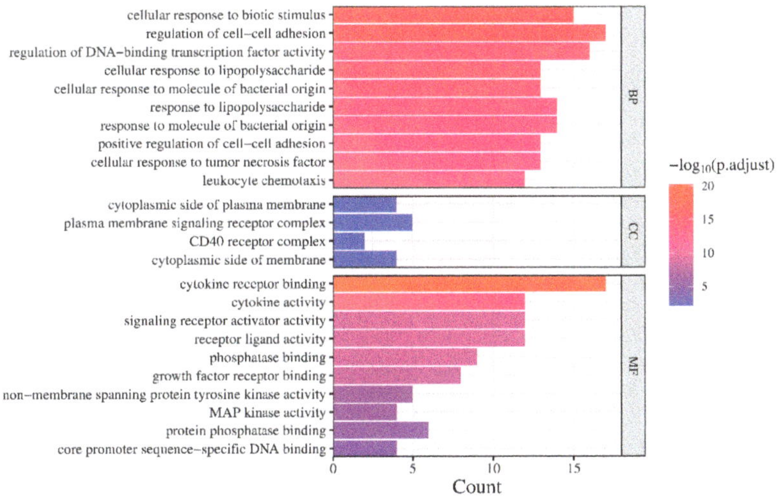

Figure 4. GO enrichment analysis.

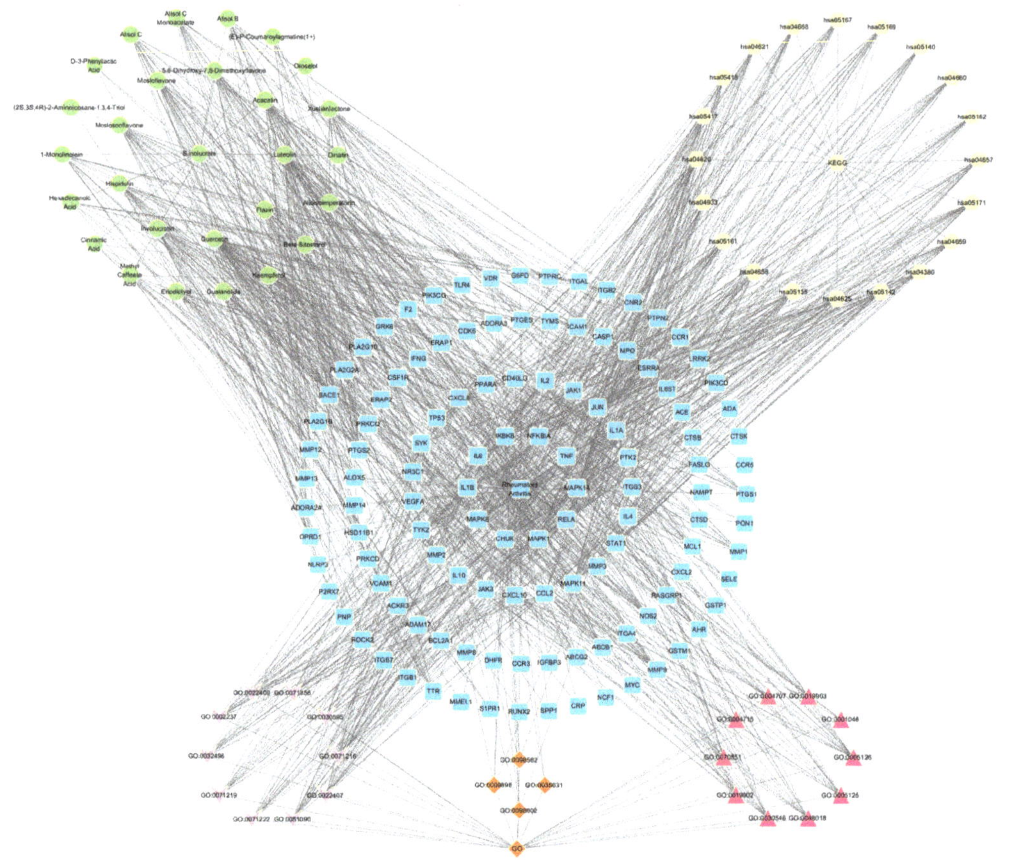

Figure 5. Network Analysis.

3.6. Molecular Docking

According to the network analysis results of Cytoscape, 10 compounds with the highest degree values, Quercetin, Luteolin, Acacetin, Xuelianlactone, Moslosooflavone, Hispidulin, Mosloflavone, Involucratin, 5,7-Dihydroxy-6,8-Dimethoxyflavone and Flazin were selected as molecular docking ligands (core components). Ten targets with the highest degree values, MAPK14, MAPK1, RELA, TNF, MAPK8, IL6, IL1B, CHUK, IKBKB and NFKBIA, were selected as the core targets for molecular docking. Nine protein structures were selected as the receptors, with CHUK and IKBKB targets located in different segments of the same protein structure (Table 3). The results of the molecular docking were visualized in the form of a heat map (Figure 6), where the color gradient shifting from red to blue indicates a decrease in affinity. Lower binding energy signifies a better binding activity between the ligand and receptor protein. In general, affinity values > −5 kcal/mol indicate no predicted binding, affinity < −5 kcal/mol suggests moderate predicted binding, and affinity < −7 kcal/mol suggests strong predicted binding [47]. In this section, all the selected ligands and receptors demonstrated excellent binding activity, as the lowest binding energy with the best ligand for each receptor was less than −7 kcal/mol. Notably, Xuelianlactone demonstrates the lowest affinity at −10.01 kcal/mol. In addition, the docking results of MAPK1, MAPK8, and TNF showed significantly lower binding affinities compared to the other targets ($p < 0.05$). However, the binding effect of IL6, ILB, CHUK, and IKBKB to each ligand is not outstanding.

Table 3. Core components.

No.	Ingredients	Degree
1	Quercetin	60
2	Luteolin	43
3	Acacetin	33
4	Xuelianlactone	26
5	Moslosooflavone	25
6	Hispidulin	24
7	Mosloflavone	24
8	Involucratin	23
9	5,6-Dihydroxy-7,8-Dimethoxyflavone	23
10	Flazin	21

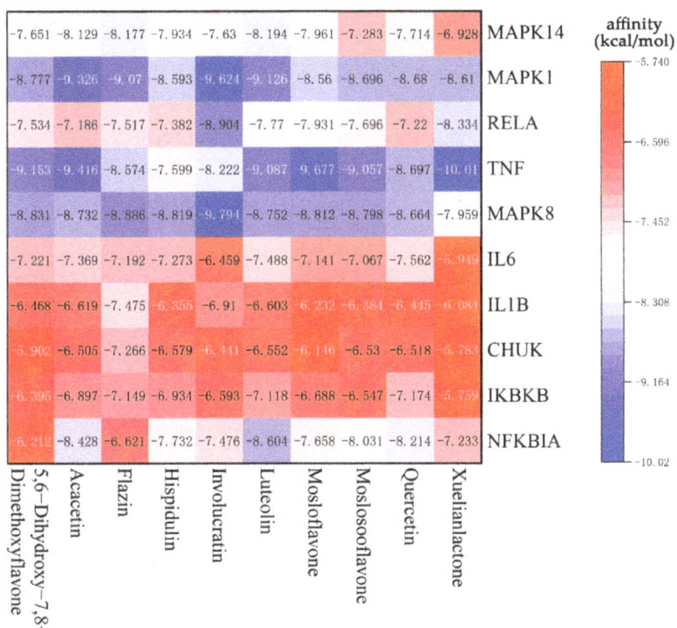

Figure 6. Heat map of lowest binding energy in molecular docking.

For each target protein, the ligand with the lowest affinity was selected from the molecular docking results. Visualization was achieved using Biovia Discovery Studio 2021 software, and the docking results are presented in Table 4 and Figure 7.

3.7. Molecular Dynamics Simulation

Based on the degree values obtained in network analysis and molecular docking results, the following study primarily focuses on the MAPK1 and TNF. For both targets, the top four compounds with the best docking results, as well as the original ligands (38Z and VGY) of the target proteins, were selected for MD simulations. In addition, for MAPK8, two compounds and the original ligand (38Z) were chosen for simulations. Considering the certainty of the target position, the simulation was conducted with NFKIBA as the representative target for the NF-κB pathway, focusing on the top two best-performing compounds based on the docking results. Table 5 and Figure 8 present the Root Mean Square Deviation (RMSD) values for each of these simulation combinations.

Table 4. Best protein–ligand complexes and their binding energies.

No.	Receptor	Degree of Receptor	Structure	Target Chain	Target Position	Ligand	Affinity (kcal/mol)
1	MAPK14	38	5WJJ	A	1–360	Luteolin	−8.194
2	MAPK1	37	4QTA	A	1–360	Involucratin	−9.624
3	RELA	35	6NV2	P	39–51	Involucratin	−8.904
4	TNF	33	7JRA	A/B/C	77–233	Xuelianlactone	−10.01
5	MAPK8	33	4QTD	A	1–363	Involucratin	−9.794
6	IL6	33	7NXZ	A	30–212	Quercetin	−7.562
7	IL1B	31	5R8Q	A	117–269	Flazin	−7.475
8	CHUK	31	3BRT	A/C	732–745	Flazin	−7.266
9	IKBKB	30	3BRT	A/C	701–730	Quercetin	−7.174
10	NFKBIA	28	1IKN	D	67–302	Luteolin	−8.604

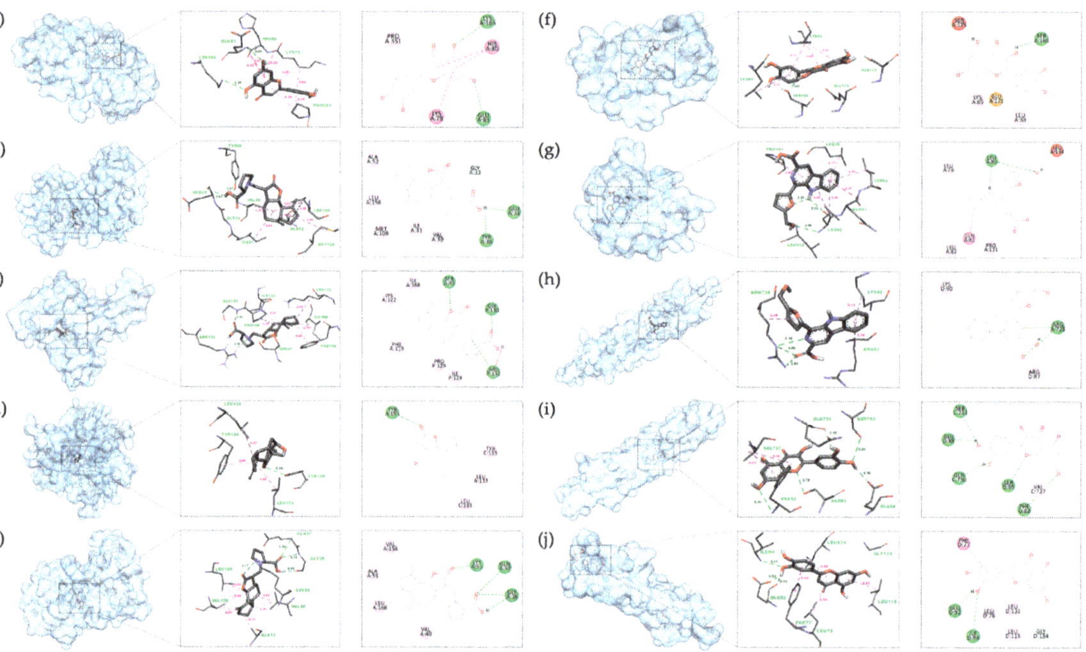

Figure 7. Molecular docking results in each target with the bioactive compound of SI: (**a**) Luteolin and MAPK14; (**b**) Involucratin and MAPK1; (**c**) Involucratin and RELA; (**d**) Xuelianlactone and TNF; (**e**) Involucratin and MAPK8; (**f**) Quercetin and IL6; (**g**) Flazin and IL1B; (**h**) Flazin and CHUK; (**i**) Quercetin and IKBKB; (**j**) Luteolin and NFKBIA. The images depict the binding positions of ligands within the protein, along with the surrounding residues, showcasing the interactions between the ligands and the residues. In this figure, pink, magenta, and purple dashed lines represent hydrophobic interactions, while the green dashed lines represent hydrogen bonds.

In MD simulations, RMSD measures the average deviation or fluctuations in atomic positions in a molecular system from their initial positions, providing insight into the stability of a target protein–ligand complex. Generally, it is considered that once the RMSD value stabilizes and the fluctuation range is less than 0.2 nm, the system can be deemed stable [48]. It can be observed that, for MAPK1, Involucratin and Luteolin reach equilibrium after about 13 ns, with smaller fluctuations than the protein's original ligand 38Z. The stabilized RMSD value for Involucratin is less than 0.4 nm, and both compounds exhibit fluctuations below 0.2 nm after stabilization. For TNF, the RMSD values for all analyzed compounds remain below 0.4 nm, with fluctuations below 0.2 nm for all except Mosloflavone. Among them, Xuelianlactone and Acacetin demonstrate the highest stability. Regarding MAPK8, the original ligand 38Z exhibits a low RMSD value, but shows significant fluctuations towards the end of the simulation. On the other hand, Flazin maintains an RMSD of 0.39, with fluctuations also within the 0.2 nm range. As for NFKIBA, both selected ligand Luteolin and Acacetin display higher overall fluctuations. In the last 5 ns, their RMSDs tend to stabilize, with fluctuations smaller than 0.2 nm. However, compared to other complexes, their stability remains poor, and thus, they cannot be considered to have achieved stable binding. Based on this, further analysis will be conducted of the following compounds: Involucratin and Luteolin for MAPK1, Xuelianlactone and Acacetin for TNF, and Flazin for MAPK8.

Table 5. The Average RMSD values for each target protein–ligand complex.

Target			MAPK1		
Compounds	38Z	Acacetin	Flazin	Involucratin	Luteolin
RMSD Average (nm)	0.567 ± 0.162	0.940 ± 0.290	0.455 ± 0.139	0.346 ± 0.048	0.650 ± 0.112
Target			TNF		
Compounds	VGY	Xuelianlactone	5,6-Dihydroxy-7,8-Dimethoxyflavone	Mosloflavone	Acacetin
RMSD Average (nm)	0.235 ± 0.049	0.295 ± 0.022	0.205 ± 0.040	0.155 ± 0.060	0.175 ± 0.034
Target		MAPK8		NFKIBA	
Compounds	38Z	Involucratin	Flazin	Luteolin	Acacetin
RMSD Average (nm)	0.251 ± 0.091	0.862 ± 0.160	0.390 ± 0.049	0.698 ± 0.199	0.686 ± 0.132

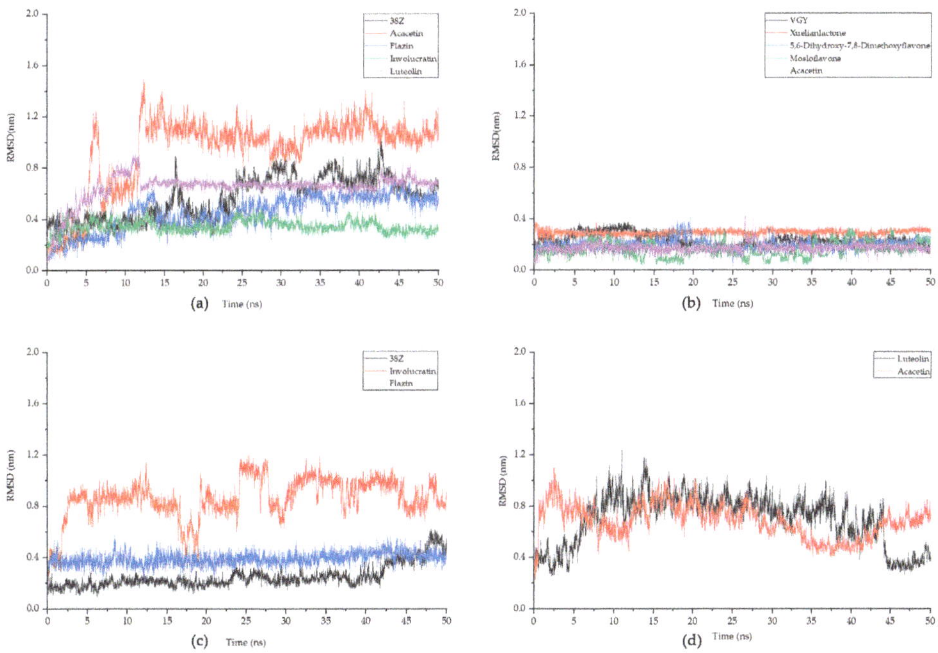

Figure 8. The fluctuation plot of the target protein–ligand complexes RMSD. (**a**) MAPK1, (**b**) TNF, (**c**) MAPK8, (**d**) NFKIBA. 38Z is the original ligand for MAPK1 and MAPK8, while VGY is for TNF, and NFKIBA does not have an original ligand.

Solvent-Accessible Surface Area (SASA) quantifies the surface area of a molecule that is accessible to solvent molecules and can indicate changes in a molecule's conformation or exposure during simulation, aiding in the assessment of binding interactions in a target protein–ligand complex. The average SASA values for complexes XT (black), AT (red), IM (blue), LM (green), and FM (purple) during MD simulation are as follows: 202.49 ± 3.72, 201.65 ± 3.17, 179.03 ± 3.25, 175.97 ± 2.59, and 179.9 ± 2.9 nm^2. Throughout the entire simulation process, the SASA values of these compounds show small fluctuations, indicating their stable interaction with the protein complexes (Figure 9).

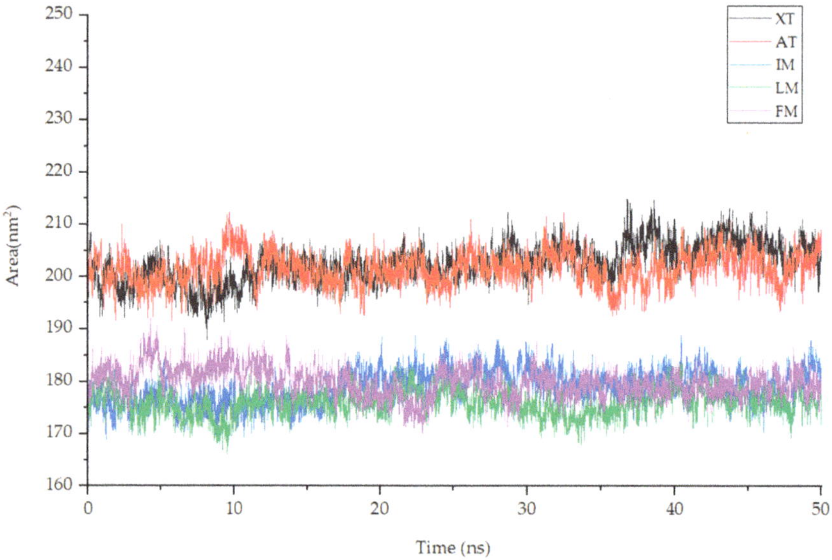

Figure 9. The fluctuation plot of the target protein–ligand complexes SASA. **Note:** XT: Xuelianlactone-TNF(7JRA), AT: Acacetin-TNF(7JRA), IM: Involucratin-MAPK1(4QTA), LM: Luteolin-MAPK1(4QTA), FM: Flazin-MAPK8(4QTD).

Molecular Mechanics–Poisson Boltzmann Surface Area (MMPBSA) is a method used to estimate the binding energy of a target protein–ligand complex by post-processing the MD trajectory. MMPBSA can characterize the strength and stability of the protein–ligand interaction by calculating the difference between the free energy of the bound state and the free energy of the unbound state. For the five complexes mentioned above, we selected segments with stable RMSD values and extracted 10 ns trajectories for MMPBSA energy analysis. The total binding energy (ΔG) is the sum of the change in enthalpy (ΔH) and the change in entropy ($-T\Delta S$) [49]. Using gmx_mmpbsa.py with a time interval of 10 ps, the total energy difference (ΔG_{total}) between the ligand, receptor and their respective complexes in the stable phase of MD simulation was calculated, as shown in Figure 10. It can be seen from the figure that the ΔG_{total} curves of each compound have small fluctuations, and the average is below −10 kcal/mol. Furthermore, by utilizing the gmx_mmpbsa.bsh script, the entropy change in each complex is calculated at a time interval of 1000 ps, allowing for the calculation of the total binding energy (ΔG). Table 6 presents the contributions of the Van der Waals force (VDW), coulomb interaction energy (COU), molecular mechanics (MM), polar solvation energy (PB) and nonpolar solvation energy (SA). The ΔH calculated by gmx_mmpbsa.bsh closely aligns with the ΔG_{total} computed using gmx_mmpbsa.py. The results from both methods exhibit a close resemblance, which enhances the credibility of the computed free energy values. It can be observed from the figure and the table that ΔG and ΔH for XT are significantly lower than that of the other ligands, consistent with the results observed in molecular docking.

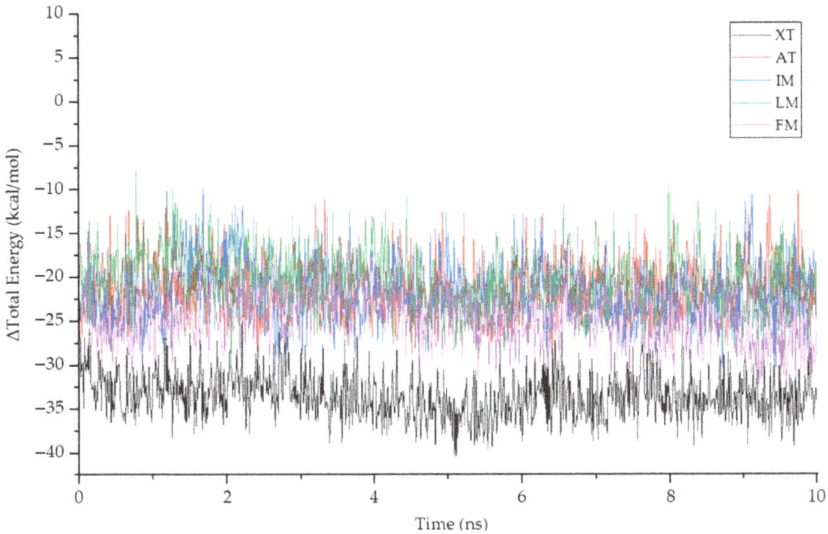

Figure 10. The fluctuation plot of the target protein–ligand complexes ΔH.

Table 6. The ΔG of each complex and the contributions of individual energy components(kcal/mol).

Complex	Contribution							
	ΔG	−TΔS	ΔH	MM	PB	SA	COU	VDW
XT	−30.03	5.35	−35.38	−45.34	14.48	−4.53	−3.20	−42.13
AT	−23.42	1.73	−25.15	−41.16	21.43	−5.42	−5.74	−35.42
IM	−11.96	3.69	−15.65	−45.88	35.93	−5.71	−9.88	−35.99
LM	−10.99	3.74	−14.73	−43.06	33.36	−5.03	−10.11	−32.95
FM	−22.00	2.89	−24.89	−43.49	23.80	−5.20	−5.47	−38.02

Note: In this table, MM is the sum of VDW and COU, while ΔH is the sum of MM, PB, and SA.

This study investigated the binding free energy and residue contributions of active components of SI to the RA target using methods such as MD simulations and MMPBSA energy calculations. As shown in Figure 11, among the four complexes, Van der Waals forces have the most significant impact in promoting protein–ligand binding, while nonpolar solvation energy has a relatively weaker influence on binding affinity. On the other hand, polar solvation energy strongly impedes the formation of the complexes. Specifically, for the MAPK1 target, we compared the results of MD simulations for the IM and LM complexes and identified four residues (36, 39, 156, and 166) that played important roles in both complexes. In the LM complex, the sum of the ΔH values for these four residues accounted for 42.9% of the total ΔH. The maximum resistance to binding was observed from residues such as 54, 151, 153, and 167, but it was insufficient to offset the binding energy. For the TNF target, in both the XT and AT complexes, four residues (133, 135, 231, and 233) made significant contributions to the binding free energy. In the AT complex, the sum of the ΔH values for these four residues accounted for 43.0% of the total ΔH, while the maximum resistance to binding came from residues 174 and 195, although their impact was relatively small, with residue 174 contributing only 0.687 kJ/mol to ΔH. Compared to complexes IM and LM, complexes AT and XT exhibit higher binding energy contributions from residues and a lower binding resistance. This observation aligns with what is reflected in the RMSD curves.

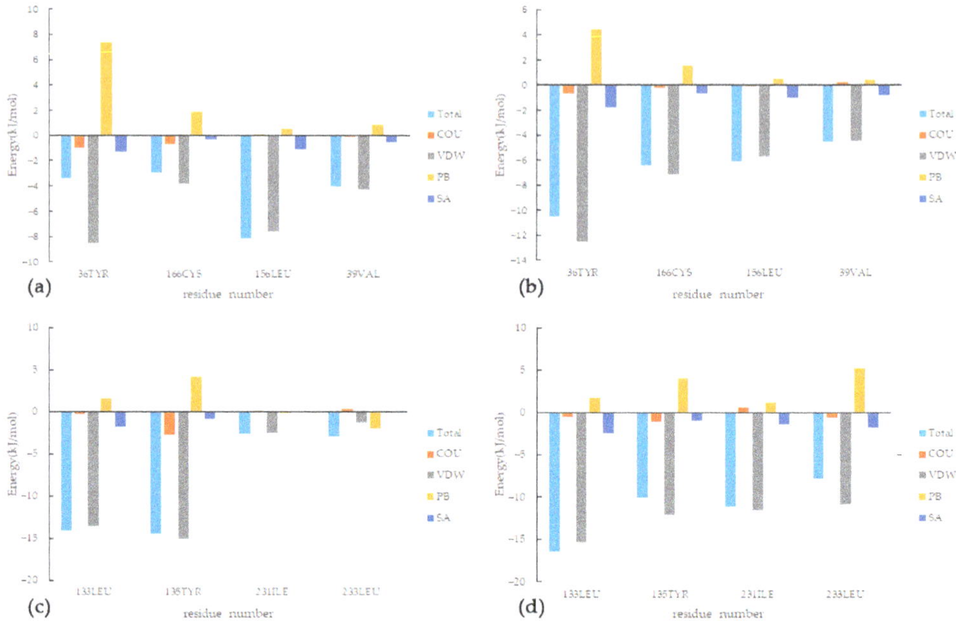

Figure 11. Energy decomposition of key residues: (**a**) IM, (**b**) LM, (**c**) XT, (**d**) AT.

The analysis of residue interactions with different ligands targeting the same receptor reveals crucial regions that facilitate complex binding. In future drug design efforts, it is essential to pay attention to the contributions of these residues. This can be achieved by introducing functional groups or optimizing their molecular spatial structures, aiming to retain residues with strong binding forces and reduce the impact of residues with significant resistance [50].

4. Discussion

In this study, we employed network pharmacology to analyze SI, resulting in the identification of 27 bioactive components and 119 targets that intersect with RA. Among these targets, 33 were identified as key targets. Additionally, we conducted KEGG and GO analyses to investigate the pathways and biological processes involved. The findings suggest a potential correlation between the components present in SI and the treatment of RA.

Among the core targets, ERK (MAPK1), JNK (MAPK8), and p38 MAPK (MAPK14) are well-defined families of MAPKs, activated by phosphorylation, and play significant roles in the inflammatory and destructive mechanisms observed in rheumatoid arthritis, including regulating pro-inflammatory cytokine production and mediating downstream signaling from IL-1, IL-17, and TNF-α receptors. These properties make them attractive therapeutic targets for rheumatic diseases [51,52]. RELA, NFKBIA, CHUK, and IKBKB are associated with the NF-κB pathway. CHUK and IKBKB serve as different catalytic subunits of the IκB kinase (IKK) complex [53,54]. Highly activated NF-κB induces the production of pro-inflammatory cytokines, including TNF-α, IL-1β, and IL-6, accelerating RA progression. The upregulation of these cytokines also triggers positive feedback, regulating NF-κB activation, and forming a vicious cycle that worsens RA development [52]. Among these targets, MAPK targets exhibit a higher degree of centrality in network analysis. According to molecular docking results, both MAPK1 and MAPK8 demonstrate prominent binding efficiency with all core components. Therefore, MAPK targets play a crucial role in the process of treating RA with IS. Regarding NF-κB-related targets, their network analysis shows lower degree centrality rankings, and taking NFKIBA as an example, the results of molecular dynamics simulations fail to confirm its stable binding. Therefore, it can be inferred that the active components of SI have a weaker effect on these targets.

From a pathway perspective, the pathways exhibiting high gene enrichment and confidence levels include IL-17, TNF, TLR (Toll-like receptor), NLR (NOD-like receptor), and CLR (C-type lectin receptor) signaling pathways, as well as Th17, Th1, and Th2 cell differentiation pathways, among which the IL-17 and Th17 pathways are the most confident. Interactions between RA, Fibroblast-Like Synoviocytes (FLSs), and Th17 cells further contribute to tumorous FLS growth and joint pannus formation [55]. Previous research has identified IL-17 as a potential therapeutic target for RA, leading to several trials being conducted [56,57]. There is also considerable confidence in the osteoclast (OC) differentiation pathway, which plays a key role in the pathological bone destruction observed in RA. Pro-inflammatory cytokines, including TNF, IL-1 and IL-17, induce OC maturation and differentiation through different signaling pathways such as NF-κB [58]. This highlights the dual therapeutic role of SI, not only targeting the inflammatory symptoms of RA but also reducing bone destruction.

The GO analysis primarily centers on responses to biotic stimuli, specifically lipopolysaccharides and other molecules of bacterial origin, known to trigger immune and inflammatory responses. Previous research has indicated that bacterial infection plays a significant role in contributing to RA pathogenesis [59]. The pathways showing the highest enrichment, such as Coronavirus disease, Chagas disease, and Yersinia infection, further reinforce this notion, as they are involved in immune responses to viruses, parasites, and bacteria. In terms of molecular function analysis, the active components primarily influence functions related to binding activities, such as cytokine receptor binding, growth factor receptor binding, and phosphatase binding, while also affecting cytokine activity and receptor ligand activity. This suggests that these components may modulate processes like phosphorylation within the pathways by binding to specific targets, thereby inhibiting excessive immune responses and achieving therapeutic effects. Additionally, in the biological process analysis, certain processes are associated with the regulation of cell–cell adhesion. Adhesion molecules are important regulators of leukocyte recruitment into the synovial tissue [60], while Leukocytes, which are aberrantly recruited and activated, are characteristic features of rheumatoid arthritis (RA), as they migrate out of the blood, cross the endothelium, and infiltrate inflamed tissues, triggering a cascade of pathological processes, particularly in the early stages of the disease [61].

Based on the above analysis results, components Luteolin, Involucratin, Xuelianlactone, Flazin, Quercetin, and Acacetin, all belonging to the flavonoid class, exhibit favorable binding effects with the targets. Quercetin exerted a bone-protective effect by reducing MMPs, RANKL production, and osteoclast formation via the MAPKs and NF-κB pathways [62]. Current animal model studies have demonstrated the effectiveness of quercetin in treating RA [63]. Some studies suggest that Luteolin can inhibit the proliferation and affect the function of stimulated rat synovial fibroblasts [64]. Furthermore, it has the ability to suppress the IL-1β-induced production of cytokines and MMPs, which are crucial in tissue degradation in rheumatoid synovium, through the activation of p38 MAPK, JNK, NF-κB, and AP-1 [65]. Acacetin inhibits p38 and JNK phosphorylation and reduces MMP-1, MMP-3, and MMP-13 expression in IL-1β-induced FLSs, suggesting that Acacetin has antiarthritic effects in FLSs [66]. In addition, it has been shown to inhibit the activation of NF-κB by stimulation with TNF-α [67]. Moreover, this study reveals the significant roles of Involucratin, Xuelianlactone, and Flazin in the process of treating RA with SI. Among all complexes, Xuelianlactone exhibits the best binding efficiency with the TNF target, displaying the lowest binding energy in both molecular docking and MD simulations, along with good binding stability. Involucratin, on the other hand, stands out in the molecular docking results, showing the lowest binding energy among ligands binding to MAPK1, MAPK8, and RELA. Flazin also demonstrates strong binding abilities with MAPK8 in MD simulations. Considering the limited number of related studies conducted on these compounds to date, they represent potential new research avenues for the development of RA treatment drugs in the future.

5. Conclusions

In summary, the network pharmacology analysis suggests that the mechanism of SI in treating RA mainly involves its flavonoids, which target key proteins through MAPK and NF-κB-related pathways. By doing so, they effectively inhibit inflammation and mitigate bone destruction, leading to therapeutic effects. The binding efficiency of complexes like XT, AT, and FM has been confirmed through MD simulations. This suggests that the action of SI in treating RA is achieved through multiple components acting on various targets. However, it is essential to note that network pharmacology is primarily a data-driven and network-based research method. Therefore, these findings should be further validated and supported by experimental studies to establish their clinical relevance and potential as RA treatment options.

Author Contributions: Methodology, J.C.; Formal analysis, J.C.; Data curation, J.C.; Writing–original draft, J.C.; Writing–review & editing, J.C., X.W. and R.Y.; Supervision, R.Y.; Project administration, R.Y.; Funding acquisition, R.Y. All authors have read and agreed to the published version of the manuscript.

Funding: This research was funded by Qinghai Provincial Natural Science Foundation General Project (Grant Number: 2022-ZJ-930), and Qinghai Provincial Key Laboratory of Tibetan Medicine Research Innovation Platform Development Special Project (Grant Number: 2022-ZJ-Y03).

Institutional Review Board Statement: Not applicable.

Informed Consent Statement: Not applicable.

Data Availability Statement: The original data are available upon reasonable request to the corresponding author.

Conflicts of Interest: The authors declare no conflict of interest.

References

1. Almutairi, K.; Nossent, J.; Preen, D.; Keen, H.; Inderjeeth, C. The global prevalence of rheumatoid arthritis: A meta-analysis based on a systematic review. *Rheumatol. Int.* **2021**, *41*, 863–877. [CrossRef] [PubMed]
2. Zeng, X.; Zhu, S.; Tan, A.; Xie, X. Disease burden and quality of life of rheumatoid arthritis in China: A systematic review. *Chin. J. Evid. Based Med.* **2013**, *13*, 300–307. [CrossRef]
3. Zeng, X.; Tian, X.; Li, M. *China Rheumatoid Arthritis Development Report 2020*; Liaoning Science and Technology Press: Shenyang, China, 2021.
4. Tian, X.; Wang, Q.; Li, M.; Zhao, Y.; Zhang, Z.; Huang, C.; Liu, Y.; Xu, H.; Chen, Y.; Wu, L. 2018 Chinese guidelines for the diagnosis and treatment of rheumatoid arthritis. *Rheumatol. Immunol. Res.* **2021**, *2*, 1–14. [CrossRef] [PubMed]
5. van Vollenhoven, R.F. Sex differences in rheumatoid arthritis: More than meets the eye. *BMC Med.* **2009**, *7*, 12.
6. Goemaere, S.; Ackerman, C.; Goethals, K.; De Keyser, F.; Van der Straeten, C.; Verbruggen, G.; Mielants, H.; Veys, E. Onset of symptoms of rheumatoid arthritis in relation to age, sex and menopausal transition. *J. Rheumatol.* **1990**, *17*, 1620–1622. [CrossRef]
7. Hitchon, C.A.; El-Gabalawy, H.S. Infection and rheumatoid arthritis: Still an open question. *Curr. Opin. Rheumatol.* **2011**, *23*, 352–357. [CrossRef]
8. Jiang, X.; Alfredsson, L. Modifiable environmental exposure and risk of rheumatoid arthritis—Current evidence from genetic studies. *Arthritis Res. Ther.* **2020**, *22*, 154. [CrossRef]
9. Wu, D.; Luo, Y.; Li, T.; Zhao, X.; Lv, T.; Fang, G.; Ou, P.; Li, H.; Luo, X.; Huang, A. Systemic complications of rheumatoid arthritis: Focus on pathogenesis and treatment. *Front. Immunol.* **2022**, *13*, 1051082. [CrossRef]
10. Zhang, W.; Anis, A.H. The economic burden of rheumatoid arthritis: Beyond health care costs. *Clin. Rheumatol.* **2011**, *30*, 25–32. [CrossRef]
11. Fidahic, M.; Kadic, A.J.; Radic, M.; Puljak, L. Celecoxib for rheumatoid arthritis. *Cochrane Database Syst. Rev.* **2017**. [CrossRef]
12. Yeo, J.; Lee, Y.M.; Lee, J.; Park, D.; Kim, K.; Kim, J.; Park, J.; Kim, W.J. Nitric oxide-scavenging nanogel for treating rheumatoid arthritis. *Nano Lett.* **2019**, *19*, 6716–6724. [CrossRef] [PubMed]
13. Abbasi, M.; Mousavi, M.J.; Jamalzehi, S.; Alimohammadi, R.; Bezvan, M.H.; Mohammadi, H.; Aslani, S. Strategies toward rheumatoid arthritis therapy; the old and the new. *J. Cell. Physiol.* **2019**, *234*, 10018–10031. [CrossRef] [PubMed]

14. Shea, B.; Swinden, M.V.; Ghogomu, E.T.; Ortiz, Z.; Katchamart, W.; Rader, T.; Bombardier, C.; Wells, G.A.; Tugwell, P. Folic acid and folinic acid for reducing side effects in patients receiving methotrexate for rheumatoid arthritis. *Cochrane Database Syst. Rev.* **2013**, *2014*, CD000951. [CrossRef]
15. Tu, A.B.; Lewis, J.S. Biomaterial-based immunotherapeutic strategies for rheumatoid arthritis. *Drug Deliv. Transl. Res.* **2021**, *11*, 2371–2393. [CrossRef] [PubMed]
16. Junshan, L.; Shaoqing, C. Advances in Chemical and Pharmacological Research of Saussurea. *Chin. Pharm. J.* **1998**, 3–6.
17. Ruiping, Y.; Yongfeng, J.; Liang, W. Research on Drug Resources of Saussurea. In Proceedings of the International Congress of Traditional Medicine, Beijing, China, 22–24 April 2000; p. 2.
18. Committee, N.P. *Pharmacopoeia of People's Republic of China. Part 1*; Medicine Science and Technology Press of China: Beijing, China, 2020; pp. 55–56.
19. Fan, W.-X.; Yang, W.-P.; Liu, H.-S. Research progress on culture technologies, chemical components, and pharmacological activities of Saussurea involucrata cells. *Chin. J. Chin. Mater. Med.* **2021**, *46*, 3522–3528. [CrossRef]
20. Chik, W.-I.; Zhu, L.; Fan, L.-L.; Yi, T.; Zhu, G.-Y.; Gou, X.-J.; Tang, Y.-N.; Xu, J.; Yeung, W.-P.; Zhao, Z.-Z. Saussurea involucrata: A review of the botany, phytochemistry and ethnopharmacology of a rare traditional herbal medicine. *J. Ethnopharmacol.* **2015**, *172*, 44–60. [CrossRef]
21. Cao, Z.-X.; Li, H.-H.; Li, A.; Liu, P.-Y.; Zhao, Y.-Y.; Mao, P.-Q.; Li, G.-L. Analysis of flavonoids and antitumor activity of transgenic Saussurea involucrate. *Chin. J. Chin. Mater. Med.* **2018**, *43*, 4491–4497. [CrossRef]
22. Jing, L.; He, L.; Fan, P.; Jia, Z.; Ma, H. Chemical constituents with anti-hypoxia activity from Saussurea involucrata. *Zhong Yao Cai* **2015**, *38*, 89–92. [CrossRef]
23. Huan, W.; Qiu, X.; Xu, F. A systematic review clinical efficacy about Xuelian treatment for rheumatoid arthritis. *Chin. Pract. Med.* **2008**, *3*, 59–60. [CrossRef]
24. Song, S.; Zhou, J.; Li, Y.; Liu, J.; Li, J.; Shu, P. Network pharmacology and experimental verification based research into the effect and mechanism of Aucklandiae Radix–Amomi Fructus against gastric cancer. *Sci. Rep.* **2022**, *12*, 9401. [CrossRef] [PubMed]
25. Na, Z.; Fengrong, Z.; Huayong, T.; Qingqing, L.; Xiulan, H.; Zhiyong, L. Benefit evaluation of Tujia medicine Tianzhusan added medicine prescription based on traditionaknowledge investigation and network pharmacology. *J. Hunan Univ. Chin. Med.* **2022**, *42*, 633–641.
26. Ye, X.W.; Wang, H.L.; Cheng, S.Q.; Xia, L.J.; Xu, X.F.; Li, X.R. Network Pharmacology-Based Strategy to Investigate the Pharmacologic Mechanisms of Coptidis Rhizoma for the Treatment of Alzheimer's Disease. *Front. Aging Neurosci.* **2022**, *14*, 890046. [CrossRef] [PubMed]
27. Yong, Y.; Jianguo, X.; Guihua, L.; Yongjun, Z.; Xincun, W.; Guipeng, X. In situ rat intestinal absorption of two active components in Saussurea involucrate. *Chin. J. Hosp. Pharm.* **2011**, *31*, 1407–1410. Available online: https://www.cnki.net/ (accessed on 12 April 2023).
28. Wu, Q.; Ma, J.; Shu, Z.; Ren, Y.; Li, D.-Z.; Zhang, Y.-L. Potential therapeutic effect of Saussureae Involucratae Herba on breast cancer and its mechanism based on network pharmacology. *Chin. J. Chin. Mater. Med.* **2021**, *46*, 4824–4832. [CrossRef]
29. Wang, D.; Sun, Y.; Liu, Q.; Ye, C.; Zhao, S.; Zhang, H. Ferula sinkiangensis against gastric cancer: A network pharmacology, molecular docking and cell experiment study. *Transl. Cancer Res.* **2023**, *12*, 743. [CrossRef]
30. Dong, Y.; Zhao, Q.; Wang, Y. Network pharmacology-based investigation of potential targets of astragalus membranaceous-angelica sinensis compound acting on diabetic nephropathy. *Sci. Rep.* **2021**, *11*, 19496. [CrossRef]
31. Choi, N.-R.; Jung, D.; Kim, S.-C.; Park, J.-W.; Choi, W.-G.; Kim, B.-J. Analysis of Network Pharmacological Efficacy and Therapeutic Effectiveness in Animal Models for Functional Dyspepsia of Foeniculi fructus. *Nutrients* **2023**, *15*, 2644. [CrossRef]
32. Khan, S.A.; Lee, T.K.W. Network-pharmacology-based study on active phytochemicals and molecular mechanism of cnidium monnieri in treating hepatocellular carcinoma. *Int. J. Mol. Sci.* **2022**, *23*, 5400. [CrossRef]
33. Shi, H.; Tian, S.; Tian, H. Network pharmacology interpretation of fuzheng–jiedu decoction against colorectal cancer. *Evid. Based Complement. Alternat. Med.* **2021**, *2021*, 4652492. [CrossRef]
34. Hu, H.; Wang, H.; Yang, X.; Li, Z.; Zhan, W.; Zhu, H.; Zhang, T. Network pharmacology analysis reveals potential targets and mechanisms of proton pump inhibitors in breast cancer with diabetes. *Sci. Rep.* **2023**, *13*, 7623. [CrossRef] [PubMed]
35. Wang, Y.; Yuan, Y.; Wang, W.; He, Y.; Zhong, H.; Zhou, X.; Chen, Y.; Cai, X.J.; Liu, L.Q. Mechanisms underlying the therapeutic effects of Qingfeiyin in treating acute lung injury based on GEO datasets, network pharmacology and molecular docking. *Comput. Biol. Med.* **2022**, *145*, 105454. [CrossRef]
36. Wu, Y.; Liu, X.; Li, G. Integrated bioinformatics and network pharmacology to identify the therapeutic target and molecular mechanisms of Huangqin decoction on ulcerative Colitis. *Sci. Rep.* **2022**, *12*, 159. [CrossRef] [PubMed]
37. Liu, H.; Mohammed, S.A.D.; Lu, F.; Chen, P.; Wang, Y.; Liu, S. Network Pharmacology and Molecular Docking-Based Mechanism Study to Reveal Antihypertensive Effect of Gedan Jiangya Decoction. *BioMed Res. Int.* **2022**, *2022*, 3353464. [CrossRef]
38. Bai, X.; Tang, Y.; Li, Q.; Chen, Y.; Liu, D.; Liu, G.; Fan, X.; Ma, R.; Wang, S.; Li, L. Network pharmacology integrated molecular docking reveals the bioactive components and potential targets of Morinda officinalis–Lycium barbarum coupled-herbs against oligoasthenozoospermia. *Sci. Rep.* **2021**, *11*, 2220. [CrossRef]

39. Xiao, Z.; Liu, C.; Duan, J.; Zhou, T.; Liu, X.; Lu, S.; Xu, F. A Network Pharmacology Approach to Investigate the Anti-Depressive Mechanism of Gardeniae fructus. *Int. J. Pharmacol.* **2020**, *16*, 382–397. [CrossRef]
40. Yan, H.-Y.; Zou, C.-C. Study on anticoagulant material basis and mechanism of Trichosanthis Semen and its shell and kernel based on spectrum-effect relationship integrated molecular docking. *Chin. J. Chin. Mater. Med.* **2022**, *47*, 1370–1382. [CrossRef]
41. Vidya, N.; Vadivukkarasi, B.; Manivannan, G.; Anbarasu, K. Molecular modeling and docking studies of glutamate racemase in Vibrio vulnificus CMCP6. *In Silico Biol.* **2008**, *8*, 471–483.
42. Cao, J.-Y.; Dong, Q.; Wang, Z.-Y.; Zhao, Y.; Ren, Y.; Liu, C.; Dang, J.; Yu, R.-T.; Tao, Y.-D. Arylnaphthalide lignans from Saussurea medusa and their anti-inflammatory activities. *Arab. J. Chem.* **2022**, *15*, 104155. [CrossRef]
43. Jiménez, J.; Doerr, S.; Martínez-Rosell, G.; Rose, A.S.; De Fabritiis, G. DeepSite: Protein-binding site predictor using 3D-convolutional neural networks. *Bioinformatics* **2017**, *33*, 3036–3042. [CrossRef]
44. Wang, Y. Study on Mechanism of Five flavonoids Inhibiting hIAPP Aggregation and NtMGAM Activity Based on Molecular Simulation. Master's Thesis, Chongqing University, Chongqing, China, 2020.
45. Zimeng, A.; Qianfang, F.; Yaruo, X.; Xinming, Y.; Yuning, G.; Xilian, Z. Based on network pharmacology, molecular docking, and molecular dynamics simulation to explore the target mechanism of Rongchang Capsules in the treatment of pediatric epilepsy. *Tianjin J. Tradit. Chin. Med.* **2023**, *40*, 495–505.
46. Valdés-Tresanco, M.S.; Valdés-Tresanco, M.E.; Valiente, P.A.; Moreno, E. gmx_MMPBSA: A New Tool to Perform End-State Free Energy Calculations with GROMACS. *J. Chem. Theory Comput.* **2021**, *17*, 6281–6291. [CrossRef] [PubMed]
47. Pantsar, T.; Poso, A. Binding Affinity via Docking: Fact and Fiction. *Molecules* **2018**, *23*, 1899. [CrossRef] [PubMed]
48. Saranya, P.; Karunya, R.; Keerthi Varshini, G.; Kowsikan, K.; Prathiksha, R. In-silico docking studies of selected phytochemicals against papain like protease of SARS-CoV-2. *Vegetos* **2023**, *36*, 188–194. [CrossRef]
49. Wilson Alphonse, C.R.; Kannan, R.R. In silico exploration of antioxidants as oxidation protectant for PITRM1 peptidase activity, an Alzheimer disease target. *J. Cell. Biochem.* **2023**, *124*, 1002–1011. [CrossRef]
50. Zhao, Q.; Deng, P.-Y.; Wang, H.-Y.; Luo, Q.; Tian, Y.-F.; Wang, G.-X.; Yang, Y.-Z.; Li, C.-G.; Chen, G. Molecular dynamics simulation of the interactions between puerarin and acetylcholinesterase. *J. At. Mol. Phys.* **2022**, *39*, 27–33. [CrossRef]
51. Ralph, J.A.; Morand, E.F. MAPK phosphatases as novel targets for rheumatoid arthritis. *Expert Opin. Ther. Targets* **2008**, *12*, 795–808. [CrossRef]
52. Liu, S.; Ma, H.; Zhang, H.; Deng, C.; Xin, P. Recent advances on signaling pathways and their inhibitors in rheumatoid arthritis. *Clin. Immunol.* **2021**, *230*, 108793. [CrossRef]
53. Ponce, C.; Torres, M.; Galleguillos, C.; Sovino, H.; Boric, M.A.; Fuentes, A.; Johnson, M.C. Nuclear factor κB pathway and interleukin-6 are affected in eutopic endometrium of women with endometriosis. *Reproduction* **2009**, *137*, 727–737. [CrossRef]
54. Liang, Y.; Zhou, Y.; Shen, P. NF-kappaB and its regulation on the immune system. *Cell. Mol. Immunol.* **2004**, *1*, 343–350.
55. Kim, E.K.; Kwon, J.-E.; Lee, S.-Y.; Lee, E.-J.; Kim, D.S.; Moon, S.-J.; Lee, J.; Kwok, S.-K.; Park, S.-H.; Cho, M.-L. IL-17-mediated mitochondrial dysfunction impairs apoptosis in rheumatoid arthritis synovial fibroblasts through activation of autophagy. *Cell Death Dis.* **2018**, *8*, e2565. [CrossRef] [PubMed]
56. Van Den Berg, W.B.; Miossec, P. IL-17 as a future therapeutic target for rheumatoid arthritis. *Nat. Rev. Rheumatol.* **2009**, *5*, 549–553. [CrossRef] [PubMed]
57. Kunwar, S.; Dahal, K.; Sharma, S. Anti-IL-17 therapy in treatment of rheumatoid arthritis: A systematic literature review and meta-analysis of randomized controlled trials. *Rheumatol. Int.* **2016**, *36*, 1065–1075. [CrossRef] [PubMed]
58. Chen, H.; Wang, Y. Function and regulation of the osteoclast in the pathological changes of bone destruction in rheumatoid arthritis. *Chin. J. Osteoporos.* **2016**, *22*, 1168–1173. [CrossRef]
59. Perricone, C.; Ceccarelli, F.; Matteo, S.; Di Carlo, G.; Bogdanos, D.P.; Lucchetti, R.; Pilloni, A.; Valesini, G.; Polimeni, A.; Conti, F. Porphyromonas gingivalis and rheumatoid arthritis. *Curr. Opin. Rheumatol.* **2019**, *31*, 517–524. [CrossRef] [PubMed]
60. Volin, M.V. Soluble adhesion molecules in the pathogenesis of rheumatoid arthritis. *Curr. Pharm. Des.* **2005**, *11*, 633–653. [CrossRef]
61. Hao, J.; Qi, F.; Wang, H.; Su, L.; Li, X.; Zhang, N.; Sun, W.; Wei, W. Network pharmacology-based prediction of inhibiting leukocyte recruitment and angiogenesis of total glucosides of peony against rheumatoid arthritis. *Ann. Palliat. Med.* **2022**, *11*, 3085101. [CrossRef]
62. Tang, M.; Zeng, Y.; Peng, W.; Xie, X.; Yang, Y.; Ji, B.; Li, F. Pharmacological aspects of natural quercetin in rheumatoid arthritis. *Drug Des. Dev. Ther.* **2022**, *ume 16*, 2043–2053. [CrossRef]
63. Liu, X.; Tao, T.; Yao, H.; Zheng, H.; Wang, F.; Gao, Y. Mechanism of action of quercetin in rheumatoid arthritis models: Meta-analysis and systematic review of animal studies. *Inflammopharmacology* **2023**, *31*, 1629–1645. [CrossRef]
64. Hou, Y.; Wu, J.; Huang, Q.; Guo, L. Luteolin inhibits proliferation and affects the function of stimulated rat synovial fibroblasts. *Cell Biol. Int.* **2009**, *33*, 135–147. [CrossRef]
65. Choi, E.M.; Lee, Y.S. Luteolin suppresses IL-1β-induced cytokines and MMPs production via p38 MAPK, JNK, NF-kappaB and AP-1 activation in human synovial sarcoma cell line, SW982. *Food Chem. Toxicol.* **2010**, *48*, 2607–2611. [CrossRef] [PubMed]

66. Chen, W.P.; Yang, Z.G.; Hu, P.F.; Bao, J.P.; Wu, L.D. Acacetin inhibits expression of matrix metalloproteinases via a MAPK-dependent mechanism in fibroblast-like synoviocytes. *J. Cell. Mol. Med.* **2015**, *19*, 1910–1915. [CrossRef] [PubMed]
67. Tanigawa, N.; Hagiwara, M.; Tada, H.; Komatsu, T.; Sugiura, S.; Kobayashi, K.; Kato, Y.; Ishida, N.; Nishida, K.; Ninomiya, M. Acacetin inhibits expression of E-selectin on endothelial cells through regulation of the MAP kinase signaling pathway and activation of NF-κB. *Immunopharmacol. Immunotoxicol.* **2013**, *35*, 471–477. [CrossRef] [PubMed]

separations

MDPI

Article

Green Extraction of Phenolic Compounds from Lotus (*Nelumbo nucifera* Gaertn) Leaf Using Deep Eutectic Solvents: Process Optimization and Antioxidant Activity

Jiwei Yang [1], Zhi Yan [2,3], Lingna Li [1], Lifen Zhang [1], Mengjian Zhao [1], Huixiang Yi [1], Ziying Wang [1], Gang Li [1], Zhenhua Wang [1], Mei Li [1,*] and Chengjun Ma [1,*]

[1] Center for Mitochondria and Healthy Aging, College of Life Sciences, Yantai University, Yantai 264005, China; jwyang12138@163.com (J.Y.); li_lingna961231@yeah.net (L.L.); 19553582206@163.com (L.Z.); zmj1428409280@163.com (M.Z.); huixiangdiyi@163.com (H.Y.); wzy610722@163.com (Z.W.); ligang@ytu.edu.cn (G.L.); skywzh@ytu.edu.cn (Z.W.)

[2] Yantai Institute of Coastal Zone Research, Chinese Academy of Sciences, Yantai 264003, China

[3] School of Ocean, Yantai University, Yantai 264005, China

* Correspondence: lmei9206@163.com (M.L.); chengjun-ma@163.com (C.M.)

Abstract: Natural deep eutectic solvents (NDESs) were used to extract flavonoids and polyphenols from lotus (*Nelumbo nucifera* Gaertn.) leaves at the same time, and the extraction process was optimized to provide reference for the effective development and utilization of lotus leaves. The deep eutectic solvents (DESs) with the highest yield of flavonoids and polyphenols were screened out from 19 different NDES combinations. The response surface method was employed to optimize the extraction process. After a rational design, a lactic acid/glycerol (molar ratio 1:2) DES was chosen as the optimal extraction solvent, and the optimum extraction parameters were as follow: water content (29%), liquid–solid ratio (37:1 mL/g), extraction time (61 min), and extraction temperature (53 °C). Compared with traditional water extraction or ethanol extraction, it improved the yield of flavonoids (126.10 mg/g) and polyphenols (126.10 mg/g). By LC–MS analysis, 19 flavonoids or organic acid compounds with known compound structural formulae were identified in the DES extract of lotus leaves. By comparing the free radical scavenging ability and total reducing ability, the extraction of lotus leaves using the NDES method was superior to both ethanol extraction and water extraction. It is a green, environmentally friendly, and efficient extraction method for antioxidants from leaves of *Nelumbo nucifera* Gaertn.

Keywords: deep eutectic solvents; lotus (*Nelumbo nucifera* Gaertn.) leaves; extraction; response surface methodology; antioxidant; flavonoids; polyphenols

1. Introduction

Lotus (*Nelumbo nucifera* Gaertn.) is a common aquatic perennial herbaceous plant that is cultivated in many regions of China. The lotus leaf was listed as a food and medicine resource by the Chinese Ministry of Health in 1991 [1,2]. In recent years, lotus leaves have attracted more and more attention due to their antioxidant, anti-inflammatory, antiobesity, and lipid-lowering activities [2]. The chemical constituents of lotus leave mainly include alkaloids, flavonoids, polyphenolic acids, volatile oil, and so on [3]. The flavonoids from lotus leaves have been reported to regulate blood lipids [4], have antibacterial [5] and antioxidant [6] properties, inhibit atherosclerosis [7], and improve liver damage [8].

The active ingredients in lotus leaves are flavonoids and phenolic acids; the identified phenolic compounds are reported to be catechin, myricetin, isoquercetin, hyperin, and kaempferol [9,10]. Solvent extraction is the most used method to extract flavonoids and polyphenolic compounds. Different types of solvent extraction methods are used, among which hot water bath extraction and soxhlet extraction are the most commonly used methods to extract the bioactive compounds of flavonoids [11]. Ultrasound-assisted extraction is a green technique for the extraction of polyphenolic compounds, and this method improves the extraction efficiency and shortens the extraction time [12]. The disadvantage of solvent extraction is the long process time, which eventually leads to thermal degradation of the compounds and reduces environmental sustainability [11].

Deep eutectic solvents (DESs) are a new type of ionic liquid analog, which are eutectics formed by two or more components with a certain ratio of hydrogen bonds [13]. DESs have the advantages of simple preparation, good stability, high chemical purity, low cost, degradability, low viscosity, etc.; moreover, the solvent polarity can be adjusted by adjusting the substance ratio of deep eutectic solvents components. At present, deep eutectic solvents have been widely used in the extraction of active ingredients in traditional Chinese medicine [14] and active substances in food, the preparation of test solutions for quality testing, electrochemistry, and materials science [15]. Leyre Sillero et al. [16]. has successfully synthesized two DESs as green solvents for the extraction of bioactive compounds. They were used as additives to aqueous mixtures to improve the selective extraction of flavonoids from pine bark. Dai et al. [17]. effectively extracted 24 phenolic compounds from safflower, including hydroxy saffron yellow A (HSYA), using the DESs system (proline: malic acid). The use of deep eutectic solvents for natural product extraction has the advantage of simplicity and efficiency. Ali et al. [18] consider the use of DESs as a medium to extract active compounds from medicinal plants as a green method superior to the use of traditional solvents. Several authors have established that DESs have low toxicity properties for human life and the living environment [19,20].

This study focused on extracting flavonoids and polyphenols from lotus leaves with green eutectic solvent, optimizing the extraction process using the response surface method, and evaluating their antioxidant activities in vitro. Flavonoids and polyphenols both have a high antioxidant capacity, and antioxidant indicators such as DPPH (1,1-Diphenyl-2-picrylhydrazyl), ABTS (2,2′-azinobis (3-ethylbenzothiazoline-6-sulfonic acid)), FRAP (Ferric reducing ability of plasma) used on the extracts verified this through antioxidant experiments. This topic provides some scientific directions for the extraction research of lotus leaves and provides an effective theoretical basis for the development and utilization of lotus leaves.

2. Materials and Methods

2.1. Materials

DPPH (1898-66-4, 99%), rutin (153-18-4, ≥95%), gallic acid (149-91-7, 99%), ABTS (28752-68-3, 99%), Folin phenol (12111-13-6, Biological reagent), D(+)-Glucose (50-99-7, Analytical purity; Sinopharm Chemical Reagent Co., Ltd., Shanghai, China), betaine (107-43-7, >99%; Refrigerant Cool Chemical Co., Ltd., Jinan, China), lactic acid (50-21-5, >90.0%), ferric trichloride (7705-08-0, Analytical purity), potassium hexacyanoferrate (13746-66-2, Analytical purity), trifluoroacetic acid (76-05-1, Analytical purity), sodium dihydrogen phosphate (89140-32-9, Analytical purity), disodium hydrogen phosphate (10039-32-4, Analytical purity), sodium chloride (7647-14-5, Analytical purity; Tianjin Beichen Founder Reagent Factory, Tianjin, China), Citric acid (77-92-9, >99.5%; Tianjin Aupu Kai Chemical Co., Ltd., Tianjin, China), malic acid (6915-15-7, >99%; Hefei Bomei Biotechnology Co., Ltd., Hefei, China), crystalline aluminum chloride (7784-13-6, >97%; Shenyang City Reagent Five Factory, Shenyang, China), glycerol (56-81-5, >99%), urea (57-13-6, >99%), propylene glycol (57-55-6, Analytical purity; Tianjin Beilian Fine Chemicals Development Co., Ltd., Tianjin, China); ethanol (64-17-5, Analytical purity), sodium hydroxide (1310-73-2, Analytical purity), Sodium nitrite (7632-00-0, Analytical purity), and sodium carbonate (497-19-8, Analytical purity; Yantai Sanhe Chemical Reagent Co., Ltd., Yantai, China) were used.

2.2. Samples

The lotus leaves (Origin: Taiyuan, China; Production date: August 2021) provided by Hebei Renxin Pharmaceutical Co., Ltd., were dried, crumbled, sieved (using a 60-mesh sieve), and then stored at 4 °C for later use.

2.3. Preparation of Deep Eutectic Solvents

A hydrogen bond acceptor and hydrogen bond donor were selected. After mixing, they were then stirred in a water bath at 80 °C with a magnetic agitator until the liquid became uniform and transparent [21]. A synopsis of the DESs prepared is shown in Table 1. The viscosity, pH, and visible properties were observed according to the literature [22,23].

Table 1. Composition and characteristics of DESs.

Number	Hydrogen Bond Receptor (HBA)	Hydrogen Bonded Donor (HBD)	Mole Ratio	Water Content (%)	Viscosity (mpa s)	PH Value	Character
DES-1	Choline chloride	Glycerol	1:2	20%	67.03	5.75	Transparent liquid
DES-2		Propylene glycol	1:2		39.1	5.88	Transparent liquid
DES-3		Lactic acid	1:2		31.3	1.22	Transparent liquid
DES-4		Citric acid	1:2		213	0.07	Transparent liquid
DES-5		Malic acid	1:2		138.8	0.11	Transparent liquid
DES-6		D(+)-Glucose	1:2		222.8	3.6	Transparent liquid
DES-7		Urea	1:2		26.4	9.28	Transparent liquid
DES-8	Betaine	Glycerol	1:2		147.3	6.82	Transparent liquid
DES-9		Propylene glycol	1:2		131.3	7.37	Transparent liquid
DES-10		Lactic acid	1:2		66.5	3.57	Transparent liquid
DES-11		Citric acid	1:2		711	2.27	Transparent liquid
DES-12		Malic acid	1:2		424.33	2.57	Transparent liquid
DES-13		D(+)-Glucose	1:2		470	5.37	Transparent liquid
DES-14	Lactic acid	Glycerol	1:2		66.03	2.11	Transparent yellow liquid
DES-15		Propylene glycol	1:2		33	2.24	Transparent yellow liquid
DES-16		D(+)-Glucose	1:2		351.17	1.85	Transparent yellow liquid
DES-17	Citric acid	Glycerol	1:2		326.67	1.75	Transparent liquid
DES-18		Propylene glycol	1:2		106.67	1.67	Transparent liquid
DES-19		D(+)-Glucose	1:2		627	1.65	Transparent liquid

2.4. Extraction of Flavonoid and Polyphenol Components

The extraction process was carried out according to previously reported methods with some modifications [24]. A sample (0.10 g) was added to the DES solution (4 mL, containing 20% water), extracted at 140 r/min for 60 min (50 °C). The extract was centrifuged at 8000 r/min for 10 min, and the supernatant was collected for later use.

2.5. Optimization of Extraction Process

The effect of extraction process parameters on the yield of flavonoids and polyphenols in lotus leaves extract was investigated by a single-factor test. Experiments were performed using a variety of different conditions: 19 different deep eutectic solvents, different molar ratios (3:1, 2:1, 1:1, 1:2, 1:3, 1:4), water contents (0%, 10%, 20%, 30%, 40%, 50%, 60%), material–liquid ratios (1:10, 1:20, 1:30, 1:40, 1:50, 1:60), extraction times (15, 30, 45, 60, 75, 90 min), and extraction temperatures (30, 40, 50, 60, 70 °C).

The Box–Behnken design (BBD) was adopted to optimize the extraction methods. Based on the above single-factor analysis of variance, four variables, namely (A) water content, (B)material-to-liquid ratio, (C)extraction temperature, (D) and extraction time, were selected as independent variables of the BBD, and the response values of the flavonoid yield (Y_1) and polyphenol yield (Y_2) were used to design a four-factor three-level response surface. A total of 29 sets of experiments were designed to optimize the four-factor three-level response surface test, as shown in Table 2.

Table 2. Response surface factor level design.

Factor	Level		
	−1	0	1
Moisture content (%)	20	30	40
Extraction temperature (°C)	40	50	60
Extraction time (min)	45	60	75
Liquid–solid ratio (mL/g)	30	40	50

2.6. Traditional Extraction Method Comparison

Compared with traditional extraction methods, 75% ethanol and water were used for the water bath (140 r/min, 50 °C, 60 min).

2.7. Determination of Total Flavonoids

The content of flavonoids was calculated using the modified method described by Ji et al. [25]. A standard solution was prepared by dissolving rutin (82.2 mg) in 60% ethanol to give a total volume of 100 mL. Rutin dilutions were prepared with mass concentrations ranging from 82.2 to 822 μg/mL. The total flavonoid content was determined by the color development method of sodium nitrite-aluminum nitrate-sodium hydroxide, and the absorbance was measured at 510 nm by UV spectrophotometer. In addition, the regression equation of total flavonoid was Y = 0.0059 X + 0.0021 (R^2 = 0.9999), where X is the mass concentration of rutin (μg/mL) and Y is the absorbance value. The concentration of rutin showed a good linear relationship with the absorbance.

2.8. Determination of Polyphenols

The total phenolic content was determined using the Folin–Ciocalteu method. The method was in reference to Sutivisedsak et al. [26] and modified appropriately. The gallic acid was accurately weighed (80.2 mg), dissolved in double-pure water, fixed into a 100 mL volumetric flask, and mixed as the mother liquor. Preparation of gallic acid dilutions with mass concentrations of 80.2–802 μg/mL. In total, 50 μL was taken from the above standard solution with different concentrations, 125 μL from Folin-Ciocalteu reagent, and 1250 μL from a 7% $NaCO_3$ solution and then added together, and the reaction was carried out at 40 °C for 90 min under light protection. After the reaction, measuring the absorbance at 760 nm using UV spectrophotometer and yielded a regression equation of polyphenols of Y = 0.0602 X + 0.0104 (R^2 = 0.9991), where X is the mass concentration of gallic acid (μg/mL) and Y is the absorbance value. The concentration of gallic acid showed a good linear relationship with the absorbance.

2.9. Antioxidant Activity

2.9.1. DPPH Radical Scavenging Rate Measurement

To evaluate the ability of extracts to eliminate DPPH free radicals, the previously reported methods were modified and used [27]. The supernatant was diluted 10 times, mixed with 9 mL of DPPH solution (200 μmol/L, dissolved in anhydrous ethanol), and allowed to react in the dark for 30 min. The standard curve was plotted with the concentration of different standards (X) as the horizontal coordinate and the scavenging rate of DPPH radicals (Y) as the vertical coordinate (Y = 0.7758 X − 4.0584 (R^2 = 0.9994)). The absorbance values were then measured at 517 nm and used to calculate the scavenging activity according to the formula:

$$\text{DPPH inhibition } (\%) = (1 - \frac{A_i - A_j}{A_0}) \times 100\%$$

where A_i is the absorbance value of the sample group, A_j is the absorbance value of the blank reagent, and A_0 is the absorbance value of the blank control sample.

2.9.2. ABTS Cation Radical Rate Determination

The supernatant (1 mL) was mixed with 10 mL of $ABTS^+$ solution (7 mmol/L ABTS aqueous solution and 2.45 mmol/L potassium persulfate aqueous solution were mixed and protected from light for 12–16 h), and the reaction was carried out for 10 min in the dark. The absorbance values were then measured at 734 nm. The standard curve was drawn with the concentration of different standards (X) as the horizontal coordinate, the scavenging rate of ABTS cationic radicals (Y) as the vertical coordinate, and the regression equation being Y = 0.113 X + 2.0628 (R^2 = 0.9934). The ABTS cationic radical scavenging rate was then calculated using the equation:

$$\text{ABTS inhibition } (\%) = (1 - \frac{A_i - A_j}{A_0}) \times 100\%$$

where A_i, is the absorbance value of the sample group, A_j is the absorbance value of the blank reagent, A_0 is the absorbance value of the blank control sample group.

2.9.3. FRAP Total Reduction Capacity Measurement

The sample solution (5 µL) was mixed with 200 µL FRAP working solution (Equal volume of phosphate buffer (pH = 6.6), 1 mg/mL ferric chloride solution, 10 mg/mL potassium ferricyanide, and 100 mg/mL trifluoroacetic acid were mixed), and the reaction was carried out at 37 °C for 5 min under light protection. The absorbance values were measured at 593 nm. The standard curve was plotted with different concentrations of Fe^{2+} (X) as the horizontal coordinate, the corresponding absorbance (Y) as the vertical coordinate, and the regression equation being Y = 0.0003 X + 0.0032 (R^2 = 0.9997), which indicated that the model fitted well.

2.10. LC–MS Structural Analysis

Chromatographic conditions: ACQUITY UPLC BEH C18 column (2.1 mm × 50 mm, 1.7 µm); column temperature 30 °C; flow rate 0.3 mL/min; injection volume 10 µL; mobile phase A: 0.1% formic acid aqueous solution, *v*/*v*; mobile phase B: 0.1% formic acid acetonitrile solution, *v*/*v*. Gradient elution conditions: 0–2 min, 30% B; 2–20 min, 30–100% B; 20–26 min, 100% B; 26–26.1 min, 100–10% B; 26.1–30 min, 10% B.

Mass spectrometry conditions: The LC–MS/MS system consists of the Waters ACQUITY UPLC system connected to the Waters Xevo TQ-S triple quadrupole time of flight mass spectrometer (Waters Corp., Milford, MA, USA). Detection was performed using MSE mode and processed using the Masslynx 4.1 software (Waters Corp.). The UPLC effluent was introduced into the mass spectrometer by positive mode electrospray ionization. The capillary voltage was 3.00 kV (ESI+), extractor voltage was 5 V, desolvation nitrogen flow rate was 800 L/h (N_2, purity 99.9%), desolvation gas temperature was 400 °C, and source temperature was 150 °C. Data were collected in centroid mode from 100 to 1500 *m*/*z*.

2.11. Statistical Analysis

The response surface design experiments and data statistics were performed with Design Expert 12.0 (Minneapolis, Minnesota, MN, USA). Analysis of variance (ANOVA) and correlation analysis were performed using SPSS 20.0 software (Amenk, New York, NY, USA) and different lowercase letters were used to indicate significant differences ($p < 0.05$). Calculation of IC_{50} using GraphPad prism8.0 (San Diego, CA, USA); Origin 2018 software (Northampton, MA, USA) was used for plotting.

3. Results and Discussion

3.1. Single-Factor Test

3.1.1. Selection of the Optimal DES

The deep eutectic solvents consist of two parts: a hydrogen bond donor and a hydrogen bond acceptor. Different combinations form hydrogen bonding forces of different strengths. The extraction rates of different deep eutectic solvents on the flavonoid and polyphenol components of lotus leaves were investigated. Four substances were selected as hydrogen bond acceptors in the experiment, namely choline chloride, betaine, lactic acid, and citric acid, where the selection of hydrogen bond donors included four donors, carboxylic acids, polyols, sugars, and amides. The yields of polyphenols and flavonoids measured under the same extraction conditions, i.e., 20% water content, 1:20 ratio, and 60 min at 50 °C, were compared with the traditional extraction method of water and 70% ethanol (Figure 1). The yield of flavonoids was slightly lower than that of the combination of betaine and propylene glycol. Considering the yield of lotus flavonoids and polyphenols and the low price of lactic acid and propanetriol, they are pure natural solvents that are green, pollution-free, and easily degradable; therefore, the combination of lactic acid and propanetriol was chosen.

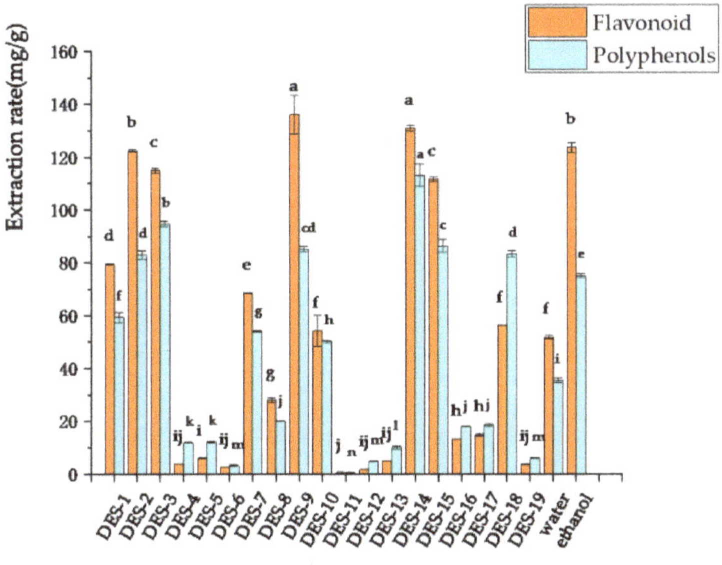

Figure 1. Effect of different solvents on the yield of flavonoids and polyphenols from lotus leaves. Different letters indicate significant differences, $p < 0.05$.

3.1.2. Selection of the Optimal DES Molar Ratio

The effect of the molar ratio of hydrogen bond acceptor to hydrogen bond donor of DESs solvent on the extraction of lotus flavonoids and polyphenols was investigated (Figure 2). The yield tended to decrease when the molar ratio gradually changed from 1:2 to 1:4. This indicated that too many hydrogen bond donors or hydrogen bond acceptors can affect the yield of phenolic compounds. This is because when the content of propanetriol increased, this significantly promoted the diffusion and mass transfer of the reaction system, which led to a higher extraction rate, whereas, when the viscosity of propanetriol is high, excess propanetriol leads to stronger spatial site resistance, which results in a lower extraction rate [28]. Therefore, the highest yield of flavonoids and polyphenols was obtained with a molar ratio of 1:2.

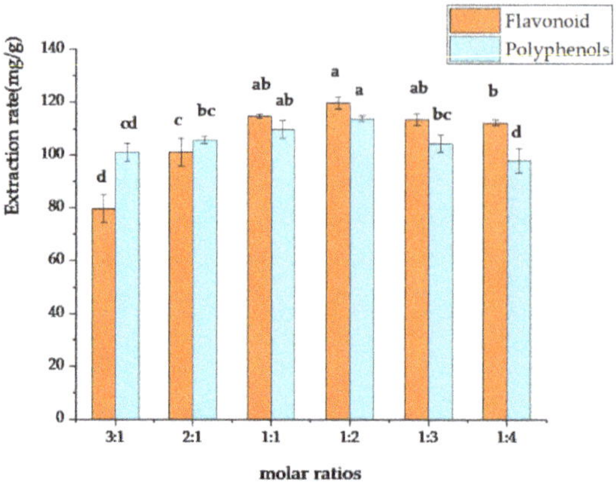

Figure 2. Effect of different molar ratios of DESs on the yields of lotus flavonoids and polyphenols. Different letters indicate significant differences, $p < 0.05$.

3.1.3. Selection of Optimal Water Content

The presence of water in deep eutectic solvents affects the physicochemical properties of the solvent [29], while the right amount of water has no significant effect on the structure of the solvent components [30]. The addition of water reduces the viscosity and surface tension of the system, increases the osmotic pressure, and enhances mass transfer, thus positively influencing the extraction [31]. The effect of increasing the water content from 0% to 10% and to 60% on the yield of lotus flavonoids and polyphenols was investigated, and the results are shown in Figure 3. The yield of flavonoids and polyphenols increased gradually with the increase in water content (0% to 30%) in the solvent system. When the water content in the solvent increased from 30% to 60%, the extraction rate decreased with the increase in water content. This may be related to the fact that the excess water in the DESs broke the structure of the DES system as well as weakened the hydrogen bonds between the constituents of the lotus leaves and DESs, which led to a decrease in the extraction rate of the target compounds [32,33]. The experimental results showed that the extraction rate of flavonoids and polyphenols of DESs reached the maximum when the water content of DESs was 30%; therefore, the optimal water content choice for the DES system was 30%.

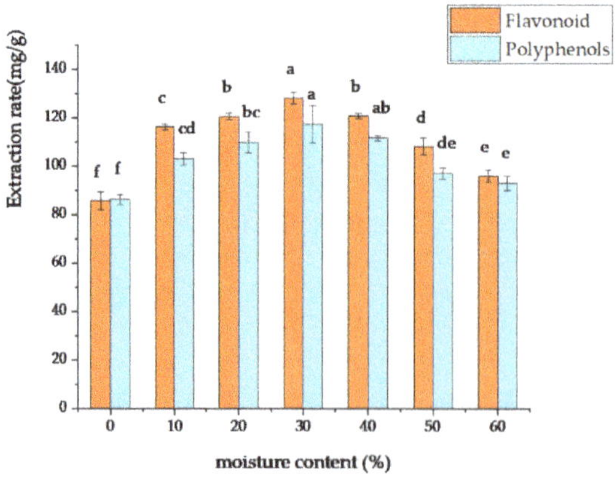

Figure 3. Effect of different water content on the yield of flavonoids and polyphenols of lotus leaves. Different letters indicate significant differences, $p < 0.05$.

3.1.4. Selection of the Optimum DESs Liquid–Solid Ratios

Considering the economics, excessive use of DES solutions for extraction can result in large losses; moreover, extractions with too little solvent will lead to incomplete extraction, so finding the right ratio of solution to material has a greater impact on extraction [28]. The effect of liquid–solid ratio of 10 mL/g, 20 mL/g, 30 mL/g, 40 mL/g, 50 mL/g and 60 mL/g on the yield of lotus flavonoids and polyphenols was investigated, and the results are shown in Figure 4. When the liquid–solid ratio was below 40 mL/g, the yield of flavonoids and phenolic compounds increased with the increase in the liquid–solid ratio and with the increase in the solvent amount, the reason being that the increase in the solvent helped more flavonoids and polyphenolic compounds to diffuse into the solvent. With the further increase in the feed–liquid ratio to 40 mL/g, the extraction rate showed a decreasing trend. The reason may be since the concentration of the solution becomes smaller with the increase in the stock–liquid ratio, and the percentage of lotus leaves per ml DES solution becomes less; therefore, a liquid–solid ratio of 40 mL/g was chosen.

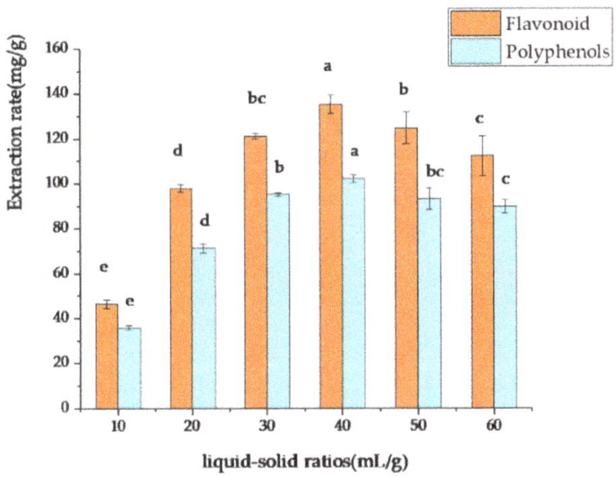

Figure 4. Effect of different liquid–solid ratios on the yields of flavonoids and polyphenols of lotus leaves. Different letters indicate significant differences, $p < 0.05$.

3.1.5. Selection of Optimum DES Extraction Time

During the extraction of lotus leaves, the yield of flavonoids and polyphenols is maximized after a certain period, and when the extraction time is extended, the active ingredients in lotus leaves will decompose and the yield will be reduced. A short extraction time will lead to the loss of raw materials, so the optimal extraction time should be selected. From 15 to 60 min, the yields of flavonoids and polyphenols in lotus leaves showed an increasing trend, and then, with the increase in extraction time, the extraction amount decreased slightly, but the difference was not significant, probably because the extraction process was very close to the solid–liquid equilibrium and the extraction reached the maximum (Figure 5). However, the flavonoids and polyphenols were decomposed in the process of continued extraction, so the extraction rate decreased slightly; therefore, 60 min was chosen as the most appropriate extraction time for the experiment.

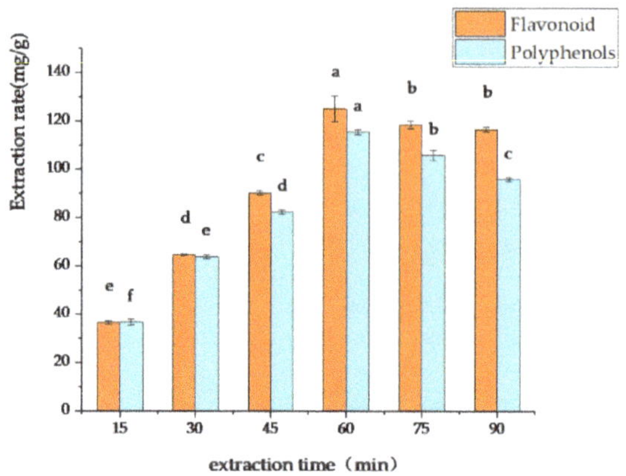

Figure 5. Effect of different extraction time on the yield of lotus leaf flavonoids and polyphenols. Different letters indicate significant differences, $p < 0.05$.

3.1.6. Selection of Optimum DES Extraction Temperature

Extraction temperature is also one of the conditions affecting the extraction of active substances extracted from lotus leaves, as increasing the temperature helps to increase the solubility of lotus active substances in DESs, decreases the viscosity, density, and surface tension of the DES solution, and increases the diffusion coefficient, thus increasing the extraction rate [15,34]. The effects of different extraction temperatures on the yield of flavonoids and polyphenols at a molar ratio of lactic acid–propanetriol of 1:2, a water content of 30%, a liquid-to-solid ratio of 40 mL/g, and an extraction time of 60 min are shown in Figure 6. Below 50 °C, the yield of lotus leaf flavonoids and polyphenols improved with the increase in temperature and attained the maximum yield at 50 °C. When the temperature exceeded 50 °C, the yields of lotus flavonoids and polyphenols decreased slightly with the increasing temperature. The reason may be that when the temperature exceeded 50 °C, the active ingredients in lotus leaves would decompose due to the increase in temperature as the extraction progressed, so the yield decreased slightly with the increase in temperature; therefore, the optimum extraction temperature was 50 °C.

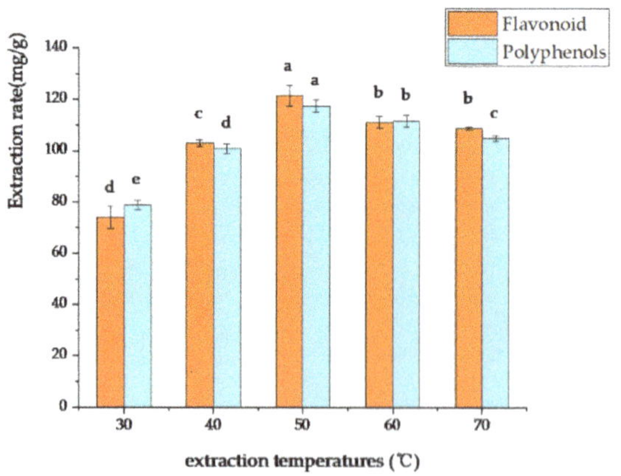

Figure 6. Effect of different extraction temperatures on the yield of lotus leaf flavonoids and polyphenols. Different letters indicate significant differences, $p < 0.05$.

3.2. *Results of Response Surface Experiments*

3.2.1. Response Surface Experimental Design and Analysis of Variance

The results of the response surface experimental design are shown in Table 3, the regression equations were fitted to the data in Table 3 using Design-Expert12 analysis software, and the quadratic multiple regression equations for each factor (A: water content, B: liquid-solid ratio, C: extraction temperature, D: extraction time) on the yield of flavonoids (Y_1) and polyphenols (Y_2) were obtained as follows:

$$Y_1 = 128.29 - 3.11\,A - 14.66\,B + 4.15\,C + 2.14\,D + 0.2420\,AB - 3.70\,AC + 2.08\,AD + 3.09\,BC - 0.7930\,BD + 1.23\,CD - 10.69\,A^2 - 14.67\,B^2 - 9.19\,C^2 - 13.06\,D^2$$

$$Y_2 = 113.04 - 1.45\,A + 2.40\,B + 6.21\,C - 0.7261\,D + 1.91\,AB - 0.2530\,AC - 0.8942\,AD - 2.05\,BC + 1.50\,BD + 5.08\,CD - 7.51\,A^2 - 3.89\,B^2 - 8.27\,C^2 - 10.24\,D^2$$

Table 3. Response surface test design and results.

Number	Factors: A: Water Content %	B: Liquid-Solid Ratio mL/g	C: Extraction Temperature °C	D: Extraction Time min	Total Flavonoid Yield mg/g	Polyphenol Yield mg/g
1	−1	−1	0	0	121.24 ± 3.22	103.93 ± 3.37
2	0	−1	1	0	117.06 ± 1.48	109.63 ± 2.15
3	0	0	−1	−1	101.06 ± 2.76	94.59 ± 1.71
4	1	1	0	0	82.37 ± 2.02	102.45 ± 4.90
5	0	0	0	0	130.83 ± 3.33	111.56 ± 3.35
6	1	0	0	1	110.49 ± 0.91	94.52 ± 1.48
7	1	0	0	−1	96.59 ± 2.41	95.95 ± 0.58
8	1	−1	0	0	116.34 ± 3.50	96.03 ± 3.99
9	0	−1	0	1	117.10 ± 4.75	91.34 ± 6.33
10	0	0	0	0	132.91 ± 4.11	114.91 ± 5.97
11	−1	0	0	1	109.32 ± 3.04	98.88 ± 4.61
12	0	1	0	−1	87.33 ± 1.96	101.01 ± 2.85
13	1	0	1	0	108.77 ± 3.31	100.35 ± 1.69
14	0	0	1	1	110.73 ± 0.75	103.57 ± 0.56
15	−1	0	1	0	121.43 ± 8.10	102.88 ± 1.45
16	−1	1	0	0	86.30 ± 0.29	102.70 ± 1.63
17	0	1	−1	0	86.63 ± 3.84	99.04 ± 4.28
18	0	0	−1	1	99.66 ± 4.36	81.17 ± 1.40
19	0	1	0	1	87.79 ± 2.19	102.53 ± 3.49
20	0	0	0	0	127.36 ± 4.29	110.26 ± 5.26
21	0	1	1	0	97.48 ± 0.80	109.17 ± 4.67
22	0	−1	−1	0	118.59 ± 2.94	91.33 ± 5.58
23	−1	0	0	−1	103.76 ± 2.94	96.72 ± 3.83
24	0	0	0	0	129.23 ± 15.84	112.54 ± 1.64
25	0	−1	0	−1	113.48 ± 3.53	95.82 ± 1.76
26	0	0	0	0	121.12 ± 3.07	115.92 ± 5.67
27	1	0	−1	0	104.50 ± 5.71	90.03 ± 1.87
28	−1	0	−1	0	102.38 ± 0.39	91.56 ± 0.31
29	0	0	1	−1	107.21 ± 1.65	96.65 ± 1.18

The ANOVA (analysis of variance) of total flavonoid yield is shown in Table 4. According to the analysis in Table 4, the model $p < 0.01$ is significant, indicating that the model was successfully established, the misfit term $p > 0.05$ is not significant, demonstrating that the model fit is good, the coefficient of determination $R^2 = 0.9619$ and the model adjustment coefficient $R_{adj}^2 = 0.9238$ both exceed 0.9 and are close to each other, indicating that the experimental values are strongly correlated with the predicted values and that the model correlation is good. From the response surface test results, the factor of liquid-to-solid ratio (B) is the most influential factor on the total flavonoid yield, followed by the extraction temperature (C). The p-values of extraction time (D) and water content (A) were not significant, which indicated that these two factors had a little effect on the total flavonoid yield.

Table 4. ANOVA of total flavonoid yield.

Source	Sum of Squares	df	Mean Square	*F*-Value	*p*-Value	
Model	5500.78	14	392.91	25.26	<0.0001	**
A	53.6	1	53.6	3.45	0.0846	
B	2578.55	1	2578.55	165.76	<0.0001	**
C	207.17	1	207.17	13.32	0.0026	**
D	54.88	1	54.88	3.53	0.0813	
AB	0.2343	1	0.2343	0.0151	0.9041	
AC	54.62	1	54.62	3.51	0.082	
AD	17.36	1	17.36	1.12	0.3087	
BC	38.31	1	38.31	2.46	0.1389	
BD	2.52	1	2.52	0.1617	0.6937	
CD	6.06	1	6.06	0.3897	0.5425	
A^2	741.76	1	741.76	47.68	<0.0001	**
B^2	1395.06	1	1395.06	89.68	<0.0001	**
C^2	548.11	1	548.11	35.23	<0.0001	**
D^2	1106.71	1	1106.71	71.14	<0.0001	**
Residual	217.78	14	15.56			
Lack of Fit	136.88	10	13.69	0.6767	0.7198	
Pure Error	80.91	4	20.23			
Cor Total	5718.57	28				

$p < 0.01$ ** means significant statistical difference; A: water content, B: liquid–solid ratio, C: extraction temperature, D: extraction time.

Figure 7 shows the response surface diagram of the interaction between the factors of total flavonoid yield, and the F-value analysis of the interaction between the factors in Table 4 shows that the interaction between water content and extraction temperature has the greatest effect on the yield of total flavonoid, and the interaction between water content and liquid–solid ratio has the least effect.

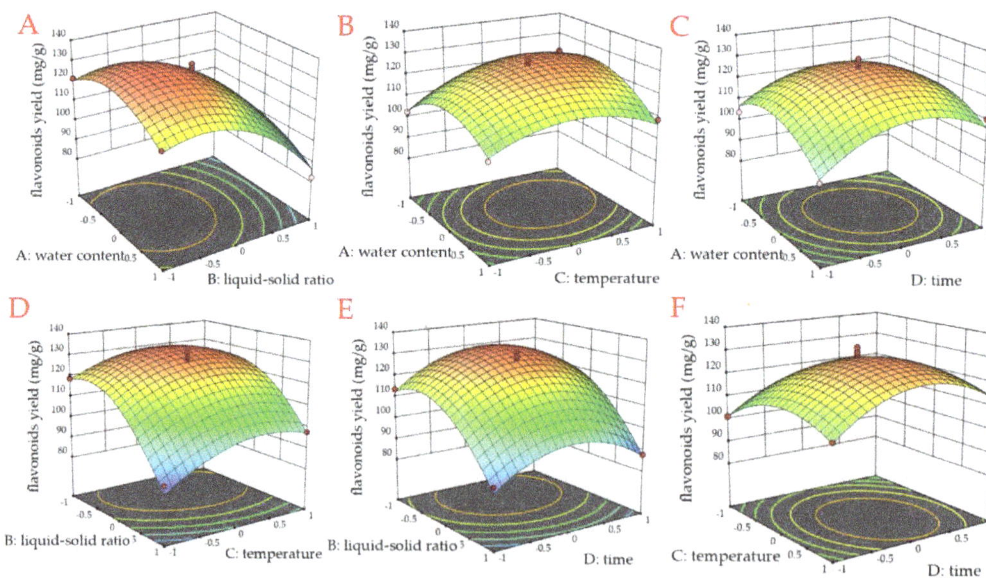

Figure 7. Response surface diagram of the interaction of different factors of total flavonoid yield. (**A**) Water content and liquid–solid ratio; (**B**) water content and temperature; (**C**) water content and time; (**D**) liquid–solid ratio and temperature; (**E**) liquid–solid ratio and time; (**F**) temperature and time.

The ANOVA of polyphenol yield is shown in Table 5, based on which we know that the experimental model $p < 0.01$ is significant, indicating successful model building. The misfit term $p > 0.05$ was not significant, indicating that the model has good fit. The coefficient of determination $R^2 = 0.9579$ and the model adjustment coefficient $R_{adj}{}^2 = 0.9159$ both exceed 0.9 and were close to each other, which shows that the experimental values were strongly correlated with the predicted values and the model correlation was good. From the results of the response surface test, the relationship between the four factors set on the polyphenol yield is as follows: C (extraction temperature) > B (liquid to solid ratio) > A (water content) > D (extraction time). The extraction temperature had the greatest effect on the yield of polyphenols, probably because of the poor stability of polyphenols, and the change of temperature had a greater effect on polyphenols.

Table 5. ANOVA of polyphenol yield.

Source	Sum of Squares	df	Mean Square	*F*-Value	*p*-Value	
Model	1824.14	14	130.3	22.77	<0.0001	**
A	25.07	1	25.07	4.38	0.055	
B	69.22	1	69.22	12.1	0.0037	**
C	462.89	1	462.89	80.9	<0.0001	**
D	6.33	1	6.33	1.11	0.3108	
AB	14.59	1	14.59	2.55	0.1326	
AC	0.256	1	0.256	0.0447	0.8355	
AD	3.2	1	3.2	0.559	0.467	
BC	16.75	1	16.75	2.93	0.1091	
BD	8.99	1	8.99	1.57	0.2305	
CD	103.37	1	103.37	18.07	0.0008	**
A^2	366.1	1	366.1	63.98	<0.0001	**
B^2	98.12	1	98.12	17.15	0.001	**
C^2	443.17	1	443.17	77.45	<0.0001	**
D^2	704.02	1	704.02	123.04	<0.0001	**
Residual	80.1	14	5.72			
Lack of Fit	58.14	10	5.81	1.06	0.5224	
Pure Error	21.96	4	5.49			
Cor Total	1904.24	28				

$p < 0.01$ ** means significant statistical difference; A: water content, B: liquid–solid ratio, C: extraction temperature, D: extraction time.

Figure 8 shows the response surface diagram of the interaction between the factors of polyphenol yield, and from the results of the analysis in Table 5, we can conclude that the relationship of the interaction between the factors is CD > BC > AB > BD > AD > AC, in which the interaction between extraction temperature and extraction time has a significant effect on the yield of polyphenol. In the extraction process, with the increase in temperature and time, the yield of polyphenols showed a tendency to increase before decreasing, because in a certain range, the increase intemperature and longer extraction time were beneficial to the extraction of polyphenols. When the temperature and time continued to increase, the yield of polyphenols showed a slightly decreasing trend, indicating that the high temperature and long extraction time had a negative effect on the yield of polyphenols, which might be caused by the decomposition of the structure of polyphenols.

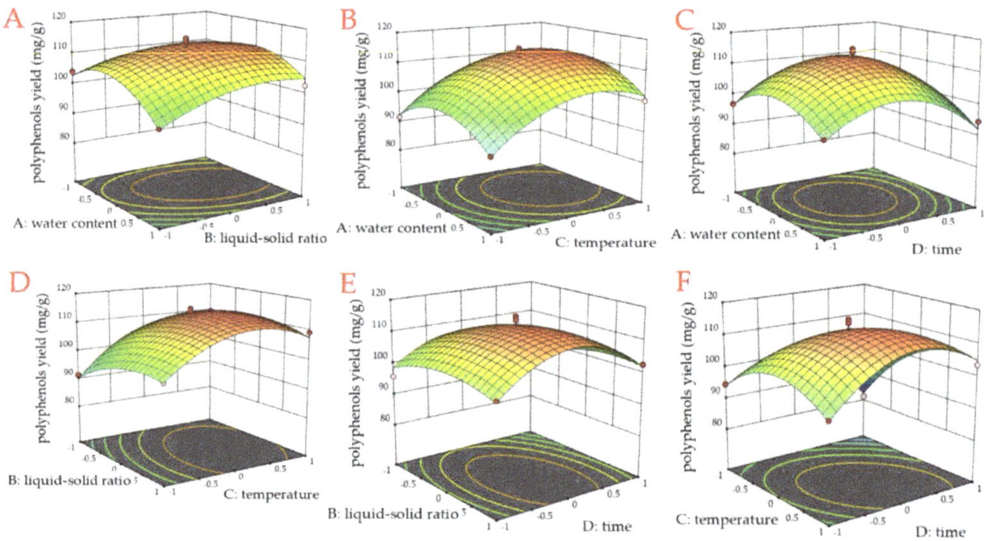

Figure 8. Response surface diagram of the interaction of different factors of polyphenols yield. (**A**)Water content and liquid–solid ratio; (**B**) water content and temperature; (**C**) water content and time; (**D**) liquid–solid ratio and temperature; (**E**) liquid–solid ratio and time; (**F**) temperature and time.

3.2.2. Analysis of Validation Test Results

A high extraction rate is the major objective of this research on the extraction of lotus leaves. The optimal extraction process was optimized by Design Expert 12.0 with the following four factors: water content 28.53%, liquid–solid ratio 37.23:1 (mL/g), extraction temperature 53.39 °C, and extraction time 60.915 min. Under the conditions of these four factors, the theoretically estimated number of flavonoids was 131.661 mg/g and the yield of polyphenols was 113.567 mg/g with 95.4% confidence. In the validation experiments, the operating parameters were adjusted to 29% water content, 37:1 liquid–solid ratio (mL/g), 53 °C extraction temperature, and 61 min extraction time, and three sets of parallel experiments were conducted, considering the actual conditions. The yield of lotus leaf flavonoids was 126.10 $\pm$ 3.64 mg/g and the yield of polyphenols was 113.12 $\pm$ 4.28 mg/g, which were 4.23% and 0.40% different from the theoretical values, indicating that the model fit well with the actual one and proved the feasibility of the model. In respect to polyphenol extraction, Viktoria Vorobyova et al. [35] investigated the extraction of polyphenols from tomato pomace with the help of ultrasound in a deep eutectic solvent based on choline chloride, and the total phenolic content of the extract was (51.75 $\pm$ 1.15 mg GAE (gallic acid equivalent)/g extract dry fraction), which was much lower than the polyphenol extraction rate of the present study.

3.2.3. Comparison of the Effects of Different Extraction Methods on Antioxidant Activity

The extracts of lotus leaves were performed with water, 70% ethanol, and a DES (lactic acid-propanetriol) to compare the antioxidant activity of the 3 extracts in terms of FRAP total reducing capacity, DPPH radicals, and ABTS cationic radical scavenging capacity, respectively. The FRAP total reducing capacity was reflected by comparing the ability of the extracts to convert Fe^{3+} to Fe^{2+}, i.e., the amount of Fe^{2+} production; therefore, a higher FRAP value in Table 6 indicates a higher total reducing capacity using this extraction method of lotus leaves. In both DPPH and ABTS free radical scavenging ability measurements, the smaller the value, the stronger the scavenging ability it represents. By comparing the values in Table 6, DES extraction has the smallest values for both DPPH radical scavenging capacity and ABTS scavenging capacity compared to the traditional water extraction and 70% ethanol extraction, while it has the largest values for total reducing capacity; therefore, a comprehensive comparison of the 3 antioxidant activities showed that DES extraction was superior to the conventional water and 70% ethanol extracts. Both the total flavonoids and the total phenolic acids showed better performance in terms of antioxidants; therefore, DES extraction has more obvious advantages in maintaining the activity of flavonoids and polyphenols. It shows that the extraction method used in this study is suitable for the extraction of lotus leaf flavonoids, as it improves the yield of active ingredients while ensuring the antioxidant activity.

Table 6. Antioxidant activity of different extracts.

	Water	Ethanol	DESs
FRAP (mmolFe^{2+}/g)	0.40	0.66	0.76
DPPH-IC50 (mg/g)	3.12	1.29	0.25
ABTS-IC50 (mg/g)	13.38	9.26	6.48

3.3. *Correlation Comparison of Different Extraction Methods*

The results of the correlation analysis are given in Table 7. Analysis of the data in Table 7 shows that the values of total polyphenol content (TPC), total flavonoid content (TFC), ABTS, DPPH, and FRAP are positive, indicating that the five factors are positively correlated with each other, and in terms of significance, the values of both comparisons are highly significant, indicating that the five factors have a strong positive correlation with each other.

Table 7. Analysis of correlation.

	TPC	TFC	ABTS	DPPH	FRAP
TPC	1				
TFC	0.972 **	1			
ABTS	0.971 **	0.941 **	1		
DPPH	0.829 **	0.773 **	0.892 **	1	
FRAP	0.843 **	0.77 **	0.877 **	0.903 **	1

$p < 0.01$ ** means significant statistical difference.

3.4. *LC–MS Detection Results*

The basal peak ion flow spectrum obtained from DES extract of lotus leaves analyzed by UPLC-QToF-MS is shown in Figure 9, from which the separation on C18 column by 2.9.1 gradient sub is better. Its main peaks were more than 20, and the peak shape was sharper. It proves that the changed conditions are suitable for LC–MS analysis.

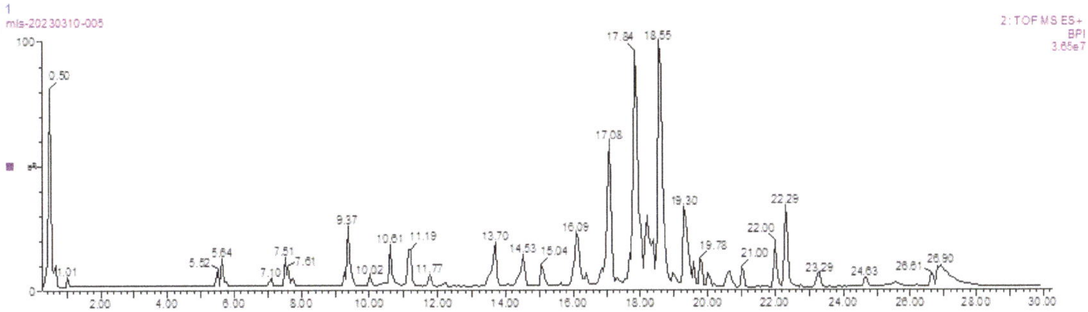

Figure 9. Example of the chromatogram of lotus leaves extract.

The results of compound analysis are shown in Table 8. It was found in the literature that most of the compounds contained in lotus leaves are flavonoids and organic acids [36,37]; therefore, 19 flavonoids or organic acid compounds with known compound structural formula were screened and determined to be contained in the DES extract of lotus leaves by MS profiling. Thus, it was demonstrated that the DES extraction of the constituents in lotus leaves was more complete.

Table 8. Identification of the chemical constituents contained in lotus leaves extract.

NO.	Rt (min)	Formula	Theoretical MASS (Da)	Calculated MASS (Da)	MASS ERROR (ppm)	Component Name
1	0.50	$C_{16}H_{12}O_5$	284.263	284.0685	−1.1	Oroxylin A
2	0.60	$C_{15}H_{10}O_7$	302.236	302.0427	1.6	Quercetin
3	0.67	$C_{15}H_{10}O_6$	286.236	286.0471	1.7	Kaempferol
4	1.14	$C_{16}H_{12}O_7$	316.2623	316.0583	−3.8	Isorhamnetin
5	10.19	$C_7H_6O_4$	154.12	154.0266	0.0	Protocatechuic acid
6	14.53	$C_{20}H_{18}O_{11}$	434.35	434.0849	1.1	Quercetin 3-O-arabinoside
7	14.58	$C_{21}H_{18}O_{13}$	478.36	478.0747	−3.3	Quercetin 3-O-glucuronide
8	14.99	$C_{22}H_{20}O_{11}$	460.4	460.1006	2.6	Oroxindin
9	15.28	$C_{21}H_{18}O_{12}$	462.36	462.0798	0.4	Kaempferol 3-O-glucuronide
10	15.99	$C_9H_8O_4$	180.157	180.0423	3.3	Caffeic acid
11	16.86	$C_{22}H_{22}O_{12}$	478.403	478.1111	−1.9	Isorhamnetin 3-O-hexose
12	16.91	$C_{22}H_{22}O_{11}$	462.41	462.1162	1.7	Diosmetin 7-O-hexose
13	17.96	$C_{21}H_{20}O_{12}$	464.376	464.1033	3.2	Quercetin 3-O-galactoside (hyperoside)
14	18.32	$C_{21}H_{20}O_{11}$	448.38	448.1006	−1.8	Kaempferol 3-O-glucoside (astragalin)
15	18.37	$C_{21}H_{20}O_{12}$	464.376	464.1033	−4.3	Quercetin 3-O-glucoside (isoquercitrin)
16	18.37	$C_{22}H_{20}O_{13}$	492.386	492.0904	−1.0	Isorhamnetin 3-O-glucuronide
17	26.80	$C_{21}H_{20}O_{13}$	480.376	480.0982	0.8	Myricetin 3-O-hexose
18	26.80	$C_{27}H_{30}O_{16}$	610.518	610.1534	4.3	Quercetin 3-O-rhamnopyranosyl-(1→2)-glucopyranoside
19	27.02	$C_{26}H_{28}O_{16}$	596.491	596.1377	2.8	Quercetin 3-O-arabinopyranosyl-(1→2)-galactopyranoside

Rt: retention time on LC–MS.

4. Conclusions

Nature deep eutectic solvents were used for the extraction of flavonoids from lotus leaves. Based on the single-factor assay, the procedure for the extraction of flavonoids and phenolic acids from lotus leaves by NDESs was optimized using the Box–Behnken design method. The optimal extraction process parameters were obtained as a DES system of lactic acid–propanetriol (molar ratio 1:2) with 29% water content, 37:1 solid–liquid ratio (mL/g), extraction temperature 53 °C, and extraction time 61 min. The yield of flavonoids under this condition was 126.0972 mg/g and the yield of polyphenols was 113.1163 mg/g, which were the same as the predicted values of the model. The extraction method used in this study improved the yield of flavonoids while increasing the antioxidant activity compared to the traditional extraction method and is suitable for the research on the extraction and antioxidant activity of lotus leaves. By comparing with the traditional extraction method, we observed that the deep eutectic solvent lactic acid–propanetriol system was superior to the traditional extraction method and that DESs were significantly better than water extraction and ethanol extraction in terms of their clearing ability of DPPH radicals and scavenging ability of ABTS cation radicals. It indicates that the extraction method used in this experiment is efficient and the application of deep eutectic solvent in the extraction of lotus leaf flavonoids is of high practical value. The DES extract of lotus leaves was analyzed by LC–MS and it was determined that 19 compounds in lotus leaves were extracted, indicating a highly efficient DES extraction. As a new extraction system, deep eutectic solvents have the advantages of being green, sustainable, and low-cost, and many studies have shown that its efficiency in extracting active ingredients is higher than that of traditional organic solvents, so deep eutectic solvents can replace traditional organic solvents to a certain extent and can be applied to functional food and pharmaceutical fields, providing a theoretical basis for further development and utilization of lotus leaves.

Author Contributions: Investigation, formal analysis, writing—original draft, visualization, J.Y.; data curation, formal analysis, writing—review and editing, Z.Y.; investigation, visualization, L.L.; investigation, data curation, L.Z.; software, data curation, M.Z.; formal analysis, H.Y.; investigation, data curation, Z.W. (Ziying Wang); methodology, resources, G.L.; methodology, resources, Z.W. (Zhenhua Wang); supervision, writing—review and editing, data curation, M.L.; supervision, funding acquisition, writing—review and editing, project administration, C.M. All authors have read and agreed to the published version of the manuscript.

Funding: This work was supported by the Shandong Provincial Natural Science Foundation, China (ZR2019MH094, ZR2020MH380), and the Innovation Platform for the Development and Construction of Special Project of Qinghai Province (2021-ZJ-T05).

Data Availability Statement: Data are available on request from the authors.

Conflicts of Interest: The authors declare no conflict of interest.

References

1. Zhili, M.; Yu, M.; Yin, L.; Bei, Z.; Yalin, Z.; Ping, W.; Dexin, Z.; Deyuan, L. Effects of maturity and processing on the volatile components, phytochemical profiles and antioxidant activity of Lotus (*Nelumbo nucifera*) Leaf. *Foods* **2023**, *12*, 198. [CrossRef]
2. Zhu, M.-Z.; Wu, W.; Jiao, L.-L.; Yang, P.-F.; Guo, M.-Q. Analysis of flavonoids in Lotus (*Nelumbo nucifera*) leaves and their antioxidant activity using macroporous resin chromatography coupled with LC-MS/MS and antioxidant biochemical assays. *Molecules* **2015**, *20*, 10553. [CrossRef]
3. Showkat, Q.A.; Rather, J.A.; Jabeen, A.; Dar, B.N.; Makroo, H.A.; Majid, D. Bioactive components, physicochemical and starch characteristics of different parts of lotus (*Nelumbo nucifera* Gaertn.) plant: A review. *Int. J. Food Sci. Technol.* **2021**, *56*, 2205–2214. [CrossRef]
4. Ahn, J.H.; Kim, E.S.; Lee, C.; Kim, S.; Cho, S.H.; Hwang, B.Y.; Lee, M.K. Chemical constituents from *Nelumbo nucifera* leaves and their anti-obesity effects. *Bioorganic Med. Chem. Lett.* **2013**, *23*, 3604–3608. [CrossRef]
5. Hammi, K.M.; Essid, R.; Khadraoui, N.; Ksouri, R.; Majdoub, H.; Tabbene, O. Antimicrobial, antioxidant and antileishmanial activities of Ziziphus lotus leaves. *Arch. Microbiol.* **2022**, *204*, 119. [CrossRef] [PubMed]
6. Da-Hee, K.; Won-Young, C.; Su-Jung, Y.; Sung-Hee, C.; Chi-Ho, L. Effects of Lotus (*Nelumbo nucifera*) Leaf on quality and antioxidant activity of Yogurt during refrigerated storage. *Food Sci. Anim. Resour.* **2019**, *39*, 792–803. [CrossRef]
7. Lee, H.-J.; Chen, C.-C.; Chou, F.-P.; Wu, C.-H.; Lai, F.-S.; Yang, M.-Y.; Wang, C.-J. Water extracts from *Nelumbo nucifera* leaf reduced plasma lipids and atherosclerosis in Cholesterol-Fed rabbits. *J. Food Biochem.* **2010**, *34*, 779–795. [CrossRef]
8. Liu, T.; Tan, F.; Long, X.; Pan, Y.; Mu, J.; Zhou, X.; Yi, R.; Zhao, X. Improvement effect of Lotus Leaf flavonoids on carbon Tetrachloride-Induced liver injury in mice. *Biomedicines* **2020**, *2*, 41. [CrossRef]
9. Zheng, H.X.; Han, L.T.; Shi, W.F.; Fang, X.P.; Hong, Y.; Cao, Y. Research advances in Lotus Leaf as Chinese Dietary Herbal Medicine. *Am. J. Chin. Med.* **2022**, *50*, 1423–1445. [CrossRef] [PubMed]
10. Wang, Z.Y.; Cheng, Y.; Zeng, M.M.; Wang, Z.J.; Qin, F.; Wang, Y.Z.; Chen, J.; He, Z.Y. Lotus (*Nelumbo nucifera* Gaertn.) leaf: A narrative review of its Phytoconstituents, health benefits and food industry applications. *Trends Food Sci. Technol.* **2021**, *112*, 631–650. [CrossRef]
11. Routray, W.; Orsat, V. Microwave-Assisted extraction of flavonoids: A Review. *Food Bioprocess Technol.* **2012**, *5*, 409–424. [CrossRef]
12. Oroian, M.; Ursachi, F.; Dranca, F. Ultrasound-Assisted extraction of polyphenols from crude pollen. *Antioxidants* **2020**, *9*, 322. [CrossRef] [PubMed]
13. Smith, E.L.; Abbott, A.P.; Ryder, K.S. Deep eutectic solvents (DESs) and their applications. *Chem. Rev.* **2014**, *114*, 11060–11082. [CrossRef] [PubMed]
14. Luo, S.B.; Ren, X.M.; Shi, X.Q.; Zhong, K.; Zhang, Z.J.; Wang, Z.T. Study on enhanced extraction and seasonal variation of secondary metabolites in Eucommia ulmoides leaves using deep eutectic solvents. *J. Pharm. Biomed. Anal.* **2022**, *209*, 114514. [CrossRef] [PubMed]
15. Babu, S.M.; Kumar, V.S.; Mansi, C.; Prashant, S. A mini review on synthesis, properties and applications of deep eutectic solvents. *J. Indian Chem. Soc.* **2021**, *98*, 100210. [CrossRef]
16. Sillero, L.; Prado, R.; Welton, T.; Labidi, J. Extraction of flavonoid compounds from bark using sustainable deep eutectic solvents. *Sustain. Chem. Pharm.* **2021**, *24*, 100544. [CrossRef]
17. Dai, Y.; Witkamp, G.J.; Verpoorte, R.; Choi, Y.H. Natural deep eutectic solvents as a new extraction media for phenolic metabolites in *Carthamus tinctorius* L. *Anal. Chem.* **2013**, *85*, 6272–6278. [CrossRef] [PubMed]
18. Sami, D.A.; Fadzelly, A.B.M.; Mohamed, A.; Fatimah, S.S.; Fathi, M.H.A.; Azman, M. Deep Eutectic Solvents (DESs) as green extraction media of beneficial bioactive phytochemicals. *Separations* **2021**, *8*, 176. [CrossRef]
19. Bárbara, S.; Vanessa, T.M.; Gerardo, Á.; Mendiola, J.A. Deep eutectic solvents for the extraction of bioactive compounds from natural sources and agricultural By-Products. *Appl. Sci.* **2021**, *11*, 4897. [CrossRef]
20. Wojeicchowski, P.; Ferreira, A.M.; Abranches, D.O.; Mafra, M.R.; Coutinho, J.A.P. Using Cosmo-Rs in the design of deep eutectic solvents for thie extraction of antioxidants from rosemary. *ACS Sustain. Chem. Eng.* **2020**, *8*, 12132–12141. [CrossRef]

21. Zhang, H.; Hao, F.; Yao, Z.; Zhu, J.; Jing, X.; Wang, X. Efficient extraction of flavonoids from Polygonatum sibiricum using a deep eutectic solvent as a green extraction solvent. *Microchem. J.* **2022**, *175*, 107168. [CrossRef]
22. Kimia, J.; Hossein, F.M.; Patrice, E. Deep eutectic solvents (DESs): A short overview of the thermophysical properties and current use as base fluid for heat transfer nanofluids. *J. Mol. Liq.* **2021**, *321*, 114752. [CrossRef]
23. Henkel, S.; Beutel, S. Messung des pH-Werts in der Biotechnologie. *Chem. Ing. Tech.* **2013**, *6*, 872–885. [CrossRef]
24. Bubalo, M.C.; Curko, N.; Tomasevic, M.; Ganic, K.K.; Redovnikovic, I.R. Green extraction of grape skin phenolics by using deep eutectic solvents. *Food Chem.* **2016**, *200*, 159–166. [CrossRef]
25. Ji, Y.B.; Guo, S.Z.; Wang, B.; Yu, M. Extraction and determination of flavonoids in Carthamus tinctorius. *Open Chem.* **2018**, *16*, 1129–1133. [CrossRef]
26. Sutivisedsak, N.; Cheng, H.N.; Willett, J.L.; Lesch, W.C.; Tangsrud, R.R.; Biswas, A. Microwave-assisted extraction of phenolics from bean (*Phaseolus vulgaris* L.). *Food Res. Int.* **2010**, *43*, 516–519. [CrossRef]
27. Chen, X.; Liang, L.; Han, C. Borate suppresses the scavenging activity of gallic acid and plant polyphenol extracts on DPPH radical: A potential interference to DPPH assay. *LWT* **2020**, *131*, 109769. [CrossRef]
28. Ali, A.R. Review on extraction of phenolic compounds from natural sources using green deep eutectic solvents. *J. Agric. Food Chem.* **2021**, *69*, 878–912. [CrossRef]
29. Dai, Y.; Witkamp, G.-J.; Verpoorte, R.; Choi, Y.H. Tailoring properties of natural deep eutectic solvents with water to facilitate their applications. *Food Chem.* **2015**, *187*, 14–19. [CrossRef] [PubMed]
30. Jablonský, M.; Škulcová, A.; Malvis, A.; Šima, J. Extraction of value-added components from food industry based and agro-forest biowastes by deep eutectic solvents. *J. Biotechnol.* **2018**, *282*, 46–66. [CrossRef]
31. Cao, Q.; Li, J.; Xia, Y.; Li, W.; Luo, S.; Ma, C.; Liu, S.; Ibañez, E.; Chemat, F. Green Extraction of Six Phenolic Compounds from Rattan (*Calamoideae faberii*) with Deep Eutectic Solvent by Homogenate-Assisted Vacuum-Cavitation Method. *Molecules* **2018**, *24*, 113. [CrossRef]
32. Alberto, G.; Mert, A.; Santiago, A. Molecular dynamics study on water confinement in deep eutectic solvents. *J. Mol. Liq.* **2021**, *339*, 116758. [CrossRef]
33. Achkar, T.E.; Fourmentin, S.; Greige-Gerges, H. Deep eutectic solvents: An overview on their interactions with water and biochemical compounds. *J. Mol. Liq.* **2019**, *288*, 111028. [CrossRef]
34. Balaraman, H.B.; Rathnasamy, S.K. Selective purification of protease from ginger and sodom apple by ultrasound assisted liquid-liquid microextraction using natural deep eutectic solvent. *Microchem. J.* **2019**, *150*, 104132. [CrossRef]
35. Vorobyova, V.; Skiba, M.; Vasyliev, G. Extraction of phenolic compounds from tomato pomace using choline chloride-based deep eutectic solvents. *J. Food Meas. Charact.* **2022**, *16*, 1087–1104. [CrossRef]
36. Chen, S.; Fang, L.C.; Xi, H.F.; Guan, L.; Fang, J.B.; Liu, Y.L.; Wu, B.H.; Li, S.H. Simultaneous qualitative assessment and quantitative analysis of flavonoids in various tissues of lotus (*Nelumbo nucifera*) using high performance liquid chromatography coupled with triple quad mass spectrometry. *Anal. Chim. Acta* **2012**, *724*, 127–135. [CrossRef]
37. Wang, Y.B.; Lin, B.J.; Li, Z.X. Effect of Lactobacillus plantarum Fermentation on Metabolites in Lotus Leaf Based on Ultra-High-Performance Liquid Chromatography-High-Resolution Mass Spectrometry. *Fermentation* **2022**, *8*, 599. [CrossRef]

nutrients

MDPI

Review

Legume-Derived Bioactive Peptides in Type 2 Diabetes: Opportunities and Challenges

Kanghong Hu †, Huizhong Huang †, Hanluo Li, Yanhong Wei and Chenguang Yao *

Sino-German Biomedical Center, Hubei Provincial Key Laboratory of Industrial Microbiology, Cooperative Innovation Center of Industrial Fermentation (Ministry of Education & Hubei Province), Key Laboratory of Fermentation Engineering (Ministry of Education), National "111" Center for Cellular Regulation and Molecular Pharmaceutics, Hubei University of Technology, Wuhan 430068, China

* Correspondence: yaochenguang@hbut.edu.cn; Tel.: +86-(027)-59750462

† These authors contributed equally to this work.

Abstract: Diabetes mellitus is a complex disorder characterized by insufficient insulin production or insulin resistance, which results in a lifelong dependence on glucose-lowering drugs for almost all patients. During the fight with diabetes, researchers are always thinking about what characteristics the ideal hypoglycemic drugs should have. From the point of view of the drugs, they should maintain effective control of blood sugar, have a very low risk of hypoglycemia, not increase or decrease body weight, improve β-cell function, and delay disease progression. Recently, the advent of oral peptide drugs, such as semaglutide, brings exciting hope to patients with chronic diabetes. Legumes, as an excellent source of protein, peptides, and phytochemicals, have played significant roles in human health throughout human history. Some legume-derived peptides with encouraging anti-diabetic potential have been gradually reported over the last two decades. Their hypoglycemic mechanisms have also been clarified at some classic diabetes treatment targets, such as the insulin receptor signaling pathway or other related pathways involved in the progress of diabetes, and key enzymes including α-amylase, α-glucosidase, and dipeptidyl peptidase-IV (DPP-4). This review summarizes the anti-diabetic activities and mechanisms of peptides from legumes and discusses the prospects of these peptide-based drugs in type 2 diabetes (T2D) management.

Keywords: bioactive peptide; legume; type 2 diabetes (T2D); hypoglycemic peptide

1. Introduction

Diabetes is a metabolic disease characterized by a persistent over-normal level of blood glucose that causes impressive morbidity and mortality worldwide [1]. Persistent hyperglycemia imposes damage on other organs, such as the eye, heart, kidney, and skin, as well as the nervous system, and is strongly correlated with a myriad of diabetes-related complications [2]. Diabetes typically develops when the pancreas does not create enough insulin, or the organs involved in glucose metabolic regulation do not effectively respond to the insulin [3]. Type 1 diabetes (T1D, 5–7%), type 2 diabetes (T2D, 90%), and gestational diabetes (GD, 2–3%) are the three most common forms of diabetes [4]. T1D is a destructive autoimmune disease of pancreatic β-cells, leading to a deficiency of insulin. T2D is the most prevalent kind of diabetes in the general population, and is frequently caused by inadequate insulin production or insulin resistance [5,6]. GD is another type of diabetes that is caused by abnormal glucose tolerance and diabetes during pregnancy [7,8]. The global prevalence of diabetes shows that 537 million adults were troubled by diabetes in 2021, and the diabetic population is estimated to rise to 643 million (11.3%) in 2030 and to 783 million (12.2%) in 2045 [9]. In recent years, the incidence of T2D cases has accelerated rapidly, and it is predicted that the T2D cases may reach 700 million in 2045 [9].

Given the grim reality of T2D, several strategies including appropriate exercise, reasonable diet, and pharmacotherapy have been applied to control postprandial hyperglycemia to prevent the development of the disease. However, pharmacotherapy is the most effective method, and is favored by T2D patients. Up to now, existing drugs such as insulin and its analogues, metformin, sulfonylurea, glucagon-like peptide-1 (GLP-1) receptor agonist, dipeptidyl peptidase IV (DPP-4) inhibitor, sodium-glucose cotransporter-2 (SGLT-2) inhibitor, α-glucosidase inhibitor, etc., have been approved for the treatment of T2D. However, because no drug has yet been identified to cure T2D, nearly all T2D patients have a lifelong dependence on glucose-lowering medications. It is worth noting that recent studies have highlighted that pretreatment via the intake of special food can significantly reduce the prevalence of T2D for high-risk groups, resulting in the minimalization of the economic impact of T2D treatment [8,10].

Biopeptides are easily absorbed food-derived protein segments that play crucial roles in controlling or pretreating metabolism-related chronic diseases, such as the mild T2D subtype [11]. Recently, legume-derived peptides, such as native peptides and hydrolytic peptides from legume proteins, have been reported to prevent or treat T2D in animal models and in clinical studies. Mechanically, these peptides regulate glucose metabolism via several ways, e.g., increasing insulin secretion, improving the sensitivity of the body's response to insulin, and inhibiting the activities of key enzymes (α-amylase, α-glucosidase, DPP-4) [12]. Aglycin family members, which are highly conserved peptides containing 37 amino acids extracted from soybeans, can resist gastric and intestinal protease degradation and exhibit insulin-like activities [13]. Legume protein hydrolysates (also called oligopeptides), always containing 2–20 amino acids produced by enzymatic hydrolysis, microbial fermentation, or food processing, have potential anti-diabetic activity because they interact with the catalytic site of the key enzymes [12,14,15]. Researchers are increasingly concerned with the development of legume-derived hypoglycemic peptide drugs and oral-specific medical foods for the control and treatment of T2D. This review summarizes the anti-diabetic activity and hypoglycemic mechanism of legume-derived peptides, which provides an option for the development of oral hypoglycemic drugs.

2. T2D and Its Therapy

2.1. *The Aberrant Glucose Metabolism in T2D*

The normal regulation of glucose metabolism is determined by a feedback loop consisting of pancreatic β-cells and insulin-responding tissues (such as the liver, skeletal muscle, and adipocytes) [5]. Pancreatic β-cells, located in the islets of Langerhans, lower postprandial blood glucose through glucose-dependent insulin secretion [16]. Insulin stimulates the liver, skeletal muscles, and adipocytes to transform glucose, amino acids, and fatty acids for energy storage. When insulin resistance occurs, the insulin-responding tissues and organs cannot sensitively utilize glucose. Hence, more insulin is needed to maintain the standard glucose tolerance, which may cause the overwork and dysfunction of islet β-cells [5]. β-cells' dysfunction results in a relative lack of insulin secretion, which causes the development of hyperglycemia or T2D [6,17].

T2D is characterized by a relative lack of insulin secretion or insulin resistance occurring in the insulin-responding organs. The current multiple drugs of T2D work mainly by reversing several physiological indexes to lower blood glucose, including an increase of insulin secretion (pancreas islet β-cells), a decrease of glucagon secretion (pancreas islet α-cells), an improvement of neurotransmitter dysfunction (brain), a decrease of hepatic glucose production (liver), an increase of peripheral glucose absorption and deceleration of lipolysis (muscle and adipose tissue), a decrease of renal reabsorption of glucose (kidney), an increase of incretin effect and decrease of glucose absorption (intestinal), an improvement of balance of gut microbiota (colon) [18]. An early start and a combination of multiple therapy drugs can bring benefits to T2D patients.

2.2. *Clinical Therapeutic Drugs and Their Targets in T2D*

Some anti-diabetic drugs targeting specific tissues and organs have been approved. The definite targets of these drugs are mainly α-amylase, α-glucosidase, dipeptidyl peptidase-4 (DPP-4), glucagon-like peptide-1 (GLP-1), gastric inhibitory peptide (GIP), gastrointestinal target hormone peptide (PYY), glucose transporters (GLUTs), and sodium-dependent glucose cotransporters (SGLTs) (Table 1) [5,19–21]. Insulin and its analogs are the most common injectable diabetes drugs for patients with severe pancreatic dysfunction. Oral anti-diabetic drugs mainly include metformin, sulfonylureas, glinides, thiazolidinediones (TZDs), DPP-4 inhibitors, SGLT-2 inhibitors, α-amylase inhibitors, and α-glucosidase inhibitors. The current medications can lessen the harm to the body brought on by hyperglycemia by regulating blood sugar levels and increasing insulin sensitivity [22].

Table 1. Clinical drugs in T2D and their target organs/tissues.

Target Organs/Tissues	Mechanism	Drug Class	Drug Name	Adverse Reaction	Drug Delivery
Pancreatic β-cell	β-cell mass restore, increasing insulin secretion	Sulfonylurea	Glibenclamide, glipizide, glimepiride, gliclazide	Cause hypoglycemia	Oral
		Meglitinide	Repaglinide, nateglinide	Not cause hypoglycemia	Oral
Pancreatic α-cell	Increasing glucagon secretion	GLP-1 agonist	Exenatide, lixisenatide, liraglutide, dulaglutide, exenatide extend-release, semaglutide, albiglutide	Gastrointestinal and hypoglycemic reactions	Inject/Oral
		Amylin analog	Pramlintide	Cause hypoglycemic	Inject
		Biguanide	Metformin	Lactic acidemia and ketouria	Oral
Liver	Decreasing hepatic glucose production	Thiazolidinedione	Pioglitazone, rosiglitazone	Weight gain, edema, cardiac problems	Oral
		Insulin	Rapid-, short-, intermediate-, long-acting insulin	Hypoglycemia and edema	Inject
		Biguanide	Metformin	Lactic acidemia and ketouria	Oral
Muscle and adipose tissue	Increasing glucose uptake and glycolysis	Biguanide	Metformin	Lactic acidemia and ketouria	Oral
		Thiazolidinedione	Pioglitazone, rosiglitazone	Weight gain, edema, cardiac problems	Oral
		Insulin	Rapid-, short-, intermediate-, long-acting insulin	Hypoglycemia and edema	Inject
		α-glucosidase inhibitor	Acarbose, miglitol, voglibose	Gastrointestinal reaction	Oral
Intestine	Increasing incretin activity, enhancing glucose absorption	DPP-4 inhibitor	Sitagliptin, saxagliptin, linagliptin, vidaglipti, alogliptin, teneligliptin, gemigliptin	Minor adverse drug reactions	Oral
		GLP-1 agonist	Exenatide, lixisenatide, liraglutide, dulaglutide, exenatide extend-release, semaglutide, albiglutide	Gastrointestinal and hypoglycemic reactions	Inject/Oral
		Biguanide	Metformin	Lactic acidemia and ketouria	Oral
Colon	Balancing gut microbiota	GLP-1 agonist	Exenatide, lixisenatide, liraglutide, dulaglutide, exenatide extend-release, semaglutide, albiglutide	Gastrointestinal and hypoglycemic reactions	Inject/Oral
Kidney	Inhibiting glucose reabsorption	SGLT-2 inhibitor	Dapagliflozin, canagliflozin, empagliflozin, ertugliflozin, Sotagliflozin	Urinary genital infection risk, ketoacidosis risk	Oral
Central nervous system	Lowing neurotransmitters	Dopamine-receptor agonist	Bromocriptine	Gastrointestinal reaction	Oral

Insulin, the most important regulator of metabolism, reduces blood sugar by preventing hepatic glucose synthesis and promoting intracellular glucose uptake by fat and muscle cells. Insulin and its analogues have a short action period and a risk of minimally invasive infection and other side effects, such as hypoglycemia, resistance, allergy, edema, and lipodystrophy [23]. The market for peptide-based medicines has been firmly established by the creation of human insulin utilizing recombinant technology, as well as other synthetic hormones [4]. Oral insulin is superior to other forms of insulin delivery because it follows the normal physiological pathway, that is, through the portal vein circulation of the liver, first reaching the liver and later the peripheral tissues [24].

Metformin, an oral medication, is used to reduce blood sugar levels in people with non-insulin-dependent diabetic mellitus. It promotes the uptake and utilization of glucose in adipocytes and muscles and improves insulin sensitivity by reducing glucose synthesis in the liver [12]. Metformin has good security, but 5–15% of the administrated patients are still troubled by side effects, such as diarrhea, nausea, indigestion, and other gastrointestinal symptoms [20]. TZDs also ameliorate insulin resistance in adipocytes, liver, and muscle [25]. Rosiglitazone and pioglitazone, peroxisome proliferator-activated receptor c (PPARc) agonists of TZDs, act as insulin sensitizers that bring benefits by maintaining long-term glycemic balance [25]. Presently, TZDs are rarely considered for the treatment of T2D due to side effects, such as cardiac issues, edema, and weight gain.

Sulfonylureas are currently used as second-line drugs for T2D or in combination with other medications. They promote insulin secretion by blocking K+ channels in pancreatic tissue, limiting gluconeogenesis, reducing the insulin clearance rate in the liver, and reducing fatty acid decomposition [26,27]. First-generation and second-generation sulfonylureas are the two categories. The tolbutamide and chlorpropamide sulfonylureas are first-generation sulfonylureas. Glyburide (also known as glibenclamide), glipizide, glimepiride, and gliclazide are second-generation sulfonylureas. These days, second-generation sulfonate drugs are used in clinical settings more frequently. All sulfonyl medications have a common side effect called hypoglycemia, along with less serious side effects like headache, nausea, dizziness, allergic reactions, and weight gain [6]. Meglitinides, non-sulfonylureas insulin secretagogues, also target pancreatic β-cell tissue, stimulating the pancreatic β-cells to secrete insulin, without hypoglycemic risk [26].

SGLT-2 inhibitors are oral hypoglycemic medications that lower blood sugar by blocking renal glucose reabsorption. They prevent about 90% of the filtered glucose reabsorption by directly inactivating the SGLT-2, a glucose transporter located in the proximal tubules' first section [20,28]. SGLT-2 inhibitors include dapagliflozin, canagliflozin, empagliflozin, ertugliflozin, and sotagliflozin. They also have side effects, such as urinary and genital infection risk (6.4%) and ketoacidosis risk [6]. Glucose reabsorption is blocked in the kidney when SGLT-2 is inhibited, resulting in insulin-independent glucose lowering as well as a reduction in weight and blood pressure [20].

GLP-1 receptor agonists, GLP-1 analogues, and incretin mimics are common hypoglycemic drugs. Injectable GLP-1 receptor agonists include exenatide, liraglutide, lixisenatide, albiglutide, and dulaglutide. They control the blood glucose balance via the enhancement of insulin release and suppression of excessive glucagon secretion by activating the GLP-1 receptor [7]. Exedin-4 is one of the most promising GLP-1 receptor agonists currently utilized to treat diabetes, and is injected twice daily [29]. Liraglutide is a once-daily GLP-1 analogue, whose homology of amino acids sequence with human GLP-1 is 97% [30]. The modification of a fatty acid at position 26, and the replacement of lysine with arginine at position 34, result in an extension of the plasma half-life of liraglutide (13 h), an increase of self-association, and a resistance to digestion of DPP-4 [31,32]. In 2019, semaglutide (Rybelsus®), the first oral hypoglycemic peptide drug, was approved by the U.S. Food and Drug Administration (FDA) to improve glycemic control in adults with T2D [33]. The combination of semaglutide and a pharmaceutical sodium 8-[(2-hydroxybenzoyl)amino]octanoate (SNAC), an absorption enhancer, leads to a better solubility of semaglutide and an increased resistance to degradation at a low pH value [31]. Despite being combined with SNAC, the oral bioavailability of Rybelsus® is only 0.4–1% [30].

DPP-4 inhibitors are oral medications that extend the half-lives of endogenous incretins by preventing the DPP-4 enzyme from digesting incretins [28,34]. These medications include sitagliptin, vildagliptin, saxagliptin, linagliptin, and alogliptin. The hypoglycemic effect of DPP-4 inhibitors is characterized by glucose concentration dependence. Therefore, they generally may not cause hypoglycemia.

Mounjaro (tirzepatide) is a "first-in-class" injectable drug that activates both GIP and GLP-1 receptors, controlling hyperglycemia through a dual mechanism of action [35,36]. Imeglimin, another "first-in-class" oral tablet, can improve insulin secretion disorders with a novel mechanism of action targeting mitochondrial bioenergetics [37]. It rebalances respiratory chain activity, resulting in less reactive oxygen species formation and the prevention of mitochondrial permeability transition pore opening [37]. Chiglitazar, a PPAR complete agonist, is a new oral drug approved by China's national medical products administration for T2D treatment in 2021; it can activate three subunits of PPAR (α, γ, and δ) [38,39].

α-glucosidase inhibitors (acarbose, miglitol, voglibose) and α-amylase inhibitors are the first-line drugs for T2D. They lower blood glucose levels by slowing down the digestion rate and inhibiting intestinal glucose absorption [40]. Their main side effect is gastrointestinal reaction.

Over the past few decades, there has been a significant increase in therapy alternatives, but none of them has prevented the decline of β-cell function. The current drugs available to treat T2D listed in Table 1 have side effects, and most of them are administered by injection. As a result, many scientists have made efforts to create alternative delivery methods, such as transdermal, oral, nasal, and ocular delivery. Due to the higher safety and compliance, the oral route remains the most appealing option for T2D patients. Currently, various oral peptide drugs have reached clinical trials, including oral insulin, calcitonin, parathyroid hormone, and vasopressin. The approval of an oral formulation of the GLP-1 receptor agonist semaglutide for the treatment of T2D represents a significant landmark in the development of oral peptide drugs [33].

3. Legume-Derived Peptides and Their Anti-Diabetic Activity

The legume is the fruit or seed of plants of the legume family, which are used for food, including lentils (*Lens culinaris*), common beans (*Phaseolus vulgaris*), broad beans (*Vicia faba*), dry peas (*Pisum sativum*), chickpeas (*Cicer arietinum*), cowpeas (*Vigna sinensis*), and mung beans (*Vigna radiata*) [41]. Legumes are an excellent source of good quality protein (20–45% protein), providing high amounts of the essential amino acids such as lysine and leucine, and lower amounts of methionine and tryptophan, complex carbohydrates, dietary fiber, unsaturated fats, vitamins, and essential minerals for the human diet [42,43].

The intake of legumes brings many benefits and positive effects for physical health, especially on metabolic syndromes, such as cardiovascular protection and the regulation of glucose and lipid metabolism [11,44]. Legume proteins can be converted into a variety of peptides that control vital biological activities, especially those involved in the endocrinology of living organisms [45,46]. Several observations of clinical statistics indicate that intake of legumes (lentils, chickpeas, and soybeans) or their protein significantly lowers the risk of T2D among Caucasians and Xanthoderms in different countries [47–50]. The relationship between the risk of T2D and the intake of legumes is listed in Table 2.

Given that legumes and their proteins benefit T2D patients, various legume-derived peptides are identified as anti-hyperglycemia agents due to their metabolic regulating bioactivity in vivo or in vitro. Plant-derived peptides have been shown to have hypoglycemic effects as well, which overcome security hurdles and yield an efficient treatment for T2D [4,51]. These agents can be divided into native proteins, peptides, and protein hydrolysates (hydrolytic peptides) [4,52]. The native proteins and peptides can be directly extracted and purified from legume storage or germinating seeds. Hydrolytic peptides, also called oligopeptides, are a mixture derived from the legume protein by digestion of various enzymes, fermentation of microorganisms, or mechanical cutting. Several studies have demonstrated the potential anti-diabetic activity of native preparations and hydrolysates in vitro, in vivo, or in clinical trials [53–55].

Table 2. Risk of T2D in relation to the average intake of legumes and their proteins.

Source	Consumption(g/d)	People Tested	HRs or RR (95% CIs)	Reference
Lentils	6.6	Caucasian	0.67 (0.46, 0.98)	[47]
Chickpea	5.0	Caucasian	0.68 (0.46, 1.00)	[47]
Soybean	32.0	Chinese women	0.57 (0.48, 0.60)	[48]
Soy protein	11.0–15.0	Chinese/Japanese	0.84 (0.75, 0.95)	[49]
Soy protein	13.6	Japanese women	0.46 (0.30, 0.70)	[50]

CIs, confidence intervals; HRs, hazard ratios; RR, relative risk.

Animal models are the most common approaches to investigate the anti-diabetic activity of drugs in vivo, including streptozotocin (STZ) and high-fat diet (HFD)-induced diabetic mice [14,56,57], KKA^y diabetic mice [58], T1D Sprague Dawley (SD) rats [14,59], STZ-induced Wistar rats [60,61], HFD-C57BL/6J mice [15], and alloxan-induced diabetic mice [62]. The potential anti-diabetic benefits of legume hydrolysates and fractions or synthesized pure peptides have been investigated by several cell line models. Glucose consumption activities were evaluated by human HepG2 [15,57,59,63,64], Caco-2 [64], 3T3-L1 [64,65], and INS-1E cells [14,66]. Furthermore, Rat L6 skeletal muscle cells [67], Min6 cell NCI-H716 [65], and human embryo kidney 293 cell models [65] were used to evaluate the activation of the insulin signaling pathway. The legume-derived peptides related to anti-diabetic activities, experimental models, and anti-diabetic mechanisms are summarized in Table 3.

Table 3. Hypoglycemic effect and mechanism of legume peptides and hydrolysates in vivo and in vitro.

Peptide	Amino Acid Sequence	Source	Model	Feeding/Treat Pattern	Hypoglycemic Effect and Index	Mechanism	Reference
Aglycin	ASCNGVCSPFEMP PCGS SACRCIPVGLVVGY CRHPSG	Soybean	STZ/HFD-induced diabetic BALB/c mice, C2C12 cell	50 mg/kg/d, 4 weeks	BG↓, OGTT↑, insulin tolerance↑, p-IR↑, p-IRS1↑, p-Akt↑, GLUT4↑, glucose uptake↑	Increasing insulin receptor via IR/IRS1 pathway, enhancing glucose uptake	[56]
Vglycin	VSCNGVCSPFEMP PCGSSACRCIPY GLVVGNCRHPSG	Pea seed/germinating pea seed	STZ/HFD-induced diabetic rats, HepG2 cell, L02 cell	4 weeks	BW↓, food intake↓, FPG↑, PARP↑, PDX1↑, GSK3α/β↑, GLUT4↑, p85-PI3-kinase↓, p-Akt↓	Impairing glucose tolerance, restoring pancreatic function, enhancing insulin signaling by activating the IR/Akt pathway	[57]
			T1D SD rat, STZ-induced T2D C57BL/6 mice, INS-1 832/13 cell	80 mg/kg/d, 4 weeks, 8 weeks	BW↓, lee's index↓, food intake↓, FPG↓, BG↓, ITT↑, pancreatic islet↑, plasma insulin↑, glucose-stimulated glucagon↓, pancreatic mass↑, β-cell area and mass↑, Ki67/PCNA immunostaining area↑, TUNEL-positive/total β-cells↓, Erk↑	Promoting the proliferation of β-cells via the IR/Akt/Erk pathway	[14]
			HFD-C57BL/6J mice, HepG2 cell	15 weeks	BW↓, FPG↓, glucose tolerance↑, ITT↑, FA β-oxidation↑, FAS↓	Improving insulin sensitivity and glucose tolerance, enhancing β-oxidation and inhibiting FAS via AMPK pathway and down-regulating the FAS	[15]
Soymorphin-5	YPFVV	Soybean	KKA^y mice	10 mg/kg/d, 5 weeks	BG↓, plasma insulin↓, TG↓, adiponectin↑, liver TG↓, Adipor2↑, PPARα↑, AOX1↑, CPT1↑, UCP2 1↑	Increasing insulin sensitivity, improving glucose and lipid metabolism via activation of the adiponectin and PPARα system	[58]
Soy protein	/	Soybean	ZDF rat	Soy protein, 11 weeks	BW↓, total adiposity↓, total and liver adiposity↓, glucose level↓, insulin↓, GLUT4↑, PPAR-r↑, FAS↓, GPDH↓	Maintenance of peripheral (adipose tissue) insulin signaling	[68]
Soy protein	/	Soybean	KKA^y mice	High content isoflavone soy protein, 9 weeks	FPG↓, insulin↓, TG↓, TC↓, GLUT2↑, GLUT3↑, Ins1↑, Ins2↑, IGF1↓, β2/Neurod1↓, cholecystokinin↓, LDLR↑	Improving glucose and insulin sensitivity	[69]

Table 3. *Cont.*

Peptide	Amino Acid Sequence	Source	Model	Feeding/Treat Pattern	Hypoglycemic Effect and Index	Mechanism	Reference
γ-conglutin	/	Lupin bean	SD rat, HepG2 cell	10 μmol/L, 24 or 48 h	Glucose consumption↑	Maintaining glucose homeostasis	[59]
γ-conglutin	/	Lupin bean	STZ-induced Wistar rat	150 mg/kg, 1 week	G6pc↓, Fbp1↓, Pck1↓	Regulating glucose metabolism mainly through G6pc inhibition	[70]
γ-conglutin	/	Lupin bean	Glucose-administrated male rat	50, 100 and 200 mg/kg BW, 0, 30, 60 and 90 min	BG↓, AUC↓	Hypoglycemic effect	[54]
γ-conglutin	/	Lupin bean	Glucose-administrated male rat	30, 60 and 120 mg/kg BW, 30, 60, 90, and 120 min	Plasma glucose↓	Hypoglycemic effect	[71]
γ-conglutin	/	Lupin bean	STZ administrated rat	120 mg/kg in saline, 1 week	Glucose↓, Ins1↑, pancreatic insulin↑, serum insulin↑	Hypoglycemic effect	[72]
γ-conglutin	/	Lupin bean	C2C12 cell	0.5 mg/mL,72 h	Plasma glucose↓, IRS1 protein↑, p85-PI3 kinase↑, Akt1 protein↑, eIF4E protein↑, p70S6 K↑, ERK1↑, ERK2↑, MHC protein↑, myogenin↑	Regulating muscle energy metabolism, protein synthesis and MHC gene transcription through insulin signaling pathway	[73]
HPI/pure peptide	AKSPLF, ATNPL, FFEELN, LSVSVL	Black bean	STZ-induced Wistar rats, Caco-2 cell	100, 150 and 200 mg HPI/kg/BW, 15 d, pure peptide (100 μM), HPI (10 mg/mL)	BW↓, BG↓, postprandial glucose level↓, insulin↓, GLP-1↑, OGTT↓, glucose absorption↓, GLUT2↓, SGLT1↓	Reducing glucose absorption via blocking glucose transporters GLUT2 and SGLT1(in silico)	[60]
Synthetic peptide	IAVPGEVA, IAVPTGVA, LPYP	Soy glycinin	HepG2 cell	50 and 100 μM	Glucose uptake↑, Akt↑, GSK3α/β↓, GLUT4↑, GLUT1↑	Enhancing glucose uptake through GLUT1 and GLUT4 activation, Akt and AMPK pathway	[63]
Hydrolysate	/	Soy protein	Alloxan-induced male Kunming mice	47.5 mg/kg/d, 3 weeks	FBG↓	Hypoglycemic effect	[62]
Hydrolytic oligopeptide	/	Pea	STZ/HFD-induced diabetic mice	800, 1600 and 3200 mg/kg BW, 4 weeks	FBG↓, BW↓, OGTT↑, serum insulin↑, TC↓, TG↓, HDL-C↑, fatty acid anion ↓, liver and muscle glycogen↑	Enhancing insulin sensitivity	[74]
Protein/peptide fraction	<10 kDa	Common bean	Male Wistar rat	0.5 and 5 mg/kg	Glucose level↓, glucose uptake↑	Hypoglycemic activity	[75]

Table 3. *Cont.*

Peptide	Amino Acid Sequence	Source	Model	Feeding/Treat Pattern	Hypoglycemic Effect and Index	Mechanism	Reference
γ-conglutin hydrolysate	/	Lupin bean	Caco-2 cells, 3T3-L1 cell, HepG2 cell	2 and 5 mg/mL	Glucose uptake↑, gluconeogenesis↓, PEPCK↓, GLUT4↑, HepG2 glucose production↓	Inhibiting DPP-4, improving insulin receptor sensitivity, inhibiting hepatic gluconeogenesis through GLUT4 activation	[64]
Peptide	/	Cowpea	Rat L6 skeletal muscle cell	Various doses	Akt↑	Activating the insulin signaling pathway	[67]
Water extract peptide	<3 kDa	Fermented soybean	3T3-L1 cell, Min6 cells NCI-H716 cell, Human embryo kidney 293 cell	5 μg/mL	Glucose uptake↑, triacylglycerol↑, PPAR-r↑, β-cell viability↑, insulin secretion↑, cell proliferation↑, PDX1↑	Increasing insulin sensitivity and exerting insulinotropic via PPAR-r activation	[65]
Hydrolysate/ fraction	<1 and 1–3 kDa	Hard-to-cook bean	INS-1E cell	1 g Hydrolysate treatment	Increase insulin secretion up to 57%	Increasing insulin secretion	[66]
Hydrolysate	/	Common Bean(G0-0h)	INS-1E pancreatic β-cell	2 mg SP/mL	Increase insulin secretion 45% from the basal state	Increasing insulin secretion	[76]

G0-0h, the non-germinated and non-hydrolyzed sample; HPI, hydrolyzed protein isolate; SP, soluble protein; ZDF, Zucker diabetic fatty; ↑stimulative effect; ↓inhibitory effect.

3.1. Native Legume Peptides

The primary elements of legume seeds are proteins and peptides generated by the connection of amino acids via peptide bonds. Native legume peptides (aglycin, vglycin and soymorphin-5) have been reported as anti-T2D agents due to their bioactivities in decreasing blood sugar levels, improving insulin sensitivity and glucose tolerance, and promoting the proliferation of β-cells (Table 3).

Aglycin, a biopeptide containing 37 amino acid residues, was identified as matching to the residues 27–63 of plant albumin 1 B precursor (PA1B) from pea seeds [56,77]. Aglycin has a high affinity with a 43 kDa basic 7S globulin protein [78]. This protein binding mode is similar to the interaction of insulin and insulin receptor; therefore, aglycin is also called leginsulin [79]. Structurally, it is made up of six cysteines embedded in three disulfide bonds (C3-C20, C7-C22, and C15-C32), which are highly conserved and can resist the degradation of pepsin, trypsin, and Glu-C protease [56,57]. Aglycin was initially thought to be a leginsulin that participates in plant signal transduction to control growth and differentiation [80]. Subsequently, Chen's group found that the oral administration of aglycin in diabetic mice effectively controlled hyperglycemia by improving the insulin-signaling pathway and enhancing glucose uptake in peripheral tissues [77]. Furthermore, a long-term administration of aglycin benefited the impaired pancreatic restoration and insulin secretion [56].

Vglycin, another leginsulin, is highly similar to aglycin in amino acid sequence and structural domain [57]. It may function with a similar mechanism to aglycin, which could be useful in T2D treatment for restoring impaired insulin signaling, glucose tolerance, and pancreatic function [14]. Other leginsulin variants identified in different cultivars, as well as their bacteria-expressed recombinants, also exert insulin-like activities in myotube-like differentiated L6 and C2C12 cells [13]. Thus, leginsulins, such as aglycin and vglycin, could be considered as potential orally administrated drugs to be developed.

Soymorphin-5 (YPFVV), a μ-opioid agonist with five amino acids, is derived from soybean β-conglycinin β-subunit, and has anxiolytic-like activity [58]. It exhibited good glucose lowing activity in diabetic KKA^y mice [58]. Soymorphin-5 lowered blood glucose levels in the glucose tolerance test (GTT) and insulin tolerance test (ITT) after acute intraperitoneal administration, implying that soymorphin-5 might increase insulin sensitivity in KKA^y mice [58]. Soymorphin-5 benefits diabetic improvement by increasing plasma insulin levels and decreasing glucose and triglyceride (TG) levels. However, des-Tyr-soymorphin-5 (PFVV) loses the μ-opioid and anxiolytic-like activities, as well as their metabolic regulating activity [58].

3.2. Legume Proteins

Legume seed proteins are the main dietary source of plant protein, in which anti-nutritional substances include lectins, hydrolase inhibitors, ribosome-inactivating proteins (RIPs), and allergens [81]. Recently, soy and lupin proteins have been reported to have hypoglycemic effects.

Most of the protein in lupin seeds (around 44% *w*/*w* of the total conglutins) belongs to the conglutin family, whose molecular mass is between 143 and 260 kDa [82]. β1-, β3-, and β6-conglutin proteins can bind to insulin in vitro, suggesting that β-conglutin proteins have potential benefits for the prevention and treatment of diabetes [83]. The second most prevalent globulin, α-conglutin, shares 33% *w*/*w* of all conglutins. The third conglutin is δ-conglutin, which accounts for 12% *w*/*w* of all conglutins and 4–5% *w*/*w* of all globulins [82]. γ-conglutin (~50 kDa) is a glycoprotein composed of two subunits (17 kDa and 29 kDa). γ-conglutin has excellent hypoglycemic effects in vitro and in vivo (Table 3). In mouse C2C12 cells, γ-conglutin activated the kinases of the synthetic protein pathway and increased glucose consumption by up-regulating muscle-specific gene MHC transcription and GLUT4 gene translocation [73]. In the STZ rat model, Ins1 gene expression and pancreatic insulin content were elevated by γ-conglutin [72]. Bertoglio's group reported that lupin γ-conglutin had a glucose-lowering effect in a clinical trial [54].

When different dosages of γ-conglutin (630, 315, and 157.5 mg) were eaten 30 min before the carbohydrate supply for 7 weeks, a relevant hypoglycemic effect could be observed in human subjects [54]. Lupin seed protein could be transported by Caco-2 cell monolayers and everted intestinal sacs, suggesting it has the potential to be developed as an oral agent to manage T2D [84].

Soybean storage proteins, such as β-conglycinin and glycinin, also promote anti-diabetic activity (Table 3). Nordentoft reported that soy protein improved insulin sensitivity and up-regulated the expression of key insulin-regulatory genes [69]. A clinical study compared the effects of the intake of 6% (*w*/*v*) whey protein isolate (WPI), whey protein hydrolysate (WPH), soy protein isolate (SPI), and 2.66% WPI, or a control (no protein added) on insulin and glucose responses in 25 healthy men. The results suggested that SPI with 6% protein enhanced insulin response and decreased the plasma glucose level compared with a control beverage [55]. Another study demonstrated that the SPI increased the insulin response compared to WPH [85].

3.3. Hydrolytic Peptides

Bioactive hydrolytic peptides are organic substances formed from amino acids and released mainly through enzymatic proteolysis or food processing (cooking, fermentation, ripening) [86,87]. Currently, the commonly used peptide and protein extraction methods mainly include aqueous, organic solvent, enzymatic, ultrasonic, two-phase aqueous, and reverse micelle extraction [86]. The two most common methods for making bioactive peptides are enzyme hydrolysis and fermentation [88]. Pepsin, trypsin, chymotrypsin, alcalase, and flavourzyme are frequently utilized for hydrolysis. Compared with microbial fermentation, these bioactive oligopeptides, occurring in different sizes and produced by enzymes, have higher scalability [4]. The peptides, after enzymatic digestion, can be recovered by desalination, membrane ultrafiltration, column chromatography, and freeze-drying [87].

Crucially, some oligopeptides with short sequences of 2–20 amino acids can be absorbed by the intestine into the blood circulation and exert systemic or local physiological anti-diabetic activities, such as decreasing blood glucose levels, improving glucose and insulin sensitivity in target tissues, and inhibiting key enzymes like α-amylase, α-glucosidase, and DPP-4 related to T2D [4,89,90].

Legume-derived hydrolysates and fractions have also been investigated in cell and animal models (Table 3). Administered with semipurified γ-conglutin, hydrolysates (5 mg/mL) from Andean lupin legumes induced a 6.5-fold glucose uptake and decreased gluconeogenesis in male SD rats by 50% [64]. In Caco-2 cells, treatment with 10 mg/mL black bean hydrolyzed protein isolate (HPI) decreased glucose absorption by 21.5%, and intake of 100–200 mg of HPI/kg BW/day lowered postprandial glucose levels by 22.7–47.7% in a hyperglycemic rat model [60]. The intake of common bean peptide fractions reduced glucose levels in male Wistar rats at the same rate as glibenclamide, keeping a stable basal level without a surge in postprandial hyperglycemia [75]. Jiang found that soybean protein hydrolysate (<5 kDa) made by ultrafiltration significantly reduced the level of fasting blood glucose (FBG) in mice [62]. Wei reported that pea oligopeptides significantly reduced blood glucose levels, lipid profiles, and liver fat deposition in diabetic mice [74].

Some pure sequence-known peptides have also shown hypoglycemic effects in animal and cell models (Table 3). LPYP, IAVPGEVA, and IAVPTGVA from soy glycinin improved glucose metabolism by increasing glucose uptake via up-regulating the expression of GLUT1 and GLUT4 in cultured hepatic cells [63]. Lammi's group developed a fast, sensitive, and cost-effective ex vivo DPP-4 assay for human serum by collecting venous blood from a healthy female volunteer and analyzing how peptides inactivated the enzyme. They discovered that hydrolytic peptides like LTFPGSAED from lupin β-conglutin and IAVPTGVA from soybean glycinin inhibited the activity of DPP-4 [91].

Furthermore, legume pure peptides and hydrolysates have been found to inhibit key enzymes (α-amylase, α-glucosidase, and DPP-4) in vitro or in silico. Herein, we summarize 40 peptides with clear amino acid sequences and their indicated targets (Table 4). A total of 19 kinds of peptides from the pinto bean, black bean, hard-to-cook bean, chickpea, and fermented bean seeds have been found to inhibit the activities of α-amylases (in biochemical assay or in silico); their sequences, sources, mass weights, and IC50 values are listed in Table 4. In the chemical assay, pinto bean peptides exhibited excellent IC50 values in inhibiting α-amylase. LSSLEMGSLGALFVCM obtained the lowest IC50 value of 0.31 mM compared with others, such as PLPLHMLP (5.92 mM), PPMHLP (6.08 mM), PPHMGGP (6.14 mM), PLPWGAGF (6.64 mM), and PPHMLP (23.33 mM) [92,93]. Some α-amylase inhibitory peptides were identified in fermented bean seeds, such as INEGSLLLPH FVVAEQAGNEEGFE, SGGGGGGVAGAATASR, GSGGGGGGGFGGPRR, GGYQGGGYG-GNSGGGYGNRG, GGSGGGGGSSSGRRP, and GDTVTVEFDTFLSR. Their IC50 values ranged from 0.04 μg/mL to 0.65 μg/mL [94]. In in silico study, some peptides seemed to provide potent inhibition against α-amylase, α-glucosidase, and DPP-4 by computational modelling. Compared with acarbose (−9.71 kcal/mol), a known α-amylase inhibitor, the free energy (interaction with the catalytic site of α-amylase) of peptides AKSPLF and WEVM were −10.2 kcal/mol and −10.1 kcal/mol, respectively [95]. QQEG from hard-to-cook beans inhibited α-amylase, and the interaction score was −7.29 REU [66]. Twelve peptides provided the potential inhibition of α-glucosidase, including aglycin, LLPLPVLK, SWLRL, WLRL, GSR, EAK, TTGGKGGK, KKSSG, GGGLHK, CPGNK, KTYGL, and YVDGSGTPLT (Table 4). The α-glucosidase inhibitory activity of aglycin from soybeans was 36.48 μmol/L [96]. GSR and EAK, identified from soybeans, had IC50 values of 20.40 μM and 520.20 μM, respectively [62]. LLPLPVLK, SWLRL, and WLRL from soy protein showed strong α-glucosidase inhibitory activity, with IC50 values of 237.43 ± 0.52 μM, 182.05 ± 0.74 μM, and 162.29 ± 0.74 μM, respectively [97]. Four synthesized peptides (KKSSG, GGGLHK, CPGNK and KTYGL) were evaluated with the α-glucosidase inhibitory ratio of 49.34 ± 6.5%, 46.10 ± 8.30%, 37.60 ± 6.8%, and 36.30 ± 8.80%, respectively [98].

Table 4. Legume-derived peptide inhibitors targeting α-amylase, α-glucosidase, and DPP-4.

NO.	Peptide Sequence	MW(DA)	Source	Target	IC50, %	Reference
1	LSSLEMGSLGALFVCM	1658.02	Pinto bean	α-amylase	0.31 mM	[92]
2	PLPLHMLP	917.18	Pinto bean	α-amylase	5.92 mM	[92]
3	PPMHLP	690.87	Pinto bean	α-amylase	6.08 mM	[92]
4	PPHMLP	690.81	Pinto bean	α-amylase	23.33 ± 0.15 mM	[93]
5	PPHMGGP	691.81	Pinto bean	α-amylase	6.14 mM	[92]
6	PLPWGAGF	843.98	Pinto bean	α-amylase	6.64 mM	[92]
7	SPQSPPFATPLW	1327.50	Chickpea	α-amylase	−8.40 kcal/mol	[99]
8	FVVAEQAGNEEGFE	1525.59	Fermented bean seed	α-amylase	0.04−0.65 μg/mL	[94]
9	SGGGGGGVAGAATASR	1232.29	Fermented bean seed	α-amylase	0.59−2.12 μg/mL	[94]
10	GSGGGGGGGFGGPRR	1232.29	Fermented bean seed	α-amylase	0.59−2.12 μg/mL	[94]
11	INEGSLLLPH	1092.26	Fermented bean seed	α-amylase	0.04−0.65 μg/mL	[94]
12	GGYQGGGYGGNSGGGYGNRG	1791.77	Fermented bean seed	α-amylase	0.59−2.12 μg/mL	[94]
13	GGSGGGGGSSSGRRP	1232.24	Fermented bean seed	α-amylase	0.59−2.12 μg/mL	[94]
14	GDTVTVEFDTFLSR	1586.72	Fermented bean seed	α-amylase	0.59−2.12 μg/mL	[94]
15	NEGEAH	655.62	Hard-to-cook bean	α-amylase	−12.84 REU	[66]
16	FFL	425.53	Hard-to-cook bean	α-amylase	−8.22 REU	[66]
17	WEVM	563.67	Black bean	α-amylase	0.04 μM (ki)	[95]
18	AKSPLF	661.79	Black bean	α-amylase, DPP-4	0.03 μM (ki), 0.08 μM (ki)	[95]
19	QQEG	460.44	Hard-to-cook bean	α-amylase, DPP-4	−7.03 REU, −7.29 REU	[66]
20	Aglycin [1]	3743.40	Soybean, pea	α-glucosidase	36.48 μM	[96]

Table 4. *Cont.*

NO.	Peptide Sequence	MW(DA)	Source	Target	IC50, %	Reference
21	LLPLPVLK	892.18	Soybean	α-glucosidase	237.43 ± 0.52 μM	[97]
22	SWLRL	673.80	Soybean	α-glucosidase	182.05 ± 0.74 μM	[97]
23	WLRL	586.73	Soybean	α-glucosidase	162.29 ± 0.74 μM	[97]
24	GSR	318.33	Soybean	α-glucosidase	20.40 μM	[62]
25	EAK	346.38	Soybean	α-glucosidase	520.20 μM	[62]
26	TTGGKGGK	704.77	Black bean	α-glucosidase	0.27 μM (ki)	[95]
27	KKSSG	505.57	Common bean	α-glucosidase, DPP-4	49.34 ± 6.5%, 0.64 ± 0.16 mg/mL	[98]
28	GGGLHK	567.65	Common bean	α-glucosidase, DPP-4	46.10 ± 8.30%, 0.61 ± 0.10 mg/mL	[98]
29	CPGNK	517.60	Common bean	α-glucosidase, DPP-4	37.60 ± 6.8%, 0.87 ± 0.02 mg/mL	[98]
30	KTYGL	580.68	Common bean	α-glucosidase, DPP-4	36.30 ± 8.80%, 0.03 mg/mL	[98]
31	YVDGSGTPLT	1009.08	Chickpea	α-glucosidase, DPP-4	−7.30 kcal/mol, −8.20 kcal/mol	[99]
32	IAVPTGVA	726.87	Soybean	DPP-4	223.20 μM (in situ)	[91]
33	LTFPGSAED	935.97	Lupin bean	DPP-4	207.50 μM (in situ)	[91]
34	EGLELLLLLLAG	1253.52	Black bean	DPP-4	0.06 μM (ki)	[95]
35	FEELN	650.69	Black bean	DPP-4	0.10 μM (ki)	[95]
36	RGPLVNPDPKPFL	1449.72	Common bean	DPP-4	14.04 kcal/mol	[76]
37	KL	259.34	Fermented soybean	DPP-4	41.40 ± 2.68 μg/mL	[100]
38	LR	287.35	Fermented soybean	DPP-4	598.02 ± 18.35 μg/mL	[100]
39	PHPATSGGGL	892.97	Chickpea	DPP-4	−8.20 kcal/mol	[99]
40	LLSL	444.57	Hard-to-cook bean	DPP-4	−11.75 REU	[66]

[1] The amino acid sequence of aglycin is in Table 3. Amino acid nomenclature: C, cysteine; H, histidine; I, isoleucine; M, methionine; S, serine; V, valine; A, alanine; G, glycine; L, leucine; P, proline; T, threonine; F, phenylalanine; R, arginine; Y, tyrosine, W, tryptophan; D, aspartic acid; N, asparagine; E, glutamic acid, Q, glutamine; K, lysine. Ki, inhibition constant expressed in μM.

Peptides from the lupin bean, soybean, fermented soybean, black bean, common bean, chickpea, and hard-to-cook bean exhibited inhibition of DPP-4. Peptides LTFPGSAED, IAVPTGVA, EGLELLLLLLAG, AKSPLF, FEELN, KKSSG, GGGLHK, CPGNK, KTYGL, KL, and LR were confirmed to inhibit the activity of DPP-4 by biochemical assay. RGPLVNPDPKPFL, PHPATSGGGL, YVDGSGTPLT, LLSL, and QQEG were identified as potential DPP-4 inhibitors by computational modelling (Table 4).

In addition, several studies showed that a hydrolysate and peptide fraction mixture had the potential to inhibit the enzymatic activities of α-amylase, α-glucosidase, and DPP-4 (Table S1). Alkaline protease was reported to be the best enzyme for producing black bean protein components with anti-diabetic potential [60,95]. Inhibition values for DPP-4, α-amylase, and α-glucosidase of alcalase fraction peptides from the black bean were 96.70%, 53.40%, and 66.10%, respectively [95]. The inhibition of α-glucosidase in different common bean cultivars' protein hydrolysates ranged from 46.90–60.00% [101], and the IC50 of DPP-4 inhibition ranged from 0.14–0.33 mg DW/mL [98]. In another in vitro study, 5 mg/mL purified γ-conglutin hydrolysates from lupin inhibited DPP-4 completely. The fact that undigested γ-conglutin did not directly inhibit DPP-4 activity demonstrated that this protein needs to be digested to produce DPP-4 enzyme inhibitory hydrolysates [64]. Bambara bean hydrolysates produced by alcalase and thermolysin exhibited similar DPP-4 inhibitory activity with an IC50 of 1.73 mg/mL [102]. Cowpea alcalase protein hydrolysis also showed strong DPP-4 inhibition [103,104]. Soybean hydrolysates had an α-glucosidase inhibitory activity with an IC50 of 0.05 mg/mL [62]. Six-days-germinated soybean protein hydrolysates inhibited DPP-4 (IC50 = 1.49 ± 0.14 mg/mL), α-amylase (IC50 = 1.70 ± 0.18 mg/mL), and sucrase activities of α-glucosidases (IC50 = 2.90 ± 0.07 mg/mL). Peptide fractions of 5–10 kDa and >10 kDa were more effective at inhibiting DPP-4 (IC50 = 0.91± 0.17 mg/mL and 1.18 ± 0.15 mg/mL, respectively) [61].

Collectively, legume peptides and hydrolysates show remarkable hypoglycemic effects through various approaches. Interest has been directed toward the acceptable oral administration of bioactive peptides, one of the main attractions for T2D patients. Based on their inherent amino acid composition and sequence, bioactive peptides exhibit different activities in regulating glucose and lipid metabolism, which exert beneficial effects on the control of diabetic progress.

4. Potential Hypoglycemic Mechanism of Bioactive Legume Peptides

The hypoglycemic mechanism of legume diabetic peptides mainly includes reducing glucose absorption, promoting pancreatic β-cells proliferation, enhancing insulin secretion and sensitivity through signaling pathways associated with diabetes, and inhibiting carbohydrate-digesting enzymes (α-amylase and α-glucosidase) and DPP-4 in target organs (Figure 1).

4.1. Targeting the Pancreas

One of the main factors contributing to the development of T2D is assumed to be a decrease in glucose-stimulated insulin secretion from pancreatic β-cells [105]. An appealing idea for treating diabetes and its complications is to restore the function of poor β-cells. The IRS (insulin receptor substrate)/AKT (protein kinase B) pathway is the primary mechanism of the hypoglycemic effect of the body's response to insulin stimulation [106]. Vglycin peptide exhibited beneficial effects on hyperglycemia by facilitating glucose metabolism and enhancing insulin sensitivity, but it could not increase insulin secretion [57]. Another study supports an apparent impact of vglycin on regulating β-cell preservation; a self-renew program was initiated in which vglycin directly promoted the proliferation of β-cells via activating the IR/Akt/Erk pathway [14]. These results reveal the protective effects of vglycin on improving β-cell function in long-term glucolipotoxicity.

Some hydrolysates and fractions also exhibited a protective effect on the dysfunctional pancreas. Hydrolysates (<3 kDa) from hard-to-cook beans and common beans were reported to increase glucose-stimulated insulin secretion up to 57% and 45% from the basal state in INS-1E pancreatic β-cells, respectively [66,76]. In another study, fermented meju water extracts (W-60), containing 15 kDa peptides, increased glucose-stimulated insulin secretion capacity and β-cell viability in Min6 insulinoma cells [65]. Previous studies have identified that amino acid metabolism, especially glutamine and alanine, is essential for the functional maintenance of pancreatic cells and insulin secretion [107]. Therefore, it can be inferred that the amino acids or oligopeptides in the hydrolysates of legumes may be beneficial for the exertion of hypoglycemic function of the pancreas directly or indirectly.

4.2. Targeting the Liver

Soymorphin-5 (YPFVV), derived from the soy conglycinin subunit, plays a role in glucose and lipid metabolism [58]. Although no differences were observed in the weights of mesenteric and epididymal fat and brown adipose tissues, plasma TG levels and liver weights in KKA^y mice were significantly reduced by soymorphin-5 treatment, suggesting that soymorphin-5 enhanced the liver lipid metabolism. In terms of mechanism, soymorphin-5 improved fatty acid β-oxidation and energy expenditure by increasing the hepatic expression of PPAR and its target genes, including Adipor2, AOX1, CPT1, and UCP2 [58]. In another study, vglycin was probably responsible for increased fatty acid β-oxidation via the AMPK pathway and inhibited fatty acid synthesis (FAS) by down-regulating expression of FAS in HFD-fed C57BL/6J mice [15]. Soy peptides IAVPGEVA, IAVPTGVA, and LPYP enhanced glucose uptake through GLUT1 and GLUT4 activation, and modulated glucose metabolism by activating Akt and AMPK pathways in HepG2 cells [63]. In addition, γ-conglutin hydrolysates decreased gluconeogenesis by 50% in a dual-layered enterocyte/hepatocyte system and down-regulated the expression of phosphoenolpyruvate carboxykinase (PEPCK) in HepG2 cells [64].

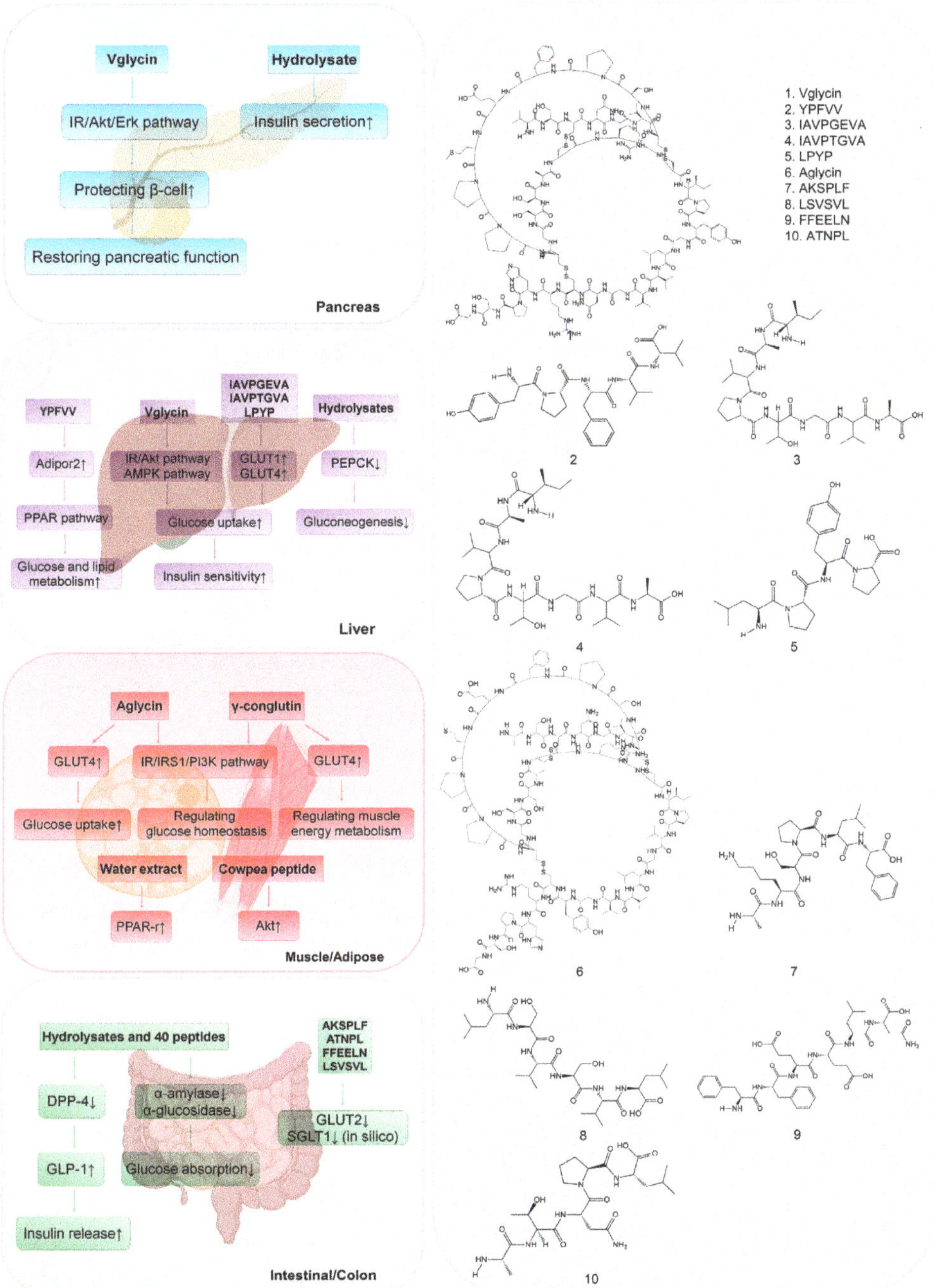

Figure 1. Mechanism of anti-diabetic effects of 10 representative legume-derived peptides. The amino acid sequence or molecular structure of the peptides are presented in the (**right**) panel. The anti-diabetic mechanisms of these peptides in corresponding organs are showed in the (**left**) panel. ↑ means a stimulative effect and ↓ means an inhibitory effect in the text. Peptide 1 works in pancreas; peptides 1 to 5 work in liver; peptide 6 works in muscle and adipose cells; and peptides 7–10 work in intestinal/colon tissue.

4.3. Targeting Muscle and Adipose Tissue

Increasing glucose absorption and transformation in muscle and adipose tissue is an effective method to control hyperglycemia. As shown in a STZ/HFD-induced diabetic mice model, oral administration of aglycin could potentially attenuate or prevent hyperglycemia via enhancing the IR/IRS1 signaling pathway in skeletal muscle [56]. Additionally, in C2C12 cells, aglycin increased glucose uptake by recruiting glucose transporter GLUT4 to the surface of cells [56]. Cowpea peptides induced the Akt phosphorylation in skeletal cells and mimicked the actions of insulin by activating the same signaling pathway [67]. Prior findings strongly implied that the translocation of GLUT4 was regulated by activation of the Akt signaling pathway in the skeletal muscle cells, which facilitated glucose uptake [108,109].

Studies of fermented soy products have suggested that the small bioactive peptides produced during fermentation may contribute to preventing or slowing the progression of T2D [65,110]. Water extracts (<3 kDa) from chungkookjang increased PPAR-r activity by about 59%, indicating that there exist certain small peptides that work as mild PPAR-r agonists in glucose and lipid metabolism [65]. γ-conglutin hydrolysates also significantly increased the insulin-induced glucose uptake in mature 3T3-L1 adipocytes through an enhanced expression of GLUT4, similar to metformin treatment [64]. Similarly, in C2C12 cells, γ-conglutin increased flottilin-2, caveolin-3 concentrations, and CBL phosphorylation, resulting in GLUT4 translocated on the cell membrane, which suggested that γ-conglutin plays an essential role in muscle energy metabolism through insulin-mimetic action [73].

4.4. Targeting the Intestine and Colon

In STZ-induced Wistar rats and the Caco-2 cell models, black bean peptides AKSPLF, ATNPL, FFEELN, and LSVSVL may have reduced glucose absorption via blocking glucose transporters GLUT2 and SGLT1 (Figure 1) [60]. In Table 4, we summarized 19 α-amylase inhibitors, 12 α-glucosidase inhibitors, and 16 DPP-4 inhibitors from legume peptides, all of which worked as potential anti-diabetic agents targeting the intestine and colon (Figure 1). The mechanism of lowering postprandial hyperglycemia by inhibition of α-amylase and α-glucosidase is to inhibit the rate of glucose release and absorption in the intestine [12]. The hypoglycemic mechanism of inhibiting the DPP-4 enzyme is to retard the decomposition of GLP-1 and increase the endogenous physiological level of GLP-1 in the human body [34]. Recently, the structure of oligopeptides and their binding modes to these enzymes have been systematically investigated, which may provide a clear anti-diabetic mechanism for these peptides [40].

α-amylase contains three distinct structural domains (A, B, and C). The active site region in domain A is associated with an extended substrate binding cleft, allowing it to recognize polymeric starch molecules [111]. Asp197, Glu233, and Asp300 are three essential catalytic carboxylic acid residues located within this active site cleft between the carboxyl ends of domains A and B. Domain B is responsible for substrate specificity and enzyme stability, and domain C helps to maintain the stability of the catalytic site. Therefore, blocking the catalytic sites was an effective way to inhibit the activity of α-amylase [40]. Peptides amply containing aromatic residues such as Leu, Pro, Gly, and Phe were effective inhibitors of α-amylase because the substrate-binding pockets of the α-amylase enzyme have many aromatic residues [111]. Hence, apart from interactions involving hydrogen bonds and electrostatic and van der Waals interactions, aromatic–aromatic interactions have also played a crucial role in α-amylase inhibitory activity [4].

The bioactive peptides LSSLEMGSLGALFVCM, PLPLHMLP, PPMHLP, PPHMLP, PPHMGGP, and PLPWGAGF, extracted from pinto beans, interacted or bound to the indicated domain of α-amylase, ultimately restricting protein conformation and affecting the degree of enclosure of the substrate. Mechanically, when the (α-amylase)–starch complex was formed, the uncompetitive peptide inhibitors bound to the complex, resulting in the starch no longer being able to hold on at its original position due to the altered conformation of α-amylase. Consequently, the starch was detached from the (α-amylase)–

starch complex [92]. The competitive inhibitors GSR and EAK formed hydrogen bonds with the catalytic residues [62].

Structural analysis has clearly shown the intimate interaction between bean-derived peptides and α-amylase catalytic residues. The interaction prevented residue Asp300 from adopting its functional position and destroyed the water channel leading from the "flexible loop" to the heart of the active-site depression [112]. Another inhibitory mechanism was identified in the interaction of porcine pancreatic α-amylase and the bean P. vulgaris-derived peptide, in which residue His305 participated in substrate binding and structural changes [113].

Similar to peptides that inhibit α-amylase, certain peptides have the potential to inhibit α-glucosidase, reducing glucose absorption and delaying carbohydrate digestion, thereby reducing postprandial blood glucose levels. Pure peptides such as KTYGL were able to inhibit the enzyme mainly through polar interactions (Asn32, Asp34, Asp38, and Asp89), hydrophobic interactions (Trp36 and Trp81), and hydrogen bonds (Ser31) with the residues from the binding pocket of the α-glucosidase [98]. AKSPLF showed only hydrogen bonding and polar interactions with α-glucosidase, and Ala and Lys were the only two amino acids interacting with ASP34, THR83, ASP89 and ASN32 [95]. Besides, α-glucosidase inhibitors also played crucial roles in the secretion of GLP-1 in T2D [114].

DPP-4 is a serine exopeptidase that cleaves X-proline or X-alanine dipeptides from the N-terminus of polypeptides, which degrades and inactivates GLP-1 and GIP. Several legume-derived peptides have been identified as promising DPP-4 inhibitors, potentially contributing to glycemic control. DPP-4 has hydrophobic pockets, which are crucial targets for inhibition of the enzyme [115]. Generally, the DPP-4 inhibitory peptides often contain high concentrations of hydrophobic amino acids such as alanine, glycine, isoleucine, leucine, phenylalanine, proline, methionine, tryptophan, and valine [4]. The interactions between DPP-4 and common bean peptides (KTYGL and AKSPLF) were mainly H-bond, hydrophobic, polar and cation π bonds [85,92]. The interactions of DPP-4 with peptide AKSPLF occurred primarily between amino acids GLU191, ASP192, ARG253, and LEU235 [95].

Collectively, legume peptides exhibit great inhibitory potential due to their affinity for and specificity of action on key enzymes such as α-amylase, α-glucosidase, and DPP-4, which are promising candidates for the development of anti-diabetic drugs. However, the structure–activity relationships between peptides and these enzymes remain to be uncovered.

5. Challenges of Legume Peptides' Development in T2D Treatment

Despite their tremendous potential value in anti-T2D therapies, legume-derived peptides have intrinsic disadvantages, including poor chemical and physical stability, poor bioavailability, short effective half-life, and inefficiency of oral delivery, which must be considered for their application as nutraceuticals or medicines [12,116]. Effectively delivering therapeutic peptides via the oral route is still a big challenge, even though some drawbacks can be solved by rational design with the increase of biological activity, selectivity, or bioavailability. Numerous studies have concentrated on creating novel technologies through physical and chemical methods, including enteric coating, enzyme inhibitors, permeability enhancers, nanoparticles, and intestinal microdevices, to improve the oral bioavailability and stability of the peptides, which overcome the absorptive barriers in the gastrointestinal tract [4,22,117].

Low selectivity, resistance to protein hydrolysis, and the demands of large-scale production are also some of the main challenges [22]. Approaches such as proteomic analysis, bioinformatics tools, pretreatments, hydrolysis mechanisms and isolation, and effective cell and animal screening models all contribute to obtaining hydrolysates or peptides with hypoglycemic activity [118]. Regarding the delivery and administration of peptides in the human body, the effectivity and stability of the peptides in the gastrointestinal tract are worth considering. Since oligopeptides are predicted to be resistant to digestive enzymes, they can be utilized as an ingredient or supplement in nutraceutical foods. Those specific peptides with long amino acid sequences or hydrolysates are still susceptible to digestive enzymes.

In addition, some legume-derived anti-diabetic peptides are mainly studied by integrated computational methods or in vitro assays, due to a lack of sufficient animal and human clinical trials. These potential anti-diabetic peptides need a deep investigation geared towards the development of nutraceuticals and drugs. On the other hand, hydrolytic peptides are generated from dietary proteins during gastrointestinal digestion or are produced by processing proteins. Their bioavailability after oral administration depends on their absorption and distribution to reach target organs [119]. The peptides in the legume hydrolysates (Table S1) should be identified, and their anti-diabetic activities and precise mechanisms need further investigation. Undoubtedly, legume-derived peptides research can benefit from pharmaceutical approaches for the discovery, design, and development of nutraceutical or oral medicinal peptides for T2D.

6. Conclusions and Perspectives

Peptides are becoming one of the most attractive candidates for the development of oral anti-diabetic drugs. The FDA has approved Rybelsus® (semaglutide) oral tablets to improve control of blood sugar in adult patients with T2D, along with diet, exercise, and other anti-diabetic drugs. The efficacy and safety of the treatment of Rybelsus®, assisted with Salcaprozate sodium, an absorption enhancer, have been considered acceptable in several clinical trials [31,120,121]. It provides a viable design for oral legume-derived drug development for T2D. The biopeptides and protein hydrolysates from legumes summarized in this review are confirmed to have anti-diabetic activities, and their anti-diabetic mechanisms are illustrated in vivo and in vitro.

The biological activity of a peptide mainly depends on its chemical structure, which determines its molecular function in target organs [44,94]. Structural modifications can enhance the enzymatic tolerance of polypeptide drugs, thereby increasing the half-life of drugs. As a native peptide, aglycin consists of 37 amino acids and contains the special cystine knot structure in the molecule, which can resist the hydrolysis of proteases in the digestive tract. This self-protective structural feature makes aglycin viable as an oral agent in the management of T2D and other metabolic syndromes.

Since its discovery, insulin has been one of the major therapeutic molecules used to control diabetes. The most common route of insulin administration is the subcutaneous route. However, oral delivery is the most convenient and patient-centered route. The human physiological system acts as a formidable barrier to insulin, limiting its bioavailability. Currently, the delivery methods enhancing the bioavailability of oral insulin and GLP-1 receptor agonists include the use of ionic liquids, hydrogels, nanoparticles, microparticles, and nano-in-microparticles [122]. These strategies provide new insights into the development of the effective delivery of orally administered protein and peptide drugs.

Supplementary Materials: The following supporting information can be downloaded at: https://www.mdpi.com/article/10.3390/nu15051096/s1, Table S1: Hydrolytic fractions from legume targeting α-amylase, α-glucosidase, and DPP-4.

Author Contributions: Conceptualization, K.H., H.H. and C.Y.; formal analysis, K.H. and C.Y.; writing—original draft preparation, H.H.; writing—review and editing, K.H., H.H. and C.Y.; comments and suggestion, H.L. and Y.W.; supervision, K.H. and C.Y. All authors have read and agreed to the published version of the manuscript.

Funding: This research was funded by Open Project Funding of the Key Laboratory of Fermentation Engineering (Ministry of Education, grant No. 202209EF09) to C.Y., by the Key R&D Project of Hubei Province (Social Development), grant No. 2022BCA018 to K.H., and by the Hubei Province Natural Science Foundation, grant No. 2021CFB289 to H.L. The APC was funded by grant No. 2022BCA018.

Institutional Review Board Statement: Not applicable.

Informed Consent Statement: Not applicable.

Data Availability Statement: Not applicable.

Acknowledgments: With many thanks to Zhengwang Chen (Huazhong University of Science and Technology), from whose instruction on the treatment of T2D, we benefited greatly.

Conflicts of Interest: The authors declare no conflict of interest.

Abbreviations

Akt	protein kinase B
AUC	area under curve
BG	blood glucose
BW	body weight
Cγ	γ-conglutin
DPP-4	dipeptidyl peptidase IV
FA	fatty acid
FAS	fatty acid synthase
FBG	fasting blood glucose
FPG	fasting plasma glucose
GIP	gastric inhibitory peptide
GLP-1	glucagon-like peptide-1
GLUT4	glucose transporter type 4
HFD	high-fat diet
IC50	half maximal inhibitory concentration
IR	insulin receptor
IRS1	insulin receptor substrate 1
ITT	insulin tolerance test
OGTT	oral glucose tolerance test
PPAR	peroxisome proliferator-activated receptor
REU	rosetta energy units
SD	Sprague Dawley
SGLT-2	sodium-glucose cotransporter-2
STZ	streptozotocin
T2D	type 2 diabetes
TG	triglyceride
TZDs	thiazolidinediones

References

1. Lin, X.; Xu, Y.; Pan, X.; Xu, J.; Ding, Y.; Sun, X.; Song, X.; Ren, Y.; Shan, P.F. Global, regional, and national burden and trend of diabetes in 195 countries and territories: An analysis from 1990 to 2025. *Sci. Rep.* **2020**, *10*, 14790. [CrossRef]
2. American Diabetes Association. 2. Classification and Diagnosis of Diabetes: Standards of Medical Care in Diabetes-2021. *Diabetes Care* **2021**, *44* (Suppl. 1), S15–S33. [CrossRef]
3. Al-Goblan, A.S.; Al-Alfi, M.A.; Khan, M.Z. Mechanism linking diabetes mellitus and obesity. *Diabetes Metab. Syndr. Obes.* **2014**, *7*, 587–591. [CrossRef]
4. Antony, P.; Vijayan, R. Bioactive Peptides as Potential Nutraceuticals for Diabetes Therapy: A Comprehensive Review. *Int. J. Mol. Sci.* **2021**, *22*, 9059. [CrossRef]
5. Kahn, S.E.; Cooper, M.E.; Del Prato, S. Pathophysiology and treatment of type 2 diabetes: Perspectives on the past, present, and future. *Lancet* **2014**, *383*, 1068–1083. [CrossRef]
6. Sterrett, J.J.; Bragg, S.; Weart, C.W. Type 2 Diabetes Medication Review. *Am. J. Med. Sci.* **2016**, *351*, 342–355. [CrossRef]
7. Acquah, C.; Dzuvor, C.K.O.; Tosh, S.; Agyei, D. Anti-diabetic effects of bioactive peptides: Recent advances and clinical implications. *Crit. Rev. Food Sci. Nutr.* **2022**, *62*, 2158–2171. [CrossRef]
8. Hewage, S.S.; Wu, S.; Neelakantan, N.; Yoong, J. Systematic review of effectiveness and cost-effectiveness of lifestyle interventions to improve clinical diabetes outcome measures in women with a history of GDM. *Clin. Nutr. ESPEN* **2020**, *35*, 20–29. [CrossRef]
9. International Diabetes Federation. IDF Diabetes Atlas, 10th ed. Available online: https://diabetesatlas.org/en/resources/ (accessed on 5 December 2022).
10. Mata-Cases, M.; Rodriguez-Sanchez, B.; Mauricio, D.; Real, J.; Vlacho, B.; Franch-Nadal, J.; Oliva, J. The Association Between Poor Glycemic Control and Health Care Costs in People with Diabetes: A Population-Based Study. *Diabetes Care* **2020**, *43*, 751–758. [CrossRef]

11. Mullins, A.P.; Arjmandi, B.H. Health Benefits of Plant-Based Nutrition: Focus on Beans in Cardiometabolic Diseases. *Nutrients* **2021**, *13*, 519. [CrossRef]
12. Moreno-Valdespino, C.A.; Luna-Vital, D.; Camacho-Ruiz, R.M.; Mojica, L. Bioactive proteins and phytochemicals from legumes: Mechanisms of action preventing obesity and type-2 diabetes. *Food Res. Int.* **2020**, *130*, 108905. [CrossRef]
13. Hashidume, T.; Sakano, T.; Mochizuki, A.; Ito, K.; Ito, S.; Kawarasaki, Y.; Miyoshi, N. Identification of soybean peptide leginsulin variants in different cultivars and their insulin-like activities. *Sci. Rep.* **2018**, *8*, 16847. [CrossRef]
14. Jiang, H.; Tong, Y.; Yan, D.; Jia, S.; Ostenson, C.G.; Chen, Z. The Soybean Peptide Vglycin Preserves the Diabetic beta-cells through Improvement of Proliferation and Inhibition of Apoptosis. *Sci. Rep.* **2015**, *5*, 15599. [CrossRef]
15. Yao, C.-C.; Tong, Y.-X.; Jiang, H.; Yang, D.-R.; Zhang, X.-J.; Zhang, P.; Su, L.; Zhao, Y.-Y.; Chen, Z.-W. Native polypeptide vglycin prevents nonalcoholic fatty liver disease in mice by activating the AMPK pathway. *J. Funct. Foods* **2020**, *73*, 104110. [CrossRef]
16. Aguayo-Mazzucato, C.; Bonner-Weir, S. Pancreatic beta Cell Regeneration as a Possible Therapy for Diabetes. *Cell Metab.* **2018**, *27*, 57–67. [CrossRef]
17. Weir, G.C.; Gaglia, J.; Bonner-Weir, S. Inadequate β-cell mass is essential for the pathogenesis of type 2 diabetes. *Lancet Diabetes Endo.* **2020**, *8*, 249–256. [CrossRef]
18. Defronzo, R.A. Banting Lecture. From the triumvirate to the ominous octet: A new paradigm for the treatment of type 2 diabetes mellitus. *Diabetes* **2009**, *58*, 773–795. [CrossRef]
19. Moller, D.E. New drug targets for type 2 diabetes and the metabolic syndrome. *Nature* **2001**, *414*, 821–827. [CrossRef]
20. Bailey, C.J. The Current Drug Treatment Landscape for Diabetes and Perspectives for the Future. *Clin. Pharmacol. Ther.* **2015**, *98*, 170–184. [CrossRef]
21. Thule, P.M. Mechanisms of current therapies for diabetes mellitus type 2. *Adv. Physiol. Educ.* **2012**, *36*, 275–283. [CrossRef]
22. Zhu, Q.; Chen, Z.; Paul, P.K.; Lu, Y.; Wu, W.; Qi, J. Oral delivery of proteins and peptides: Challenges, status quo and future perspectives. *Acta Pharm. Sin. B* **2021**, *11*, 2416–2448. [CrossRef]
23. Yari, Z.; Behrouz, V.; Zand, H.; Pourvali, K. New insight into diabetes management: From glycemic index to dietary insulin index. *Curr. Diabetes Rev.* **2020**, *16*, 293–300. [CrossRef]
24. Rekha, M.R.; Sharma, C.P. Oral delivery of therapeutic protein/peptide for diabetes–future perspectives. *Int. J. Pharm.* **2013**, *440*, 48–62. [CrossRef]
25. Soccio, R.E.; Chen, E.R.; Lazar, M.A. Thiazolidinediones and the promise of insulin sensitization in type 2 diabetes. *Cell Metab.* **2014**, *20*, 573–591. [CrossRef]
26. Akter, H. Review on diabetics and anti-diabetic drugs. *AJPTI* **2014**, *2*, 1–16.
27. DeFronzo, R.A. Pharmacologic Therapy for Type 2 Diabetes Mellitus. *Ann. Intern. Med.* **1999**, *131*, 281–303. [CrossRef]
28. Bailey, C.J.; Tahrani, A.A.; Barnett, A.H. Future glucose-lowering drugs for type 2 diabetes. *Lancet Diabetes Endo.* **2016**, *4*, 350–359. [CrossRef]
29. Furman, B.L. The development of Byetta (exenatide) from the venom of the Gila monster as an anti-diabetic agent. *Toxicon* **2012**, *59*, 464–471. [CrossRef]
30. Liao, H.J.; Tzen, J.T.C. Investigating Potential GLP-1 Receptor Agonists in Cyclopeptides from Pseudostellaria heterophylla, Linum usitatissimum, and Drymaria diandra, and Peptides Derived from Heterophyllin B for the Treatment of Type 2 Diabetes: An In Silico Study. *Metabolites* **2022**, *12*, 549. [CrossRef]
31. Knudsen, L.B.; Lau, J. The Discovery and Development of Liraglutide and Semaglutide. *Front. Endocrinol.* **2019**, *10*, 155. [CrossRef]
32. Scott, L.J. Liraglutide: A review of its use in adult patients with type 2 diabetes mellitus. *Drugs* **2014**, *74*, 2161–2174. [CrossRef]
33. Drucker, D.J. Advances in oral peptide therapeutics. *Nat. Rev. Drug Discov.* **2020**, *19*, 277–289. [CrossRef]
34. Ahren, B. DPP-4 Inhibition and the Path to Clinical Proof. *Front. Endocrinol.* **2019**, *10*, 376. [CrossRef]
35. Syed, Y.Y. Tirzepatide: First Approval. *Drugs* **2022**, *82*, 1213–1220. [CrossRef]
36. Chavda, V.P.; Ajabiya, J.; Teli, D.; Bojarska, J.; Apostolopoulos, V. Tirzepatide, a New Era of Dual-Targeted Treatment for Diabetes and Obesity: A Mini-Review. *Molecules* **2022**, *27*, 4315. [CrossRef]
37. Hallakou-Bozec, S.; Vial, G.; Kergoat, M.; Fouqueray, P.; Bolze, S.; Borel, A.L.; Fontaine, E.; Moller, D.E. Mechanism of action of Imeglimin: A novel therapeutic agent for type 2 diabetes. *Diabetes Obes. Metab.* **2021**, *23*, 664–673. [CrossRef]
38. DeFronzo, R.A. Chiglitazar: A novel pan-PPAR agonist. *Sci. Bull.* **2021**, *66*, 1497–1498. [CrossRef]
39. Xu, H.-R.; Zhang, J.-W.; Chen, W.-L.; Ning, Z.-Q.; Li, X.-N. Pharmacokinetics, Safety and Tolerability of Chiglitazar, A Novel Peroxisome Proliferator-Activated Receptor (PPAR) Pan-Agonist, in Healthy Chinese Volunteers: A Phase I Study. *Clin. Drug Investig.* **2019**, *39*, 553–563. [CrossRef]
40. Yan, J.; Zhao, J.; Yang, R.; Zhao, W. Bioactive peptides with antidiabetic properties: A review. *Int. J. Food Sci. Technol.* **2019**, *54*, 1909–1919. [CrossRef]
41. Food and Agriculture Organization of the United Nations. Definition and Classification of Commodities: Pulses and Derived Products. 1994. Available online: http://www.fao.org/es/faodef/fdef04e.htm (accessed on 2 June 2015).
42. Singhal, P.; Kaushik, G.; Mathur, P. Antidiabetic potential of commonly consumed legumes: A review. *Crit. Rev. Food Sci. Nutr.* **2014**, *54*, 655–672. [CrossRef]
43. Kamran, F.; Reddy, N. Bioactive peptides from legumes: Functional and nutraceutical potential. *Recent Adv. Food Sci.* **2018**, *1*, 134–149.

44. Jakubczyk, A.; Karas, M.; Rybczynska-Tkaczyk, K.; Zielinska, E.; Zielinski, D. Current Trends of Bioactive Peptides-New Sources and Therapeutic Effect. *Foods* **2020**, *9*, 846. [CrossRef]
45. Baldeon, M.E.; Felix, C.; Fornasini, M.; Zertuche, F.; Largo, C.; Paucar, M.J.; Ponce, L.; Rangarajan, S.; Yusuf, S.; Lopez-Jaramillo, P. Prevalence of metabolic syndrome and diabetes mellitus type-2 and their association with intake of dairy and legume in Andean communities of Ecuador. *PLoS ONE* **2021**, *16*, e0254812. [CrossRef]
46. Rizzello, C.G.; Tagliazucchi, D.; Babini, E.; Sefora Rutella, G.; Taneyo Saa, D.L.; Gianotti, A. Bioactive peptides from vegetable food matrices: Research trends and novel biotechnologies for synthesis and recovery. *J. Funct. Foods* **2016**, *27*, 549–569. [CrossRef]
47. Becerra-Tomas, N.; Diaz-Lopez, A.; Rosique-Esteban, N.; Ros, E.; Buil-Cosiales, P.; Corella, D.; Estruch, R.; Fito, M.; Serra-Majem, L.; Aros, F.; et al. Legume consumption is inversely associated with type 2 diabetes incidence in adults: A prospective assessment from the PREDIMED study. *Clin. Nutr.* **2018**, *37*, 906–913. [CrossRef]
48. Villegas, R.; Gao, Y.T.; Yang, G.; Li, H.L.; Elasy, T.A.; Zheng, W.; Shu, X.O. Legume and soy food intake and the incidence of type 2 diabetes in the Shanghai Women's Health Study. *Am. J. Clin. Nutr.* **2008**, *87*, 162–167. [CrossRef]
49. Tang, J.; Wan, Y.; Zhao, M.; Zhong, H.; Zheng, J.S.; Feng, F. Legume and soy intake and risk of type 2 diabetes: A systematic review and meta-analysis of prospective cohort studies. *Am. J. Clin. Nutr.* **2020**, *111*, 677–688. [CrossRef]
50. Konishi, K.; Wada, K.; Yamakawa, M.; Goto, Y.; Mizuta, F.; Koda, S.; Uji, T.; Tsuji, M.; Nagata, C. Dietary Soy Intake Is Inversely Associated with Risk of Type 2 Diabetes in Japanese Women but Not in Men. *J. Nutr.* **2019**, *149*, 1208–1214. [CrossRef]
51. Chelliah, R.; Wei, S.; Daliri, E.B.; Elahi, F.; Yeon, S.J.; Tyagi, A.; Liu, S.; Madar, I.H.; Sultan, G.; Oh, D.H. The Role of Bioactive Peptides in Diabetes and Obesity. *Foods* **2021**, *10*, 2220. [CrossRef]
52. Marya; Khan, H.; Nabavi, S.M.; Habtemariam, S. Anti-diabetic potential of peptides: Future prospects as therapeutic agents. *Life Sci.* **2018**, *193*, 153–158. [CrossRef]
53. Rivero-Pino, F.; Espejo-Carpio, F.J.; Guadix, E.M. Antidiabetic Food-Derived Peptides for Functional Feeding: Production, Functionality and In Vivo Evidences. *Foods* **2020**, *9*, 983. [CrossRef]
54. Bertoglio, J.C.; Calvo, M.A.; Hancke, J.L.; Burgos, R.A.; Riva, A.; Morazzoni, P.; Ponzone, C.; Magni, C.; Duranti, M. Hypoglycemic effect of lupin seed gamma-conglutin in experimental animals and healthy human subjects. *Fitoterapia* **2011**, *82*, 933–938. [CrossRef]
55. Méric, E.; Lemieux, S.; Turgeon, S.L.; Bazinet, L. Insulin and glucose responses after ingestion of different loads and forms of vegetable or animal proteins in protein enriched fruit beverages. *J. Funct. Foods* **2014**, *10*, 95–103. [CrossRef]
56. Lu, J.; Zeng, Y.; Hou, W.; Zhang, S.; Li, L.; Luo, X.; Xi, W.; Chen, Z.; Xiang, M. The soybean peptide aglycin regulates glucose homeostasis in type 2 diabetic mice via IR/IRS1 pathway. *J. Nutr. Biochem.* **2012**, *23*, 1449–1457. [CrossRef]
57. Jiang, H.; Feng, J.; Du, Z.; Zhen, H.; Lin, M.; Jia, S.; Li, T.; Huang, X.; Ostenson, C.G.; Chen, Z. Oral administration of soybean peptide Vglycin normalizes fasting glucose and restores impaired pancreatic function in Type 2 diabetic Wistar rats. *J. Nutr. Biochem.* **2014**, *25*, 954–963. [CrossRef]
58. Yamada, Y.; Muraki, A.; Oie, M.; Kanegawa, N.; Oda, A.; Sawashi, Y.; Kaneko, K.; Yoshikawa, M.; Goto, T.; Takahashi, N.; et al. Soymorphin-5, a soy-derived mu-opioid peptide, decreases glucose and triglyceride levels through activating adiponectin and PPARalpha systems in diabetic KKA^y mice. *Am. J. Physiol. Endocrinol. Metab.* **2012**, *302*, E433–E440. [CrossRef]
59. Lovati, M.R.; Manzoni, C.; Castiglioni, S.; Parolari, A.; Magni, C.; Duranti, M. Lupin seed gamma-conglutin lowers blood glucose in hyperglycaemic rats and increases glucose consumption of HepG2 cells. *Br. J. Nutr.* **2012**, *107*, 67–73. [CrossRef]
60. Mojica, L.; Gonzalez de Mejia, E.; Granados-Silvestre, M.Á.; Menjivar, M. Evaluation of the hypoglycemic potential of a black bean hydrolyzed protein isolate and its pure peptides using in silico, in vitro and in vivo approaches. *J. Funct. Foods* **2017**, *31*, 274–286. [CrossRef]
61. Gonzalez-Montoya, M.; Hernandez-Ledesma, B.; Mora-Escobedo, R.; Martinez-Villaluenga, C. Bioactive Peptides from Germinated Soybean with Anti-Diabetic Potential by Inhibition of Dipeptidyl Peptidase-IV, alpha-Amylase, and alpha-Glucosidase Enzymes. *Int. J. Mol. Sci.* **2018**, *19*, 2883. [CrossRef]
62. Jiang, M.; Yan, H.; He, R.; Ma, Y. Purification and a molecular docking study of α-glucosidase-inhibitory peptides from a soybean protein hydrolysate with ultrasonic pretreatment. *Eur. Food Res. Technol.* **2018**, *244*, 1995–2005. [CrossRef]
63. Lammi, C.; Zanoni, C.; Arnoldi, A. Three Peptides from Soy Glycinin Modulate Glucose Metabolism in Human Hepatic HepG2 Cells. *Int. J. Mol. Sci.* **2015**, *16*, 27362–27370. [CrossRef]
64. Muñoz, E.B.; Luna-Vital, D.A.; Fornasini, M.; Baldeón, M.E.; Gonzalez de Mejia, E. Gamma-conglutin peptides from Andean lupin legume (*Lupinus mutabilis* Sweet) enhanced glucose uptake and reduced gluconeogenesis in vitro. *J. Funct. Foods* **2018**, *45*, 339–347. [CrossRef]
65. Kwon, D.Y.; Hong, S.M.; Ahn, I.S.; Kim, M.J.; Yang, H.J.; Park, S. Isoflavonoids and peptides from meju, long-term fermented soybeans, increase insulin sensitivity and exert insulinotropic effects in vitro. *Nutrition* **2011**, *27*, 244–252. [CrossRef]
66. Oseguera-Toledo, M.E.; Gonzalez de Mejia, E.; Amaya-Llano, S.L. Hard-to-cook bean (*Phaseolus vulgaris* L.) proteins hydrolyzed by alcalase and bromelain produced bioactive peptide fractions that inhibit targets of type-2 diabetes and oxidative stress. *Food Res. Int.* **2015**, *76*, 839–851. [CrossRef]
67. Barnes, M.J.; Uruakpa, F.O.; Udenigwe, C.C. Influence of Cowpea (*Vigna unguiculata*) Peptides on Insulin Resistance. *J. Nutrit. Health Food Sci.* **2015**, *3*, 1–3.

68. Davis, J.; Higginbotham, A.; O'Connor, T.; Moustaid-Moussa, N.; Tebbe, A.; Kim, Y.C.; Cho, K.W.; Shay, N.; Adler, S.; Peterson, R.; et al. Soy protein and isoflavones influence adiposity and development of metabolic syndrome in the obese male ZDF rat. *Ann. Nutr. Metab.* **2007**, *51*, 42–52. [CrossRef]
69. Nordentoft, I.; Jeppesen, P.B.; Hong, J.; Abudula, R.; Hermansen, K. Increased Insulin Sensitivity and Changes in the Expression Profile of Key Insulin Regulatory Genes and Beta Cell Transcription Factors in Diabetic KKAy-Mice after Feeding with a Soy Bean Protein Rich Diet High in Isoflavone Content. *J. Agric. Food Chem.* **2008**, *56*, 4377–4385. [CrossRef]
70. Gonzalez-Santiago, A.E.; Vargas-Guerrero, B.; Garcia-Lopez, P.M.; Martinez-Ayala, A.L.; Dominguez-Rosales, J.A.; Gurrola-Diaz, C.M. *Lupinus albus* Conglutin Gamma Modifies the Gene Expressions of Enzymes Involved in Glucose Hepatic Production In Vivo. *Plant Foods Hum. Nutr.* **2017**, *72*, 134–140. [CrossRef]
71. Magni, C.; Sessa, F.; Accardo, E.; Vanoni, M.; Morazzoni, P.; Scarafoni, A.; Duranti, M. Conglutin gamma, a lupin seed protein, binds insulin in vitro and reduces plasma glucose levels of hyperglycemic rats. *J. Nutr. Biochem.* **2004**, *15*, 646–650. [CrossRef]
72. Vargas-Guerrero, B.; Garcia-Lopez, P.M.; Martinez-Ayala, A.L.; Dominguez-Rosales, J.A.; Gurrola-Diaz, C.M. Administration of *Lupinus albus* gamma conglutin (Cgamma) to n5 STZ rats augmented Ins-1 gene expression and pancreatic insulin content. *Plant Foods Hum. Nutr.* **2014**, *69*, 241–247. [CrossRef]
73. Terruzzi, I.; Senesi, P.; Magni, C.; Montesano, A.; Scarafoni, A.; Luzi, L.; Duranti, M. Insulin-mimetic action of conglutin-gamma, a lupin seed protein, in mouse myoblasts. *Nutr. Metab. Cardiovasc. Dis.* **2011**, *21*, 197–205. [CrossRef]
74. Wei, Y.; Zhang, R.; Fang, L.; Qin, X.; Cai, M.; Gu, R.; Lu, J.; Wang, Y. Hypoglycemic effects and biochemical mechanisms of Pea oligopeptide on high-fat diet and streptozotocin-induced diabetic mice. *J. Food Biochem.* **2019**, *43*, e13055. [CrossRef]
75. Valencia-Mejia, E.; Batista, K.A.; Fernandez, J.J.A.; Fernandes, K.F. Antihyperglycemic and hypoglycemic activity of naturally occurring peptides and protein hydrolysates from easy-to-cook and hard-to-cook beans (*Phaseolus vulgaris* L.). *Food Res. Int.* **2019**, *121*, 238–246. [CrossRef]
76. de Souza Rocha, T.; Hernandez, L.M.R.; Mojica, L.; Johnson, M.H.; Chang, Y.K.; González de Mejía, E. Germination of *Phaseolus vulgaris* and alcalase hydrolysis of its proteins produced bioactive peptides capable of improving markers related to type-2 diabetes in vitro. *Food Res. Int.* **2015**, *76*, 150–159. [CrossRef]
77. Dun, X.P.; Wang, J.H.; Chen, L.; Lu, J.; Li, F.F.; Zhao, Y.Y.; Cederlund, E.; Bryzgalova, G.; Efendic, S.; Jornvall, H.; et al. Activity of the plant peptide aglycin in mammalian systems. *FEBS J.* **2007**, *274*, 751–759. [CrossRef]
78. Hirano, K.; Hirano, H. Interaction of a 43-kDa Receptor-like Protein with a 4-kDa Hormone-like Peptide in Soybean. *Biochemistry* **2004**, *43*, 12105–12112.
79. Watanbe, Y. A peptide that stimulates phosphorylation of the plant insulin-binding protein Isolation, primary structure and cDNA cloning. *Eur. J. Biochem.* **1994**, *224*, 167–172. [CrossRef]
80. Gressent, F.; Duport, G.; Rahioui, I.; Pauchet, Y.; Bolland, P.; Specty, O.; Rahbe, Y. Biological activity and binding site characteristics of the PA1b Entomotoxin on insects from different orders. *J. Insect. Sci.* **2007**, *7*, 12. [CrossRef]
81. Domoney, C. Inhibitors of legume seeds. In *Seed Proteins*; Shewry, P.R., Casey, R., Eds.; Springer: Dordrecht, The Netherlands, 1999; pp. 635–655.
82. Mane, S.P.; Johnson, S.K.; Duranti, M.; Pareek, V.K.; Utikar, R.P. Lupin seed γ-conglutin: Extraction and purification methods—A review. *Trends Food Sci. Technol.* **2018**, *73*, 1–11. [CrossRef]
83. Lima-Cabello, E.; Robles-Bolivar, P.; Alché, J.D.; Jimenez-Lopez, J.C. Narrow Leafed Lupin Beta-Conglutin Proteins Epitopes Identification and Molecular Features Analysis Involved in Cross-Allergenicity to Peanut and Other Legumes. *GCB* **2016**, *2*, e29. [CrossRef]
84. Jessica Capraro, A.C.; Luis, A.R.; Chiara, M.; Alessio, S.; Marcello, D. Assessment of the lupin seed glucose-lowering protein intestinal absorption by using in vitro and ex vivo models. *Food Chem.* **2011**, *125*, 1279–1283. [CrossRef]
85. Claessens, M.; Saris, W.H.; Van Baak, M.A. Glucagon and insulin responses after ingestion of different amounts of intact and hydrolysed proteins. *Br. J. Nutr.* **2008**, *100*, 61–69. [CrossRef]
86. Sánchez, A.; Vázquez, A. Bioactive peptides: A review. *FQS* **2017**, *1*, 29–46. [CrossRef]
87. Daliri, E.B.; Oh, D.H.; Lee, B.H. Bioactive Peptides. *Foods* **2017**, *6*, 32. [CrossRef]
88. Agyei, D. Bioactive Proteins and Peptides from Soybeans. *Recent Pat. Food Nutr. Agric.* **2015**, *7*, 100–107. [CrossRef]
89. Chatterjee, C.; Gleddie, S.; Xiao, C.W. Soybean Bioactive Peptides and Their Functional Properties. *Nutrients* **2018**, *10*, 1211. [CrossRef]
90. Shahidi, F.; Zhong, Y. Bioactive Peptides. *J. Aoac. Int.* **2008**, *9*, 914–931. [CrossRef]
91. Lammi, C.; Bollati, C.; Ferruzza, S.; Ranaldi, G.; Sambuy, Y.; Arnoldi, A. Soybean- and Lupin-Derived Peptides Inhibit DPP-IV Activity on In Situ Human Intestinal Caco-2 Cells and Ex Vivo Human Serum. *Nutrients* **2018**, *10*, 1082. [CrossRef]
92. Ngoh, Y.Y.; Tye, G.J.; Gan, C.Y. The investigation of α-amylase inhibitory activity of selected Pinto bean peptides via preclinical study using AR42J cell. *J. Funct. Foods* **2017**, *35*, 641–647. [CrossRef]
93. Ngoh, Y.Y.; Gan, C.Y. Identification of Pinto bean peptides with inhibitory effects on alpha-amylase and angiotensin converting enzyme (ACE) activities using an integrated bioinformatics-assisted approach. *Food Chem.* **2018**, *267*, 124–131. [CrossRef]
94. Jakubczyk, A.; Karas, M.; Zlotek, U.; Szymanowska, U. Identification of potential inhibitory peptides of enzymes involved in the metabolic syndrome obtained by simulated gastrointestinal digestion of fermented bean (*Phaseolus vulgaris* L.) seeds. *Food Res. Int.* **2017**, *100*, 489–496. [CrossRef]

95. Mojica, L.; de Mejia, E.G. Optimization of enzymatic production of anti-diabetic peptides from black bean (*Phaseolus vulgaris* L.) proteins, their characterization and biological potential. *Food Funct.* **2016**, *7*, 713–727. [CrossRef]
96. Huang, M.H.; Lin, J.L.; Wang, M.; Ma, Y.; Wang, J.F. High-level expression and activity determination of hypoglycemic peptide aglycin. *Mod. Food Sci. Technol.* **2020**, *36*, 143–149. [CrossRef]
97. Wang, R.; Zhao, H.; Pan, X.; Orfila, C.; Lu, W.; Ma, Y. Preparation of bioactive peptides with antidiabetic, antihypertensive, and antioxidant activities and identification of alpha-glucosidase inhibitory peptides from soy protein. *Food Sci. Nutr.* **2019**, *7*, 1848–1856. [CrossRef]
98. Mojica, L.; Luna-Vital, D.A.; Gonzalez de Mejia, E. Characterization of peptides from common bean protein isolates and their potential to inhibit markers of type-2 diabetes, hypertension and oxidative stress. *J. Sci. Food Agric.* **2017**, *97*, 2401–2410. [CrossRef]
99. Chandrasekaran, S.; Luna-Vital, D.; de Mejia, E.G. Identification and Comparison of Peptides from Chickpea Protein Hydrolysates Using Either Bromelain or Gastrointestinal Enzymes and Their Relationship with Markers of Type 2 Diabetes and Bitterness. *Nutrients* **2020**, *12*, 3843. [CrossRef]
100. Sato, K.; Miyasaka, S.; Tsuji, A.; Tachi, H. Isolation and characterization of peptides with dipeptidyl peptidase IV (DPPIV) inhibitory activity from natto using DPPIV from Aspergillus oryzae. *Food Chem.* **2018**, *261*, 51–56. [CrossRef]
101. Mojica, L.; Chen, K.; de Mejia, E.G. Impact of commercial precooking of common bean (*Phaseolus vulgaris*) on the generation of peptides, after pepsin-pancreatin hydrolysis, capable to inhibit dipeptidyl peptidase-IV. *J. Food. Sci.* **2015**, *80*, H188–H198. [CrossRef]
102. Mune Mune, M.A.; Minka, S.R.; Henle, T. Investigation on antioxidant, angiotensin converting enzyme and dipeptidyl peptidase IV inhibitory activity of Bambara bean protein hydrolysates. *Food Chem.* **2018**, *250*, 162–169. [CrossRef]
103. de Souza Rocha, T.; Hernandez, L.M.R.; Chang, Y.K.; de Mejia, E.G. Impact of germination and enzymatic hydrolysis of cowpea bean (*Vigna unguiculata*) on the generation of peptides capable of inhibiting dipeptidyl peptidase IV. *Food Res. Int.* **2014**, *64*, 799–809. [CrossRef]
104. Castañeda-Pérez, E.; Jiménez-Morales, K.; Quintal-Novelo, C.; Moo-Puc, R.; Chel-Guerrero, L.; Betancur-Ancona, D. Enzymatic protein hydrolysates and ultrafiltered peptide fractions from Cowpea *Vigna unguiculata* L bean with in vitro antidiabetic potential. *J. Iran. Chem. Soc.* **2019**, *16*, 1773–1781. [CrossRef]
105. Cnop, M.; Welsh, N.; Jonas, J.C.; Jörns, A.; Lenzen, S.; Eizirik, D.L. Mechanisms of pancreatic beta-cell death in type 1 and type 2 diabetes: Many differences, few similarities. *Diabetes* **2005**, *54*, S97–S107. [CrossRef]
106. Guo, S.D. Insulin signaling, resistance, and the metabolic syndrome: Insights from mouse models into disease mechanisms. *J. Endocrinol.* **2014**, *220*, T1–T23. [CrossRef]
107. Newsholme, P.; Bender, K.; Kiely, A.; Brennan, L. Amino acid metabolism, insulin secretion and diabetes. *Biochem. Soc. Trans.* **2007**, *35*, 1180–1186. [CrossRef]
108. Hilder, T.L.; Baer, L.A.; Fuller, P.M.; Fuller, C.A.; Grindeland, R.E.; Wade, C.E.; Graves, L.M. Insulin-independent pathways mediating glucose uptake in hindlimb-suspended skeletal muscle. *J. Appl. Physiol.* **2005**, *99*, 2181–2188. [CrossRef]
109. Huang, S.; Czech, M.P. The GLUT4 glucose transporter. *Cell Metab.* **2007**, *5*, 237–252. [CrossRef]
110. Kwon, D.Y.; Daily, J.W., 3rd; Kim, H.J.; Park, S. Antidiabetic effects of fermented soybean products on type 2 diabetes. *Nutr. Res.* **2010**, *30*, 1–13. [CrossRef]
111. Ngoh, Y.Y.; Gan, C.Y. Enzyme-assisted extraction and identification of antioxidative and alpha-amylase inhibitory peptides from Pinto beans (*Phaseolus vulgaris* cv. Pinto). *Food Chem.* **2016**, *190*, 331–337. [CrossRef]
112. Bompard-Gilles, C.; Rousseau, P.; Rougé, P.; Payan, F. Substrate mimicry in the active center of a mammalian α amylase: Structural analysis of an enzyme–inhibitor complex. *Structure* **1996**, *4*, 1441–1452. [CrossRef]
113. Nahoum, V.; Farisei, F.; Le-Berre-Anton, V.; Egloff, M.P.; Rouge, P.; Poerio, E.; Payan, F. A plant-seed inhibitor of two classes of alpha-amylases: X-ray analysis of Tenebrio molitor larvae alpha-amylase in complex with the bean *Phaseolus vulgaris* inhibitor. *Acta Crystallogr. Sect. D Struct. Biol.* **1999**, *55*, 360–362. [CrossRef]
114. Patil, P.; Mandal, S.; Tomar, S.K.; Anand, S. Food protein-derived bioactive peptides in management of type 2 diabetes. *Eur. J. Nutr.* **2015**, *54*, 863–880. [CrossRef]
115. Arulmozhiraja, S.; Matsuo, N.; Ishitsubo, E.; Okazaki, S.; Shimano, H.; Tokiwa, H. Comparative Binding Analysis of Dipeptidyl Peptidase IV (DPP-4) with Antidiabetic Drugs—An Ab Initio Fragment Molecular Orbital Study. *PLoS ONE* **2016**, *11*, e0166275. [CrossRef]
116. Zizzari, A.T.; Pliatsika, D.; Gall, F.M.; Fischer, T.; Riedl, R. New perspectives in oral peptide delivery. *Drug Discov. Today* **2021**, *26*, 1097–1105. [CrossRef]
117. Li, Y.; Zhang, W.; Zhao, R.; Zhang, X. Advances in oral peptide drug nanoparticles for diabetes mellitus treatment. *Bioact. Mater.* **2022**, *15*, 392–408. [CrossRef]
118. Yap, P.G.; Gan, C.Y. In vivo challenges of anti-diabetic peptide therapeutics: Gastrointestinal stability, toxicity and allergenicity. *Trends Food Sci. Technol.* **2020**, *105*, 161–175. [CrossRef]
119. Oseguera-Toledo, M.E. Proteins and bioactive peptides: Mechanism of action in diabetes management. *Nutrafoods* **2014**, *13*, 147–157. [CrossRef]

120. Rosenstock, J.; Allison, D.; Birkenfeld, A.L.; Blicher, T.M.; Deenadayalan, S.; Jacobsen, J.B.; Serusclat, P.; Violante, R.; Watada, H.; Davies, M.; et al. Effect of Additional Oral Semaglutide vs Sitagliptin on Glycated Hemoglobin in Adults with Type 2 Diabetes Uncontrolled with Metformin Alone or with Sulfonylurea: The PIONEER 3 Randomized Clinical Trial. *JAMA* **2019**, *321*, 1466–1480. [CrossRef]
121. Davies, M.; Pieber, T.R.; Hartoft-Nielsen, M.L.; Hansen, O.K.H.; Jabbour, S.; Rosenstock, J. Effect of Oral Semaglutide Compared with Placebo and Subcutaneous Semaglutide on Glycemic Control in Patients with Type 2 Diabetes: A Randomized Clinical Trial. *JAMA* **2017**, *318*, 1460–1470. [CrossRef]
122. Poudwal, S.; Misra, A.; Shende, P. Role of lipid nanocarriers for enhancing oral absorption and bioavailability of insulin and GLP-1 receptor agonists. *J. Drug Target.* **2021**, *29*, 834–847. [CrossRef]

antioxidants

MDPI

Article

Shallow- and Deep-Water *Ophiura* Species Produce a Panel of Chlorin Compounds with Potent Photodynamic Anticancer Activities

Antonina Klimenko [1,2,†], Robin Huber [3,4,†], Laurence Marcourt [3,4], Dmitry Tabakaev [5], Alexey Koval [1], Salim Sh. Dautov [6], Tatyana N. Dautova [6], Jean-Luc Wolfender [3,4,*], Rob Thew [5], Yuri Khotimchenko [2,6], Emerson Ferreira Queiroz [3,4,*] and Vladimir L. Katanaev [1,2,*]

1 Translational Research Center in Oncohaematology, Department of Cell Physiology and Metabolism, Faculty of Medicine, University of Geneva, Rue Michel-Servet 1, CH-1206 Geneva, Switzerland
2 Institute of Life Sciences and Biomedicine, Far Eastern Federal University, 690090 Vladivostok, Russia
3 School of Pharmaceutical Sciences, University of Geneva, Rue Michel-Servet 1, CH-1206 Geneva, Switzerland
4 Institute of Pharmaceutical Sciences of Western Switzerland, University of Geneva, CMU, Rue Michel-Servet 1, CH-1206 Geneva, Switzerland
5 Department of Applied Physics, Faculty of Sciences, University of Geneva, Rue de l'Ecole-De-Médecine 20, CH-1205 Geneva, Switzerland
6 A.V. Zhirmunsky National Scientific Center of Marine Biology, Far East Branch of Russian Academy of Sciences, Palchevsky St. 17, 690041 Vladivostok, Russia
* Correspondence: jean-luc.wolfender@unige.ch (J.-L.W.); emerson.ferreira@unige.ch (E.F.Q.); vladimir.katanaev@unige.ch (V.L.K.)
† These authors contributed equally to this work.

Abstract: A Pacific brittle star *Ophiura sarsii* has previously been shown to produce a chlorin (3*S*,4*S*)-14-Ethyl-9-(hydroxymethyl)-4,8,13,18-tetramethyl-20-oxo-3-phorbinepropanoic acid (ETPA) (**1**) with potent phototoxic activities, making it applicable to photodynamic therapy. Using extensive LC-MS metabolite profiling, molecular network analysis, and targeted isolation with de novo NMR structure elucidation, we herein identify five additional chlorin compounds from *O. sarsii* and its deep-sea relative *O. ooplax*: 10S-Hydroxypheophorbide a (**2**), Pheophorbide a (**3**), Pyropheophorbide a (**4**), (3*S*,4*S*,21*R*)-14-Ethyl-9-(hydroxymethyl)-21-(methoxycarbonyl)-4,8,13,18-tetramethyl-20-oxo-3-phorbinepropanoic acid (**5**), and (3*S*,4*S*,21*R*)-14-Ethyl-21-hydroxy-9-(hydroxymethyl)-4,8,13,18-tetramethyl-20-oxo-3-phorbinepropanoic acid (**6**). Chlorins **5** and **6** have not been previously reported in natural sources. Interestingly, low amounts of chlorins **1–4** and **6** could also be identified in a distant species, the basket star *Gorgonocephalus* cf. *eucnemis*, demonstrating that chlorins are produced by a wide spectrum of marine invertebrates of the class Ophiuroidea. Following the purification of these major *Ophiura* chlorin metabolites, we discovered the significant singlet oxygen quantum yield upon their photoinduction and the resulting phototoxicity against triple-negative breast cancer BT-20 cells. These studies identify an arsenal of brittle star chlorins as natural photosensitizers with potential photodynamic therapy applications.

Keywords: marine organisms; chlorins; photodynamic therapy; brittle stars; Ophiuroidea; phototoxicity; cancer

1. Introduction

Photodynamic therapy (PDT) is a powerful alternative to other treatment options for cancer [1], dermatological aberrations [2], infectious diseases [3], or even cosmetics [4]. It is based on the activity of photosensitizers–compounds that are harmless unless excited with light of the proper wavelength. From the photoactivated state, a photosensitizer generates reactive oxygen species that are highly cytotoxic [5]. The systemic application of non-activated photosensitizers combined with the focal activation at the disease site with a laser makes PDT a unique therapeutic approach bordering between general and targeted treatments.

As with many other drugs, photosensitizers used in the clinic are derived from or inspired by nature [6]. Marine compounds are gaining interest as a source of new drugs [7–9]. Curiously, some natural metabolites with photosensitizer properties are used in their hosts for what can be considered a natural PDT. For example, bonellin, a chlorin-type compound synthesized by females of the sea worm *Bonellia viridis*, controls the sex determination of this polychete. Larvae of *B. viridis* develop into males when settled in the physical proximity of an adult female; the photodynamic action of bonellin is believed to play the key role in this process [10]. Photosensitizers also mediate the chemical defense function of their hosts against predators [10,11].

The number of factors determines whether a given photosensitizer can become a good candidate for medical PDT applications. One such factor is the excitation wavelength—the further in the red zone of the spectrum it is, the deeper the activating light can penetrate through biological tissues. Another is the singlet oxygen quantum yield of the compound; the higher, the better. Lack of toxicity at high concentrations of the non-activated photosensitizer is also an important factor. These and other pharmacokinetic/pharmacodynamic considerations frame the never-stopping search for and development of novel photosensitizers for PDT [12]. Much interest in this regard is devoted to chlorins that, in general, are powerful photosensitizers [13].

In our previous studies, we discovered the chlorin (3*S*,4*S*)-14-Ethyl-9-(hydroxymethyl)-4,8,13,18-tetramethyl-20-oxo-3-phorbinepropanoic acid (ETPA) from a Pacific brittle star *Ophiura sarsii* [14]. This major metabolite is easily purifiable and shows low cytotoxicity unless photoactivated. Red-light illumination escalates its potent submicromolar toxicity against a panel of cancer cell lines [15]. We further provided a proof-of-concept in vivo PDT application of ETPA in a mouse model of glioblastoma. These findings highlighted the promise of this brittle star chlorin for diverse PDT applications [14,15].

As ETPA is endogenously produced by *O. sarsii* [15], we wondered whether this brittle star might synthesize other chlorin compounds. As previously, the class Ophiuroidea has not been known to produce chlorins [11,16]. We also questioned whether other representatives of these marine invertebrates could constitute sources of natural photosensitizers for potential PDT applications. Here, we discover a family of chlorins in *O. sarsii* and other Ophiuroidea species, some of which were never identified as natural compounds previously. The strong phototoxic anticancer effects of these chlorins make them interesting candidates for further developments for PDT applications, as single compounds or as cocktails.

2. Materials and Methods

2.1. Materials

Brittle stars *Ophiura sarsii* (Figure 1A) were collected at depths of 15–18 m in the Peter the Great Gulf (Sea of Japan) in May 2021; for location, see [15]. *Ophiura ooplax* [17] (Figure 1B) and the basket star *Gorgonocephalus* cf. *eucnemis* [18] (Figure 1C) were collected in July-August 2021 from the Koko guyot (Pacific Ocean, 35.60 N 171.23 E, depth 750 m, and 33.75 N, 171.92 E, depth 865 m, respectively, Figure 1D) using the remotely operated vehicle (ROV) Sub-Atlantic Comanche 18. These deep-sea samples were collected during the expedition of the A.V. Zhirmunsky National Scientific Center of Marine Biology (Far East Branch, Russian Academy of Sciences, Vladivostok, Russia) aboard the vessel R/V Akademik M. Lavrentyev (Cruise No. 94) to the seamounts of the Emperor Chain (Pacific Ocean) in July–September 2021. Sample collection was performed by the standards approved by the Ministry of Science and Higher Education (Russia); all efforts were made to minimize animal suffering. Species were identified by S.S.D. at the Laboratory of Embryology of the A.V. Zhirmunsky National Scientific Center of Marine Biology using morphological taxonomic characters. Freshly caught animals were washed twice under running water and frozen at −80 °C. One day after freezing, the animals were dried in a lyophilic dryer (Labconco FreeZone, Kansas City, MO, USA) and further stored at −23 °C.

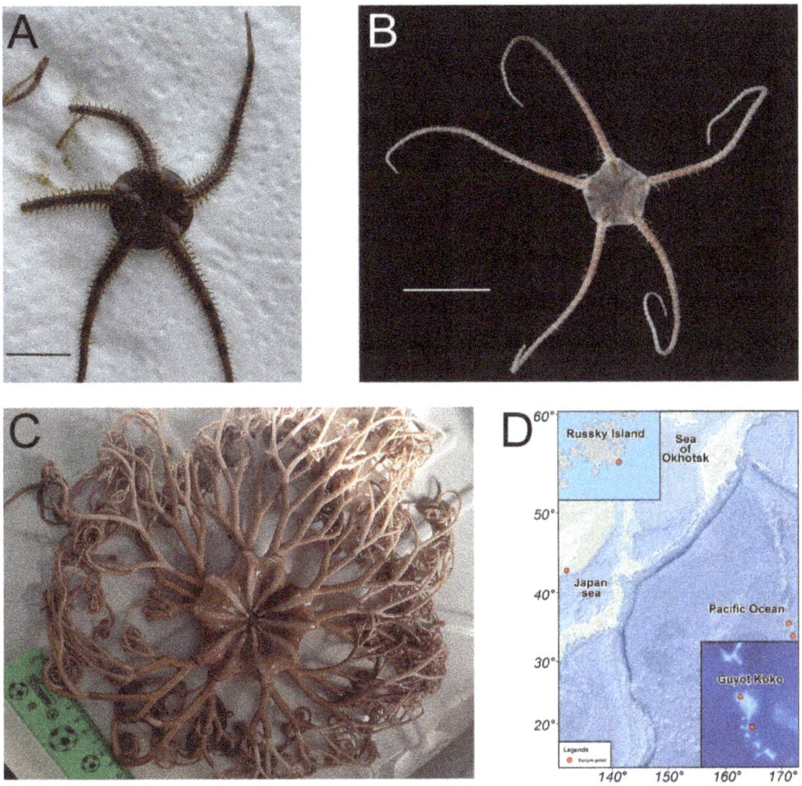

Figure 1. (**A**,**B**) Brittle stars *Ophiura sarsii* (**A**) and *Ophiura ooplax* (**B**). Scale bars: 1 cm. (**C**) Basket star *Gorgonocephalus* cf. *eucnemis*. (**D**) Map depicting the sample collection locations: Russky Island in the Japan sea for *O. sarsii*, Guyot Koko in the Pacific Ocean for *O. ooplax*, and *G. cf. eucnemis*.

2.2. Extraction

Before extraction, the material was lyophilized and homogenized using a Retsch MM301 mixer mill (Retsch, Eragny, France) at a vibration frequency of 1500 rpm for 2 min to obtain a homogeneous powder. 40 g of *O. sarsii* powder was poured into the Dionex ASE 350 solvent extraction system (Thermo Scientific, Bremen, Germany) and successively extracted by solvent of increasing polarity at 40 °C and using a holding time of 10 min for each cycle (50 mL/cycle). The solvents and their volumes were 800 mL of hexane, 250 mL of ethyl acetate (EtOAc), 250 mL of methanol (MeOH), and 200 mL of water. The extracts were dried using a rotary evaporator and/or lyophilization. The masses of the obtained extracts of *O. sarsii* were 459 mg of hexane, 51 mg of EtOAc, 1999 mg of MeOH, and 400 mg of water. The total yield of extraction was about 7%. The MeOH extract was further treated by liquid–liquid extraction to remove most of the polar compounds. The extract was solubilized in 120 mL of *n*-butanol and washed 3 times with 200 mL of H_2O in a separating funnel. The butanol phase was dried on a rotary evaporator (250 mg).

A similar procedure was performed with *O. ooplax* and *G.* cf. *eucnemis*. A total of 29 g of *O. ooplax* were taken, ground into powder, and extracted in the ASE system (same parameters as described before) using 600 mL of hexane, 300 mL of EtOAc, 300 mL of MeOH, and 100 mL of water. The obtained extracts were dried using rotary evaporation and/or lyophilization. The weights of the obtained extracts of *O. ooplax* were 343 mg of hexane, 59.5 mg of EtOAc, 1598 mg of MeOH, and 267 mg of water. The total yield of extraction was about 8%. A total of 50 g of homogenized dry material of *G.* cf. *eucnemis* was extracted in the ASE system using solvents: 800 mL of hexane, 400 mL of EtOAc, 450 mL of MeOH, and 200 mL of water. The total weights of the extracts were hexane 1235 mg, EtOAc 116 mg, MeOH 2012 mg, and water 917 mg. The total yield of extraction was about 9%.

2.3. General Analytical Procedures

The optical rotations were measured in MeOH on a JASCO P-1030 polarimeter (Loveland, CO, USA) in a 10 cm tube. The UV–Vis and ECD spectra were recorded on a JASCO J-815 spectrometer (Loveland, CO, USA) in MeOH using a 1 cm cell. Scan speed was set at 200 nm/min in continuous mode between 800 and 190 nm with 3 accumulations. NMR spectroscopic data were recorded on a Bruker Avance Neo 600 MHz NMR spectrometer equipped with a QCI 5 mm cryoprobe and a SampleJet automated sample changer (Bruker BioSpin, Rheinstetten, Germany). One-dimensional and two-dimensional NMR experiments (^{1}H, COSY, ROESY, and edited-HSQC) were recorded in DMSO-d_6. Chemical shifts are reported in parts per million (δ) and coupling constants (*J*) in Hz. The residual DMSO-d_6 signal (δ_H 2.50; δ_C 39.5) was used as internal standards for ^{1}H and ^{13}C NMR, respectively.

2.4. UHPLC-PDA-ELSD-MS Analysis

Chromatographic data were obtained on an ultra-high-performance liquid chromatography system equipped with a photodiode array, an evaporative light-scattering detector, and a single quadrupole detector using heated electrospray ionization (UHPLC-PDA-ELSD-MS) (Waters, Milford, MA, USA). The ESI parameters were the following: capillary voltage 800 V, cone voltage 15 V, source temperature 120 °C, and probe temperature 600 °C. Acquisition was performed in positive ionization mode with an *m/z* range of 150−1000 Da. The chromatographic separation was performed on an Acquity UPLC BEH C_{18} column (50 × 2.1 mm i.d., 1.7 μm; Waters) at 0.6 mL/min, 40 °C with H_2O (A) and MeCN (B), both containing 0.1% formic acid as solvents. The gradient was carried out as follows: 5–100% B in 7 min, 1 min at 100% B, and a re-equilibration step at 5% B for 2 min. The ELSD temperature was fixed at 45 °C, with a gain of 9. The PDA data were acquired from 190 to 500 nm, with a resolution of 1.2 nm. The sampling rate was set at 20 points/s.

2.5. UHPLC-PDA-CAD-HRMS Analysis, Data-Processing, and Feature-Based Molecular Network Generation

Chromatographic data with high-resolution MS were obtained on a Waters Acquity UHPLC system equipped with a Q-Exactive Focus mass spectrometer (Thermo Scientific, Bremen, Germany), using heated electrospray ionization source (HESI-II). The chromatographic separation was carried out on an Acquity UPLC BEH C_{18} column (50 × 2.1 mm i.d., 1.7 μm; Waters) at 0.6 mL/min, 40 °C with H_2O (A) and MeCN (B) both containing 0.1% formic acid as solvents. The gradient was carried out as follows: 5%–100% B in 7 min, 1 min at 100% B, and a re-equilibration step at 5% B in 2 min. The ionization parameters were the same as used in [19]. The raw UHPLC-HRMS/MS files were converted into mzXML files using the MSConvert software. The mzXML files were then processed using the open software MZmine (2.53) [20]. Mass detection step was performed using centroid mass detector with a noise level set at 5E4 for MS^1 and 0 for MS^2. The ADAP chromatogram builder was employed with a minimum group size of scans of 5, a minimum group intensity threshold of 1E4, a minimum highest intensity of 1E4, and an *m/z* tolerance of 8 ppm. The deconvolution was carried out with the ADAP (Wavelets) algorithm, using a signal-to-noise threshold of 10, a minimum feature height of 10, a coefficient/area threshold of 110, a peak duration range between 0.01 and 2.0 min, and a wavelet range between 0.01 and 0.10 min. The *m/z* and retention time (RT) ranges for MS^2 scan pairing were, respectively, set to

0.005 Da and 0.1 min. The isotopes were grouped using the isotope peak grouper algorithm with an *m/z* tolerance of 8 ppm, an RT tolerance of 0.01 min, and a maximum charge of 2, using the most intense isotope as the representative one. The alignment was carried out with the join aligner with an *m/z* tolerance of 8 ppm, an RT tolerance of 0.1 min, and a weight tolerance for *m/z* and RT of 10 each. The MZmine aligned table was exported in MGF format for the processing of the Feature-based molecular network (FBMN). The spectral data were uploaded on the Global Natural Products Social (GNPS) platform [21]. A network was generated with a minimum cosine score of 0.65 and a minimum of 5 matching peaks. The experimental spectra were searched against GNPS' spectral libraries. The obtained network was visualized in the software Cytoscape (3.7.2, Institute of Systems Biology, Seattle, WA, USA) [22].

2.6. Chromatographic Optimization and Semi-Preparative Isolation

The separation conditions of the MeOH and EtOAc extracts were optimized on an HP 1260 Agilent High-Performance liquid chromatography equipped with a photodiode array detector and an ELSD detector (HPLC-PDA-ELSD) (Agilent Technologies, Santa Clara, CA, USA). The chromatographic separation was performed on an XBridge C_{18} column (250×4.6 mm i.d., 5 μm; Waters) equipped with a C_{18} pre-column at 1 mL/min, with H_2O (A) and MeCN (B), both containing 0.1% formic acid as solvents. The UV absorbance was measured at 280 and 360 nm, and UV–Vis spectra were recorded between 190 and 600 nm (step 2 nm). The optimized gradient used for the MeOH extract was from 45 to 100% of MeCN in 60 min, with 10 min of washing at 100% MeCN. The optimized gradient used for the EtOAc extract was from 55% to 90% MeCN in 60 min, with 10 min of washing at 100% MeCN. These chromatographic methods were geometrically transferred [23] to the semi-preparative scale on a Shimadzu system equipped with an LC-20 A module pumps, an SPD-20 A UV/VIS, a 7725I Rheodyne® valve, and an FRC-40 fraction collector (Shimadzu, Kyoto, Japan). The separation was performed on an XBridge C_{18} column (250 mm × 19 mm i.d., 5 μm; Waters) equipped with a C_{18} pre-column cartridge holder (10 mm × 19 mm i.d., 5 μm; Waters) at 17 mL/min, with H_2O (A) and MeCN (B) both containing 0.1% formic acid as solvents. The UV detection was set at 280 and 360 nm. The mixtures were injected into the semi-preparative HPLC column using a dry-load methodology developed in our laboratory [24]. Two injections of 50 mg were performed for the MeOH extract and one injection of 50 mg for the EtOAc extract. Six compounds were obtained (the yields for each compound are the sum of the compound isolated from the two extracts): **1** (2 mg, 70% purity), **2** (0.6 mg, 75% purity), **3** (3.8 mg, 85% purity), **4** (1.4 mg, 65% purity), **5** (0.3 mg, 75% purity), and **6** (0.8 mg, 70% purity). Purity estimation was based on the ^{1}H-NMR spectra.

2.7. Description of the Isolated Compounds

(**1**): (3*S*,4*S*)-14-Ethyl-9-(hydroxymethyl)-4,8,13,18-tetramethyl-20-oxo-3-phorbinepropanoic acid (**ETPA**) **[14]** $[\alpha]^{25}_D$ +300 (c 0.01, MeOH). UV (MeCN) λ_{max} (log ε) 269 (4.94), 320 (4.16), 375 (4.54) (sh), 393 (4.64) (sh), 408 (4.69), 504 (3.73), 535 (3.73), 604 (3.69), 661 (4.37) nm. ECD (c 20 μM, MeOH) λ_{max} ([θ]) 405 (+25,900), 660 (−22,200) nm. ^{1}H NMR (DMSO-d_6, 600 MHz) δ 0.33 (1H, s, NH15), 1.64 (3H, t, *J* = 7.6 Hz, H_3-4b), 1.77 (3H, d, *J* = 7.2 Hz, H_3-8a), 2.10 (1H, m, H-7a″), 2.32 (1H, m, H-7b″), 2.55 (1H, m, H-7b′), 2.61 (1H, m, H-7a′), 3.24 (3H, s, H_3-3a), 3.38 (3H, overlapped, H_3-1a), 3.62 (3H, s, H_3-5a), 3.73 (2H, q, *J* = 7.6 Hz, H_2-4a), 4.32 (1H, dt, *J* = 10.1, 3.0 Hz, H-7), 4.58 (1H, qd, *J* = 7.2, 3.0 Hz, H-8), 5.12 (1H, d, *J* = 19.4 Hz, H-10b″), 5.22 (1H, d, *J* = 19.4 Hz, H-10b′), 5.74 (2H, s, H_2-2a), 8.83 (1H, s, H-δ), 9.56 (1H, s, H-α), 9.73 (1H, s, H-β); ^{13}C NMR (DMSO-d_6, 151 MHz) δ 10.8 (CH_3-1a), 11.0 (CH_3-3a), 11.7 (CH_3-5a), 17.5 (CH_3-4b), 18.7 (CH_2-4a), 22.9 (CH_3-8a), 29.5 (CH_2-7a), 30.9 (CH_2-7b), 47.5 (CH_2-10), 49.3 (CH-8), 51.1 (CH-7), 54.4 (CH_2-2a), 93.6 (CH-δ), 97.0 (CH-α), 104.3 (CH-β), 106.0 (C-γ), 127.8 (C-5), 130.0 (C-6), 133.4 (C-1), 135.9 (C-3), 136.2 (C-12), 137.0 (C-15), 138.6 (C-2), 141.0 (C-11), 145.0 (C-4), 148.0 (C-16), 150.0 (C-14), 154.4 (C-13), 161.2 (C-17), 172.5 (C-18), 174.3 (C-7c), 195.3 (C-9). HR-ESI/MS analysis: *m/z* 539.2657 $[M+H]^+$, (calcd for

$C_{32}H_{35}N_4O_4^+$, 539.2653, Δ = 0.8 ppm). MS/MS spectrum: CCMSLIB00010128700. SMILES: OC(CC[C@H]1[C@@H](C2=N/C1=C(CC3=O)\C4=C3C(C)=C(N4)/C=C5N=C(C(C)=C\5CC)/C=C(N/6)/C(CO)=C(C6=C\2)C)C)=O. ^{1}H, COSY, ^{13}C-DEPTQ, HSQC, HMBC, and ROESY NMR spectra of compound **1** are shown in Supplementary Figures S1–S6, respectively.

(**2**): (3*S*,4*S*,21*S*)-9-Ethenyl-14-ethyl-21-hydroxy-21-(methoxycarbonyl)-4,8,13,18-tetramethyl-20-oxo-3-phorbinepropanoic acid (**(10S)-Hydroxypheophorbide a**) [25,26]: $[\alpha]^{25}{}_D$ +65 (c 0.01, MeOH). UV (MeCN) λ_{max} (log ε) 275 (4.46), 329 (4.44) (sh), 370 (4.64) (sh), 408 (4.80), 500 (3.94), 535 (3.82), 609 (3.73), 665 (4.34) nm ECD (c 10 μM, MeOH) λ_{max} ([θ]) 406 (+20,400), 662 (−32,300) nm. ^{1}H NMR (DMSO-d_6, 600 MHz) δ 1.55 (3H, d, *J* = 7.4 Hz, H_3-8a), 1.66 (3H, t, *J* = 7.7 Hz, H_3-4b), 3.28 (3H, s, H_3-3a), 3.47 (3H, s, H_3-1a), 3.58 (3H, s, H_3-10b), 3.71 (3H, s, H_3-5a), 3.78 (2H, q, *J* = 7.7 Hz, H_2-4a), 4.11 (1H, overlapped, H-7), 4.62 (1H, q, *J* = 7.4 Hz, H-8), 6.25 (1H, d, *J* = 11.7 Hz, H-2b″), 6.44 (1H, d, *J* = 17.9 Hz, H-2b′), 7.74 (1H, s, OH10), 8.28 (1H, dd, *J* = 17.9, 11.7 Hz, H-2a), 9.01 (1H, s, H-δ), 9.60 (1H, s, H-α), 9.92 (1H, s, H-β); ^{13}C NMR (DMSO-d_6, 151 MHz) δ 11.0 (CH_3-3a), 11.7 (CH_3-5a), 12.0 (CH_3-1a), 17.5 (CH_3-4b), 18.7 (CH_2-4a), 22.6 (CH_3-8a), 49.3 (CH-8), 51.4 (CH-7), 52.6 (CH_3-10b), 94.3 (CH-δ), 97.5 (CH-α), 104.9 (CH-β), 109.5 (C-γ), 123.5 (CH_2-2b), 126.8 (C-6), 128.9 (CH-2a), 129.2 (C-5), 132.3 (C-1), 135.8 (C-2), 136.7 (C-3), 137.1 (C-15), 141.5 (C-11), 145.3 (C-4), 150.6 (C-14), 154.6 (C-13), 171.3 (C-10a), 173.3 (C-18), 189.2 (C-9). HR-ESI/MS analysis: *m/z* 609.2718 [M+H]$^+$, (calcd for $C_{35}H_{37}N_6O_6^+$, 609.2708, Δ = 1.7 ppm). MS/MS spectrum: CCMSLIB00010128701. SMILES: OC(CC[C@H]1[C@@H](C2=N/C1=C([C@](C(OC)=O)(O)C3=O)\C4=C3C(C)=C(N4)/C=C5N=C(C(C)=C\5CC)/C=C(N/6)/C(C=C)=C(C6=C\2)C)C)=O. ^{1}H, COSY, HSQC, HMBC, and ROESY NMR spectra of compound **2** are shown in Supplementary Figures S7–S11, respectively.

(**3**): (3*S*,4*S*,21*R*)-9-Ethenyl-14-ethyl-21-(methoxycarbonyl)-4,8,13,18-tetramethyl-20-oxo-3-phorbinepropanoic acid (**Pheophorbide a**) [27]: $[\alpha]^{25}{}_D$ +400 (c 0.02, MeOH). UV (MeCN) λ_{max} (log ε) 275 (4.01), 328 (4.19) (sh), 374 (4.56) (sh), 406 (4.74), 502 (3.80), 536 (3.74), 605 (3.72), 665 (4.38) nm. ECD (c 15 μM, MeOH) λ_{max} ([θ]) 400 (+18,700), 662 (−10,700) nm. ^{1}H NMR (DMSO-d_6, 600 MHz) δ 0.41 (1H, s, NH15), 1.62 (3H, t, J = 7.7 Hz, H_3-4b), 1.76 (3H, d, J = 7.3 Hz, H_3-8a), 2.15 (1H, m, H-7a″), 2.24 (1H, m, H-7b″), 2.44 (1H, m, 7b′), 2.58 (1H, m, 7a′), 3.21 (3H, s, H_3-3a), 3.43 (3H, s, H_3-1a), 3.64 (3H, s, H_3-5a), 3.70 (2H, q, J = 7.7 Hz, H_2-4a), 3.83 (3H, s, H_3-10b), 4.05 (1H, dt, J = 9.5, 2.8 Hz, H-7), 4.58 (1H, qd, J = 7.3, 2.2 Hz, H-8), 6.22 (1H, d, J = 11.6 Hz, H-2b″), 6.40 (1H, d, J = 17.8 Hz, H-2b′), 6.42 (1H, s, H-10), 8.21 (1H, dd, J = 17.8, 11.6 Hz, H-2a), 8.91 (1H, s, H-*δ*), 9.44 (1H, s, H-*α*), 9.77 (1H, s, H-*β*), 12.05 (1H, s, COOH); ^{13}C NMR (DMSO-d_6, 151 MHz) δ 10.9 (CH_3-3a), 11.7 (CH_3-5a), 12.0 (CH_3-1a), 17.4 (CH_3-4b), 18.6 (CH_2-4a), 22.9 (CH_3-8a), 29.0 (CH_2-7a), 30.7 (CH_2-7b), 49.2 (CH-8), 50.8 (CH-7), 52.7 (CH_3-10b), 64.2 (CH-10), 94.0 (CH-*δ*), 97.0 (CH-*α*), 105.0 (CH-*β*), 105.4 (C-*γ*), 123.3 (CH_2-2b), 128.5 (C-6), 128.9 (C-5), 128.9 (CH-2a), 132.3 (C-1), 135.6 (C-2), 135.9 (C-12), 136.4 (C-3), 137.2 (C-15), 141.5 (C-11), 145.3 (C-4), 148.8 (C-16), 150.4 (C-14), 154.9 (C-13), 161.8 (C-17), 169.3 (C-10a), 173.2 (C-18), 174.0 (C-7c), 189.2 (C-9). Confirmed by comparison with the standard compound. HR-ESI/MS analysis: *m/z* 593.2745 [M+H]$^+$, (calcd for $C_{35}H_{37}N_4O_5^+$, 593.2758, Δ = 2.3 ppm). MS/MS spectrum: CCMSLIB00010128702. SMILES: OC(CC[C@H]1[C@@H](C2=N/C1=C([C@@H](C(OC)=O)C3=O)\C4=C3C(C)=C(N4)/C=C5N=C(C(C)=C\5CC)/C=C(N/6)/C(C=C)=C(C6=C\2)C)C)=O. ^{1}H, COSY, ^{13}C-DEPTQ, HSQC, HMBC, and ROESY NMR spectra of compound **3** are shown in Supplementary Figures S12–S17, respectively.

(**4**): (3*S*,4*S*)-9-Ethenyl-14-ethyl-4,8,13,18-tetramethyl-20-oxo-3-phorbinepropanoic acid (**Pyropheophorbide a) [28]**: $[\alpha]^{25}{}_D$ +250 (c 0.01, MeOH). UV (MeCN) λ_{max} (log ε) 275 (4.17), 323 (4.22), 374 (4.48) (sh), 396 (4.62) (sh), 412 (4.68), 507 (3.73), 539 (3.70), 606 (3.64), 667 (4.20) nm. ECD (c 12 μM, MeOH) λ_{max} ([θ]) 412 (+12,600), 668 (−15,000) nm. ^{1}H NMR (DMSO-d_6, 600 MHz) δ 0.29 (1H, s, NH15), 1.64 (3H, t, J = 7.7 Hz, H_3-4b), 1.78 (3H, d, J = 7.4 Hz, H_3-8a), 2.12 (1H, m, H-7a″), 2.33 (1H, m, H-7b″), 2.56 (1H, m, H-7b′), 2.63 (1H, m, H-7a′), 3.25 (3H, s, H_3-3a), 3.45 (3H, s, H_3-1a), 3.64 (3H, s, H_3-5a), 3.73 (2H, q, J = 7.7 Hz, H_2-4a), 4.33 (1H, d, J = 9.6 Hz, H-7), 4.60 (1H, q, J = 7.8 Hz, H-8), 5.14 (1H, d, J = 19.5 Hz, H-10″), 5.24 (1H, d, J = 19.5 Hz, H-10′), 6.23 (1H, d, J = 11.6 Hz, H-2b″), 6.41 (1H, d, J = 17.7 Hz, H-2b′), 8.25 (1H, dd, J = 17.7, 11.6 Hz, H-2a), 8.91 (1H, s, H-*δ*), 9.48 (1H, s, H-*α*), 9.77 (1H, s, H-*β*); ^{13}C NMR (DMSO-d_6, 151 MHz) δ 11.0 (CH_3-3a), 11.7 (CH_3-5a), 12.0 (CH_3-1a), 17.4 (CH_3-4b), 18.7 (CH_2-4a), 22.9 (CH_3-8a), 29.4 (CH_2-7a), 30.8 (CH_2-7b), 47.5 (CH_2-10), 49.3 (CH-8), 51.0

(CH-7), 106.2 (C-11), 123.1 (CH_2-2b), 128.1 (C-5), 129.1 (CH-2a), 130.1 (C-6), 131.9 (C-1), 135.1 (C-2), 136.2 (C-3), 137.3 (C-15), 140.7 (C-11), 145.0 (C-4), 148.0 (C-9), 150.1 (C-14), 154.2 (C-13), 172.4 (C-18), 174.2 (C-7c), 195.3 (C-9). HR-ESI/MS analysis: *m/z* 535.2698 $[M+H]^+$, (calcd for $C_{33}H_{35}N_4O_3{}^+$, 535.2704, Δ = 1.1 ppm). MS/MS spectrum: CCMSLIB00010128703. SMILES: OC(CC[C@H]1[C@@H](C2=N/C1=C(CC3=O)\C4=C3C(C)=C(N4)/C=C5N=C(C(C)=C\5C C)/C=C(N/6)/C(C=C)=C(C6=C\2)C)C)=O. ^{1}H, COSY, HSQC, HMBC, and ROESY NMR spectra of compound **4** are shown in Supplementary Figures S18–S22, respectively.

(**5**): (3*S*,4*S*,21*R*)-14-Ethyl-9-(hydroxymethyl)-21-(methoxycarbonyl)-4,8,13,18-tetramethyl-20-oxo-3-phorbinepropanoic acid (**2-Hydroxymethyl-2-devinyl pheophorbide-a**) [29]: $[\alpha]^{25}{}_D$ +300 (c 0.01, MeOH). UV (MeCN) λ_{max} (log ε) 272 (4.02), 324 (4.19) (sh), 371 (4.54), 399 (4.73), 500 (3.79), 533 (3.68), 600 (3.64), 663 (4.35) nm. ECD (c 15 μM, MeOH) λ_{max} ([θ]) 399 (+32,500), 661 (−20,800) nm. ^{1}H NMR (DMSO-d_6, 600 MHz) δ 0.47 (1H, s, NH15), 1.64 (3H, t, J = 7.7 Hz, H_3-4b), 1.74 (3H, d, J = 7.4 Hz, H_3-8a), 2.11 (1H, m, H-7a″), 2.17 (1H, m, H-7a′), 2.20 (1H, m, H-7b″), 2.44 (1H, m, H-7b′), 3.25 (3H, s, H_3-3a), 3.38 (3H, s, H_3-1a), 3.65 (3H, s, H_3-5a), 3.74 (2H, q, J = 7.7 Hz, H_2-4a), 3.82 (3H, s, H_3-10b), 4.03 (1H, m, H-7), 4.57 (1H, q, J = 7.4 Hz, H-8), 5.74 (2H, d, J = 5.8 Hz, H_2-2a), 5.84 (1H, t, J = 5.8 Hz, OH2a), 6.41 (1H, s, H-10), 8.84 (1H, s, H-δ), 9.58 (1H, s, H-α), 9.79 (1H, s, H-β); ^{13}C NMR (DMSO-d_6, 151 MHz) δ 10.8 (CH_3-1a), 11.0 (CH_3-3a), 11.7 (CH_3-5a), 17.5 (CH_3-4b), 18.7 (CH_2-4a), 22.9 (CH_3-8a), 49.3 (CH-8), 50.7 (CH-7), 52.6 (CH_3-10b), 64.2 (CH-10), 93.8 (CH-δ), 97.5 (CH-α), 104.8 (CH-β), 128.1 (C-6), 128.6 (C-5), 134.0 (C-1), 136.2 (C-3), 136.9 (C-12), 137.1 (C-15), 139.1 (C-2), 141.6 (C-11), 145.4 (C-4), 148.8 (C-16), 150.4 (C-14), 155.1 (C-13), 169.2 (C-10a), 173.5 (C-18), 174.2 (C-7c), 189.2 (C-9). HR-ESI/MS analysis: *m/z* 597.2703 $[M+H]^+$, (calcd for $C_{34}H_{37}N_4O_6{}^+$, 597.2708, Δ = 0.8 ppm). MS/MS spectrum: CCMSLIB00010128704. SMILES: OC(CC[C@H]1[C@@H](C2=N/C1=C([C@@H](C(OC)=O)C3=O)\C4=C3C(C)=C(N4)/C=C5N =C(C(C)=C\5CC)/C=C(N/6)/C(CO)=C(C6=C\2)C)C)=O. ^{1}H, COSY, HSQC, HMBC, and ROESY NMR spectra of compound **5** are shown in Supplementary Figures S23–S27, respectively.

(**6**): (3*S*,4*S*,21*R*)-14-Ethyl-21-hydroxy-9-(hydroxymethyl)-4,8,13,18-tetramethyl-20-oxo-3-phorbinepropanoic acid (**(10*R*)-hydroxy-ETPA**): $[\alpha]^{25}{}_D$ +200 (c 0.01, MeOH). UV (MeOH) λ_{max} (log ε) 283 (4.03), 312 (4.05), 360 (4.38) (sh), 398 (4.75), 494 (3.71), 500 (3.68), 525 (3.49), 606 (3.47), 665 (4.21) nm. ECD (c 12 μM, MeOH) λ_{max} ([θ]) 400 (+8080), 667 (−20,800) nm. ^{1}H NMR (DMSO-d_6, 600 MHz) δ 1.69 (3H, t, J = 7.7 Hz, H_3-4b), 1.95 (3H, d, J = 7.3 Hz, H_3-8a), 2.17 (3H, m, H_2-7a, H-7b″), 2.97 (1H, m, H-7b′), 3.30 (3H, s, H_3-3a), 3.45 (3H, s, H_3-1a), 3.82 (2H, q, J = 7.7 Hz, H_2-4a), 3.88 (3H, s, H_3-5a), 4.39 (1H, qd, J = 7.3, 3.1 Hz, H-8), 4.61 (1H, s, H-10), 4.94 (1H, dt, J = 12.1, 3.1 Hz, H-7), 5.80 (2H, s, H_2-2a), 8.99 (1H, s, H-δ), 9.79 (1H, s, H-α), 9.90 (1H, s, H-β); ^{1}H NMR (DMSO-d_6, 151 MHz) δ 10.8 (CH_3-1a), 11.0 (CH_3-3a), 12.0 (CH_3-5a), 17.7 (CH_3-4b), 18.9 (CH_2-4a), 23.6 (CH_3-8a), 29.3 (CH_2-7a), 33.8 (CH_2-7b), 51.4 (CH-8), 53.9 (CH-7), 54.6 (CH_2-2a), 75.1 (CH-10), 93.4 (CH-δ), 99.2 (CH-α), 102.7 (CH-β), 112.8 (C-6), 130.6 (C-5), 132.8 (C-1), 135.5 (C-12), 136.2 (C-3), 137.3 (C-15), 138.5 (C-2), 145.0 (C-4), 154.2 (C-13), 171.7 (C-18), 174.6 (C-7c). HR-ESI/MS analysis: *m/z* 555.2600 $[M+H]^+$, (calcd for $C_{32}H_{35}N_4O_5{}^+$, 555.2602, Δ = 0.3 ppm). MS/MS spectrum: CCMSLIB00010128699. SMILES: OC(CC[C@H]1[C@@H](C2=N/C1=C([C@@H](O)C3=O)\C4=C3C(C)=C(N4)/C=C5N=C(C (C)=C\5CC)/C=C(N/6)/C(CO)=C(C6=C\2)C)C)=O. ^{1}H, COSY, HSQC, HMBC, and ROESY NMR spectra of compound **6** are shown in Supplementary Figures S28–S32, respectively.

2.8. UV–Vis Spectrophotometry and Fluorescence Spectra

UV–Vis spectra were recorded on a spectrophotometer Agilent Cary 60 UV–Vis (Santa-Clara, CA, USA) in MeOH in the wavelength range from 200 to 800 nm. Fluorescence spectra were obtained from 50 μL of 500 μM stocks of compounds in anhydrous MeOH in black 384-well plates in Tecan M200Pro reader. Excitation wavelength was 350 nm (9 nm bandpass), and emission range was from 400 to 850 nm (20 nm bandpass) with the 2 nm step.

2.9. Relative Singlet Oxygen Quantum Yield Measurements and Calculations

To measure the relative singlet oxygen quantum yield via its phosphorescence intensity, a 637.5 nm laser diode beam was focused through one of the ports of a cuvette holder (Thorlabs CVH100/M) to a 2-mm cuvette by an A-coated lens L1 with 5 cm focal distance (Thorlabs LBF254-050-A). The cuvette was filled with a sample and fixed in the cuvette holder. Another C-coated lens L2 with 2 cm focal distance (Thorlabs LA1074-C) was mounted in the orthogonal port of the cuvette holder to collect and collimate the singlet oxygen phosphorescence. A bandpass filter IFB with a central wavelength of 1277 nm and a bandwidth of 20 nm (Oceanoptics) was installed between this lens and the cuvette. Another C-coated lens with 3 mm focal distance (Thorlabs) focused the collected phosphorescence to an optical fiber connected to a free-running multimode single-photon detector (SPAD, modification of ID Quantique ID220).

The number of detected phosphorescence photons R_d, caused by singlet oxygen relaxation is as follows:

$$R_d = \mathrm{ClN}_A \sigma R_L \eta_d \eta_l \eta_q \tag{1}$$

where C is a concentration of a derivative in MeOH [mol/L], l is a cuvette length, N_A is the Avogadro number, σ is a single-photon absorption cross-section [cm^2] at the wavelength of laser excitation, R_L is a laser excitation rate, i.e., the number of photons per second incident to the sample, η_d is a combined collection and detection efficiency of the setup, η_l is the amount of losses that are unrelated to the absorption by the sample (reflection by the cuvette's glass, scattering and absorption in MeOH, etc.), and η_q is a quantum yield of singlet oxygen. Concentrations of compounds were 0.95–1 μM, except for compound **6** (0.36 μM).

We start by finding η_l. We put the pure MeOH as a sample and measure the incident laser power before and after the cuvette. The ratio of these two gives us $\theta_l = 0.85$. We calculate $\sigma = \ln(10)\frac{10^3}{N_A}\,\epsilon$, where ϵ is a molar extinction coefficient or absorbance [$\mathrm{cm}^{-1}\mathrm{M}^{-1}$]. The concentration is given, however η_d and η_q are unknown. To factor out the η_d, we use commercially available Pheophorbide a (Santa Cruz Biotechnology, Texas, USA) with a known $\eta_q^{ph} = 0.69$ and $\sigma^{ph} = 2.71 \times 10^{-17}$ cm^2 [30,31] as a reference and plug it back to 1, writing the equation for a singlet oxygen quantum yield of singlet oxygen as

$$\eta_q = \frac{R_d}{R_d^{Ph}} \frac{C^{Ph}}{C} \frac{\sigma^{Ph}}{\sigma} \frac{R_L^{Ph}}{R_L} \eta_q^{Ph} \tag{2}$$

We averaged over 10 s measuring R_d when the signal was distinguishable from the noise; otherwise, we measured during 100 s. Power of the laser was averaged over the same time periods. The value of relative singlet oxygen quantum yield for Pheophorbide a was double-checked using rhodamine 6G as a reference, obtaining the value of 0.677. We next used commercial pheophorbide a as a reference to measure how much power is absorbed by a layer l of pheophorbide a of concentration C^{ph} under the excitation I_0^{ph}

$$I_{abs}^{Ph} = C^{Ph} \sigma^{Ph} I_0^{Ph} \tag{3}$$

$$I_{abs} = C \sigma I_0, \tag{4}$$

where I_{abs}, C, σ, I_0, are absorbed power, concentration, absorption cross-section, and excitation power for all other compounds. We measure I_{abs} or I_{abs}^{Ph}, subtracting the power value measure behind the cuvette from the excitation power I_0. So we can write that

$$\sigma = \frac{I_{abs}}{I_{abs}^{Ph}} \frac{I_0^{Ph}}{I_0} \frac{C^{Ph}}{C} \sigma^{Ph} \tag{5}$$

The resulting relative quantum yields of singlet oxygen for the new compounds are given as η_q^{res} in the text.

2.10. Cell Culture

Triple-negative human breast cancer cells of the BT-20 cell line were cultivated in DMEM medium + GlutaMAX supplement, with FBS 10% (both Gibco, Gaithersburg MD, USA) without antibiotics at 37 °C and 5% CO_2. For all experiments, the minimum cell viability considered for plating was 95%, using the trypan blue test.

For the MTT cell survival assay, BT-20 cells were seeded in DMEM medium supplemented with 10% FBS and 1% gentamicin in a 384-well flat-bottomed transparent plate (Greiner, Monroe, NC, USA). Cells were seeded at a density of 3000 cells/well in a final medium volume of 30 µL of medium and cultured overnight in a CO_2 incubator at 37 °C. The day after removal of the medium, 50 µL DMEM was added with serial dilutions of chlorins starting at 50 µg/mL. Cells with the compounds were incubated for 72 h. Cells in DMEM without added compounds served as positive controls; DMEM wells without cells served as negative controls. The resulting concentration of DMSO in the wells was maintained at 0.5%. Each experiment was conducted in four replicates.

2.11. Phototoxicity Assay

The phototoxic analysis was made using an LED lamp with a maximum wavelength of 730–870 nm and a power of 50W. Fluence was measured as 25 J/cm^2 using a Newport Optical Power Meter 842-PE, MKS Instruments, Norwood, MA, USA. For phototoxicity studies, BT-20 cells were seeded in 384-well plates in DMEM medium supplemented with 10% FBS at a density of 3000 cells/well in a final medium volume of 30 µL and cultured overnight in a CO_2 incubator at 37 °C. The next day, the chlorins were dissolved in DMSO and added to the cells in DMEM medium in series dilutions starting at 25 µg/mL for each. The cells were incubated for 2 h with the chlorin compounds to allow the cellular uptake of the chlorins, after which DMEM medium was replaced with 20 µL of transparent DPBS, and the plate was irradiated with a red LED lamp for 30 min. Next, 80 µL of the culture medium was added to each well for further cultivation. Wells with no cells were used as positive controls; wells without cells were used as negative controls. The resulting concentration of DMSO in the wells was maintained at 0.5%. After 72 h, the wells were emptied, and 30 µL of MTT reagent dissolved in PBS at 0.5 mg/mL, and after 3.5 h, the formazan crystals formed were solubilized with 50 µL of DMSO. In 5 min, optical density of the solution was measured at the wavelength of 590 nm by the Infinite M Plex multifunctional plate reader (Tecan, Switzerland).

3. Results

3.1. Isolation of Multiple Chlorins from *Ophiura sarsii*

In our previous work, a chlorin compound, (3*S*,4*S*)-14-Ethyl-9-(hydroxymethyl)-4,8,13,18-tetramethyl-20-oxo-3-phorbinepropanoic acid (ETPA), was isolated from a Pacific brittle star *Ophiura sarsii* [14]. In a subsequent study, this compound was shown to be endogenous to the species and to possess powerful phototoxicity against a panel of cancer cell lines; these findings led to a proof-of-concept application of ETPA for photodynamic therapy in a mouse glioblastoma model [15]. While ETPA is a major metabolite in *O. sarsii* [14,15], natural products are often present as a variety of structural analogs in plants and marine organisms [32].

This motivated a new sample collection to search for natural analogs of ETPA in May 2021. The samples were homogenized and extracted with solvents of increasing polarity (hexane, EtOAc, MeOH, and water). The MeOH extract was further treated by liquid–liquid extraction (butanol–water) to remove most of the salts and polar primary metabolites. In the extraction process, the hexane and water extracts were not considered for analysis because they are known to contain mainly lipids and saccharides, respectively. The EtOAc and MeOH (butanolic fraction) extracts were profiled by untargeted UHPLC-PDA-CAD-HRMS/MS in the data-dependent mode to highlight the presence of chlorin analogs. The obtained data were processed on the MZmine software and uploaded to the Global Natural Products Social (GNPS) platform [21] to generate a Feature-Based Molecular Network

(FBMN). An FBMN represents "features" (an MS^2 spectrum associated with a retention time) as nodes. Two nodes are connected by an edge if their spectral similarity (based on a cosine score) is above a defined level. This visualization allows the organization of a large amount of MS^2 data and can facilitate the search for analogs.

Such processing of the LC-MS/MS data on both extracts allowed the detection of 1202 features in positive ionization mode. The node ($[M+H]^+$) associated with the previously isolated compound ETPA was highlighted (based on LC-MS analysis of the standard) in the FBMN by a diamond (Figure 2A,C). This compound is in a cluster of spectrally correlated features, which probably correspond to other chlorin analogs. Most of the features detected were found in both MeOH and EtOAc extracts. To further confirm the nature of the other nodes, the natural product classifier (NPClassifier) tool [33], which classifies compounds into a natural products ontology, was used on ETPA and assigns them to the superclass "tryptophan alkaloid". The spectral data exported from MZmine were then processed with the SIRIUS software [34] and, in particular, the CANOPUS module, which allows chemical class prediction from an MS^2 spectrum. The predicted chemical class of all features was then exported, and the "tryptophan alkaloid" superclass was mapped on the FBMN and confirmed that the nodes in the same cluster as the ETPA were mostly annotated with this superclass (Figure 2A). At a higher level, the predicted NP pathways (alkaloids, terpenoids, etc.) were also mapped on the FBMN (Supplementary Figure S33), which provides a quick overview of the chemical diversity of the extracts, which are mainly rich in fatty acids. This enabled us to highlight the 10 most intense features found in the chlorin cluster in the chromatogram of the MeOH extract (butanol fraction) of *O. sarsii* in view of the isolation (Figure 2D,E). These most intense MS peaks all have corresponding UV signals at 360 nm, typical of chlorins. This wavelength was, therefore, used to track the targeted peaks during the isolation process.

Targeted isolation of ETPA-related compounds was performed from both MeOH and EtOAc extracts. Chromatographic conditions were first optimized on an HPLC-PDA-ELSD instrument on a C_{18} column. The optimized gradients were geometrically transferred to the semipreparative HPLC scale [23] and injected in the column using a dry load method to maintain chromatographic resolution [24] (Figure 3 for the MeOH extract, Supplementary Figure S34 for the EtOAc extract). Six chlorins were isolated and fully characterized by HRMS, NMR, UV, ECD, and optical rotation using this approach. Among them, five were already known: (3*S*,4*S*)-14-Ethyl-9-(hydroxymethyl)-4,8,13,18-tetramethyl-20-oxo-3-phorbinepropanoic acid (ETPA) (**1**) that we previously isolated from this brittle star [14,15]; (10*S*)-Hydroxypheophorbide a (**2**) previously isolated from the microalgae *Chlorella regulans* [25] and the plant *Clerodendrum calamitosum* [26]; Pheophorbide a (**3**) previously isolated from the plant *Artemisia capillaris* [27]; Pyropheophorbide a (**4**) previously isolated from diverse species such as the plant *Atalantia monophyla* [35] *or the sea mussel Musculus senhousei* [28]; and (3*S*,4*S*,21*R*)-14-Ethyl-9-(hydroxymethyl)-21-(methoxycarbonyl)-4,8,13,18-tetramethyl-20-oxo-3-phorbinepropanoic acid (2-Hydroxymethyl-2-devinyl pheophorbide-a, (**5**) previously not reported from natural sources but cited in a synthesis patent [29]. Being less abundant and stable than the other chlorins, 2-Hydroxymethyl-2-devinyl pheophorbide-a was omitted from some of the following biophysical and cellular experiments.

Compound **6**, as compounds **1-5**, displayed the UV–Vis spectra typical for chlorin-type compounds (see below). The ^1H NMR spectrum of compound **6** showed close similarities to that of compound **1**: three deshielded aromatic protons at δ_H 8.99 (1H, s, H-δ), 9.79 (1H, s, H-α), and 9.90 (1H, s, H-β), oxygenated methylene at δ_H 5.80 (2H, s, H_2-2a), three deshielded methyl singlets at δ_H 3.30 (3H, s, H_3-3a), 3.45 (3H, s, H_3-1a), and 3.88 (3H, s, H_3-5a), the typical ethylene group at δ_H 3.82 (2H, q, J = 7.7 Hz, H_2-4a), and 1.69 (3H, t, J = 7.7 Hz, H_3-4b), as well as a methyl doublet at δ_H 1.95 (3H, d, J = 7.3 Hz, H_3-8a), and the two methine proton at δ_H 4.39 (1H, qd, J = 7.3, 3.1 Hz, H-8), and 4.94 (1H, dt, J = 12.1, 3.1 Hz, H-7). When compared to compound **1**, the two doublets from the methylene protons in C-10 (δ_H 5.12 and 5.22, J = 19.4 Hz) were missing and replaced by a singlet at δ_H/δ_C 4.61/75.1

indicating a hydroxyl in C-10. The ROESY correlations from H_2-7a to H-8 and H-10 indicate that the three methines, H-8, H-7, and H-10, were *trans*-oriented. The ROESY from H-7 to the methyl H_3-8a and the deshielding of H-7 (δ_H 4.94) compared to Pheophorbide a (δ_H 4.05) confirmed the *trans* configuration of H-7 and H-8 and that the hydroxyl in C-10 was in the same side than H-7. The positive Cotton effect at 400 nm and negative at 667 nm confirmed that, like other chlorins isolated, the configuration at C-8 and C-7 of **1** was *S*, *S*. Compound **6** was thus identified as (3*S*,4*S*,21*R*)-14-Ethyl-21-hydroxy-9-(hydroxymethyl)-4,8,13,18-tetramethyl-20-oxo-3-phorbinepropanoic acid ((10*R*)-hydroxy-ETPA), that has never been reported. Furthermore, to our knowledge, this is the first report of a chlorin with hydrogen and a hydroxyl group in C-10 isolated from natural sources.

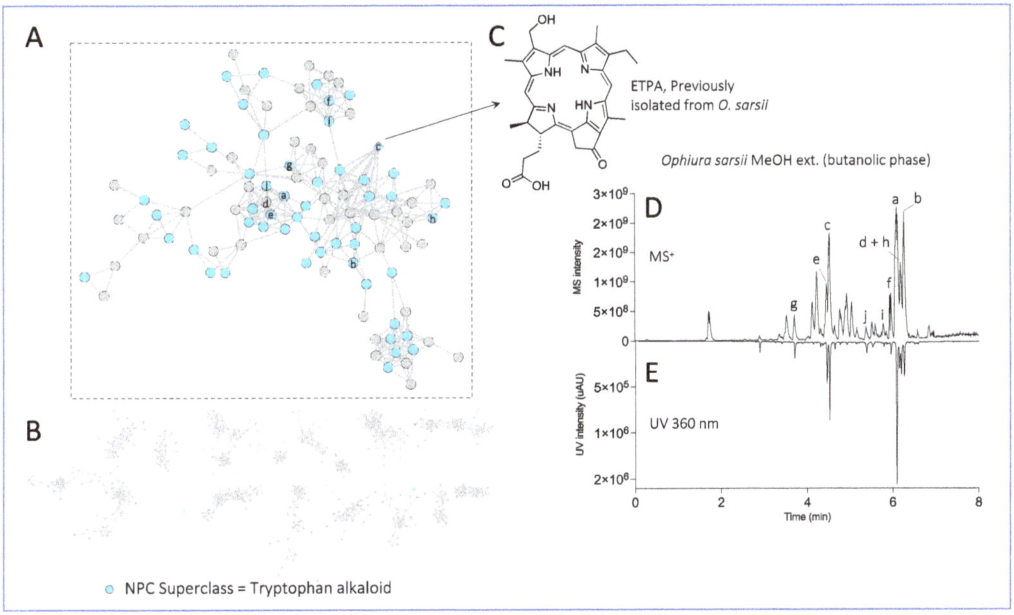

Figure 2. Feature-based Molecular Network of the EtOAc and MeOH (butanolic fraction) extracts of *Ophiura sarsii*. Nodes colored in blue belong to the "tryptophan alkaloid" predicted natural product superclass (NPClassifier). The previously isolated ETPA is displayed as a diamond. (**A**) The cluster containing chlorin ETPA and several related compounds. (**B**) Other major clusters of the Feature-Based Molecular Network. (**C**) Structure of the previously isolated ETPA. (**D**) UHPLC-MS profile of the MeOH extract (butanolic fraction) of *O. sarsii* with the 10 most intense ions of the chlorin cluster indicated with letters. (**E**) UHPLC-UV profile at 360 nm of the same extract. The same network mapped with the predicted natural product pathways is displayed in Supplementary Figure S33.

The elucidated structures of the chlorin compounds **1** to **6** from *O. sarsii* are shown in Figure 4. The Figure also provides the yields of these compounds, as isolated from EtOAc and/or MeOH extracts, starting from the dry mass of *O. sarsii* of 40 g. It can be seen that all six isolated chlorins are major metabolites, comparable in content to the ETPA we initially isolated from this brittle star.

3.2. *Absorbance Spectra and Singlet Oxygen Production by Chlorins of O. sarsii*

The isolated natural chlorin compounds show typical absorption and fluorescence spectra of chlorins such as the commercially available Pheophorbide a or the ETPA previously characterized by us [14,15] (Figure 5A and Supplementary Figures S35 and S36 for the UV–Vis, ECD, and fluorescence spectra). We next aimed at quantifying their relative singlet oxygen quantum yield using the device schematized in Figure 5B as described in Materials and Methods. Commercial Pheophorbide a was used as the standard.

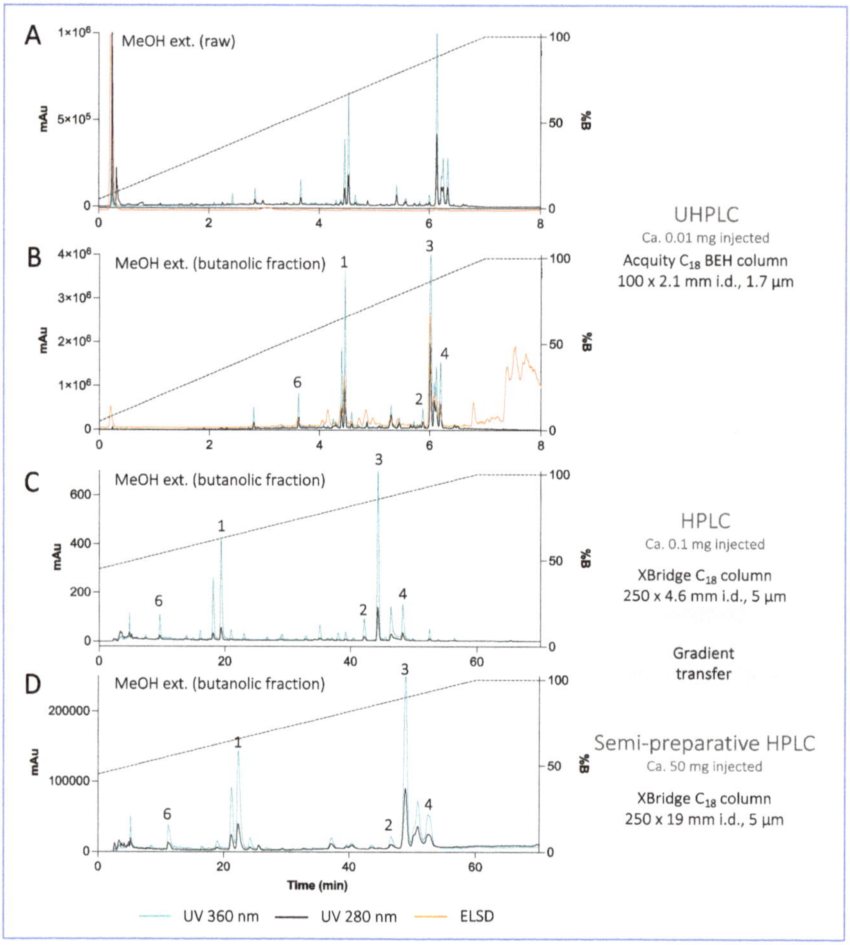

Figure 3. (**A**,**B**) UHPLC-PDA-ELSD analysis of the raw MeOH extract of *Ophiura sarsii* and its butanolic fraction. (**C**) Optimized HPLC-PDA-ELSD analysis of the MeOH extract (butanolic fraction) of *O. sarsii*. (**D**) semi-preparative HPLC-UV analysis after gradient transfer using a dry load injection. See Supplementary Figure S34 for the chromatograms of the EtOAc extract.

The results of this analysis are depicted in Figure 5C. Surprisingly, the relative singlet oxygen quantum yield of Pheophorbide a isolated from *O. sarsii* was lower than that of the commercial analog (0.57 vs. 0.68 of commercial Pheophorbide a). Additionally, we previously used two different methods to calculate the singlet oxygen quantum yield of ETPA as 0.8 [15], which was considerably higher than the values we obtained for the current isolate (Figure 5C). We conclude that impurities in the current small-scale isolations of the chlorin compounds (see Materials and Methods) confound the correct quantification of the singlet oxygen quantum yield. However, the measured values still permit us to conclude that the arsenal of chlorins present in *O. sarsii* possesses significant singlet oxygen quantum yield properties.

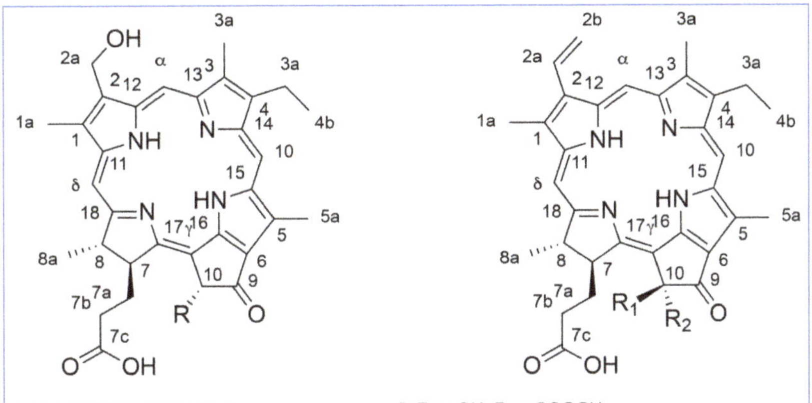

1 R = H (ETPA, yield: 2mg)

5 R = $COOCH_3$ (2-Hydroxymethyl-2-devinyl pheophorbide-a, 0.3mg)

6 R = OH ((10*R*)-hydroxy-ETPA, 0.8mg)

2 R_1 = OH, R_2 = $COOCH_3$ ((10*S*)-Hydroxyphephorbide a, yield: 0.6mg)

3 R_1 = H, R_2 = $COOCH_3$ (Pheophorbide a, 3.8mg)

4 R_1 = R_2 = H (Pyropheophorbide a, 1.4mg)

Figure 4. Structures and the yields of the chlorin compounds isolated from *O. sarsii.*

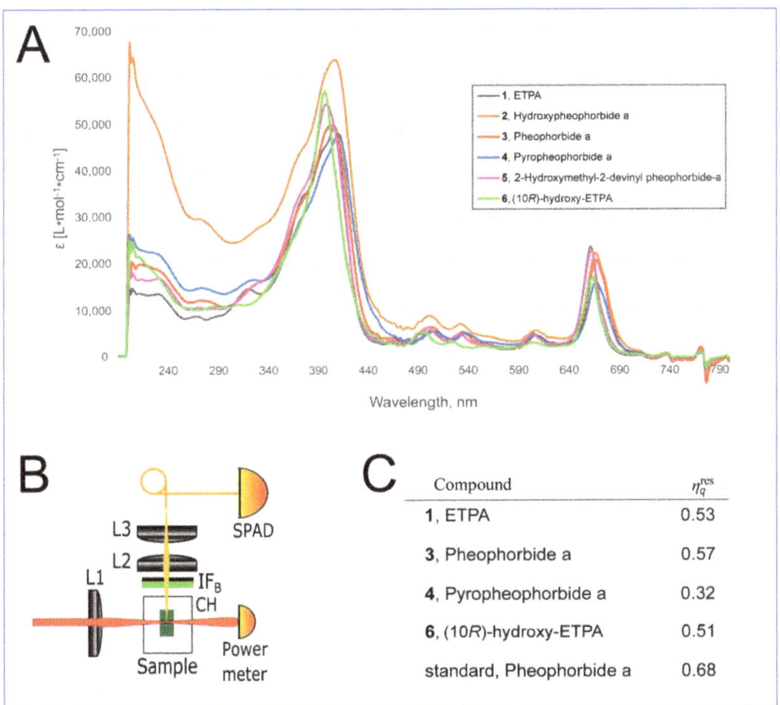

Figure 5. Physical properties of chlorin compounds from O. sarsii. (**A**) UV-Vis absorbance spectra of the chlorins. (**B**) Scheme of the device for measurement of the singlet oxygen generation. IF_B—bandpass interference filter; L1—laser beam focusing lens; Sample—cell with chlorin solution; CH—cuvette holder; L2—singlet oxygen phosphorescence collecting lens; L3—phosphorescence focusing lens; SPAD—single-photon avalanche diode. (**C**) Quantification of the relative singlet oxygen quantum yield.

3.3. Phototoxicity of *O. sarsii* Chlorins against Cancer Cells

We next assessed the phototoxicity of the chlorin compounds isolated from *O. sarsii*, against the triple-negative breast cancer cell line BT-20. In the dark, when the chlorin compounds are not activated, their toxicities were low, with the IC_{50}s in the range of 40–80 μM, corresponding to our previous findings on ETPA [14,15] (Figure 6A); commercial Pheophorbide a produced a similar value.

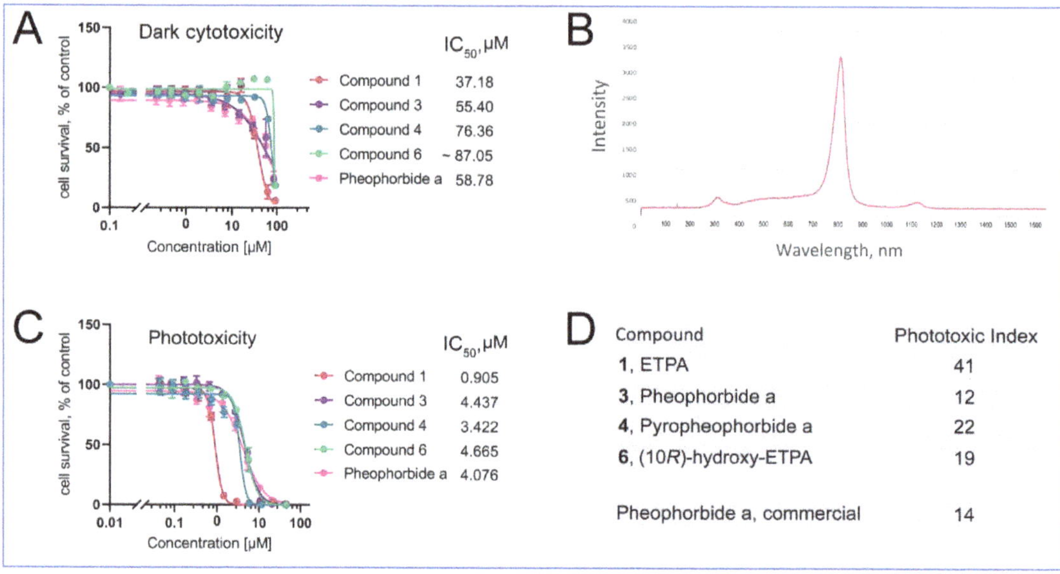

Figure 6. Phototoxicity of chlorins from *O. sarsii* against triple-negative breast cancer BT-20 cells. (**A**) Dark cytotoxicity of the compounds. (**B**) Emission spectrum of the LED lamp used in the phototoxicity experiment. (**C**) Phototoxicity of the compounds. (**D**) Phototoxic Index (PI) of the compounds. Commercial Pheophorbide a was used as a control in the experiments. The data are representatives of four independent experiments.

Photoactivation of the chlorins was achieved with an LED lamp, with the emission maximum partially covering the absorbance maximum of ca. 680 nm of chlorins (Figure 6B). Upon illumination with this lamp (see Materials and Methods for details), phototoxicity of the chlorin compounds was induced (Figure 6C) with the micomolar-to-submicromolar IC_{50}s. Other isolates of compounds **1** and **3** give similar values (Supplementary Figure S37). The ratio of dark cytotoxicity IC_{50} to that of the phototoxicity gives the Phototoxic Index (PI)—the characteristic value of photosensitizers used in PDT. We find the PI values to vary from 12 to 41, being highest for ETPA among the tested compounds, in agreement with our previous findings [15].

3.4. Identification of Chlorins in a Deep-Sea Pacific Brittle Star *O. ooplax* and a Deep-Sea Pacific Basket Star *Gorgonocephalus cf. eucnemis*

Prior to our identification of the chlorin ETPA in *O. sarsii* [14,15], chlorin-type compounds were considered absent in the class Ophiurodea [11,16]. Although we have proven the endogenous (rather than exogenous, such as dietary) origin of ETPA in *O. sarsii* [15], the valid question is whether chlorins can be found in other representatives of the class, and if yes, whether the same set of chlorin compounds would be present in the other species. Additionally, an ecogeographical aspect could be considered: *O. sarsii* is mostly a shallow-waters brittle star that we collected in the Sea of Japan next to Russky Island (Figure 1D). Would deep-waters brittle stars living in other locations also carry chlorin compounds?

To address these questions, we took part in the expedition of the A.V. Zhirmunsky National Scientific Center of Marine Biology (Far East Branch, Russian Academy of Sciences) aboard the vessel R/V Akademik M. Lavrentyev (Cruise No. 94) to the seamounts of the Emperor Chain (Pacific Ocean) in July–September 2021. During this expedition, we collected invertebrate samples from depths of 750–1000 m near the Koko guyot (Pacific Ocean, Figure 1D). Among the samples, we collected and analyzed two representatives of the class Ophiuroidea: the brittle star *Ophiura ooplax* (Figure 1B) and the basket star *Gorgonocephalus* cf. *eucnemis* (Figure 1C).

O. ooplax (order Ophiurida, family Ophiuridae) has previously been identified at the coasts of Japan, Australia, and New Zealand, at depths ranging from 100 to 1170 m [17,36–38] and belongs to the same *Ophiura* genus as *O. sarsii*. In contrast, *Gorgonocephalus* cf. *eucnemis* [18] (order Phrynophiurida, family Gorgonocephalidae) is a distant member of the class Ophiurodea found in the northern hemisphere, including the Atlantic, Arctic, and Pacific Oceans at various depths reaching 4000 m (obis.org/taxon/124969) [39].

Samples of *O. ooplax* and *G.* cf. *eucnemis* were extracted in the same manner as described for *O. sarsii* (see Materials and Methods). EtOAc and MeOH extracts were profiled with UHPLC-PDA-CAD-HRMS/MS. The obtained data were again processed with MZmine with the EtOAc and MeOH extracts of *O. sarsii* (for the alignment step). The generated aligned feature table was exported, and the intensities (MS peak area) for each of the six isolated compounds in each extract were plotted (Figure 7). Most of the features corresponding to the six chlorin compounds were detected in all samples, but with important variations in MS intensities. In order to highlight the presence/absence of chlorins in the different samples, a logarithm was applied to the MS intensities for visualization purposes. The obtained results show that all isolated chlorins are found in both *O. sarsii* and *O. ooplax*. In the case of *G.* cf. *eucnemis*, five of the six chlorins are also detected (**1**, **2**, **3**, **4**, and **6**), but these are very minor compounds in the extracts. It should be noted, however, that the analysis we performed is only semi-quantitative, as the concentrations of the extracts were not standardized before the analysis. These data suggest that chlorins are not exclusive to the species *O. sarsii*, nor even to the genus *Ophiura*, but are likely present in different invertebrates of the class Ophiuroidea, albeit in different amounts and chemical representatives.

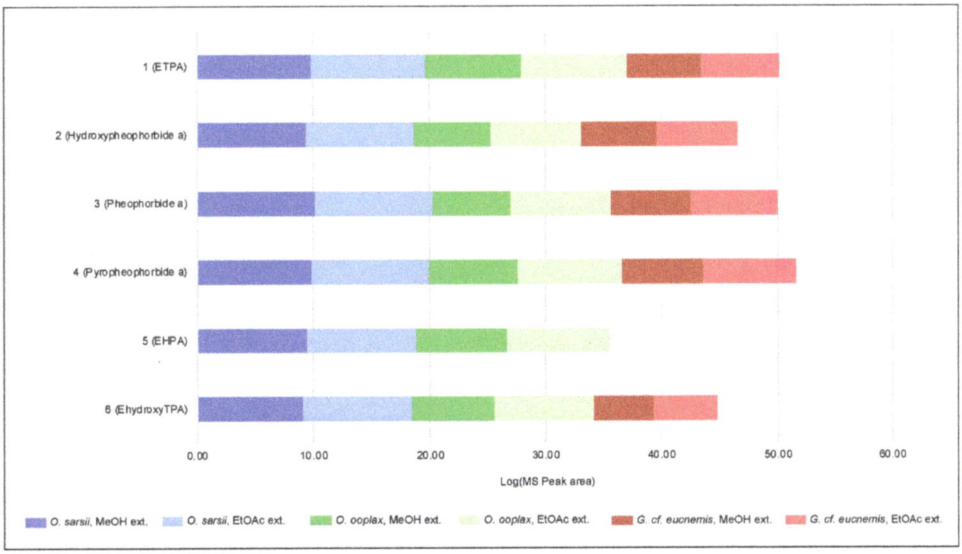

Figure 7. Log_{10} of the MS peak area (from UHPLC-HRMS/MS analysis) of the 6 isolated chlorins in the EtOAc and MeOH extracts of *Ophiura sarsii*, *Ophiura ooplax*, and *Gorgonocephalus* cf. *eucnemis*.

4. Discussion

Our findings characterize the marine invertebrates of the class Ophiuroidea as a rich source of natural photosensitizers. Six chlorins with photosensitizer properties emerge as major metabolites of the shallow- and deep-water brittle stars *Ophiura sarsii* and *Ophiura ooplax*, and five of the same chlorins can be found as minor metabolites in the basket star *Gorgonocephalus* cf. *eucnemis*. The class Ophiuroidea consists of >2000 known species (of which 400 are in the North Pacific), falling into 16 families [40]. A wider investigation involving more diverse brittle star and basket star (that represent the two orders within the class Ophiuroidea) species would be useful to draw conclusions on the chemodiversity and abundance of chlorins in these curious marine organisms. The role(s) they might play in their hosts is also open to further investigation.

We provide a detailed physical and biological characterization of the six Ophiuroidea chlorins, two of which have never been found in natural sources before. All chlorins emerge as photosensitizers with significant photodynamic properties against cancer cells, being well-tolerable without photoactivation by the red-spectrum light. These features make these natural chlorins interesting candidates for development in prospective PDT applications. The most powerful of the six, the chlorin ETPA, has been applied by us in a proof-of-concept in vivo PDT treatment of glioblastoma [15]—the most common brain tumor that is poorly treatable and has a bad prognosis, with a median survival below two years [41]. In the future, we plan to investigate this and the other Ophiuroidea chlorins in a panel of PDT applications in cancer, dermatology, and infectious disease indications [1–3]. Studying these natural chlorins, in solo or as cocktails/extracts, for cosmetics applications may also be attractive [4].

Such developments in natural chlorins will raise the need to solve the supply chain task—the common theme for marine-derived drugs [42]. Although *O. sarsii* represents an abundant shallow-waters brittle star in the North Pacific that is easily harvested, e.g., in the vicinity of the Russky Island, mariculture of this species appears as the best solution in case mass production becomes needed [43]. Chemical synthesis represents another possibility [44,45].

5. Conclusions

In conclusion, we discover an arsenal of photosensitizers in three species of North Pacific Ophiuroidea, shallow- and deep-water inhabitants. These natural chlorins possess attractive biophysical and anticancer properties. Our discoveries pave the way for further interdisciplinary investigations of the taxonomic chemodiversity of marine invertebrates and translational developments of their metabolites for diverse PDT applications.

Supplementary Materials: The following supporting information can be downloaded at: https://www.mdpi.com/article/10.3390/antiox12020386/s1, Figure S1: ^{1}H NMR spectrum of compound **1**; Figure S2: COSY NMR spectrum of compound **1**; Figure S3: ^{13}C-DEPTQ NMR spectrum of compound **1**; Figure S4: HSQC NMR spectrum of compound **1**; Figure S5: HMBC NMR spectrum of compound **1**; Figure S6: ROESY NMR spectrum of compound **1**; Figure S7: ^{1}H NMR spectrum of compound **2**; Figure S8: COSY NMR spectrum of compound **2**; Figure S9: HSQC NMR spectrum of compound **2**; Figure S10: HMBC NMR spectrum of compound **2**; Figure S11: ROESY NMR spectrum of compound **2**; Figure S12: ^{1}H NMR spectrum of compound **3**; Figure S13: COSY NMR spectrum of compound **3**; Figure S14: ^{13}C-DEPTQ NMR spectrum of compound **3**; Figure S15: HSQC NMR spectrum of compound **3**; Figure S16: HMBC NMR spectrum of compound **3**; Figure S17: ROESY NMR spectrum of compound **3**; Figure S18: ^{1}H NMR spectrum of compound **4**; Figure S19: COSY NMR spectrum of compound **4**; Figure S20: HSQC NMR spectrum of compound **4**; Figure S21: HMBC NMR spectrum of compound **4**; Figure S22: ROESY NMR spectrum of compound **4**; Figure S23: ^{1}H NMR spectrum of compound **5**; Figure S24: COSY NMR spectrum of compound **5**; Figure S25: HSQC NMR spectrum of compound **5**; Figure S26: HMBC NMR spectrum of compound **5**; Figure S27: ROESY NMR spectrum of compound **5**; Figure S28: ^{1}H NMR spectrum of compound **6**; Figure S29: COSY NMR spectrum of compound **6**; Figure S30: HSQC NMR spectrum of compound **6**; Figure S31: HMBC NMR spectrum of compound **6**; Figure S32: ROESY NMR spectrum of compound **6**; Figure S33:

Feature-based Molecular Network of the EtOAc and MeOH (butanolic fraction) extracts of *Ophiura sarsii*; Figure S34: UHPLC-PDA-ELSD analysis of extracts of *Ophiura sarsii*; Figure S35: UV–Vis and ECD spectra of the isolated compounds; Figure S36: Fluorescence spectra of the isolated compounds; Figure S37: Phototoxicity of compounds **1** and **3** from MeOH and EtOAc extracts.

Author Contributions: Conceptualization, V.L.K.; methodology, R.H., L.M., D.T. and S.S.D.; validation, A.K. (Alexey Koval), J.-L.W., Y.K., E.F.Q. and V.L.K.; formal analysis, L.M.; investigation, A.K. (Antonina Klimenko), R.H. and D.T.; resources, T.N.D. and Y.K.; writing, A.K. (Antonina Klimenko), R.H., L.M. and V.L.K.; writing—review and editing, R.H., J.-L.W., E.F.Q. and V.L.K.; supervision, A.K (Alexey Koval)., J.-L.W., R.T., Y.K., E.F.Q. and V.L.K.; project administration, J.-L.W., R.T., Y.K., E.F.Q. and V.L.K.; funding acquisition, J.-L.W. and Y.K. All authors have read and agreed to the published version of the manuscript.

Funding: This research was funded by the Ministry of Science and Higher Education of the Russian Federation, grant 13.1902.21.0012, "Fundamental problems of investigation and preservation of deep-sea ecosystems of potentially ore-bearing regions of the Northwestern Pacific" (Contract No. 075-15-2020-796). The School of Pharmaceutical Sciences of the University of Geneva is thankful to the Swiss National Science Foundation for the support in the acquisition of the NMR 600 MHz (SNF R'Equip grant 316030_164095 to J.-L.W.).

Institutional Review Board Statement: Not applicable.

Informed Consent Statement: Not applicable.

Data Availability Statement: The MS^2 spectrum of each isolated compound has its own accession number CCMSLIB00010128XXX on the Global Natural Product Social Molecular Networking (GNPS) (accessed via: https://gnps.ucsd.edu/ProteoSAFe/static/gnps-splash.jsp, accessed on 15 December 2022).

Conflicts of Interest: The authors declare no conflict of interest.

References

1. Li, X.; Lovell, J.F.; Yoon, J.; Chen, X. Clinical development and potential of photothermal and photodynamic therapies for cancer. *Nat. Rev. Clin. Oncol.* **2020**, *17*, 657–674. [CrossRef] [PubMed]
2. Queiros, C.; Garrido, P.M.; Maia Silva, J.; Filipe, P. Photodynamic therapy in dermatology: Beyond current indications. *Dermatol. Ther.* **2020**, *33*, e13997. [CrossRef] [PubMed]
3. Aroso, R.T.; Schaberle, F.A.; Arnaut, L.G.; Pereira, M.M. Photodynamic disinfection and its role in controlling infectious diseases. *Photochem. Photobiol. Sci.* **2021**, *20*, 1497–1545. [CrossRef] [PubMed]
4. Gold, M.H. (Ed.) *Cosmetic Photodynamic Therapy*; Karger: Basel, Switzerland, 2016; pp. VIII + 136 p. ISBN 978-3-318-02556-9.
5. Arnaut, L.G. Chapter 5—Design of porphyrin-based photosensitizers for photodynamic therapy. In *Advances in Inorganic Chemistry*; Eldik, R.V., Stochel, G., Eds.; Academic Press: Cambridge, MA, USA, 2011; Volume 63, pp. 187–233.
6. Pandey, R.K.; Goswami, L.N.; Chen, Y.; Gryshuk, A.; Missert, J.R.; Oseroff, A.; Dougherty, T.J. Nature: A rich source for developing multifunctional agents. Tumor-imaging and photodynamic therapy. *Lasers Surg. Med.* **2006**, *38*, 445–467. [CrossRef] [PubMed]
7. Katanaev, V.L.; Di Falco, S.; Khotimchenko, Y. The Anticancer Drug Discovery Potential of Marine Invertebrates from Russian Pacific. *Mar. Drugs* **2019**, *17*, 474. [CrossRef]
8. Katanaev, V.L.; Blagodatski, A.; Xu, J.; Khotimchenko, Y.; Koval, A. Mining Natural Compounds to Target WNT Signaling: Land and Sea Tales. *Handb. Exp. Pharmacol.* **2021**, *269*, 215–248. [CrossRef] [PubMed]
9. Khotimchenko, Y.S.; Silachev, D.N.; Katanaev, V.L. Marine Natural Products from the Russian Pacific as Sources of Drugs for Neurodegenerative Diseases. *Mar. Drugs* **2022**, *20*, 708. [CrossRef]
10. Agius, L.; Jaccarini, V.; Ballantine, J.A.; Ferrito, V.; Pelter, A.; Psaila, A.F.; Zammit, V.A. Photodynamic action of bonellin, an integumentary chlorin of Bonellia viridis, Rolando (echiura, bonelliidae). *Comp. Biochem. Physiol. B* **1979**, *63*, 109–117. [CrossRef]
11. Bandaranayake, W.M. The nature and role of pigments of marine invertebrates. *Nat. Prod. Rep.* **2006**, *23*, 223–255. [CrossRef]
12. Hamblin, M.R. Photodynamic Therapy for Cancer: What's Past is Prologue. *Photochem. Photobiol.* **2020**, *96*, 506–516. [CrossRef]
13. Zhu, W.; Gao, Y.H.; Liao, P.Y.; Chen, D.Y.; Sun, N.N.; Nguyen Thi, P.A.; Yan, Y.J.; Wu, X.F.; Chen, Z.L. Comparison between porphin, chlorin and bacteriochlorin derivatives for photodynamic therapy: Synthesis, photophysical properties, and biological activity. *Eur. J. Med. Chem.* **2018**, *160*, 146–156. [CrossRef] [PubMed]
14. Klimenko, A.; Huber, R.; Marcourt, L.; Chardonnens, E.; Koval, A.; Khotimchenko, Y.S.; Ferreira Queiroz, E.; Wolfender, J.L.; Katanaev, V.L. A Cytotoxic Porphyrin from North Pacific Brittle Star Ophiura sarsii. *Mar. Drugs* **2021**, *19*, 11. [CrossRef] [PubMed]
15. Klimenko, A.; Rodina, E.E.; Silachev, D.; Begun, M.; Babenko, V.A.; Benditkis, A.S.; Kozlov, A.S.; Krasnovsky, A.A.; Khotimchenko, Y.S.; Katanaev, V.L. Chlorin Endogenous to the North Pacific Brittle Star Ophiura sarsii for Photodynamic Therapy Applications in Breast Cancer and Glioblastoma Models. *Biomedicines* **2022**, *10*, 134. [CrossRef] [PubMed]

16. Kennedy, G.Y. Porphyrins in invertebrates. *Ann. New York Acad. Sci.* **1975**, *244*, 662–673. [CrossRef]
17. Clark, H.L. *North Pacific Ophiurans in the Collection of the United States National Museum*; United States National Museum: Washington, DC, USA, 1911; Volume 75.
18. Müller, J.; Troschel, F.H. *System der Asteriden.1. Asteriae. 2. Ophiuridae*; Vieweg: Braunschweig, Germany, 1842; pp. 1–134.
19. Rutz, A.; Dounoue-Kubo, M.; Ollivier, S.; Bisson, J.; Bagheri, M.; Saesong, T.; Ebrahimi, S.N.; Ingkaninan, K.; Wolfender, J.L.; Allard, P.M. Taxonomically Informed Scoring Enhances Confidence in Natural Products Annotation. *Front. Plant Sci.* **2019**, *10*, 1329. [CrossRef]
20. Pluskal, T.; Castillo, S.; Villar-Briones, A.; Orešič, M. MZmine 2: Modular framework for processing, visualizing, and analyzing mass spectrometry-based molecular profile data. *BMC Bioinform.* **2010**, *11*, 395. [CrossRef]
21. Wang, M.; Carver, J.J.; Phelan, V.V.; Sanchez, L.M.; Garg, N.; Peng, Y.; Nguyen, D.D.; Watrous, J.; Kapono, C.A.; Luzzatto-Knaan, T.; et al. Sharing and community curation of mass spectrometry data with Global Natural Products Social Molecular Networking. *Nat. Biotechnol.* **2016**, *34*, 828–837. [CrossRef]
22. Smoot, M.E.; Ono, K.; Ruscheinski, J.; Wang, P.L.; Ideker, T. Cytoscape 2.8: New features for data integration and network visualization. *Bioinformatics* **2010**, *27*, 431–432. [CrossRef]
23. Guillarme, D.; Nguyen, D.T.; Rudaz, S.; Veuthey, J.L. Method transfer for fast liquid chromatography in pharmaceutical analysis: Application to short columns packed with small particle. Part II: Gradient experiments. *Eur. J. Pharm. Biopharm.* **2008**, *68*, 430–440. [CrossRef]
24. Queiroz, E.F.; Alfattani, A.; Afzan, A.; Marcourt, L.; Guillarme, D.; Wolfender, J.L. Utility of dry load injection for an efficient natural products isolation at the semi-preparative chromatographic scale. *J. Chromatogr. A* **2019**, *1598*, 85–91. [CrossRef]
25. Endo, H.; Hosoya, H.; Koyama, T.; Ichioka, M. Isolation of 10-Hydroxypheophorbide a as a Photosensitizing Pigment from Alcohol-treated Chlorella Cells. *Agric. Biol. Chem.* **1982**, *46*, 2183–2193. [CrossRef]
26. Cheng, H.H.; Wang, H.K.; Ito, J.; Bastow, K.F.; Tachibana, Y.; Nakanishi, Y.; Xu, Z.; Luo, T.Y.; Lee, K.H. Cytotoxic pheophorbide-related compounds from Clerodendrum calamitosum and C. cyrtophyllum. *J. Nat. Prod.* **2001**, *64*, 915–919. [CrossRef]
27. Ohshima, T.; Hirata, M.; Oda, T.; Sasaki, A.; Shiratsuchi, M. Pheophorbide a, a potent endothelin receptor antagonist for both ETA and ETB subtypes. *Chem. Pharm. Bull. (Tokyo)* **1994**, *42*, 2174–2176. [CrossRef]
28. Chen, D.; Lu, S.; Yang, G.; Pan, X.; Fan, S.; Xie, X.; Chen, Q.; Li, F.; Li, Z.; Wu, S.; et al. The seafood Musculus senhousei shows anti-influenza A virus activity by targeting virion envelope lipids. *Biochem. Pharm.* **2020**, *177*, 113982. [CrossRef]
29. Sim, Y.G.; Yoo, J.H.; Oyunbileg, G.; Bayarmaa, B.; Wang, J.J.; Cui, B.C. Preparation of chlorin derivatives as antitumor agents. KR2009027470, 17 March 2009.
30. Fernandez, J.M.; Bilgin, M.D.; Grossweiner, L.I. Singlet oxygen generation by photodynamic agents. *J. Photochem. Photobiol. B* **1997**, *37*, 131–140. [CrossRef]
31. Eichwurzel, I.; Stiel, H.; Röder, B. Photophysical studies of the pheophorbide a dimer. *J. Photochem. Photobiol. B* **2000**, *54*, 194–200. [CrossRef]
32. Atanasov, A.G.; Zotchev, S.B.; Dirsch, V.M.; Supuran, C.T. Natural products in drug discovery: Advances and opportunities. *Nat. Rev. Drug Discov.* **2021**, *20*, 200–216. [CrossRef] [PubMed]
33. Kim, H.W.; Wang, M.; Leber, C.A.; Nothias, L.F.; Reher, R.; Kang, K.B.; van der Hooft, J.J.J.; Dorrestein, P.C.; Gerwick, W.H.; Cottrell, G.W. NPClassifier: A Deep Neural Network-Based Structural Classification Tool for Natural Products. *J. Nat. Prod.* **2021**, *84*, 2795–2807. [CrossRef] [PubMed]
34. Dührkop, K.; Fleischauer, M.; Ludwig, M.; Aksenov, A.A.; Melnik, A.V.; Meusel, M.; Dorrestein, P.C.; Rousu, J.; Böcker, S. SIRIUS 4: A rapid tool for turning tandem mass spectra into metabolite structure information. *Nat. Methods* **2019**, *16*, 299–302. [CrossRef] [PubMed]
35. Chansakaow, S.; Ruangrungsi, N.; Ishikawa, T. Isolation of pyropheophorbide a from the leaves of Atalantia monophylla (ROXB.) CORR. (Rutaceae) as a possible antiviral active principle against herpes simplex virus type 2. *Chem. Pharm. Bull.* **1996**, *44*, 1415–1417. [CrossRef] [PubMed]
36. Murakami, S. Ophiurans of Izu, Japan. *J. Fac. Agric. Kyushu Univ.* **1942**, *7*, 1–36. [CrossRef] [PubMed]
37. Baker, A.N. Some Ophiuroidea from the Tasman Sea and adjacent waters. *New Zealand J. Zool.* **1979**, *6*, 21–51. [CrossRef]
38. McEnnulty, F.R.; Gowlett-Holmes, K.; Williams, A.; Althaus, F.; Fromont, J.; Poore, G.; O'Hara, T.; Marsh, L.; Kott, P.; Slack-Smith, S.; et al. The deepwater megabenthic invertebrates on the continental margin of Australia (100–1100 m depths): Composition, distribution and novelty. *Rec. West Aust. Mus. Suppl.* **2011**, *80*, 1–191. [CrossRef]
39. Djakonov, A.M. *Les Échinodermes Des Mers Arctiques*; Academy of sciences of the USSR: Leningrad, Russia, 1933; Volume 8, pp. 1–166.
40. Stöhr, S.; O'Hara, T.D.; Thuy, B. Global diversity of brittle stars (Echinodermata: Ophiuroidea). *PLoS ONE* **2012**, *7*, e31940. [CrossRef]
41. Tan, A.C.; Ashley, D.M.; Lopez, G.Y.; Malinzak, M.; Friedman, H.S.; Khasraw, M. Management of glioblastoma: State of the art and future directions. *CA Cancer J. Clin.* **2020**, *70*, 299–312. [CrossRef]
42. Gomes, N.; Dasari, R.; Chandra, S.; Kiss, R.; Kornienko, A. Marine Invertebrate Metabolites with Anticancer Activities: Solutions to the "Supply Problem". *Mar. Drugs* **2016**, *14*, 98. [CrossRef]
43. Gavrilova, G.S.; Kucheryavenko, A.V. Commercial rearing of the sea cucumber Apostichopus japonicus in Peter the great bay: Methodical peculiarities and results of the work of a mariculture farm in Sukhodol Bight. *Russ. J. Mar. Biol.* **2010**, *36*, 539–547. [CrossRef]

44. O'Nea, W.G.; Jacobi, P.A. Toward a General Synthesis of Chlorins. *J. Am. Chem. Soc.* **2008**, *130*, 1102–1108. [CrossRef]
45. Jacobi, P.A.; Lanz, S.; Ghosh, I.; Leung, S.H.; Löwer, F.; Pippin, D. A New Synthesis of Chlorins. *Org. Lett.* **2001**, *3*, 831–834. [CrossRef]

nutrients MDPI

Article

Molecular Mechanism of Fucoidan Nanoparticles as Protector on Endothelial Cell Dysfunction in Diabetic Rats' Aortas

Giftania Wardani [1,2], Jusak Nugraha [3], Rochmah Kurnijasanti [4], Mohammad Rais Mustafa [5] and Sri Agus Sudjarwo [4,*]

1 Doctoral Program of Medical Science, Faculty of Medicine, Universitas Airlangga, Surabaya 60115, Indonesia
2 Program Study of Pharmacy, Faculty of Medicine, Hang Tuah University, Surabaya 28125, Indonesia
3 Department of Clinical Pathology, Dr. Soetomo Hospital, Universitas Airlangga, Surabaya 60115, Indonesia
4 Department of Pharmacology, Faculty of Veterinary Medicine, Universitas Airlangga, Surabaya 60115, Indonesia
5 Department of Pharmacology, Faculty of Medicine, University of Malaya, Kuala Lumpur 50603, Malaysia
* Correspondence: ags158@yahoo.com; Tel.: +62-85-6450-00684

Abstract: Antioxidants have an important role in protecting against diabetes complications such as vascular endothelial cell damage. Fucoidan has strong antioxidant properties, therefore the aim of this study was to investigate the protective mechanism of fucoidan nanoparticles through the pathway of antioxidant activity against streptozotocin-induced diabetic aortic endothelial cell dysfunction in rats. Fucoidan nanoparticles are made utilizing high-energy ball milling. This research consists of five groups, namely: control rats, rats were administered aquadest; diabetic rats, rats were administered streptozotocin (STZ); fucoidan nanoparticle rats, rats were administered STZ and fucoidan nanoparticles. Aortic tissue was collected for the evaluation of ROS (reactive oxygen species), Malondialdehyde (MDA), superoxide Dismutase (SOD), Glutathione Peroxidase (GPx), Nuclear factor erythroid-2-related factor 2 (Nrf2), Nitric Oxide (NO), cyclic Guanosine Monophosphate (cGMP), relaxation response of acetylcholine (Ach), and the diameter of the aorta. The size distribution of the fucoidan nanoparticles was 267.2 ± 42.8 nm. Administration of fucoidan nanoparticles decreased the levels of ROS and MDA, and increased the levels of SOD, levels of GPx, Nrf2 expression, NO levels, cGMP expression, the relaxation response of Ach, and lumen diameter of the aorta, which are significantly different when compared with diabetic rats, $p < 0.05$. In this study, we concluded that the mechanism pathway of fucoidan nanoparticles prevents aortic endothelial cell dysfunction in diabetic rats through antioxidant activity by reducing ROS and MDA and incrementing SOD levels, GPx levels, and Nrf2 expression. All of these can lead to an elevated relaxation response effect of Ach and an increase in the lumen diameter of the aorta, which indicates a protective effect of fucoidan nanoparticles on aortic endothelial cells.

Keywords: fucoidan nanoparticle; antioxidant; endothelial cell; diabetes

1. Introduction

One of the markers of diabetes mellitus is hyperglycemia, which can cause complications in various organs such as the liver, kidneys, nerves, eyes, and heart, as well as endothelial dysfunction of blood vessels. This is due to an impaired pancreas to secrete insulin or because of insulin resistance [1,2]. Diabetes mellitus is one of the major risk factors for cardiovascular disease, which is the most common cause of death in diabetic complications. In addition to the well-recognized microvascular diabetic complications, such as nephropathy, retinopathy, and neuropathy, there is a growing epidemic of macrovascular diabetic complications, including coronary artery disease, peripheral artery disease, and vascular endothelial cell dysfunction. Endothelial cell dysfunction can be due to glycometabolic disorder, genetics, oxidative stress, inflammatory cytokines, and apoptosis, which are the main causes of cardiovascular diseases such as atherosclerosis. Oxidative stress plays a crucial role in causing endothelial cell dysfunction in diabetic complications [3–5]. Oxidative stress can be caused by the overproduction of reactive oxygen species such as hydroxyl radicals (OH-), superoxide anions (O_2^-), and hydrogen peroxide (H_2O_2), and a lower antioxidant defense system such as SOD, GPx, and catalase. Excessive ROS formation occurs through the polyol pathway, increased production of advanced glycation end-products (AGEs), the hexosamine pathway, and protein kinase C activation, which can lead to diabetic complications [6–8]. Increased ROS levels in diabetes can lead to decreased production of SOD, GPx, and catalase. The ROS will oxidize polyunsaturated fatty acids (PUFA) that are abundant in cell membranes to form MDA. This MDA can be used as an indicator of the cell damage caused by free radicals under conditions of oxidative stress [9,10].

Increased ROS and decreased antioxidants can also occur in diabetic rat models injected with intraperitoneal streptozotocin. Previous studies revealed that administration of streptozotocin can reduce the expression of Nrf2, which is the main regulator for the formation of antioxidants; so lower SOD, GPx, catalase, and higher MDA in the aortic tissue of diabetic rats [11,12]. It has been reported that increasing ROS can inactivate Nrf2, resulting in a decrease in Nrf2 expression. This increase in ROS will cause cysteine damage in Keap1, disrupt the Keap1-Cul3 ubiquitination mechanism, and mediate Nrf2 degradation by the 26S proteasome so that Nrf2 has a short half-life, which can result in decreased expression of Nrf2 [13,14]. Animal experiments have shown that the Nrf2/Keap1 system is an important defense pathway for protecting against cell damage under conditions of oxidative stress. Decreased expression of Nrf2 can reduce the expression of cytoprotective antioxidants (SOD, GPx, and Cat) in transgenic mouse cells and exacerbate oxidative cell damage [15,16].

In a diabetic rat model, injection of STZ increased ROS and caused endothelial cell dysfunction, which resulted in decreased formation of NO and cGMP in aortic tissue. Therefore, natural products that have antioxidant effects can be used to prevent endothelial cell damage in diabetes [17–19]. The antioxidants from natural products such as Cinnamomum cassia and Heterotrigona itama could be used as protection against endothelial cell dysfunction in diabetic complications, as they are shown to decrease ROS and increase the NOS, NO, and cGMP in rat aortic tissue that was given streptozotocin intraperitoneally [20,21]. Fucoidan derived from seaweed is reported to have strong antioxidant activity. Recently, many researchers have conducted studies on the potential and pharmacological activities of fucoidan, such as anti-inflammatory, antibacterial, anti-apoptotic, immunostimulant, anti-atherosclerotic, anti-diabetic, and antioxidant [22–25].

In recent times, there have been many studies using nanotechnology to make nanoparticles of natural materials. Natural-product nanoparticles are considered to have an important role in treating and preventing diseases, both in humans and animals. Natural-product nanoparticles based on the nanoparticle size scale are more beneficial for increasing solubility, absorption, bioavailability, stability, distribution, and effectiveness in prevention and treatment [26,27].

Fucoidan has anti-diabetic and antioxidant effects, therefore, this study aims to make preparations of fucoidan nanoparticles that are used to prove the molecular mechanisms of fucoidan nanoparticles, to protect against endothelial cell dysfunction in rats induced by streptozotocin.

2. Materials and Methods

2.1. Fucoidan Nanoparticles Preparation

Fucoidan nanoparticles are made utilizing the high-energy ball milling method, which was carried out according to the instructions of the nanomachine manufacturer [28]. Furthermore, size of fucoidan nanoparticles was characterized by dynamic light scattering (Horiba LA 900, Kyoto, Japan).

2.2. Experimental Methods of Animals

Body weight of Wistar rats was 280–300 g; rats were obtained from LPPT, Universitas Gajah Mada, Indonesia. Prior to the experiment, rats were acclimatized for one week in plastic cages with a 12 h light/dark cycle at 26 ± 2 °C. All rats were given commercial pellets and drinking water ad libitum. All procedural experiments were approved by the Medical Ethics for Research in Preclinical trials of Hang Tuah University of Medical Sciences (approval number: No. 283/FK. UHT/II/2022).

2.3. Model of Diabetic Rat

After the rats fasted for 12 h, then the rats were given intraperitoneally a single dose of streptozotocin of 55 mg/kg BW. Streptozotocin was dissolved in citrate buffer 0.1 M (pH 4.5). The rat blood was checked for blood sugar levels with Accu-check glucometer (Roche Diagnostic) 3 days after the injection of streptozotocin. Rats with blood sugar levels > 200 mg/dL were used in the experiment.

2.4. Experimental Design

The rats were randomly divided into five groups (n = 10 in each group): control rats, rats were administered aquadest; diabetic rats, rats were injected intraperitoneally with a single dose of streptozotocin of 55 mg/kg BW; fucoidan nanoparticles rats, rats were injected with streptozotocin 55 mg/kg BW intraperitoneally and then after 3 days rats were administered fucoidan nanoparticles at doses of 75, 150, and 300 mg/kg BW, orally, once a day, for 75 days. At the end of the research, all rat aortas from various treatments were collected to evaluate MDA, SOD, GPx, Nrf2, NO, cGMP, relaxation response of Ach, and diameter of the aortic lumen.

2.5. Measurement of ROS in Aortic Endothelial Cells

Rats is anesthetized with ketamine intraperitoneally and the chest was opened to remove the aorta with dissection scissors. Then, the aorta was inserted into cold (sterile) PBS, and the container was moved to laminar airflow. A 1 mL syringe, equipped with a 25 G needle, was inserted into one end of the aorta, and the aorta was gently flushed with cold PBS to remove blood. The aorta was transferred to 20% fetal bovine serum (FBS)-DMEM medium. The aorta was cut into 1 mm rings and opened using sterile micro-dissection scissors to harvest endothelial cells of approximately 8–10 rings per aorta.

The using fluorescent probe, DCFH-DA was used to examine the levels of ROS in aortic endothelial cells (Sigma Aldrich; Merck, Germany). Endothelial cells were rinsed with PBS and added to 10 μM DCHF-DA for 30 min at 37 °C in darkness. The fluorescent signal of DCHF-DA was analyzed by flow cytometry (BD Vioscience, Franklin Lakes, NJ, USA) with Cell Quest Software version 5.1.

2.6. Measurement of SOD and GPx Levels of Aortic Tissue

Fifty milligrams of aortic tissue was washed five times with phosphate buffer saline (PBS) until clean. Then, sample was added to 0.5 mL of PBS and crushed with a mortar. Next, it was centrifuged at 10,000 rpm for 10 min. SOD levels in the supernatant were measured with a rat SOD ELISA kit (Bio-Vision K335–100, Milpitas, CA, USA); GPx was measured with a rat GPx ELISA kit (Bio-Vision K 762–100, Milpitas, CA, USA), according to the manufacturer's protocol. Sample was put into a microplate and incubated for 90 min at 37 °C. Afterward, it was incubated with the biotinylated antibody at 37 °C for 60 min. Then, rinsed with PBS three times and incubated at 37 °C for 30 min with working solution of avidin–biotin complex with PBS. Next, the sample was incubated with TMB color development at 37 °C for 30 min. Finally, the TMB stop solution was added and the OD value was read by microplate reader at 450 nm. SOD and GPx levels were expressed in U/mg protein.

2.7. Extraction of RNA and RT-PCR Analysis for Nrf2 Detection

Trizol solution was used in isolating total RNA from rat kidneys, in addition, it was re-suspended in 50 L of water with pyrocarbonate and at 80 °C it was stored. Furthermore, Promega reverse transcription was used to synthesize cDNA for Nrf2 detection (5); 5- TTGTAGATGACCATGAGTCGC-3 for forward and 5- TGTCCTGCTGTATGCTGCTT-3 for reverse are the specific primers used in this case. This is because mouse-actin mRNA amplification controls in each sample use a primer, the primer used for forward is 5-GAGGCTCAGAGCAAGAGAGG -3, while for retreat they use 5 TGACATCTCGCACAA-TCTCC-3. All polymerase chain reactions were brought out by tagging DNA polymerase (Life Technology Inc., Monza, Italy) with 200 ng cDNA, which were for 30 amplification cycles each; consisting of one minute for the denatured phase at 94 °C, 30 °C; seconds for phase annealing at 65 °C; and the elongation in 1 min at 72 °C. Furthermore, on the 2% agarose gel, the polymerase chain reaction product was amplified and then separated and the band was visualized using ethidium bromide. Scion Image software was used with densitometry to measure the density of the Nrf2 expression band (Scion Corporation, Frederick, MD, USA).

2.8. Measurement of NO Levels in Aortic Tissue

Griess reagent was used to evaluate NO levels in aortic tissue. For this, 100 µL homogenate of aortic tissue was mixed with 100 µL Griess reagent (1% Sulfanilamide and 0.1% Naphthylethylenediamine Dihydrochloride in 5% phosphoric acid) and incubated at room temperature for 10 min. The absorbance was measured by microplate reader at 540 nm. NO levels were expressed in terms of µg equivalence of $NANO_2$/mg protein.

2.9. Immunohistochemical Staining of MDA and cGMP in Aortic Tissues

The cGMP was determined by immunohistochemistry. To suppress endogenous peroxide, 4 µm aorta tissue slices were deparaffinized and then exposed to hydrogen peroxide at 37 °C for 10 min. Furthermore, a tris-buffered salt solution was added, and temperature was maintained at 37 °C for 30 min. They are then washed in 3× PBS and incubated with a secondary antibody from Thermofisher Scientific for 30 min at room temperture. The immunostaining was visualised using 3,3′-Diaminobenzidine (DAB, Sigma-Aldrich, St. Louis, MO, USA) for 4 min at room temperature for 30 minUTES. The sections were counterstained with hematoxylin. All slides were randomly scored in ten microscopic fields at 400× magnification. Score 0 indicates that there are no immunopositive cells; score 1 indicates that there are between 1 and 25% immunopositive cells; score 2 indicates that there are between 26 and 50% immunopositive cells; score 3 indicates that there are between 51 and 75% immunopositive cells; and score 4 indicates that there are more than 75% immunopositive cells.

2.10. Measurement of Endothelial Function (Responses to Acetylcholine on Contraction of Norepinephrine (NE))

Ring segment rat aortas were cut (3 mm long) and hung vertically in an organ bath (organ bath system-820, MO, USA) containing 10 mL Krebs solution (composition in mM: NaCl 118; KCl 4.7; KH_2PO_4 1.2; $MgSO_4$ 1.18; $NaHCO_3$ 25; D-Glucose 5.5, and $CaCl_2$) at 37 °C and oxygenated with 95% O_2 and 5% CO_2. The ring of the aorta was equilibrated at a baseline of 1 g for 60 min and then exposed to Potassium Chloride 60 mM twice. Afterward, the ring of the aorta was exposed to Norepinephrine (1 µM), and, after a steady contraction, acetylcholine (1 µM) was added to assess endothelial cell function.

2.11. Histopathological Evaluation

Rat aortic tissue was fixed in 10% formalin buffer solution, dehydrated in ethanol, and embedded in paraffin. Furthermore, it was sliced at 4 µm and stained with Hematoxylin Eosin. Then, tissue was evaluated under a microscope to assess the aortic lumen diameter.

2.12. Statistical Analysis

The results are expressed as mean and standard deviation. The difference between groups was compared using a one-way analysis of variance (ANOVA), followed by Tukey's post hoc test. The values are considered significant if $p < 0.05$.

3. Results

3.1. Dynamic Light Scattering Used to Characterize Fucoidan Nanoparticles

The particle size distribution of the Fucoidan nanoparticles was 267.2 ± 42.8 nm, which was analyzed by DLS, as shown in Figure 1.

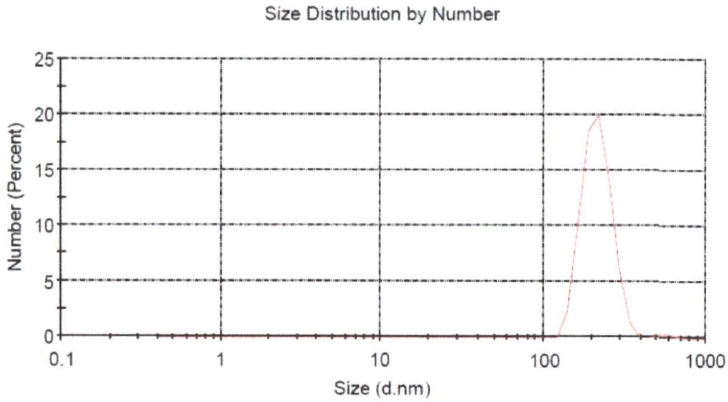

Figure 1. Fucoidan nanoparticle size distribution.

3.2. Effect of Fucoidan Nanoparticles on ROS in Aortic Endothelial Cells of Diabetic Rats

The levels of ROS can be utilized as a marker for the presence of oxidative stress in cell damage. ROS levels of aortic endothelial cells from various treatments can be seen in Figure 2. ROS levels in diabetic rats increased with a significant difference when compared with the control rats at $p < 0.05$. However, dose-dependent administration of fucoidan nanoparticles decreased the level of ROS in the aortic endothelial cells of diabetic rats. Only the administration of fucoidan nanoparticles at a dose of 300 mg/kg BW significantly decreased the levels of ROS in the aortic endothelial cells of diabetic rats.

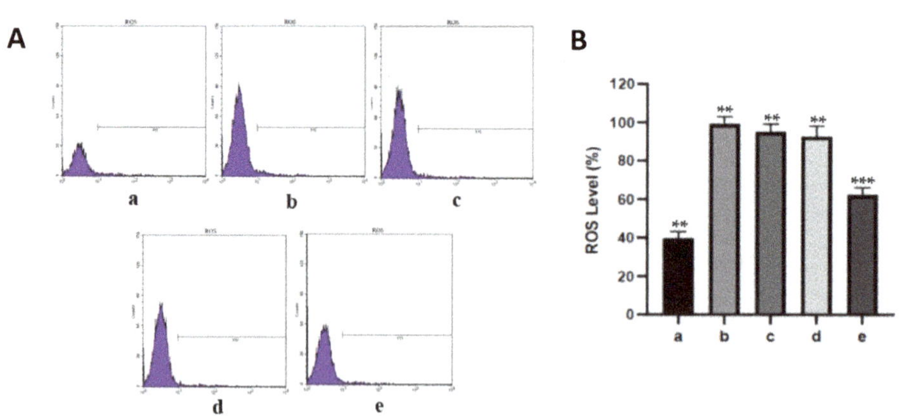

Figure 2. (**A**). Flow cytometry assay using DCFH-DA dye on fucoidan nanoparticles to assess effect on preventing oxidative stress. (**B**). The level of ROS in aortic endothelial cells was analyzed by flow cytometry. Control rats a; diabetic rats b; fucoidan nanoparticle rats, at doses of 75 c, 150 d, and 300 mg/kg BW e. **, *** The columns with different letters show significance between groups ($p < 0.05$).

3.3. Fucoidan Nanoparticles' Effects on the Levels of SOD and GPx in Diabetic Rats' Aortas

Table 1 shows the SOD and GPx levels in aorta tissue from the various treatments. SOD and GPx are endogenous antioxidant enzymes that scavenge free radicals resulting in the inhibition of oxidative stress. In rats injected with streptozotocin, levels of SOD and GPx in the aortic tissue were decreased, which was significantly different when compared with the control rats, $p < 0.05$. On the other hand, the administration of fucoidan nanoparticles, depending on the dose, increased SOD and GPx levels in the aortic tissue of diabetic rats. Administration of fucoidan nanoparticles, only at a dose of 300 mg/kg BW, was significantly able to increase levels of SOD and GPx in the aortic tissue of diabetic rats, $p < 0.05$.

Table 1. Fucoidan Nanoparticles Effect on SOD and GPx Levels in aortic tissue from various treatments.

Group	SOD Levels (U/mg Protein) $X \pm SD$	GPx Levels (U/mg Protein) $X \pm SD$
Control Rats	$5.98^{a} \pm 0.43$	$49.0^{a} \pm 2.6$
Diabetic Rats	$2.76^{b} \pm 0.29$	$29.0^{b} \pm 2.4$
Fucoidan nano 75 mg/kg bw	$2.70^{b} \pm 0.24$	$28.3^{b} \pm 1.7$
Fucoidan nano 150 mg/kg bw	$2.90^{b} \pm 0.25$	$30.8^{b} \pm 1.8$
Fucoidan nano 300 mg/kg bw	$3.88^{c} \pm 0.35$	$35.6^{c} \pm 2.1$

[a–c] The different superscript in each column show significantly diference between the means ($p < 0.05$).

3.4. Effect of Fucoidan Nanoparticles on the Expression of Nrf2 in Diabetic Rats' Aortas

The regulation of cellular antioxidants by Nrf2 plays a role in the defense against oxidative stress. The Nrf2 expression in aortic tissue from the various treatments is shown in Figure 3. Diabetes can significantly decrease Nrf2 expression in aortic tissue when compared with the control rats, $p < 0.05$. Meanwhile, dose-dependent administration of fucoidan nanoparticles increased Nrf2 expression in the aortic tissue of diabetic rats, and only a dose of 300 mg/kg BW significantly increased Nrf2 expression when compared to diabetic rats, $p < 0.05$.

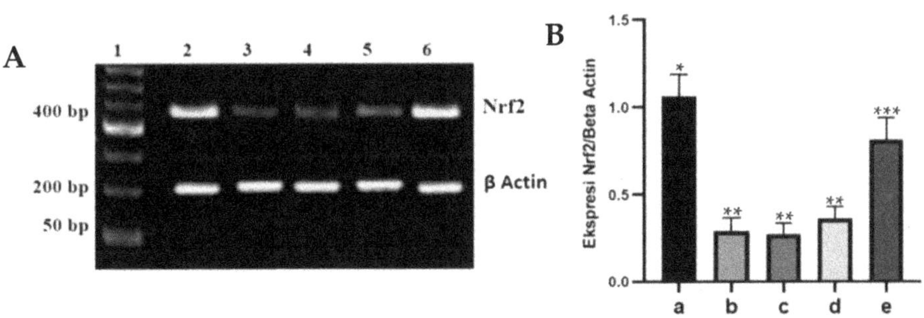

Figure 3. (**A**). Fucoidan nanoparticles' effect on Nrf2 expression in aortic tissue of various treatments. (**A**). Nrf2 expression in aortic tissue: marker (1); control rats (2); diabetic rats (3); fucoidan nanoparticles at doses of 75 (4), 150 (5), and 300 mg/kg BW (6). (**B**). Fucoidan nanoparticles' effect on Nrf2/β actin in aortic tissue: control rats a; diabetic rats b, Fucoidan nanoparticles at doses of 75 c, 150 d, and 300 mg/kg BW e. *, **, *** Columns with different letters statistically differ at $p < 0.05$.

3.5. Fucoidan Nanoparticles' Effect on NO Levels in Endothelial Cells of Diabetic Rats' Aortas

NO compounds can cause vasodilation and act as a regulator of vascular smooth muscle tone through the activation of soluble guanylate cyclase. The results of NO levels in aortic tissue from the various treatments are presented in Table 2. The diabetic rat group showed significantly decreased NO levels in the endothelial cells of the aorta when compared with the control rats, $p < 0.05$. However, depending on the dose, the administration of fucoidan nanoparticles increased the NO levels in the endothelial cell of the diabetic rats' aortas, and only at a dose of 300 mg/kg BW. This shows how fucoidan nanoparticles are significantly able to increase NO levels in the endothelial cells of diabetic rats' aortas, $p < 0.05$.

Table 2. Fucoidan nanoparticles effects on NO levels aortic tissue of various treatment.

Group	NO Level Aorta (nmol/mg) X ± SD
Control Rats	$1.47^{a} \pm 0.21$
Diabetic Rats	$0.41^{b} \pm 0.37$
Fucoidan Nano Rats 75 mg/kg bw	$0.39^{b} \pm 0.31$
Fucoidan Nano Rats 150 mg/kg bw	$0.42^{b} \pm 0.26$
Fucoidan Nano Rats 300 mg/kg bw	$0.94^{c} \pm 0.37$

$^{a–c}$ The different superscript in each column show significantly diference between the means ($p < 0.05$).

3.6. Effect of Fucoidan Nanoparticles on the Expression of cGMP in Diabetic Rats' Aortas

Cyclic GMP in vascular smooth muscle can cause vasodilation. The results of the immunohistochemistry testing of cGMP expression in aortic tissue from the various treatments are shown in Figure 4. In the diabetic rat group, cGMP production in aortic tissue decreased, which was significantly different when compared with the control rat group, $p < 0.05$. Meanwhile, diabetic rats administered with fucoidan nanoparticles increased cGMP production in the aortic tissue. Only a dose of 300 mg/kg BW significantly increased cGMP production when compared with diabetic rats, $p < 0.05$.

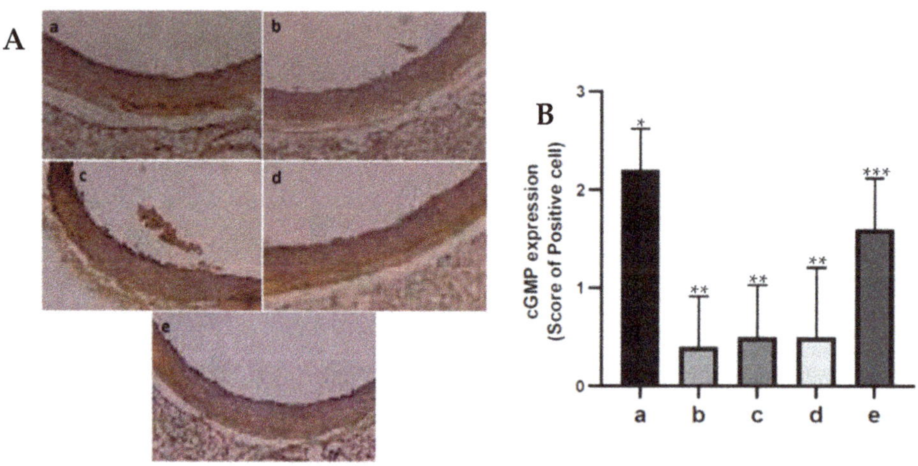

Figure 4. (**A**). Immunohistochemistry of the expression of cGMP in aortic tissue of diabetic rats: control rats a; diabetic rats b; fucoidan nanoparticles at doses of 75 c, 150 d, and 300 mg/kg BW e. (400×). (**B**). The number of cGMP-expressing cells that are immunoreactive. *, **, *** The columns with different letters show significance between groups ($p < 0.05$).

3.7. Fucoidan Nanoparticles' Effect on Response Relaxation of Ach in Diabetic Rats' Aortas

The acetylcholine smooth muscle relaxation response (vasodilation) can be used as a marker for endothelial cell damage. Figure 5 shows the response of Ach relaxation to NE contractions from the various treatments in the rats' aortas. In the diabetic rat group, the inhibition of the relaxation response of 1 μM Ach to 1 μM NE contractions on the aorta within endothelial cells was significantly different, and the relaxation response was lower when compared to the control rats, $p < 0.05$. On the other hand, administration of fucoidan nanoparticles significantly increased the relaxation response of 1 μM Ach to 1 μM NE contractions on the aorta within endothelial cells of diabetic rats, $p < 0.05$. These results indicate that the administration of fucoidan nanoparticles can prevent aortic endothelial cell dysfunction in diabetic rats.

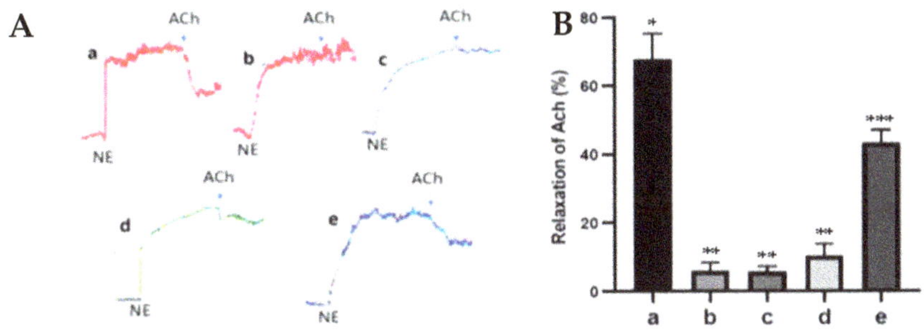

Figure 5. (**A**). The response of 1 μM Ach relaxation to 1 μM NE contractions from various treatments in rats' aortas: control rats a; diabetic rats b; fucoidan nanoparticles at doses of 75 c, 150 d, and 300 mg/kg BW e. (**B**). The relaxation of Ach to NE contractions expressed in %. *, **, *** The columns with different letters show significance between groups ($p < 0.05$).

3.8. Fucoidan Nanoparticles' Effect on Diameter of Aortic Lumens of Diabetic Rats

An increase or decrease in the diameter of the aortic lumen indicates vasodilatation or vasoconstriction in the aortic vessels. The diameter of the aortic lumen from the various treatments can be seen in Figure 6. Narrowing of the aortic lumen (vasoconstriction) occurred in the group of diabetic rats, which was significantly different and had a lower diameter than the control rats, $p < 0.05$. In diabetic rats, administering fucoidan nanoparticles increased the diameter of diabetic rats' aortic lumens, and only at a dose of 300 mg/kg BW. The fucoidan nanoparticles significantly increased the diameter of the diabetic rats' aortic lumens, $p < 0.05$. These results show that the administration of fucoidan nanoparticles can prevent the narrowing of the aortic lumen (vasoconstriction) in diabetic rats.

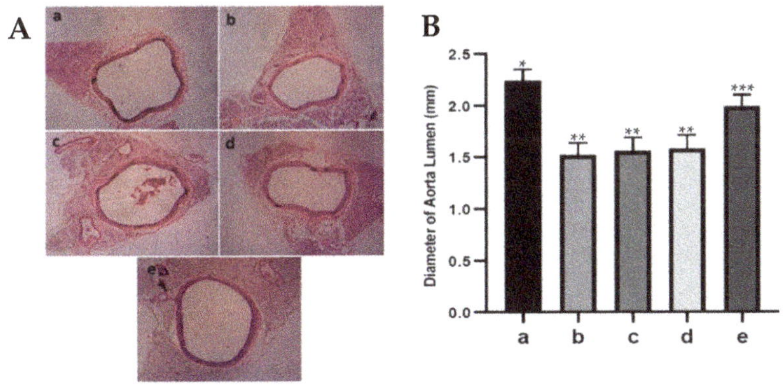

Figure 6. (**A**). The diameter of the aortic lumen from various treatments: control rats a; diabetic rats b; fucoidan nanoparticles at doses of 75 c, 150 d, and 300 mg/kg BW e. (400×). (**B**). The diameter of aortic lumens expressed in mm. *, **, *** The columns with different letters show significance between groups ($p < 0.05$).

4. Discussion

The progress of nanotechnology is quite rapid and the effectiveness of nanomaterials is extraordinary, so much so that nanotechnology is a new solution for the treatment of diabetes complications. Fucoidan nanoparticles are made into nano-size by the ball milling method, a technique that is widely used recently [26–28]. Size characterization of fucoidan nanoparticles was carried out using DLS, which showed a size distribution of 201.8 ± 14.6 nm. Fucoidan nanoparticles are considered an alternative solution to increase solubility, absorption, and bioavailability, as well as to increase their protective effect on complications of diabetes mellitus, especially in the dysfunction and damage of aortic endothelial cells. Oxidative stress has a major role in causing diabetes complications. Oxidative stress can increase the expression of inflammatory cytokines, which are both a consequence and a trigger for diabetes complications. Oxidative stress can occur due to the excessive formation of ROS and lower endogenous antioxidant defense systems [2,6,15].

In the diabetic rat model, STZ increases ROS, and induces oxidative stress, which plays an important role in endothelial cell dysfunction. Therefore, it has been necessary to investigate several parameters of oxidative stress and endothelial cell dysfunction, such as MDA, SOD, GPx, Nrf2, NO, cGMP, and the relaxation response of Ach in diabetic rat tissue [9,20,21]. STZ inhibits the secretion of insulin in the Langerhans islet beta cell, which leads to hyperglycemia complications such as endothelial cell dysfunction. The purpose of this research was to prove the antioxidant activity of fucoidan nanoparticles is able to protect against aortic endothelial cell dysfunctions in diabetic rats.

An increase in the amount of ROS in the body can cause oxidative stress and lipid peroxidation, namely the reaction of ROS with polyunsaturated fatty acids (PUFA) in cell membranes, which will produce MDA (Malondialdehyde) products. MDA can be used as a marker for the presence of free radicals, which can cause cell or tissue damage. The higher the level of MDA in the tissue, the higher the degree of tissue damage [2,6,7]. Our results showed that oral administration of fucoidan nanoparticles inhibited the increase in ROS levels in diabetic rat aortic tissue, which was significantly different when compared to the streptozotocin group at $p < 0.05$. Antioxidant compounds from fucoidan are able to scavenge and neutralize free radicals, thereby preventing an increase in MDA levels and the occurrence of oxidative stress. The antioxidant termination reaction of fucoidan can occur by capturing hydroxyl radicals (*OH) in the peroxidation reactions of lipids, proteins, or other molecules in the cell membranes so that the increase in MDA levels can be inhibited and cell damage can be avoided [24,25]. Fucoidan can also inactivate protein kinase C (PKC), causing the expression of various genes such as TGF-β, PAI-1, NF-κB, and NAD(P)H oxidase to decrease so that the production of ROS and MDA also decreases [29,30]

SOD and GPx are antioxidants that play an important role in tackling free radicals, namely superoxide anions and hydroxyl groups. SOD is present in almost all cells and is the first line of defense against ROS. SOD converts superoxide ions (O_2^-) to Hydrogen Peroxide (H_2O_2). Because Hydrogen Peroxide still reacts with other ROS, it needs to be degraded by other antioxidants, namely GPx. GPx detoxifies H2O2 by converting it into water and oxygen molecules. SOD and GPx work synergistically to support each other's defenses against ROS. In addition, SOD and GPx inhibit oxidative stress, which is one of the diabetes biomarkers, the levels of which have been extensively examined in various diabetes complication studies [31,32]. In the results of this study, administering fucoidan nanoparticles inhibited the reduction in SOD and GPx levels in the aortic tissue of diabetic rats. Fucoidan is a polysaccharide substance that can inhibit the oxidation of important molecules such as proteins, lipids, and DNA caused by free radicals; they do so by donating electrons, so that they can inhibit the formation of free radicals and prevent oxidative stress, which in turn can inhibit vascular aortic damage, especially in endothelial cell dysfunction in diabetic complications [22,33,34]. The same results have been proven by Uslu et al. (2018), who reported that the administration of the antioxidant Cinnamomum cassia extract can inhibit the decrease in SOD and GPx levels of aortic tissue in rats injected intraperitoneally with streptozotocin. Wardani et al. (2022) also reported that the administration of fucoidan nanoparticles displayed antioxidant activity and inhibited the decrease in SOD and GPx levels in the kidney tissue of diabetic rats.

Cellular antioxidant regulation by Nrf2 plays a role in defense against oxidative stress. Nrf2 activity and expression decrease in diabetes caused by oxidative stress, which can weaken the induction of genes encoding antioxidants, resulting in decreased production of endogenous antioxidants such as SOD, GPx, and catalase [12,35]. Several researchers reported that streptozotocin can cause oxidative stress that occurs due to an imbalance between increased ROS production and decreased antioxidant capacity. This increase in ROS will cause cysteine damage in Keap1, disrupt the Keap1-Cul3 ubiquitination mechanism and mediate Nrf2 degradation by the 26S proteasome so that Nrf2 has a short half-life, which can result in a decreased expression of Nrf2 [13,36]. In rats injected with streptozotocin, administration of fucoidan nanoparticles orally inhibited the decrease in Nrf2 expression in the aortic tissue of diabetic rats. This is because fucoidan has a strong antioxidant effect and is a polysaccharide that has an OH group that can react with hydroxyl free radicals (∗OH), resulting in the inhibition of oxidative stress that can lead to an increase in Nrf2 expression. In addition to that, the strong antioxidant effect of fucoidan is able to reduce ROS so that cysteine damage does not occur in Keap1, which further inhibits the Keap1-Cul3 ubiquitination mechanism and Nrf2 degradation and can cause an increase in Nrf2 expression. The same results were reported that administration of the antioxidant fucoidan could inhibit oxidative stress and inhibit the decrease in Nrf2 expression in liver tissue induced by acetaminophen [14]. Administering the antioxidant chitosan nanoparticles orally to diabetic rats can also inhibit oxidative stress and inhibit the decrease in Nrf2 expression in heart tissue [15].

Nitric oxide (NO) is an endothelium-derived relaxing factor (EDRF) that under physiological conditions is released from endothelial cells in response to mechanical stimulation, acetylcholine, and increased intracellular calcium. NO compounds can cause vasodilation and act as a regulator of vascular smooth muscle tone through the activation of soluble guanylate cyclase [21,37]. The results of this study indicated that the administration of fucoidan nanoparticles orally increased eNOS expression and NO levels of aortic tissue in diabetic rats. It has been reported that antioxidants can be used to inhibit vascular endothelial cell dysfunction in diabetes by inhibiting ROS production so as to inhibit lipid peroxidation and prevent oxidation of cell membrane lipids, which can reduce MDA levels and increase SOD and GPx expression by inhibiting the reduction of Nrf2 expression, further inhibiting endothelial cell damage. This causes eNOS to remain active in producing NO, which causes vasodilation of the blood vessels [4,5]. Fucoidan has an activity to scavenge excessive superoxide anion free radicals, so that oxidation of the important cofactor tetrahydrobiopterin (BH4), which is required for the formation of eNOS, does not occur and can further increase NO production. Yeoh et al. (2021) reported the same results, which proved that giving the antioxidant propolis from Stingless Bees (Heterotrigona Itama) could increase eNOS expression and NO levels in aortic endothelial cells of diabetic rats.

Endothelial cells produce NO which will diffuse into the blood vessels' smooth muscle cells and activate the soluble guanylate cyclase (sGC) enzyme, which can lead to increased formation of cyclic GMP from its GTP precursor. Cyclic GMP stimulates the relaxation of the smooth muscles of blood vessels so that vasodilation will occur [38]. Our results of this research show that oral administration of fucoidan nanoparticles increased cGMP expression in aortic tissue in diabetic rats. Administering exogenous antioxidants can increase NO formation and cGMP production so that aortic vasodilation can occur [20,21]. The results of this study indicate that the antioxidant activity of fucoidan nanoparticles with a scavenger can inhibit the reaction of superoxide ions with NO so that peroxynitrite which is toxic to endothelial cells is not formed, therefore, fucoidan can increase the formation of NO and cGMP. Yeohi et al. (2019) proved that administration of the antioxidant from Stingless Bees could increase endothelium-dependent relaxation of aortic smooth muscle by increasing the formation of NO and cGMP.

Endothelial cells actively regulate the relaxation and contraction of vascular smooth muscle under physiological and pathological conditions. Ach can cause relaxation of the smooth muscle of the aortic blood vessels (vasodilation) depending on the presence of endothelial cells because the administration of Ach can activate eNOS resulting in an increase in NO formation in endothelial cells, which in turn can activate soluble guanylate cyclase and increase the formation of cGMP that can cause vasodilation. Ach can be used to prove the occurrence of endothelial cell dysfunction. In diabetes, there is an inhibition of the Ach relaxation response due to endothelial cell dysfunction [19,20]. The results of this study show that the antioxidant activity of fucoidan nanoparticles increased the ACh relaxation response to norepinephrine contractions in the aortic blood vessels of diabetic rats. This is because the fucoidan nanoparticles work by donating their electrons so they can inhibit the formation of free radicals, increase the expression of SOD and GPx, and inhibit oxidative stress, which contributes to inhibiting the aortic endothelial cell dysfunction of diabetic rats. Furthermore, it can increase the production of NO and cGMP, so can cause aortic vasodilation and can increase the diameter of the aortic lumen. The same results also occur in the administration of propolis antioxidant from Heterotrigona itama, which can increase the relaxation response of acetylcholine to contraction of phenylephrine in the aorta of diabetic rats and works by increasing the production of NO and cGMP [20].

An increase or decrease in the diameter of the aortic lumen indicates vasoconstriction or vasodilation of the aortic blood vessels, which can cause narrowing or widening of the diameter of the aortic lumen [17,38]. Administration of fucoidan nanoparticles increased the diameter (dilation) of the diabetic rats' aortic lumen. It has been reported that fucoidan has a strong antioxidant effect that can inhibit the process of lipid peroxidation because it can capture ROS in diabetic rats, thereby preventing endothelial cell damage; in addition, the eNOS remains active in converting L-arginine to NO. This NO can activate soluble guanylate cyclase in producing cGMP and cause an increase in the diameter (dilation) of the aortic lumen in diabetic rats.

Antioxidants are one option to prevent endothelial cell dysfunction in diabetes complications associated with oxidative stress. A number of studies have focused on the use of antioxidants to prevent diabetes complications such as neuropathy, retinopathy, nephropathy, hepatopathy, atherosclerosis, and vascular endothelial cell dysfunction. However, whether antioxidants have preventive and/or therapeutic value remains to be conducted in clinical trials on diabetics.

5. Conclusions

The results of this study can be concluded that fucoidan nanoparticles are natural-product antioxidants that can be used to prevent damage to aortic endothelial cells in the complications of diabetes, whose mechanism of action is through decreased levels of ROS and MDA, as well as increased expression of Nrf2, SOD, and GPx levels. This results in increased NO production and cGMP, which can increase the lumen diameter (vasodilation) of the diabetic rat aorta. Henceforth, it is necessary to study the antioxidant activity associated with inflammation and apoptosis in preventing endothelial cell dysfunction in diabetes complications.

Author Contributions: G.W., S.A.S. and J.N. conceptualization; G.W. and R.K. contributed to the animal study; G.W. analyzed data and draft preparation; S.A.S. and M.R.M. review and editing. All authors have read and agreed to the published version of the manuscript.

Funding: This study was funded by the Ministry of Finance, Education Fund Management Institution (LPDP), the Republic of Indonesia, through the Doctoral Program of Medical Science, Faculty of Medicine, Airlangga University, Indonesia.

Institutional Review Board Statement: The research treatment on rats has been approved by Airlangga University and the Faculty of Veterinary Medicine by the Animal Care and Ethics Committee. All research is in accordance with the Association for Assessment and Accreditation of Animal Care International Laboratory.

Informed Consent Statement: Not applicable.

Data Availability Statement: Data are presented within the article.

Conflicts of Interest: The authors declare no conflict of interest.

References

1. Ochiagu, F.O.; Chikezie, P.C.; Chikezie, C.M. Pathophysiology of diabetes melitus and its complications: Metabolic events and control. *Biomed. Res. Ther.* **2021**, *8*, 4243–4257. [CrossRef]
2. Sing, A.; Kikreti, R.; Saso, L.; Kukreti, S. Mechanistic insight into oxidative stress-triggered signaling pathway and type 2 diabetes. *Molecules* **2022**, *27*, 950. [CrossRef] [PubMed]
3. Awad, E.M.; Ahmed, A.F.; El-Daly, M.; Wagdy, A.; Taye, A. Role of apoptosis and oxidative stress in high glucose-induced endothelial dysfunction in isolated aortic rings. *J. Adv. Bimed. Pharm. Sci.* **2022**, *5*, 23–28. [CrossRef]
4. Maruhashi, T.; Higashi, Y. Pathophysiological association between diabetes mellitus and endothelial dysfunction. *Antioxidants* **2021**, *10*, 1306. [CrossRef] [PubMed]
5. Ozturk, Z. Diabetes, oxidative stress and endothelial dysfunction. *Bezmiâlem Sci.* **2019**, *7*, 52–57. [CrossRef]
6. Alkadi, H. A review on free radicals and antioxidants. *Infect. Disord. Drug Target.* **2020**, *20*, 16–26.
7. Ghasemi-Dehnoo, M.; Amini-Khoei, H.; Lorigooini, Z.; Rafician-Kopaei, M. Oxidative stress and antioxidants in diabetes mellitus. *Asian Pac. J. Trop. Med.* **2020**, *13*, 431–438.
8. Vassalle, C.; Gaggini, M. Type 2 diabetes and oxidative stress and inflammation pathophysiological mechanism and possible therapeutic options. *Antioxidants* **2022**, *11*, 953. [CrossRef]
9. Yan, L.J. The Nicotamide/Streptozotocin rodent model type 2 diabetes: Renal Pathophysiology and redox imbalance features. *Biomolecules* **2022**, *12*, 1225. [CrossRef]
10. Zhang, P.; Li, T.; Wu, X.; Nice, E.C.; Huang, C.; Zhang, Y. Oxidative stress and diabetes: Antioxidative strategies. *Font. Med.* **2020**, *14*, 583–600. [CrossRef]
11. Salazar-Garcia, M.; Corona, J.C. The use of natural compounds as a strategy to counteract oxidative stress in animal model of diabetes mellitus. *Int. J. Mol. Sci.* **2021**, *22*, 7009. [CrossRef] [PubMed]
12. Wardani, G.; Ernawati; Sudjarwo, S.A. The potency of fucoidan nanoparticles as antioxidant and anti-caspase 3 in against lung cell damage on wistar rat diabetic. *Intercientia J.* **2020**, *45*, 83–96.
13. Rampin, A.; Carrabba, M.; Mutoli, M.; Spineeti, G. Recent advances in KEAP1/NRF2-targeting strategies by phytochemical antioxidants, nanoparticles, and biocompatible scaffolds for the treatment of diabetic cardiovascular complications. *Antioxid. Redox. Signal.* **2022**, *36*, 10–12. [CrossRef]
14. Wang, R.; Liu, L.; Liu, H.; Wu, K.; Qi, B.; Zhang, L. Nrf2 protects against diabetic dysfunction of endothelial progenitor cells via regulating cell senescence. *Int. J. Mol. Med.* **2018**, *42*, 1327–1340. [CrossRef] [PubMed]
15. Wardani, G.; Jusak, N.; Mustafa, M.R.; Kurnijasanti, R.; Sudjarwo, S.A. Antioxidative Stress and Antiapoptosis Effect of Chitosan nanoparticles to protect cardiac cell damage on streptozotocin-induced diabetic rat. *Oxidative Med. Cell. Longev.* **2022**, *2022*, 3081397. [CrossRef] [PubMed]
16. Wang, Y.Q.; Wei, J.G.; Tu, M.J.; Gu, J.G.; Zhang, W. Fucoidan alleviates acetaminophen-induced hepatotoxicity via oxidative stress inhibition and Nrf2 translocation. *Int. J. Mol. Sci.* **2018**, *19*, 4050. [CrossRef]
17. Beck, L.; Comerma-Steffensen, S.; Pinilla, E.; Carlsson, R.; Simonsen, U. Endothelial dysfunction and passive changes in the aorta and coronary arteries of diabetic db/db mice. *Front. Physiol.* **2020**, *11*, 667. [CrossRef]
18. Li, J.C.; Velagic, A.; Qin, C.X.; Li, M.; Ritchie, R.H.; Woodman, Q.L. Diabetes attenuates the contribution of endogenous nitric oxide but not nitroxyl to endothelium dependent relaxation of rat carotid arteries. *Front. Pharmacol.* **2021**, *11*, 585740. [CrossRef]
19. Mustapha, S.; Azemi, A.K.; Wan Ahmad, W.A.N.; Mustafa, M.R.; Mokhtar, S.S. Inhibition of endoplasmic reticulum stress improve Acetylcholine-mediated relaxation in the aorta of type 2 diabetic rats. *Molecules* **2022**, *27*, 5107. [CrossRef]
20. Yeoh, B.S.; Omar, N.; Mohammad, M.; Mokhtar, S.S.; Ahmad, R. Antioxidative propolis from stingless bees (*Heterotrigona itama*) preserves endothelium dependent aortic relaxation of disbetic rats: The role of nitric oxide and cyclic guanosine monophosphate. *Braz. J. Pharm. Sci.* **2021**, *57*, e19187. [CrossRef]
21. Uslu, G.A.; Gelen, V.; Uslu, H.; Ozen, H. Effects of *Cinnamomum cassia* extract on oxidative stress, immunoreactivity of iNOS and impaired thoracic aortic reactivity induced by type II diabetes in rats. *Braz. J. Pharm. Sci.* **2018**, *54*, 17785. [CrossRef]
22. Wang, Y.; Xing, M.; Cao, Q. Biological activities of fucoidan and the factor mediating its therapeutic effect: A review of recent studies. *Mar. Drugs* **2019**, *17*, 183. [CrossRef] [PubMed]
23. Aleissa, M.S.; Alkahtani, S.; Abd Eldaim, M.A.; Mohammed, A.M.; Abdel-Daim, M.M. Fucoidan ameliorates oxidative stress, inflammation, DNA damage, and hepatorenal injuries in diabetic rats intoxicated with aflatoxin B1. *Oxidative Med. Cell. Longev.* **2020**, *2020*, 9316751. [CrossRef] [PubMed]
24. Husni, M.A.; Izmi, N.; Ayunani, F.Z.; Kartini, A.; Husnayain, N.; Isnansetyo, A. Characteristic and antioxidant activity of fucoidan from *Sargassum hystrix*: Effect of extraction. *Int. J. Food. Sci.* **2022**, *2022*, 3689724. [CrossRef] [PubMed]
25. Somanath, D.; Vijayakumar, J.; Suriyakumari; Vijayaraghavan, R. Effect of fucoidan on regulation of antioxidant enzymes in hepatorenal tissues of streptozotocin-induced diabetes rats. *Indian J. Pharm. Sci.* **2021**, *83*, 1164–1173. [CrossRef]
26. Chenthamara, D.; Subramaniam, S.; Ramakrishnan, S.G.; Lin, F.; Qoronfleh, M.W. Therapeutic efficacy of nanoparticles and routes of administration. *Biomater. Res.* **2019**, *23*, 20–49. [CrossRef]
27. Khan, I.; Saeed, K.; Idrees, K. Nanoparticles: Properties, applications and toxicities. *Arab. J. Chem.* **2019**, *12*, 908–931. [CrossRef]
28. Aman, K.; Singh, R.K.; Kumar, R.; Ghosh, A.K. Effect of high energy ball milling grinding on physicochemical, morphological, and optical properties of *Curcuma longa* nanoparticle powder. *Int. J. Pharm. Sci. Res.* **2018**, *9*, 672–677.

29. Xu, J.; Wang, Y.; Wang, Z.; Guo, L.; Li, X. Fucoidan mitigated diabetic nephropathy trough the downregulation of PKC and modulation of NF-kB signaling pathway: In vitro and in vivo investigations. *Phytother. Res.* **2021**, *4*, 2133–2144. [CrossRef]
30. Phull, A.R.; Kim, S.J. Fucoidan as bio-functional molecule: Insights into the anti-inflammatory potential and associated molecular mechanisms. *J. Funct. Foods* **2017**, *38*, 415–426. [CrossRef]
31. Neha, K.; Haider, M.R.; Pathak, A.; Yar, M.S. Medicinal prospects of antioxidant: A review. *Eur. J. Med. Chem.* **2019**, *178*, 687–704. [CrossRef] [PubMed]
32. Luthuli, S.; Wu, S.; Cheng, Y.; Zheng, X.; Tong, H. Therapeutic effects of fucoidan: A review on recent studies. *Mar. Drugs* **2019**, *17*, 487. [CrossRef]
33. Wu, J.; Sun, X.C.; Jiang, Z.; Jiang, J.; Wu, H. Protective role of Nrf2 in macrovascular complication of diabetes. *J. Cell. Mol. Med.* **2020**, *16*, 8903–8917. [CrossRef]
34. Gerardi, G.; Cavia-Saiz, M.; Pino-Garcia, R.; Pilar-Muniz, P. Wine pomace product ameliorates hypertensive and diabetic aorta vascular remodeling through antioxidant and anti-inflammatory action. *J. Funct. Foods* **2020**, *66*, 103794. [CrossRef]
35. Tanase, D.M.; Gosav, E.M.; Anton, M.I.; Floria, M.; Rezus, C. Oxidative stress and Nrf2/Keap1/Are pathway in diabetic kidney disease (DKD): New perspectives. *Biomolecules* **2022**, *12*, 1227. [CrossRef]
36. Tran, N.; Garcia, T.; Aniqa, M.; Ali, S.; Ally, A.; Nauli, S.M. Endothelial nitric oxide synthase (eNOS) and the cardiovascular system: In physiology and in disease states. *Am. J. Biomed. Sci. Res.* **2022**, *15*, 153–177.
37. Ataabadi, E.A.; Golshiri, K.; Jan Danser, A.H.; Roks, A.J.M. Nitric oxide-cGMP signaling in hypertension, current and future options for pharmacotherapy. *Hypertension* **2020**, *76*, 1055–1068. [CrossRef] [PubMed]
38. Chen, T.; Yang, X.; Fang, X.; Tang, L.; Mao, P.; Xu, B.; Chen, X. Potential influencing factors of aortic diameter at specific segments in population with cardiovascular risk. *BMC Cardiovasc. Disord.* **2022**, *22*, 32. [CrossRef] [PubMed]

nutrients

MDPI

Article

Identification of Kynurenic Acid-Induced Apoptotic Biomarkers in Gastric Cancer-Derived AGS Cells through Next-Generation Transcriptome Sequencing Analysis

Hun Hwan Kim [1], Sang Eun Ha [2], Min Yeong Park [1], Se Hyo Jeong [1], Pritam Bhagwan Bhosale [1], Abuyaseer Abusaliya [1], Chung Kil Won [1], Jeong Doo Heo [2], Meejung Ahn [3], Je Kyung Seong [4], Hyun Wook Kim [5] and Gon Sup Kim [1,*]

1 Department of Veterinary Medicine, Research Institute of Life Science, Gyeongsang National University, Jinju-daero, Jinju 52828, Republic of Korea
2 Biological Resources Research Group, Gyeongnam Department of Environment Toxicology and Chemistry, Korea Institute of Toxicology, 17 Jegok-gil, Jinju 52834, Republic of Korea
3 Department of Animal Science, College of Life Science, Sangji University, Wonju 26339, Republic of Korea
4 Laboratory of Developmental Biology and Genomics, BK21 PLUS Program for Creative Veterinary Science Research, Research Institute for Veterinary Science, College of Veterinary Medicine, Seoul National University, Seoul 08826, Republic of Korea
5 Division of Animal Bioscience & Intergrated Biotechnology, Jinju 52725, Republic of Korea
* Correspondence: gonskim@gnu.ac.kr; Tel.: +82-55-772-2346

Abstract: Understanding the triggers and therapeutic targets for gastric cancer, one of the most common cancers worldwide, can provide helpful information for the development of therapeutics. RNA sequencing technology can be utilized to identify complex disease targets and therapeutic applications. In the present study, we aimed to establish the pharmacological target of Kynurenic acid (KYNA) for gastric cancer AGS cells and to identify the biological network. RNA sequencing identified differentially expressed genes (DEGs) between KYNA-treated and untreated cells. A total of 278 genes were differentially expressed, of which 120 genes were up-regulated, and 158 genes were down-regulated. Gene ontology results confirmed that KYNA had effects such as a reduction in genes related to DNA replication and nucleosome organization on AGS cells. Protein–protein interaction was confirmed through STRING analysis, and it was confirmed that cancer cell growth and proliferation were inhibited through KEGG, Reactome, and Wiki pathway analysis, and various signaling pathways related to cancer cell death were induced. It was confirmed that KYNA treatment reduced the gene expression of cancer-causing AP-1 factors (Fos, Jun, ATF, and JDP) in AGS cell lines derived from gastric cancer. Overall, using next-generation transcriptome sequencing data and bioinformatics tools, we confirmed that KYNA had an apoptosis effect by inducing changes in various genes, including factor AP-1, in gastric cancer AGS cells. This study can identify pharmacological targets for gastric cancer treatment and provide a valuable resource for drug development.

Keywords: next-generation sequencing; RNA sequencing; AP-1; AGS cells; DEGs

1. Introduction

Gastric cancer was the fourth leading cause of cancer-related deaths in 2020 and is one of the most common cancers worldwide [1]. It is a malignant tumor that threatens human life and health and is mainly treated through resection [2]. However, chemotherapy is still used in the early stages to relieve symptoms and suppress metastasis [3]. Cisplatin and fluorouracil, used primarily as chemotherapeutic agents, cause various side effects in patients, including vomiting and hemotoxicity [4]. Therefore, there is a need to develop a therapeutically effective drug with low toxicity to treat gastric cancer.

Among approaches for cancer treatment, it is essential to understand changes in the molecular pathways and signaling mechanisms of tumor cells through drugs [5].

When normal cells become cancerous, various genes and proteins are involved in the transformation [6]. Although it is relatively difficult to identify the mechanism of action according to drug treatment, next-generation drugs focus on developing methods targeting specific genes and proteins [7]. Obtaining information about the target and its mechanism of action can provide precise insight into the treatment of the disease. In addition, targeted treatment methods can minimize cytotoxicity and side effects compared to conventional anticancer drugs [8]. It has been confirmed that tumors are caused by various factors, including genes, proteins, and metabolites [9].

Network pharmacology is a study that utilizes computer network analysis and biomedical data, and helps to discover the underlying mechanisms between drugs and their target agents [10]. Transcriptome analysis is a method to identify differentially expressed genes during drug treatment using bioinformatics, and is a technique that helps to understand the discovery of essential genes and the mechanism of action of drugs [11]. It is possible to quickly identify differentially expressed genes and secure a target to accelerate treatment. However, it is still a problematic study to predict the onset of gastric cancer and to identify target factors for early treatment and treatment. Therefore, there is a need for a process to acquire more target factors to improve treatment.

The AP-1 complex is a dimeric transcription factor including Jun (c-Jun, JunB, and JunD), Fos (c-Fos, FosB, Fra2, and FosL), and ATF (ATF2, ATF3, and ATF7), and regulates a variety of cellular processes, including apoptosis, survival, migration, and differentiation [12,13]. It has been reported that C-Fos, together with interleukin-1 receptor type 2 (IL1R2), promotes angiogenesis in human colon cancer cells to promote tumor progression [14]. Therefore, AP-1 is an essential target for cancer treatment, and the related mechanism is being studied [15]. Therefore, this suggests that drug-mediated alteration of the corresponding biomarkers can control a variety of cells, including cancer migration, growth, and proliferation.

Kynurenic acid (KYNA) is a phenolic compound with a phenol ring and various physiological activities. It is a metabolite of the kynurenine pathway, which is the catabolic process of tryptophan [16]. KYNA has been reported as an inhibitor of p38 in renal cancer cells and renal cell carcinoma Caki-2 cells [17], and it inhibits the proliferation of cancer cells by affecting other signaling factors such as MAPK, ERK, and AKT turnout [16]. The present study performed transcriptome analysis and network pharmacology analysis to identify potential targets of KYNA for gastric cancer cell AGS. We discovered AP-1 as an anti-tumor regulator that KYNA induces significant changes in AGS cells and secured primary data on changes in other genes.

2. Materials and Methods

2.1. Cell Culture

AGS human gastric cancer cells (Korea Cell Line Bank, Seoul, Republic of Korea) were cultured in RPMI medium (Gibco; BRL Life Technologies, Grand Island, NY, USA) containing 10% fetal bovine serum (FBS) (Gibco; BRL Life Technologies, Grand Island, NY, USA) and 1% penicillin/streptomycin (P/S) (Gibco; BRL Life Technologies, Grand Island, NY, USA) at 37 °C in a humidified atmosphere of 5% CO_2. Kynurenic acid (KYNA) was purchased from Sigma-Aldrich Corp. (St. Louis, MO, USA).

2.2. Isolation of RNA for Sequencing

AGS cells were seeded into 60 mm plates at 1×10^6 and treated with 250 μM of Kynurenic acid (KYNA) for 24 h at 37 °C. After incubation, total RNAs were extracted using TRIzol. A spectrophotometer was used to measure the amount of RNA. The sequencing of isolated total RNA was then used to determine the expression levels.

2.3. Library Preparation and Sequencing

According to the following methodology, the mRNA sequencing was prepared by Theragenbio (Seongnam-si, Gyeonggi-do, Republic of Korea). We created 151 bp paired-end sequencing libraries using the TruSeq stranded mRNA Sample Preparation Kit (Illumina, CA, USA). Utilizing oligo (dT) magnetic beads, mRNA molecules were specifically isolated and fragmented from 1 μg of total RNA. Through random hexamer priming, single-stranded cDNAs were created from the fragmented mRNAs. Double-stranded cDNA was created by using this as a template for second-strand synthesis. After end repair, A-tailing and adapter ligation were completed in order, and cDNA libraries were amplified using PCR (Polymerase Chain Reaction). The Agilent 2100 BioAnalyzer (Agilent, CA, USA) was used to assess these cDNA libraries' quality. According to the manufacturer's library quantification methodology, they were measured using the KAPA library quantification kit (Kapa Biosystems, MA, USA). After cluster amplification of denatured templates, Illumina NovaSeq6000 (Illumina, CA, USA) was used to advance the sequencing process as paired-end (2 × 151 bp).

2.4. Transcriptome Data Analysis

2.4.1. Filtering and Sequence Alignment

Adapter sequences and read ends with a Phred quality score of less than 20 were deleted throughout the filtering process, and reads less than 50 bp were also eliminated using cutadapt v.2.8. Following ENCODE standard choices and the "quantMode TranscriptomeSAM" option (refer to "Alignment" of "Help" section in the Html report) for estimation of transcriptome expression level, filtered reads were mapped to the reference genome associated with the species using the aligner STAR [18].

2.4.2. Gene-Expression Estimation

By utilizing the option "strandedness", the RSEM v.1.3.1 [19] program estimated gene expression while taking into account the orientation of the reads about the library protocol. The "estimate-rspd" option was used to increase measurement accuracy. The default settings were used for all other parameters. Values for FPKM and TPM were generated to standardize depth across samples.

2.4.3. Gene Ontology (GO) Analysis

The GO database was used to analyze biological process (BP), cellular component (CC), and molecular function (MF). A GO-based trend test was performed for DEG functional characterization using the Wallenius non-central hypergeometric distribution and the R package GOseq [20]. Following the test, selected genes with a p-value of 0.05 or below were considered statistically significant.

2.4.4. Differentially Expressed Gene (DEG) Analysis

Using the TCC v.1.26.0 [21] R package, DEGs were found based on the projected read counts from the previous phase. The TCC package compares tag-count data using effective normalizing techniques. Normalization factors were computed using the iterative DESeq2 [22]/edgeR [23] technique. Using the p.adjust function of the R package with the default parameter values, the Q-value was determined based on the p-value. A q-value criterion of less than 0.05 was used to identify the DEGs and adjust for multiple testing mistakes.

2.5. STRING Network and Enrichment Pathway Analysis

The protein–protein interaction (PPI) for the top 30 genes among up-regulated and down-regulated DEGs was performed using an online tool Search Tool for the Retrieval of Interacting Genes/Proteins (STRING, version 9.1) (http://string-db.org (accessed on 8 February 2022)). The PPI score was set based on medium confidence (0.4). In the PPI network, each node depicts a protein, while the edges represent the strength of the relationship between proteins. Likewise, for the top 30 DEGs, all functionally enriched pathways of significantly expressed genes were determined using the Kyoto Encyclopedia of Genes and Genomes (KEGG), Reactome, and Wiki pathway databases. Additionally, annotated keywords were also identified.

2.6. Drug and Disease Association Analysis

Drug and disease association analyses were performed using WEB-based GEne SeT AnaLysis (WebGestalt), which is an online toolkit for functional genomic enrichment. The significance was set at FDR < 0.05, and the gene count was set at $\geq$5.

2.7. Molecular Docking Analysis

To perform molecular docking analysis, we retrieved the protein structure from PDB (https://www.rcsb.org/, accessed on 1 May 2021) using the search ID 5VPD (AP-1), and the compound structures (Dacarvazine and Kynurenic acid) were downloaded from PubChem (https://pubchem.ncbi.nlm.nih.gov/, accessed on 1 May 2021). Docking analysis was performed using pyMol and USCF chimera with the default parameters. The affinity of the binding is determined using estimated free energy binding and total intermolecular energy.

2.8. Analysis of Protein Expression by Western Blot

AGS cells were seeded into 60 mm plates at 4×10^5 cells per well and treated with the indicated concentrations of KYNA of (0, 150, 200, and 250) μM for 24 h. Cells were lysed using radioimmunoprecipitation assay (RIPA) buffer (iNtRON Biotechnology, Seoul, Republic of Korea) containing phosphatase and protease inhibitor cocktail (Thermo Scientific, Rockford, IL, USA). Protein concentrations were determined using a Pierce™ BCA assay (Thermo Fisher Scientific, Rockford, IL, USA). An equal quantity of protein (10 μg) from each sample was electrophoresed on (8–15%) SDS-polyacrylamide gels and transferred to a polyvinylidene difluoride (PVDF) membrane (ATTO Co., Ltd., Tokyo, Japan), and then the membrane was incubated with the primary antibodies followed by a conjugated secondary antibody to peroxidase. The obtained proteins were detected by an electrochemiluminescence (ECL) detection system (Bio-Rad Laboratory, Hercules, CA, USA), and analyzed using the Image Lab 4.1 (Bio-Rad) program. The densitometry readings of the protein bands were normalized by comparison with the expression of β-actin as control, using the ImageJ software program (U.S. National Institutes of Health, Bethesda, MD, USA). Antibodies of c-Fos (Cat. #2250S), c-Jun (Cat. #9165S), p-c-Fos (Cat. #5348S), and p-c-Jun (Cat. #9261S) were purchased from Cell Signaling Technology (Danvers, Ma, USA).

2.9. Statistical Analysis

All the experimental data were analyzed using GraphPad Prism version 8.0.2 (GraphPad Software). The results were expressed as the means ± standard deviation (SD). Results were evaluated using the Student's *t*-test, and a *p*-value < 0.05 was considered statistically significant.

3. Results

3.1. Identification of Genes and DEGs

It was confirmed in a previous study [24] that KYNA treatment induces tumor cell death in AGS cells. A total of 278 DEGs ($\log_2$ (Fold Change) > 1.0 and *p*-value < 0.05) were identified in the KYNA treatment group, of which 120 up-regulated genes and 158 down-regulated genes were identified (Table 1). Additionally, the R-Bioconductor volcanic pilot revealed DEGs among the total genes (Figure 1).

3.2. Functional and Enrichment Analysis

Gene ontology was used to identify a representative class of genes or proteins that were excessively changed by KYNA in AGS cells. Gene groups corresponding to molecular functions, biological processes, and cellular components were analyzed (Figure 2 and Table 2). As a result of molecular function, the structural constituent of the extracellular matrix was the most decreased, followed by a decrease in protein heterodimerization activity, showing a tendency to decrease in genes related to cell differentiation and growth. The biological process also showed a decrease in genes involved in DNA replication and nucleosome construction in cells with a similar trend. In the cellular component, genes related to extracellular regions and neuronal signaling were decreased. This suggests that KYNA suppressed the expression of genes involved in the growth and proliferation of AGS cells.

Table 1. Sequencing statistics data.

No	Name	Type	Reads	Bases	Bases (Gb)	GC	N	Q30
1	Control	Raw	41,131,670 (100%)	6,210,882,170 (100%)	6.21	3,103,637,588 (49.97%)	33,918 (0%)	5,558,401,799 (89.49%)
1	Control	Clean	39,692,472 (96.5%)	5,845,982,692 (94.12%)	5.85	2,891,132,459 (49.46%)	32,209 (0%)	5,314,657,230 (90.91%)
2	Test	Raw	43,673,272 (100%)	6,594,664,072 (100%)	6.59	3,299,521,366 (50.03%)	35,186 (0%)	6,041,568,334 (91.61%)
2	Test	Clean	42,815,932 (98.04%)	6,224,436,097 (94.39%)	6.22	3,100,915,971 (49.82%)	34,024 (0%)	5,764,074,214 (82.6%)

Reads: Number of reads (Reads/Raw reads × 100); Bases: Number of bases (Bases/Raw bases × 100); Bases (Gb): Number of bases (in Giga base unit); GC: Number of G and C bases (GC/Bases × 100); N: Number of N bases (N/Bases × 100); Q30: Number of over Q30 bases (Q30: 99.9% Base Call Accuracy) (Q30/Bases × 100); Q20: Number of over-Q20 bases (Q20: 99% Base Call Accuracy) (Q20/Bases × 100).

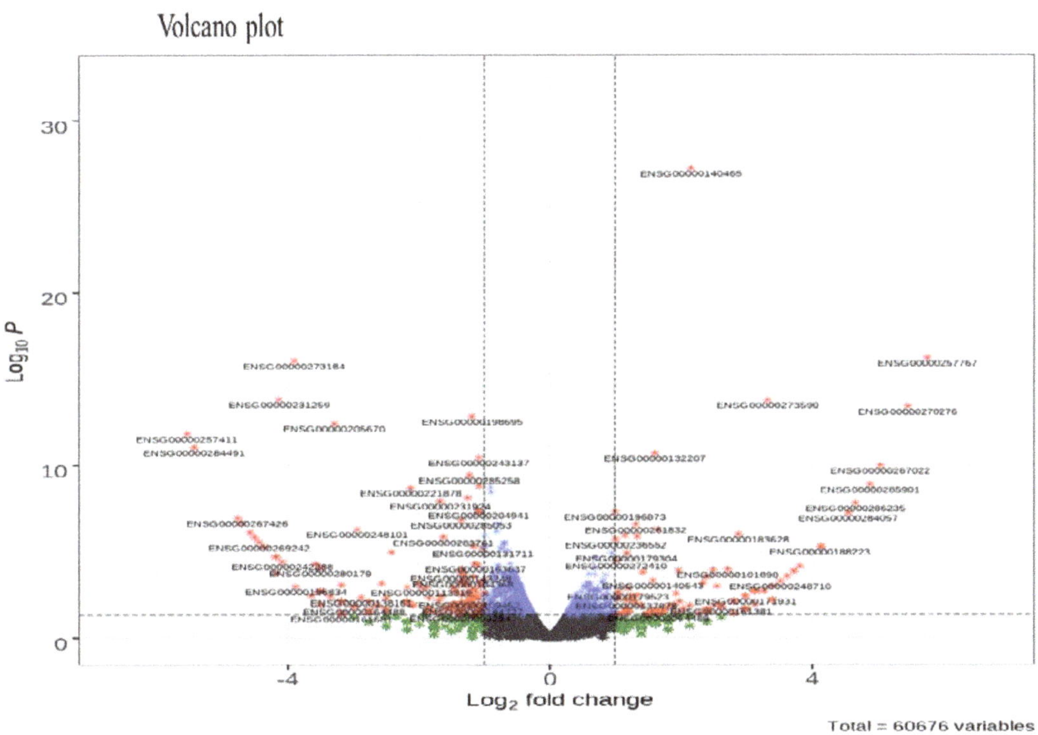

Figure 1. Volcano plot of differentially expressed genes (DEGs). A total of 60,676 variables were considered for the plot. The fold-change was plotted based on $\log_2$ FC and *p*-value.

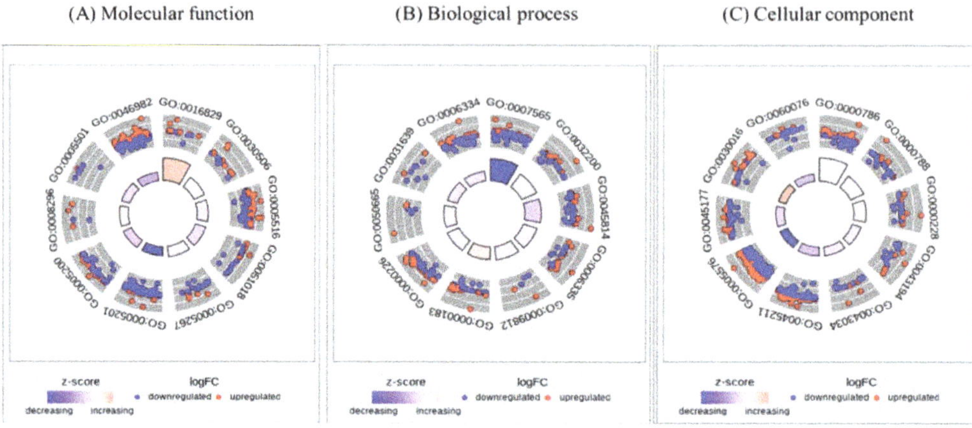

Figure 2. Circos plot representation of gene enrichment ontology analysis plotted in terms of molecular function, biological process, and cellular component from differentially regulated genes of KYNA against AGS cells. Blue: down-regulated, Red: up-regulated.

Table 2. List of enriched gene ontology in terms of molecular function, biological process, and cellular component.

	(A) Molecular Function	
Gene ID	**Term**	**z-score**
GO:0005201	extracellular matrix structural constituent	−5.422
GO:0046982	protein heterodimerization activity	−2.366
GO:0005200	structural constituent of cytoskeleton	−1.732
GO:0051018	protein kinase A binding	−1.342
GO:0005501	retinoid binding	−1.342
GO:0005516	calmodulin binding	−0.728
GO:0005267	potassium channel activity	−0.535
GO:0030506	ankyrin binding	0
GO:0008296	3′-5′-exodeoxyribonuclease activity	0.447
GO:0016829	lyase activity	1.732
	(B) Biological Process	
Gene ID	**Term**	**z-score**
GO:0007565	female pregnancy	−3.457
GO:0045814	negative regulation of gene expression, epigenetic	−1.043
GO:0031639	plasminogen activation	−0.707
GO:0006334	nucleosome assembly	−0.688
GO:0009812	flavonoid metabolic process	−0.447
GO:0006335	DNA replication-dependent nucleosome assembly	−0.408
GO:0050665	hydrogen peroxide biosynthetic process	−0.378
GO:0000226	microtubule cytoskeleton organization	−0.305
GO:0032200	telomere organization	−0.229
GO:0000183	chromatin silencing at rDNA	0.557
	(C) Cellular Component	
Gene ID	**Term**	**z-score**
GO:0005576	extracellular region	−4.899
GO:0045211	postsynaptic membrane	−1.841
GO:0060076	excitatory synapse	−1.807
GO:0045177	apical part of cell	−1.457
GO:0043034	costamere	−1.0
GO:0043194	axon initial segment	−0.775
GO:0000788	nuclear nucleosome	−0.408
GO:0000786	nucleosome	−0.119
GO:0000228	nuclear chromosome	0.0
GO:0030016	myofibril	1.789

The top 10 genes with high significance are listed with their function and z-score of the respective term.

3.3. Protein–Protein Interaction (PPI) and Enrichment Pathway of DEGs

Protein–protein interaction (PPI) network analysis was constructed using the STRING database for the top 30 differentially expressed genes (DEGs) up and down (Figure 3), and the related enrichment pathways were analyzed (Table 3). The results of the PPI STRING analysis of up-regulated genes were divided into two groups, and down-regulated genes were divided into three groups. Up-regulated DEGs were involved in various apoptoses such as in the PI3K-AKT signaling pathway and the Ras signaling pathway in the KEGG pathway analysis, and DNA damage-related results were also obtained in the Wiki pathway. In the Reactome pathway, pathways related to cell signal transduction were identified, and in the annotated keywords, results related to DNA damage, repair, and recombination were also confirmed. This suggests that KYNA induces apoptosis of AGS cells through the up-regulation of up-regulated genes. KEGG, wiki, and Reactome pathways in down-regulated genes confirmed the results of metabolic processes and DNA replication related to cell proliferation. This suggests that KYNA down-regulated genes are involved in AGS cell metabolism and DNA replication.

Table 3. KEGG, Wiki, and Reactome pathways and annotated keyword classification and functional enrichment for the up-regulation and down-regulation DEGs.

	Up-regulation DEGs		
KEGG Pathways	**Description**	**Strength**	**FDR**
hsa04014	Ras signaling pathway	1.27	0.0000138
hsa04151	PI3K-AKT signaling pathway	1.15	0.00000999
hsa04218	Cellular senescence	1.15	0.0194
hsa05202	Transcriptional misregulation in cancer	1.09	0.0268
hsa04727	GABAergic synapse	1.75	0.00000000998
hsa04926	Relaxin signaling pathway	1.58	0.0000000247
hsa04728	Dopaminergic synapse	1.58	0.0000000247
hsa04371	Apelin signaling pathway	1.57	0.0000000247
hsa04062	Chemokine signaling pathway	1.42	0.000000192
Wiki pathways	**Description**	**Strength**	**FDR**
WP1545	miRNAs involved in DNA damage response	1.97	0.0149
WP2516	ATM signaling pathway	1.73	0.002
WP4016	DNA IR-damage and cellular response via ATR	1.66	0.0000131
WP3959	DNA IR-double-strand breaks and cellular response via ATM	1.59	0.0045
WP4172	PI3K-AKT signaling pathway	1.16	0.0000347
WP3932	Focal adhesion: PI3K-AKT-mTOR signaling pathway	1.14	0.0003
Reactome pathways	**Description**	**Strength**	**FDR**
HAS-392851	Prostacyclin signaling through prostacyclin receptor	2.34	0.000000000201
HAS-8964616	G beta: gamma signaling through CDC42	2.32	0.000000000227
HAS-418217	G beta: gamma signaling through PLC beta	2.32	0.000000000227
HAS-202040	G-protein activation	2.24	0.0000000000383
HAS-392451	G beta: gamma signaling through PI3Kgamma	2.22	0.000000000441
HAS-6803204	TP53 regulates transcription of genes involved in cytochrome C release	1.87	0.0096
HSA-69473	G2/M DNA damage checkpoint	1.55	0.00018
HSA-2559580	Oxidative stress-induced senescence	1.35	0.0082
HSA-73894	DNA repair	1.31	0.0000000205
HSA-69620	Cell-cycle checkpoints	1.11	0.0012
Annotated keywords	**Description**	**Strength**	**FDR**
KW-0233	DNA recombination	1.45	0.0316
KW-0255	Endonuclease	1.43	0.0316
KW-0013	ADP-ribosylation	1.32	0.0406
KW-0234	DNA repair	1.24	0.00000466
KW-0227	DNA damage	1.22	0.00000156

Table 3. *Cont.*

Down-regulation DEGs			
KEGG pathways	**Description**	**Strength**	**FDR**
hsa00630	Glyoxylate and dicarboxylate metabolism	2.06	0.00043
hsa03030	DNA replication	1.98	0.00043
hsa00260	Glycine, serine, and threonine metabolism	1.96	0.00043
hsa04610	Complement and coagulation cascades	1.85	0.00000307
hsa4724	Glutamatergic synapse	1.62	0.00043
hsa01200	Carbon metabolism	1.47	0.008
Wiki pathways	**Description**	**Strength**	**FDR**
WP4705	Pathways of nucleic acid metabolism and innate immune sensing	2.33	0.00018
WP4875	Disruption of postsynaptic signaling by CNV	2.03	0.00079
Reactome pathways	**Description**	**Strength**	**FDR**
HAS-140837	Intrinsic pathway of fibrin clot formation	2.06	0.02940
HAS-442982	Ras activation upon Ca^{2+} influx through NMDA receptor	1.57	0.0011
HAS-8957275	Post-translational protein phosphorylation	1.51	0.024
Annotated keywords	**Description**	**Strength**	**FDR**
KW-0225	Disease mutation	0.56	0.0102

FDR: False-discovery rate.

3.4. Expression Comparison of AP-1 Factors and Molecular Docking with KYNA

The expression of AP-1 factors related to tumor growth and proliferation was confirmed (Table 4). Fos, Jun, JDP (Jun dimerization protein), and ATF (Activating transcription factor) constituting AP-1 were decreased upon KYNA treatment, suggesting that KYNA inhibits the growth and proliferation of AGS cells. Additionally, ligand–protein docking analysis was performed through UCSF Chimera software. Both ligands AP-1 and KYNA were found to occupy the active site, as illustrated in Figure 4. In addition, many active sites have been shown to aid ligand binding. Active sites involved in the binding of AP-1 to KYNA were identified as ALA281, ALA168, ALA169, ALA185, GLU192, ASN165, LYS166, GLN189, GLU191, CYS285, LYS284, ARG288, ARG164, and ASP188 (Table 5). The molecular binding energy score was found to be −6.3 kcal/mol.

Table 4. Expression comparison of AP-1 factors.

Gene ID	Symbol	RPKM	
		C	T
ENSG00000075426	FOS L2	14.98	13.7
ENSG00000125740	FOS B	0.6	0.34
ENSG00000130522	JUN D	53.29	48.77
ENSG00000170345	FOS	5.06	4.84
ENSG00000171223	JUN B	21.87	19.96
ENSG00000175592	FOS L1	24.33	22.91
ENSG00000177606	JUN	51.06	48.78
ENSG00000140044	JDP 2	2.41	2.17
ENSG00000115966	ATF 2	11.32	10.56
ENSG00000170653	ATF 7	9.38	8.82

RPKM: reads per kilobase of per million mapped reads. C: without KYNA, T: with KYNA 250 μM.

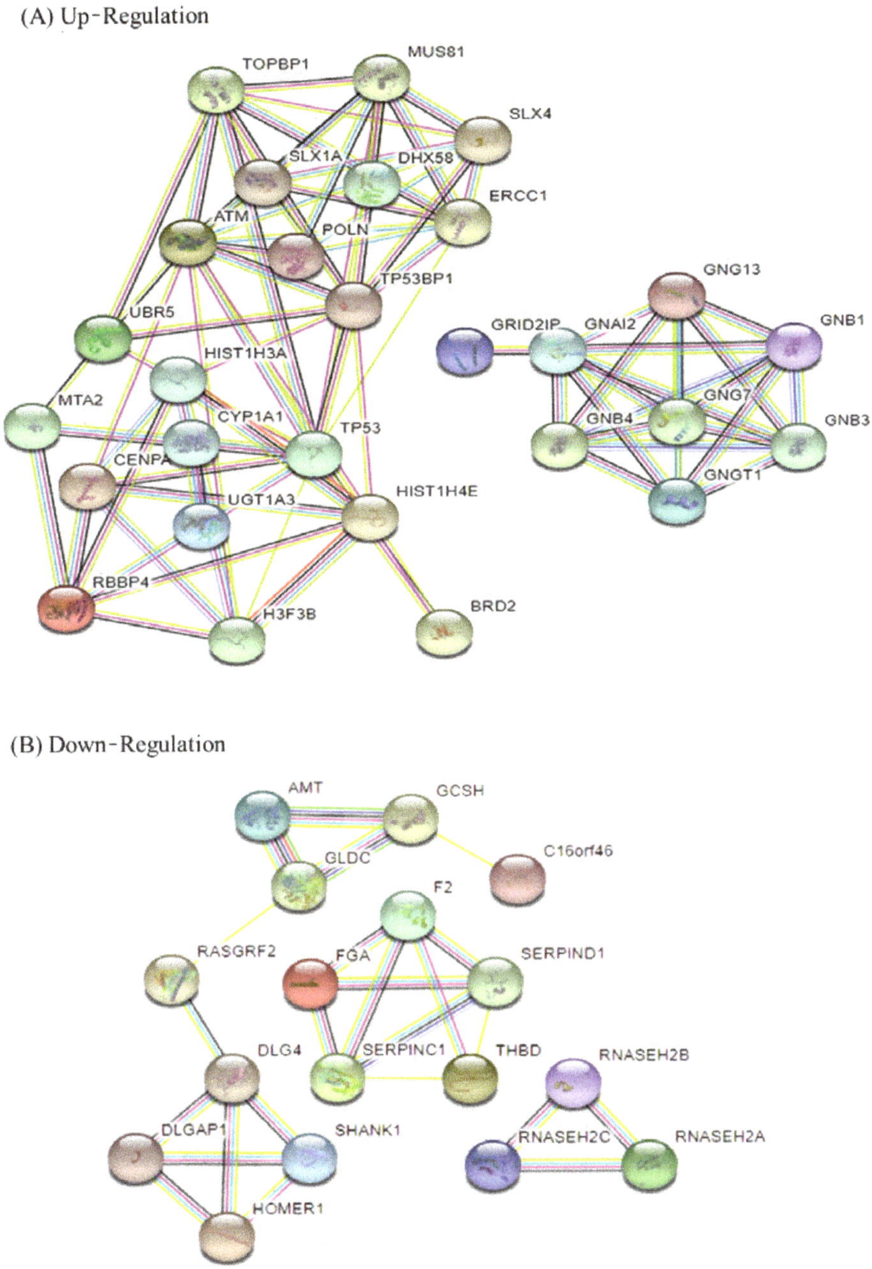

Figure 3. Protein—protein interaction (PPI) analysis of up-regulation and down-regulation DEGs analyzed by STRING software. The network nodes represent genes (showing the interactions), and the round nodes denote individual genes. The line color indicates the type of interaction evidence.

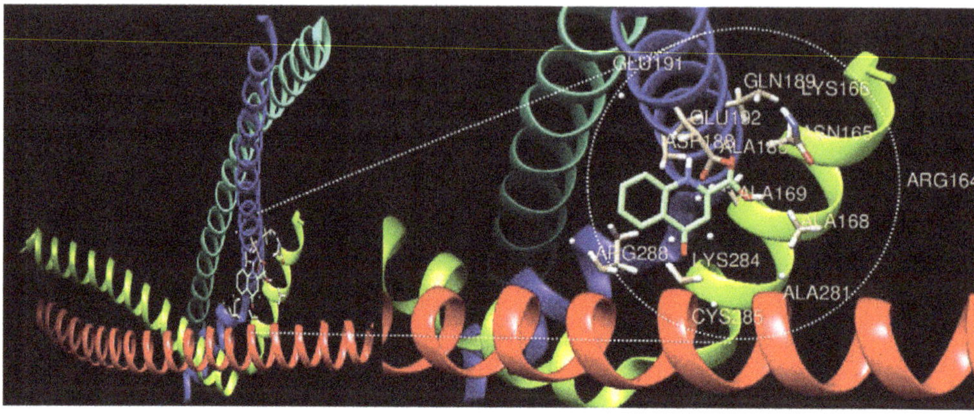

Figure 4. Molecular docking analysis of the AP-1 complex (c-Jun and c-Fos) and Kynurenic acid. The 3D structure of AP-1 factors is bound efficiently with Kynurenic acid.

Table 5. Molecular docking studies of Kynurenic acid with the AP-1 complex and their binding energy.

Compound-Protein	Interacting Amino Acid Residues	Final Intermolecular Energy
Kynurenic acid	ALA281, ALA168, ALA169, ALA185, GLU192, ASN165, LYS166, GLN189, GLU191, CYS285, LYS284, ARG288, ARG164, ASP188	−6.3 kcal/mol

The table shows the list of interacting amino acids and their binding energy.

3.5. Validation of AP-1 Factor Expression Using Western Blot Analysis

Western blot analysis of AGS cells during KYNA treatment confirmed the expression of c-Fos and c-Jun, which are AP-1 factors (Figure 5). It was confirmed that the expression of p-c-Fos and p-c-Jun proteins decreased by inhibiting phosphorylation of c-Fos and c-Jun proteins during KYNA treatment. This result was consistent with the decreased expression of AP-1 factors obtained through transcriptome analysis, further proving the role of KYNA in regulating the expression of important factors in AGS cells.

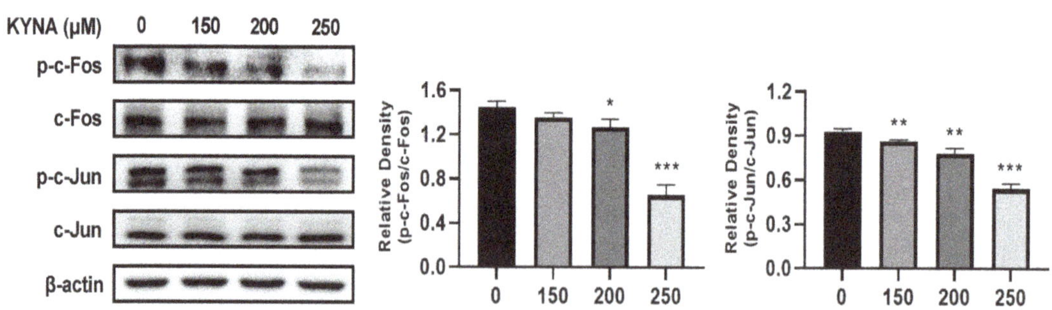

Figure 5. Western blot validation of crucial targets of KYNA against AGS cells. Protein expression of crucial proteins c-Fos and c-Jun on KYNA-treated AGS cells for 24 hr. The results obtained from three independent experiments are expressed as mean ± standard deviation (SD) compared with the control group. * $p < 0.05$, ** $p < 0.01$, *** $p < 0.001$.

3.6. Therapeutic Drug and Disease Association and Molecular Docking Analysis

Through drug and disease association analysis, the top 10 drugs significantly related to differentially regulated genes were selected (Table 6). Among the selected drugs, Dacarbazine was approved by the FDA (Abbreviated New Drug Application (ANDA) number; 075371, Fresenius, Kabi, Illinois, IL, USA), and it was confirmed that it was used as an anticancer drug. Drug and protein molecular docking were performed to confirm the molecular binding of Dacarbazine to AP-1 (Figure 6). In ligand–protein docking using UCSF Chimera software, it was found that a binding site was shared between the two factors, as illustrated in the figure. In addition, various active sites have been shown to aid in ligand uptake. Mutual binding amino residues were found to be GLU191, GLU193, GLU192, ASP188, GLN189, ALA185, ARG288, LYS166, ASN165, ALA169, LYS284, CYS285, CYS172, ALA168, and ALA281 (Table 7), with a molecular binding score of −5.2 kcal/mol demonstrating the molecular binding energy of autodock.

Table 6. Results of drug and disease association analysis.

Gene Set	Description	Size	Expect	Ratio	*p*-Value
DB04953	Ezogabine	10	0.017071	117.16	0.00010437
DB01095	Fluvastatin	18	0.030727	65.089	0.0035292
DB00586	Diclofenac	28	0.047798	41.843	0.00086596
DB00197	Troglitazone	30	0.051212	39.053	0.00099517
DB00633	Dexmedetomidine	5	0.0085353	117.16	0.0085120
DB00740	Riluzole	5	0.0085353	117.16	0.0085120
DB00851	**Dacarbazine**	**5**	**0.0085353**	**117.16**	**0.0085120**
DB00889	Granisetron	5	0.0085353	117.16	0.0085120
DB04905	Tesmilifene	5	0.0085353	117.16	0.0085120
DB06089	ICA-105665	5	0.0085353	117.16	0.0085120

A list of enriched drugs concerning differentially expressed gene sets is depicted. The top 10 drugs were chosen based on their significance rate.

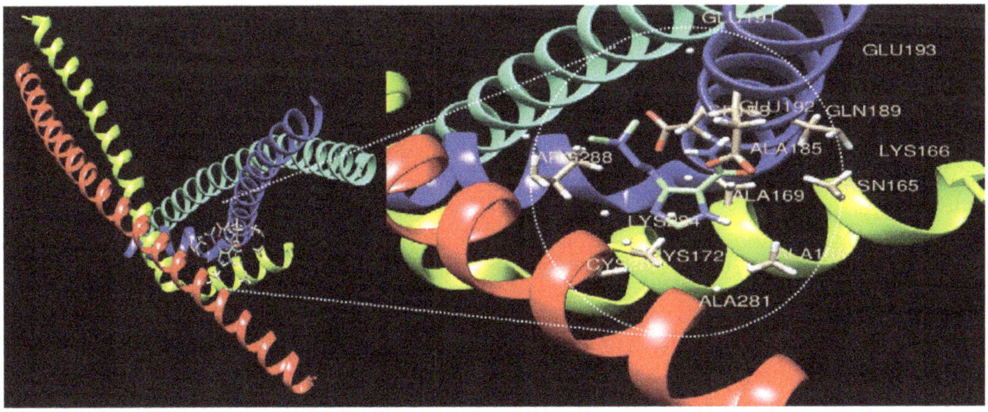

Figure 6. Molecular docking analysis of the AP-1 complex (c-Jun and c-Fos) and Dacarbazine. The 3D structure of AP-1 factors is bound efficiently with the drug Dacarbazine.

Table 7. Molecular docking studies of Dacarbazine with the AP-1 complex and their binding energy.

Compound-Protein	Interacting Amino Acid Residues	Final Intermolecular Energy
Dacarbazine	GLU191, GLU193, GLU192, ASP188, GLN189, ALA185, ARG288, LYS166, ASN165, ALA169, LYS284, CYS285, CYS172, ALA168, ALA281	−5.2 kcal/mol

The table shows the list of interacting amino acids and their binding energy.

4. Discussion

Understanding disease-causing factors provides a roadmap for the development of new therapeutic drugs [25]. RNA sequencing technology is used for disease diagnosis and therapeutic applications by identifying the targets of various diseases, including cancer [26]. Complex relationships can be understood through network analysis, usually using bioinformatics and pharmacology to help elucidate mechanisms between drugs and their targets [27]. Through this, targeted drug treatment by identifying tumor-specific expressed genes can provide patients with a variety of treatment options.

The effect of KYNA on the genetic change in AGS cells was analyzed using RNA seq. A total of 60,676 genes were identified, and gene ontology changes (Figure 2) and differentially expressed genes (DEGs) were confirmed between the KYNA-treated group and the KYNA-untreated group (Figure 1). Genes related to cell differentiation and growth decreased in molecular function, genes related to DNA replication and nucleosome construction decreased in biological process, and genes related to synaptic signal transduction decreased in cellular components (Table 2). Through GO analysis, it was confirmed that KYNA had a negative effect on tumor cells.

The association of 30 differentially expressed genes (DEGs) was confirmed through protein–protein interaction (PPI) network analysis. The up-regulated genes showed interaction in a total of two groups, and the down-regulated genes consisted of a total of three groups (Figure 3). Up-regulated interacting genes affected various signaling pathways, including the PI3K-AKT signaling pathway in the KEGG pathway. In the Wiki pathway, signaling pathways related to the ATM signaling pathway and DNA damage were also shown, and in the Reactome pathway, results such as cell-cycle checkpoint and DNA repair were shown. Down-regulated genes obtained results related to cell proliferation, metabolism, and DNA replication in the KEGG, wiki, and Reactome pathways (Table 3). These results suggest that KYNA induces apoptosis of AGS.

AP-1 [28], which affects various regulatory processes including tumor growth, proliferation, migration, cell cycle, and apoptosis, has members Jun, Fos, and ATF [29]. In particular, Fos and Jun are involved in DNA synthesis and G0-G1 during the cell cycle and are known to generate CD8 T-lymphocytes of T-cells [30]. In addition, c-Fos expression in gastric cancer cells is associated with lymph node metastasis, invasion, and short survival, and has been reported to have a poor prognosis [31]. In this study, as a result of analyzing the expression level of AP-1 members, it was confirmed that Fos, Jun, ATF, and JDP were decreased upon KYNA treatment (Table 4). Additionally, as a result of confirming the binding affinity of KYNA and the AP-1 complex (Jun and Fos) through molecular docking analysis, a binding force of −6.3 kcal/mol was confirmed (Figure 4 and Table 5). In addition, as a result of analyzing the protein expression of Jun and Fos through Western blot analysis, it was confirmed that AP-1 factors decreased in a concentration-dependent manner when KYNA was treated (Figure 5). This suggests that KYNA treatment in AGS cells suppresses the expression of AP-1 factors, thereby inhibiting tumor growth and proliferation. The top 10 drugs related to DEGs were obtained through drug and disease association analysis (Table 6). Among them, Dacarbazine was approved by the FDA and confirmed to be used as an anticancer agent [32]. As a result of confirming the binding affinity between Dacarbazine and the AP-1 complex (Jun and Fos) through molecular docking analysis, a binding force of −5.2 kcal/mol was shown (Figure 6 and Table 7). AP-1, which induces tumor growth and proliferation, showed a somewhat higher binding force with KYNA than Dacarbazine, which is currently used as a drug. This suggests that KYNA induces inhibition of AP-1.

KYNA is a physiologically active ingredient found in various herbs [33] which induces apoptosis through cell-cycle regulation and signaling pathways in colorectal and renal cancer cells [17]. It has also been reported to inhibit cell proliferation and growth through the PI3K/AKT and MAPK signaling pathways in adenocarcinoma [16]. It has been demonstrated that KYNA has a direct effect on the gastric wall to prevent gastric ulcers [34]. In a previous study, KYNA was confirmed to induce apoptosis in gastric cancer-derived AGS cells [24]. In this study, it was confirmed that KYNA inhibits the growth and proliferation of cancer cells through the identification of biomarkers. These results suggest that KYNA can have an anti-tumor effect in gastric cancer, and it is judged that it can be used as basic data for the development of gastric cancer therapeutics.

5. Conclusions

Transcriptome analysis results provide potential insights into tumor therapeutics in KYNA-treated AGS cells. In this study, it was found that KYNA induces the expression of genes that responds to apoptosis and, in particular, up-regulates the expression of AP-1 factors. In addition, the results of this study show the effect of KYNA on the gene expression of AGS cells, and provide a novel research method that can be used to confirm the effects of other drugs on other cancer cells. Results suggest that KYNA can be considered for the development of treatment for gastric cancer.

Author Contributions: Conceptualization, H.H.K.; Methodology, H.H.K. and S.E.H.; Software, H.H.K. and M.Y.P.; Validation, S.H.J.; Formal analysis, H.H.K. and S.H.J.; Investigation, P.B.B.; Resources, A.A.; Data curation, C.K.W.; Writing-original draft preparation, H.H.K.; Writing-review and editing, H.H.K.; Visualization, J.D.H. and M.A.; Supervision, G.S.K.; Project administration, J.K.S., H.W.K. and G.S.K.; Funding acquisition, G.S.K. All authors have read and agreed to the published version of the manuscript.

Funding: This study was supported by the National Research Foundation of Korea funded by the Ministry of Science and ICT (grant no. 2020R1A2B5B01001807 and 2022R1A6A3A01086899).

Institutional Review Board Statement: Not applicable.

Informed Consent Statement: Not applicable.

Data Availability Statement: The data used to support the findings of this study are available upon request from the corresponding author.

Conflicts of Interest: The authors declare no conflict of interest.

References

1. Sung, H.; Ferlay, J.; Siegel, R.L.; Laversanne, M.; Soerjomataram, I.; Jemal, A.; Bray, F. Global Cancer Statistics 2020: GLOBOCAN Estimates of Incidence and Mortality Worldwide for 36 Cancers in 185 Countries. *CA Cancer J. Clin.* **2021**, *71*, 209–249. [CrossRef] [PubMed]
2. Smyth, E.C.; Nilsson, M.; Grabsch, H.I.; van Grieken, N.C.; Lordick, F. Gastric cancer. *Lancet* **2020**, *396*, 635–648. [CrossRef] [PubMed]
3. Casaretto, L.; Sousa, P.L.; Mari, J.J. Chemotherapy versus support cancer treatment in advanced gastric cancer: A meta-analysis. *Braz. J. Med. Biol. Res.* **2006**, *39*, 431–440. [CrossRef] [PubMed]
4. Sastre, J.; Garcia-Saenz, J.A.; Diaz-Rubio, E. Chemotherapy for gastric cancer. *World J. Gastroenterol.* **2006**, *12*, 204–213. [CrossRef] [PubMed]
5. Baretton, G.B.; Aust, D.E. Current biomarkers for gastric cancer. *Pathologe* **2017**, *38*, 93–97. [CrossRef]
6. Ang, T.L.; Fock, K.M. Clinical epidemiology of gastric cancer. *Singap. Med. J.* **2014**, *55*, 621–628. [CrossRef]
7. Housman, G.; Byler, S.; Heerboth, S.; Lapinska, K.; Longacre, M.; Snyder, N.; Sarkar, S. Drug resistance in cancer: An overview. *Cancers* **2014**, *6*, 1769–1792. [CrossRef]
8. Bayat Mokhtari, R.; Homayouni, T.S.; Baluch, N.; Morgatskaya, E.; Kumar, S.; Das, B.; Yeger, H. Combination therapy in combating cancer. *Oncotarget* **2017**, *8*, 38022–38043. [CrossRef]
9. Sia, D.; Villanueva, A.; Friedman, S.L.; Llovet, J.M. Liver Cancer Cell of Origin, Molecular Class, and Effects on Patient Prognosis. *Gastroenterology* **2017**, *152*, 745–761. [CrossRef]
10. Zhang, J.; Liu, X.; Zhou, W.; Cheng, G.; Wu, J.; Guo, S.; Jia, S.; Liu, Y.; Li, B.; Zhang, X.; et al. A bioinformatics investigation into molecular mechanism of Yinzhihuang granules for treating hepatitis B by network pharmacology and molecular docking verification. *Sci. Rep.* **2020**, *10*, 11448. [CrossRef]
11. Wang, D.; Zhao, L.; Wang, D.; Liu, J.; Yu, X.; Wei, Y.; Ouyang, Z. Transcriptome analysis and identification of key genes involved in 1-deoxynojirimycin biosynthesis of mulberry (*Morus alba* L.). *PeerJ* **2018**, *6*, e5443. [CrossRef] [PubMed]
12. Ye, N.; Ding, Y.; Wild, C.; Shen, Q.; Zhou, J. Small molecule inhibitors targeting activator protein 1 (AP-1). *J. Med. Chem.* **2014**, *57*, 6930–6948. [CrossRef] [PubMed]
13. Wagner, E.F.; Eferl, R. Fos/AP-1 proteins in bone and the immune system. *Immunol. Rev.* **2005**, *208*, 126–140. [CrossRef] [PubMed]

14. Mar, A.C.; Chu, C.H.; Lee, H.J.; Chien, C.W.; Cheng, J.J.; Yang, S.H.; Jiang, J.K.; Lee, T.C. Interleukin-1 Receptor Type 2 Acts with c-Fos to Enhance the Expression of Interleukin-6 and Vascular Endothelial Growth Factor A in Colon Cancer Cells and Induce Angiogenesis. *J. Biol. Chem.* **2015**, *290*, 22212–22224. [CrossRef]
15. Verde, P.; Casalino, L.; Talotta, F.; Yaniv, M.; Weitzman, J.B. Deciphering AP-1 function in tumorigenesis: Fra-ternizing on target promoters. *Cell Cycle* **2007**, *6*, 2633–2639. [CrossRef]
16. Walczak, K.; Turski, W.A.; Rajtar, G. Kynurenic acid inhibits colon cancer proliferation in vitro: Effects on signaling pathways. *Amino Acids* **2014**, *46*, 2393–2401. [CrossRef]
17. Walczak, K.; Zurawska, M.; Kis, J.; Starownik, R.; Zgrajka, W.; Bar, K.; Turski, W.A.; Rzeski, W. Kynurenic acid in human renal cell carcinoma: Its antiproliferative and antimigrative action on Caki-2 cells. *Amino Acids* **2012**, *43*, 1663–1670. [CrossRef]
18. Dobin, A.; Davis, C.A.; Schlesinger, F.; Drenkow, J.; Zaleski, C.; Jha, S.; Batut, P.; Chaisson, M.; Gingeras, T.R. STAR: Ultrafast universal RNA-seq aligner. *Bioinformatics* **2013**, *29*, 15–21. [CrossRef]
19. Li, B.; Dewey, C.N. RSEM: Accurate transcript quantification from RNA-Seq data with or without a reference genome. *BMC Bioinform.* **2011**, *12*, 323. [CrossRef]
20. Young, M.D.; Wakefield, M.J.; Smyth, G.K.; Oshlack, A. Gene ontology analysis for RNA-seq: Accounting for selection bias. *Genome Biol.* **2010**, *11*, R14. [CrossRef]
21. Sun, J.; Nishiyama, T.; Shimizu, K.; Kadota, K. TCC: An R package for comparing tag count data with robust normalization strategies. *BMC Bioinform.* **2013**, *14*, 219. [CrossRef] [PubMed]
22. Love, M.I.; Huber, W.; Anders, S. Moderated estimation of fold change and dispersion for RNA-seq data with DESeq2. *Genome Biol.* **2014**, *15*, 550. [CrossRef] [PubMed]
23. Robinson, M.D.; McCarthy, D.J.; Smyth, G.K. edgeR: A Bioconductor package for differential expression analysis of digital gene expression data. *Bioinformatics* **2010**, *26*, 139–140. [CrossRef]
24. Kim, H.H.; Jeong, S.H.; Ha, S.E.; Park, M.Y.; Bhosale, P.B.; Abusaliya, A.; Won, C.K.; Heo, J.D.; Kim, H.W.; Kim, G.S. Cellular Regulation of Kynurenic Acid-Induced Cell Apoptosis Pathways in AGS Cells. *Int. J. Mol. Sci.* **2022**, *23*, 8894. [CrossRef]
25. Ren, H.; Zhu, J.; Yu, H.; Bazhin, A.V.; Westphalen, C.B.; Renz, B.W.; Jacob, S.N.; Lampert, C.; Werner, J.; Angele, M.K.; et al. Angiogenesis-Related Gene Expression Signatures Predicting Prognosis in Gastric Cancer Patients. *Cancers* **2020**, *12*, 3685. [CrossRef]
26. Byron, S.A.; Van Keuren-Jensen, K.R.; Engelthaler, D.M.; Carpten, J.D.; Craig, D.W. Translating RNA sequencing into clinical diagnostics: Opportunities and challenges. *Nat. Rev. Genet.* **2016**, *17*, 257–271. [CrossRef]
27. Sakle, N.S.; More, S.A.; Mokale, S.N. A network pharmacology-based approach to explore potential targets of Caesalpinia pulcherima: An updated prototype in drug discovery. *Sci. Rep.* **2020**, *10*, 17217. [CrossRef]
28. Vesely, P.W.; Staber, P.B.; Hoefler, G.; Kenner, L. Translational regulation mechanisms of AP-1 proteins. *Mutat. Res.* **2009**, *682*, 7–12. [CrossRef]
29. Zarubin, T.; Han, J. Activation and signaling of the p38 MAP kinase pathway. *Cell Res.* **2005**, *15*, 11–18. [CrossRef]
30. Grausz, J.D.; Fradelizi, D.; Dautry, F.; Monier, R.; Lehn, P. Modulation of c-fos and c-myc mRNA levels in normal human lymphocytes by calcium ionophore A23187 and phorbol ester. *Eur. J. Immunol.* **1986**, *16*, 1217–1221. [CrossRef]
31. Jin, S.P.; Kim, J.H.; Kim, M.A.; Yang, H.K.; Lee, H.E.; Lee, H.S.; Kim, W.H. Prognostic significance of loss of c-fos protein in gastric carcinoma. *Pathol. Oncol. Res.* **2007**, *13*, 284–289. [CrossRef] [PubMed]
32. World Health Organization. World Health Organization Model List of Essential Medicines: 21st List 2019. 2019. Available online: https://apps.who.int/iris/handle/10665/325771 (accessed on 8 February 2022).
33. Turski, M.P.; Turska, M.; Zgrajka, W.; Bartnik, M.; Kocki, T.; Turski, W.A. Distribution, synthesis, and absorption of kynurenic acid in plants. *Planta Med.* **2011**, *77*, 858–864. [CrossRef] [PubMed]
34. Glavin, G.B.; Pinsky, C. Kynurenic acid attenuates experimental ulcer formation and basal gastric acid secretion in rats. *Res. Commun. Chem. Pathol. Pharmacol.* **1989**, *64*, 111–119. [PubMed]

separations

MDPI

Article

Efficient Production of Antioxidants from Rape Pollen via a Chromatographic Strategy

Liugen Jin [1], Haiqing Liu [2], Xueliang Liu [2], Ke Gu [3], Minchen Wu [4,*] and Jianfeng Huang [3,*]

1 Department of Gastrointestinal Surgery, Affiliated Hospital of Jiangnan University, Wuxi 214122, China
2 Qinghai Center for Drug Evaluation and Inspection, Xining 810007, China
3 Department of Radiation Oncology, Affiliated Hospital of Jiangnan University, Wuxi 214122, China
4 Wuxi School of Medicine, Jiangnan University, Wuxi 214000, China
* Correspondence: biowmc@126.com (M.W.); 9862019007@jiangnan.edu.cn (J.H.)

Abstract: Rape pollen has always been considered as a research hotspot in health foods and pharmaceuticals due to its abundance of natural active ingredients. In this work, a compound with antioxidant activity was directly isolated from the methanol extract of rape pollen using a two-step procedure, under the supervision of online HPLC−1,1-diphenyl-2-picrylhydrazyl (HPLC-DPPH) detection. Firstly, online HPLC−DPPH detection was used to identify the active peaks in the methanol extract of rape pollen, and then the methanol extract was pretreated via medium-pressure liquid chromatography (MPLC) to obtain the target fraction 3 (Fr3). Fr3 was further purified using HPLC to finally obtain the target fraction 3-1, which was identified as kaempferol 3,4′-di-O-β-D-glucopyranoside through NMR and mass spectrometry. To further explore the free radical scavenging activity of this compound, its DPPH scavenging ability was determined, and two proteins related to the antioxidant pathway were used for molecular docking. The results revealed that the chromatographic strategy used in this study was efficient and reliable in separating high−purity antioxidants from rape pollen. A strategy such as this, meanwhile, also holds promise for qualitatively identifying and specifically isolating active compounds from other natural products.

Keywords: rape pollen; online HPLC−1,1-diphenyl-2-picrylhydrazyl detection; medium pressure liquid chromatography; antioxidants

1. Introduction

Rape (*Brassica rapa* var. oleifera), a species of the *Brassica* genus Gruciferous, is the largest cultivated and most widely distributed nectar crop in China, as well as one of the major oil crops [1–3]. Its by-product, rape pollen, is recognized as a natural health food. Rape pollen contains a large number of proteins, vitamins, lipids, and active small molecule compounds, which have various effects, such as anti-atherogenic, antioxidant, inhibiting prostate enlargement, and promoting the function of the nervous system [4–7]. Modern phytochemical technology analysis shows that rape pollen is rich in polyphenols and flavonoids and has a significant antioxidant capacity, making it an ideal research target for health foods and pharmaceuticals [8,9]. However, few studies have been reported on the antioxidant active components of rape pollen. In order to further promote the development of deep processing of rapeseed pollen and related industries, a suitable chromatographic purification method for exploring the chemical composition of rapeseed pollen is particularly essential [10–12].

The health industry has been growing quickly in recent years based on a variety of human health demands, and concepts such as "health care", "oxidative stress", and "antioxidant" have received more attention [13]. Studies have shown that aging, cancer, and cardiovascular and neurodegenerative diseases of the human body are all related to oxidative stress [14–17]. The condition known as oxidative stress occurs when the body's oxidation and antioxidant systems are out of balance, which is a negative effect of excessive levels of free radicals in the body [18–20]. Endogenous free radical inhibitors are often insufficient to cope with this state, and the intervention of exogenous free radical inhibitors is very important at this time [21]. Natural products with large resources and many active ingredients are an important source for obtaining exogenous free radical inhibitors [22]. Currently, there are various ways for identifying antioxidants from natural products, among which online HPLC−DPPH detection has gained popularity among researchers due to its stability, online access, and high efficiency [23–25].

Not surprisingly, some non-target components (pigments, macromolecular polymers, etc.) will be co-eluted with active ingredients when extracting chemical constituents from natural products. If the crude extract is directly prepared via HPLC, the preparative column will be irreparably damaged, thereby shortening the service life of the preparative column and reducing the column efficiency [26]. Therefore, a suitable pretreatment approach is needed to remove these non-target components prior to HPLC preparation. MPLC is now able to perform such a function. MPLC is formed by connecting a medium-pressure column with liquid chromatography. By setting different elution conditions and column packing, the objectives of online separation, automatic operation, and high-throughput processing can be achieved. With a low column pressure, large particle size of packing (>20 μm), and adjustable column length, MPLC is ideal for the pretreatment of natural products [27,28]. At the same time, suitable MPLC pretreatment techniques also have the potential to form a two-dimensional liquid chromatography system with subsequent HPLC preparation, which facilitates the acquisition of high-purity compounds.

Considering the multiple reports listed previously, a rapid chromatographic strategy for the preparation of antioxidants from rape pollen was developed in this paper. An online HPLC−DPPH detection was used for the qualitative identification of antioxidants, MPLC was used for sample pretreatment, and HPLC was utilized to obtain free radical inhibitors directly from the target fraction. In addition, a DPPH scavenging assay and molecular docking were used to further explore the antioxidant ability of the isolated high-purity compound. The results showed that this combined chromatographic strategy is reliable and efficient, and the isolated free radical inhibitor was beneficial for future research on deep processing and high value-added products of rape pollen. It is also worth mentioning that the chromatographic strategy established in this paper is expected to make achievements in the future development of food and pharmaceutical products.

2. Materials and Methods

2.1. Instrumentation and Reagents

NMR spectra were obtained on a Bruker Avance 600 MHz (Bruker, Karlsruhe, Germany), and ESI-MS spectra were collected from a Waters QDa ESI mass spectrometer (Waters, Milford, MA, USA). The online HPLC-DPPH detection was performed using LC-10AD (Shimadzu, Kyoto, Japan) and LC-16 (Shimadzu, Shanghai, China) instruments. A triple valve and an 18 m long reaction coil (polyetheretherketone) were used to connect these instruments. Sample separation was performed via a preparative HPLC system (Hanbon, Huai'an, China). For this work, the following chromatographic columns and separation materials were employed: MCI GEL®CHP20P (120 μm) used in a medium-pressure column (49 × 460 mm) was purchased from Mitsubishi Chemical Corporation (Kyoto, Japan). ReproSil-Pur C18 AQ analytical column (4.6 × 250 mm, 5 μm) and ReproSil-Pur C18 AQ preparative column (20 × 250 mm, 5 μm) were supplied by Maisch Corporation (Munich, Germany). Additionally, the UV absorbance values of the samples were read with a ReadMax 1900 microplate reader (Flash, Shanghai, China).

DPPH was purchased from Sigma-Aldrich (Steinheim, Germany). All reagents used in the experiments, including analytical methanol (MeOH), HPLC-grade acetonitrile (ACN), and MeOH were obtained from Xinlanjing Chemical Industry (Yuxi, China). HPLC-grade H_2O was prepared using a Moore water purification instrument (Chongqing, China).

2.2. Sample Extraction, MPLC Pretreatment and Active Peaks Recognition

A total of 1 kg of rape pollen gifted by Qinghai Ruihu Bioresource Development Co., Ltd. was extracted directly with 8 L of MeOH (extracted twice for 24 h, room temperature). The extract was combined, filtered, and concentrated using a rotary evaporator at 40 °C. After the volume of this extract solution was reduced to about 0.3 L, it was mixed with 100 g of dried amorphous silica gel and dried in an oven at a temperature of 40 °C.

A total of 182.4 g of extract−silica gel mixture was obtained after drying, which was calculated to be about 82.4 g of crude sample (yield of about 8.24%). Then the generated mixture was added to an empty chromatographic tower (49 × 100 mm) and coupled to an MCI medium-pressure column (49 × 460 mm) and liquid chromatography for pretreatment. MeOH and H_2O were utilized as mobile phases, and the elution procedure was set as follows: 0–30 min, 100% H_2O; 30–150 min, 0–100% MeOH; 150–240 min, 100% MeOH. The flow rate was 30 mL/min, and the absorbance was recorded at 254 nm. After 18 repeated elution procedures, five fractions were recovered (labeled Fr1, Fr2, Fr3, Fr4, and Fr5).

An additional 3 mg of rape pollen was weighed and dissolved in 1 mL of MeOH, then passed through an organic filter membrane (0.45 μm) for subsequent activity determination. The online HPLC−DPPH detection system was used to screen for active peaks in crude sample on ReproSil-Pur C18 AQ analytical column. This system consists of two HPLCs connected by a triple valve and reaction coils. The sample is detected through the first HPLC and then pumped to the second HPLC, where it is mixed with the DPPH solution (pumped in as mobile phase) and detected again. The active ingredients reacting with DPPH decrease the absorption at 517 nm, thus forming observable inverted peaks. The conditions for activity determination were as follows: for the first HPLC analysis, the flow rate was 1 mL/min, H_2O and ACN made up the mobile phase, and 5–50% ACN was linearly eluted for 60 min. Simultaneously, for the second HPLC, the flow rate of DPPH solution was 0.8 mL/min, and the DPPH concentration was 50 μg/mL. Chromatographic information of rape pollen was gathered at 254 nm. The data of free radical scavenging activity were recorded at 517 nm. In addition, the five recovered fractions as well as the crude sample were analyzed under the same chromatographic conditions.

2.3. Directed Separation of Antioxidants from the Target Fraction

A total of 1 g of Fr3 was completely dissolved in 8 mL of MeOH and passed through a 0.45 μm organic membrane for subsequent activity determination and separation. The conditions for activity determination were as follows: the mobile phase consisted of H_2O and ACN, with a flow rate of 1 mL/min, and the isocratic elution was 0–60 min at 13% ACN. As for online HPLC-DPPH detection, the flow rate of DPPH solution was 0.8 mL/min, and the DPPH concentration was 50 μg/mL. Chromatographic information was gathered at 254 nm. The data of free radical scavenging activity were recorded at 517 nm.

The antioxidant in Fr3 was purified using a ReproSil-Pur C18 AQ preparative column with a mobile phase composed of ACN and H_2O. The isocratic elution mode was used with the ACN content kept at 13% for 60 min. The eluent flow rate was constant at 19 mL/min, and chromatograms were collected at 254 nm. After 16 cycles of preparation, the target compound Fr3-1 was obtained, which was concentrated under reduced pressure and weighed as 406.7 mg.

2.4. Assessment of Activity and Purity of Antioxidants

Through the online HPLC−DPPH detection, the extracted compound's purity and free radical scavenging ability were verified; ACN and H_2O were utilized as the mobile phases, respectively. An amount of 5–50% ACN was eluted linearly over 60 min at 1 mL/min. At the same time, the concentration of DPPH solution was 50 μg/mL, and the flow rate was 0.8 mL/min. The data of free radical scavenging activity were measured at 517 nm.

Furthermore, the DPPH scavenging assay method was utilized to further explore the free radical scavenging activity of the isolated compound. Sample solutions containing compounds were prepared at various concentrations (0.1, 1, 10, 50, 200, and 500 μg/mL). In a 96-well microtiter plate, 30 μL sample solutions of various concentrations were mixed with 70 μL DPPH (0.25 mg/mL) solution and incubated in a shaker for 30 min. Finally, the absorbance at 517 nm of each well was measured using a microplate reader. The antioxidant capacity of the compound was obtained using the following formula:

$$\text{Inhibitory activity (\%)} = [1 - (A_1 - A_2)/A_3] \times 100\%$$

A_1 indicates the sample solution's absorbance, A_2 indicates the blank's absorbance, and A_3 indicates the control solution's absorbance.

2.5. Molecular Docking

The 3D structure of Fr3−1 was drawn and output via ChemBio3D software (16.0, CambridgeSoft, Cambridge, MA, USA). The crystal structures of Nrf2 protein (PDB ID: 4IQK) and HO-1 protein (PDB ID: 1N3U) were retrieved from the RCSB Protein Data Bank (https://www.rcsb.org/ (accessed on 2 October 2022)). After preparing these files of ligand and receptor, the receptor proteins were dehydrated and ligands were removed via PyMOL software (2.3.0, DeLano Scientific LLC, Shanghai, China). Employing the AutoDock Tools, the charge and hydrogen bonding of receptor proteins were calculated and added. Moreover, the active pocket locations where small molecule ligands attach was defined as characteristics of the receptor protein docking site, and the molecular docking between ligand and receptor proteins was displayed using AutoDock software (https://autodock.scripps.edu/ (accessed on 10 November 2022)). Eventually, a total of 100 peptide conformation results were obtained, and then the results with the lowest binding energy were visualized with PyMOL.

2.6. Statistical Analysis

The statistical analysis was conducted using SPSS 20.0 (SPSS, Chicago, IL, USA), and values were expressed as mean ± SD. All data given represented three repeat experiments. The nonlinear regression was used to calculate the concentration of the isolated compound that caused 50% inhibition (IC_{50}) of the scavenging activities. The curve representing free radical scavenging activities was created using Prism 8.0.

3. Results and Discussion

3.1. MPLC Pretreatment and Active Peaks Recognition

Considering its inexpensive cost and relative environmental friendliness, MeOH was chosen as the extraction solvent. Mixing and drying the concentrated extract with amorphous silica gel can maintain the stability and reproducibility of subsequent sample pretreatment as much as possible. At the same time, this form of dry loading is also useful for exploring the maximum sample loading during the pretreatment process. The weights of the five fractions recovered were as follows: Fr1 1.4 g, Fr2 1.3 g, Fr3 18.7 g, Fr4 37.4 g, and Fr5 1.3 g, with a recovery of 72.9%. According to the preparation diagram in Figure 1, it is found that under such elution conditions, the baseline separation between each fraction was largely achieved without having an impact on the sample recovery.

An online HPLC−DPPH detection was used to identify active peaks from rape pollen crude samples. In addition, HPLC analysis was performed on five fractions as well as the crude sample to observe the pretreatment effect. As shown in Figure 2, a clear active peak (inverted peak at 517 nm) can be detected at a retention time of roughly 26 min. From Figure 3, it can be seen that there is basically no overlap between the five fractions, encompassing all chromatographic peaks of the crude sample. At the same time, analysis of Figure 2 in conjunction with Figure 3 reveals that the active peak identified through the online HPLC−DPPH detection was effectively enriched in Fr3. Taken together, these chromatographic behaviors indicated that the MCI−MPLC pretreatment was satisfactory and saved the workload of the next separation step. In order to further explore the antioxidant active components in rape pollen, Fr3 was selected as the target fraction for the next separation.

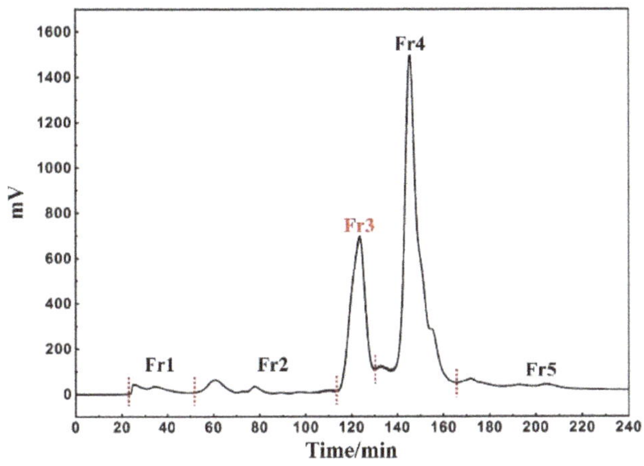

Figure 1. Chromatogram of rape pollen extract pretreatment with MCI-MPLC.

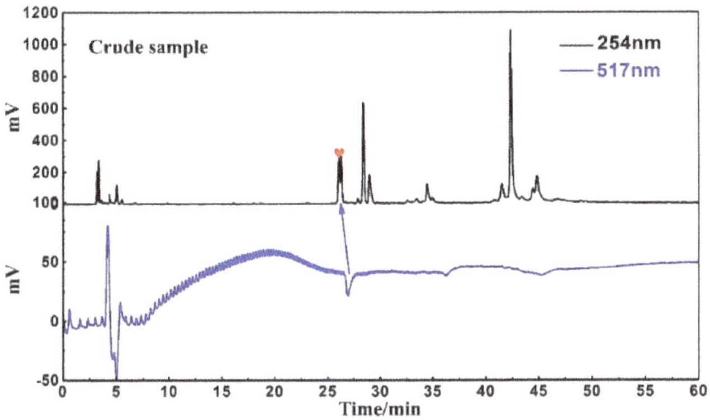

Figure 2. Online HPLC−DPPH detection chromatogram of crude sample.

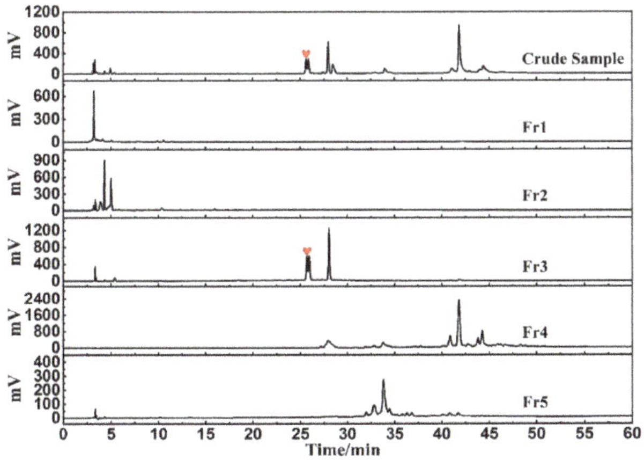

Figure 3. Analysis chromatograms of crude sample, Fr1, Fr2, Fr3, Fr4, and Fr5 under the same chromatographic condition.

3.2. Directed Separation of Active Compound from the Target Fraction

It can be seen from Figure 3 that Fr3 has two chromatographic peaks at a retention time of 26 min. To obtain greater peak resolution during the following HPLC preparation, the chromatographic conditions for Fr3 were further optimized to a 13% ACN isocratic elution for 60 min. Considering the directional separation of the high-purity free radical inhibitor in the next step, online HPLC−DPPH detection was again used to screen the active peaks under the optimized chromatographic conditions (Figure 4A). Based on the order in which the peaks appear in Figure 4A, the first peak was identified as the active peak (marked with a red graphic), and subsequent preparations will be focused on recovering this peak.

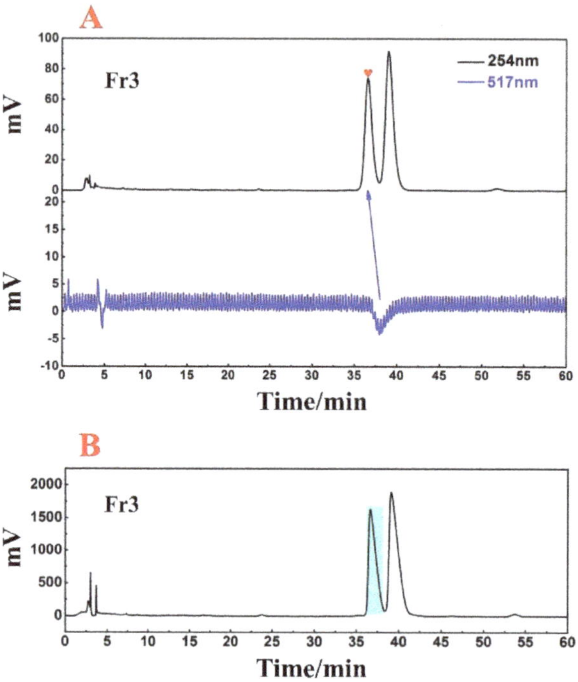

Figure 4. Online HPLC−DPPH detection chromatogram of Fr3 (**A**); preparation chromatogram of Fr3 (**B**).

A high-pressure preparation of the active peak in Fr3 via final optimized chromatographic conditions with suitable parameters such as injection volume and flow rate were selected to obtain good reproducibility. Finally, the preparative chromatogram is shown in Figure 4B, and a light blue label was placed on the prepared target peak. A comparison of Figure 4A and B makes it evident that active chromatographic peaks have nearly identical retention times on the ReproSil-Pur C18 AQ analytical column and the ReproSil-Pur C18 AQ preparative column, ensuring an accurate and efficient recovery of target peaks. After 16 cycles of preparation, the eluted solutions were combined and concentrated to finally obtain the target compound, named Fr3−1 (406.7 mg, with a yield of approximately 40.7%).

3.3. Purity, Structural Characterization and Activity of the Isolated Compound

The activity and purity of the isolated compound Fr3−1 were determined via online HPLC-DPPH detection with the ReproSil-Pur C18 AQ analytical column. According to Figure 5A, the purity of Fr3−1 is over 95%.

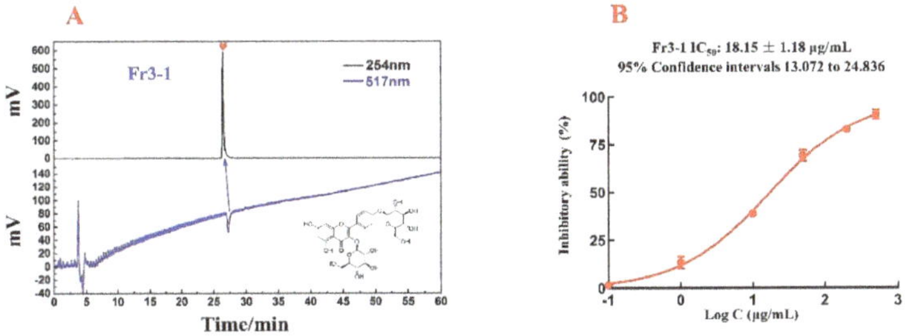

Figure 5. Purity and activity verification chromatogram of Fr3−1, as well as its chemical structure (**A**); DPPH inhibition activity of Fr3−1 at different concentrations were fitted with a logistic function to count the IC_{50} value (**B**).

NMR and ESI-MS data were obtained to elucidate the structure of the isolated compound and were compared with the data reported in the literature. More detailed spectral data on this compound are available in the Supporting Information.

Fr3-1 (kaempferol 3,4′-di-O-β-D-glucopyranoside, yellow powder, 406.7 mg, ESI-MS m/z 609.45, $[M-H]^-$, calc. For $C_{27}H_{30}O_{16}$, m/z 610.15); ^{1}H NMR (600 MHz, DMSO-d_6): 8.12 (2H, d, J = 9.0 Hz, H-2′, 6′), 7.15 (2H, d, J = 9.0 Hz, H-3′, 5′), 6.46 (1H, d, J = 2.1 Hz, H-8), 6.22 (1H, d, J = 2.1 Hz, H-6), 5.48 (1H, d, J = 7.6 Hz, H-1″), 5.02 (1H, d, J = 7.4 Hz, H-1‴); ^{13}C NMR(151 MHz, DMSO-d_6): 177.6 (C-4), 164.3 (C-7), 161.3 (C-5), 159.3 (C-4′), 156.5 (C-2), 155.6 (C-9), 133.7 (C-3), 130.6 (C-2′, 6′), 123.7 (C-1′), 115.8 (C-3′, 5′), 104.1 (C-10), 100.8 (C-1″), 100.0 (C-1‴), 98.8 (C-6), 93.8 (C-8), 77.6 (C-5″), 77.1 (C-5‴), 76.5 (C-3″), 76.4 (C-3‴), 74.2 (C-2″), 73.2(C-2‴), 69.9 (C-4″), 69.6 (C-4‴), 60.9 (C-6″), 60.6 (C-6‴). The data were consistent with kaempferol 3,4′-di-O-β-D-glucopyranoside [29].

With the aim to evaluate in vitro DPPH scavenging activities of Fr3−1, a DPPH scavenging assay was used in this paper with minor modifications [30]. As shown in Figure 5B, the IC_{50} value of Fr3−1 was 18.15 μg/mL. Flavonoids are a well-recognized class of compounds with a wide range of biological activities. As a flavonoid with the parent nucleus kaempferol, kaempferol 3,4′-di-O-β-D-glucopyranoside showed significant antioxidant activity in this experiment, validating the reliability of the online HPLC−DPPH assay. In view of the correlation between oxidative stress and multiple diseases, this compound is expected to be actively explored in future studies for its potential to treat other diseases.

3.4. Molecular Docking

Oxidative stress is a complex pathological process involving several signaling pathways and related proteins. As one of the vital antioxidant pathways, Nrf2/HO-1 can regulate the expression of antioxidant enzymes that contribute to the restoration of the cellular redox state, and this pathway is also engaged in the regulation of inflammation, epilepsy, cerebral ischemia, and other related pathological processes. In this study, Fr3−1 was molecularly docked to Nrf2 and HO-1, and the results are visualized in Figure 6. The minimum binding energies of Fr3−1 to Nrf2 and HO-1 were −6.1 Kcal/mol and −5.34 Kcal/mol. For Nrf2, Fr3−1 was bound to a pocket with Ser363, Ala556, Ser555, Ala510, Ser 508, and Val463 as amino acid residues. For HO-1, Fr3−1 was located in a pocket of activity surrounded by multiple amino acids, His25, Gln38, Thr135, and Tyr134. Therefore, it is reasonable to speculate that Fr3−1 exerts its free radical scavenging activity through the Nrf2/HO-1 pathway. The antioxidant activity of this compound has been verified through chromatography, in vitro assays, and molecular docking. However, considering the complexity of the organism, its detailed and rigorous antioxidant mechanism needs to be elucidated by further cellular or animal experiments.

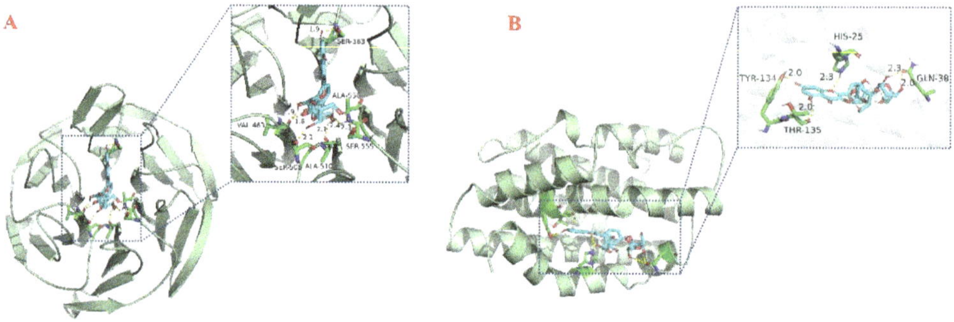

Figure 6. Molecular docking analysis of Nrf2 (**A**) and HO-1 (**B**) during binding to Fr3-1.

4. Conclusions

The appropriate chromatographic strategy has a significant effect in coping with the isolation and purification of natural products' active ingredients. In this study, online HPLC-DPPH detection was conducted for the qualitative identification of free radical inhibitors in rape pollen; MPLC pretreatment and HPLC preparation were employed for the isolation and purification of antioxidants from rape pollen. Finally, a free radical inhibitor (kaempferol 3,4′-di-O-β-D-glucopyranoside) was obtained from Fr3, its antioxidant capacity was detected through the DPPH method, and then the interaction between this compound and related proteins was theoretically investigated through a molecular docking experiment. This paper has demonstrated that the integrated chromatographic strategy of "online recognition, targeted enrichment and directed separation" is reliable and efficient for the rapid isolation of antioxidants from rape pollen and will provide theoretical support for future research on the deep processing and high value-added products of rape pollen. At the same time, the recognition and purification techniques of active compounds in other natural products can also be learned from this paper in the future.

Author Contributions: Methodology, L.J., H.L. and X.L.; data curation, L.J. and H.L.; funding acquisition, L.J., H.L. and J.H.; writing—original draft preparation, L.J. and H.L.; visualization, X.L. and K.G.; writing—review and editing, L.J. and M.W.; supervision, M.W. and J.H. All authors have read and agreed to the published version of the manuscript.

Funding: This research was funded by the Wuxi Taihu Talent Training Project (Double hundred Medical Youth Professionals Program, No. HB2020054), Scientific Research Project of Jiangsu Commission of Health (M2020005), Qinghai Basic Research Project (2020-ZJ747).

Data Availability Statement: All data are available on request from the authors.

Conflicts of Interest: The authors declare no conflict of interest.

References

1. Zhang, Z.; Cao, H.G.; Chen, C.; Chen, X.; Wei, Q.; Zhao, F.Y. Effects of fermentation by Ganoderma lucidum and Saccharomyces cerevisiae on rape pollen morphology and its wall. *J. Food. Sci. Technol.* **2017**, *54*, 4026–4034. [CrossRef] [PubMed]
2. Zhu, S.; Wang, S.; Wang, L.B.; Huang, D.J.; Chen, S.W. Identification and characterization of an angiotensin-I converting enzyme inhibitory peptide from enzymatic hydrolysate of rape (*Brassica napus* L.) bee pollen. *LWT Food. Sci. Technol.* **2021**, *147*, 111502. [CrossRef]
3. Ares, A.M.; Valverde, S.; Bernal, J.L.; Nozal, M.J.; Bernal, J. Extraction and determination of bioactive compounds from bee pollen. *J. Pharmaceut. Biomed.* **2018**, *147*, 110–124. [CrossRef] [PubMed]
4. Guo, J.L.; Yang, Y.N.; He, J.; Zhang, Z.W.; Zhang, P.C. Two new furan derivatives from bee-collected rape pollen. *J. Asian Nat. Prod. Res.* **2011**, *13*, 930–933. [CrossRef] [PubMed]
5. Rzepecka-Stojko, A.; Stojko, J.; Jasik, K.; Buszman, E. Anti-atherogenic activity of polyphenol-rich extract from bee pollen. *Nutrients* **2017**, *12*, 1369. [CrossRef]
6. Cheng, N.; Chen, S.N.; Liu, X.Y.; Zhao, H.A.; Cao, W. Impact of schisandrachinensis bee pollen on nonalcoholic fatty liver disease and gut microbiota in high fat diet induced obese mice. *Nutrients* **2019**, *2*, 346. [CrossRef]

7. Liao, Y.L.; Bae, H.J.; Zhang, J.B.; Kwon, Y.B.; Koo, B.; Jung, I.H.; Kim, H.M.; Park, J.H.; Lew, J.H.; Ryu, J.H. The ameliorating effects of bee pollen on scopolamine-induced cognitive impairment in mice. *Biol. Pharm. Bull.* **2019**, *3*, 379–388. [CrossRef]
8. Lv, H.H.; Wang, X.Y.; He, Y.F.; Wang, H.L.; Suo, Y.R. Identification and quantification of flavonoid aglycones in rape bee pollen from Qinghai-Tibetan Plateau by HPLC-DAD-APCI/MS. *J. Food Compos. Anal.* **2015**, *38*, 49–54. [CrossRef]
9. Fang, H.L.; Zhang, J.; Zhao, Y.W.; Han, N.J.; Wang, W.D.; Li, Y. Antioxidant and anti-aging mechanism of wall broken rape pollen. *Sci. Technol. Food Ind.* **2022**, *43*, 378–384. [CrossRef]
10. Hao, Z. The effect and research progress of rape pollen. *Cereal. Oil* **2020**, *8*, 4–6. Available online: https://lsyy.cbpt.cnki.net/WKC2/WebPublication/paperDigest.aspx?paperID=8dc2904d-5c5a-4f17-b76d-5f3d6b709ec0# (accessed on 20 October 2022).
11. Yao, Q.P.; Li, J.; Hu, J.; Huang, Y.F. Studies on quality evaluation of rape pollen based on HPLC fingerprint. *Zhongguo Shipin Xuebao* **2012**, *8*, 203–209. [CrossRef]
12. Xu, X.; Sun, L.P.; Dong, J.; Zhang, H.C. Breaking the cells of rape bee pollen and consecutive extraction of functional oil with supercritical carbon dioxide. *Innov. Food. Sci. Emerg.* **2009**, *10*, 42–46. [CrossRef]
13. Aceto, G.; Persico, V.; Pescapé, A. Industry 4.0 and health: Internet of things, big data, and cloud computing for healthcare 4.0. *J. Ind. Inf. Integr.* **2020**, *18*, 100129. [CrossRef]
14. Jadalla, B.M.I.S.; Moser, J.J.; Sharma, R.; Etsassala, N.G.E.R.; Egieyeh, S.A.; Badmus, J.A.; Marnewick, J.L.; Beukes, D.; Cupido, C.N.; Hussein, A.A. In vitro alpha-glucosidase and alpha-amylase inhibitory activities and antioxidant capacity of Helichrysum cymosum and Helichrysum pandurifolium schrank constituents. *Separations* **2022**, *8*, 190. [CrossRef]
15. Viñas, G.; Puig, T.; Porta, R. Oxidative stress in patients with cancer: Two sides of the same coin. *Med. Clin.* **2012**, *4*, 171–175. [CrossRef] [PubMed]
16. Wang, X.Y.; Zhou, Y.X.; Gao, Q.N.; Ping, D.N.; Wang, Y.L.; Wu, W.; Lin, X.; Fang, Y.J.; Zhang, J.M.; Shao, A.W. The role of exosomal microRNAs and oxidative stress in neurodegenerative diseases. *Oxid. Med. Cell Longev.* **2020**, *4*, 171–175. [CrossRef] [PubMed]
17. Salmon, A.B.; Richardson, A.; Pérez, V.I. Update on the oxidative stress theory of aging: Does oxidative stress play a role in aging or healthy aging? *Free. Radic. Biol. Med.* **2010**, *5*, 642–655. [CrossRef]
18. Hajam, Y.A.; Rani, R.; Ganie, S.Y.; Sheikh, T.A.; Javaid, D.; Qadri, S.S.; Pramodh, S.; Alsulimani, A.; Alkhanani, M.; Harakeh, S.; et al. Oxidative stress in human pathology and aging: Molecular mechanisms and perspectives. *Cells* **2022**, *3*, 552. [CrossRef]
19. Tain, Y.L.; Hsu, C.N. Oxidative stress-induced hypertension of developmental origins: Preventive aspects of antioxidant therapy. *Antioxidants* **2022**, *3*, 511. [CrossRef]
20. Hirschenson, J.; Melgar-Bermudez, E.; Mailloux, R.J. The uncoupling proteins: A systematic review on the mechanism used in the prevention of oxidative stress. *Antioxidants* **2022**, *2*, 322. [CrossRef]
21. Martemucci, G.; Costagliola, C.; Mariano, M.; D'andrea, L.; Napolitano, P.; D'Alessandro, A.G. Free radical properties, source and targets, antioxidant consumption and health. *Oxygen* **2022**, *2*, 48–78. [CrossRef]
22. Agraharam, G.; Girigoswami, A.; Girigoswami, K. Myricetin: A multifunctional flavonol in biomedicine. *Curr. Pharmacol. Rep.* **2022**, *8*, 48–61. [CrossRef] [PubMed]
23. Dawa, Y.; Du, Y.R.; Wang, Q.; Chen, C.B.; Zou, D.L.; Qi, D.S.; Ma, J.B.; Dang, J. Targeted isolation of 1, 1-diphenyl-2-picrylhydrazyl inhibitors from *Saxifraga atrata* using medium-and high-pressure liquid chromatography combined with online high performance liquid chromatography-1,1-diphenyl-2-picrylhydrazyl detection. *J. Chromatogr. A* **2021**, *1635*, 461690. [CrossRef]
24. Liu, C.; Lei, Y.Q.; Dang, J.; Wang, W.D.; Zhang, L.; Mei, L.J.; Liu, Z.G.; Tao, Y.D.; Shao, Y. Preparative isolation of 1, 1-diphenyl-2-picrylhydrazyl inhibitors from *Ribes himalense* using medium-pressure and two-dimensional reversed-phase/reversed-phase liquid chromatography guided by an online HPLC-1,1-diphenyl-2-picrylhydrazyl assay. *J. Sep. Sci.* **2021**, *7*, 1345–1352. [CrossRef]
25. Dang, J.; Ma, J.B.; Dawa, Y.; Liu, C.; Ji, T.F.; Wang, Q.L. Preparative separation of 1, 1-diphenyl-2-picrylhydrazyl inhibitors originating from *Saxifraga sinomontana* employing medium-pressure liquid chromatography in combination with reversed-phase liquid chromatography. *RSC Adv.* **2021**, *61*, 38739–38749. [CrossRef] [PubMed]
26. Yuan, C.; Dang, J.; Han, Y.; Liu, C.; Yu, S.; Lv, Y.; Cui, Y.B.; Wang, Z.H.; Li, G. Preparative isolation of maltol glycoside from *Dianthus superbus* and its anti-inflammatory activity in vitro. *RSC Adv.* **2022**, *8*, 5031–5041. [CrossRef]
27. Cheng, Y.J.; Liang, Q.L.; Ping, H.; Wang, Y.M.; Jun, F.W.; Luo, G.A. Combination of normal-phase medium-pressure liquid chromatography and high-performance counter-current chromatography for preparation of ginsenoside-Ro from *panax ginseng* with high recovery and efficiency. *Sep. Purif. Technol.* **2010**, *3*, 397–402. [CrossRef]
28. Li, Y.J.; Lin, H.M.; Zhang, J.B.; Deng, X.; Li, J.A. An efficient procedure for preparing high-purity pingyangmycin and boanmycin from *Streptomyces verticillus* var. *pingyangensis fermentation broth via macroporous cation-exchange resin and subsequent reversed-phase preparative chromatography. J. Chromatogr. B* **2020**, *1136*, 121883. [CrossRef]
29. Feng, Z.F.; Chen, X.F.; Di, D.L. Online extraction and isolation of highly polar chemical constituents from *Brassica napus* L. pollen by high shear technique coupled with high-performance counter-current chromatography. *J. Sep. Sci.* **2012**, *35*, 625–632. [CrossRef]
30. Lv, Y.; Wang, Z.; Wu, Q.; Fang, Y.; Wang, Q.L.; Li, G.; Dang, J. Preparation and Antioxidant Activities of Phenylethanoids from Dracocephalum heterophyllum. *Separations* **2022**, *5*, 111. [CrossRef]

separations

MDPI

Article

Target Discovery of Flavonoids from *Elymus nutans* Griseb Using Medium- and High-Pressure Liquid Chromatography Combined with Online High-Performance Liquid Chromatography–1,1-diphenyl-2-picrylhydrazyl Detection

Lili Sheng [1,2], Zhaofei Hou [1,2,*] and Yufeng Hu [3,*]

1 Minmetals Salt Lake Co., Ltd., Xining 810008, China
2 China Minmetals Co., Ltd., Beijing 100010, China
3 School of Chemical Engineering and Environment, University of Petroleum, Beijing 100010, China
* Correspondence: sdhzhzf09@126.com (Z.H.); huyf3581@sina.com (Y.H.)

Abstract: Forage-based nutrients constitute the main forage value of forage grass. *Elymus nutans* Griseb possesses a wide ecological adaptability, enhanced crude protein content, good palatability, and excellent genes. Herein, employing medium- (MPLC) and high-pressure liquid chromatography (HPLC), along with online HPLC-DPPH (OHD)-based identification, two primary radical scavenging compounds were extracted and identified from the methanolic extract of *Elymus nutans* Griseb. With a starting material of 300 g of *Elymus nutans* Griseb, 5.95 g of the target DPPH suppressors fraction (Fr6) was separated following one cycle of MCI GEL® CHP20P medium pressure liquid chromatography. A Kromasil 100-5-Phenyl column was subsequently employed for further purification of the fraction, which yielded 432.16 mg of Fr62 (7.26% recovery) and 489.01 mg of Fr63 (8.22% recovery). The target compounds were then assessed based on their structure and purity, and two compounds (salcolin A and tricin) were extracted with > 95% purity. This newly designed procedure was highly effective for the targeted flavonoids, and high-purity radical scavenger extraction from forage extracts. This methodology can potentially provide a scientific basis for their quality evaluation.

Keywords: *Elymus nutans* Griseb; preparative isolation; DPPH inhibitors; flavonoids

1. Introduction

Oxidative stress is a physiological event whereby excess stress results in the large accumulation of free radicals and reactive oxygen species, which in turn, diminishes the antioxidant defense capacity of the body [1,2]. Oxidative stress often causes biomolecular damage, as well as metabolic and physiological dysregulation, which subsequently tips the delicate balance between in immune function and inflammatory response in animals [3–5]. Oxidative stress and the inflammatory responses are integrated and amplified in specific cell types to enhance disease progression. Inflammatory diseases can decrease the production performance, reproductive performance, life span and quality of livestock products. This can not only result in huge economic losses to farms, but also endanger the health of consumers [6,7]. Therefore, early regulation of livestock and poultry diets are necessary for intervention, not only to alleviate antibiotics usage to combat drug residues and bacterial resistance challenges while reducing antibiotics costs, but also to protect the health of the animal organism [8,9].

Elymus nutans Griseb. (*E. nutans*) is a perennial, tufted and self-pollinated plant belonging to the *Elymus* L. genus of the Poaceae family. It inhabits the grasslands, thickets, river banks, mountain slopes, and forest margins, of the Inner Mongolia Autonomous Region, Gansu Province, Hebei Province, Shaanxi Province, Qinghai Province, Sichuan Province, Xinjiang Uygur Autonomous Region and Tibet Autonomous Region. *E. nutans* possesses broad-ranging ecological adaptability, cold and drought tolerance, elevated crude protein content, good palatability, and excellent genes that are lacking in other wheat crops, such as disease and insect resistance [10]. It is widely used in the improvement of alpine degraded pastures and the construction of artificial grasses, and it is an excellent source of forage. High quality forage is the key to enhancing animal husbandry, and the nutritional quality of forage will not only impact the growth and development of livestock, but also modulate the yield and quality of products. Hence, forage quality evaluation is of particular importance to the animal husbandry industry [11,12]. *E. nutans*, is a well-established high quality forage grass, which is rich in flavonoids. Flavonoids are essential nutrients that directly scavenge free radicals, and augment antioxidant enzyme activity. Using *E. nutans* in animal feed can ensure adequate flavonoids supplementation in animals, which can be beneficial to their health and the quality of their meat products.

Antioxidant active substances are generally assessed using two procedures, namely, traditional and online modes [13,14]. The traditional involves hydroxyl radical scavenging and the superoxide anion method. In contrast, the on-line mode involves HPLC-DPPH, with the added benefits of automation, stabilization, and rapidity. In addition, this mode simultaneously analyzes and evaluates the antioxidant activity of a single component in traditional Chinese medicine [15,16]. Subsequently, the potential antioxidant components are separated using preparative chromatography, which can efficiently achieve the preparative separation of antioxidant active substances within samples.

Quality forage is an indispensable feed material for cattle, sheep and other herbivores, and is of great importance to the development of animal husbandry [11,17]. The antioxidant active substance enrichment in forage grasses is critical for sustaining the normal physiological growth requirements of livestock and poultry [18]. It is well reported that *E. nutans* is a high-quality forage grass preferred by horses, cattle and sheep. Currently, most studies on *E. nutans* have examined genetic diversity and strategies to enhance yield. This study, examining the *E. nutans* quality using antioxidant active substances as indicators, is the first report of its kind. Herein, an HPLC-1,1-diphenyl-2-picrylhydrazyl (HPLC-DPPH) on-line analytical procedure was developed for the rapid selection of antioxidant active components from complex chemical compositions. After on-line analysis of the crude ethanol based *E. nutans* extract, the main components were quickly identified as having certain antioxidant activities. The main component was enriched using MCI GEL® CHP20P medium-pressure liquid chromatography (MPLC), and was detected in fraction Fr6 after liquid chromatography analysis. The Kromasil 100-5-Phenyl column was selected for further preparative separation of the two potential antioxidant active components in Fr6 after the analysis of Fr6 using different columns. Finally, using HPLC-DPPH accompanied by the medium- and high-pressure liquid chromatography method, the two potential antioxidant flavonoid main components were successfully identified and separated from *E. nutans*, providing a scientific basis for their quality evaluation.

2. Materials and Methods

2.1. Apparatus and Reagents

LC-10AD and LC-16 HPLC apparatuses were utilized to generate an online HPLC-DPPH identification system. An NU3000 UV-Vis detector, two NP7000 prep-HPLC pumps, a 5 mL manual administrator, and an LC workstation were employed in a preparative MPLC workstation (Hanbon Science & Technology Co., Ltd., Jiangsu, China). Samples were degassed with DGU-20A3R (Shimadzu Instruments Co., Ltd., Beijing, China) prior to HPLC analyses via an LC-16A equipment with attached autosampler and column thermostat. The Waters QDa electrospray ionization (ESI) mass spectrometer (Waters Instruments Co., Ltd., Milford, MA, USA) was used to acquire the ESI-MS data. The ^{1}H and ^{13}C NMR spectra were measured via the Bruker Avance 600 MHz (Bruker, Karlsruhe, Germany) using the DMSO-d_6 solvent. An UV absorbance reading was acquired via a Readmax 1900 microplate reader (Shanghai Shanpu Biotechnology Co., Ltd. Shanghai, China).

MCI GEL® CHP20P (120 μm) separation materials were collected from Mitsubishi Chemical Corporation (Japan). Odyssil C18 column (4.6 × 250 mm, 5 μm) was from Agela Technologies (Tianjin, China). Two Kromasil 100-5-Phenyl columns (4.6 × 250 mm, 5 μm and 20 × 250 mm, 5 μm) were supplied by Nouryon Kromasil Corporation (Sweden). Ethanol, preparative acetonitrile (ACN), and HPLC grade ACN were acquired from Kelon Chemical Reagent Factory (Chengdu, China). DPPH was obtained from Sigma Aldrich (Berlin, Germany). Moore water purification station was used to obtain ultrapure water from deionized water for use in HPLC (Chongqing, China).

2.2. Sample Preparation, DPPH Suppressor Identification, and Active Fraction Enrichment

The medicinal material of *E. nutans* was acquired in July 2020 from the Goluo Tibetan Autonomous Prefecture, Qinghai Province (4200 m, N 34°28′, 17″, E 100°14′, 41″) and was subsequently identified as *E. nutans* by Lijuan Mei of the Northwest Institute of Plateau Biology, Chinese Academy of Sciences. The acquired samples were housed in the Key Laboratory of Adaptation and Evolution of Plateau Biota, Chinese Academy of Sciences under the number No. 20200709.

The sample underwent air drying in a cool place prior to being crushed into powder, then 300 g of *E. nutans* was accumulated and isolated two times with methanol (4.0 L for 24 h per isolation). The resulting extract (8 L) underwent filtration, and was further concentrated via evaporation under reduced pressure to a 500 mL volume. Next, this was combined with silica gel (10 g), followed by drying at 40 °C. Subsequently, the sample was ground, then sifted to achieve a 48.0 g weight (12.67% yield). DPPH suppressors were then identified within the *E. nutans* extract, using the online HPLC-DPPH technique. The methanolic extract was separated on the Odyssil C18 (4.6 × 250 mm, 5 μm) column. A gradient elution was performed using a linear rise in ACN (mobile phase B) concentration in 0.1% v/v formic acid aqueous solution (HCOOH, mobile phase A) from 5 to 95% B over a 60 min period. In this case, the eluent flow rate was 1.0 mL/min, and the administration volume was 1 μL. Post-column derivatization, a methanolic solution of DPPH (50 μg/mL) was applied at a flow rate of 0.8 mL/min, and the absorbance was monitored at 517 nm.

The dried silica gel mixture was then placed into a medium pressure chromatography tower (49 × 100 mm), attached to a medium pressure chromatography column (49 × 460 mm) with 1.2 L MCI GEL CHP20P stationary phase. The elution step was performed with ACN/water for 0–120 min (5–95% ACN) at a flow rate of 57.0 mL/min and a detection wavelength of 254 nm. Following one experimental operation, the process yielded a 5.95 g sample after concentration of the condensed target fraction (Fr6), with recovery of 15.66%.

2.3. Identification and Isolation of Potential DPPH Suppressors Based on High-Pressure Liquid Chromatography Separation

To further separate Fr6, 20 mg of the sample was suspended in methanol/water solution (1.0 mL, 9:1 v/v), and prior to filtration, a 0.45 μm organic filter membrane (20.0 mg/mL). DPPH suppressors were identified in the targeted fraction Fr6 via the online HPLC-DPPH approach. HPLC was conducted as follows: Using the Odyssil C18 analytical column and an elution gradient, ACN (mobile phase B) was dropped linearly from 5% to 95% B into 0.1% v/v formic acid in water (mobile phase A), over 30 min. The flow rate and injection volume were 1.0 mL/min, 10 μL, respectively. It was detected at 254 nm. The column oven temperature was 30 °C. To conduct post-column derivatization, a 25 μg/mL solution of 100% DPPH anhydrous ethanol was used. The DPPH flow rate was 0.8 mL/min. The absorption was measured, at 517 nm.

The fraction analysis indicated that the Fr6 fraction possessed active compounds. For Fr6 (5.95 g), preparative separation was performed on a preparative Kromasil 100-5-Phenyl column (20 × 250 mm, 5 μm). The 0.1% v/v formic acid in water served as mobile phase A, while the acetonitrile solution (analytical purity) served as mobile phase B. Elution conditions were determined by an isocratic elution with 35% acetonitrile for 20 min. The flow rate was 19.0 mL/min, the detection wavelength was 254 nm. The preparation was performed at room temperature. Lastly, Fr62 and Fr63 were acquired and condensed to yield 432.16 and 489.01 mg respectively with a net recovery rate of 15.48%.

2.4. Purity and Activity Evaluation of the Extracted DPPH Suppressors

The Odyssil C18 analytical column was used to assess the purity of the isolated DPPH inhibitors. The mobile phase A was formic acid in water at 0.1% v/v, while the mobile phase B was acetonitrile. The analytical column was employed with gradient elution for 60 min in 5–95% acetonitrile, with a flow rate of 1.0 mL/min and an injection volume of 1 μL, respectively. The wavelength of detection was recorded at 254 nm.

3. Results and Discussion

3.1. Sample Pretreatment, DPPH Suppressor Identification, and MCI GEL® CHP20P Medium Pressure Liquid Chromatography Enrichment

DPPH is a stably present free radical with the potential to chemically react with the active hydrogen of antioxidant substances, thereby altering the chemical structure of the antioxidant substances. The two HPLCs were attached in series by a three-way valve and a polyether ether ketone (PEEK) tube approximately 18 m in length and 0.25 μm in radius. Owing to the presence of free radical suppressors within the sample which interacted with DPPH, the absorption value at 517 nm is reduced to an inverted peak. The chromatograms of the two HPLC analyses were compared, which led to the rapid identification of free radical suppressors in the samples [19,20].

Owing to the extremely limited information on *E. nutans* based DPPH suppressors, the condensed *E. nutans* methanol extract (500.0 mL) was identified using the online HPLC-DPPH system with a Odyssil C18 analytical column (4.6 × 250 mm, 5 μm), and the identification chromatogram is presented in Figure 1B (Figure 1A depicts the actual online HPLC-DPPH system). As illustrated in Figure 1B, the main DPPH suppressor peaks (marked with hearts in Figure 1B) were evident at retention durations between 30–32.5 min of *E. nutans* methanol extract.

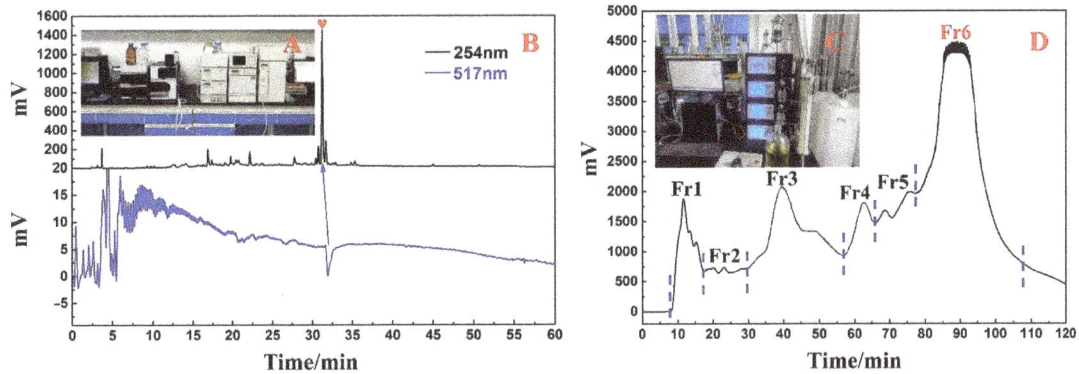

Figure 1. The actual online HPLC-DPPH system (**A**) and the analytical chromatogram on a Odyssil C18 analytical column and DPPH inhibitory activity profile of the *E. nutans* crude sample (**B**). The actual micro gel chp20p medium pressure liquid chromatography system (**C**) and *E. nutans* amorphous silica gel mixture separation chromatogram (**D**).

There was a considerable amount of chlorophyll in the methanol *E. nutans* extract. These substances can interfere with the subsequent separation and can easily contaminate the column. Hence, chlorophyll elimination was performed before chromatographic evaluations. It is well established that the MCI GEL® CHP20P filler for medium pressure chromatographic separation is composed of styrene-divinylbenzene copolymer matrix, which stabilizes the spherical structure and properties in extreme acid-base solutions and organic solvents, which in turn, guarantees target compound repeatability during purification. This approach allows for process development and separation optimization, to yield enhanced resolution and product recovery. Dry sample loading was performed by placing 48.0 g of the combined sample to a small medium pressure column (49 × 100 mm) and connecting it to a medium pressure column (49 × 460 mm) equipped with 1.2 L of MCI GEL® CHP20P for dry sample loading preparation (Figure 1C). Figure 1D depicts the chromatogram for extract separation using MCI GEL® CHP20P and methanol–water eluent. After one cycle, Fr1, Fr2, Fr3, Fr4, Fr5, and Fr6 were obtained by collecting, condensing, and weighing the desired component.

To further analyze the sample, these fractions were resuspended in a methanol/water mixture (9:1 *v*/*v*, 1.0 mL, 20.0 mg/mL) prior to filtration through a 0.45 µM organic filter membrane. Subsequently, the accumulated fractions Fr1-Fr6 were assessed via a Odyssil C18 analytical column under the identical parameters as in Figure 1B. The chromatogram of the analysis of the crude sample of *E. nutans* and fractions Fr1-Fr6 is shown in Figure 2. As shown in Figure 2, the main DPPH inhibitors of the *E. nutans* crude sample were efficiently enriched in fraction Fr6. A solution for further chromatographic separation was obtained by resuspending Fr6 in 60.0 mL of water/methanol (1:9 *v*/*v*), followed by filtering through a 0.45 µm filter.

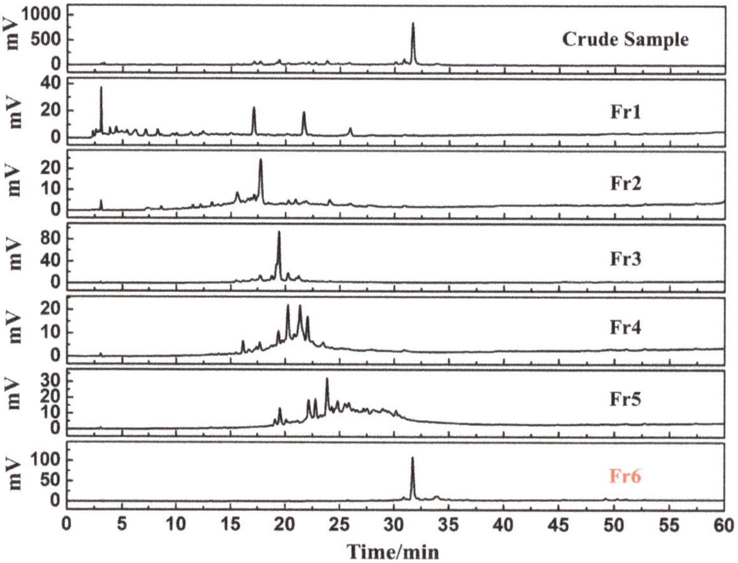

Figure 2. HPLC analysis of the *E. nutans* crude extract and Fr1-Fr6 on the Odyssil C18 analytical column.

3.2. *Identification and Extraction of Candidate DPPH Suppressors Based on High-Pressure Liquid Chromatography Separation*

The target fraction Fr6 was initially assessed by a Odyssil C18 column (4.6 × 250 mm, 5 µm). As depicted in Figure 3A, a primary peak was evident with asymmetric peak shape for Fr6 on the Odyssil C18 column. Hence, its separation on the Odyssil C18 column did not achieve good results. Subsequently, we chose to analyze it on a Kromasil 100-5-Phenyl column. The analytical chromatogram is illustrated in Figure 3B. Based on our results, Fr6 was able to achieve a good separation on the Kromasil 100-5-Phenyl column, with four symmetrical peaks obtained (peaks 1–4). By comparison, the Kromasil 100-5-Phenyl column was chosen for further Fr6 separation and purification in order to improve the separation efficiency.

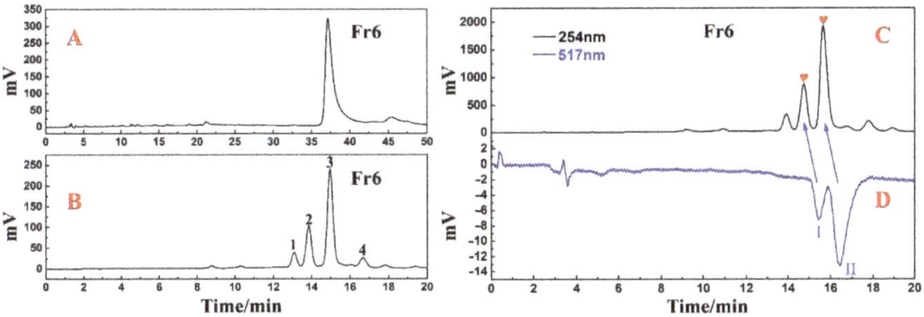

Figure 3. HPLC analysis of *E. nutans* Fr6 on the Odyssil C18 analytical column (**A**) and on a Kromasil 100-5-Phenyl analytical column (**B**). The analytical chromatogram (**C**) and DPPH radical scavenging profile (**D**) of the *E. nutans* target Fr6 sample on the Kromasil 100-5-Phenyl analytical column analytical column. The numbers 1, 2, 3 and, 4 represent four different peaks. Red hearts indicate peaks with antioxidant activity, and I and II correspond to corresponding inverted peaks, indicated by arrows.

An online HPLC-DPPH approach was employed to quickly screen for free radical suppressors in Fr6. The *E. nutans* Fr6 sample was identified with the online HPLC-DPPH system using the Kromasil 100-5-Phenyl column and the recognition chromatogram is displayed in Figure 3C,D. DPPH suppressors peaks (negative peaks I–II in Figure 3D corresponds to the red heart in Figure 3C) were strongly visible in the *E. nutans* target fraction Fr6.

Based on the aforementioned analytical findings, a Kromasil 100-5-Phenyl preparative column (20 × 250 mm, 5 μm) was selected for additional preparation to enhance the DPPH suppressor purity. Under the condition of isocratic elution of acetonitrile-0.1% *v*/*v* formic acid in water (0–20 min, 35% acetonitrile), the DPPH suppressor peaks showed sufficient resolution, as indicated in Figure 3C,D. Hence, subsequent examinations were made under this setting. Following linear amplification, the DPPH inhibitor peaks were separated and purified on the Kromasil 100-5-Phenyl preparative column under optimized conditions. The result is presented in Figure 4. It can be seen from the figure that good baseline separation of Fr62, Fr63 can be achieved on the Kromasil 100-5-Phenyl column, and the peak shapes revealed good symmetry. This explains the good complementary selectivity of Odyssil C18 and Kromasil 100-5-Phenyl columns, which can be used in combination to improve separation efficiency and monomer purity in natural product separation and purification work. Fr62 and Fr63 were accrued and condensed after passing through 75 replicates, yielding 432.16 and 489.01 mg, respectively, and providing a net recovery of 15.48%.

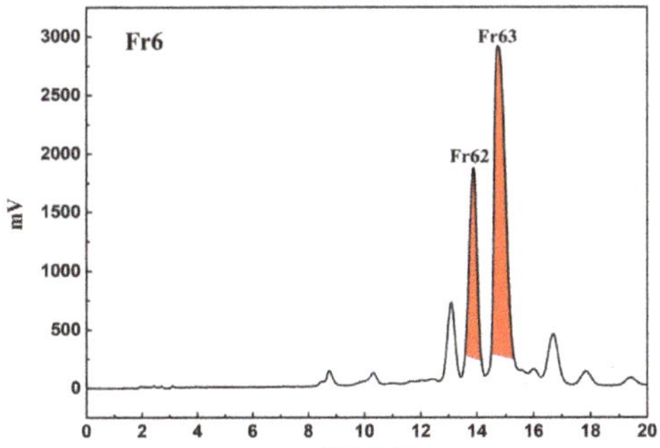

Figure 4. The preparative chromatogram of the *E. nutans* target Fr6 sample on a Kromasil 100-5-Phenyl preparative column. The red part represents the target component (Fr62 and Fr63).

3.3. Purity, Activity and Structural Characterization of the Isolated DPPH Suppressors

The extracted DPPH suppressors, Fr62 and Fr63 activities, and purity were re-evaluated using the online HPLC- DPPH system with a Odyssil C18 analytical column. As depicted in Figure 5, all compounds possessed purities above 95%.

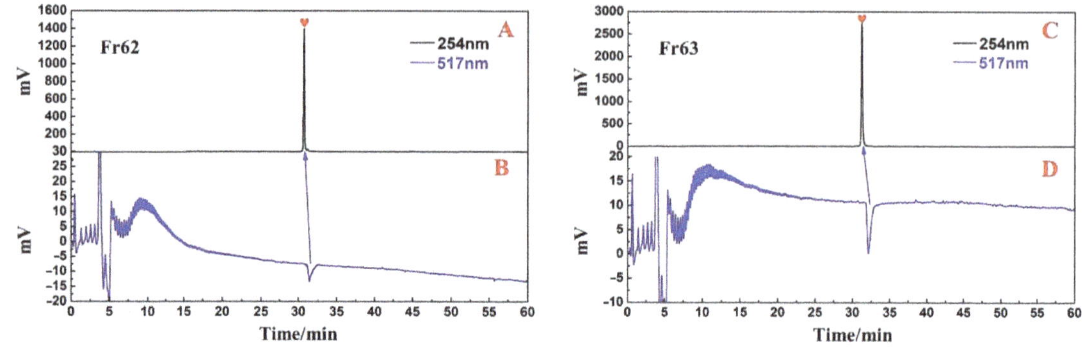

Figure 5. Purity and DPPH inhibitory activity of the target fraction activity verification chromatogram of the isolated Fr62 (**A**,**B**), and Fr63 (**C**,**D**) fractions on the Odyssil C18 analytical column. Red hearts indicate peaks with antioxidant activity, indicated by arrows.

The resulting ESI-MS, ^{1}H NMR and ^{13}C NMR spectra were compared against the published literature to delineate the structure of the target DPPH suppressors Fr62 and Fr63 (Figure 6). The structural identification of Fr62 and Fr63 from the supplementary information are presented in Figures S1–S6 (Supplementary Materials). The two DPPH suppressors Fr62 and Fr63 match the data for salcolin A and tricin, respectively, based on all spectrum data [21,22].

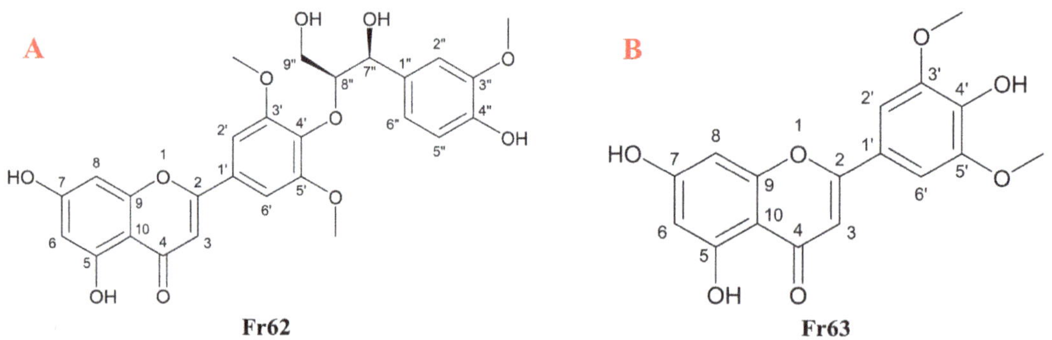

Figure 6. Chemical structures of the isolated DPPH inhibitors. (**A**,**B**) represent the chemical structure of Fr62 and Fr63, respectively.

Compound Fr62 (salcolin A, 432.16 mg, yellow powder, ESI-MS m/z: 525.39 [M-H]$^-$, calc. for $C_{27}H_{26}O_{11}$ m/z 526.1475): ^{1}H NMR (600 MHz, DMSO-d_6) 7.31 (2H, s, H-2′, 6′), 6.93 (1H, d, J = 1.8 Hz, H-2″), 6.75 (1H, dd, J = 8.1, 1.8 Hz, H-6″), 6.70 (1H, d, J = 8.1 Hz, H-5″), 6.69 (1H, s, H-3), 6.56 (1H, d, J = 2.0 Hz, H-8), 6.21 (1H, d, J = 2.0 Hz, H-6), 5.17 (1H, m, H-7″), 4.35 (1H, ddd, J = 5.2, 5.1, 3.7 Hz, H-8″), 3.88 (6H, s, 3′, 5′-OCH_3), 3.75 (3H, s, 3″-OCH_3), 3.49 (1H, dd, J = 11.5, 5.2 Hz, H-9″a), 3.44 (1H, dd, J = 11.5, 5.1 Hz, H-9″b); ^{13}C NMR (151 MHz, DMSO- d_6) 181.8 (C-4), 164.7 (C-7), 163.0 (C-2), 161.4 (C-5), 157.4 (C-9), 153.0 (C-3′, 5′), 147.0 (C-3″), 145.4 (C-4″), 139.5 (C-4′), 133.2 (C-1″), 125.2 (C-1′), 119.4 (C-6″), 114.7 (C-5″), 111.0 (C-2″), 104.8 (C-3), 104.3 (C-10), 103.7 (C-2′, 6′), 99.0 (C-6), 94.4 (C-8), 86.5 (C-8″), 72.2 (C-7″), 60.2 (C-9″), 56.4 (C-3′, 5′-OCH_3), 55.5 (C-3″-OCH_3). According to our ESI-MS, ^{1}H NMR and ^{13}C NMR data, as well as in the literature review, the compound was identified as salcolin A [21].

Compound Fr63 (tricin, 489.01 mg, yellow powder, ESI-MS m/z: 329.21 [M-H]$^-$, calc. for $C_{17}H_{14}O_7$ m/z 330.0740): ^{1}H NMR (600 MHz, DMSO-d_6) 3.88 (6H, s, 2OCH$_3$), 6.20 (1H, d, J = 2.0 Hz, H-6), 6.56 (1H, d, J = 2.0 Hz, H-8), 6.98 (1H, s, H-3), 7.32 (2H, s, H-2′, 6′); ^{13}C NMR (151 MHz, DMSO-d_6) 181.8 (C-4), 164.3 (C-7), 163·6 (C-2), 161.4 (C-9), 157.4 (C-5), 148.2 (C-3′, 5′), 139.9 (C-4′), 120.4 (C-1′), 104.4 (C-2′, 6′), 103.7 (C-10), 103.6 (C-3), 98.9 (C-6), 94.2 (C-8), 56.4 (OCH$_3$). According to our ESI-MS, ^{1}H NMR and ^{13}C NMR data, as well as in the literature review, the compound was identified as tricin, by a comparison with the compound in the literature [22].

Sacolin A and tricin participate in a myriad of biological activities, namely, anti-inflammatory, antioxidant, antiviral, antitumor and immunomodulatory, especially anti-inflammatory effects. Both compounds are flavonoids, which are commonly found in graminaceous plants, such as bamboo, barley, rice, wheat, and maize, and are considered to be healthy and harmless nutrients. The present study demonstrated that sacolin A and tricin are abundant in *E. nutans*, thus, providing insight into the extraction and purification of sacolin A and tricin.

4. Conclusions

Flavonoids are widely available in a variety of forage grasses. Owing to their numerous biological functions, the application of flavonoids can significantly improve animal production performance, enhance animal body resistance to disease and improve animal body immune function [23]. Flavonoids also possess weak estrogenic activity, which can markedly enhance animal growth, the egg-laying performance of poultry, promote reproductive system development, and improve fertility. Moreover, flavonoids augment the immune function of T cells, natural killer cells, and killer cells. Lastly, owing to their excellent antioxidant activity, flavonoids scavenge free radicals and reduce their production.

Herein, we employed a rapid and efficient method based on a combination of medium- and high-pressure chromatography, and online HPLC-DPPH analysis was designed to screen, isolate and purify flavonoids from *E. nutans*. By pre-processing the sample using MCI GEL® CHP20P MPLC, the process yielded 5.95 g of the target fraction Fr6. Further, Kromasil 100-5-Phenyl column was used for the separation and purification of target fraction Fr6, yielding 432.16 mg of Fr62 (7.26% recovery) and 489.01 mg of Fr63 (8.22% recovery). The reassessment of purity and radical scavenging activity showed that all compounds are active with >95% purity. In all, two flavonoids were isolated with satisfactory purity from the target sample, which indicated that the combination of medium- and high-pressure chromatography and online HPLC-DPPH method was efficient for preparative separation of the flavonoids from *E. nutans*. Moreover, this procedure is significant for the isolation and purification of flavonoids from other forage grasses.

Supplementary Materials: The following supporting information can be downloaded at: https://www.mdpi.com/article/10.3390/separations9120437/s1, Figure S1: ESI mass spectrum of salcolin A; Figure S2: ^{1}H NMR Spectrum (600 MHz) of salcolin A (in DMSO-d_6); Figure S3: ^{13}C NMR Spectrum (151 MHz) of salcolin A (in DMSO-d_6). Figure S4: ESI mass spectrum of tricin; Figure S5: ^{1}H NMR Spectrum (600 MHz) of tricin (in DMSO-d_6); Figure S6: ^{13}C NMR Spectrum (151 MHz) of tricin (in DMSO-d_6).

Author Contributions: Writing—original draft, methodology, data curation, formal analysis, investigation L.S.; writing—review and editing, conceptualization, project administration and funding acquisition Z.H.; data curation, formal analysis Y.H. All authors have read and agreed to the published version of the manuscript.

Funding: This research was funded by the Fund of Technical and Economic Research Institute of China Minmetals Salt Lake Co., Ltd. [2022].

Institutional Review Board Statement: Not applicable.

Informed Consent Statement: Not applicable.

Data Availability Statement: All data generated or analyzed during this study are included in this published article (and its Supplementary Materials).

Conflicts of Interest: The authors declare no conflict of interest.

References

1. Sies, H. Oxidative stress: A concept in redox biology and medicine. *Redox. Biol.* **2015**, *4*, 180–183. [CrossRef] [PubMed]
2. Forman, H.J.; Zhang, H. Targeting oxidative stress in disease: Promise and limitations of antioxidant therapy. *Nat. Rev. Drug. Discov.* **2021**, *20*, 689–709. [CrossRef] [PubMed]
3. Senoner, T.; Dichtl, W. Oxidative Stress in Cardiovascular Diseases: Still a Therapeutic Target? *Nutrients* **2019**, *11*, 2090. [CrossRef] [PubMed]
4. Ighodaro, O.M. Molecular pathways associated with oxidative stress in diabetes mellitus. *Biomed. Pharmacother.* **2018**, *108*, 656–662. [CrossRef] [PubMed]
5. Poprac, P.; Jomova, K.; Simunkova, M.; Kollar, V.; Rhodes, C.J.; Valko, M. Targeting Free Radicals in Oxidative Stress-Related Human Diseases. *Trends. Pharmacol. Sci.* **2017**, *38*, 592–607. [CrossRef] [PubMed]
6. Tan, B.L.; Norhaizan, M.E. Effect of High-Fat Diets on Oxidative Stress, Cellular Inflammatory Response and Cognitive Function. *Nutrients* **2019**, *11*, 2579. [CrossRef]
7. Dutta, S.; Sengupta, P.; Slama, P.; Roychoudhury, S. Oxidative Stress, Testicular Inflammatory Pathways, and Male Reproduction. *Int. J. Mol Sci.* **2021**, *22*, 10043. [CrossRef]
8. McGarry, T.; Biniecka, M.; Veale, D.J.; Fearon, U. Hypoxia, oxidative stress and inflammation. *Free. Radic. Biol. Med.* **2018**, *125*, 15–24. [CrossRef]
9. Mavangira, V.; Sordillo, L.M. Role of lipid mediators in the regulation of oxidative stress and inflammatory responses in dairy cattle. *Res. Vet. Sci.* **2018**, *116*, 4–14. [CrossRef]
10. Yang, Y.; He, T.; Lu, S.; Huang, R.; Wang, Z. *Records of Tibetan Medicine*; Qinghai Publishing House: Qinghai, China, 1991; pp. 450–451.
11. Capstaff, N.M.; Miller, A.J. Improving the Yield and Nutritional Quality of Forage Crops. *Front. Plant. Sci.* **2018**, *9*, 535. [CrossRef]
12. Manzanares, C.; Yates, S.; Ruckle, M.; Nay, M.; Studer, B. TILLING in forage grasses for gene discovery and breeding improvement. *N. Biotechnol.* **2016**, *33*, 594–603. [CrossRef]
13. Macáková, K.; Afonso, R.; Saso, L.; Mladěnka, P. The influence of alkaloids on oxidative stress and related signaling pathways. *Free. Radic. Biol. Med.* **2019**, *134*, 429–444. [CrossRef]
14. Dawa, Y.; Du, Y.; Wang, Q.; Chen, C.; Zou, D.; Qi, D.; Ma, J.; Dang, J. Targeted isolation of 1,1-diphenyl-2-picrylhydrazyl inhibitors from *Saxifraga atrata* using medium- and high- pressure liquid chromatography combined with online high performance liquid chromatography-1,1-diphenyl-2- picrylhydrazyl detection. *J. Chromatogr. A* **2021**, *1635*, 461690. [CrossRef]
15. Ionita, P. The Chemistry of DPPH· Free Radical and Congeners. *Int. J. Mol. Sci.* **2021**, *22*, 1545. [CrossRef]
16. Gulcin, İ. Antioxidants and antioxidant methods: An updated overview. *Arch. Toxicol.* **2020**, *94*, 651–715. [CrossRef]
17. Zhou, M.; Wei, L.; Sun, Z.; Gao, L.; Meng, Y.; Tang, Y.; Wu, Y. Production and transcriptional regulation of proanthocyanidin biosynthesis in forage legumes. *Appl. Microbiol. Biotechnol.* **2015**, *99*, 3797–3806. [CrossRef]
18. Lee, M.R. Forage polyphenol oxidase and ruminant livestock nutrition. *Front. Plant. Sci.* **2014**, *5*, 694. [CrossRef]
19. Cui, Y.; Shen, N.; Yuan, X.; Dang, J.; Shao, Y.; Mei, L.; Tao, Y.; Wang, Q.; Liu, Z. Two-dimensional chromatography based on on-line HPLC-DPPH bioactivity-guided assay for the preparative isolation of analogue antioxidant compound from *Arenaria kansuensis*. *J. Chromatogr. B.* **2017**, *1046*, 81–86. [CrossRef]
20. Fang, Y.; Dawa, Y.; Wang, Q.; Lv, Y.; Yu, W.; Li, G.; Dang, J. Targeted isolation of 1,1-diphenyl-2-picrylhydrazyl inhibitors from *Saxifraga atrata* and their antioxidant activities. *J. Sep. Sci.* **2022**, *45*, 2435–2445. [CrossRef]
21. Jung, Y.J.; Park, J.H.; Cho, J.G.; Seo, K.H.; Lee, D.S.; Kim, Y.C.; Kang, H.C.; Song, M.C.; Baek, N.I. Lignan and flavonoids from the stems of Zea mays and their anti-inflammatory and neuroprotective activities. *Arch. Pharm. Res.* **2015**, *38*, 178–185. [CrossRef]
22. Zhang, X.Q.; Jiang, W.W.; Wang, Y.; Li, Y.L.; Ye, W.C. A new phenylpropanoic acid derivatives from the roots of *Ficus stenophylla*. *Yao. Xue. Xue. Bao.* **2008**, *43*, 281–283. [PubMed]
23. Gholami, A.; De Geyter, N.; Pollier, J.; Goormachtig, S.; Goossens, A. Natural product biosynthesis in Medicago species. *Nat. Prod. Rep.* **2014**, *31*, 356–380. [CrossRef] [PubMed]

separations

MDPI

Article

Medium- and High-Pressure Integrated Chromatographic Strategies for the Isolation and Purification of Free Radical Inhibitors from *Dracocephalum heterophyllum*

Yue Lv [1,2], Ze Wang [3], Qilan Wang [1] and Jun Dang [1,*]

[1] Qinghai Provincial Key Laboratory of Tibetan Medicine Research, Key Laboratory of Tibetan Medicine Research, Northwest Institute of Plateau Biology, Chinese Academy of Sciences, Xining 810001, China
[2] Center for Mitochondria and Healthy Aging, College of Life Sciences, Yantai University, Yantai 264005, China
[3] College of Pharmacy, Qinghai Nationalities University, Xining 810007, China
* Correspondence: dangjun@nwipb.cas.cn; Tel.: +86-971-6143-282

Abstract: *Dracocephalum heterophyllum* has been reported as a traditional Tibetan medicine with diverse therapeutic benefits for the effective treatment of various diseases. However, only a few reports on its free radical inhibitors are limited due to its complex chemical composition and difficult isolation and purification processes. In this study, five free radical inhibitors are isolated by an integrated chromatographic method from *Dracocephalum heterophyllum*, followed by an investigation of the in vitro antioxidant activity utilizing 1,1-diphenyl-2-picrylhydrazyl (DPPH) assay. Medium-pressure liquid chromatography was used for the pretreatment of the crude extract of *Dracocephalum heterophyllum* and targeted separation and purification of the free radical inhibitors using high-pressure liquid chromatography; the antioxidant peaks are recognized by the separation and purification process in combination with an online HPLC-DPPH system. Five free radical inhibitors with purity higher than 95% were obtained, namely xanthotoxol, 5-hydroxy-8-methoxypsoralen, luteolin, methyl rosmarinate, and ethyl rosmarinate. Finally, DPPH assays are performed, and their IC_{50} values for isolated compounds are 250.39 ± 13.32 μM, 26.91 ± 1.93 μM, 66.87 ± 14.33 μM, 21.99 ± 3.17 μM, and 36.96 ± 1.72 μM, respectively. This method is effective in isolating free radical inhibitors from *Dracocephalum heterophyllum*, and it has the potential to be adopted for the isolation of antioxidants from other plants of medicinal value as well.

Keywords: *Dracocephalum heterophyllum*; medium-pressure liquid chromatography; high-pressure liquid chromatography; online HPLC-1,1-diphenyl-2-picrylhydrazyl

1. Introduction

Dracocephalum heterophyllum Benth is commonly used in Tibetan herbal medicine in ethnic areas, and its name is "Ji Zi Qing Bao" in Tibetan and "Bai Hua Zhi Zi Hua" in Chinese pharmacopeia [1]. It is a perennial herb of the Lamiaceae family, with the effect of liver diarrhea and clearing of heat [2]. It is commonly used in Tibetan medicine to treat jaundiced hepatitis and mouth ulcers. It is recorded in ancient texts that *D. heterophyllum* is effective in treating mouth ulcers and has anti-inflammatory properties [3,4]. The constituents of *D. heterophyllum* are mainly volatile oils, terpenoids, flavonoids, and phenylpropanoids [5–8]. Modern pharmacological studies have provided evidence for the pharmacological effects of *D. heterophyllum*, such as inhibition of anti-tumor, cardiac hypertrophy, anti-inflammatory, antioxidant and free radical scavenging, anti-viral, anti-hypoxia, anti-hypertensive, and cardio protection [9–12].

Antioxidants are chemicals which can regulate oxidative stress [13]. Antioxidant chemicals act through various mechanisms, such as transition metal chelation, single electron transfer (SET), and hydrogen atom transfer (HAT). Antioxidants exert their physiological effects by protecting cellular structures from damage caused by free radicals in chemical reactions [14]. Previous data suggest that free radicals are significant in many important physiological activities, and oxidative stress determines the etiology of prevalent diseases, such as atherosclerosis, chronic renal failure, and diabetes. The common antioxidants nowadays are natural and synthetic [15]. Synthetic antioxidants are less harmful to the body, and it has become a trend to look for natural antioxidants [16].

The discovery and screening of antioxidants have shown significant progress due to online HPLC-1,1-diphenyl-2-picrylhydrazyl (HPLC-DPPH) screening. DPPH is coupled with the HPLC stream after the reduced absorption detected in the column, and the antioxidant contents at specific visible wavelengths are determined to effectively recognize free radical inhibitors in various extracts from natural products [17,18]. In traditional methods for isolating complex plant extracts, open-column chromatographic steps on polyamide, Sephadex LH-20 columns, or silica gel are required; however, they have limitations of complex processes, have irreversible adsorption, are time-consuming, and have poor reproducibility [19]. Preparative HPLC is a powerful separation and purification method, employing online detection and automatic control to purify target compounds efficiently. This approach has many advantages, including good reproducibility, high resolution, and high efficiency [20,21]. However, untreated samples that are separated directly with a high-pressure column can easily reduce the life of the stationary phase [22]. Therefore, samples are treated with medium-pressure chromatographic columns (MPCCs) before separation to extend the service life of high-pressure columns and save column costs. The traditional use of MPCCs is generally open, hindering online data monitoring. When MPCCs are applied to preparative HPLC, a variety of medium- and high-pressure columns combination could be obtained for realizing the isolation and purification of different types of natural products.

In previous studies, we successfully isolated four phenylethanols (decaffeoylverbascoside, rosmarinic acid, acteoside, and 2′-*O*-acetylplantamajoside) from *D. heterophyllum* by developing the MPCCs (silica gel × MCI GEL®CHP20P) combined with the high-pressure hilic/reversed-phase chromatography columns (Click XIon × Phenyl) [23]. Four kinds of MPCCs (silica gel × MCI GEL®CHP20P × diol × spherical C18) combined with high-pressure reversed-phase/reversed-phase chromatography columns (C18 AQ × Phenyl) were used for the separation of the four gingerols (5-methoxy-6-gingerol, 6-shogaol, 6-paradol, and diacetoxy-6-gingerdiol) [24]. Four furanocoumarins (isodemethylfuropinarine, demethylfuropinarine, alloimperatorin, and alloisoimperatorin) were isolated from the fractions of *D. heterophyllum* using three steps of MPCCs (silica gel × MCI GEL®CHP20P × diol) combined with the reversed-phase/reversed-phase (C18 AQ × 7-X10) high-pressure chromatography columns [25]. A lignin-like compound (Samwinol) was also isolated from the same subfraction with the MPCCs (silica gel × MCI GEL® CHP20P × diol × spherical C18) combined with a reversed-phase C18 high-pressure chromatography column (C18 AQ × C18 AQ) [11]. Different fraction samples cannot be separated using the same chromatographic strategy. A combination of different classes of medium- and high-pressure chromatography strategies should be developed for different compounds. For the bioactivity assessment and quality control, it is crucial for developing more reproducibility techniques to isolate and purify more free radical inhibitors from *D. heterophyllum*. This work used an online HPLC-DPPH system to recognize free radical inhibitors. An integrated medium- and high-pressure integrated chromatographic strategy were utilized to separate and purify different free radical inhibitors from *D. heterophyllum*. In addition, the antioxidant activity of isolated free radical inhibitors was tested using a DPPH assay.

2. Materials and Methods

2.1. Instrumentation, Separation Medium, and Reagents

LC-10AD HPLC device (Shimadzu Instruments, Co., Kyoto, Japan) and Essentia LC-16 (Shimadzu Instruments, Co., Shanghai, China) were used for online HPLC–DPPH systems, connected with the polyether ether ketone reaction coils (18.0 m × 0.25 mm i.d.) and a triple valve. The LC-10AD determined the DPPH screening profile, and HPLC analysis was conducted utilizing LC-16. The medium- and high-pressure preparative isolations were performed on a nonstandard NP7000 preparative liquid chromatography and a maximum of 100 mL/min of each pump (Hanbon Science & Technology Co., Huaian, China). Agilent 6500 Q-TOF mass spectrometer acquired HRESI-MS spectra of samples. The Bruker Avance (600 MHz) was utilized to obtain ^{1}H and ^{13}C NMR spectra (Bruker, Karlsruhe, Germany). UV absorbance values for the DPPH assays were obtained by employing a Readmax 1900 microplate reader (Flash, Co., Shanghai, China). MCI GEL®CHP20P (120 μm) was acquired from Mitsubishi Chemical Corporation (Kyoto, Japan). The silica was obtained from Qingdao Ocean Chemical Corporation (Qingdao, China). Analytical and preparative columns (ReproSil-Pur C18 AQ) were provided by Maisch Corporation (Munich, Germany). ACCHROM Corporation (Beijing, China) supplied the Click XIon analytical and preparative columns. Sigma-Aldrich (Steinheim, Germany) provided the DPPH standard substance. Dichloromethane (CH_2Cl_2), methanol (MeOH), and acetonitrile (ACN) were obtained from Kelon Chemical Reagent Factory (Chengdu, China). HPLC grade H_2O was prepared using a water purifier from Moore (Chongqing, China). ACN and MeOH (HPLC grade) were supplied by Kelon Chemical Reagent Factory (Chengdu, China).

2.2. Sample Extraction and Medium-Pressure Liquid Chromatography Separation

The collection of the whole *D. heterophyllum* herb was carried out from North Mountain in Huzhu, Qinghai. The authentication of the herb was carried out by Prof. Lijuan Mei (Northwest Institute of Plateau Biology). The plant sample (voucher number: nwipb-2016-10-10) was stored in the Qinghai-Tibet Plateau Biological Museum. Utilizing 80.0 L MeOH, 10 kg *D. heterophyllum* (dry in the shade herb) was extracted at room temperature thrice for 12 h, each of which was then filtered (240.0 L) and concentrated to 5.0 L, and 1.5 kg of silica gel (amorphous) was mixed with the extract and dried at 40 °C. The final 2.8 kg of a dried mixture of a silica gel-sample was pretreated with an amorphous silica gel medium-pressure liquid chromatography (MPLC) column, using the mobile phases of MeOH and CH_2Cl_2 elution gradients of 0–30 min, 0% MeOH; 30–60 min, 0–100% MeOH; and 60–90 min, 100% MeOH at a 57.0 mL/min flow rate and the 65 g once loading sample. Through 43 repeated treatments, 205.5 g fraction Fr1 was obtained.

MeOH (2.0 L) was used to re-dissolve Fr1 (205.5 g); then amorphous silica (234.0 g) was added and dried at 40 °C. The pretreatment of 439.5 g of the dried mixed sample was carried out with MCI GEL®CHP20P MPCC (49 × 460 mm) utilizing a mobile phase (M.P) system of MeOH/H_2O and eluted with 0–150 min, 20–100% MeOH and 150–210 min, 100% MeOH with 57.0 mL/min flow rate followed by the recording of the elution chromatograms at 210 nm. After 8 repetitions, the fraction Fr1-3 was collected and concentrated, and 31.62 g of sample was obtained after drying and selected to elaborate the medium- and high-pressure integrated chromatographic strategies.

2.3. High-Pressure Liquid Chromatography Isolation and Purification of Free Radical Inhibitors from Fr1-3

Fraction Fr1-3 (31.6 g) was redissolved in MeOH (1.0 L), mixed with amorphous silica gel (30.0 g), and dried at 40 °C to obtain 61.6 g of silica gel mixed sample. Fr1-3 was separated using a preparative ReproSil-Pur C18 AQ column (20 × 250 mm, 5 μm). M.P A and B were HPLC-grade water and ACN, respectively. Conditions for elution were 0–60 min, 20–50% B with 19.0 mL/min flow rate followed by the recording the chromatogram at 210 nm. The single loading sample was 10 g. After 6 repeated preparations, Fr1-3-1 to Fr1-3-7 fractions were obtained. Under the recognition results of active peaks, the fractions Fr1-3-2 (100 mg), Fr1-3-3 (138 mg), Fr1-3-4 (219 mg), and Fr1-3-5 (216 mg) were selected as the target fractions.

Subsequently, the separation of Fr1-3-2 and Fr1-3-3 has also been performed on the ReproSil-Pur C18 AQ (20 × 250 mm, 5 μm) preparative column. The M.P and flow rate were identical to those used for preparing Fr1-3, and the only difference was the elution conditions, 15% acetonitrile isocratic for 60 min for Fr1-3-2 and 20% acetonitrile isocratic for 60 min for Fr1-3-3. Finally, 2.55 mg of Fr1-3-2-1 and 5.00 mg of Fr1-3-3-1 were obtained, respectively.

Further isolation of Fr1-3-4 and Fr1-3-5 was performed on the preparative column Click XIon (20 × 250 mm, 5 μm). The M.P system was acetonitrile/water for 0–30 min, 100–85% acetonitrile at 19.0 mL/min, and 210 nm. The 16.96 mg active fraction Fr1-3-4-4 and 23.91 mg active fraction Fr1-3-5-4 were obtained, respectively. For Fr1-3-4-4 and Fr1-3-5-4, the final purification step was performed with the help of ReproSil-Pur C18 AQ while employing an ACN/water system. Fr1-3-4-4 was isocratically eluted with 18% acetonitrile for 70 min, and Fr1-3-5-4 was isocratically eluted with 22% acetonitrile for 55 min. Other conditions were the same as before. The final purification yielded 3.44 mg of Fr1-3-4-4-1, 6.85 mg of Fr1-3-4-4-2, and 8.40 mg of Fr1-3-5-4-1.

2.4. Free Radical Inhibitors Activity

The study utilized an online system of HPLC-DPPH to test the activity of Fr1-3-2-1, Fr1-3-3-1, Fr1-3-4-4-1, Fr1-3-4-4-2, and Fr1-3-5-4-1. While the analysis of the isolated antioxidants was carried out utilizing the analytical column of the ReproSil-Pur C18 AQ (4.6 × 250 mm, 5 μm), M.P A and B were HPLC-grade water and ACN, respectively. The conditions for elution were 0–60 min and 0–60% B at 1.0 mL/min and 210 nm. The DPPH (25 μg/mL) was used at a 0.8 mL/min flow rate and wavelength of 517 nm.

2.5. DPPH Assays

Appropriate amounts of Fr1-3-2-1, Fr1-3-3-1, Fr1-3-4-4-1, Fr1-3-4-4-2, and Fr1-3-5-4-1 were prepared as sample solutions over a range of (0.1, 1, 10, 50, 100, 500 μg/mL). DPPH was prepared with ethanol to 25 μg/mL concentration. The 96-well plate was added with a ratio of 3:7 sample solution and DPPH solution and incubated for 30 min in the dark, followed by the determination of the absorbance at 517 nm on a microplate reader. As a positive standard control, quercetin was utilized. The rate of DPPH radical scavenging was estimated as follows: Before calculation, the sample concentrations were converted to molar concentrations based on molecular weight.

$$\text{DPPH scavenging rate (\%)} = [1 - (A - A0)/A1] \times 100\%$$

where A, A0, and A1 were experimental, blank, and control groups absorbance, respectively.

2.6. Statistical Analysis

The IC_{50} of DPPH scavenging rate was calculated by SPSS 18.0 version (SPSS, Chicago, IL, USA). All experimental data are shown as the mean ± standard deviation in triplicate.

3. Results and Discussion

3.1. Sample Extraction and Application of Medium-Pressure Liquid Chromatography for Its Pretreatment

The proposed method is green and environment-friendly since methanol is chosen as the extraction. Air-dried *D. heterophyllum* whole grass (10.0 kg) yielded a crude sample of 1.3 kg at a 13.4% extraction yield. To eliminate polymers and sugars, the crude samples are pretreated with silica gel MPLC. Two medium-pressure columns of different sizes (49 × 100 mm and 49 × 460 mm) in the MPLC are connected into a single-column system to increase preparation efficiency and loading capacity. A baseline separation between two fractions is achieved (Figure 1A). Coarse separation of the crude sample into two fractions is easy to achieve. After 43 replicate separations, two fractions were acquired, with 205.5 g of the target fraction Fr1 (15.8% recovery).

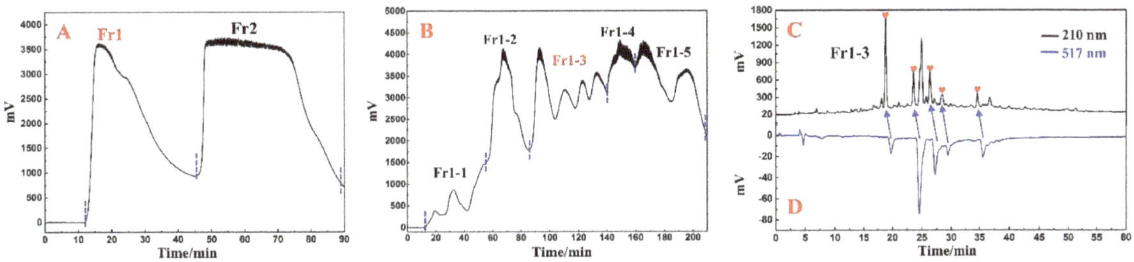

Figure 1. Chromatogram for separating *D. heterophyllum* extract (**A**) using silica gel MPLC system and the pretreatment chromatogram (**B**) of Fr1 from *D. heterophyllum* with MCI GEL®CHP20P MPLC. The analytical chromatogram (**C**) on the ReproSil-Pur C18 AQ column and DPPH radical scavenging profile (**D**) of fraction Fr1-3 sample.

The sample Fr1 also contains a large amount of chlorophyll, which may be deadened to the preparative column stationary phase, thus contaminating the column, reducing the column efficiency, and decreasing the column life. Therefore, chlorophyll removal before further preparative separations is necessary. Based on previous work in the laboratory [26], the pretreatment of Fr1 was conducted with MCI GEL®CHP20P MPCC to remove chlorophyll and enrich active components. Five fractions (Fr1-1 to Fr1-5) were collected after eight replicates (Figure 1B). To isolate more of the same categories of free radical inhibitors and to pave the way for the subsequent experiments to compare the structure-activity relationship of the same category compounds. In this paper, Fr1-3 (31.62 g) is chosen for the target free radical inhibitors separations and to evaluate the integrated chromatographic strategies.

Approximately 100 mg from fraction Fr1-3 was dissolved in MeOH (1.0 mL) followed by filtration via membrane filter (0.45 μm) to obtain a sample of fraction Fr1-3, recognized for antioxidant peaks in Fr1-3 by an online HPLC-DPPH system. The screening of antioxidant activity peaks was obtained after optimizing the analytical conditions of Fr1-3 on a ReproSil-Pur C18 AQ analytical column (Figure 1C,D). There are five main negative peaks at 517 nm in Fr1-3 (Figure 1D), indicating at least five antioxidant peaks in Fr1-3. Then, all main negative peaks at 517 nm were separated and purified.

3.2. *Target Preparation of Free Radical Inhibitor of Fr1-3 with High-Pressure Liquid Chromatography*

Figure 2A shows the preparative chromatogram of directly linearly amplified analytical conditions in Figure 1C of the Fr1-3 fraction. The preparation of this step subdivided the Fr1-3 fraction into a total of seven subfractions of Fr1-3-1 to Fr 1-3-7. The fraction Fr1-3 and its obtained subfractions were re-analyzed using the same chromatographic conditions to determine which subfraction the active peak was located, and the analytical comparison chromatograms were depicted in Figure 2B. The composition in subfractions Fr1-3-2 to Fr1-3-5 contains the time range in which negative peaks appear in Fr1-3. These four fractions were then used as the focal targets to purify the free radical inhibitors.

To further determine the reliability of the method, the Fr1-3-2 to Fr1-3-5 were identified on the online HPLC-DPPH system utilizing optimized conditions (Figure 3A–H). A negative peak in each fraction indicates that the target fractions were selected correctly and that at least one free radical inhibitor was present in each fraction. In the Fr1-3-2 fraction, peak 1 in Figure 3A corresponds to the negative peak I in Figure 3B, peak 2 in the Fr1-3-3 fraction in Figure 3C corresponds to negative peak II in Figure 3D, peak 3 in the Fr1-3-4 fraction in Figure 3E corresponds to negative peak III in Figure 3F, peak 3 is wrapped by two peaks, and peak 4 in the Fr1-3-5 fraction in Figure 3G corresponds to negative peak IV in Figure 3H. This is more relevant for the next step of purification and separation.

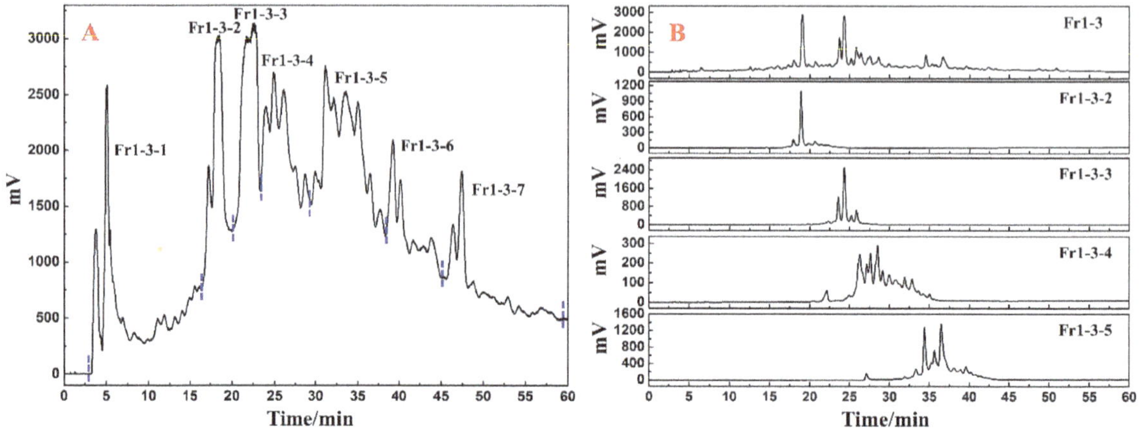

Figure 2. Preparation chromatograms (**A**) on the ReproSil-Pur C18 AQ preparative column of Fr1-3. Analytical comparison chromatograms (**B**) between fraction Fr1-3 and subfractions Fr1-3-2, Fr1-3-3, Fr1-3-4, and Fr1-3-5.

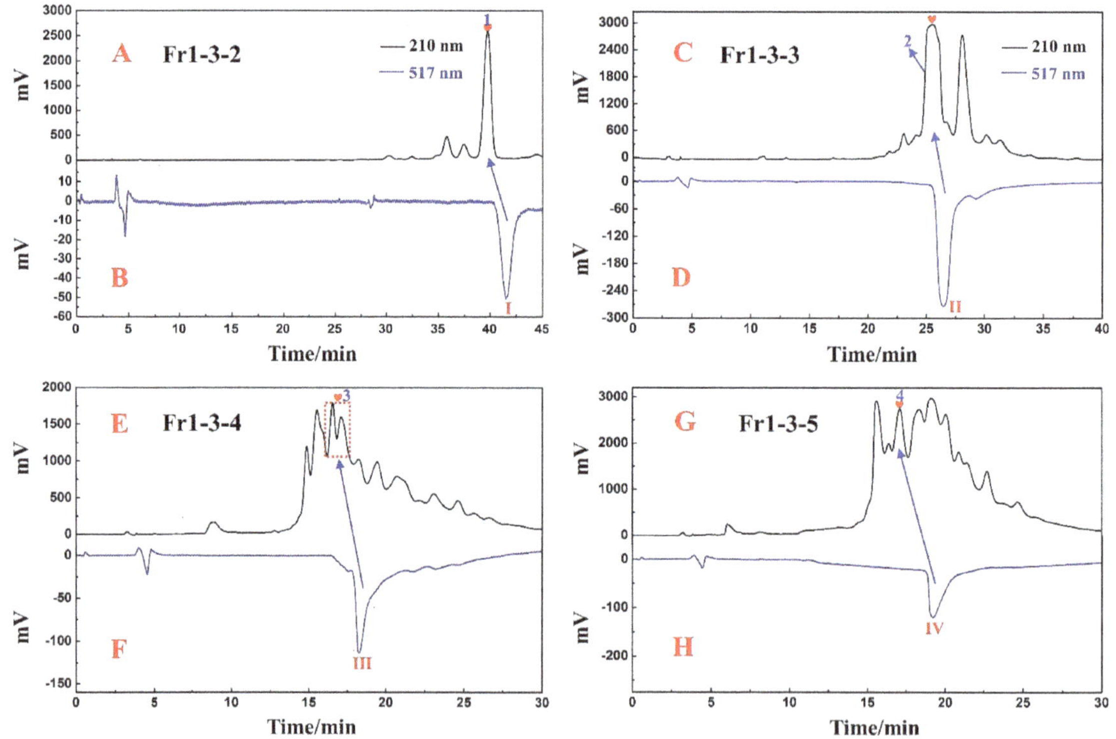

Figure 3. Chromatogram of the Fr1-3-2 verifying the DPPH inhibitory activity (**A**,**B**), Fr1-3-3 (**C**,**D**), Fr1-3-4 (**E**,**F**), Fr1-3-5 (**G**,**H**) on the ReproSil-Pur C18 AQ analytical column. Conditions for HPLC1 (**A**,**C**,**E**,**G**): M.P A: HPLC-grade water, B: acetonitrile (ACN); gradient: 20% ACN isocratic (**A**); 28% ACN (**C**,**E**); 32% ACN isocratic (**G**); wavelength: 210 nm; flow rate: 1.0 mL/min. Conditions for HPLC2 (**B**,**D**,**F**,**H**): DPPH solution flow rate: 0.8 mL/min; monitoring wavelength: 517 nm.

Figure 3A,C shows that the analytical column ReproSil-Pur C18 AQ can separate peaks 1 and 2 and other impurity peaks well; therefore, this column was selected for the next purification step. The chromatographic conditions were optimized in this work to obtain satisfactory separation curves based on the analytical conditions (Figure 3A,C). Figure 4A,C shows the optimized chromatograms; peaks 1 and 2 are well separated from the surrounding impurity peaks. However, Figure 3E,G shows that both fractions Fr1-3-4 and Fr1-3-5 were packed in a pile of peaks on the ReproSil-Pur C18 AQ analytical column with poor resolution for the next separation step. A different analytical strategy might be able to solve this problem. The separation mechanism of the hydrophilic column is different from the conventional reversed-phase column, and the hydrophilic column can be considered for the next step of purification as well as separation [27].

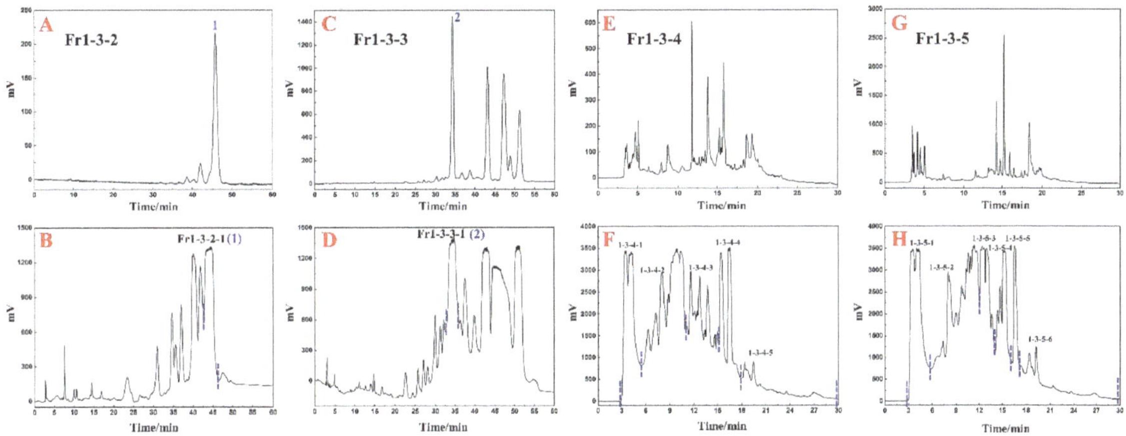

Figure 4. Fr1-3-2 and Fr1-3-3 in the analytical chromatograms (**A**,**C**) and preparative chromatograms (**B**,**D**) of the ReproSil-Pur C18 AQ column, respectively. Fr1-3-4 and Fr1-3-5 in the analytical chromatograms (**E**,**G**) and preparative chromatograms (**F**,**H**) of the Click XIon column, respectively.

Under optimized conditions, the analytical conditions were scaled up linearly for the Fr1-3-2 and Fr1-3-3, and the targeted preparation was performed on the ReproSil-Pur C18 AQ preparative column. Figure 4A,C depicts the preparative chromatograms of Fr1-3-2 and Fr1-3-3 fractions, respectively. Similar retention times for active peak 1 and active peak 2 were observed on the ReproSil-Pur C18 AQ preparative column (Figure 4B,D) and the analytical column (Figure 4A,C). Since the columns contained the same packing material, the retention of samples was the same; thus, the peaks appeared at similar times. After repeated chromatographic separations, 2.55 mg of Fr1-3-2-1 and 5.00 mg of Fr1-3-3-1 were purified from the two subfractions (Fr1-3-2 and Fr1-3-3), respectively.

For the Fr1-3-4 and Fr1-3-5, a Click XIon analytical column was chosen, and the final optimized profiles are shown in Figure 4E,G. Fr1-3-4 and Fr1-3-5 were evenly dispersed on the column rather than piled up in a mountain of peaks. Fr1-3-4 and Fr1-3-5 were suitable for this separation step with the Click XIon column. After linearly scaling up the optimized analytical conditions, the preparative chromatograms of Fr1-3-4 and Fr1-3-5 were obtained in Figure 4F,H, respectively. Fr1-3-4 was subdivided into five fractions, and Fr1-3-5 was subdivided into six fractions.

To investigate which subfractions the free radical inhibitors existed, each subfraction was re-analyzed by the ReproSil-Pur C18 AQ column under the same chromatographic conditions, and the composition of the subfractions was compared with Fr1-3-4 and Fr1-3-5, respectively. The final analytical comparison results are shown in Figure 5A–D, with peaks at 16-18 min (peak 3) corresponding to Fr1-3-4-4 and Fr1-3-4 and peaks at 17 min (peak 4) in Fr1-3-5-4 and Fr1-3-5. To determine the reliability of this result, the inverse peak recognition was performed on the online HPLC-DPPH system under the same chromatographic conditions. The recognition results are shown in Figure 5E–H, respectively. Negative peaks III (Figure 5F) and IV (Figure 5H) were present in Fr1-3-4-4 and Fr1-3-5-4, indicating that the free radical inhibitors in Fr1-3-4 and Fr1-3-5 were present in Fr1-3-4-4 and Fr1-3-5-4, respectively. These two subfractions became the target for the next purification step.

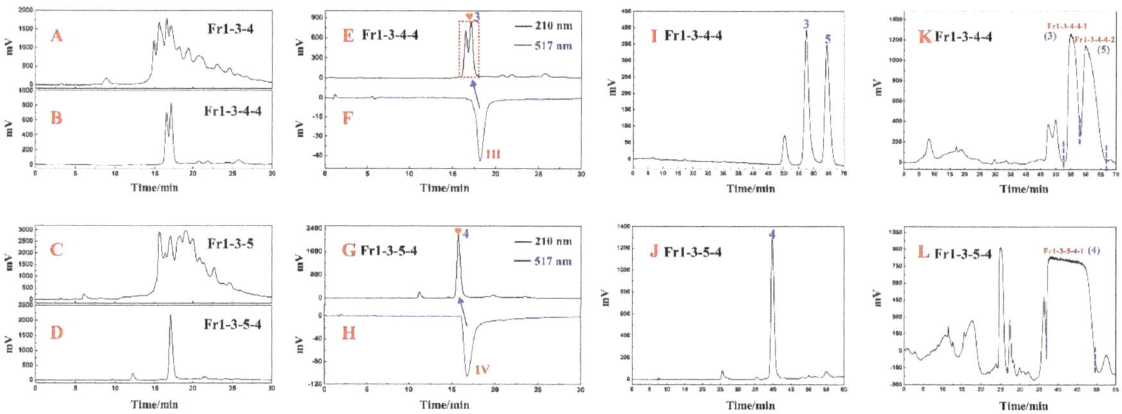

Figure 5. Analytical comparison chromatograms of Fr1-3-4 and Fr1-3-4-4 (**A**,**B**). Analytical comparison chromatograms of Fr1-3-5 and Fr1-3-5-4 (**C**,**D**). DPPH inhibitory activity verification chromatogram of the Fr1-3-4-4 (**E**,**F**), Fr1-3-5-4 (**G**,**H**) on the ReproSil-Pur C18 AQ analytical column. Fr1-3-4-4 and Fr1-3-5-4 in the analytical chromatograms (**I**,**J**) and preparative chromatograms (**K**,**L**) of the ReproSil-Pur C18 AQ column, respectively.

For Fr1-3-4-4 and Fr1-3-5-4, the chromatographic conditions were optimized to obtain the analytical chromatograms (Figure 5I,J). The previous hump was optimized (Figure 5I) into two single chromatographic peaks (peak 3 and peak 5) with good resolution. The main peak (peak 4) was well separated from the surrounding impurity peaks (Figure 5G) and conducive to the direct purification of the free radical inhibitor by linear amplification. Based on the analytical conditions, the analytical conditions were linearly amplified directly, and the final purification step for Fr1-3-4-4 and Fr1-3-5-4 was carried out using the preparative ReproSil-Pur C18 AQ column, and the preparative chromatograms are shown in Figure 5K,L. Fr1-3-4-4 was purified to obtain two free radical inhibitors (Fr1-3-4-4-1 and Fr1-3-4-4-2) with masses of 3.44 and 6.85 mg, respectively. Fr1-3-5-4 yielded a free radical inhibitor named Fr1-3-5-4-1 (8.40 mg).

3.3. Purity, Activity and Structural of Isolated Free Radical Inhibitors

The purity of the isolated Fr1-3-2-1, Fr1-3-3-1, Fr1-3-4-4-1, Fr1-3-4-4-2, and Fr1-3-5-4-1 were re-evaluated using the ReproSil-Pur C18 AQ analytical column and online HPLC-DPPH system. Figure 6A–J show that the purity of the five free radical inhibitors was much higher than 95% according to the calculation of the peak area percentage. Fr1-3-2-1, Fr1-3-3-1, Fr1-3-4-4-1, Fr1-3-4-4-2, and Fr1-3-5-4-1 were identified by HRESI-MS and NMR spectral data to elucidate the structures of the target free radical inhibitors with the literature data. Figures S1–S15 in the supplemental material showed the full spectra of the five free radical inhibitors structurally identified. The NMR and mass spectral data of Fr1-3-2-1, Fr1-3-3-1, Fr1-3-4-4-1, Fr1-3-4-4-2, and Fr1-3-5-4-1 were compared with xanthotoxol, 5-hydroxy-8-methoxypsoralen, luteolin, methyl rosmarinate, and ethyl rosmarinate, respectively (Figure 6K–O).

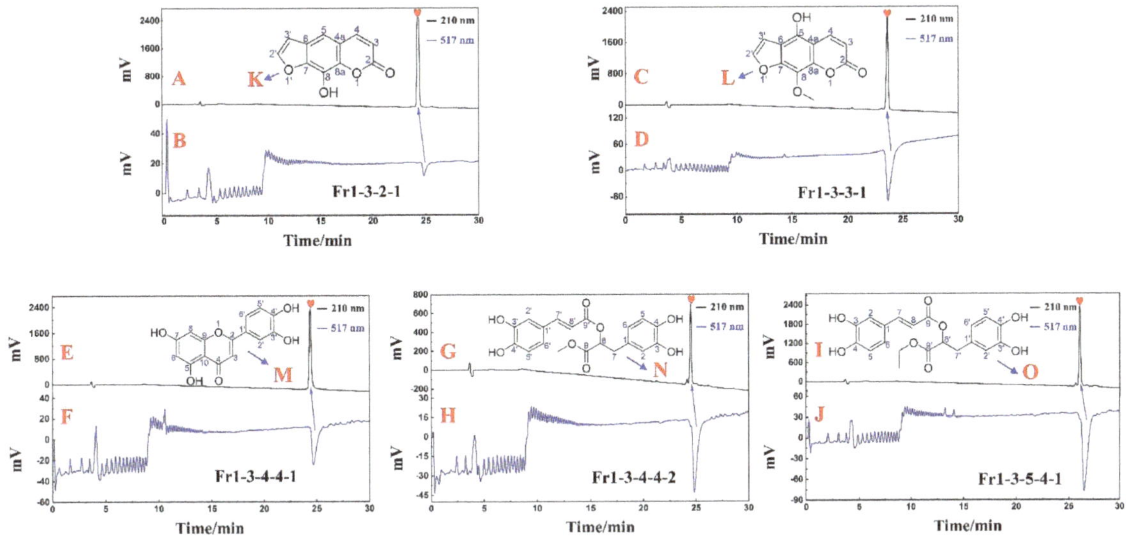

Figure 6. Purity and DPPH inhibitory activity verification chromatogram of the isolated Fr1-3-2-1 (**A**,**B**), Fr1-3-3-1 (**C**,**D**), Fr1-3-4-4-1 (**E**,**F**), Fr1-3-4-4-2 (**G**,**H**), and Fr1-3-5-4-1 (**I**,**J**). Chemical structures of Fr1-3-2-1 (**K**), Fr1-3-3-1 (**L**), Fr1-3-4-4-1 (**M**), Fr1-3-4-4-2 (**N**), and Fr1-3-5-4-1 (**O**) isolated from Fr1-3 of *D. heterophyllum*.

Fr1-3-2-1: (yellow powder, peak 1, xanthotoxol, 2.55 mg), HRESI-MS m/z: 201.0265 $[M-H]^-$. ^{1}H NMR (600 MHz, DMSO-d_6) δ: 8.12 (1H, d, J = 9.5 Hz, 4-H), 8.07 (1H, d, J = 2.1 Hz, 2′-H), 7.45 (1H, s, 5-H), 7.04 (1H, d, J = 2.1 Hz, 3′-H), 6.40 (1H, d, J = 9.5, 3-H). ^{13}C NMR (151 MHz, DMSO-d_6) δ: 160.1 (C-2), 147.5 (C-2′), 145.6 (C-7), 145.4 (C-4), 139.8 (C-8a), 130.1 (C-8), 125.2 (C-5), 116.3 (C-6), 113.8 (C-4a), 110.2 (C-3), 107.1 (C-3′), consistent with published data for xanthotoxol [28].

Fr1-3-3-1: (yellow powder, peak 2, 5-hydroxy-8-methoxypsoralen, 5.00 mg), HRESI-MS m/z: 231.0372 $[M-H]^-$. ^{1}H NMR (600 MHz, DMSO-d_6) δ: 10.10 (1H, s, 5-OH), 8.17 (1H, d, J = 9.8 Hz, 4-H), 8.05 (1H, d, J = 2.3 Hz, 2′-H), 7.29 (1H, d, J = 2.3 Hz, 3′-H), 6.32 (1H, d, J = 9.8 Hz, 3-H), 4.09 (3H, s, 8-OCH_3). ^{13}C NMR (151 MHz, DMSO-d_6) δ: 159.9 (C-2), 147.1 (C-2′), 146.2 (C-7), 141.2 (C-4), 139.9 (C-8a), 139.6 (C-8), 125.5 (C-5), 114.8 (C-6), 112.4 (C-4a), 107.1 (C-3), 105.4 (C-3′), 61.1 (C-9), consistent with the literature data for 5-hydroxy-8-methoxypsoralen [29].

Fr1-3-4-4-1: (yellow needles, peak 3, luteolin, 3.44 mg), HRESI-MS m/z: 309.0478 $[M+Na]^+$. ^{1}H NMR (600 MHz, DMSO-d_6) δ: 12.97 (1H, s, 5-OH), 10.83 (1H, s, 7-OH), 9.92 (1H, s, 3′-OH), 10.83 (1H, s, 4′-OH), 7.41 (1H, dd, J = 8.3, 2.1 Hz, 6′-H), 7.39 (1H, d, J = 2.1 Hz, 2′-H) 6.89 (1H, d, J = 8.3 Hz, 5′-H), 6.67 (1H, s, 3-H), 6.44 (1H, d, J = 1.9 Hz, 8-H), 6.19 (1H, d, J = 1.9 Hz, 6-H). ^{13}C NMR (151 MHz, DMSO-d_6) δ: 181.7 (C-4), 164.1 (C-7), 163.9 (C-2), 161.5 (C-5), 157.3 (C-9), 149.7 (C-4′), 145.7 (C-3′), 121.5 (C-1′), 119.0 (C-6′), 116.0 (C-5′), 113.4 (C-2′), 103.7 (C-10), 102.9 (C-3), 98.8 (C-6), 93.8 (C-8). The data supported the compound's identity as luteolin [30].

Fr1-3-4-4-2: (yellow powder, peak 5, methyl rosmarinate, 6.85 mg), HRESI-MS m/z: 397.1002 $[M+Na]^+$. ^{1}H NMR (600 MHz, DMSO-d_6) δ: 9.66 (1H, s, 4′-OH), 9.16 (1H, s, 3′-OH), 8.81 (1H, s, 4-OH), 8.75 (1H, s, 3-OH), 7.48 (1H, d, J = 15.8 Hz, 7′-H), 7.06 (1H, d, J = 1.8 Hz, 2′-H), 7.02 (1H, dd, J = 8.2, 1.8 Hz, 6′-H), 6.77 (1H, d, J = 8.2 Hz, 5′-H), 6.65 (1H, d, J = 1.7 Hz, 2-H), 6.64 (1H, d, J = 8.0 Hz, 5-H), 6.50 (1H, dd, J = 8.0, 1.7 Hz, 6-H), 6.26 (1H, d, J = 15.9 Hz, 8′-H), 5.12 (1H, dd, J = 7.5, 5.1 Hz, 8-H), 3.63 (1H, s, 9-OCH_3), 2.96 (2H, m, 7-H). ^{13}C NMR (151 MHz, DMSO-d_6) δ: 169.9 (C-9), 165.9 (C-9′), 148.8 (C-4′), 146.4 (C-7′), 145.6 (C-3′), 145.0 (C-3), 144.1 (C-4), 126.6 (C-1), 125.2 (C-1′), 121.7 (C-6′), 120.1 (C-6), 116.7 (C-2), 115.8 (C-5′),

115.4 (C-5), 115.0 (C-2′). 112.8 (C-8′), 72.8 (C-8), 52.0 (C-10), 36.2 (C-7). The compound was identified as methyl rosmarinate [31].

Fr1-3-5-4-1: (yellow powder, peak 4, ethyl rosmarinate, 8.40 mg,), HRESI-MS m/z: 411.1157 $[M+Na]^+$. ^{1}H NMR (600 MHz, DMSO-d_6) δ: 9.65 (1H, s, 4′-OH), 9.15 (1H, s, 4-OH), 8.80 (1H, s, 3′-OH), 8.74 (1H, s, 3-OH), 7.49 (1H, d, J = 15.8 Hz, 7-H), 7.06 (1H, d, J = 2.0 Hz, 2-H), 7.02 (1H, d, J = 8.2, 2.0 Hz, 6-H), 6.77 (1H, d, J = 8.2 Hz, 5-H), 6.66 (1H, d, J = 2.0 Hz, 2′-H), 6.64 (1H, d, J = 7.9 Hz, 5′-H), 6.51 (1H, dd, J = 7.9, 2.0 Hz, 6′-H), 6.27 (1H, d, J = 15.8 Hz, 8-H), 5.08 (1H, dd, J = 7.0, 5.8 Hz, 8′-H), 4.09 (2H, q, J = 6.9 Hz, 10-H), 3.44 (1H, dd, J = 14.0, 7.0 Hz, 7′a-H), 2.95 (1H, t, J = 14.0, 5.8 Hz, 7′b-H), 1.14 (3H, t, J = 14.3, 6.9 Hz, 11-H), ^{13}C NMR (151 MHz, DMSO-d_6) δ: 169.4 (C-9′), 165.9 (C-9), 148.7 (C-4), 146.3 (C-7), 145.6 (C-3),145.0 (C-3′), 144.1 (C-4′), 126.6 (C-1′), 125.3 (C-1), 121.7 (C-6), 120.1 (C-6′), 116.7 (C-2′), 115.8 (C-5), 115.4 (C-5′), 115.0 (C-2), 112.9 (C-8), 72.9 (C-8′), 60.8 (C-10), 36.2 (C-7′), 14.0 (C-11). The above data were compared with those reported in the literature [31] and were consistent with ethyl rosmarinate.

A slight modification was conducted in the DPPH assay to quantify the antioxidant activity of the isolated free radical inhibitors [32], the DPPH radicals scavenging rate by free radical inhibitors was determined, and the IC_{50} values were calculated according to the formula. Their IC_{50} values were 250.39 ± 13.32 µM for xanthotoxol, 26.91 ± 1.93 µM for 5-hydroxy-8-methoxypsoralen, 66.87 ± 14.33 µM for luteolin, 21.99 ± 3.17 µM for methyl rosmarinate, and 36.96 ± 1.72 µM for ethyl rosmarinate, respectively (Figure 7). Compared with the positive control quercetin (IC_{50} value was 10.33 µM), Fr1-3-3-1 and Fr1-3-4-4-2 were slightly less effective in free radicals scavenging than quercetin; however, the overall effect was comparable. When comparing the IC_{50} values of Fr1-3-2-1 and Fr1-3-3-1, the antioxidant activity of Fr1-3-3-1 was stronger compared with Fr1-3-2-1 because of a lower IC_{50} value since it has substituents at both C5 and C8 positions, and the methoxylation of the C5 position significantly enhances its free radicals scavenging ability. The difference in the substitution groups ultimately leads to the difference in the ability to scavenge DPPH radicals.

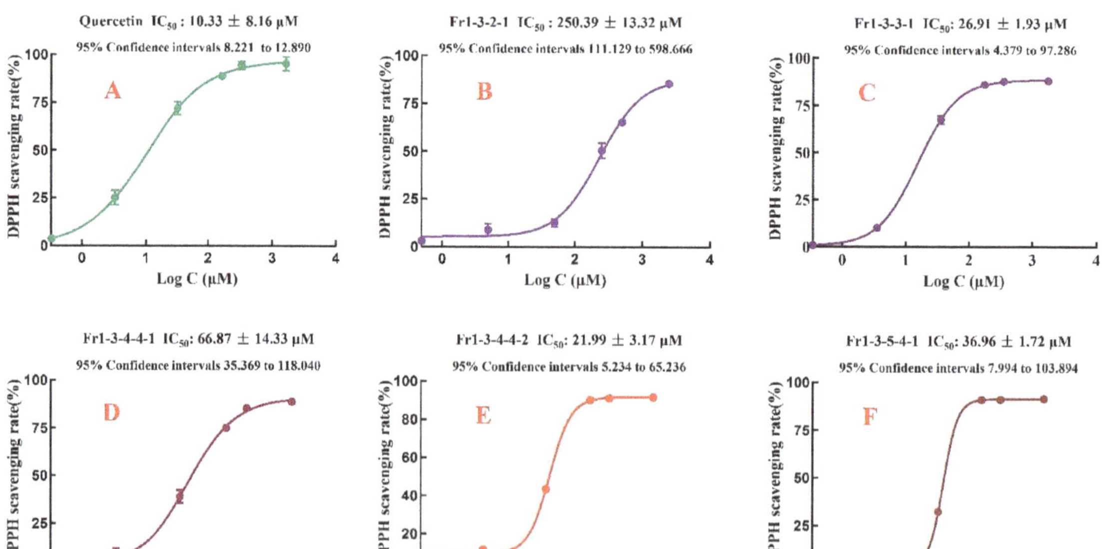

Figure 7. DPPH scavenging rate curves of quercetin (**A**), Fr1-3-2-1 (**B**), Fr1-3-3-1 (**C**), Fr1-3-4-4-1 (**D**), Fr1-3-4-4-2 (**E**), and Fr1-3-5-4-1 (**F**) and their IC_{50} values.

4. Conclusions

In this work, an online HPLC-DPPH system was used to recognize free radical inhibitors in *D. heterophyllum*, combining medium- and high-pressure integrated chromatographic methods for the separation and purification of five free radical inhibitors. Sample pretreatment was performed on the silica gel and MCI GEL®CHP20P MPCCs. Subsequently, the integration of reversed-phase and hydrophilic high-pressure liquid chromatography was applied in separating and purifying five free radical inhibitors, namely xanthotoxol, 5-hydroxy-8-methoxypsoralen, luteolin, methyl rosmarinate, and ethyl rosmarinate with purity higher than 95%. DPPH assays were also performed to evaluate these compounds' antioxidant capacity and finally concluded that these free radical inhibitors possess good antioxidant capacity. However, their mechanisms of action still need to be explored by different methods, such as ABTS, CUPRAC, and FRAP, to study various antioxidant mechanisms in cellular experiments. To the best of our knowledge, the described method lays the foundation for the isolation and purification of free radical inhibitors with good activity from various natural products.

Supplementary Materials: The following supporting information can be downloaded at: https://www.mdpi.com/article/10.3390/separations9120420/s1, Figure S1: High-resolution mass spectrum of xanthotoxol (Fr1-3-2-1). Figure S2: ^{1}H NMR Spectrum (600 MHz) of xanthotoxol (Fr1-3-2-1) (in DMSO-d_6). Figure S3: ^{13}C NMR Spectrum (151 MHz) of xanthotoxol (Fr1-3-2-1) (in DMSO-d_6). Figure S4: High-resolution mass spectrum of 5-hydroxy-8-methoxypsoralen (Fr1-3-3-1). Figure S5: ^{1}H NMR Spectrum (600 MHz) of 5-hydroxy-8-methoxypsoralen (Fr1-3-3-1) (in DMSO-d_6). Figure S6: ^{13}C NMR Spectrum (151 MHz) of 5-hydroxy-8-methoxypsoralen (Fr1-3-3-1) (in DMSO-d_6). Figure S7: High-resolution mass spectrum of luteolin (Fr1-3-4-4-1). Figure S8: ^{1}H NMR Spectrum (600 MHz) of luteolin (Fr1-3-4-4-1) (in DMSO-d_6). Figure S9: ^{13}C NMR Spectrum (151 MHz) of luteolin (Fr1-3-4-4-1) (in DMSO-d_6). Figure S10: High-resolution mass spectrum of methyl rosmarinate (Fr1-3-4-4-2). Figure S11: ^{1}H NMR Spectrum (600 MHz) of methyl rosmarinate (Fr1-3-4-4-2) (in DMSO-d_6). Figure S12: ^{13}C NMR Spectrum (151 MHz) of methyl rosmarinate (Fr1-3-4-4-2) (in DMSO-d_6). Figure S13: High-resolution mass spectrum of ethyl rosmarinate (Fr1-3-5-4-1). Figure S14: ^{1}H NMR Spectrum (600 MHz) of ethyl rosmarinate (Fr1-3-5-4-1) (in DMSO-d_6). Figure S15: ^{13}C NMR Spectrum (151 MHz) of ethyl rosmarinate (Fr1-3-5-4-1) (in DMSO-d_6).

Author Contributions: Conceptualization, methodology, J.D. and Z.W.; writing—original draft, Y.L. and J.D.; formal analysis, investigation, data curation, Q.W. and Y.L.; supervision, project administration, and funding acquisition, J.D. All authors have read and agreed to the published version of the manuscript.

Funding: This research was funded by the Applied Basic Research Project of Qinghai Province (2020-ZJ-706).

Institutional Review Board Statement: Not applicable.

Informed Consent Statement: Not applicable.

Data Availability Statement: Data are available on request from the authors.

Conflicts of Interest: The authors declare no conflict of interest.

References

1. Dang, J.; Zhang, L.; Shao, Y.; Mei, L.; Liu, Z.; Yue, H.; Wang, Q.; Tao, Y. Preparative isolation of antioxidative compounds from *Dracocephalum heterophyllum* using off-line two-dimensional reversed-phase liquid chromatography/hydrophilic interaction chromatography guided by on-line HPLC-DPPH assay. *J. Chromatogr. B* **2018**, *1095*, 267–274. [CrossRef] [PubMed]
2. Liu, J.Y.; He, J.X.; Shi, G.X.; An, L.Z.; Öpik, M.; Feng, H.Y. Diverse communities of arbuscular mycorrhizal fungi inhabit sites with very high altitude in Tibet Plateau. *FEMS Microbiol. Ecol.* **2011**, *78*, 355–365. [CrossRef] [PubMed]
3. Zeng, Q.; Jin, H.Z.; Qin, J.J.; Fu, J.J.; Hu, X.J.; Liu, J.H.; Yan, L.; Chen, M.; Zhang, W.D. Chemical Constituents of Plants from the Genus *Dracocephalum*. *Chem. Biodivers.* **2010**, *7*, 1911–1929. [CrossRef] [PubMed]
4. Numonov, S.; Sharopov, F.; Qureshi, M.N.; Gaforzoda, L.; Gulmurodov, I.; Khalilov, Q.; Setzer, W.N.; Habasi, M.; Aisa, H.A. The Ursolic Acid-Rich Extract of *Dracocephalum heterophyllum* Benth. with Potent Antidiabetic and Cytotoxic Activities. *Appl. Sci.* **2020**, *10*, 6505. [CrossRef]

5. Numonov, S.R.; Usmanova, S.K.; Aisa, H.A. Chemical composition of *Dracocephalum heterophyllum*. *Chem. Nat. Compd.* **2013**, *49*, 511–513. [CrossRef]
6. Shi, Q.Q.; Zhao, J.Q.; Dang, J.; Yuan, X.; Wang, Q.L. Triterpenes, flavonoids, and lignans from *Dracocephalum heterophyllum*. *Chem. Nat. Compd.* **2018**, *54*, 970–972. [CrossRef]
7. Stappen, I.; Wanner, J.; Tabanca, N.; Wedge, D.E.; Ali, A.; Kaul, V.K.; Lal, B.; Jaitak, V.; Gochev, V.K.; Schmidt, E.; et al. Chemical composition and biological activity of essential oils of *Dracocephalum heterophyllum* and *Hyssopus officinalis* from Western Himalaya. *Nat. Prod. Commun.* **2015**, *10*, 133–138. [CrossRef]
8. Singh, N.; Kaul, V.K.; Megeji, N.W.; Singh, V.; Ahuja, P.S. Essential oil composition of three accessions of *Dracocephalum heterophyllum* Benth. cultivated at Palampur, India. *Nat. Prod. Res.* **2008**, *22*, 927–936. [CrossRef]
9. Fang, Y.; Sun, D.; Li, G.; Lv, Y.; Li, J.; Wang, Q.; Dang, J. Ethyl Acetate Extract of *Dracocephalum heterophyllum* Benth Ameliorates Nonalcoholic Steatohepatitis and Fibrosis via Regulating Bile Acid Metabolism, Oxidative Stress and Inhibiting Inflammation. *Separations* **2022**, *9*, 273. [CrossRef]
10. Shi, Q.Q.; Dang, J.; Wen, H.X.; Yuan, X.; Tao, Y.D.; Wang, Q.L. Anti-hepatitis, antioxidant activities and bioactive compounds of *Dracocephalum heterophyllum* extracts. *Bot. Stud.* **2016**, *57*, 16. [CrossRef]
11. Li, C.; Dang, J.; Lv, Y.; Fang, Y.; Ma, C.; Wang, Q.; Li, G. The Isolation and Preparation of Samwinol from *Dracocephalum heterophyllum* and Prevention on $A\beta_{25-35}$-Induced Neuroinflammation in PC-12 Cells. *Int. J. Mol. Sci.* **2022**, *23*, 11572. [CrossRef] [PubMed]
12. Wang, Y.; Lai, D.; Geng, Y.; Shang, P.; Wang, P. Therapeutic effects of *Dracocephalum heterophyllum* in collagen-induced arthritis. *AAPS Open* **2022**, *8*, 4. [CrossRef]
13. Ahmed, S.; Habiba, M.; Hossain, M.; Hoque, S.A.; Rahman, M. Retardation of oxidative rancidity in ghee adding orange peel powder at different storage temperature. *J. Food Sci. Technol.* **2022**, 1–9. [CrossRef]
14. Hu, J.; Yang, L.; Yang, P.; Jiang, S.; Liu, X.; Li, Y. Polydopamine free radical scavengers. *Biomater. Sci.* **2020**, *8*, 4940–4950. [CrossRef]
15. Jawad, A.; Zhan, K.; Wang, H.; Shahzad, A.; Zeng, Z.; Wang, J.; Zhou, X.; Ullah, H.; Chen, Z.; Chen, Z. Tuning of persulfate activation from a free radical to a nonradical pathway through the incorporation of non-redox magnesium oxide. *Environ. Sci. Technol.* **2020**, *54*, 2476–2488. [CrossRef] [PubMed]
16. Dungan, A.M.; Bulach, D.; Lin, H.; van Oppen, M.J.; Blackall, L.L. Development of a free radical scavenging bacterial consortium to mitigate oxidative stress in cnidarians. *Microb. Biotechnol.* **2021**, *14*, 2025–2040. [CrossRef] [PubMed]
17. Dang, J.; Chen, C.; Ma, J.; Dawa, Y.; Wang, Q.; Tao, Y.; Wang, Q.; Ji, T. Preparative isolation of highly polar free radical inhibitor from *Floccularia luteovirens* using hydrophilic interaction chromatography directed by on-line HPLC-DPPH assay. *J. Chromatogr. B* **2020**, *1142*, 122043. [CrossRef]
18. Wang, X.; Zhang, Y.; Wu, N.; Cao, J.; Tao, Y.; Yu, R. A Method to Separate Two Main Antioxidants from *Lepidium latifolium* L. Extracts Using Online Medium Pressure Chromatography Tower and Two-Dimensional Inversion/Hydrophobic Interaction Chromatography Based on Online HPLC-DPPH Assay. *Separations* **2021**, *8*, 238. [CrossRef]
19. Dang, J.; Wang, Q.; Wang, Q.L.; Yuan, C.; Li, G.; Ji, T.F. Preparative isolation of antioxidative gallic acid derivatives from *Saxifraga tangutica* using a class separation method based on medium-pressure liquid chromatography and reversed-phase liquid chromatography. *J. Sep. Sci.* **2021**, *44*, 3734–3746. [CrossRef]
20. Yang, X.; Rajivgandhi, G.N.; Ramachandran, G.; Alharbi, N.S.; Kadaikunnan, S.; Khaled, J.M.; Almanaa, T.N.; Manoharan, N.; Viji, R. Preparative HPLC fraction of *Hibiscus rosa-sinensis* essential oil against biofilm forming *Klebsiella pneumoniae*. *Saudi J. Biol. Sci.* **2020**, *27*, 2853–2862. [CrossRef]
21. Jibril, S.; Basar, N.; Sirat, H.M.; Wahab, R.A.; Mahat, N.A.; Nahar, L.; Sarker, S.D. Application of Box–Behnken design for ultrasound-assisted extraction and recycling preparative HPLC for isolation of anthraquinones from *Cassia singueana*. *Phytochem Anal.* **2019**, *30*, 101–109. [CrossRef] [PubMed]
22. Dawa, Y.Z.; Du, Y.R.; Wang, Q.; Chen, C.B.; Zou, D.L.; Qi, D.S.; Ma, J.B.; Dang, J. Targeted isolation of 1,1-diphenyl-2-picrylhydrazyl inhibitors from *Saxifraga atrata* using medium- and high-pressure liquid chromatography combined with online high performance liquid chromatography-1,1-diphenyl-2-picrylhydrazyl detection. *J. Chromatogr. A* **2021**, *1635*, 461690. [CrossRef] [PubMed]
23. Lv, Y.; Wang, Z.; Wu, Q.; Fang, Y.; Wang, Q.; Li, G.; Dang, J. Preparation and Antioxidant Activities of Phenylethanoids from *Dracocephalum heterophyllum*. *Separations* **2022**, *9*, 111. [CrossRef]
24. Dang, J.; Lv, Y.; Li, C.; Fang, Y.; Li, G.; Wang, Q. Integrated chromatographic approach for the discovery of gingerol antioxidants from *Dracocephalum heterophyllum* and their potential targets. *Anal. Methods* **2022**, *14*, 4133–4145. [CrossRef]
25. Lv, Y.; Li, C.; Wang, Z.; Wang, Q.; Li, G.; Dang, J. Preparative isolation of antioxidative furanocoumarins from *Dracocephalum heterophyllum* and their potential action target. *J. Sep. Sci.* **2022**, *24*. [CrossRef]
26. Yuan, C.; Dang, J.; Han, Y.; Liu, C.; Yu, S.; Lv, Y.; Cui, Y.B.; Wang, Z.H.; Li, G. Preparative isolation of maltol glycoside from *Dianthus superbus* and its anti-inflammatory activity in vitro. *RSC Adv.* **2022**, *12*, 5031–5041. [CrossRef]
27. Dang, J.; Zhang, L.; Wang, Q.; Mei, L.; Yue, H.; Liu, Z.; Shao, Y.; Gao, Q.; Tao, Y. Target separation of flavonoids from *Saxifraga tangutica* using two-dimensional hydrophilic interaction chromatography/reversed-phase liquid chromatography. *J. Sep. Sci.* **2018**, *41*, 4419–4429. [CrossRef]
28. Waight, E.S.; Razdan, T.K.; Qadri, B.; Harkar, S. Chromones and coumarins from *Skimmia laureola*. *Phytochemistry* **1987**, *26*, 2063–2069. [CrossRef]

29. Deng, G.G.; Yang, X.W.; Zhang, Y.B.; Xu, W.; Wei, W.; Chen, T.L. Chemical constituents from lipophilic parts in roots of *Angelica dahurica var. formosana* cv. Chuanbaizhi. *China J. Chin. Mater. Med.* **2015**, *40*, 2148–2156.
30. Youssef, D.; Frahm, A.W. Constituents of the Egyptian *Centaurea scoparia*; III. Phenolic constituents of the aerial parts. *Planta Med.* **1995**, *61*, 570–573. [CrossRef]
31. Woo, E.R.; Piao, M.S. Antioxidative constituents from *Lycopus lucidus*. *Arch. Pharm Res.* **2004**, *27*, 173–176. [CrossRef] [PubMed]
32. Sethi, S.; Joshi, A.; Arora, B.; Bhowmik, A.; Sharma, R.R.; Kumar, P. Significance of FRAP, DPPH, and CUPRAC assays for antioxidant activity determination in apple fruit extracts. *Eur. Food Res. Technol.* **2020**, *246*, 591–598. [CrossRef]

nutrients

MDPI

Article

Moderate Hyperglycemia-Preventive Effect and Mechanism of Action of *Periplaneta americana* Oligosaccharides in Streptozotocin-Induced Diabetic Mice

Kaimin Lu [1,2,†], Yufei He [1,†], Chuanfang Wu [1,*] and Jinku Bao [1,*]

[1] Key Laboratory of Bio-Resource and Eco-Environment of Ministry of Education, College of Life Sciences, Sichuan University, Chengdu 610065, China
[2] Pharmacy Research Center, Binzhou Medical University, Yantai 264003, China
* Correspondence: wuchuanfang@scu.edu.cn (C.W.); baojinku@scu.edu.cn (J.B.); Tel.: +86-28-8541-5171 (J.B.)
† These authors contributed equally to this work.

Abstract: *Periplaneta americana* is a kind of medicinal and edible insect, and its oligosaccharides (PAOS) have been reported to exert anti-inflammatory effects by regulating immunity, reducing oxidative stress, and meliorating gut microbiota. We hypothesized PAOS might benefit experimental diabetes mellitus (DM), an inflammatory disease coordinated by both innate and adaptive immunity. This study aimed to evaluate the effect of PAOS on glycemia and its potential mechanisms. Mice model of diabetes was established, and then the potential effects of PAOS was tested in vivo. Here, we found that PAOS triggered a moderate hyperglycemia-preventive effect on DM mice, showing markedly alleviated symptoms of DM, reduced blood glucose, and meliorated functions of liver and pancreas β cell. Deciphering the underlying mechanism of PAOS-improving diabetes, the results revealed that PAOS downregulated the blood glucose level by activating PI3K/AKT/mTOR and Keap/Nrf2/HO-1 pathways, meanwhile inhibiting TLR4/MAPK/NF-κB, Beclin1/LC3, and NLRP3/caspase1 pathways in vivo. Furthermore, analyses of the microbial community intriguingly exhibited that PAOS promoted the communities of bacteria producing short-chain fatty acids (SCFAs), whereas attenuating lipopolysaccharides (LPS)-producing ones that favored inflammatory tolerance. Collectively, balancing the intestinal bacterial communities by PAOS, which favored anabolism but suppressed inflammatory responses, contributed substantially to the glycemia improvement of PAOS in DM mice. Accordingly, PAOS might function as complementary and alternative medicine for DM.

Keywords: diabetes mellitus (DM); oligosaccharides; inflammation; gut microbiota; oxidative stress; *Periplaneta americana*

1. Introduction

Diabetes mellitus (DM), of any type, is a severe metabolic disease characterized by high blood glucose caused by insulin production defects or inefficient insulin utilization [1]. DM, is related to the reduced quality of life and substantial socioeconomic burden [2]. World Health Organization (WHO) has proposed that 537 million people suffer from diabetes of any type in 2021, and this number will increase to 783 million by 2045 [3].

Type 1 DM is an autoimmune disease resulting from an immune system attack on the islet β cells that produce insulin, leading to an inflammatory process and a lack of insulin in the body [4]. It is usually diagnosed in children and young adults and is determined mainly by host genetics [5]. Furthermore, growing evidence shows that environmental factors, such as diet and intestinal microbiota, play essential roles in the type 1 DM development process [6]. The gut microbiota has been a target to the treatment of type 1 DM [7]. Nowadays, there is considerable interest in searching for high-active compounds from natural products having multiple beneficial effects on glycemia, microbiota, and inflammation, that could help preventing DM or that can be of an additional help for DM treatment.

Periplaneta americana is the part of Insecta class, Dictyoptera order, and Blattidae family [8], and is widely distributed in tropical area, which as a medicinal insect is first recorded in an ancient Chinese pharmacopeia "Shen Nong Ben Cao Jing" [9]. The main chemical constituents of *Periplaneta americana* include pheromones, proteins, fatty acids, and esters, amino acids, alkaloids, alkanes, polysaccharides, isofavones, cockroach oil, and peptides, which has been used to treat arthritis, gastric ulcer reverse, fever, carbuncles, pains, and inflammation of the extremities for several hundred years [8,9]. Nature products have great potential for cost-effective benefits with high safety, such as functional oligosaccharides [10]. Our previous study has reported that *Periplaneta americana* oligosaccharides (PAOS) exert anti-inflammatory activity by modulating immune responses, reducing oxidative stress, inhibiting Toll-like receptor 4 (TLR4)/mitogen-activated protein kinase (MAPK)/nuclear factor kappa-B (NF-κB) pathway, preserving intestinal barrier integrity, and regulating gut microbiota with high safety in vivo [11]. However, no investigation has been undertaken to determine the effect of PAOS on glycemia. Thus, it is worth exploring whether PAOS has blood glucose-lowering activity. In this study, a moderate hyperglycemia-preventive effect of PAOS was examined, and its underlying mechanism was investigated in vivo. These findings highlight a new compound from a natural source that could be of additional help in DM therapeutics.

2. Materials and Methods

2.1. Materials and Chemicals

The *Periplaneta americana* residues were collected from the Sichuan Gooddoctor-Panxi Pharmaceutical Company (Xichang, Sichuan Province, China).

2.2. Preparation of PAOS

The PAOS was obtained following our previous methods [11]. The crude PAOS was extracted by PBS buffer (pH 6.5) in a ratio of 1:10 (w/w) at 560 w for 60 s in single-mode microwave-assisted synthesis equipment (Monowave 300, Anton Parr, Graz, Austria), and then extracted by 10,000 u papain papaya (Solarbio, Beijing, China) at 65 °C for 4 h. The PAOS was purified by gel filtration chromatography with Sephacry S-100 high resolution column (1.5 × 95 cm, GE, American). The third peak was collected, concentrated, and lyophilized for further research. PAOS consist of 83% glucose, 6% galactose, and 11% xylose with a molecular mass of 1.0 kDa, and the main backbone of PAOS is 1,4-Glcp with 7% branching degree [11].

2.3. Animals

Male 6-weeks-old C57BL/6 mice were purchased from Dashuo Laboratory Animal Technology Co. in Chengdu, China. All animal experiments were performed according to the Animal Care and Use Committee of China guidelines. The study was in complete compliance with the National Institutes of Health Guide for the Care and Use of Laboratory Animals and approved by Research Ethics Committee of Sichuan University (NO.20190402001). Prior to the experiments, the mice were housed for at least 1 week at 25 °C under 12 h light/dark cycles with access to standard diet pellets (3.85 kcal/g, about 76% of energy of carbohydrates, 9% of energy of fat, 15% of energy of protein) and water.

2.4. Establishment of the DM Model and PAOS Treatment

The mice (n = 40) of DM model were induced by a single intraperitoneal injection of freshly prepared streptozotocin (STZ, 180 mg/kg) dissolved in 0.1 M cold citrate buffer (pH 4.4) [12]. The level of fasting blood glucose (FBG) was tested after 72 h of STZ injection using ACCU-CHEK Performa glucometer (Roche, Basel, Switzerland), and mice were considered diabetic when FBG levels were above 11.1 mmol/L for over one week. After a week, 34 mice successfully developed DM, as confirmed by testing the FBG, 2 mice failed to develop DM, and 4 mice died.

Subsequently, the C57BL/6 mice (n = 8 per group) were randomly divided into control group (Con), model group (M), control + low-dose PAOS group (Con + L), control + high-dose PAOS group (Con + H), control + positive group (Con + P), model + low-dose PAOS group (M + L), model + high-dose PAOS group (M + H), model + positive group (M + P). Glibenclamide is a drug used in type 2 diabetes for increasing the release of insulin from the B cells of the pancreas, so it can be used as a positive drug. The low-dose, high-dose PAOS groups and the positive group were treated orally with 100 mg/kg PAOS, 300 mg/kg PAOS, and 25 mg/kg glibenclamide for 35 days, respectively. Mice of the Con and M groups were given an equal amount of normal saline by intragastric administration for 35 days. The mice were fed with standard diets during the whole experiment. The FBG levels and weight were measured once a week. Mice were sacrificed euthanized with CO_2 on day 35. The liver was collected and stored at 80 °C for further analysis. Mice feces were collected for intestinal microbiota analysis.

2.5. Fasting Serum Insulin Levels

The fasting insulin levels in serum were measured by ELISA kit (Mlbio, Shanghai, China). The homeostasis model of assessment of β-cell function (HOMA-β) was calculated using the following equation [13]:

$$\text{HOMA} - \beta = 20 \times \text{fasting insulin (mU/L)/FBG (mmol/L)} - 3.5$$

2.6. Measurement of Cytokines, Serum Parameters and Organ Indexes

Serum was collected after 2000 g centrifugation of blood at 4 °C for 15 min and was used to measure the levels of cytokines and serum parameters. Alanine transaminase (ALT), serum triglyceride (TC), total cholesterol (TG), and low-density lipoprotein cholesterol (LDL-C) levels were determined by the AU5800 Automatic biochemical detector (Beckman, CA, USA). The levels of interleukin (IL)-1β, IL-6, IL-10 and tumor necrosis factor α (TNF-α) in the liver were measured by ELISA kit (Mlbio, Shanghai, China). Spleen and thymus were weighed, and then spleen index and thymus index were calculated using the following equation:

$$\text{Spleen or thymus index} = \text{spleen or thymus weight (mg)/body weight (g)}$$

2.7. Measurement of Liver Function and Antioxidant Parameters

The liver tissues were homogenized, and protein concentration was performed by the BCA Protein Assay Kit (NCM, Suzhou, China). The superoxide dismutase (SOD), malondialdehyde (MDA), and glycogen levels in the liver were measured by ELISA kit (Mlbio, Shanghai, China). The levels of aspartate aminotransferase (AST), ALT, albumin (ALB), and total protein (TP) were measured via an AU5800 Automatic biochemical detector (Beckman, CA, USA).

2.8. Immunohistochemistry Staining

Pancreas tissues were fixed in 4% paraformaldehyde and embedded in paraffin. The embedded tissues were cut into 4 μm thin sections. Pancreas sections were incubated with antibodies against insulin or glucagon (Abcam, Cambridge, England). Then, colon sections were co-incubated with caspase-3 (Abcam, Cambridge, England). The results of immunohistochemical staining were visualized under a fluorescence microscope equipped with a charge-coupled device camera (Nikon, Tokyo, Japan).

2.9. Western Blot

The liver tissues were homogenized, and protein concentration was performed using the BCA Protein Assay Kit (NCM, Suzhou, China). Then, 25 μg proteins were separated with 12% SDS-PAGE gel and then transferred to the PVDF membrane. The membranes were incubated with primary antibodies against Toll-like receptor 4 (TLR4), p65, phosphorylated (P)-p65, p38, P-p38, extracellular signal-regulated kinase (ERK1/2), p-ERK1/2, Jun

N-terminal kinase (JNK), P-JNK (Affinity Biosciences, Changzhou, China), phosphatidylinositol 3-hydroxy kinase (PI3K), P-PI3K, protein kinase B (AKT), P-AKT, Foxo1, P-Foxo1, mammalian target of rapamycin (mTOR), P-mTOR, glycogen synthase kinase (GSK3β), P-GSK3β, LC3, Beclin1, Keap1, Nrf2, Heme Oxygenase-1 (HO-1), NOD-like receptor thermal protein domain associated protein 3 (NLRP3), caspase1 or GAPDH (Abcam, Cambridge, England), followed by incubation with secondary antibodies. The signals were developed using an ECL Western blot detection kit (Affinity Biosciences, Changzhou, China) and analyzed by Image J.

2.10. Microbial Community Analysis

Mice feces were collected and stored at −80 °C. The DNA of total bacteria in mice feces was extracted with QIAamp® Fast DNA Stool Mini Kit. The V4 region of the 16S rRNA gene was amplified using the barcoded primers. The PCR products were purified using the Qubit 2.0 (Thermo Fisher, Waltham, MA, USA) and sequenced using the Illumina MiSeq platform. All the results were based on sequenced reads and operational taxonomic units (OTUs).

2.11. Statistical Analysis

Results were expressed as mean ± SD. The two-way ANOVA test determined differences between groups, followed by Tukey's post-test using GraphPad Prism version 5. A value of $p < 0.05$ was considered statistically significant and $p < 0.01$ was considered highly significant.

3. Results

3.1. Effects of PAOS on DM Were Revealed by Body Weight, FBG, Insulin and HOMA-β

The DM mice model was established to investigate the effects of PAOS on DM. STZ treatment induced a marked decrease in body weight (Figure 1A), insulin ($p = 0.0029$, Figure 1C) and HOMA-β ($p = 0.0002$, Figure 1D), and induced an increase in FBG (>11.1 mmol/L, $p < 0.001$, Figure 1B). There was no significant difference in weight between the model group and DM groups treatment with PAOS (Figure 1A). During the administration period, the weight of DM model group tended to be lower, while in the low-dose PAOS or glibenclamide treatment groups the weight did no change and showed lower fluctuation (Figure 1A). On the contrary, the value of FBG showed a lower fluctuation in DM model group, while the value of FBG tended to be (at 14 and 21 days) or was significantly (at 28 and 35 days) lower in glibenclamide group, and the value of FBG rose first and then decreased to be stable in low-dose PAOS group (Figure 1B). Compared to DM model group, low-dose PAOS or glibenclamide treatment were lower by 15.7%, 41.7% for FBG (Figure 1B), were higher by 33.5%, 31.3% for insulin (Figure 1C), and were higher by 98.6%, 177.4% for HOMA-β (Figure 1D), respectively. The control mice treatment with PAOS or glibenclamide groups had no significant difference with control group. These results suggested that PAOS or glibenclamide treatment had a preventive effect on the clinical symptoms of STZ-induced DM.

3.2. PAOS Regulated Immune Responses in DM Mice

DM is an autoimmune disease, so the effects of PAOS on the cytokines and immune organs index were explored. The levels of cytokines, including IL-1β, TNF-α, IL-6, and IL-10, were showed in Figure 2A–D. Compared to the control group, the levels of proinflammatory cytokines (IL-1β and IL-6) in serum were markedly higher ($p = 0.019$, $p = 0.0362$), and the level of anti-inflammatory cytokine (IL-10) in serum was lower in DM model group ($p = 0.0013$). As shown in Figure 2A–D, in low dose PAOS or glibenclamide treatment group, the levels of IL-1β ($p = 0.0021$, $p = 0.003$) were lower, and the level of IL-10 ($p = 0.0056$, $p = 0.014$) were higher in DM group. As regards to the level of IL-6, glibenclamide treatment did not conduct to a different value ($p = 0.2035$), while low dose PAOS treatment led to a significant lower value ($p = 0.0236$). As depicted in Figure 2E, F, the spleen and thymus indexes were lower by 20.9% and 52.7% in DM, respectively. Low dose PAOS or glibenclamide administration were higher by 39.4% or 41.3% of thymus index. There was no significant difference between the control group of treatment with PAOS or glibenclamide and the control group. These findings indicated that PAOS relieved symptoms of DM by preventing inflammation to occur and immunomodulatory effects.

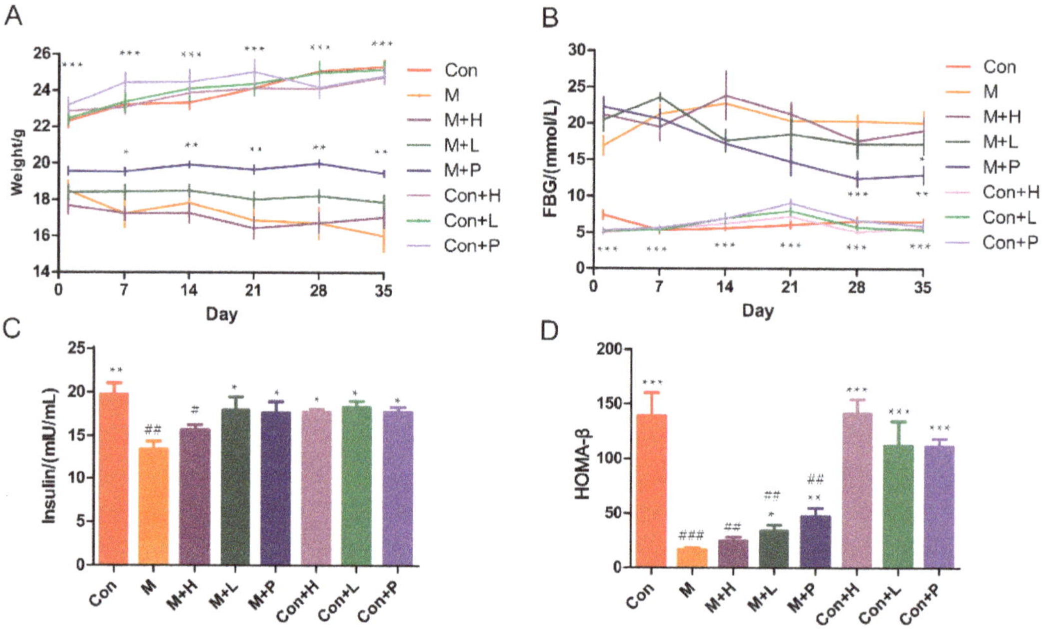

Figure 1. Effects of PAOS on body weight, FBG, insulin, and HOMA-β in TIDM. (**A**) The changes in weight during the experiment; (**B**) the changes in FBG levels during the experiment; (**C**) the level of insulin in serum; (**D**) HOMA-β. Data were expressed as the mean ± SD (n = 8). Con: control group, M: DM model group, M + H: DM + high dose of PAOS group; M + L: DM + low dose of PAOS group, M + P: DM + glibenclamide group; Con + H: control + high dose of PAOS group; Con + L: control + low dose of PAOS group; Con + P: control + glibenclamide group. *** $p < 0.001$, ** $p < 0.01$, * $p < 0.05$ vs. M group; ### $p < 0.001$, ## $p < 0.01$, # $p < 0.05$ vs. Con group.

3.3. PAOS Reduced Serum Parameterslevels

The serum parameters levels were displayed in Figure 2G–J. In DM, the serum parameters, including ALT, LDL-C, TC, and TG, were markedly higher ($p = 0.0282$, $p = 0.0011$, $p = 0.0027$, $p = 0.004$) than control group mice. After administration of low dose PAOS or glibenclamide, the levels of ALT (Figure 2G), LDL-C (Figure 2H), TC (Figure 2I), and TG (Figure 2J) were lower by 15.7% or 19.1%, 24.5% or 23.5%, 15.8% or 14.9 and 40.9% or 46.8%, respectively, compared to DM model mice. PAOS or glibenclamide had no significant effects on serum parameters levels in control mice. These results suggested that PAOS eased DM symptoms by reducing serum parameters levels.

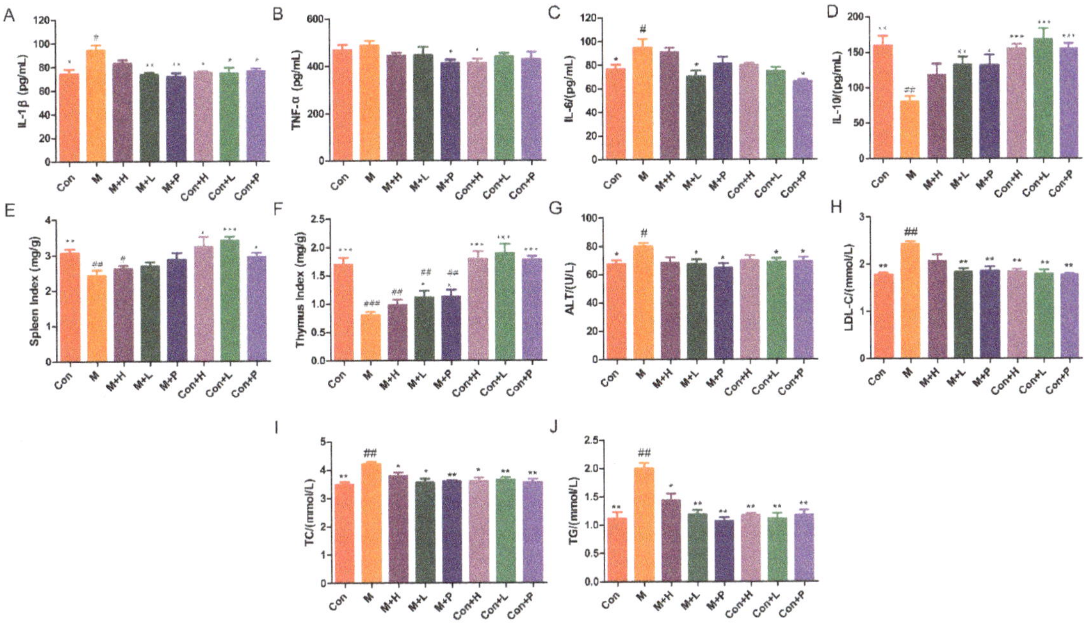

Figure 2. Effects of PAOS on the levels of cytokines in serum, immune organ indexes and serum parameters. Levels of IL-1β (**A**), TNF-α (**B**), IL-6 (**C**), IL-10 (**D**) in serum, spleen index (**E**), thymus index (**F**), and ALT (**G**), LDL-C (**H**), TC (**I**) and TG (**J**) in serum. Data were expressed as the mean ± SD (n = 8). Con: control group, M: DM model group, M + H: DM + high dose of PAOS group; M + L: DM + low dose of PAOS group, M + P: DM + glibenclamide group; Con + H: control + high dose of PAOS group; Con + L: control + low dose of PAOS group; Con + P: control + glibenclamide group. *** $p < 0.001$, ** $p < 0.01$, * $p < 0.05$ vs. M group; ### $p < 0.001$, ## $p < 0.01$, # $p < 0.05$ vs. Con group.

3.4. PAOS Benefited Liver Function and Antioxidant Parameters in DM Mice

The liver is an important site where glucose is converted into glycogen. The effects of PAOS on the parameters of liver function and antioxidant were explored. As shown in Figure 3A–D, compared with control mice, the liver function parameters (ALB, TP, ALT and AST) were abnormal in DM, which suggested that liver function in mice with diabetes was abnormal. The levels of ALB (Figure 3A) and TP (Figure 3B) were lower by 30.2% and 20.7%, and the contents of ALT (Figure 3C) and AST (Figure 3D) were higher by 98.5-fold and 69.2% in DM, respectively. The mice in treatment with low-dose PAOS or glibenclamide showed higher ALB ($p = 0.0329$, $p = 0.0169$) and TP ($p = 0.028$, $p = 0.0404$), and dramatically lower ALT (82% or 80.5%, respectively) and AST (40.4% or 44%, respectively) than model group. As shown in Figure 3E, liver glycogen level was lower in DM ($p = 0.0028$), while it was higher in the PAOS or glibenclamide-treated DM groups ($p = 0.0019$, $p = 0.0004$, $p = 0.0027$). Compared with the DM group, the level of antioxidant enzyme SOD in PAOS or glibenclamide treatment group was significantly higher (Figure 3F, $p = 0.0589$, $p = 0.0353$, $p = 0.0128$). On the contrary, the level of MDA (maker of oxidative stress) in liver tissues in low-dose PAOS or glibenclamide treatment group was lower by 44.3% or 43.5%, respectively (Figure 3G). However, PAOS or glibenclamide had no significant effect on liver function and antioxidant parameters of control mice. These findings demonstrated that PAOS or glibenclamide had potential efficacy of improving liver function and reducing oxidative stress.

3.5. PAOS Improved Islet β Cell Function and Downregulated Its Apoptosis in DM Mice

The pancreas function was detected by immunohistochemistry. As shown in Figure 4A,B, the insulin-positive β-cells and glucagon-positive α-cells were analyzed, respectively. Compared to the control group, the immunofluorescence staining exhibited that the insulin expression (β cells) was decreased and glucagon expression (α cells) were increased in pancreatic islets of diabetic mice. PAOS or glibenclamide treatment prevented these changes, the insulin expression β-cells were elevated and glucagon expression α-cells were reduced in diabetic mice. Moreover, the caspase-3 positive cells in islet β- and α-cells were analyzed (Figure 4A,B). In diabetes mice, the apoptosis-positive of islet β-cells was increased. After administration of PAOS or glibenclamide, the apoptosis-positive of islet β-cells was diminished in diabetic mice. These results suggested that PAOS or glibenclamide could rise insulin expression via inhibiting the apoptosis of islet β-cells.

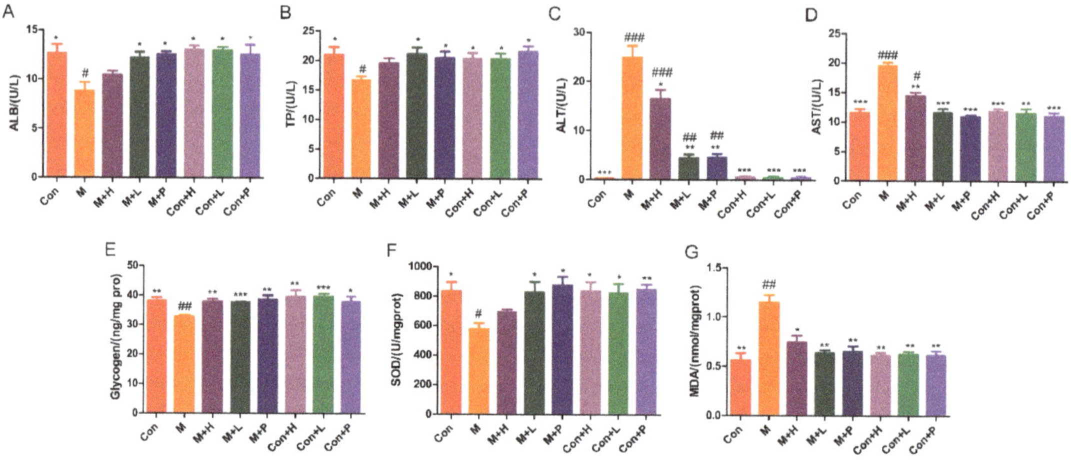

Figure 3. PAOS benefited the liver function and oxidative stress parameters. Levels of ALB (**A**), TP (**B**), ALT (**C**), AST (**D**), glycogen (**E**), SOD (**F**), and MDA (**G**) in liver. Data were expressed as the mean ± SD (n = 8). Con: control group, M: DM model group, M + H: DM + high dose of PAOS group; M + L: DM + low dose of PAOS group, M + P: DM + glibenclamide group; Con + H: control + high dose of PAOS group; Con + L: control + low dose of PAOS group; Con + P: control + glibenclamide group. *** $p < 0.001$, ** $p < 0.01$, * $p < 0.05$ vs. M group; ### $p < 0.001$, ## $p < 0.01$, # $p < 0.05$ vs. Con group.

3.6. PAOS Regulated Signal Pathways in the Livers of TIDM Mice

TLR4/MAPK/NF-κB pathway has been shown to contribute to the inflammatory response. The expressions of key components in the TLR4/MAPK/NF-κB signaling pathway are shown in Figure 5A. Compared with the control group, the levels of some important proteins (including, P-p38, P-ERK1/2, P-JNK1/2/3 and P-p65) in TLR4/MAPK/NF-κB pathway were higher ($p = 0.0722$, $p = 0.0329$, $p = 0.0077$, $p = 0.0012$) in DM. Low dose of PAOS inhibited the expression levels of TLR4 ($p = 0.001$), and PAOS or glibenclamide significantly inhibited the phosphorylation of ERK1/2, JNK, and p65. There was no significant effect on TLR4/MAPK/NF-κB signaling pathway in control mice treated with PAOS or glibenclamide. These results revealed the anti-inflammatory effects of PAOS via suppressing TLR4/MAPK (ERK1/2 and JNK)/NF-κB pathway. The glucose metabolism PI3K/AKT/mTOR signaling pathway was remarkably downregulated in DM (Figure 5B). Moreover, the protein expressions of P-Foxo1 and P-GSK3β were upregulated in the livers of DM mice (Figure 5B). The treatment of PAOS or glibenclamide normalized the glucose metabolism, gluconeogenesis, and glycogen synthesis (Figure 5B), suggesting that PAOS or glibenclamide reduced the blood glucose via activating PI3K/AKT/mTOR pathway.

PAOS or glibenclamide had no significant effects on glucose metabolism in control mice. Expressions of key proteins in the autophagy signaling pathway are depicted in Figure 5C. The levels of LC3 and Beclin1 were significantly higher in DM (p = 0.0036, p = 0.0105), PAOS or glibenclamide could downregulate the expression of LC3 and Beclin1. PAOS or glibenclamide had no significant effects on the level of LC3 and Beclin1 in control mice. As shown in Figure 5D, compared with the control group, expression of Keap1, Nrf2 and HO-1 (the key proteins in the antioxidative pathway) were abnormal in DM. After administration of PAOS or glibenclamide, the level of Keap1 was significantly downregulated (p = 0.0024, p = 0.0005, p = 0.0029), and the expressions of Nrf2 and HO-1 were upregulated (p = 0.0188, p = 0.0057, p = 0.007; p = 0.0007, p = 0.0104, p = 0.0012) in DM. These findings confirmed the previous results of reducing oxidative stress. The levels of important proteins in the pyroptosis signaling pathway, including NLRP3 and caspase1, were analyzed in Figure 5E. The expression of NLRP3 and caspase1 were remarkably higher (p = 0.0005, p = 0.0267), PAOS or glibenclamide downregulated the levels of NLRP3 and caspase1 (p = 0.0243, p = 0.001, p = 0.0475; p = 0.0336, p =0.001, p = 0.0013) in DM, suggesting that PAOS or glibenclamide downregulated the pyroptosis signaling pathway.

3.7. PAOS Regulated the Gut Microbiota in Control Mice

To investigate PAOS's role on gut microbiota in control mice, the relative abundance at phylum level and genus level, sankeyplot of high abundance genus are shown in Figure 6A–E. Venn diagram (Figure 6A) shows the logical connection between each group, and shows that 73.51% of the intestinal microbiota was overlapping. As shown in Figure 6B, compared with control group, the level of Epsilonbacteraeota in all PAOS treatment control group was lower, and the levels of Verrucomicrobia in the low-dose PAOS and glibenclamide group were lower. Compared with the control group, the level of Catenibacterium was higher, and the levels of Staphylococcus, Prevotellaceae UGG-004, Helicobacter, and Bacteroides were lower in all PAOS or glibenclamide treatment control group (Figure 6C, D). The alpha diversity represented by Chao1, ACE, Simpson and Shannon is displayed in Figure 7A–D. Compared with the control group, the indexes of Chao1, Ace and Shannon were significantly higher (p = 0.0331, p = 0.0383, p = 0.0102) in the low-dose PAOS treatment control group, suggesting low-dose PAOS increased the diversity of gut microbiota in standard mice. To explore the biomarkers of gut microbiota among each group, random forest and LEFse analysis were depicted in Figure 7E–G. The microbiota such as *Catenibacterium, Faecalibacterium, Bacteroides,* and *Muribaculum* with high values of mean decrease Gini, was influential in the classifying groups (Figure 7E). As seen in Figure 7F,G, the prominent and important intestinal microbiota in the gut were *Actinobacteria, Prevotellaceae,* and *Bacteroidaceae* in the control group; the prominent and crucial intestinal microbiota in the gut was *Muribaculum* in the high-dose PAOS treatment standard mice group; the prominent and essential intestinal microbiota in the gut was *Rhodospirillales* in low-dose PAOS treatment control mice group; the prominent and vital intestinal microbiota in the gut was *Coriobacterlia* in glibenclamide treatment control mice group.

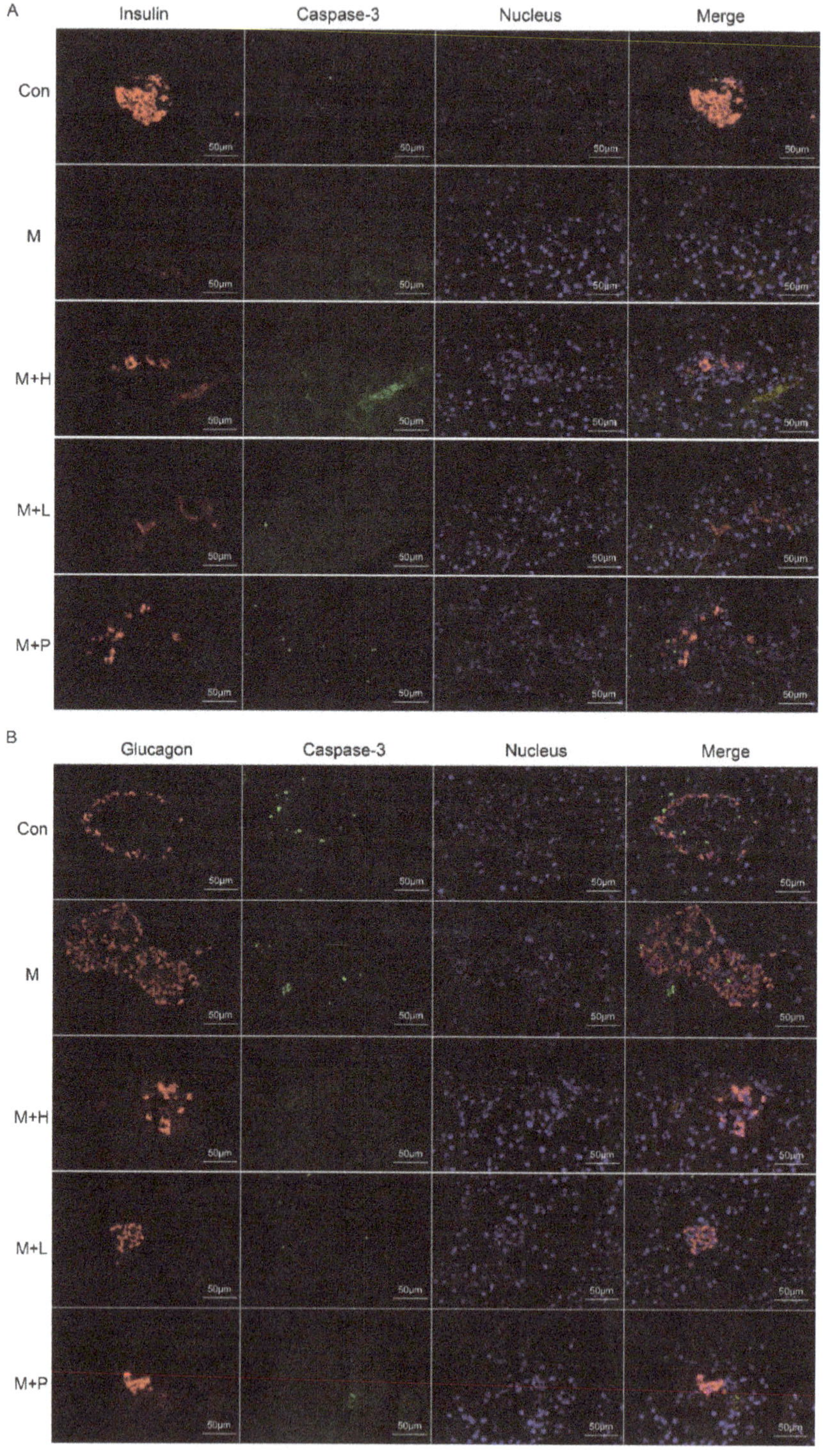

Figure 4. PAOS improved islet β cell function and downregulated its apoptosis in the pancreas.

(**A**) The effects of PAOS on insulin (β-cells) and apoptosis of β cells in the pancreas. The red fluorescence was insulin, the green fluorescence was caspase-3, the blue fluorescence was the nucleus, and the Merge fluorescence was the overlap of the three kinds of fluorescence. (**B**) The effects of PAOS on glucagon (α cells) and apoptosis of α cells in the pancreas. The red fluorescence was glucagon, the green fluorescence was caspase-3, the blue fluorescence was the nucleus, and the Merge fluorescence was the overlap of the three kinds of fluorescence. Con: control group, M: DM model group, M + H: DM + high dose of PAOS group; M + L: DM + low dose of PAOS group, M + P: DM + glibenclamide group.

3.8. PAOS Ameliorated on Gut Microbiota in DM Mice

To explore the effects of PAOS on gut microbiota in DM mice, the relative abundance at phylum level and genus level, sankeyplot of high abundance genus are shown in Figure 8A–D. Venn diagram (Figure 8A) showed 77.99% of the intestinal microbiota in each group was overlapping. As shown in Figure 8B, compared with the control group, the levels of Bacteroidetes, Proteobacteria, and Actinobacteria were higher, the levels of Firmicutes and Verrucomicrobia were lower, and the ratio of Firmicutes/Bacteroidetes was lower in DM mice. The PAOS could elevate the level of Firmicutes, Verrucomicrobia, and the ratio of Firmicutes/ Bacteroidetes, and reduce the levels of Bacteroidetes and Proteobacteria in DM mice. As seen in Figure 8C,D, compared with the control group, the levels of *Prevotellaceae UGG-004, Prevotellaceae UGG-001, Prevotella1, Prevotellaceae Ga6A1 group, Ralstonia Proteus*, and *Bacteroides* were higher, and the levels of *Akkermansia, Allobaculum, Ruminococcus2, Ileibacterium*, and *Odoribacter* were lower in DM mice. The treatment of PAOS or glibenclamide prevented such changes. The alpha diversity represented by Chao1, ACE, Simpson, and Shannon were displayed in Figure 9A–D. Compared with the control group, the indexes of Chao1, Ace, and Shannon had no significant difference in DM group. The low-dose PAOS treatment elevated the index of Shannon ($p = 0.0438$) in DM. To explore the biomarkers of gut microbiota among each group, the random forest and LEFse analyses were depicted in Figure 9E–G. The microbiota, such as *Ruminococcaceae UGG-010* and *Vagococcus* with high values of mean decrease Gini, were crucial in classifying groups (Figure 9E). As seen in Figure 9F,G, the prominent and influential intestinal microbiota in the gut was *Alloprevotella* in the DM group; the prominent and essential intestinal microbiota in the gut were *A2* and *Rikenellaceae RC9 gut group* in the low-dose PAOS treatment DM group; the prominent and vital intestinal microbiota in the gut was *Odoribacter* in glibenclamide treatment DM group. The Figure 10A,B showed that compared with control group, the amount of Bacteroidetes was increased in DM, and the low-dose of PAOS reduced the amount of Bacteroidetes. These results indicated that PAOS improved the gut microbiota in DM mice.

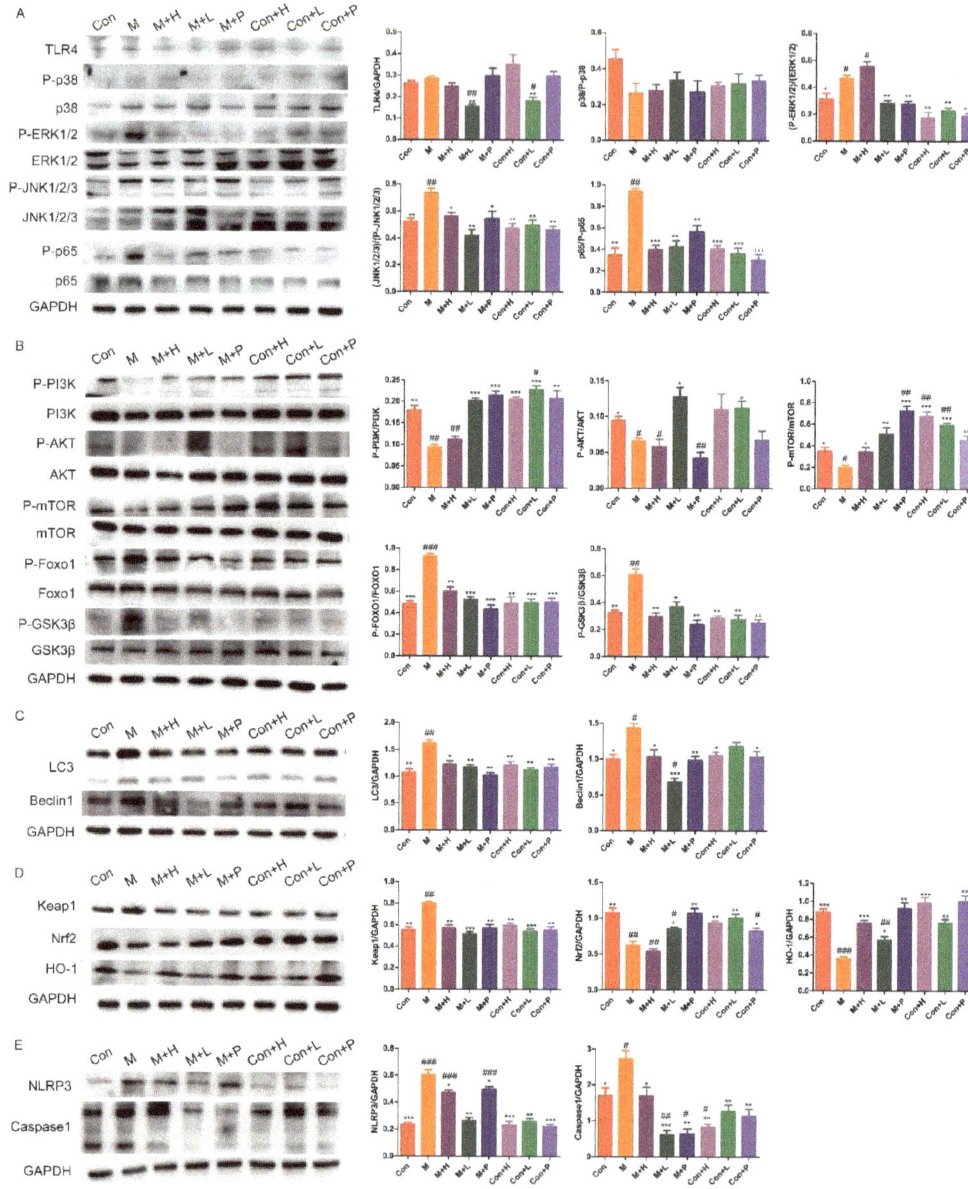

Figure 5. Effects of PAOS on the related signal pathways in DM mice. The effects of PAOS on the TLR4/MAPK/NF-κB (**A**), PI3K/AKT (**B**), Beclin1/LC3 (**C**), Keap1/Nrf2/HO-1 (**D**) and NLRP3/caspase1 (**E**) pathways in the liver. Con: control group, M: DM model group, M + H: DM + high dose of PAOS group; M + L: DM + low dose of PAOS group, M + P: DM + glibenclamide group; Con + H: control + high dose of PAOS group; Con + L: control + low dose of PAOS group; Con + P: control + glibenclamide group. *** $p < 0.001$, ** $p < 0.01$, * $p < 0.05$ vs. M group; ### $p < 0.001$, ## $p < 0.01$, # $p < 0.05$ vs. Con group.

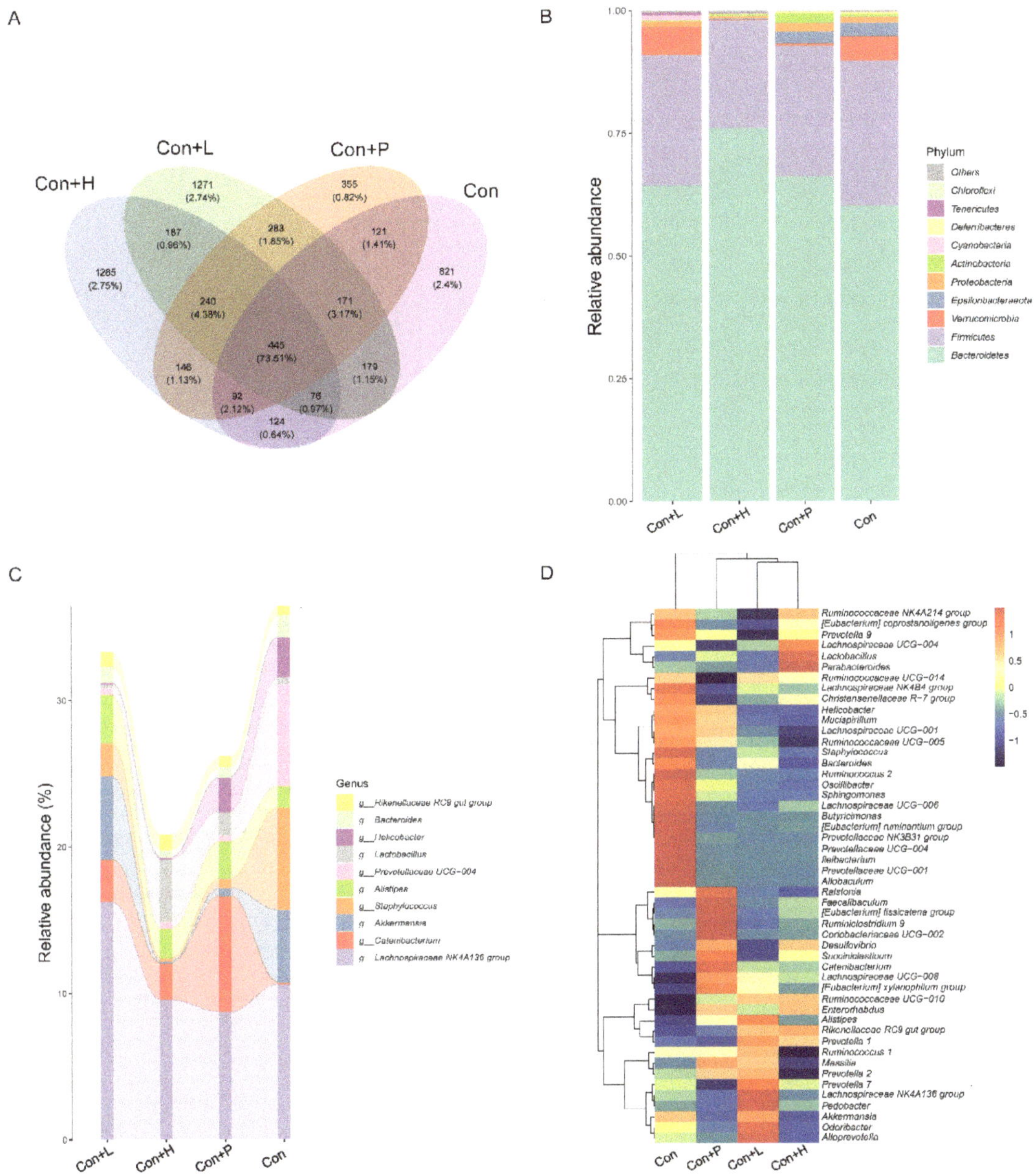

Figure 6. Effects of PAOS on gut microbiota at phylum and genus levels in control mice. (**A**) Venn chart; (**B**) the relative abundance at the phylum level. (**C**) The analysis of sankeyplot of high abundance genus; (**D**) the heap maps of relative abundance at the genus level. Con: control group; Con + H: control + high dose of PAOS group; Con + L: control + low dose of PAOS group; Con + P: control + glibenclamide group.

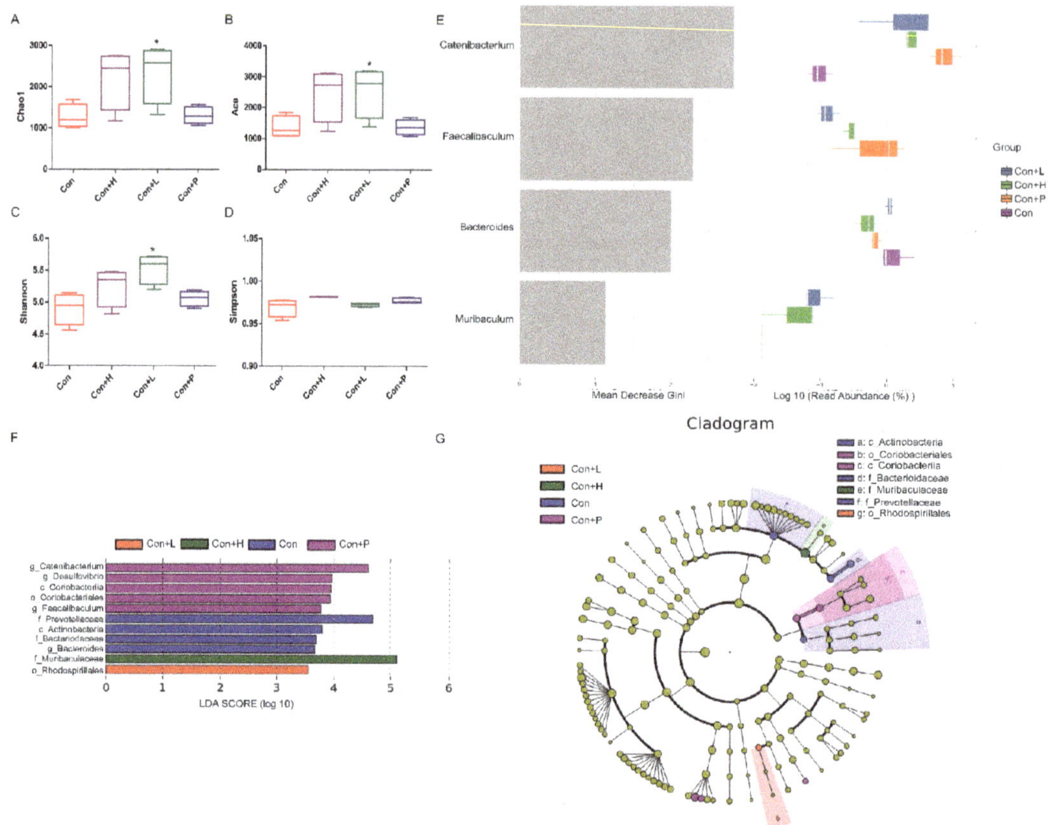

Figure 7. Effects of PAOS on the alpha diversity and the biomarkers of gut microbiota in control mice. Chao1 (**A**), Shannon (**B**), Simpson (**C**), Faith's PD (**D**) of gut microbiota, respectively; the random forest analysis (**E**); LDA score of Lefse (**F**); Cladogram of Lefse (**G**). Con: control group; Con + H: control + high dose of PAOS group; Con + L: control + low dose of PAOS group; Con + P: control + glibenclamide group. * $p < 0.05$ vs. Con group.

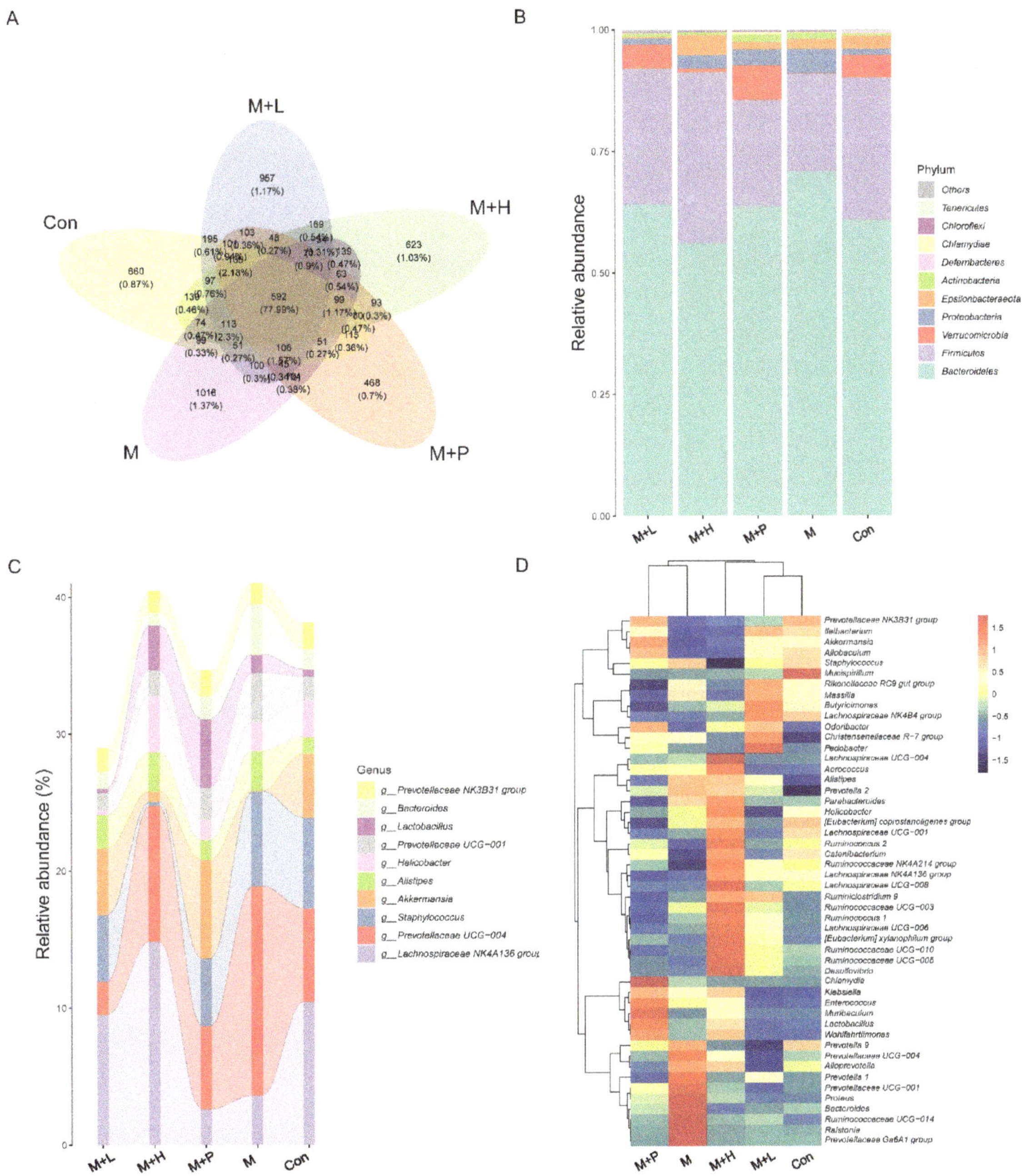

Figure 8. Effects of PAOS on gut microbiota at phylum and genus level in DM. (**A**) Venn chart; (**B**) The relative abundance at the phylum level. (**C**) The analysis of sankeyplot of high abundance genus; (**D**) The heap maps of relative abundance at the genus level. Con: control group, M: DM model group, M + H: DM + high dose of PAOS group; M + L: DM + low dose of PAOS group, M + P: DM + glibenclamide group.

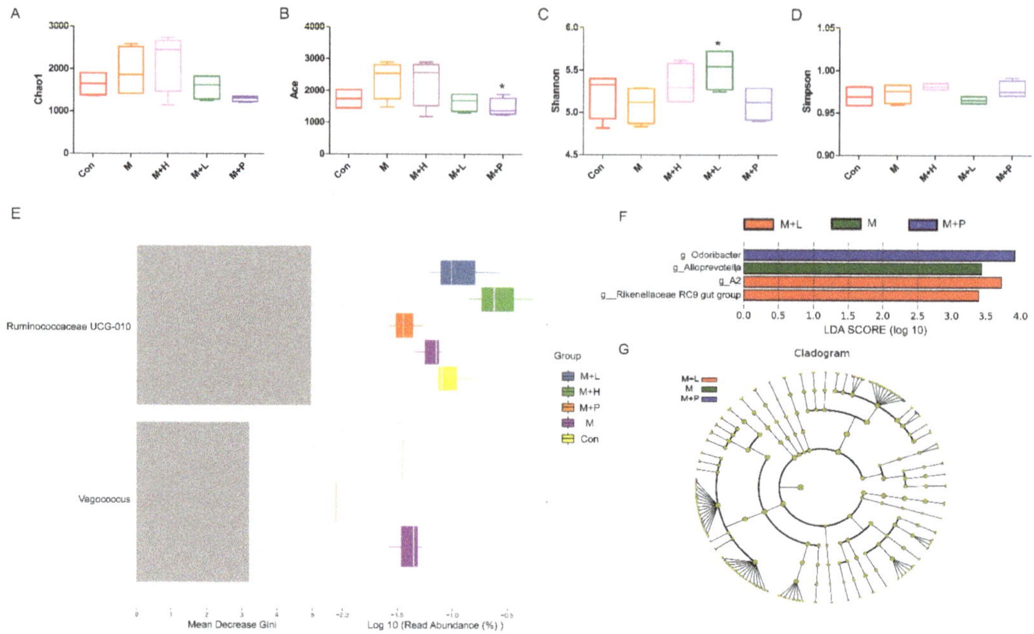

Figure 9. Effects of PAOS on the alpha diversity and the biomarkers of gut microbiota in DM. Chao1 (**A**), Shannon (**B**), Simpson (**C**), Faith's PD (**D**) of gut microbiota, respectively; the random forest analysis (**E**); LDA score of Lefse (**F**); Cladogram of Lefse (**G**). Con: control group, M: DM model group, M + H: DM + high dose of PAOS group; M + L: DM + low dose of PAOS group, M + P: DM + glibenclamide group. * $p < 0.05$ vs. M group.

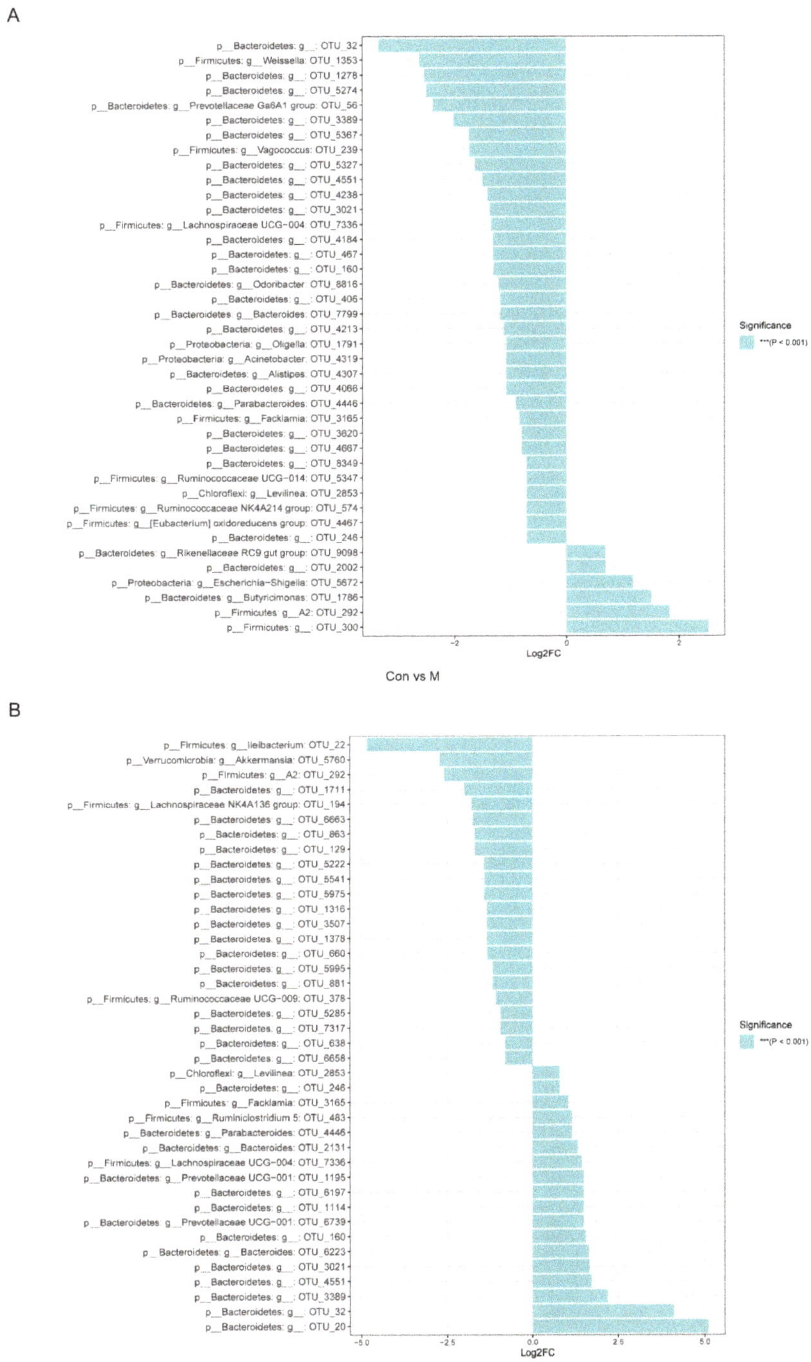

Figure 10. MetagenomeSeq analysis of gut microbiota in DM. (**A**) MetagenomeSeq analysis of Con VS M group; (**B**) MetagenomeSeq analysis of M vs. M + L group. Con: control group, M: DM model group; M + L: DM + low dose of PAOS group.

4. Discussion

STZ is the most widely used chemical drug for establishing the diabetes mice or rat model, which causes pancreatic islet damage and thus reduces insulin secretion [14]. Some natural products exert antidiabetic effects via several mechanisms, including promoting insulin secretion, inhibition of carbohydrate metabolizing enzymes and regeneration of β-cells, such as alkaloids, flavonoids, phenolic acids, saponins, and terpenoids [15]. Some studies have reported that functional oligosaccharides have antidiabetic activity, such as fructo-oligosaccharides (FOSs) [16], mannan-oligosaccharides (MOSs) [17], and chito-oligosaccharides (COSs) [18]. In this study, we demonstrated that PAOS improved glucose-lipid metabolic disorder and glycemic control to mitigate risks of DM through modulation in inflammation, oxidative stress, and gut microbiota.

DM is considered a β-cell-mediated pro-inflammatory state induced by innate and adaptive immunity. TLR4/MAPK/NF-κB pathway is the primary mediator of inflammatory responses, which plays a crucial role in the immune and inflammatory response [19], which regulates the release of many proinflammatory cytokines and then causes β-cell death in DM [20]. Pyroptosis is a form of pro-inflammatory cell death [21], induced by the classic pathway (depended on caspase 1) or non-classic pathway (depended on caspase 4/5/11). PAOS inhibited the expression of TLR4, then down-regulated the phosphorylation of ERK and JNK in the MAPK family and p65 in the NF-κB pathway, which reduced the expression of proinflammatory cytokines. Moreover, PAOS suppressed the classic pyrolysis pathway. These findings indicated that PAOS relieved DM by reducing inflammation.

Significantly lack of insulin and high blood glucose are the features of DM. HOMA-β is the usual assessment of islet β-cell function that releases insulin [22]. Insulin regulates glucose homeostasis via promoting glucose transport into muscle and adipose cells, while binding to the insulin receptor and then actives insulin cascade [23]. FOSs increased insulin secretion and improved β-cell function in DM mice [24]. PAOS also recovered the HOMA-β via reducing the apoptosis of islet β-cell and then elevating insulin secretion. The activation of the insulin pathway, PI3K/AKT/mTOR pathway, reduces blood glucose by inhibiting gluconeogenesis and stimulating glycogen synthesis [23,25]. PAOS down-regulated the PI3K/AKT pathway, then downregulated the phosphorylation of GSK-3β and FOXO1, which suggested that PAOS suppressed gluconeogenesis and promoted glycogen synthesis. The liver glycogen is crucial for maintaining blood glucose levels [14]. PAOS increased liver glycogen levels by improving liver function parameters (ALB, TP, ALT and AST). Aberrant blood lipid metabolism is critical for DM progression [26]. Oligo-N-acetylglucosamine can significantly reduce the lipid profile, including TG, TC, and LDL [27]. PAOS reduced the levels of ALT, LDL-C, TC, and TG. These results showed that PAOS ameliorated symptoms of DM via activating insulin cascade, reducing the blood lipid and improving liver function.

Hyperglycemia induces reactive oxygen species production and leads to oxidative stress in DM. Moreover, oxidative stress can lead to cell autophagy death and inflammation, so lowering the oxidative injury is essential for DM treatment [28,29]. COSs exhibits oxidation resistance bioactivities in alloxan-induced DM [30]. Keap1/Nrf2 pathway is an endogenous antioxidant signaling pathway. PAOS unbound Nrf2 with Keap1 in the cytoplasm, then activated Nrf2 was transported to the nucleus and stimulated the expression of antioxidase HO-1. Meanwhile, PAOS increased the level of SOD and decreased the MDA level. Beclin1, LC3, and mTOR play essential roles in autophagy. PAOS elevated the phosphorylation of mTOR and then down-regulated the expression of Beclin1 and LC3, which suggested that PAOS inhibited autophagy pathway. These findings suggested that PAOS reduced blood glucose by lowering oxidative stress and suppressing autophagy.

Interactions of gut microbiota components play key roles in immune and inflammatory functions [7]. Studies have shown that the composition of major microbial groups differs between healthy individuals and those with DM. The ratio of Firmicutes to Bacteroidetes (F/B) may be the early diagnostic marker of DM [31]. PAOS elevated the ratio of F/B in DM mice. The LPS derived from microbiota in the gut can promote the release of proinflammatory cytokines and damage pancreatic β-cell function [32,33]. The study has reported that hosts with DM have higher LPS and LPS-producing bacteria than healthy hosts. LPS may act as the link between inflammation, gut microbiota, and DM [34]. Functional oligosaccharides could reduce LPS and then reduce inflammation, such as FOS [24]. PAOS reduced the amounts of LPS producing bacteria, such as Bacteroidetes and Proteobacteria, and then inhibited the downstream TLR4/MAPK/NF-κB pathway in DM mice. Bacterial-producing short-chain fatty acids (SCFAs, such as butyrate and acetate) were reduced in DM [35]. SCFAs play an essential role in metabolic, immune response, and inflammatory diseases, such as DM [36]. Functional oligosaccharides improve glucose metabolism by regulating intestinal microbiota and increasing the secretion of SCFAs [37]. PAOS increased the amounts of SCFAs producing bacteria, such as *Odoribacter*, *Ruminococcus2*, and *Allobaculum*, which regulated blood glucose by decreasing inflammation. Moreover, PAOS increased the *Akkermansia* that could reduce the risk of diseases, such as obesity, diabetes, and inflammation. All these results indicated that PAOS regulated blood glucose by improving the structure of gut microbiota and downregulated the TLR4/MAPK/NF-κB pathway.

In conclusion, PAOS exerted a hyperglycemia-reducing effect by reducing inflammation and oxidative stress, improving pancreas function, enhancing immunity, and regulating gut microbiota. Inflammation, immune, oxidative stress, and gut microbiota could form an interactive network to regulate blood glucose in DM mice. All these results may pave a new way for developing effective drugs with high safety that can be applied in DM treatment in the future.

Author Contributions: Conceptualization, J.B.; methodology, K.L.; data curation, K.L. and Y.H.; writing—original draft preparation, K.L. and Y.H.; writing—review and editing, C.W. and J.B.; project administration, K.L.; funding acquisition, C.W. and J.B. All authors have read and agreed to the published version of the manuscript.

Funding: This research was funded by the National Nature Science Foundation of China [grant numbers: No. 32071275, U20A20410, 31971162], the Key Program of Science and Technology Department of Sichuan province [grant number 2018SZ0026], Youth Natural Science Foundation of Shandong province [grant number: ZR2022QH350] and Sichuan Gooddoctor-Panxi Pharmaceutical Company Limited and Key Laboratory of Bio-Resource and Eco-Environment of Ministry of Education.

Institutional Review Board Statement: The animal study protocol was approved by the Institutional Review Board (or Ethics Committee) of Research Ethics Committee of Sichuan University (protocol code: NO.20190402001).

Informed Consent Statement: Not applicable.

Conflicts of Interest: The authors declare no conflict of interest.

References

1. Cole, J.B.; Florez, J.C. Genetics of diabetes mellitus and diabetes complications. *Nat. Rev. Nephrol.* **2020**, *16*, 377–390. [CrossRef] [PubMed]
2. Hu, F.B.; Satija, A.; Manson, J.E. Curbing the Diabetes Pandemic: The Need for Global Policy Solutions. *JAMA* **2015**, *313*, 2319–2320. [CrossRef]
3. International Diabetes Federation. IDF Diabetes Atlas. In *Idf Diabetes Atlas*; International Diabetes Federation: Brussels, Belgium, 2021.
4. Kerru, N.; Singh-Pillay, A.; Awolade, P.; Singh, P. Current anti-diabetic agents and their molecular targets: A review. *Eur. J. Med. Chem.* **2018**, *152*, 436–488. [CrossRef]
5. Buzzetti, R.; Zampetti, S.; Maddaloni, E. Adult-onset autoimmune diabetes: Current knowledge and implications for management. *Nat. Rev. Endocrinol.* **2017**, *13*, 674–686. [CrossRef] [PubMed]
6. Zou, J.; Reddivari, L.; Shi, Z.; Li, S.; Wang, Y.; Bretin, A.; Ngo, V.L.; Flythe, M.; Pellizzon, M.; Chassaing, B.; et al. Inulin Fermentable Fiber Ameliorates Type I Diabetes via IL22 and Short-Chain Fatty Acids in Experimental Models. *Cell. Mol. Gastroenterol. Hepatol.* **2021**, *12*, 983–1000. [CrossRef]
7. Knip, M.; Siljander, H. The role of the intestinal microbiota in type 1 diabetes mellitus. *Nat. Rev. Endocrinol.* **2016**, *12*, 154–167. [CrossRef] [PubMed]
8. Zhao, Y.; Yang, A.; Tu, P.; Hu, Z. Anti-tumor effects of the American cockroach, Periplaneta americana. *Chin. Med.* **2017**, *12*, 26. [CrossRef]

9. Nguyen, T.; Chen, X.; Chai, J.; Li, R.; Han, X.; Chen, X.; Liu, S.; Chen, M.; Xu, X. Antipyretic, anti-inflammatory and analgesic activities of Periplaneta americana extract and underlying mechanisms. *Biomed. Pharmacother.* **2020**, *123*, 109753. [CrossRef]
10. Zhu, D.; Yan, Q.; Liu, J.; Wu, X.; Jiang, Z. Can functional oligosaccharides reduce the risk of diabetes mellitus? *FASEB J.* **2019**, *33*, 11655–11667. [CrossRef]
11. Lu, K.M.; Zhou, J.; Deng, J.; Li, Y.J.; Wu, C.F.; Bao, J.K. Periplaneta americana Oligosaccharides Exert Anti-Inflammatory Activity through Immunoregulation and Modulation of Gut Microbiota in Acute Colitis Mice Model. *Molecules* **2021**, *26*, 1718. [CrossRef]
12. Dhuria, R.S.; Singh, G.; Kaur, A.; Kaur, R.; Kaur, T. Current status and patent prospective of animal models in diabetic research. *Adv. Biomed. Res.* **2015**, *4*, 117. [CrossRef] [PubMed]
13. Matthews, D.R.; Hosker, J.P.; Rudenski, A.S.; Naylor, B.A.; Treacher, D.F.; Turner, R.C. Homeostasis model assessment: Insulin resistance and beta-cell function from fasting plasma glucose and insulin concentrations in man. *Diabetologia* **1985**, *28*, 412–419. [CrossRef] [PubMed]
14. Hu, Z.; Li, E.; Sullivan, M.A.; Tan, X.; Deng, B.; Gilbert, R.G.; Li, C. Glycogen structure in type 1 diabetic mice: Towards understanding the origin of diabetic glycogen molecular fragility. *Int. J. Biol. Macromol.* **2019**, *128*, 665–672. [CrossRef] [PubMed]
15. Kumar, V.; Veeranjaneyulu, A. *Herbs for Diabetes and Neurological Disease Management*; CRC Press: Boca Raton, FL, USA, 2017.
16. Cani, P.D.; Knauf, C.; Iglesias, M.A.; Drucker, D.J.; Delzenne, N.M.; Burcelin, R. Improvement of glucose tolerance and hepatic insulin sensitivity by oligofructose requires a functional glucagon-like peptide 1 receptor. *Diabetes* **2006**, *55*, 1484–1490. [CrossRef]
17. Wang, H.; Zhang, X.; Wang, S.; Li, H.; Lu, Z.; Shi, J.; Xu, Z. Mannan-oligosaccharide modulates the obesity and gut microbiota in high-fat diet-fed mice. *Food Funct.* **2018**, *9*, 3916–3929. [CrossRef]
18. Katiyar, D.; Singh, B.; Lall, A.M.; Haldar, C. Efficacy of chitooligosaccharides for the management of diabetes in alloxan induced mice: A correlative study with antihyperlipidemic and antioxidative activity. *Eur. J. Pharm. Sci.* **2011**, *44*, 534–543. [CrossRef]
19. Ortega-González, M.; Ocón, B.; Romero-Calvo, I.; Anzola, A.; Guadix, E.; Zarzuelo, A.; Suárez, M.D.; de Medina, F.S.; Martínez-Augustin, O. Nondigestible oligosaccharides exert nonprebiotic effects on intestinal epithelial cells enhancing the immune response via activation of TLR4-NFκB. *Mol. Nutr. Food Res.* **2014**, *58*, 384–393. [CrossRef]
20. Chen, L.; Chen, R.; Wang, H.; Liang, F. Mechanisms Linking Inflammation to Insulin Resistance. *Int. J. Endocrinol.* **2015**, *2015*, 508409. [CrossRef]
21. Zhu, W.; Li, Y.Y.; Zeng, H.X.; Liu, X.Q.; Sun, Y.T.; Jiang, L.; Xia, L.L.; Wu, Y.G. Carnosine alleviates podocyte injury in diabetic nephropathy by targeting caspase-1-mediated pyroptosis. *Int. Immunopharmacol.* **2021**, *101*, 108236. [CrossRef]
22. Cobelli, C.; Toffolo, G.M.; Man, C.D.; Campioni, M.; Denti, P.; Caumo, A.; Butler, P.; Rizza, R. Assessment of beta-cell function in humans, simultaneously with insulin sensitivity and hepatic extraction, from intravenous and oral glucose tests. *Am. J. Physiol. Endocrinol. Metab.* **2007**, *293*, E1–E15. [CrossRef]
23. Obafemi, T.O.; Olaleye, M.T.; Akinmoladun, A.C. Antidiabetic property of miracle fruit plant (Synsepalum dulcificum Shumach. & Thonn. Daniell) leaf extracts in fructose-fed streptozotocin-injected rats via anti-inflammatory activity and inhibition of carbohydrate metabolizing enzymes. *J. Ethnopharmacol.* **2019**, *244*, 112124. [CrossRef] [PubMed]
24. Dehghan, P.; Gargari, B.P.; Jafar-abadi, M.A. Oligofructose-enriched inulin improves some inflammatory markers and metabolic endotoxemia in women with type 2 diabetes mellitus: A randomized controlled clinical trial. *Nutrition* **2014**, *30*, 418–423. [CrossRef] [PubMed]
25. Arneth, B.; Arneth, R.; Shams, M. Metabolomics of Type 1 and Type 2 Diabetes. *Int. J. Mol. Sci.* **2019**, *20*, 2467. [CrossRef] [PubMed]
26. Sun, Y.; Li, L.; Wu, J.; Gong, B.; Liu, H. Germacrone cooperates with dexmedetomidine to alleviate high-fat diet-induced type 2 diabetes mellitus via upregulating AMPKα1 expression. *Exp. Ther. Med.* **2019**, *18*, 3514–3524. [CrossRef] [PubMed]
27. Ohashi, N.; Morino, K.; Ida, S.; Sekine, O.; Lemecha, M.; Kume, S.; Park, S.-Y.; Choi, C.S.; Ugi, S.; Maegawa, H. Pivotal Role of O-GlcNAc Modification in Cold-Induced Thermogenesis by Brown Adipose Tissue Through Mitochondrial Biogenesis. *Diabetes* **2017**, *66*, 2351–2362. [CrossRef] [PubMed]
28. Dubey, R.; Minj, P.; Malik, N.; Sardesai, D.M.; Kulkarni, S.H.; Acharya, J.D.; Bhavesh, N.S.; Sharma, S.; Kumar, A. Recombinant human islet amyloid polypeptide forms shorter fibrils and mediates β-cell apoptosis via generation of oxidative stress. *Biochem. J.* **2017**, *474*, 3915–3934. [CrossRef]
29. Ige, A.O.; Adewoye, E.O. Oral Magnesium Treatment Reduces Anemia and Levels of Inflammatory Markers in Experimental Diabetes. *J. Diet. Suppl.* **2017**, *14*, 76–88. [CrossRef]
30. Sangwan, V.; Tomar, S.K.; Ali, B.; Singh, R.R.; Singh, A.K. Hypoglycaemic effect of galactooligosaccharides in alloxan-induced diabetic rats. *J. Dairy Res.* **2015**, *82*, 70–77. [CrossRef]
31. Giongo, A.; Gano, K.A.; Crabb, D.B.; Mukherjee, N.; Novelo, L.L.; Casella, G.; Drew, J.C.; Ilonen, J.; Knip, M.; Hyöty, H.; et al. Toward defining the autoimmune microbiome for type 1 diabetes. *ISME J.* **2011**, *5*, 82–91. [CrossRef]
32. Allin, K.H.; Nielsen, T.; Pedersen, O. Mechanisms in endocrinology: Gut microbiota in patients with type 2 diabetes mellitus. *Eur. J. Endocrinol.* **2015**, *172*, R167–R177. [CrossRef]
33. Pussinen, P.J.; Havulinna, A.S.; Lehto, M.; Sundvall, J.; Salomaa, V. Endotoxemia is associated with an increased risk of incident diabetes. *Diabetes Care* **2011**, *34*, 392–397. [CrossRef]
34. Han, H.; Li, Y.; Fang, J.; Liu, G.; Yin, J.; Li, T.; Yin, Y. Gut Microbiota and Type 1 Diabetes. *Int. J. Mol. Sci.* **2018**, *19*, 995. [CrossRef] [PubMed]

35. Zhao, G.; Vatanen, T.; Droit, L.; Park, A.; Kostic, A.D.; Poon, T.W.; Vlamakis, H.; Siljander, H.; Härkönen, T.; Hämäläinen, A.-M.; et al. Intestinal virome changes precede autoimmunity in type I diabetes-susceptible children. *Proc. Natl. Acad. Sci. USA* **2017**, *114*, E6166–E6175. [CrossRef] [PubMed]
36. Albenberg, L.G.; Wu, G.D. Diet and the intestinal microbiome: Associations, functions, and implications for health and disease. *Gastroenterology* **2014**, *146*, 1564–1572. [CrossRef] [PubMed]
37. Kirpich, I.A.; Marsano, L.S.; McClain, C.J. Gut-liver axis, nutrition, and non-alcoholic fatty liver disease. *Clin. Biochem.* **2015**, *48*, 923–930. [CrossRef] [PubMed]

separations

MDPI

Article

Amelioration of Alcoholic Liver Disease by Activating PXR-Cytochrome P450s Axis with Blackberry Extract

Ting Xiao [1,2], Zhenghong Guo [3,*], Min Fu [2], Jiaoyan Huang [2], Xiaowei Wang [2], Yuqing Zhao [4], Ling Tao [1,2] and Xiangchun Shen [1,2,*]

1 The State Key Laboratory of Functions and Applications of Medicinal Plants, The Department of Pharmaceutic Preparation of Chinse Medicine, The High Educational Key Laboratory of Guizhou Province for Natural Medicinal Pharmacology and Druggability, School of Pharmaceutical Sciences, Guizhou Medical University, Guiyang 550025, China

2 The Key Laboratory of Optimal Utilization of Natural Medicine Resources, School of Pharmaceutical Sciences, Guizhou Medical University, University Town, Guian New District, Guiyang 550025, China

3 School of Pharmacy, Guizhou University of Traditional Chinese Medicine, Guiyang 550025, China

4 School of Functional Food and Wine, Shenyang Pharmaceutical University, Shenyang 110016, China

* Correspondence: sxc@gmc.edu.cn (X.S.); guo_zhenghong@163.com (Z.G.)

Abstract: Blackberry is widely used in diets for its rich biological phytochemicals and health benefits. However, the relationship between the effect of blackberry extract (BBE) on ameliorating alcoholic liver disease (ALD) and the PXR-Cytochrome P450s axis in vivo and in vitro is unknown. In this study, 50% and 30% ethanol by gavage were used to establish acute and subacute ALD. Male mice were intragastrically administered BBE with 25, 50, and 100 mg/kg BW in the treatment groups. In the experiment, samples were collected, and related indices and histopathological observation were measured. In addition, the potential mechanism was predicted by network and docking studies, which were verified by qRT-PCR analysis, the detection of apoptosis, the measurement of mitochondrial membrane potential, the detection of ROS levels, and Western blotting in liver tissues and HepG2 cells. The acute and subacute ALD experiments indicated BBE ameliorated liver indices, AST, ALT, SOD, and MDA in serum, and the histopathology changed, as observed via H&E, Sirius red, and oil red O staining. The potential mechanism was predicted by network and docking studies, which were verified by experiments. Western blotting suggested BBE reduced the protein expression of NF-κB, TGF-β, IL-6, and α-SMA, and enhanced PXR and CAR in livers. In addition, qRT-PCR showed BBE significantly elevated the mRNA levels of *PXR*, *CAR*, *CYP3A25*, *CYP3A11*, and *CYP2B10*. In the experiment of the ethanol-induced apoptosis of HepG2 cells, BBE reduced the apoptosis of HepG2 cells by boosting mitochondrial membrane potential, reducing the apoptotic rate and ROS content, lessening the expression of Bax, and inducing the expression of PXR. For the first time, this study demonstrated BBE's preventive effects on ALD, which are associated with the antioxidation and stimulation of the PXR-Cytochrome P450s axis. In addition, BBE is available as a nutritional agent.

Keywords: blackberry; PXR-Cytochrome P450s; alcoholic liver disease; mechanism; nutritional agent

1. Introduction

Alcohol is regarded as a primary carcinogen by the international agency for research on cancer (IARC). According to the reports, more than 740,000 new cancer cases are associated with alcohol consumption in 2020, and it is critical to heightening public health intervention, which is crucial to mitigate the negative effect of alcohol [1].

The liver is the major organ of heterologous metabolism, and a multitude of toxic chemicals, and drugs could give rise to liver damage [2]. Alcoholic liver disease (ALD) is the main cause of the incidence rate and mortality of liver diseases. It results in fatty degeneration, hepatitis, progressive fibrosis, cirrhosis, liver cancer, and psychiatric illnesses [3,4].

Alcohol abuse and alcoholism have triggered a worldwide public health issue worldwide, and the burden of ALD accounts for 33% of all chronic liver diseases [5]. Many factors, such as nutrition, gene, heredity, and environment, are involved in the process of ALD degenerating into other serious diseases [6]. The forms of treatments, including nutritional therapy, drug therapy, psychotherapy, and liver transplantation depend on the different stages of liver disease. Abstinence is effective and essential to prevent ALD [7]. Corticosteroids have been used for the treatment of alcohol-associated hepatitis, which is the most extensive manifestation of ALD, for many decades [8]. The condition of macronutrient and micronutrient malnutrition is widespread in patients with ALD. Thus, the intake of supplemental protein and energy and some micronutrients is used as nutritional therapy [9]. Some anti-inflammatory agents and attractive targets have been studied in ALD therapies because of inflammation in liver injury associated with alcohol use [10]. Therapies for stimulating liver regeneration and a few agents with antioxidant properties have been considered as alternative options [3,11]. Unfortunately, these therapies for ALD have limited applicability and efficacy.

Pregnane X receptor (PXR), a member of metabolic NRs, plays a vital role in xenobiotic and endobiotic metabolism in mammals [12]. It is highly expressed in the liver and gastrointestinal tract. PXR could be activated by various ingredients, such as derivatives, pregnane steroids, and some herbal extracts. The ligand of PXR in active state is combined with retinoid X receptor alpha (RXRα) to form a heterodimer, which controls the transcription of various proteins encoding detoxification, such as phase I enzymes cytochrome P450, phase II enzymes sulfotransferases, glutathione transferases, and the transporters of metabolite elimination [13]. However, the physiological and pathophysiological roles of PXR on ALD remain unknown.

Berries have positive effects originating from their health-promoting benefits [14]. The World Health Organization (WHO) declares the natural anthocyanins from berries as excellent antioxidants. Blackberry (*Rubus fruticosus* Pollich), belonging to the family Rosaceae, is listed as a third-generation fruit and praised as the "black diamond" and "fruit of life" [15,16]. Moreover, it is one of the earliest fruits used for medicinal purposes due to its various nutritional ingredients. Blackberry is also a great source of multifarious active phytochemical constituents, especially anthocyanins and polyphenols, which have potential health benefits, such as anticancer, antioxidant, anti-inflammatory, antianxiety, antibacterial, hypoglycemic, hypolipidemic, liver protection, neuroprotection, and vascular protection [17–19]. The fruit of blackberry could be processed into foods, juice, wine, and syrup. Blackberry anthocyanins have been reported to impose obvious inhibitory effects on hepatic steatosis induced by oleic acid [20].

The activity of anthocyanins from black raspberry (*Rubus occidentalis* L.) against ALD has been studied by the authors in vivo and in vitro [21], However, the ameliorative effect of blackberry, which is a different plant species with different chemical constituents, on ALD has never been reported. In the present study, the PXR-Cytochrome P450s axis was activated for ameliorating ALD with blackberry extract (BBE). Furthermore, the network pharmacology of cyanidin-3-*O*-glucoside was analyzed by molecular docking and networking. This study was the first to investigate BBE in terms of preventing ALD in vivo and in vitro.

2. Materials and Methods

2.1. Materials and Reagents

Blackberry was purchased from Youguowei organic blackberry and blueberry planting base, Nanjing, China. The voucher specimens (No. 202006) have been displayed in the herbarium of Guizhou Medical University. Cyanidin-3-*O*-glucoside, gallic acid, and catechin (the purity all higher than 95%) were purchased from Chengdu Purifa Technology Development Co., Ltd., Chengdu, China. The 2,2-diphenyl-1-picrylhydrazyl (DPPH), 2,2′-azino-bis (3-ethyl- benzothiazoline-6-sulfonic acid) (ABTS), 2,4,6-tris(2-pyridyl)-s-triazine (TPTZ), and Folin–Ciocalteu reagent were purchased from Sigma-Aldrich (St. Louis, MO,

USA). Ascorbic acid (V_C) was purchased from Sinopharm Chemical Reagent Co., Ltd., Shanghai, China. Fetal bovine serum, Dulbecco's Modified Eagle's medium (DMEM), and penicillin-streptomycin were purchased from Thermo Fisher Scientific Co., Ltd. (St. Wyman, Grand Island, MA, USA). MTT (3-(4,5-Dimethylthiazol-2-yl)-2,5-diphenyltetrazolium bromide) reagent was acquired from Guangzhou Solarbio Life Sciences Co., Ltd., Guangzhou, China. An Annexin V-FITC Kit (Cat. No.: 40302ES60) was purchased from Shanghai Yisheng Biotechnology Co., Ltd., Shanghai, China. JC-1 (Cat. No.: C2005) and a DCFH-DA (Cat. No.: S0033S) Kit were purchased from Beyotime Biotechnology Co., Ltd., Shanghai, China. Glyceraldehyde-3-phosphate dehydrogenase antibody (GAPDH, Cat. No.: 56t2759), nuclear factor-kappa b antibody (NF-κB, Cat. No.: BF8005), transforming growth factor-β antibody (TGF-β, Cat. No.: AF1027), interleukin-6 antibody (IL-6, Cat. No.: DF6087), constitutive androstane receptor antibody (CAR, Cat. No.: DF6725) were purchased from Affinity Biosciences (USA), Shanghai, China, and pregnane x receptor antibody (PXR, Cat. No.: 118336, Abcame Biosciences (UK), Shanghai, China, Anti-alpha smooth muscle actin antibody (α-SMA, Cat. No.: ab7817) from Abcam Biosciences (UK), Shanghai, China. Ethanol and HCl of analytical purity were purchased from Merck Chemical Technology (Shanghai) Co., Ltd., Shanghai, China.

2.2. Preparation of the Blackberry Extract

We refer to our previous research and the stability of anthocyanins under acidic conditions [22]. Blackberry fresh fruits were washed and vacuum freeze-dried, and then powdered. A total of 300 g powder was extracted by ultrasonic with ethanol-water (75:25, v/v, containing 0.1% HCl) at 35 °C 3 times, each time lasting for 1 h to obtain 70 g of blackberry extract (BBE), which was rich in crude anthocyanins, and then filtered with a Buchner funnel. BBE was obtained after the solvents were removed under vacuum using a rotary evaporation device, and the BBEs were stored at −20 °C before use. All processes are dark operations with black film and tin foil wrapping and stored away from light.

2.3. Polyphenol, Flavonoids, and Anthocyanin Contents

The experiments were implemented according to our previous research [22]. The Folin–ciocalteu method was used to detect the total phenolic content (TPC) of BBE, which was expressed as mg GAE/g DW according to the gallic acid calibration curve. The content of total flavonoids (TFC) in the BBE was determined by colorimetry, and the results were expressed as the average of milligrams catechin equivalents (CE)/g dry weight (DW). The anthocyanin content (TMA) was determined by the pH differential method [23], and the results were calculated as mg of cyanidin-3-*O*-glucoside equivalents/g dry weight (DW).

2.4. Antioxidant Activities

We refer to the method reported previously [22]. The antioxidant capacity of BBE was conducted with DPPH and ABTS radical scavenging assays and ferric reducing antioxidant power (FRAP) assays. Vitamin C was the antioxidant standard.

2.5. Animals and Treatment

2.5.1. Animals

Male Kunming mice weighing 18.0–22.0 g were purchased from the experimental animal center of Guizhou Medical University. The animals were subjected to a cycle of 12 h light/dark with conditions of 22 °C in an animal room free of specific pathogens with a humidity of 60% ± 5%. They were allowed free access to water and food. All animal operating procedures obey the regulations on animal experiments issued by the National Science and Technology Commission of the People's Republic of China and the guidelines for the care and use of laboratory animals issued by the National Institutes of Health (Experimental facility certification No.: SYXK (Guizhou) 2018-0001).

2.5.2. Experimental Design

The mice were adaptively fed for one week and randomly assigned to 10 groups with 10 mice per group. During the experiment, records of the food and water intake of mice once a day were processed. In acute and subacute ALD mice, these groups included a control group, a model group, and three treatment groups (25, 50, and 100 mg BBE/kg BW; suspension was prepared with 0.5% carboxymethyl cellulose CMC). The experiment lasted for one month, carried out as reported previously [21] (Figure 1). The control group was intragastrically administered an equal volume of saline during the experiment. In the acute experiment, the low, medium, and high dose groups were intragastrically administered with corresponding doses of BBE once, and the model group was administered with an equal volume of saline. Four hours after the last administration, the model and treatment groups were given 50% ethanol by gavage (12 mL/kg BW). All groups fasted for 16 h, and the mice were anesthetized by an intraperitoneal injection of pentobarbital sodium 60 mg/kg BW.

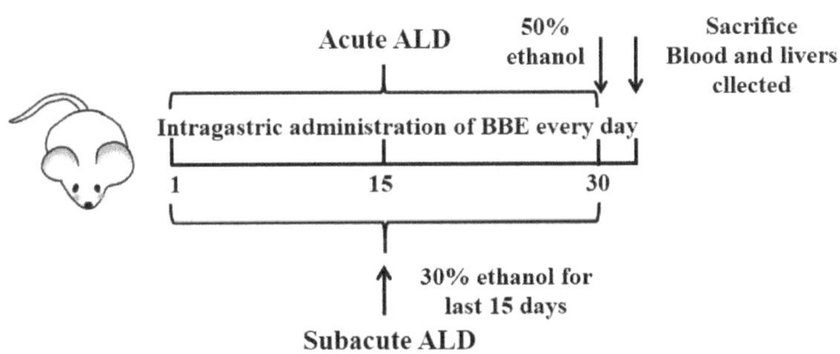

Figure 1. Experimental protocol for the establishment of ALD and the treatment schedule.

In the subacute experiment, the model group was given the same dose of saline for 15 days once a day, and the next with 30% ethanol (10 mL/kg BW) for 15 days. The low-, medium-, and high-dose groups were given BBE for 30 days and then treated with 30% ethanol once a day for the last 15 days. The interval between the two administrations was 4 h. Then, all groups fasted for 4 h, and all mice were anesthetized with pentobarbital sodium.

2.5.3. Measurement of Related Indices

The percentage of liver weight/body weight was used to calculate liver indexes. Blood was collected from the retroorbital venous plexus and the levels of aspartate aminotransferase (AST), Alanine aminotransferase (ALT), superoxide dismutase (SOD), and malondialdehyde (MDA) were measured. After coagulation, AST, ALT, SOD, and MDA in serum were detected by an automatic biochemical analyzer (Chemray 800, Shenzhen redu Life Technology, Shenzhen, China)

2.5.4. Histopathological Observation

All mouse livers were fixed in 4% paraformaldehyde for 48 h with paraffin-embedded tissues and cut into sections 5–6 μm thick. They were then placed on microscope slides for H&E staining and Sirius red staining and then observed under a microscope (Mshot MF53, Mingmei Photoelectric Technology Co., Ltd., Guangzhou, China).

In addition, oil red O staining with a 10 μm frozen section of liver tissue was applied to evaluate steatosis under a microscope.

2.5.5. Network Pharmacological Analysis of Cyanidin-3-O-glucoside

We searched the SMILES number of cyanidin-3-O-glucoside in the PubChem database (the main component of BBE) and then entered the Swiss Target Prediction Database (http://www.swisstargetprediction.Ch/) (accessed on 1 September 2020). The species was defined as "Homo sapiens", and the targets related to cyanidin-3-O-glucoside were acquired. The keyword "ALD" was used in the GeneCards Database (https://www.Genecards.org/) (accessed on 15 September 2020), and the condition was "score > 20"; the targets related to ALD were selected. Then, the screened component targets and disease targets of cyanidin-3-O-glucoside and ALD were located to obtain the cross targets with Venn diagrams (http://bioinformatics.psb.ugent.be/webtools/Venn/) (accessed on 30 September 2020).

2.5.6. Establishment of PPI Network

The cross-targets of active components and disease were inputted into the STRING Database (https://string-db.org/) (accessed on 5 October 2020). The species was "H. sapiens", and the selected condition was the comprehensive score of protein interaction > 0.4. Then, the relationship between the target interaction network and PPI was established. Then, the Cytoscape 3.7.2 software was used for network data analysis with the TSV format exported from the network.

2.5.7. Analysis of Target Pathways

R × 64 (4.0.2) was used for the analysis of the intersection targets for the enrichment analysis of the GO and KEGG pathways. The top 20 channels were collected, and a visual analysis of the histograms was displayed.

2.5.8. Construction of Regulatory Network for Cyanidin-3-O-glucoside-Targets-Pathways-Disease

From the enrichment analysis of the KEGG results, the construction of 18 low *p*-value target pathways related to ALD was carried out, and the Cytoscape 3.7.2 software was processed to construct the "components-target pathway-disease" network with the common targeting. In the established network, the putative targets of cyanidin-3-O-glucoside on ALD were marked green, while the pathways related to ALD were marked red. The interactions between cyanidin-3-O-glucoside, targets, pathways, and disease were represented by black edges.

2.5.9. Analysis of Gene Ontology and KEGG

The molecular function (MF), biological process (BP), and cellular component (CC) were collected from the Gene Ontology (GO) Database (http://geneontology.org/) (accessed on 25 October 2020), which can be used to predict the biological mechanisms analysis of high-throughput genomic or transcriptome data. The compound was cyanidin-3-O-glucoside and targeted ALD. The function and biological correlation of candidate targets can be selected in the KEGG database (https://www.kegg.jp/) (accessed on 25 October 2020) [24]. In the study, the analysis of the GO and KEGG pathways was carried out with the "ClusterProfiler" package in R. In these enrichment analysis results, the name of the pathway was located on the Y-axis, and the X-axis was the enrichment factor. The bubble size represented the number of genes belonging to this pathway in the target genes, and the bubble color was the degree of enrichment, i.e., the value of *p*.adjust. The threshold was set to *p*-value < 0.01.

2.5.10. In Silico Molecular Docking Study

The top one of the KEGG pathways in the drug-target network was selected for molecular docking. In order to evaluate the efficacy of the main anthocyanins (cyanidin-3-O-glucoside) in BBE as inhibitors of PXR [25], Cyt P450 1B1, Bcl-2, Caspase 9, and an activator of Cytochrome c, the analysis of molecular docking was processed to predict the ligand within the restriction of receptor binding sites. The crystal structures of PXR, Cyt P450 1B1, Bcl-2, Caspase 9, and Cytochrome c were downloaded with IDs 1NRL, 3PM0, IDs, 4LVT, 4RHW, 2BC5 from PDB. ChemBioDraw (PerkinElmer) and AutoDock Tools

(ADT, version: 1.5.6) were used for the docking process, and the structure exhibition was displayed by Discovery Studio 2016 Client. Genetic Algorithm was used for Blind docking, and the conformations of the most favorable binding energy were used to investigate the resultant complex structures.

2.5.11. qRT-PCR Analysis

The total RNA of liver tissue was extracted and isolated with a total RNA kit (Wuhan Servicebio Technology Co., Ltd., Wuhan, China) for qRT-PCR under the guidance of the instructions, and then the cDNA was synthesized. RT-PCR amplification scheme was as follows: initial denaturation at 95 °C for 10 min, denaturation at 95 °C for 15 s, annealing at 60 °C for 30 s, melting curve at 65 °C to 95 °C, temperature rise 0.3 °C every 15 s, and cycle 40 times. The transcription level was related to the *GAPDH* mRNA level, and the transcription levels were calculated by the $2^{-\Delta\Delta CT}$ method. All the above primers were synthesized by Wuhan Servicebio Technology Co., Ltd., (Wuhan, China). The primers are listed in Table 1.

Table 1. Quantitative real-time PCR primers.

Gene	Forward (5′-3′)	Reverse (5′-3′)
PXR	AGACGGCAGCATCTGGAACTAC	GTTTCTGGAAGCCACCATTAGG
CAR	CCACAGGCTATCATTTCCACG	CCTTCCAGCAAACGGACAGAT
CYP3A25	GGAGGCCTGAACTGCTAAAG	GTAGTTGAAAATGGTGCCAAGTAAC
CYP3A11	GGTGCTCCTAGCAATCAGCTT	AAGGAGAGGCGTTTGACCATC
CYP2B10	TCTGCCCTTCTCAACAGGAAAG	AAGGAGAGGCGTTTGACCATC
GAPDH	TTGGAGCCCTGGAGATTTGGA	TGAGGTCAATGAAGGGGTCGT

2.6. Potential Mechanisms of BBE against HepG2 Cells

2.6.1. Cell Viability Assay

The cytotoxicity of HepG2 cells induced by 200 mM ethanol was measured with an MTT assay. Cells (5000 cells/well) were inoculated into 96-well plates and cultured overnight. Then, the cells were treated with a mixture of 200 mM ethanol and different concentrations of BBE (150, 250, and 450 μg/mL, dissolved in PBS) for 24 h. After the treatments, formazan crystals were then formed after 0.5 mg/mL MTT was added to each well and cultured for 4 h. After removing the supernatant, 150 mL DMSO was added to dissolve the crystals. The absorbance of formazan crystals formed was quantified at 490 nm using a microplate reader (Bio-Rad iMARK, Berkeley, CA, USA). The data were calculated as a percentage of survival compared with untreated control cells.

2.6.2. Detection of Apoptosis by Flow Cytometry in HepG2 Cells

Referring to the manufacturer's instructions (ACEA Bioscience, Inc., Hangzhou, China), the Annexin V-FITC apoptosis kit was used to determine the apoptotic effect induced by the mixture of 200 mM ethanol and different concentrations of BBE. In short, HepG2 cells were spread evenly on a six-well plate (2×10^5/well) and incubated for 24 h. After the treatment of 200 mM ethanol and different concentrations of BBE for 24 h, the cells were collected by centrifugation and washed with PBS. Thereafter, 100 μL binding buffer was added to resuspend cells and Annexin V-FITC and propidium iodide were used to stain for 15 min in the dark at room temperature. At last, the cells were evaluated by flow cytometry after staining within 1 h, and the data were analyzed using NovoExpress software (version 1.2.5) (ACEA Bioscience, Inc., Hangzhou, China).

2.6.3. Measurement of Mitochondrial Membrane Potential in HepG2 Cells

JC-1 kit was used to measure the loss of mitochondrial membrane potential by fluorescent probe under the guidance of instructions. The cultured cells were incubated with a 2.0 mg/mL JC-1 fluorescent probe for 30 min at 37 °C. After washing with ice-cold PBS, HepG2 cells were observed on a Leica DM4B inverted microscope (100× magnification).

The loss of mitochondrial membrane potential drives the formation of red fluorescing JC-1 dimers.

2.6.4. Detection of ROS Levels in HepG2 Cells

HepG2 cells were treated with 200 mM ethanol, and DCFH-DA fluorescent probe was used to detect intracellular reactive oxygen species (ROS). In brief, HepG2 cells were diluted into approximately 2×10^5 cells/well on 6-well plates (JET BIOFIL, Guangzhou, China) in DMEM medium (Gibco, Grand Island, NY, USA) using a DCFH-DA fluorescent probe for 10 min, and luminescence was detected by flow cytometry at the excitation wavelength of 488 nm and emission wavelength of 525 nm, and the data were analyzed using NovoExpress software.

2.7. Western Blotting

After treatment, the mice livers or cells were obtained, and the total proteins were collected from the tissue or cells using RIPA lysis buffer, and a BCA assay was used to measure the concentration. Briefly, 10% SDS-PAGE was used to separate equal amounts of proteins, then proteins were transferred to polyvinylidene fluoride membranes. Additionally, membranes were incubated with NF-κB (1:2000), TGF-β (1:2000), PXR (1:3000), IL-6 (1:1000), CAR (1:1000), and α-SMA (1:2000) antibodies and Bax (1:2000) antibodies overnight at 4 °C. Membranes and the appropriate secondary antibodies were incubated together for 1 h at room temperature. Then, ECL reagents (Beyotime Institute of Biotechnology, Shanghai, China) were used to display positive bands with the ChemiDoc MP Imaging System (Bio-Rad, Hercules, CA, USA). The protein blot intensities were quantified using Image J Software (1.48 v) and normalized to the housekeeping protein (GAPDH) levels.

2.8. Data and Statistical Analysis

All data were repeated three times, and the values are expressed as mean ± SD. One-way analysis of variance (ANOVA) was used to test differences between groups, and LSD was used for average separation ($p \leq 0.05$) using the GraphPad Prism program (Version 6.01) for statistical analysis.

3. Results

3.1. The Contents of Polyphenols, Flavonoids, and Anthocyanins

In BBE, the total polyphenols and flavonoids of blackberry were 5.70 ± 1.34 and 105.70 ± 12.11 mg/g DW, respectively (Table 2). Polyphenols and flavonols, which are almost completely glycosylated, are rich in berries [26]. For instance, the highest content of ellagic acid in blackberry of the Boysen variety was 13.67% [27]. The total monomeric anthocyanin content of blackberry was 24.50 ± 3.49 mg/g DW. Cyanidin, the main anthocyanin in blackberry fruits, especially cyanidin-3-*O*-glucoside, accounts for more than 80% of total anthocyanins [25].

Table 2. The total phenolic contents, total flavonoid, total monomeric anthocyanin, and the antioxidant activities of DPPH, ABTS, and FRAP assays of blackberry.

Species	TP [a]	TF [b]	TMA [c]	DPPH [d]	ABTS [d]	FRAP [e]
Blackberry	5.70 ± 1.34	105.70 ± 12.11	24.50 ± 3.49	22.08 ± 7.13	51.69 ± 7.84	2.93
Vc				4.76 ± 1.15	36.23 ± 5.78	1

Values with the different superscript in the same column indicate significant statistical differences ($p < 0.05$); n = 3. [a] The total phenolic (TP) content of species is expressed as mg gallic acid equivalents (GAE)/g dry weight (DW). [b] The total flavonoid (TF) content of species is expressed as mg catechin equivalents (CE)/g dry weight (DW). [c] The total monomeric anthocyanin (TMA) is expressed as mg cyanidin-3-*O*-glucoside equivalents/g dry weight (DW). [d] The DPPH and ABTS activities are expressed as EC_{50} and IC_{50} in μg/mL for extracts. [e] In FRAP activities, the value "1" of Vc was defined as the quantity of Vc generating 100 μM Fe^{2+}, and the value of species is expressed as the times of the ability of Vc.

3.2. Antioxidant Activities

The results of the DPPH assay confirmed that the radical scavenging activities of BBE were lower than that of the positive control (V_C, 4.76 ± 1.15 μg/mL), with EC_{50} of 22.08 ± 7.13 μg/mL. Similar conclusions were found in the ABTS assay with an EC_{50} of 51.69 ± 7.84 μg/mL of BBE, which was weaker than the Vc (36.23 ± 5.78 μg/mL) for free radical scavenging capacity. The results indicated that BBE has good free radical scavenging ability. In the FRAP assay, the FRAP value was expressed as a μM $FeSO_4$/μM sample under the same absorbance. The FRAP value of BBE was 2.93, indicating that it is a powerful ferric-reducing antioxidant compared with vitamin C. The results suggested that BBE possesses excellent electron-transfer capacity and total antioxidant activity (Table 2) [22,28].

3.3. Measurement of Related Indices

The effects of BBE on growth performance and liver indices were displayed in Table 2. The liver weight and index of the BBE-treated groups decreased with no significant difference compared with those of the model group. Meanwhile, no difference was observed in the liver weight among the low-, medium-, and high-dose BBE groups in the acute and subacute ALD experiments.

In the acute and subacute ALD experiments, the levels of ALT, AST, and MDA in the model groups increased, whereas the SOD level decreased. In the treatment groups (low-, medium-, and high-dose groups), these markers shifted distinctly to normal levels in a dose-dependent manner. The results (Table 3) indicated that administering BBE enormously suppressed liver injury, lessened the release of these markers into blood, and promoted the antioxidant capacity of liver tissues. In the subacute ALD experiments, the treatment groups showed extensive enhancement compared to the model group ($p < 0.001$). The reason may be related to the inhibitory effects of anthocyanins with strong antioxidant activity in oxidative stress, which resulted in ALD [29]. This study is the first investigation of blackberry on the inhibitory effect on ALD in vivo.

Table 3. Effect of BBE on the activity of biochemical parameters.

Treatment Group	Final Weight (g)	Liver Index (%)	AST (U/L)	ALT (U/L)	SOD (U/mL)	MDA (U/mL)
			(a) Subacute ALD mice			
Control	41.45 ± 2.78	4.23 ± 0.24	135.60 ± 8.75	55.07 ± 7.03	260.13 ± 17.52	5.76 ± 0.24
Model	34.48 ± 3.45	3.76 ± 0.31	189.92 ± 15.87 ***	94.08 ± 1.55 ***	177.88 ± 3.24 ***	11.37 ± 0.14
Low-dose BBE	36.69 ± 4.05	3.81 ± 0.55	169.60 ± 11.35 ###	82.01 ± 1.09 ###	191.01 ± 2.89 ###	8.79 ± 0.24 ###
Medium-dose BBE	35.87 ± 3.61	3.71 ± 0.39	163.73 ± 10.24 ###	72.28 ± 2.23 ###	229.02 ± 6.96 ###	8.19 ± 0.65 ###
High-dose BBE	36.12 ± 3.34	3.69 ± 0.25	151.18 ± 5.27 ###	61.57 ± 3.97 ###	235.07 ± 3.15 ###	8.03 ± 0.42 ###
			(b) Acute ALD mice			
Control	40.90 ± 0.45	3.29 ± 0.30	121.14 ± 9.95	44.71 ± 7.13	306.80 ± 17.14	6.37 ± 0.42
Model	41.00 ± 0.31	4.30 ± 0.21	210.14 ± 22.60	72.65 ± 0.55	231.62 ± 4.29	8.94 ± 0.21
Low-dose BBE	41.31 ± 0.62	4.04 ± 0.57	176.69 ± 14.77	70.82 ± 1.19	245.44 ± 3.58	8.49 ± 0.08
Medium-dose BBE	41.58 ± 0.45	3.33 ± 0.22	158.99 ± 10.16	60.01 ± 1.23	253.22 ± 7.68	7.28 ± 0.16
High-dose BBE	41.69 ± 0.56	3.10 ± 1.27	151.37 ± 3.76	53.94 ± 4.97	266.19 ± 2.55	7.12 ± 0.21

Values are the mean ± standard deviation of 10 determinations. Compared with control: ***, $p < 0.001$. Compared with model: ###, $p < 0.001$.

3.4. Histopathological Observation

Histological evaluation is applied to assess the severity of ALD. In this study, it was used to estimate the amelioration of BBE on hepatic steatosis, hepatic fibrosis, and liver pathological changes on the basis of liver sections. Representative micrographs of the liver histology were elucidated in Figure 2. In the acute or subacute ALD experiments, the control groups exhibited normality in appearance, color, and liver status (Figure 2A). On the contrary, the livers of the model groups were pale, hard, large, and rough. The pathological state of the liver treated with BBE was modified in a dose-dependent manner, coinciding with the results of the pathological sections. In the H&E staining (Figure 2B), the subjects in the acute or subacute ALD experiments exhibited a large amount of fat accumulation and a process into steatohepatitis and fibrosis, which were characterized by hepatocyte expansion, scattered lobular inflammatory cell infiltration, inflammatory lesions, and some severe cellular fibrosis. After Sirius red staining was applied in the model group (Figure 2C), collagen fibers extended outward along the vascular wall of the portal area, and the amount of product was significantly higher than that in the control group. Obvious changes in the morphology of hepatocytes, such as cell cavities, uneven arrangement, and cell shrinkage, were observed. The accumulation of fat, steatohepatitis, and fibrosis were eased when the animals were administered BBE. In addition, a large area of fat deposition and a large, dark halo of fat droplets were detected in the model group after oil red O staining (Figure 2D). These results indicated that BBE relieved hepatic steatosis, necroinflammation, and hepatic fibrosis.

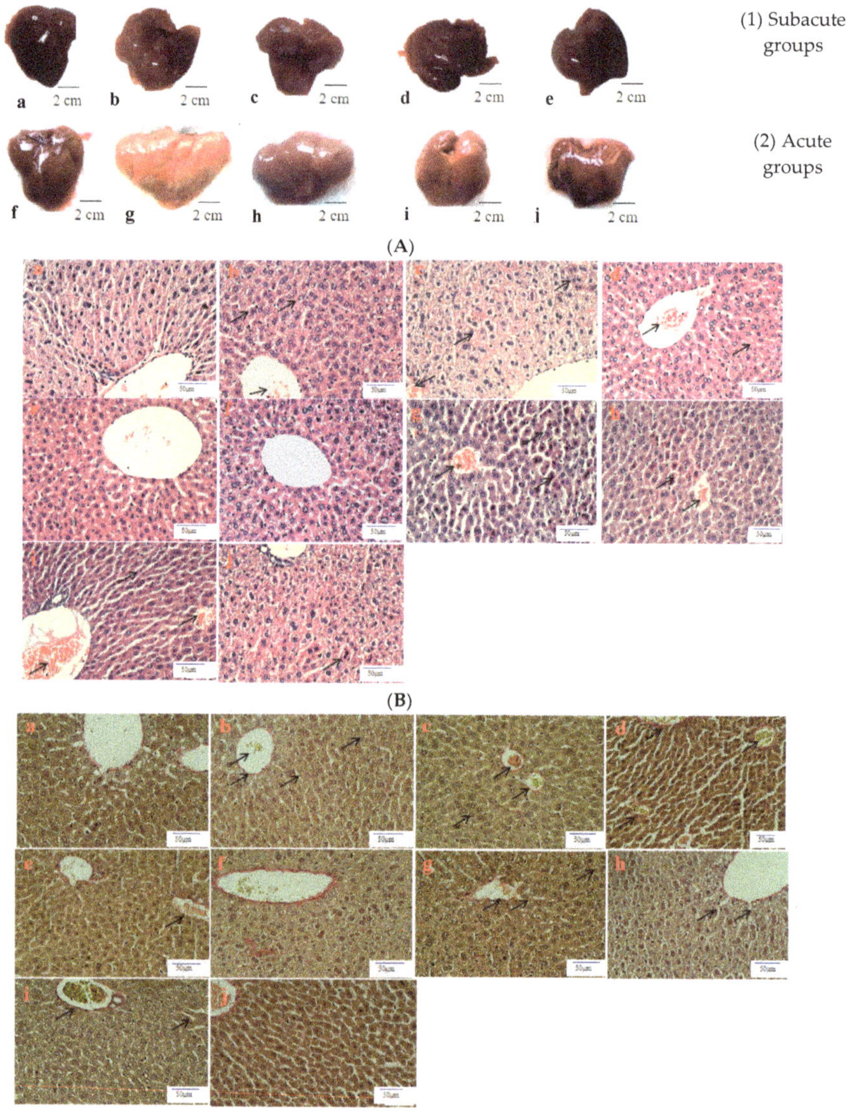

Figure 2. *Cont.*

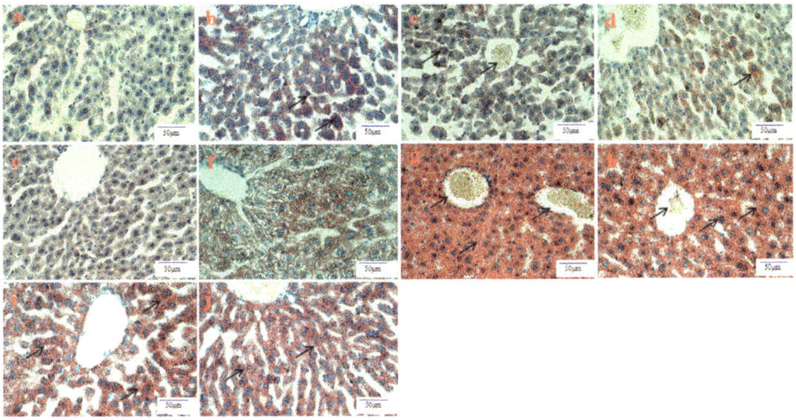

(D)

Figure 2. The histopathological observation of BBE on subacute and acute alcohol-induced liver damage (liver appearance, (**A**); analysis of BBE with H&E staining ((**B**), ×400), Sirius red staining ((**C**), ×400), and oil red O staining ((**D**), ×400) ((**a**), subacute control group; (**b**), subacute model group; (**c**), subacute low-dose BBE group; (**d**), subacute medium-dose BBE group; (**e**), subacute high-dose BBE group; (**f**), acute control group; (**g**), acute model group; (**h**), acute low-dose BBE group; (**i**), acute medium-dose BBE group; (**j**), acute high-dose BBE group)).

3.5. Network Pharmacological Analysis of Cyanidin-3-O-glucoside

The SMILES number of cyanidin-3-*O*-glucoside retrieved on the PubChem database was C1=CC(=C(C=C1C2=[O+]C3=CC(=CC(=C3C=C2OC4C(C(C(C(O4)CO)O)O)O)O)O)O)O. A total of 100 related targets of cyanidin-3-*O*-glucoside were searched on the Swiss Target Prediction database (Figure S1A). A total of 5389 ALD-related targets were screened on the GeneCards database to reveal a Venn diagram (Figure S1B). These two kinds of targets were mapped to each other to collect 82 shared targets (Table S1).

3.6. Establishment of PPI Network

The shared targets between cyanidin-3-*O*-glucoside and ALD were inputted into the STRING database, and the protein interaction network was conducted on Cytoscape 3.7.2 (Figure S2). A total of 82 nodes and 112 edges were surveyed in the network. The average degree of nodes and the local clustering coefficient were 10.6 and 0.519, respectively. Refined with degree value, the degrees of AKT1, TNF, SRC, EGFR, PTGS2, and PIK3R were greater than the average node degree.

3.7. Analysis of Target Pathways

As a key technology in systems biology, network pharmacology attaches great importance to the molecular mechanism of complex diseases [30]. As shown in Figure S3A–C, the top five PPI network targets involved in the metabolic process were the response to oxidative stress, the cellular response to chemical stress, the cellular response to oxidative stress, peptidyl-tyrosine phosphorylation, and peptidyl-tyrosine modification. The analysis of CC demonstrated that these targets are related to the membrane raft, membrane microdomain, cell projection membrane, membrane region, and apical part of the cell, which are ranked as the top five. According to the analysis of MF, the top five targets were connected with protein serine/threonine kinase activity, protein tyrosine kinase activity, transmembrane receptor protein tyrosine kinase activity, transmembrane receptor protein kinase activity, and lyase activity.

As shown in Figure S4, enrichment analysis of the KEGG pathway showed that these targets involved signal pathways including EGFR tyrosine kinase inhibitor resistance, proteoglycans in cancer, nitrogen metabolism, endocrine resistance, and PI3K-Akt, which were in the top five. These results certified that the targets of cyanidin-3-*O*-glucoside were distributed in different metabolic pathways. The mechanism of ALD treatment is possible "multi-targets, and multi-pathways" mutual regulation.

3.8. Construction of Regulatory Network for Cyanidin-3-O-glucoside-Targets-Pathways-Disease

An interaction network was conducted on Cytoscape 3.7.2 to clarify the mechanism of cyanidin-3-*O*-glucoside on ALD. The pathway diagram of "component-target-pathway-disease" was shown in Figure S5. The network consisted of 224 nodes and 434 edges. Among the nodes, 82 nodes were green, indicating these targets were common, and 29 nodes were red, which suggested these were related to KEGG pathways. The pink and yellow nodes were cyanidin-3-*O*-glucoside and ALD, respectively. According to the degree of the pathway, the mechanisms involved were EGFR tyrosine kinase inhibitor resistance, proteoglycans in cancer, nitrogen metabolism, endocrine resistance, and the PI3K-Akt signaling pathway and other pathways. In this study, the PI3K-Akt signaling pathway was selected for mechanism verification.

3.9. In Silico Molecular Docking Study

As an important tool of computer-aided molecular design, molecular docking predicts biological experiments that were conducted by simulating the interaction between small molecules and biological macromolecules.

The binding energy and binding mode of cyanidin-3-*O*-glucoside with PXR, Cyt P450 1B1, Bcl-2, Caspase 9, and as Cytochrome c activator were shown in Table 4 and Figure 3. The lower the binding energy is, the easier it is to bind to proteins. Cyanidin-3-*O*-glucoside was transplanted compatibly into the binding domain of Cyt P450 1B1, Bcl-2, Caspase 9, and Cytochrome c, and binding energies were −8.7, −8.2, −7.3, −7.2, and −7.6 kcal/mol, respectively. Furthermore, cyanidin-3-*O*-glucoside bound to PXR easily and it was matched with the PXR-Cytochrome P450s axis appropriately.

Table 4. Molecular docking mode for Cyanidin-3-*O*-glucoside with PXR, Bcl-2, Caspase 9, and Cytochrome c.

Targets	Binding Free Energy (kcal/mol)	Numbers of Bonds
PXR	−8.7	10
Cyt P450 1B1	−8.2	14
Bcl-2	−7.3	6
Caspase 9	−7.2	5
Cytochrome c	−7.6	4

3.10. qRT-PCR Analysis

The mRNA level of liver tissues was detected by qRT-PCR to determine the expression of the PXR-Cytochrome P450s axis in ALD. In the acute and subacute experiments, *PXR* decreased significantly in the model groups ($p < 0.05$). It increased significantly in the low-dose BBE group of the acute model ($p < 0.001$), and the medium- and high-dose BBE groups ($p < 0.001$) of the subacute model (Figure 4A).

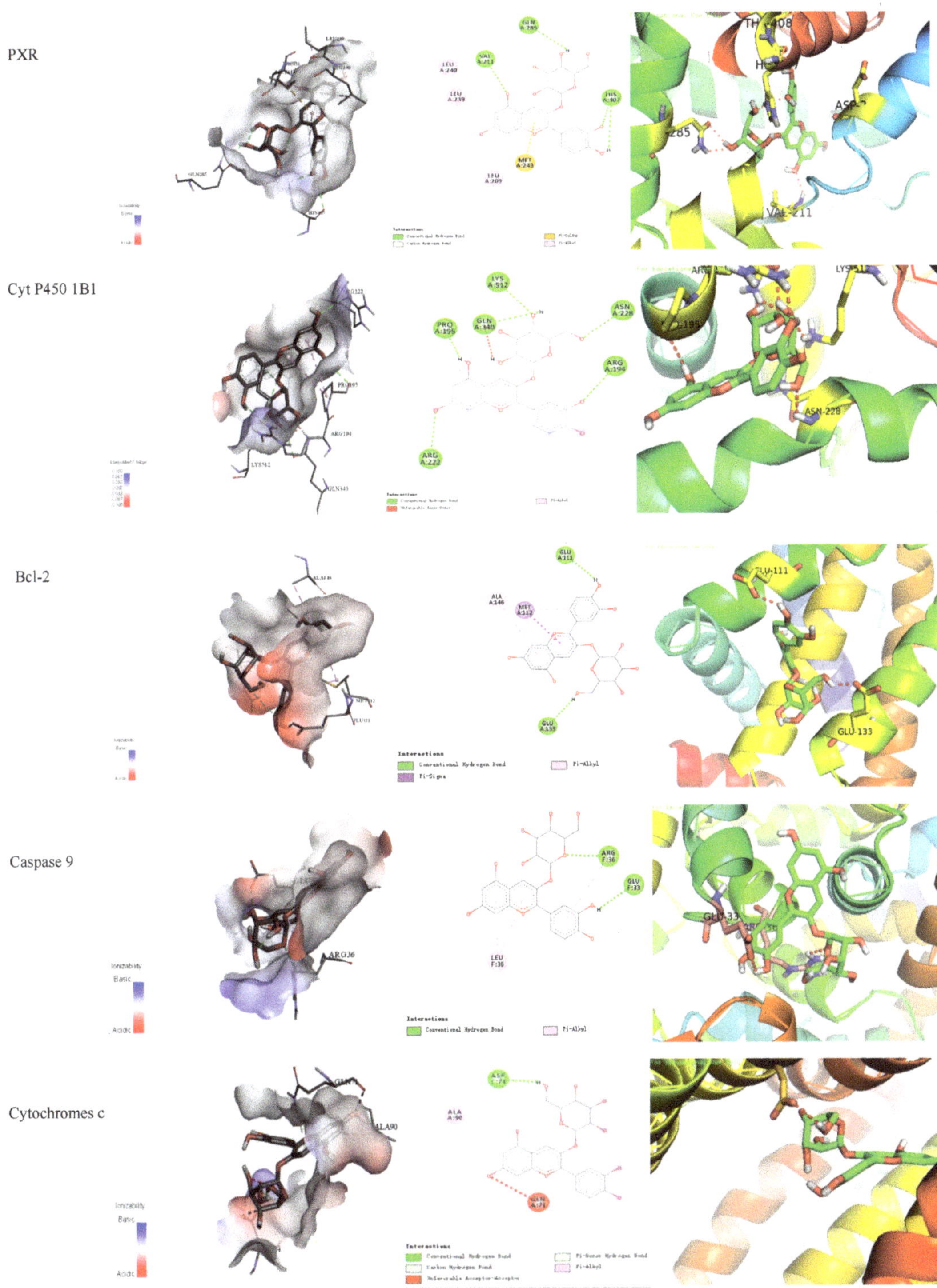

Figure 3. Cyanidin-3-*O*-glucoside-proteins docking combination.

The mRNA expression of *CAR* in the model group decreased in the acute ALD mice and increased in the low-, and medium-dose BBE groups. Meanwhile, no significant difference was found between the model group and the control group, and between the BBE groups and the model group. In the subacute ALD mice, CAR increased significantly ($p < 0.05$) in the high-dose BBE groups (Figure 4B).

Similarly, the mRNA expression of *CYP3A25* (Figure 4C), *CYP3A11* (Figure 4D), and *CYP2B10* (Figure 4E) were reduced in the model groups of acute and subacute experiments and increased in all BBE groups. A notable detail is that *CYP2B10* decreased significantly ($p < 0.01$) in the model group, and increased significantly ($p < 0.05$) in the high-dose BBE group of the acute experiment. Meanwhile, *CYP3A25*, *CYP3A11*, and *CYP2B10* enhanced significantly in the high-dose BBE group of the subacute experiment. The results indicated that the benefits of BBE in subacute ALD are superior to that in acute ALD.

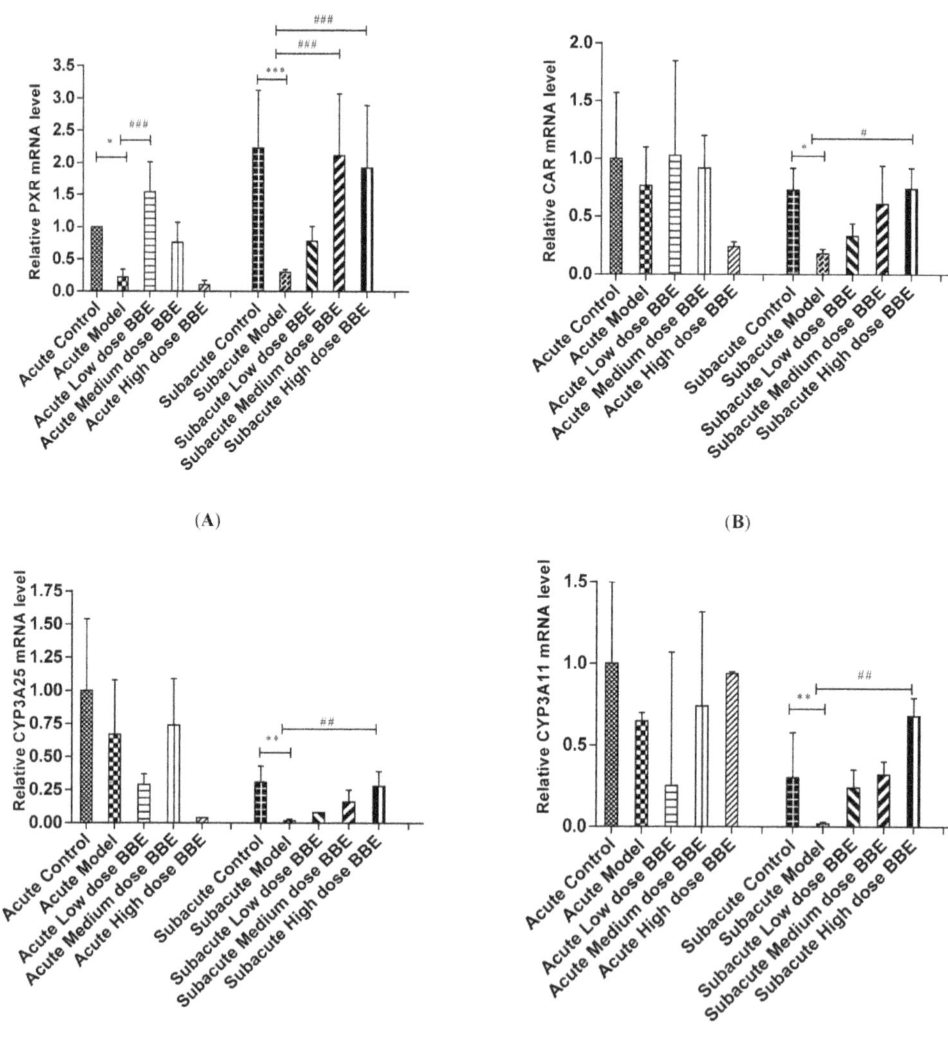

Figure 4. *Cont.*

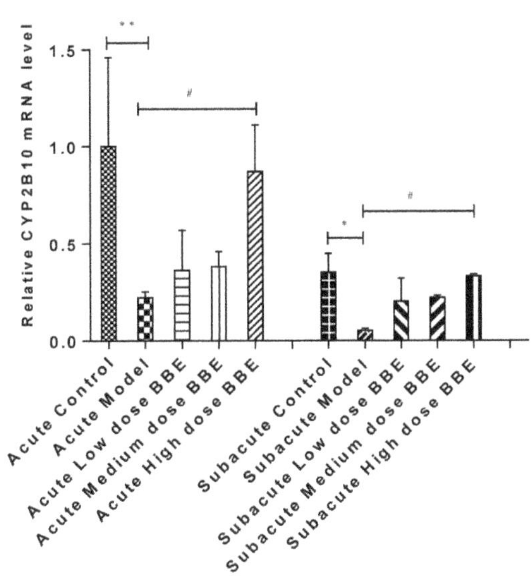

(E)

Figure 4. The qRT-PCR analysis of the PXR-Cytochrome P450s axis in ALD (**A–E**). Values are the mean ± standard deviation. Compared with control: *, $p < 0.05$; **, $p < 0.01$; ***, $p < 0.001$. Compared with model: $^{\#}$, $p < 0.05$; $^{\#\#}$, $p < 0.01$; $^{\#\#\#}$, $p < 0.001$.

3.11. Detection of Apoptosis by Flow Cytometry in HepG2 Cells

The injury of HepG2 cells induced by 200 mM ethanol was used to simulate the effect of ALD in vitro and explore the effect of BBE on ALD. An Annexin V-FITC assay was carried out to determine the effects of BBE on the apoptosis of HepG2 cells.

BBE upgraded the cell viability in a dose-dependent manner in HepG2 cells (Figure 5A,B). Late and early apoptotic cells appeared in Q2 and Q4, respectively. The results suggested that BBE (150, 250, and 450 μg/mL) ameliorated ethanol-induced apoptosis compared with the model group. The apoptotic rates of the control group, the model group, and the low-, medium-, and high-dose groups were 6.48 ± 1.48%, 9.60 ± 2.15%, and 9.42 ± 2.07%, 7.21 ± 1.58%, and 6.98 ± 1.23%, respectively. The middle- ($p < 0.05$) and high-dose BBE groups ($p < 0.01$) showed a significant protective effect on the ethanol-induced apoptosis of HepG2 cells.

3.12. Measurement of Mitochondrial Membrane Potential in HepG2 Cells

Changes in the mitochondrial membrane potential of HepG2 cells were studied to examine whether the improvement of this event is consistent with the antiapoptotic effect of BBE. With the depolarization of the mitochondria, the cell fluorescence changed from red to green with the help of membrane-permeant JC-1 dye (Figure 6). The results revealed that the intensity of red fluorescence decreased in the model group, suggesting progressive depolarization in the mitochondria. The intensity of red fluorescence increased with the pretreatment of BBE and 200 mM ethanol. The results were consistent with those of the Annexin V-FITC analysis pretreated with BBE previously. Overall, these results indicated that BBE prevents mitochondrial membrane depolarization induced by ethanol, and anthocyanins, especially cyanidin-3-*O*-glucoside, may be the active components.

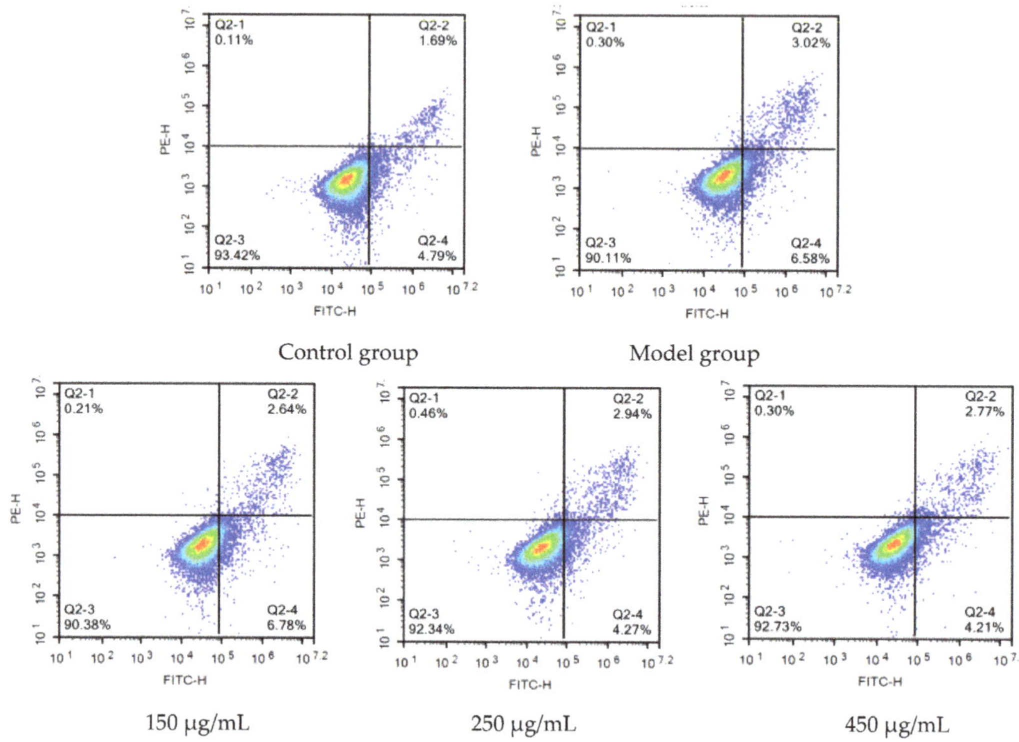

(A)

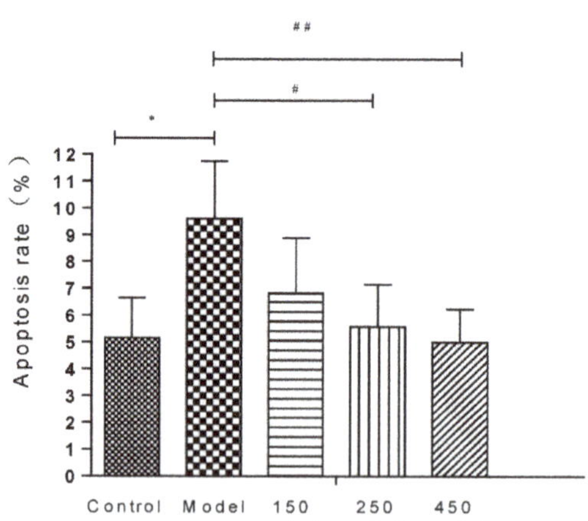

(B)

Figure 5. Annexin V-FITC Apoptosis Detection by Flow Cytometry in HepG2 cells (**A**,**B**). Values are the mean ± standard deviation. Compared with control: *, $p < 0.05$. Compared with model: #, $p < 0.05$, ##, $p < 0.01$.

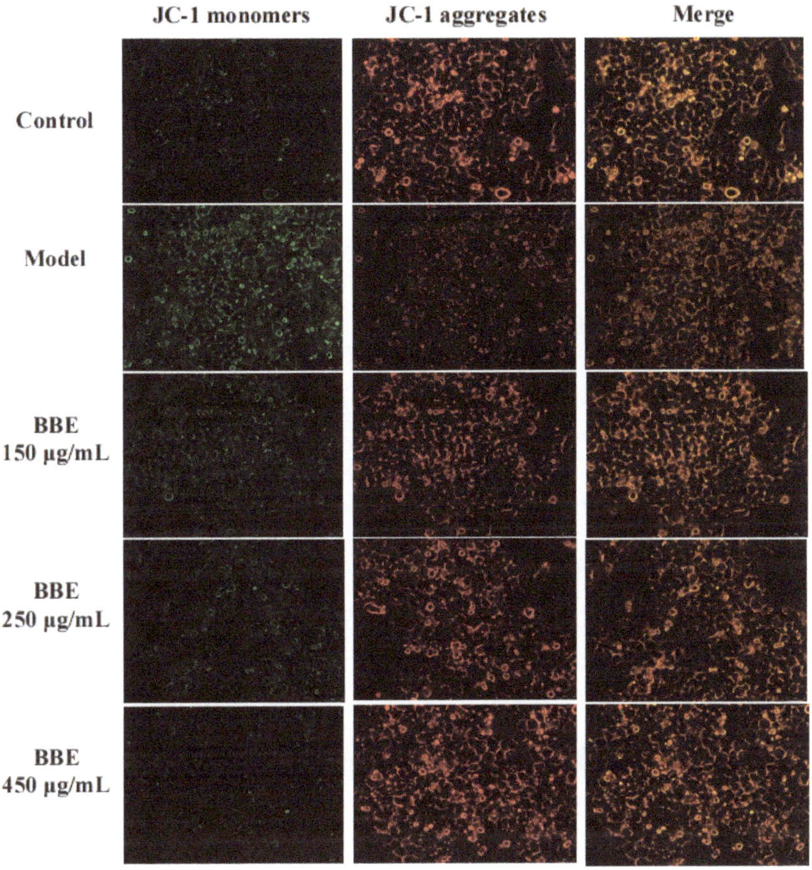

Figure 6. Measurement of mitochondrial membrane potential in HepG2 cells. Cells were stained with JC-1 and visualized on an inverted fluorescence microscope (200× magnification). Red fluorescence of JC-1 dimers was present in the cell areas with high mitochondrial membrane potential, while the green fluorescence of JC-1 monomers was prevalent in the cell areas with low mitochondrial membrane potential.

3.13. Detection of ROS Levels in HepG2 cells

Most polyphenols, flavonoids, and anthocyanins in berries are natural antioxidants. The capacity of blackberry to reduce ethanol-induced oxidative stress was investigated (Figure 7A,B). In HepG2 cells, three BBE treatment groups showed a significant decrease in the production of intracellular ROS initiated by ethanol injury ($p < 0.001$). The strong free radical scavenging activity of BBE could be attributed to its high content of natural antioxidants [22,28]. In this study, after being pre-incubated with BBE, the cells showed significantly relieved ALD-induced oxidative damage and reduced apoptosis. This finding suggested that ROS plays a vital role in ethanol-induced apoptosis and free radical scavenging activity, and BBE could restrain or ease the process. The results coincided with the mitochondrial membrane potential of HepG2 cells.

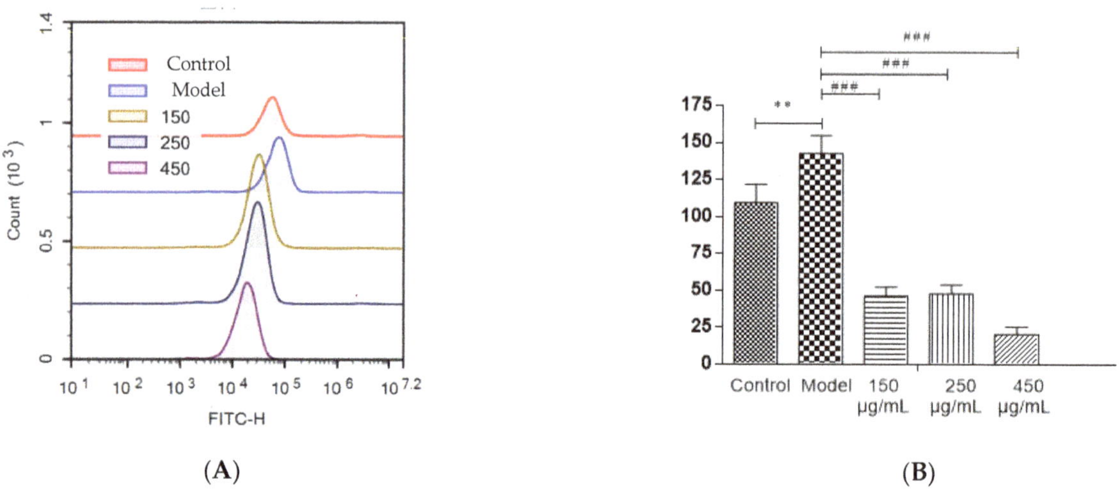

Figure 7. The detection of ROS levels in HepG2 cells (**A**,**B**). Values are the mean ± standard deviation. Compared with control: **, $p < 0.01$. Compared with model: ###, $p < 0.001$.

3.14. Western Blotting

Western blotting was used to evaluate the protein expression of NF-κB, TGF-β, α-SMA, PXR, CAR, and IL-6 in each group to research the effect of BBE on the PXR/PI3K/Akt signaling pathway in the liver (Figure 8A–H). In acute ALD, the expression of NF-κB, TGF-β, IL-6, and α-SMA ($p < 0.001$) in the model group was higher than those in the control group, whereas the expression of PXR and CAR protein was lower. After BBE was intragastrically administered, the expression of NF-κB ($p < 0.05$), TGF-β ($p < 0.001$), IL-6 ($p < 0.001$), and α-SMA ($p < 0.01$) in the livers significantly decreased compared with that in the model group, whereas that of PXR ($p < 0.01$, $p < 0.001$) and CAR ($p < 0.001$) significantly increased. In subacute ALD, the trend of protein expression was more obvious than that in acute ALD. The expression of NF-κB ($p < 0.05$), TGF-β ($p < 0.05$), IL-6 ($p < 0.05$), and α-SMA ($p < 0.001$) in the model group was higher than that in the control group, whereas the expression of PXR ($p < 0.001$) and CAR ($p < 0.05$) protein was lower. After BBE was administered, the expression of NF-κB ($p < 0.05$, $p < 0.001$, $p < 0.001$), TGF-β ($p < 0.05$, $p < 0.001$, $p < 0.001$), IL-6 ($p < 0.05$, $p < 0.001$, $p < 0.001$), and α-SMA ($p < 0.001$, $p < 0.001$, $p < 0.001$) in the livers significantly decreased compared with that in the model group, whereas the expression of PXR ($p < 0.05$) and CAR ($p < 0.05$, $p < 0.01$, $p < 0.001$) significantly increased. These results suggested that BBE has a good regulatory effect on hepatic metabolic disorder, inflammation, and fibrosis through the PXR-Cytochrome P450s axis.

In HepG2 cells, the expression of Bax, a pro-apoptosis protein, decreased ($p < 0.01$, $p < 0.001$), whereas that of PXR ($p < 0.05$, $p < 0.01$) was increased after BBE treatment on ethanol-induced cells. These results indicated that blackberry may prevent cell apoptosis induced by ethanol and elevate the metabolism of alcohol in cells (Figure 8I,J). BBE manifested excellent efficacy in inhibiting liver cell apoptosis through improving the metabolism in liver cells.

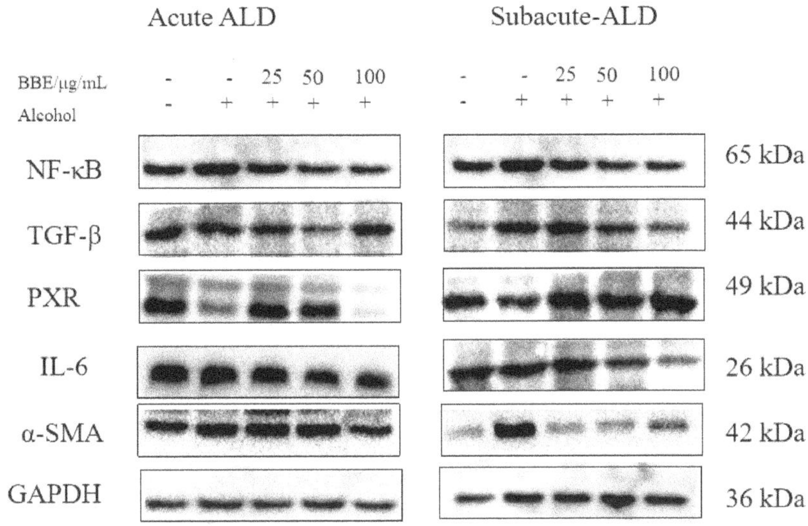

(**A**)

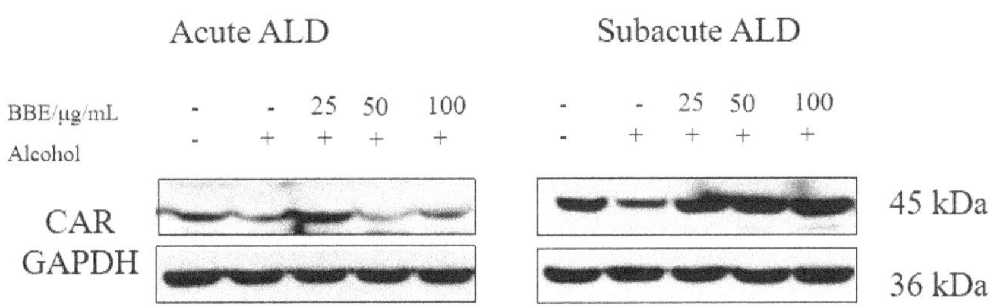

(**B**)

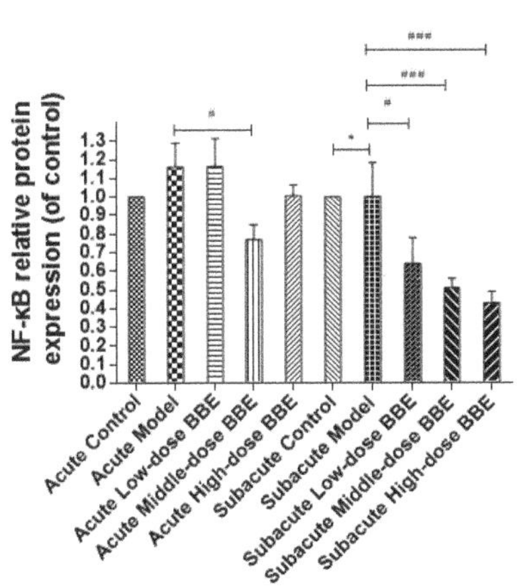

(**C**)

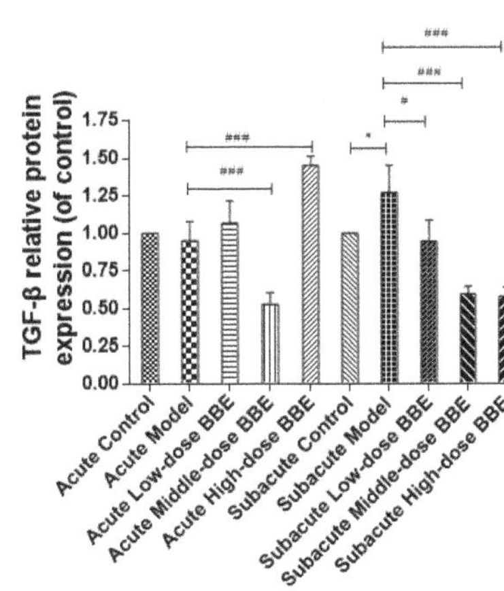

(**D**)

Figure 8. *Cont.*

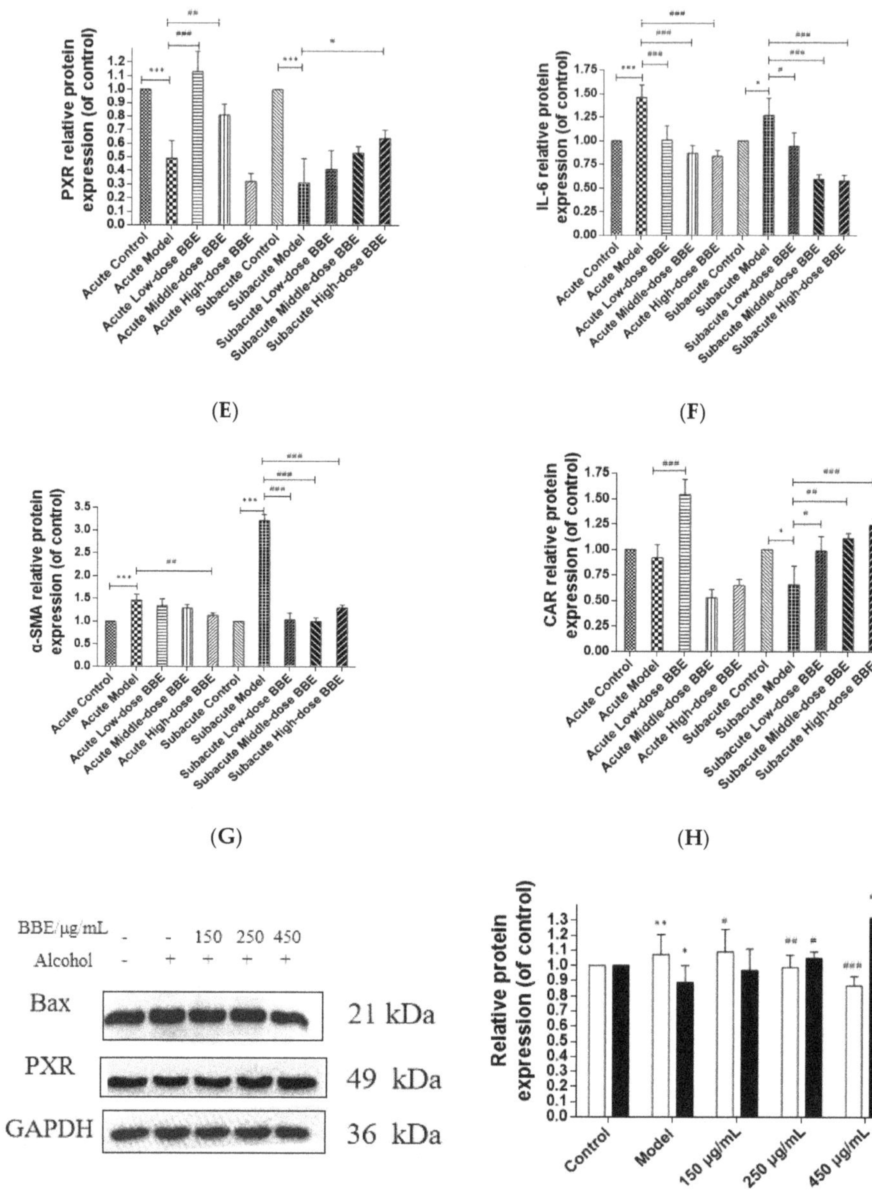

Figure 8. Effects of BBE on the expression of PXR/PI3K/Akt pathways in liver and HepG2 cells (**A–J**). Western blotting analysis of NF-κB, TGF-β, PXR, IL-6, α-SMA in livers, and the datas were normalized to that of GAPDH (**A–H**), Western blotting analysis of Bax, and PXR in HepG2 cells, and the datas were normalized to that of GAPDH (**H**,**I**). Values are the mean ± standard deviation. Compared with control: *, $p < 0.05$, **, $p < 0.01$, ***, $p < 0.001$. Compared with model: #, $p < 0.05$, ##, $p < 0.01$. ###, $p < 0.001$.

4. Discussion

Polyphenols are widely distributed in organisms as secondary metabolites. Flavonoids are recognized as natural antioxidants in the diet. Anthocyanins, which are water-soluble pigments, are rich in colored berries, fruits, and vegetables. They prevent high glucose-induced hepatocytes from oxidative damage by improving antioxidant status and inhibiting mitochondrial apoptosis. The mechanism is involved in preventing hyperglycemia-induced mitochondrial depolarization and maintaining its function [31]. In our study, BBE is rich in polyphenols, flavonoids, and anthocyanins. The six main anthocyanins glycosides in nature are cyanidin, followed by delphinidin, peonidin, petunidin, pelargonidin, and malvidin [32]. According to the reports, cyanidin, the main anthocyanin in blackberry fruits, especially cyanidin-3-*O*-glucoside, accounts for more than 80% of total anthocyanins [25].

An increasing number of polyphenols, as natural antioxidants, have attracted the attention of scientists due to their favorable influences on human health. Reactive oxygen and nitrogen species may lead to disastrous consequences, including cancer, cardiovascular disease, diabetes, and neurodegeneration. Polyphenols, which are rich in berries, could eliminate reactive oxygen and nitrogen species and be absorbed from the daily diet or dietary supplementation [33]. BBE is a good natural antioxidant in our study. Several methods, such as DPPH, ABTS, and FRAP, have been frequently utilized to measure the antioxidant capacities of extracts from fresh fruits and vegetables. These assays are simple and practicable, without the need for expensive equipment. However, their principles are different. DPPH and ABTS assays are used to evaluate the free radical scavenging ability of extracts, while the FRAP is used to estimate the electron transfer capacity [34].

Liver injury accounts for liver enlargement, growth retardation, and cirrhosis, and the liver index is an indicator of liver damage [35]. Alcohol retains macromolecules in cells that constitutively secrete protein, triggering increases in liver weights and index in the model group, and finally leading to liver swelling or "balloon", which is a feature of ALD. Long-term excessive alcohol consumption provokes the decline of appetite and absorption function in mice [36], which apparently results in malnutrition and weight loss [37].

Cellular enzymes, as vital catalysts, play a considerable role in human metabolism [38]. Disorders in lipid metabolism and changes in transaminase activity will occur in ALD. Intemperance severely damages the permeability of cell membranes, and cellular enzymes stored in the liver leak into plasma [39]. ALT, AST, SOD, and MDA levels are essential diagnostic indices of liver function. They are closely related to hepatocyte membrane injury, metabolic syndrome, and hepatic lipid metabolism [40]. The measurement of related indices confirmed these results.

Briefly, 80% alcohol is oxidized and decomposed in the liver after absorption. Heavy drinking causes an imbalance of the antioxidant system and oxidative stress in vivo. Persistent oxidative stress could result in liver steatosis, hepatitis, liver fibrosis, liver cirrhosis, and liver cancer [40]. However, ALD usually begins with fatty liver [41]. In our study, the pathological state of the liver treated with BBE was modified in a dose-dependent manner with the observation of H&E staining, Sirius red staining, and oil red O staining.

PXR plays a critical role in the process of exogenous drug metabolism and endogenous lipid and bile acid metabolism [42]. As a nuclear receptor, PXR forms a heterodimer with CAR, enters the nucleus, identifies its corresponding response elements, and finally activates the transcription and expression of its target genes [43]. PXR and CAR regulate the target genes with phase I and phase II drug-metabolizing enzymes and some drug members of the transporter family [44]. CYP3A and CYP2B are phase I-related enzymes of chemical metabolism in vivo. CYP3A11, CYP3A25, and CYP2B10 are the main metabolic enzyme genes expressed in mouse hepatocytes.

CYP3A involves the metabolism of more than 50% of clinical drugs, including a large number of hepatotoxic drugs [45,46]. CYP3A4 and CYP3A11 are the most significant subtypes in humans and mice, respectively [47]. Inhibiting these metabolic enzymes could ameliorate ALD. The results of the qRT-PCR analysis indicated that the benefits of BBE in subacute ALD are superior to that in acute ALD. Maybe the reason is that ALD caused by high-dose ethanol intake may have a devastating effect on liver pathophysiology and lead to multiple organ and system failures [48]. Recovery is also difficult to achieve in a short time. However, the liver damage caused by low-dose ethanol intake is not as severe as that caused by high-dose ethanol. A report revealed that low-dose alcohol intake has a protective effect on the liver to some extent [49].

The development of the reproductive system is significantly affected by the imbalance between cell proliferation and death, such as during folliculogenesis and spermatogenesis [50]. BBE showed a significant protective effect on the ethanol-induced apoptosis of HepG2 cells in our study.

In the reproductive system, oxidative stress is the key pathological basis of liver injury and the major cause of the progression from simple steatosis to steatohepatitis [51]. The imbalance between excessive oxidants and antioxidants gives rise to oxidative stress. In addition, ROS mainly originates from the mitochondria, and antioxidants prevent the organelles from producing ROS to avoid oxidative injury. A large amount of polyphenolic compounds not only directly obliterates reactive species but also indirectly controls the redox environment. Furthermore, multiple cell models showed that polyphenols have the ability to regulate mitochondrial biogenesis and control mitochondrial membrane potential and oxidative phosphorylation [52]. Mitochondrial dysfunction and cellular apoptosis correlate closely with mitochondrial membrane depolarization [53]. In our study, the results indicated that BBE prevents mitochondrial membrane depolarization induced by ethanol. Additionally, BBE, as a natural antioxidant, showed significantly relieved ALD-induced oxidative damage and reduced apoptosis (Figure 9).

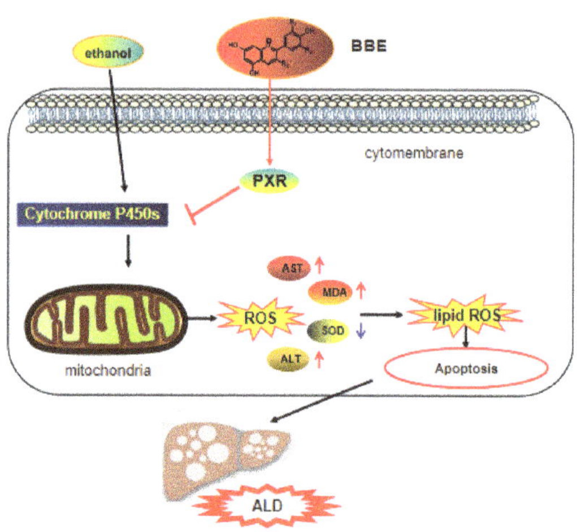

Figure 9. The mechanism of BBE regulating of activating the PXR-Cytochrome P450s axis.

PXR is a ligand-activated transcription factor highly expressed in the liver and gastrointestinal tract [54]. It has the dual identity of xenobiotic sensor and endobiotic receptor for its key role in homeostasis [55], and it plays a vital role in physiological processes, including glucose and lipid metabolism, steroid hormone homeostasis, cholic acid and bilirubin detoxification, bone mineral balance, and immune inflammatory response. The activation of PXR regulates the PI3K/Akt signaling pathway [56], which involves protein synthesis, metabolism, cell cycle regulation, proliferation, and apoptosis [21,57]. This pathway regulates the proliferation and survival of tumor cells and plays a strong part in the process of apoptosis. By inhibiting the PI3K/Akt signaling pathway, many active components of medicinal herbs could mediate cancer cell apoptosis [58].

The pro-apoptotic protein Bax belongs to the Bcl-2 family. It balances the change in $\Delta\Psi m$, which regulates the intrinsic apoptotic pathway by the mitochondrial apoptotic pathway [59]. Most drug interaction mechanisms are related to drug metabolism, especially CYP450. The content of the CYP3A4 sub-enzyme is higher than 50% in the liver, which plays an important role in drug metabolism. Recent studies have found that the PXR receptor is the key regulator of CYP3A4 gene transcription, thereby revealing the mechanism of PXR protective effects from exogenous substances at the molecular level. As the "main foreign body receptor", PXR plays a crucial role in heterologous substances (such as food, drugs, and other components). Alcohol metabolism activates the NF-κB signaling pathway in the liver and other inflammatory pathways, which lead to the release of a large number of chemokines and inflammatory mediators from damaged hepatocytes and promote the progress of ALD [60]. Additionally, TGF-β is a crucial element involved in liver fibrogenesis [61]. In addition, IL-6 can activate the signal transducer and activator of transcription 3 (STAT3), thereby regulating liver fibrosis and inflammation [62]. α-SMA is a pathological marker of liver fibrosis, for its expression can promote the secretion of ECM in HSC and the progression of liver fibrosis [63,64]. The present study demonstrated that BBE has a good regulatory effect on hepatic metabolic disorder, inflammation, and fibrosis through the PXR-Cytochrome P450s axis, and BBE manifested excellent efficacy in inhibiting liver cell apoptosis through improving the metabolism in liver cells (Figure 9).

5. Conclusions

Alcohol abuse provokes a sharp increase in oxidative stress markers, nutritional disorders, inflammatory response, and histological changes in liver tissue. Heavy drinking is an addictive disease that accounts for hepatitis, fibrosis, cirrhosis, and cancers. As a natural product, blackberry plays an indispensable role in health supplements due to its potential beneficial pharmacological effects. PXR, which could be activated by various compounds, is highly expressed in the liver. Ligand-activated PXR regulates the transcription of a group of genes encoding detoxification-related proteins and transporters involved in metabolite elimination. Therefore, the activation of the PXR-Cytochrome P450s axis is significantly essential for enhancing and accelerating ALD.

In this study, DPPH, ABTS, and FRAP assays showed that BBE has excellent antioxidant activity. The administration of BBE could extensively decrease the biochemical parameters of ALT, AST, MDA, and SOD in vivo. These results suggested the protective effect of BBE on ALD, as confirmed by liver indices and histopathological observation, including H&E staining, oil red O staining, and Sirius red staining. Network analysis and docking studies revealed that BBE improved apoptosis via the PI3K-Akt signaling pathway, which has a preventive effect on ALD. Furthermore, Western blot and qRT-PCR results proved that BBE regulated liver metabolic disorder, inflammation, and fibrosis in ALD models. This study demonstrated the protective effect of BBE on ALD for the first time. The protective mechanisms may be attributed to the strong antioxidant activities of its anthocyanins. In addition, ethanol-induced HepG2 cells as a model of ALD in vitro showed that BBE improved apoptosis in a dose-dependent manner, which was consistent with the mitochondrial membrane potential of HepG2 cells. BBE also significantly reduced ALD-induced oxidative damage and apoptosis by down-regulating the ROS content and Bax protein expression and up-regulating the PXR level. The amelioration of ALD by blackberry is in connection with activating the PXR-Cytochrome P450s axis (Figure 9). This study provides a new and promising natural product for the treatment of alcoholic liver injury.

Supplementary Materials: The following supporting information can be downloaded at: https://www.mdpi.com/article/10.3390/separations9100321/s1, Figure S1: Network pharmacology Diagram of Cyanidin-3-*O*-glucoside. (A) Related targets of cyanidin-3-*O*-glucoside, the green circular and red polygons respectively represented cyanidin-3-*O*-glucoside -targeted genes and cyanidin-3-*O*-glucoside. (B) Venn map of cyanidin-3-*O*-glucoside target and ALD target; Table S1: Shared target information of cyanidin-3-*O*-glucoside; Figure S2: PPI network of the intersection target of cyanidin-3-*O*-glucoside for ALD; Figure S3: Histogram of Go analysis of cyanidin-3-*O*-glucoside (A) The enriched terms in biological process (BP); (B) The enriched terms in cellular component

(CC); (C) The enriched terms in molecular function (MF); Figure S4: KEGG pathway diagram of cyanidin-3-*O*-glucoside; Figure S5: "Component-target-pathway-disease" network diagram.

Author Contributions: T.X.: Conceptualization, Methodology, Investigation, Project administration, Validation, Visualization, Writing—original draft. Z.G.: Formal analysis, Resources, investigation, Writing—review and editing. M.F.: Resources, Data curation. J.H. and X.W.: Resources, funding acquisition. Y.Z. and L.T.: Resources. X.S.: Methodology, Visualization, Resources, Supervision, Writing—review and editing. All authors have read and agreed to the published version of the manuscript.

Funding: This research was supported by a grant from the Basic Scientific Research Project of Guizhou Province (grant number [2021] 535), the Doctoral Fund of Guizhou Medical University (grant number [2018] 013), the Fund of Science and Technology Project of Guizhou provincial health commission (gzwjkj 2019-1-181), the Guizhou Medical University Breeding programs of National Natural Science Foundation of China (grant number 19NSP074).

Institutional Review Board Statement: The experiments were conducted according to the guidelines of the Declaration of Helsinki and were approved by the Institutional Review Board (or Ethics Committee) of Guizhou Medical University. All animal operating procedures obey the regulations on animal experiments issued by the National Science and Technology Commission of the People's Republic of China and the guidelines for the care and use of laboratory animals issued by the National Institutes of Health (Experimental facility certification No.: SYXK (Guizhou) 2018-0001).

Informed Consent Statement: Not applicable.

Data Availability Statement: Data are contained within the manuscript and Supplementary Materials.

Conflicts of Interest: The authors declare no conflict of interest.

Abbreviations

PXR, pregnane X receptor; ALD, alcoholic liver disease; P450, cytochrome P450 oxidase; AST, aspartate aminotransferase; alanine aminotransferase; SOD, superoxide dismutase; MDA, malondialdehyde; BBE, extract of blackberry; NF-κB, nuclear factor kappa-B; TGF-β, transforming growth factor-β; IL-6, interleukin- 6; CAR, constitutive androstane receptor; CYP3A25, cytocherome P450-3A25; CYP3A11, cytocherome P450-3A11; CYP2B10-cytocherome P450-2B10; IARC, international agency for research on cancer; NRs, nuclear receptors; RXRα, retinoid X receptor alpha; DPPH, 2,2-diphenyl-1-picrylhydrazyl; ABTS, 3-ethyl- benzothiazoline-6-sulfonic acid; TPTZ, 2,4,6-tris(2-pyridyl)-s-triazine; V_C, ascorbic acid; TPC, total phenolic content; TFC, total flavonoids content; TMA, total anthocyanin content; FRAP, ferric reducing antioxidant power; CMC, carboxymethylcellulose; BW, body weight; PPI, protein protein interaction; GO, gene ontology; KEGG, Kyoto Encyclopedia of Genes and Genomes; MF, molecular function; BP, biological process; CC, cellular component; RT-PCR, reverse transcription-polymerase chain reaction; DMSO, dimethylsulfoxide; DMEM, dulbecco's modified eagle medium; DHE, dihydroethidium; SDS-PAGE, sodium dodecyl sulfate polyacrylamide gel electrophoresis.

References

1. Justice, A.C. Alcohol and the global burden of cancer: What are we missing? *Lancet Oncol.* **2021**, *22*, 1048–1049. [CrossRef]
2. Li, Y.G.; Ji, D.F.; Zhong, S.; Shi, L.G.; Hu, G.Y.; Chen, S. Saponins from Panax japonicus Protect against Alcohol-Induced Hepatic Injury in Mice by Up-regulating the Expression of GPX3, SOD1 and SOD3. *Alcohol Alcohol.* **2010**, *45*, 320–331. [CrossRef]
3. Rattan, P.; Shah, V.H. Review article: Current and emerging therapies for acute alcohol-associated hepatitis. *Aliment. Pharmacol. Ther.* **2022**, *56*, 28–40. [CrossRef]
4. Lee, D.U.; Chou, H.; Wang, E.; Fan, G.H.; Han, J.; Chang, K.; Kwon, J.; Lee, K.J.; Blanchard, J.; Urrunaga, N.H. The clinical implication of psychiatric illnesses in patients with alcoholic liver disease: An analysis of US hospitals. *Expert Rev. Gastroenterol. Hepatol.* **2022**, *16*, 689–697. [CrossRef]
5. Singal, A.K.; Arsalan, A.; Dunn, W.; Arab, J.P.; Wong, R.J.; Kuo, Y.F.; Kamath, P.S.; Shah, V.H. Alcohol- associated liver disease in the United States is associated with severe forms of disease among young, females and Hispanics. *Aliment. Pharmacol. Ther.* **2021**, *54*, 451–461. [CrossRef] [PubMed]

6. Wu, S.; Yue, Y.; Tian, H.; Li, X.; He, W.; Ding, H. Carthamus red from Carthamus tinctorius L. exerts antioxidant and hepatoprotective effect against CCl_4-induced liver damage in rats via the Nrf2 pathway. *J. Ethnopharmacol.* **2013**, *148*, 570–578. [CrossRef]
7. Potts, J.R.; Goubet, S.; Heneghan, M.A.; Verma, S. Determinants of long-term outcome in severe alcoholic hepatitis. *Aliment. Pharmacol. Ther.* **2013**, *38*, 584–595. [CrossRef] [PubMed]
8. Thursz, M.R.; Richardson, P.; Allison, M.; Austin, A.; Bowers, M.; Day, C.P.; Downs, N.; Gleeson, D.; Macgilchrist, A.; Grant, A.; et al. Prednisolone or pentoxifylline for alcoholic hepatitis. *New Engl. J. Med.* **2015**, *372*, 1619–1628. [CrossRef]
9. Plauth, M.; Bernal, W.; Dasarathy, S.; Merli, M.; Plank, L.D.; Schütz, T.; Bischoff, S. ESPEN guideline on clinical nutrition in liver disease. *Clin. Nutr.* **2019**, *38*, 485–521. [CrossRef]
10. Petrasek, J.; Bala, S.; Csak, T.; Lippai, D.; Kodys, K.; Menashy, V.; Barrieau, M.; Min, S.; Kurt-Jones, E.A.; Szabo, G. IL-1 receptor antagonist ameliorates inflammasome- dependent alcoholic steatohepatitis in mice. *J. Clin. Investig.* **2012**, *122*, 3476–3489. [CrossRef] [PubMed]
11. Aghemo, A.; Alekseeva, O.P.; Angelico, F.; Bakulin, I.G.; Bakulina, N.V.; Bordin, D.; Bueverov, A.O.; Drapkina, O.M.; Gillessen, A.; Kagarmanova, E.M.; et al. Role of silymarin as antioxidant in clinical management of chronic liver diseases: A narrative review. *Ann. Med.* **2022**, *54*, 1548–1560. [CrossRef] [PubMed]
12. Zhang, B.; Xie, W.; Krasowski, M.D. PXR: A xenobiotic receptor of diverse function implicated in pharmacogenetics. *Pharmacogenomics* **2008**, *9*, 1695–1709. [CrossRef] [PubMed]
13. Oladimeji, P.O.; Chen, T. PXR: More than just a master xenobiotic receptor. *Mol. Pharmacol.* **2018**, *93*, 119–127. [CrossRef]
14. Ghareaghajlou, N.; Hallaj-Nezhadi, S.; Ghasempour, Z. Red cabbage anthocyanins: Stability, extraction, biological activities and applications in food systems. *Food Chem.* **2021**, *365*, 130482. [CrossRef]
15. Fernández-Demeneghi, R.; Rodríguez-Landa, J.; Guzmán-Gerónimo, R.; Acosta-Mesa, H.; Meza-Alvarado, E.; Vargas-Moreno, I.; Herrera-Meza, S. Effect of blackberry juice (*Rubus fruticosus* L.) on anxiety-like behaviour in Wistar rats. *Int. J. Food Sci. Nutr.* **2019**, *70*, 856–867. [CrossRef] [PubMed]
16. Kim, H.; Jeong, D.; Kim, S.; Lee, S.; Sin, H.; Yu, K.; Jeong, S.; Kim, S. Fermentation of Blackberry with L. plantarum JBMI F5 Enhance the Protection Effect on UVB-Mediated Photoaging in Human Foreskin Fibroblast and Hairless Mice through Regulation of MAPK/NF-κB Signaling. *Nutrients* **2019**, *11*, 2429. [CrossRef] [PubMed]
17. Figueira, I.; Tavares, L.; Jardim, C.; Costa, I.; Terrasso, A.P.; Almeida, A.F.; Santo, C.N. Blood-brain barrier transport and neuroprotective potential of blackberry-digested polyphenols: An in vitro study. *Eur. J. Nutr.* **2019**, *58*, 113–130. [CrossRef]
18. Cenk, E.; Schmutz, C.; Pahlke, G.; Oertel, A.; Kollarova, J.; Mock, H.P.; Matros, A.; Marko, D. Immunomodulatory Properties of blackberry anthocyanins in THP-1 derived macrophages. *Int. J. Mol. Sci.* **2021**, *22*, 10483. [CrossRef]
19. Tatar, M.; Bagheri, Z.; Varedi, M.; Naghibalhossaini, F. Blackberry extract inhibits telomerase activity in human colorectal cancer cells. *Nutrtion Cancer Int. J.* **2019**, *71*, 461–471. [CrossRef]
20. Wang, Y.; Zhao, Y.; Wang, D.; Huo, Y.; Ji, B. Anthocyanin-rich extracts from blackberry, wild blueberry, strawberry, and chokeberry: Antioxidant activity and inhibitory effect on oleic acid-induced hepatic steatosis in vitro. *Int. J. Food Sci. Nutr.* **2016**, *96*, 2494–2503. [CrossRef]
21. Xiao, T.; Luo, Z.; Guo, Z.; Wang, X.; Ding, M.; Wang, W.; Shen, X.; Zhao, Y. Multiple Roles of Black Raspberry Anthocyanins Protecting against Alcoholic Liver Disease. *Molecules* **2021**, *26*, 2313. [CrossRef] [PubMed]
22. Xiao, T.; Guo, Z.; Sun, B.; Zhao, Y. Identification of Anthocyanins from Four Kinds of Berries and Their Inhibition Activity to α-Glycosidase and Protein Tyrosine Phosphatase 1B by HPLC FT-ICR MS/MS. *J. Agric. Food Chem.* **2017**, *65*, 6211–6221. [CrossRef] [PubMed]
23. Zheng, J.; Zheng, X.; Zhao, L.; Yi, J.; Cai, S. Effects and interaction mechanism of soybean 7S and 11S globulins on anthocyanin stability and antioxidant activity during in vitro simulated digestion. *Curr. Res. Food Sci.* **2021**, *4*, 543–550. [CrossRef] [PubMed]
24. Zhang, G.; Wang, H.; Zhu, K.; Yang, Y.; Li, J.; Jiang, H.; Liu, Z. Investigation of candidate molecular biomarkers for expression profile analysis of the Gene expression omnibus (GEO) in acute lymphocytic leukemia (ALL). *Biomed. Pharm.* **2019**, *120*, 109530. [CrossRef] [PubMed]
25. Jakobek, L.; Seruga, M.; Medvidovic-Kosanovic, M.; Novak, I. Anthocyanin content and antioxidant activity of various red fruit juices. *Dtsch. Lebensm. Rundsch.* **2007**, *103*, 58–64.
26. Cho, M.J.; Howard, L.R.; Prior, R.L.; Clark, J.R. Flavonoid glycosides and antioxidant capacity of various blackberry, blueberry and red grape genotypes determined by high-performance liquid chromatography/mass spectrometry. *J. Sci. Food Agric.* **2004**, *84*, 1771–1782. [CrossRef]
27. Zhao, H.; Wu, W.; Lü, L.; Li, W. Change Regularity of Polyphenol Content in Blackberry Fruit during Growth and Development. *J. Jilin Agric. Univ.* **2013**, *35*, 457–462.
28. Xiao, T.; Guo, Z.; Bi, X.; Zhao, Y. Polyphenolic profile as well as anti-oxidant and anti-diabetes effects of extracts from freeze-dried black raspberries. *J. Funct. Foods* **2017**, *31*, 179–187. [CrossRef]
29. Sozio, M.; Crabb, D.W. Alcohol and lipid metabolism. *Am. J. Physiol. Endocrinol. Metab.* **2008**, *295*, E10–E16. [CrossRef]
30. Li, S.; Fan, T.P.; Jia, W.; Lu, A.; Zhang, W. Network Pharmacology in Traditional Chinese Medicine. *Evid. Based Complement. Altern. Med.* **2014**, *2014*, 138460. [CrossRef]

31. Jiang, X.; Tang, X.; Zhang, P.; Liu, G.; Guo, H. Cyanidin-3-O-b-glucoside protects primary mouse hepatocytes against high glucose-induced apoptosis by modulating mitochondrial dysfunction and the PI3K/Akt pathway. *Biochem. Pharmacol.* **2014**, *90*, 135–144. [CrossRef] [PubMed]
32. Prior, R.L.; Wu, X. Anthocyanins: Structural characteristics that result in unique metabolic patterns and biological activities. *Free Radic. Res.* **2006**, *40*, 1014–1028. [CrossRef] [PubMed]
33. Nakamura, T.; Lipton, S.A. Preventing Ca^{2+}-mediated nitrosative stress in neurodegenerative diseases: Possible pharmacological strategies. *Cell Calcium* **2010**, *47*, 190–197. [CrossRef] [PubMed]
34. Thaipong, K.; Boonprakob, U.; Crosby, K.; Cisneros-Zevallos, L.; Byrne, D.H. Comparison of ABTS, DPPH, FRAP, and ORAC assays for estimating antioxidant activity from guava fruit extracts. *J. Food Compos. Anal.* **2006**, *19*, 669–675. [CrossRef]
35. Xiang, J.; Zhu, W.; Li, Z.; Ling, S. Effect of juice and fermented vinegar from Hovenia dulcis peduncles on chronically alcohol induced liver damage in mice. *Food Funct.* **2012**, *3*, 628–634. [CrossRef] [PubMed]
36. Lieber, C.S. Alcoholic fatty liver: Its pathogenesis and mechanism of progression to inflammation and fibrosis. *Alcohol* **2004**, *34*, 9–19. [CrossRef] [PubMed]
37. Wu, W.; Chen, J.; Liu, C.; Kong, P.; Yan, J.; Cheng, H. Protective Effect of Green Tea Polyphenols against Chronic Alcoholic Hepatic Injury in Mice. *Food Sci.* **2011**, *32*, 310–313.
38. He, Z.; Wang, Y.; Liu, L.; Lou, Z. Effects of Panax Japonicus Extractions on Serum Biochemical Indices and Inflammatory Factors in Mice with Alcoholic Liver Injury. *Zhejiang J. Integr. Tradit. Chin. West. Med.* **2018**, *28*, 21–24.
39. Baldi, E.; Burra, P.; Plebani, M.; Salvagnini, M. Serum malondialdehyde and mitochondrial aspartate aminotransferase activity as markers of chronic alcohol intake and alcoholic liver disease. *Ital. J. Gastroenterol. Hepatol.* **1993**, *25*, 429–432.
40. Sun, H.; Mu, T.; Liu, X.; Zhang, M.; Chen, J. Purple sweet potato (*Lpomoea batatas* L.) anthocyanins: Preventive effect on acute and subacute alcoholic liver damage and dealcoholic effect. *J. Agric. Food Chem.* **2014**, *62*, 2364–2373. [CrossRef]
41. Yang, C.; Liao, A.; Cui, Y.; Yu, G.; Hou, Y.; Pan, L.; Chen, W.; Zheng, S.; Li, X.; Ma, J.; et al. Wheat embryo globulin protects against acute alcohol-induced liver injury in mice. *Food Chem. Toxicol.* **2021**, *153*, 112240. [CrossRef] [PubMed]
42. Zeng, H.; Jiang, Y.; Chen, P.; Fan, X.; Li, D.; Liu, A.; Ma, X.; Xie, W.; Liu, P.; Gonzalez, F.J.; et al. Schisandrol B protects against cholestatic liver injury through pregnane X receptors. *Br. J. Pharmacol.* **2017**, *174*, 672–688. [CrossRef] [PubMed]
43. Ostberg, T.; Bertilsson, G.; Jendeberg, L.; Berkenstam, A.; Uppenberg, J. Identification of residues in the PXR ligand binding domain critical for species specific and constitutive activation. *Eur. J. Biochem.* **2002**, *269*, 4896–4904. [CrossRef] [PubMed]
44. Jia, Y.; Viswakarma, N.; Reddy, J.K. Med1 subunit of the mediator complex in nuclear receptor-regulated energy metabolism, liver regeneration, and hepatocarcinogenesis. *Gene Expr.* **2014**, *16*, 63–75. [CrossRef]
45. Wilkinson, G.R. Cytochrome P4503A (CYP3A) metabolism: Prediction of in vivo activity in humans. *J. Pharmacokinet. Biopharm.* **1996**, *24*, 475–490. [CrossRef]
46. Jones, B.C.; Rollison, H.; Johansson, S.; Kanebratt, K.P.; Lambert, C.; Vishwanathan, K.; Andersson, T.B. Managing the risk of CYP3A induction in drug development: A strategic approach. *Drug Metab. Dispos.* **2017**, *45*, 35–41. [CrossRef]
47. Komura, H.; Iwaki, M. Species differences in in vitro and in vivo small intestinal metabolism of CYP3A substrates. *J. Pharm. Sci.* **2008**, *97*, 1775–1800. [CrossRef] [PubMed]
48. Christidis, C.; Karatayli, E.; Hall, R.A.; Weber, S.N.; Reichert, M.C.; Hohl, M.; Qiao, S.; Boehm, U.; Lütjohann, D.; Lammert, F.; et al. Fibroblast Growth Factor 21 Response in a Preclinical Alcohol Model of Acute-on-Chronic Liver Injury. *Int. J. Mol. Sci.* **2021**, *22*, 7898. [CrossRef] [PubMed]
49. Liu, F.; Yu, H.; Liao, C.; Chou, A.; Lee, H. The Timing and Effects of Low-Dose Ethanol T reatment on Acetaminophen-Induced Liver Injury. *Life* **2021**, *11*, 1094. [CrossRef]
50. Larsen, B.D.; Sørensen, C.S. The caspase-activated DNase: Apoptosis and beyond. *FEBS J.* **2017**, *284*, 1160–1170. [CrossRef]
51. Sumida, Y.; Niki, E.; Naito, Y.; Yoshikawa, T. Involvement of free radicals and oxidative stress in NAFLD/NASH. *Free Radic. Res.* **2013**, *47*, 869–880. [CrossRef] [PubMed]
52. Serrano, J.C.; Cassanye, A.; Martín-Gari, M.; Granado-Serrano, A.B.; Portero-Otín, M. Effect of dietary bioactive compounds on mitochondrial and metabolic flexibility. *Diseases* **2016**, *4*, 14. [CrossRef]
53. Fulda, S. Modulation of mitochondrial apoptosis by PI3K inhibitors. *Mitochondrion* **2013**, *13*, 195–198. [CrossRef]
54. Handschin, C.; Podvinec, M.; Meyer, U.A. CXR, a chicken xenobiotic-sensing orphan nuclear receptor, is related to both mammalian pregnane X receptor (PXR) and constitutive androstane receptor (CAR). *Proc. Natl. Acad. Sci. USA* **2000**, *97*, 10769–10774. [CrossRef]
55. Garcia, M.; Thirouard, L.; Sedes, L.; Monrose, M.; Holota, H.; Caira, F.; Volle, D.H.; Beaudoin, C. Nuclear receptor metabolism of bile acids and xenobiotics: A coordinated detoxification system with impact on health and diseases. *Int. J. Mol. Sci.* **2018**, *19*, 3630. [CrossRef] [PubMed]
56. Luan, Z.; Wei, Y.; Huo, X.; Sun, X.; Zhang, C.; Ming, W.; Luo, Z.; Du, C.; Li, Y.; Xu, H.; et al. Pregnane X receptor (PXR) protects against cisplatin-induced acute kidney injury in mice. *BBA-Mol. Basis Dis.* **2021**, *1867*, 165996. [CrossRef]
57. Yan, W.; Ma, X.; Zhao, X.; Zhang, S. Baicalein induces apoptosis and autophagy of breast cancer cells via inhibiting PI3K/AKT pathway in vivo and vitro. *Drug Des. Dev. Ther.* **2018**, *12*, 3961–3972. [CrossRef]
58. Feng, L.-X.; Sun, P.; Mi, T.; Liu, M.; Liu, W.; Yao, S.; Cao, Y.-M.; Yu, X.-L.; Wu, W.-Y.; Jiang, B.-H. Agglutinin isolated from Arisema heterophyllum Blume induces apoptosis and autophagy in A549 cells through inhibiting PI3K/Akt pathway and inducing ER stress. *Chin. J. Nat. Med.* **2016**, *14*, 856–864. [CrossRef]

59. Gu, X.; Yao, Y.; Cheng, R.; Zhang, Y.; Dai, Z.; Wan, G.; Yang, Z.; Cai, W.; Gao, G.; Yang, X. Plasminogen K5 activates mitochondrial apoptosis pathway in endothelial cells by regulating Bak and Bcl-xL subcellular distribution. *Apoptosis* **2011**, *16*, 846–855. [CrossRef]
60. Zhao, N.; Xia, G.; Cai, J.; Li, Z.; Lv, X. Adenosine receptor A2B mediates alcoholic hepatitis by regulating cAMP levels and the NF-KB pathway. *Toxicol. Lett.* **2022**, *359*, 84–95. [CrossRef] [PubMed]
61. Kartasheva-Ebertz, D.; Gaston, J.; Lair-Mehiri, L.; Massault, P.; Scatton, O.; Vaillant, J.; Morozov, V.-A.; Pol, S.; Lagaye, S. Adult human liver slice cultures: Modelling of liver fibrosis and evaluation of new anti-fibrotic drugs. *World J. Hepatol.* **2021**, *13*, 187–217. [CrossRef] [PubMed]
62. Al-Humadi, H.-W.; Al-Saigh, R.; Sahib, A. The impact of low alcohol consumption on the liver and inflammatory cytokines in diabetic rats. *Adv. Clin. Exp. Med.* **2019**, *28*, 331–337. [CrossRef] [PubMed]
63. Ramachandran, P.; Unny, A.K.; Vij, M.; Safwan, M.; Balaji, M.S.; Rela, M. α-Smooth muscle actin expression predicts the outcome of Kasai portoenterostomy in biliary atresia. *Saudi J. Gastroenterol.* **2019**, *25*, 101–105. [CrossRef]
64. Roehlen, N.; Crouchet, E.; Baumert, T.F. Liver fibrosis: Mechanistic concepts and therapeutic perspectives. *Cells* **2020**, *9*, 875. [CrossRef]

separations

MDPI

Article

Synthesis and Characterization with Computational Studies of Metal Complexes of Methyl 2-((4-cyanophenyl)(hydroxy) methyl)acrylate: A New Biologically Active Multi-Functional Adduct

Shazia Ishfaq [1], Shazia Nisar [1,*], Amtul Qayum [2], Sadaf Iqbal [1], Nasreen Fatima [1], Fatmah Ali Alasmary [3], Amani Salem Almalki [3], ElSayed M. Tag El Din [4,*], Muhammad Sufyan Javed [5,*] and Patrizia Bocchetta [6]

[1] Department of Chemistry, Faculty of Sciences, University of Karachi, Karachi 75270, Pakistan
[2] Department of Chemistry, Faculty of Science, N.E.D University of Engineering and Technology, Karachi 75270, Pakistan
[3] Chemistry Department, College of Science, King Saud University, Riyadh 11451, Saudi Arabia
[4] Electrical Engineering Department, Faculty of Engineering & Technology, Future University in Egypt, New Cairo 11835, Egypt
[5] School of Physical Science and Technology, Lanzhou University, Lanzhou 730000, China
[6] Dipartimento di Ingegneria dell'Innovazione, Università del Salento, Via Monteroni, 73100 Lecce, Italy
* Correspondence: shazian@uok.edu.pk (S.N.); elsayed.tageldin@fue.edu.eg (E.M.T.E.D.); safisabri@gmail.com (M.S.J.)

Abstract: The title ligand (L''_x), methyl 2-((4-cyanophenyl)(hydroxy)methyl)acrylate was synthesized following the Morita-Baylis-Hillman reaction scheme. Spectroscopic techniques such as: UV- Visible, FT-IR, ESI-MS, and ^1H NMR helped in characterization of the L''_x. Complexes of Cr^{3+}, Co^{3+}, Ni^{2+}, Mn^{2+}, Cu^{2+} with L''_x were prepared and characterized by UV- Visible, FT-IR and powder-XRD. FTIR spectrum of the L''_x generated through DFT B3LYP method and 6-311++ G (d,p) basis set was found in good agreement with experimental spectrum. Additionally, the semi-empirical PM6 method optimization helped propose the most suitable geometries of the complexes with Cr^{3+}, Co^{3+} possessing octahedral, Ni^{2+} square planner, Mn^{2+} and Cu^{2+} tetrahedral geometries. Powder-XRD patterns of the complexes have revealed cubic crystal class for Cr^{3+} and Co^{3+}, whereas hexagonal, orthorhombic, and monoclinic for Ni^{2+}, Mn^{2+}, and Cu^{2+} complexes were observed, respectively. In addition, the nano-particle size was found in the range of 8.2560–4.5316 nm for complexes. Antibacterial activity against *S. aureus*, *E. coli*, *B. pumilis* and *S. typhi* confirmed a substantially high potential, as endorsed by their Molecular docking studies, of Ni^{2+} and Cu^{2+} complexes against each bacterial strain. Moreover, all compounds exhibited positive antioxidant activities, but have no antifungal potential except L''_x. The current study demonstrates the usefulness of these novel transition metal complexes as possible potent antibacterial and antioxidant agents.

Keywords: Morita-Baylis-Hillman; XRD; biological assays; PM6 method; molecular docking

1. Introduction

In synthetic organic chemistry, the carbon-carbon bond formation is one of the essential tools to prepare novel compounds and hence is a challenging and fascinating field [1,2] for synthetic chemists. The primary requirement in such a synthesis is the production of a C-C bond at a particular site when more than one competitive position is available. Such selections tend to improve the procedure for manufacturing an organic network through inspiration, novelty, and logical contribution [3–5]. In this regard, the Morita-Baylis-Hillman (MBH) reaction has proven to be one of the best approaches due to its ease of execution and methodology [6]. MBH adducts are prepared via coupling between alkenes or alkynes at α-position and aldehydes in the presence of a suitable catalyst, most probably tertiary amines or phosphine. The reaction has been reported to be extremely useful in synthesizing a novel class of bioactive compounds with the potential to discover new cheaper, and more efficient drugs [7].

Moreover, this reaction congruently provides an approved atom economical approach for synthesizing medicinally useful multifunctional molecules. The aromatic aldehydes offer a unique class of compounds when introduced with multifunctional groups rather than the aliphatic ones [8,9]. The prepared adduct-type molecules have been utilized extensively as starting materials in preparing organic and inorganic molecules for various medicinal applications [10,11]. Numerous protocols have been adopted to achieve a pure high yield in a minimum period of time [12].

Moreover, MBH adduct derivatives bearing numerous functional groups such as acetate, ester, alcoholic, nitrates, and halogen in a single compound [7,13] have demonstrated prominent pharmacological activities [14–16].

As a part of our ongoing research on MBH adducts, we report herein the synthesis and characterization of a new multifunctional MBH adduct ligand Methyl 2-((4-cyanophenyl)(hydroxy)methyl)acrylate (L''_x) and its corresponding metal complexes with Cr^{3+}, Co^{3+}, Ni^{2+}, Mn^{2+}, and Cu^{2+} ions. Nature has endowed metals with unique characteristics such as variable coordination modes, redox activity, catalysis, and reactivity towards organic substrates to make them suitable as essential cellular components to perform several functions in biochemical processes for living organisms. [17]. Additionally, the transition metal complexes based on the leading group of transition series have attracted greater attention due to the change in coordination state after coordination, regular geometry, formation of color compounds, binding variety, and hybridization [18]. Though all of these properties are not accessible in organic drug compounds because the carbon atom does not exceed the coordination number of four, owing to the presence of transition metal, the complex compounds retain these properties in their molecular structures [19]. Hence, it is considered that the coordination of organic-based biomolecules with transition metals should improve their biological properties [20].

Among natural sciences, synthetic compounds' critical implications for treating diseases in the living system are one of the essential properties [21,22] in the field of bioinorganic chemistry. In the various steps of drug discovery and designing, the computational science of chemicals and their methodologies belong to a set of valuable scientific tools often practiced [23]. Furthermore, to better understand bioactive compounds' behavior, quantum calculations and molecular mechanics are widely used in the modern pharmaceutical industry for chemical research [24]. Comparison of the molecular modeling data with the experimental characterization procedures helps expand the frontiers of medicinal and structural chemistry [25].

The objective of the present study is to discuss the ease of synthesis of a new MBH multifunctional adduct through a simple one-pot economical procedure, its characterization, and evaluation of the possibility of its participation in developing new MBH adduct-based drugs as a ligand or in the form of metal complexes.

2. Experimental

2.1. Materials and Methods

The current study used various A.R. grades solvents, such as *n*-hexane, methanol, and ethyl acetate. Additionally, Methyl Acrylate, NaCl, $MgSO_4$ anhydrous, NaOH (Dae-Jung Kosdaq Reagents and Chemicals), DABCO (1,4-diazabicyclo [2.2.2]octane), $NiCl_2{\cdot}H_2O$, $CuCl_2{\cdot}2H_2O$, $MnCl_2{\cdot}2H_2O$, $CoCl_3{\cdot}6H_2O$, $CrCl_3{\cdot}6H_2O$, and 4-Cyanobenzaldehyde, (Sigma Aldrich, St. Louis, MO, USA) were also used. A U.V. lamp (monitoring TLC card), digital hotplate with constant temperature and stirring system, Gallen Kamp melting point instrument (SPW, Ambala Cantt, Haryana, India), LAMBDA 1050+ U.V./Vis/NIR spectrophotometer, FTIR spectrophotometer Shimadzu Company (Kanda Nishiki-cho, Chiyoda-ku, Tokyo 101-8448, Japan) prestige-21 (4000–500 cm^{-1}), AVANCE NEO 1H-NMR spectrophotometer (500 MHz in $CDCl_3$), LECO CHNS 932 model microanalytical elemental analyzer instrument (Model: AV500, BRUKER, Bath, UK) (±0.3%), JEOL 600H-1 Mass spectrophotometer (ionization mode EI+) by Direct Probe Inlet and XRD Panalytical company (Lelyweg 1, Almelo, Netherland) X-pro serial No. DYH313 (Goniometer Radius mm = 240.00 and Dist. Focus-Diverg. Slit mm = 91.00) with Cu- anode material, Kα [Å] = 1.54060 and generator settings 30 mA, 40 kV) were the main instruments used during this research. Thermal stability of the complexes was studied by using a TA Instruments Trios V4.5.1.42498 SDT 650 Simultaneous Thermal Analyzer, (TA Instruments, New Castle, DE, USA). The analysis was carried out under an N_2 atmosphere with the flow time of 1 mg min^{-1} at a heating rate of 20 °C min^{-1}.

2.2. Synthesis of Methyl 2-((4-cyanophenyl)(hydroxy)methyl)acrylate MBH Adduct

Methyl 2-((4-cyanophenyl)(hydroxy)methyl)acrylate (L''_x) was synthesized by mixing five equivalent methyl acrylate and one equivalent 4-cyano benzaldehyde in the presence of 0.65 equivalents of DABCO (catalyst) in a round-bottomed flask at room temperature and constant stirring [26]. The reaction mixture was checked after half-hour intervals using TLC plates under a UV lamp. The completion of the reaction took almost one day, as revealed by TLC results. A gummy crude material was obtained 24 h after an excess of the methyl acrylate was evaporated [11]. The glutinous crude was diluted by adding 15 mL each of ethyl acetate and brine solution. The complete organic and inorganic layers were separated in a separating funnel, and the mixture was collected thrice after running through the solvent. Through evaporation of EtOAc under reduced pressure, the organic phase was concentrated.

Furthermore, crude was subjected to column chromatography for further purification. The mobile phase system was constituted in a 10:90 to 20:70 (v/v) ratio of ethyl acetate and n-hexane. The prominent spot was collected as a pure product with an 85% yield, further confirmed through spectral analysis [2,7,27]. Scheme 1 here shows the whole setup for the preparation of MBH Adduct.

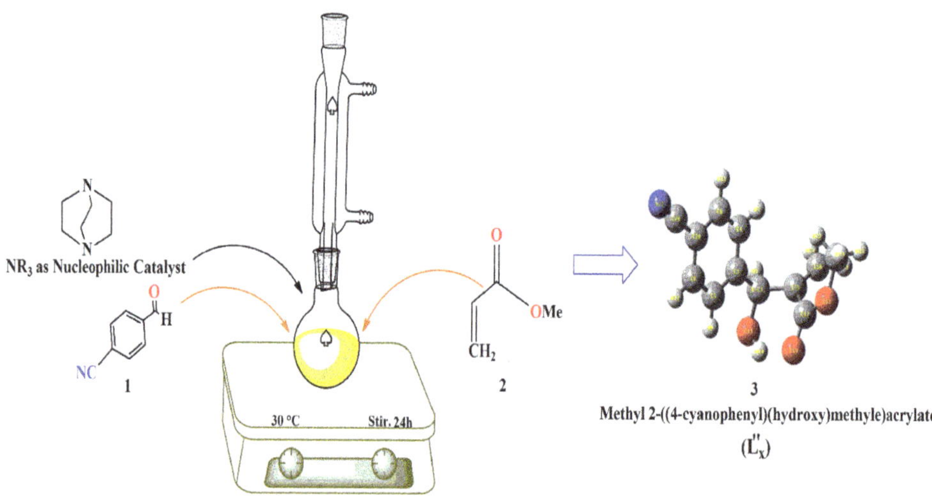

Scheme 1. Synthesis of Methyl 2-((4-cyanophenyl)(hydroxy)methyl)acrylate MBH adduct (L''_x).

Analytical Data for L''_x (Compound **3**)

M.P. 120.5–123.4 °C; 217.07 (g/mol) yield 87%. Color: Milky white. λ (nm): 269. ε ($mol^{-1}cm^{-1}L$): 762.63. FT-IR (KBr, ῡ=cm^{-1}): 3437 alcoholic (-OH), 2954 (=C-H), 3000 (sp^3 C-H stretch), 2229 (-C≡N), 1718 (ester C=O), 1629 (aromatic C=C), 1600, 1053 (-OH bend). 1H NMR (500MHz, $CDCl_3$-D-1): δ 3.203 (s, 1H, OH), 3.693 (s, 3H, OCH_3), 5.488 (s, 1H, CH_2), 5.804 (s, 1H, CH_2), 6.307 (s, 1H, CH), 7.240 (m, 4H, H-2, H-3, H-5, H-6). Mass spectrum [*m/z*

(%)]: 216 (52) M^+, 185 (48), 184 (15), 158 (17), 157 (80), 156 (11), 142 (14), 140 (19), 130 (100), 128 (10), 102 (17), 104 (23), 77 (12), 55 (14). Anal. Calculated for $C_{12}H_{11}NO_3$ (%): 217.07 (100), Found (%):218.08 (52.2). Elemental Anal. Calc. (%): C, 66.35; H, 5.10; N, 6.45, Found: C, 66.36; H, 4.93; N, 6.48

2.3. Synthesis of Metal Complexes of L''_x

About 20 mL of 0.042M solution of L''_x in hot ethanol and 0.0201M transition metal salt solutions of $CoCl_3 \cdot 6H_2O$, $NiCl_2 \cdot 6H_2O$, $MnCl_2 \cdot 2H_2O$, $CrCl_3 \cdot 6H_2O$ and $CuCl_2 \cdot 2H_2O$ in distilled water were prepared separately. The metal ions were added dropwise to the L''_x solution with continuous stirring. The pH was maintained at ten by adding a few drops of NaOH solution, and the mixture was refluxed at 60–70 °C for about 5–6 h until a solid mass was formed. The progress of the reaction was continuously checked via TLC under a UV lamp [28]. After the completion of the response, as indicated by a single spot under the UV lamp, the cooled product was collected employing vacuum filtration. Though the single crystal formation of these complexes remained unsuccessful despite many attempts of different procedures for crystallization, we collected the product in an amorphous state for subsequent analyses. The product was washed with water and ethanol thrice and dried in a desiccator [29,30]. Each metal complex was characterized through UV- Visible, FTIR, and percentage analysis to determine the molecular and structural formula. Computational studies geometrically optimized the Synthesized compounds. Further, the crystal class of these novel crystal compounds of metal complexes was obtained through XRD powder diffraction. Scheme 2 outlines the synthesis of these metal complexes of L''_x.

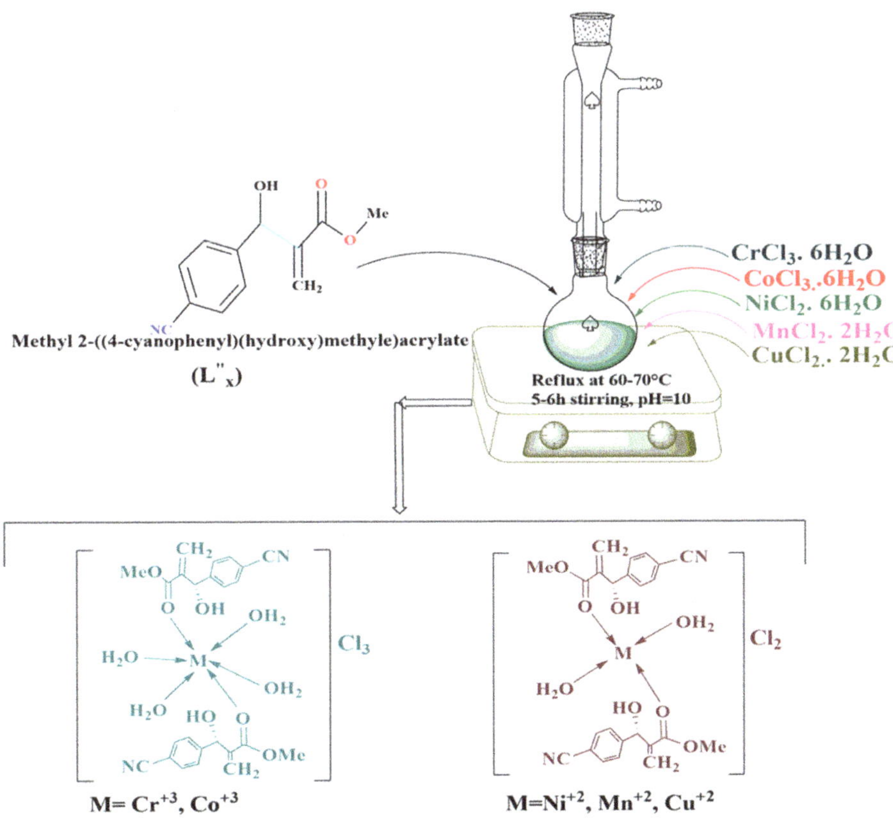

Scheme 2. Synthesis of the L''_x Tansition Metal Complexes.

2.4. Analytical Data of Transition Metal Complexes

2.4.1. $Cr^{3+}L''_x$ Complex (Compound **4**)

M.P: >300 °C. 558.50 (g/mol): Color: Sky blue. λmax (nm): 371.5. ε ($mol^{-1}cm^{-1}L$): 238.09. FT-IR (KBr, ῡ=cm^{-1}): 3450–3380 alcoholic (-OH), 2850 (=C-H), 2900–2800 (sp^3 C-H stretch), 2374 (-C≡N), 1608 (aromatic C=C), 850 (M-OH_2), 607 (M-O). Mass spectrum [*m/z* (%)], for $C_{24}H_{30}CrN_2O_{10}{}^{3+}M^+$: Anal. Calculated for (%):186.04 (100.0), Found (%): 185.47 (83.3). Elemental Anal. Calc. (%): C, 51.61; H, 5.41; N, 5.02, Found: C, 51.58; H, 4.89; N, 5.10.

2.4.2. $Co^{3+}L''_x$ Complex (Compound **5**)

M.P: >300 °C. 565.43 (g/mol): Color: Teal blue. λmax (nm): 361. ε ($mol^{-1}cm^{-1}L$): 224.23. FT-IR (KBr, ῡ=cm^{-1}): 3500–3350 alcoholic (-OH), 2900 (=C-H), 2850 (sp^3 C-H stretch), 2210 (-C≡N), 1716 small (ester C=O) 1635 (aromatic C=C), 835 (M-OH_2), 653 (M-O). Mass spectrum [*m/z* (%)], for $C_{24}H_{30}CoN_2O_{10}{}^{3+}M^+$ (%): 188.37 (100), Found (%): 188.39 (26.6). Elemental Anal. Calc. (%): C, 50.98; H, 5.35; N, 4.95, Found: C, 50.80; H, 5.54; N, 4.78.

2.4.3. $Ni^{2+}L''_x$ Complex (Compound **6**)

M.P: >300 °C. 529.16 (g/mol): Color: Cadet blue. λmax (nm): 360. ε ($mol^{-1}cm^{-1}L$): 309.81. FT-IR (KBr, ῡ=cm^{-1}): 3550–3450 alcoholic (-OH), 2950 (=C-H), 2850 (sp^3 C-H stretch), 1640 (ester C=O), 1625 (aromatic C=C), 605 (M-O). Mass spectrum [*m/z* (%)] for $C_{24}H_{26}N_2NiO_8{}^{2+}$ M^+ (%): 264.05 (100.0), Found (%): 265.10 (38.7). Elemental Anal. Calc. (%): C, 54.47; H, 4.95; N, 5.29, Found: 54.50; H, 4.87; N, 4.94.

2.4.4. $Mn^{2+}L''_x$ Complex (Compound **7**)

M.P: >300 °C. 525.41 (g/mol): Color: Wine red. λmax (nm): 372. ε ($mol^{-1}cm^{-1}L$): 168.57. FT-IR (KBr, ῡ=cm^{-1}): 3450–3350 alcoholic (-OH), 2954 (=C-H), 2875 (sp^3 C-H stretch), 2229 min (-C≡N), 1722 (ester C=O), 1625 (aromatic C=C), 613 (M-O). Mass spectrum [*m/z* (%)], for $C_{24}H_{26}MnN_2O_8{}^{2+}$ M^+ (%): 262.55 (100.0), Found (%): 263.10 (26.6). Elemental Anal. Calc. (%): C, 54.86; H, 4.99; N, 5.33, Found: C, 54.45; H, 4.41; N, 5.03.

2.4.5. $Cu^{2+}L''_x$ Complex (Compound **8**)

M.P: >300 °C. 533.06 (g/mol): Color: Hunter green. λmax (nm): 371. ε ($mol^{-1}cm^{-1}L$): 120.11. FT-IR (KBr, ῡ=cm^{-1}): 3500–3470 alcoholic (-OH), 2900 (=C-H), 2875 (sp^3 C-H stretch), 1673 (aromatic C=C), 603 (M-O). Mass spectrum [*m/z* (%)], for $[C_{24}H_{26}CuN_2O_8]^{2+}$ M^+, Calc. (%): 266.55 (100.0), Found (%): 265.87 (49.3). Elemental Anal. Calc. (%): C, 53.98; H, 4.91; N, 5.25, Found: C, 54.02; H, 4.95; N, 5.31.

2.5. Antibacterial Assay for Compounds **3–8**

The agar disc diffusion method [31,32] was used to determine the antibacterial activities of the compounds **3–8** against four bacterial strains *Staphylococcus aureus, Escherichia coli* (Gram-negative), and *Bacillus pumilis, Salmonella typhi* (Gram-positive). A sterile membrane syringe filter of pore size 0.45 μm (Millipore) was used for extraction. To 100 mL antibiotic agar No.11 (45 °C), 1mL of culture suspension (25 T%, 530 nm) of each strain was added and intermingled. 25mL of each agar medium was poured into separate Petri dishes (20 × 100 mm) and solidified. Four holes were made after solidifying by expending a sterile borer of 8mm diameter with (6 mm inner diameter). Each extract (100 μL) was poured into the marked holes and incubated at 37 °C for 24 h. These experiments were performed under a severe aseptic environment in triplicate. The inhibition (mm) of the incubation zone produced via individual extract demonstrated antibacterial activity. Finally, the % inhibition was computed. The standard antibiotic Gentamycin (0.3%) was used as a standard [33].

2.6. Determination of DPPH Radical Scavenging Activity of Compounds **3–8**

The DPPH (2,2-diphenyl-1-picrylhydrazyl) radical scavenging method has been extensively used to determine free extreme scavenging action [34]. The same was applied in our work with some modifications. 0.3 mM solution of DPPH was prepared in methanol. 10μL of varying concentrations (25–100 mg) of each compound **3–8** was mixed with 1.0 mL of DPPH solution. At 37 °C, the reaction mixture was incubated for about half an hour. The absorbance was measured at 515 nm. In contrast to methanol-treated control percent, radical scavenging activity was determined when ascorbic acid was used as a standard for sample analysis. The antioxidant activity was determined [9,35].

2.7. Antifungal Assay for Compounds **3–8**

The antifungal activity of the compounds **3–8** was measured by well-known quantitative agar well diffusion method [36,37]. About 1 mL of the compound suspension was mixed with 100 mL of 4.0% Sabouraud Dextrose Agar (SDA) and transferred into plate. Wells of 8 mm were prepared and 100μL of test compounds were poured to positive control into respective wells after the solid mass have been prepared. The test plates were left for 5 days at room temperature and then incubated for further 5 days at same temperature. Zones of inhibitions were measured with reference to the plant extract of 100 μL to be assayed and Ketoconazole 1.0 mg mL^{-1} was used for instance positive control [36,38].

2.8. Computational Studies

All the optimization and frequency calculations were performed with the Gaussian 16W [39] program package on an ACPI x64 Core i7 laptop with a 3.0 GHz processor and 16 GB Ram. The molecular structure of the ligand (L''_x) was optimized by using the DFT B3LYP method and 6-311++ G (d,p) basis set [40–42]. All metal complexes' molecular structures were optimized using the semi-empirical PM6 method [43], which was justified by the absence of imaginary frequency. The assignment of the calculated wavenumbers was aided by the animation option of Gauss View 6.0 graphical interface for the Gaussian program, which gives a visual presentation of the shape of the vibrational modes. Furthermore, for molecular docking, structures of ligand and complexes were taken from their optimized geometries calculated by Gaussian. The crystal structures of *Escherichia coli, Staphylococcus aureus,* and *Salmonella typhi* proteins were fetched from the Protein data bank (PDB) using IDs; 1AJ6 [44], 4URO [45], and 1WVG [46], respectively. Polar hydrogen atoms and Kollman united atom charges were added using AutoDock Tools [47]. Docking calculations were performed with AutoDock Vina using the Lamarckian Genetic Algorithm [48]. A grid box size of 31 × 37 × 35 Å points for *E.coli*, 35 × 30 × 38 Å points for *Staphylococcus aureus*, and 40 × 35 × 37 Å points for *Salmonella typhi* with a grid spacing of 0.375 Å was generated using AutoGrid. The coordinates of active site for *E.coli* are x = 60.29, y = −8.53, z = 36.67, for *Staphylococcus aureus* are x = 2.51, y = −54.72, z = −13.36, and for *Salmonella typhi* are x = 63.95, y = 21.80, z = 49.35, respectively.

3. Results and Discussion

3.1. Physical Characteristics and Elemental Analysis

The MBH adduct ligand (L''_x) and its corresponding metal complexes were analyzed by physical as well as comparative elemental analysis (Table 1). It has already been stated that pure L''_x is a viscous liquid. In contrast, its corresponding metal complexes are amorphous solids (compounds **4–8**). The prepared complexes (compounds **4–8**) are all colored compounds, stable at room temperature, insoluble in water, and most organic solvents, such as acetone, DMF, methanol, and ethanol, but soluble to a lesser extent in DMSO. Several oxygen atom-containing organic ligands prefer an essential medium for complexation when more than one chelation site is available in a compound for coordination [49,50]. Under such conditions, hydrated hydroxide can be formed, which can further participate in complex formation if the incoming ligand is substantial [51]. The physical analysis, e.g., color, melting point, and molecular formula, are preliminary examination-based tests to observe the formation of new species. For example, manganese forms a stable complex in the essential medium of dark red to brown shades. Color change of transition metals after the formation of the complexes is meaningful property as it can be a consequence of either charge transfer or changes in the d-d transitions of the metal ions [52]. The yield was found to be in the range of 60–85%.

Table 1. Physical Properties and analytical data of compounds **3–8**.

Compounds	Molecular Formula	M. Wt (g/mol)	Color	M.P (°C)	Elemental Analysis (%) Calc. (Found) C	H	N
L''_x	$C_{12}H_{11}NO_3$	217.07	Milky white	120.5–123.4	66.35 (66.36)	5.10 (4.93)	6.45 (6.48)
$Cr^{3+}L''_x$	$C_{24}H_{26}CrN_2O_8{}^{3+}$	558.50	Sky blue	>300	51.61 (51.58)	5.41 (4.89)	5.02 (5.10)
$Co^{3+}L''_x$	$C_{24}H_{26}CoN_2O_8{}^{3+}$	565.43	Teal blue	>300	50.98 (50.80)	5.35 (5.54)	4.95 (4.78)
$Ni^{2+}L''_x$	$C_{24}H_{22}N_2NiO_6{}^{2+}$	529.16	Cadet blue	>300	54.47 (54.50)	4.95 (4.87)	5.29 (4.94)
$Mn^{2+}L''_x$	$C_{24}H_{26}MnN_2O_8{}^{2+}$	561.13	Wine red	>300	54.86 (54.45)	4.99 (4.41)	5.33 (5.03)
$Cu^{2+}L''_x$	$C_{24}H_{22}CuN_2O_6{}^{2+}$	533.06	Hunter green	>300	53.98 (54.02)	4.91 (4.95)	4.99 (5.31)

The elemental analysis (%) results confirmed that the counter ions might not contain carbon, hydrogen, and nitrogen atoms; if they are present, then there will be higher percentages of these elements rather than observed [49]. The results have also confirmed the formation of complexes of L''_x with desired metal ions (Cr^{3+}, Co^{3+}, Ni^{2+}, Cu^{2+}, Mn^{2+}) in a molar ratio of 2:1 (L''_x: M). The molecular formulas of complexes were confirmed by computational data obtained through the semi-empirical PM6 method. These transition metal complexes with organic adduct-based ligands have also been studied and reported in the literature [23,53–55]. The physical data, along with the estimated elemental analysis, have been summarized in Table 1.

3.2. Electronic Spectroscopy

The UV-Vis spectra of compounds **3–8** have provided knowledge about the changes that occurred upon complex formation, as reported in Table 2. The bands at 251 and 265 nm in the UV spectrum of compound **3** in DMSO are assigned to the $\pi \rightarrow \pi^*$ transitions. The spectrum has also presented a half curve at 269 nm and a strong band at 272 nm due to the $n \rightarrow \pi^*$ evolution of the unshared pairs of electrons found in the cyno-group of the nitrogen at the para position of the aromatic ring (Table 2). The $n \rightarrow \pi^*$ transition is also a characteristic of the aldehyde groups in a compound [56,57]. It has been observed that the $\pi \rightarrow \pi^*$ and $n \rightarrow \pi^*$ transitions were shifted after the metal ions were coordinated to L''_x. This change supports that the oxygen atoms of the esoteric carbonyl group in L''_x contribute to the coordination towards the central transition metal ions. By observing changes in the electronic spectrum of L''_x upon complex formation with the metal ions, it can be concluded that compounds **4–8** show a characteristic band in the region of 360–372 nm that is absent in compound **3**. These bands have shallow values of molar absorptivity coefficients and can be assigned to d-d transitions in the metal complexes.

Table 2. Investigated UV-Vis data for the Methyl 2-((4-cyanophenyl)(hydroxy)methyl)acrylate MBH adduct and and its formed complexes.

Samples	Concentration 1×10^{-3} (M)	Observed λmax (nm)	ε ($mol^{-1}cm^{-1}L$)	Absorbance (A)
L''_x	1.049	251, 265, 269	762.63 (269 nm)	0.65, 0.54, 0.80
$Cr^{3+}L''_x$	1.050	256.5, 275, 371	238.10 (371 nm)	2.8, 1.538, 0.25
$Co^{3+}L''_x$	1.048	256.5, 275, 361	224.24 (361 nm)	2.949, 1.453, 0.235
$Ni^{2+}L''_x$	1.049	254.5, 271.5, 360	309.81 (360 nm)	3.656, 1.741, 0.325
$Mn^{2+}L''_x$	1.050	265, 292, 372	168.57 (372 nm)	0.266, 0.214, 0.177
$Cu^{2+}L''_x$	1.049	264, 291, 371	120.11 (371 nm)	0.367, 0.207, 0.126

All compounds were dissolved in DMSO to observe the UV-Visible spectrum, ε ($mol^{-1}cm^{-1}L$) values were calculated a respective λ in the range 360–372 nm.

3.3. Theoratical and Experimental FT-IR of Ligand L''_x (Compound **3***)*

The FTIR spectra of MBH Adduct (L''_x) and its metal complexes were recorded between 4000–500 cm^{-1} using a KBr disk, and the data is presented in Table 3. The FTIR spectral data of compound **3** has shown the characteristics -OH broad peak at 3437 cm^{-1}, a prominent stretch of =C-H at 2954 cm^{-1} and sp^3 C-H stretch at 3000 cm^{-1} [58], and the band observed at 1718 cm^{-1} is due to ester carbonyl vibration. Furthermore, the $\bar{\upsilon}$ of C=C aromatic, -CH_3, C-O, and C-CN were assigned as 1629 cm^{-1}, 1440 cm^{-1}, 1247 cm^{-1}, and 2229 cm^{-1}, respectively (Figure 1a). Moreover, in theoretical IR analysis, it was observed that -OH peak is somewhat different in shape, may be due to some content of moisture present in the sample during the examination, from the observed spectrum however it retains its position. Furthermore, the rest of the fragments above (Figure 1b) show a good agreement of frequencies in both the experimental and theoretical spectrum. A slight change might be observed because of the theoretical calculations of the range corresponding to the isolated functional groups in the gaseous state. At the same time, the experimental results belong to the molecules in a solid state [59,60]. The close resemblance of DFT-based IR and calculated $\bar{\upsilon}$ results have made us suggest the molecular structure of Methyl 2-((4-cyanophenyl)(hydroxy)methyl)acrylate MBH Adduct (L''_x) as presented in Figure 2a.

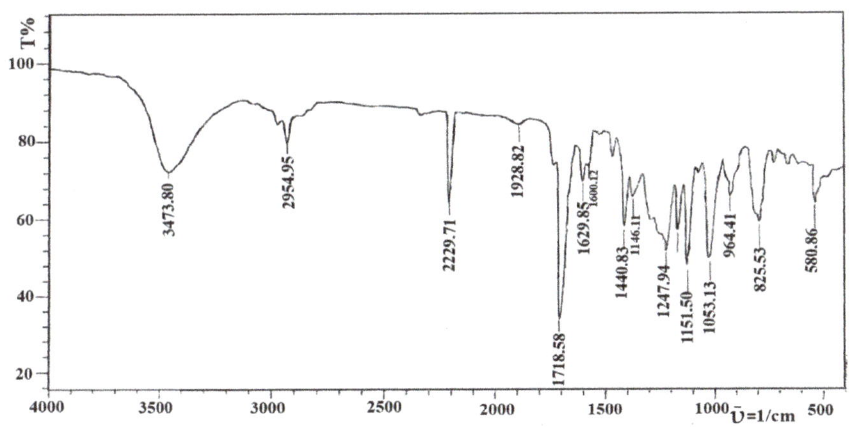

(**a**)

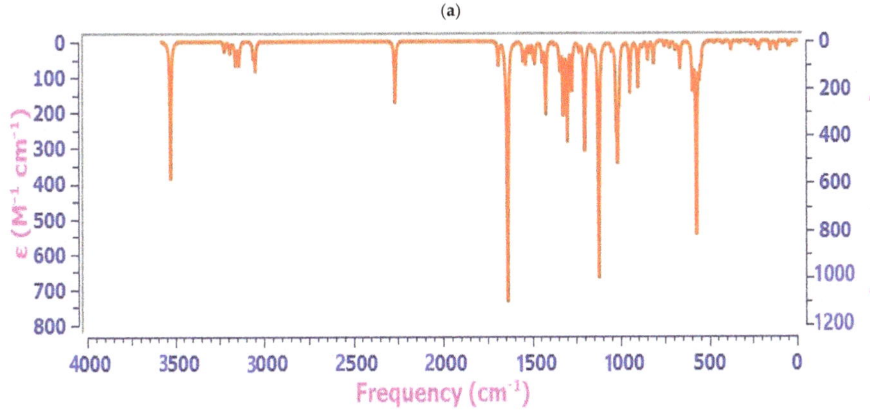

(**b**)

Figure 1. (**a**) Experimental FT-IR Spectrum of Compound **3**. (**b**) Theoretical FT-IR Spectrum of Compound **3**.

Table 3. Characteristic FTIR bands of the MBH Adduct (L″$_x$) and its metal complexes (cm^{-1}) $\bar{\upsilon}$.

Functional Groups	L″$_x$	Calc. L″$_x$	Cr^{3+}L″$_x$	Co^{3+}L″$_x$	Ni^{2+}L″$_x$	Mn^{2+}L″$_x$	Cu^{2+}L″$_x$
$\bar{\upsilon}$(-OH)	3437	3524	3450–3380	3500–3350	3550–3450	3450–3350	3500–3470
$\bar{\upsilon}$(=C-H)	2954	3221	2850	2900	2950	2954	2900
$\bar{\upsilon}$(sp^3 C-H stretch),	3000	3046	2900–2800	2850	2850	2875	2875
$\bar{\upsilon}$(-C≡N)	2229	2264	2374	2210	-	2229	-
$\bar{\upsilon}$(ester C=O),	1718	1687	-	-	1640	-	-
$\bar{\upsilon}$(aromatic C=C),	1629	1635	1608	1635	1625	1625	1673
$\bar{\upsilon}$C=C	1600	1635	1630	1571	-	1568	1604
$\bar{\upsilon}$(-CH_3)	1440	1490	1556	1450	-	1436	1400
$\bar{\upsilon}$(C-O)	1247	1201, 1274	1390	1396	1388	1390	1388
$\bar{\upsilon}$(C-OCH_3)	1151	1121	1120	1107	1112	1107	1111
$\bar{\upsilon}$(-OH bend)	1053	1023, 570	-		-	-	-
$\bar{\upsilon}$(=C-H aromatic)	825	845, 900	700	-	-	833	-
$\bar{\upsilon}$(M-O)	-		607	653	605	613	603
$\bar{\upsilon}$(M-OH_2)	-		550	535	520	525	527

Only the observed changes in specified functional groups are presented.

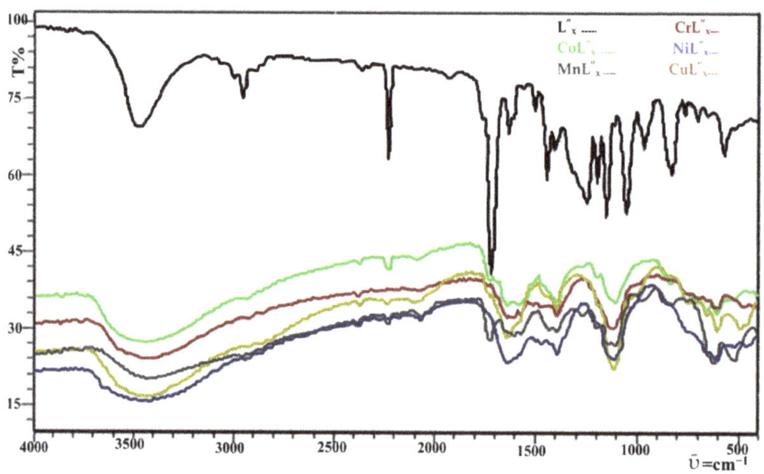

Figure 2. Experimental FT-IR Spectrum of Transition Metals Complexes with MBH Adduct (L″$_x$).

3.4. *Experimental FT-IR Spectroscopyof Complexes* **4–8**

A detailed explanation of experimental FT-IR spectroscopy results has been summarized in Table 3. In experimental FT-IR, a characteristic band of the –OH functional group was observed in the region of 3350–3550 cm^{-1} in the IR spectra of the compounds **4–8**, proposing its nonparticipation in coordinate bond formation towards all metal ions in these compounds. Furthermore, the broadness of this peak was increased after coordination, clearly seen in Figure 2. This may either be due to coordinated water molecules in the complexes or the moisture in the sample [23,61,62]. Common and robust evidence regarding the coordination of Ligand (L″ $_x$) towards the central metal ion is the disappearance of the C=O peak, which originated at 1680–1720 cm^{-1} (Figure 2) in both theoretical and experimental spectrum (Figure 1a,b) of the compound 3. The results in Table 3 revealed the disappearance of the characteristic peak of the C=O group from compounds **4–8** except compound **6** (Ni^{2+}L″ $_x$), where the mountain has merely shifted to 1640 cm^{-1}. The disappearance of the peak endorses the formation of a coordination bond through the oxygen of the C=O group with the central metal ion, which eventually diminishes the strength of the carbonyl group in complexes after bonding. The literature also supports such a way of coordination [63,64]. In compound **6**, we can observe that the peak intensity is also very low rather than the more intense appearing in the Ligand [61]. This significant change is good support for justifying that the coordination of Ligand towards the Ni^{2+} metal ions is from this definite functional group (Figure 2).

Table 3 also shows the shift of Ligand's ester (C-O) group from 1247 cm^{-1} to 1390 cm^{-1} in compound **4** may be attributable to the environmental effect after complex formation. Moreover, the additional peaks have also been observed at 607 and 550 cm^{-1} and assigned to the Cr-O and Cr-OH_2, respectively [61]. Further, it is inferred that the C=C group doesn't participate in complexation. Because there were no significant changes in the IR frequency of the C=C double bond seen upon complex formation, based on these observations, the molecular and structural formulae of the compound **4** were deduced as $[Cr(L''_x)2(H_2O)_4]\cdot 3Cl^-$. Both compounds **4** and **5** have shown peak shifting with low intensity of the Ligand's cyano (-C≡N) group to a region of 2374–2210 cm^{-1}. The little shift and peak intensity difference might be due to the environmental effect [65] and ligand coordination [66]. The involvement of the carbonyl group (1718 cm^{-1}) (L''_x) in coordinate bond formation has been proved and already reported in the literature [67], thus confirming the coordination of this Ligand's carbonyl site towards the Co+3 metal ions. Table 3 shows an exceptional signal attributable to Co-O appearing at 653 cm^{-1} and another noticeable difference in Co-OH_2 frequency from 535 cm^{-1}. Based on comprehensive information, the molecular formula $[Co(L''_x)_2(H_2O)_4]Cl^-{}_3$ was established for compound **5**.

The detailed inspection of the data based on the FT-IR analysis (Table 3) has led us to elucidate the structural formula for compounds **6–8** and presented peaks for all the conspicuous functional groups, which revealed the complex formation along with some informative shifts. Such as an extremely weak band, almost negligible at 1640 cm^{-1}, corresponds to the C=O group, which was comparatively at a lower frequency than its precursor C=O absorption (1718 cm^{-1}) in compound **6**. In addition, the –OH and =CH groups exhibited peaks at 3450–3350 cm^{-1} (broad) and 2950 cm^{-1}, respectively. Furthermore, we have also observed peaks for the C=C bond at 1625 cm^{-1} with no noticeable shift, simultaneously signifying that C=C does not participate in coordination bond formation. Further, in compound **7**, we have also observed a broad peak at 3450–3350 cm^{-1} of the same (-OH) functional group. The difference from precursor ligand –OH is may due to the presence of moisture in the sample, which has provided interference during the recording of the spectrum. Similarly, the remaining functional groups show a slight change in the calculated values, as is evident from their sharp pointed peaks at exact frequencies. FTIR results for compound **8** have revealed the presence of the –OH functional group by a height almost at a similar position (3500–3470 cm^{-1}) as that of the ligand forerunner. Around about similar results were gained of the complex for the presence of sp^2 and sp^3 C-H bonds, i.e., their peaks were observed at 2900, 2875 cm^{-1}, respectively. The ester carbonyl absorption has disappeared as compared to that of the ligand carbonyl (1718 cm^{-1}), suggesting its participation in complex formation. No remarkable change was observed in the frequency due to aliphatic and aromatic C=C double bonds not contributing to complex formation. These assumptions were further supported by the appearance of IR peaks at 605 cm^{-1} and 520 cm^{-1} in Compound **6** were assigned to Ni-O and Ni-OH_2 groups, respectively while in Compound **7** revealed the $\bar{\upsilon}$ at 603 cm^{-1}, and 527 cm^{-1} due to the presence of Cu-O and Cu-OH_2 bond (Table 3, Figure 2). Upon physical, analytical and spectral results basis the prepared complexes (compounds **6–8**) were assigned the structure presented above in Scheme 2 formulated as $[M(L''_x)_2(H_2O)_2]Cl^-{}_2$, where, M= Ni^{2+}, Mn^{2+}, Cu^{2+}.

3.5. Mass Spectroscopy

The molecular weight of the Compound **3** was determined through mass spectroscopy based. The results have shown *m/z* 130, 70.2%, with a total of 349 ions. The finest ions with the lowest % are 77 and appear because of the phenyl group ($C_6H_6{}^+$) at the lowest m/e (12%) comparatively. A fragment detected with a mass of 104 matches with $C_6H_6CN^+$ at 23%, while the ionic chip (130) next to this ion is present in the highest *m/z*, i.e., 100%. This molecular ion fragment is the precise result of the molecular weight of $C_7H_8OCN^+$. Further, it was observed in the mass spectrum that the $C_9H^{11}OCN^+$ with the molar mass

157 appears at 80% m/e. Additionally, the molecular ion fragments $C_{11}H_{13}O_2CN^+$ (185) and $C_{11}H_{13}O_3CN^+$ (216) were also observed at 56% and 51%, respectively. Hence, these results also confirm the purity of compound **3** obtained through this technique [15,68,69].

Experimentally, mass spectroscopy of compound **4–8** could not be possible due to the insolubility of these metal complexes in any suitable solvent other than pure DMSO [70,71]. However, the estimated Mass spectrum of the Cr^{3+} complex showed a molecular ion peak M^+ at *m/z* 185.47 that is equivalent to its molecular mass, while that of Co^{3+} at *m/z* 188.39 is attributable to [M^+]. Ni^{2+}, Mn^{2+}, and Cu^{2+} complexes are suggested to have two water molecules and thereby display [M^+] fragments at *m/z* 265.10, 265.87, and 263.10, respectively. Furthermore, [M^+] peaks are in good agreement with the structures proposed (Scheme 2) by estimated elemental analysis, spectral data, and molar stoichiometry [58,72,73].

3.6. ^1H *NMR Spectroscopy*

^1H NMR spectrum of ligand L''_x (compound **3**) was observed in $CDCl_3$ solvent at 500MHz by keeping TMS as internal reference. The data obtained in the form of spectrum showed five signals as singlet at 3.203, 3.693, 5.488, 5.804, and 6.307 ppm, because of the -OH, -OCH_3, =CH_2, =CH_2, and –CH protons, respectively. However, only one signal of multiplet, which is certainly due to the aromatic protons at 7.240 ppm was also observed. These aromatic protons were located at the same chemical shift, because of their identical chemical environment [58].

3.7. *Molecular Modeling*

DFT B3LYP method and 6-311++ G (d,p) basis set were used for geometrical optimization and frequency calculation of the ligand (L''_x). Consequently, the FT-IR spectrum of the synthesized ligand was computed theoretically and found in good agreement with the experimental FT-IR range. The ligand (L''_x) was subsequently used in the synthesis of five novel transition metal complexes (compounds **4–8**) (Scheme 2). These metal complexes were further analyzed by physical, analytical, and spectral analyses to confirm their proposed structures. The synthesized metal complexes' best possible geometry has been submitted using the semi-empirical PM6 method. Geometrical optimization of metal complexes demonstrates their proposed designs best fit the experimental findings. For example, the Cr^{3+} complex (compound **4**) is optimized in tetrahedral geometry with high spin and quartet multiplicity. The Co^{3+} complex (compound **5**) is found in distorted octahedral geometry with low spin and singlet multiplicity. Mn^{2+} and Cu^{2+} complexes (compounds **6** and **7**) attain identical spin (down) as well as geometries (tetrahedral). The assortment adjusted in theoretical calculations is sextet for Mn^{2+} (d^5), while doublet is found for Cu^{2+} (d^9). However, Ni^{2+} (d^8) complex (compound **8**) is observed in a low spin with singlet multiplicity and square planner geometry. This structural analysis for geometry optimization of metal complexes is well presented in the literature [74–76]. Computational studies on the synthesized ligand and its metal complexes provided reasonable geometrical shapes, which correlate well with the experimental results. The results of these optimized structures are presented in Figure 3.

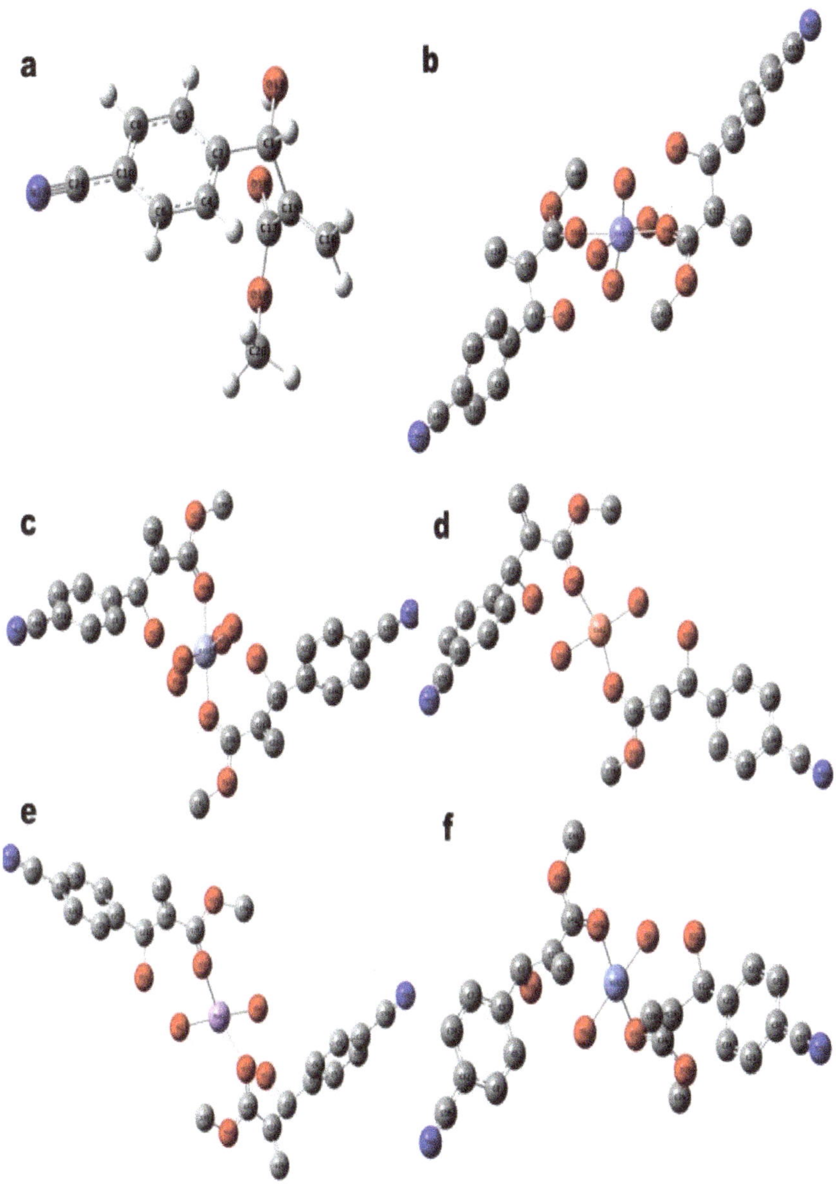

Figure 3. Theoretically Optimized Geometries of (**a**) MBHA (L''_x), and its Corresponding Complexes, (**b**) CoL''_x, (**c**) CrL''_x, (**d**) CuL''_x, (**e**) MnL''_x and (**f**) NiL''_x. The results have confirmed that each metal is coordinated by two ligand molecules. Cr^{+3}, Co^{+3} are octahedral and Ni^{+2} is square planner, whereas, Mn^{+2} and Cu^{+2} are tetrahedral as per optimized geometrical structures. Hydrogen atoms are removed from metal complexes for geometry clarity.

3.8. X-ray Diffraction

Powder X-ray diffraction was performed to confirm the crystal structure of transition metal complexes with L''_x. Single crystal XRD of these synthesized compounds was not possible because the crystals of the complexes could not be grown despite many attempts to crystallize a single crystal perfect for the analysis. However, powder XRD has also proved to be a handy tool for determining crystal class whenever we have the product in the crystalline form [67,77,78]. The patterns of these diffractograms for compounds **4–8** are given in Figure 4. The ways provide an idea of the coordination of oxygen atoms from the ligand to the metal ions. Furthermore, these patterns also indicate the crystalline nature of all the complexes [58]. It can be observed that mainly the remaining diffractograms of all these compounds differ due to their different crystalline structures [79]. This difference might be due to the coordinated water molecules in the coordination sphere [80] that give an appropriate and unique crystal class [78]. Their subsequent XRD results, such as; calculated density, specified volume, radius intensity ratio, and lattice parameters (a, b, c, α, β, γ) with crystal class,, have been given in Table 4.

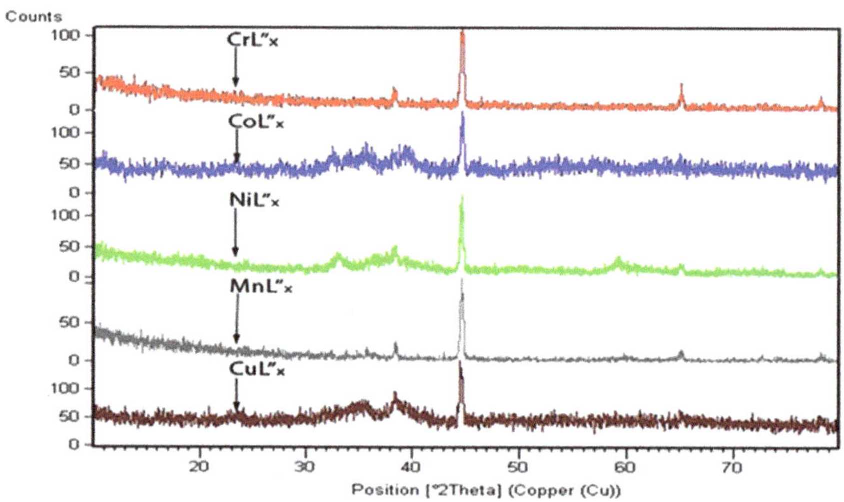

Figure 4. X-ray Diffraction Patterns of Compounds **4–8**.

Table 4. Crystallographic data and observed refinement parameters for compounds **4–8**.

Complexes	S. Group (G. No.)	Volume (10^{-6} pm^3)	Density (g/cm³)	Unit Cell Dimensions (Å)	Crystal Class	No. of Unit Cells (Z)	Reference Intensity Ratio (RIR)
CrL″x	Pm-3n (223)	93.82	6.09	a = b = c a = 2.8787 b = 2.8787 c = 2.8787	Cubic α = β = γ = 90°	2	6.39
CoL″x	Pm-3n (223)	93.82	6.09	a = b = c a = 4.5440 b = 4.5440 c = 4.5440	Cubic α = β = γ = 90°	2	6.39
NiL″x	P6322 (182)	79.31	7.96	a = b ≠ c a = 4.6160 b = 4.6160 c = 4.2980	Hexagonal α = β = 90° γ = 120	2	6.40
MnL″x	Pnma (62)	119.62	4.83	a ≠ b ≠ c a = 9.2660 b = 2.8607 c = 4.5128	Orthorhombic α = β = γ = 90°	4	3.46
CuL″x	C2/c (15)	82.14	6.43	a ≠ b ≠ c a = 4.6890 b = 3.4200 c = 5.1300	Monoclinic α = γ = 90° β ≠ 90°	4	3.69

Powder X-ray diffraction was performed to confirm the crystal structure of transition metal complexes with L''_x. Single crystal XRD of these synthesized compounds was not possible because the crystals of the complexes could not be grown despite many attempts to crystallize a single crystal perfect for the analysis. However, powder XRD has also proved to be a handy tool for determining crystal class whenever we have the product in the crystalline form [67,77,78]. The patterns of these diffractograms for compounds **4**–**8** are given in Figure 4. The ways provide an idea of the coordination of oxygen atoms from the ligand to the metal ions. Furthermore, these patterns also indicate the crystalline nature of all the complexes [58]. It can be observed that mainly the remaining diffractograms of all these compounds differ due to their different crystalline structures [79]. This difference might be due to the coordinated water molecules in the coordination sphere [80] that give an appropriate and unique crystal class [78]. Their subsequent XRD results, such as; calculated density, specified volume, radius intensity ratio, and lattice parameters (a, b, c, α, β, γ) with crystal class, have been given in Table 4. It is essential that the complex $Mn^{2+}L''_x$ (compound **7**) was found to have orthorhombic crystalline nature, having space group Pnma (62) with a Z value of 4. The indexing related [67,81] to their structure elucidation, peak intensities, and diffraction angles (2θ) is given in Table 5. Compound **8** belongs to the monoclinic crystal class, which provides it with a unique identity among these compounds. The other important properties, including the space group, unit cell number, and radius intensity ratio, depending upon the crystal class [80,81]. These findings, together with the results from computational modeling, have strengthened our conclusions on the energy and mass of our metal complexes.

Table 5. Crystal lattice Data and Summary of Data Collection and Refinement for Compounds **4**–**8**.

Complexes	Miller Indices h	k	l	d [Å]	2°θ	Intensity (%)	FWHMI (β)	S (nm)
$[Cr(L''_x)_2(H_2O)_4]Cl_3$	1	1	0	2.03	44.6	100	0.3444	5.9055
	2	0	0	1.44	64.678	17		
	2	1	1	1.17	82.352	30		
	2	2	0	0.91	115.66	3		
$[Co(L''_x)_2(H_2O)_4]Cl_3$	1	0	0	2.3027	39.086	33.9	0.246	8.256
	0	0	2	2.167	41.644	32		
	1	0	1	2.0335	44.518	100		
	1	0	2	1.5781	58.434	6		
$[Ni(L''_x)_2(H_2O)_2]Cl_2$	1	1	0	2.308	38.993	18.8	0.2952	6.8805
	1	1	1	2.0333	44.522	100		
	1	1	2	1.572	58.651	14.7		
	3	0	0	1.3325	70.631	11.5		
$[Mn(L''_x)_2(H_2O)_2]Cl_2$	1	0	1	4.507	21.89	100	0.3444	4.5316
	3	0	1	2.5459	35.179	38		
	2	1	0	2.434	36.9	29		
	1	1	1	2.338	38.473	31		
$[Cu(L''_x)_2(H_2O)_2]Cl_2$	−1	1	1	2.5438	35.253	100	0.246	7.389
	0	0	2	2.5244	35.533	34.2		
	1	1	1	2.334	58.538	81.3		
	−1	1	2	2.308	38.989	28.3		

Each set of indices was chosen on the basis of highest intensity (%) of sharp peak.

Moreover, the peaks of the highest intensities of all complexes, along with the values of miller indices, d-spacing, and position (2θ), are given in Table 5. The grain size of amorphous compounds is also significant to confirm their stability. XRD- powder diffraction is a method used for this purpose. Scherer's equation can calculate the size of the grain. This equation is formulated as:

$$S = \frac{\lambda m}{\beta \cos \theta} \quad (1)$$

In Formula (1), $\boldsymbol{\lambda}$ shows X-ray wavelength, $\boldsymbol{\theta}$ shows Bragg's diffraction angle, **m** is a constant value (0.94), and $\boldsymbol{\beta}$ shows full width of half maximum intensity (FWHMI). In this research the average grain size (**S**) in nm of a complex was calculated from the highest peak intensity (Table 5).

3.9. Thermal Analysis

Thermal stability of Co and Ni complexes (compounds **5** and **6**) was studied by TGA. It is an essential technique that has been used to determine the compound's stability [82]. TGA measurements were carried out from room temperature to 1000 °C and obtained curves for the metal complexes are illustrated in Figure 5A,B). Figure 5A presents three decomposition steps for compound **5**. The first miniature weight loss with respect to temprature 31.30 °C probably shows the removal of any moisture present in the sample. After 17 min at the temperature of about 355 °C, 31.46% weight loss was observed (calc. 32.5%), which might be due to the water molecules, OCH_3, $-CH_2$ as well as -OH fragments from the ligand (L''_x). The residual complex was stable upto the temperature 614.20 °C and then decomposed with weight loss 37.11% (calc. 37.1%). This degradation was a little larger than the previous one, because of the removal of cyanide from the coordinated ligand molecules (Figure 5A). Upon further heating, most of the part of the ligand in the form of gases was evaporated and the metal oxide was left as final residue 56.98% (calc. 57.12%) (Figure 5A). Almost similar changes have been observed in Ni L''_x (compound **6**) TGA curve (Figure 5B). However, the stability of intermediate residue is less than compound **5** and the complex gradually decomposes completely at comparatively low temperature. The loss of water molecules and the organic moities results in 26.5% (calc. 27.7%) residue at about 200 °C. The second weight loss 33.6% (32.30%) was observed at 320 °C, again due to the first weightt loss along with the cyanide group from both of the ligands. In last step, the final residue left over 55.7% (calc. 56.4%), because of the Ni^{2+} oxides. The stabilities of other complexes of these transition metals are known and support our findings too [83,84].

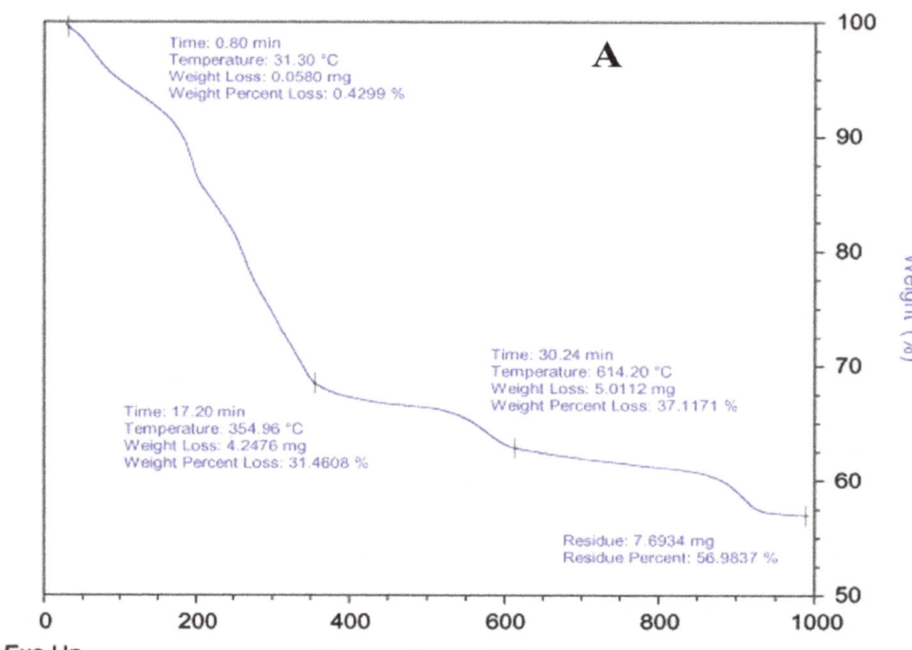

Figure 5. *Cont.*

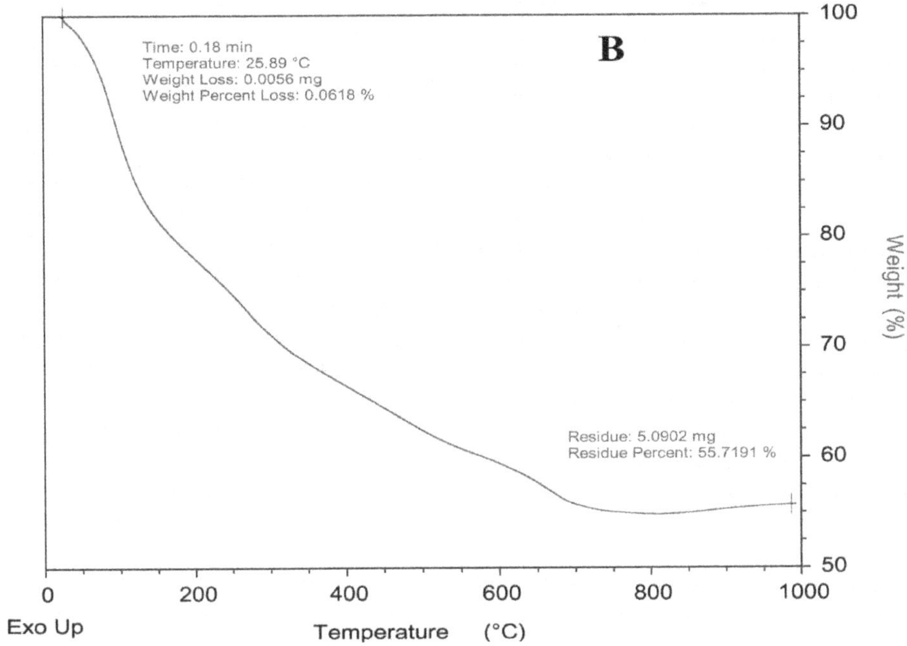

Figure 5. (**A**) Thermo Gravimetric Analysis (TGA) Curve of Compound **5**. (**B**) Thermo Gravimetric Analysis (TGA) Curve of Compound **6**.

3.10. Antibacterial Assay

The antibacterial assay of compounds **3–8** was performed using the agar disc diffusion method [85] against four bacterial strains (*S. aureus*, *E. coli*, *B. pupils*, and *S. typhi*) employing Gentamycin as standard (Table 6). The following relation has been used to calculate the activity index of the tested compounds.

$$\text{Activity index } (\%) = \frac{\text{Inhibition zone of compound (mm)} \times 100}{\text{Inhibition zone of a standard drug (mm)}} \quad (2)$$

Table 6. Antibacterial Activities of Compound **3–8**.

Ligand/Complexes	*S. aureus* (%)	*E. coli* (%)	*B. pumilis* (%)	*S. typhi* (%)
L''_x	(-ve)	83.3	70.3	83.3
CrL''_x	(-ve)	33.1	37	54.1
CoL''_x	57.14	85	51.8	50
NiL''_x	71.4	75	51.8	55
MnL''_x	(-ve)	(-ve)	(-ve)	(-ve)
CuL''_x	(-ve)	(-ve)	(-ve)	(-ve)

Antimicrobial activity, expressed as inhibition zone diameter in millimeters (mm), of compounds **3–8** against pathological strains based on agar well diffusion assays at 1 mg mL^{-1}. The experiment was carried out in triplicate and the average zone of inhibition was calculated. (-ve) = Non active inhibition zone.

L''_x (compound **3**), MnL''_x (compound **7**), and CuL''_x (compound **8**) were found incompetent against the *S. aureus* strain. At the same time, it's CoL''_x and NiL''_x (compounds **5** and **6**) metal complexes presented significant potential, i.e., 57.14% and 71.4%, respectively. This change has been attributed to the coordination of ligands with the metal ions, which enhances the capability to fight against the bacterial pathogenic strain [58,86]. Moreover, compounds **7** & **8** were inactive against all the music selected for this study. All other compounds show at least some activity against these strains with variable potential in each case. It is interesting to notice that compound **5** has a higher inhibition potency toward *E. coli* as compared to L''_x (compound **3**), and NiL''_x complex (compound **6**) has also exhibited fairly well (Figure 6).

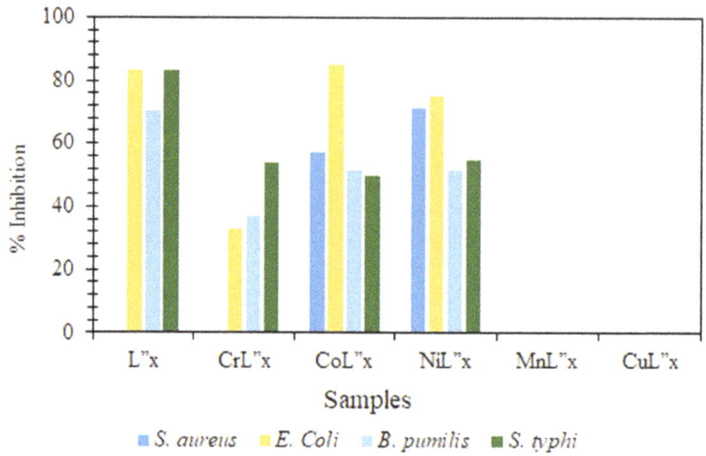

Figure 6. Comparative Histograms Showing Inhibition Zone in Antibacterial Assays of Compounds **3–8**.

3.11. Antioxidant Activity

The synthesized compounds were tested to determine their efficiency as an antioxidant comparable to ascorbic acid as standard by using DPPH (α,α-diphenyl-β-picrylhydrazyl) free radical scavenging method [87]. The potential compounds were mixed with DPPH solution, and absorbance was noted after a definite period. However, with the progression and superiority in instrumental methods, the process has been modified, but the fundamental aspects remain similar [88,89]. The absorbance at 515 nm was measured by spectrophotometer, and radical scavenging activity (%) was determined compared to the methanol-treated control according to the following relation. Where 'E' is the absorbance of the control (extreme). The results of the study have been presented graphically in Figure 7.

$$\text{DPPH scavenging efficiency (\%)} = \frac{[\text{E(radical)} - \text{E(standard)}]}{\text{E(radical)}} \times 100 \quad (3)$$

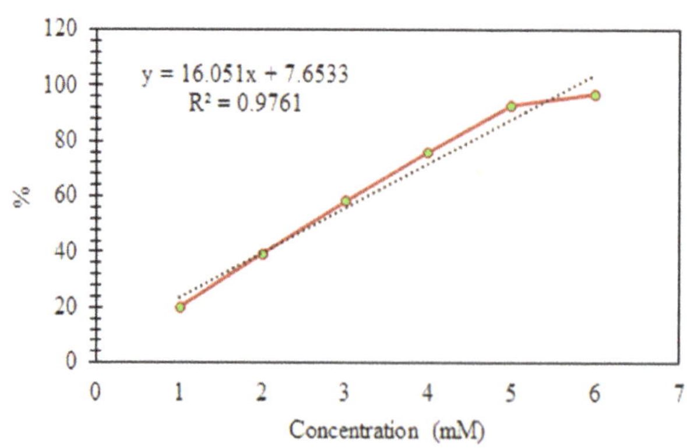

Figure 7. Antioxidant Activities of the Standard (Ascorbic Acid).

The results of compounds **3–8** have been manipulated in Figure 8. Compound **3** contains an alcoholic, an ester functional group, and an aromatic ring in its structure. These types of compounds are known to be exceptionally active in exhibiting antioxidant potential [9,90]. Moreover, the results also signify that compound **3** has the highest antioxidant activity compared to its novel transition metal complexes synthesized here.

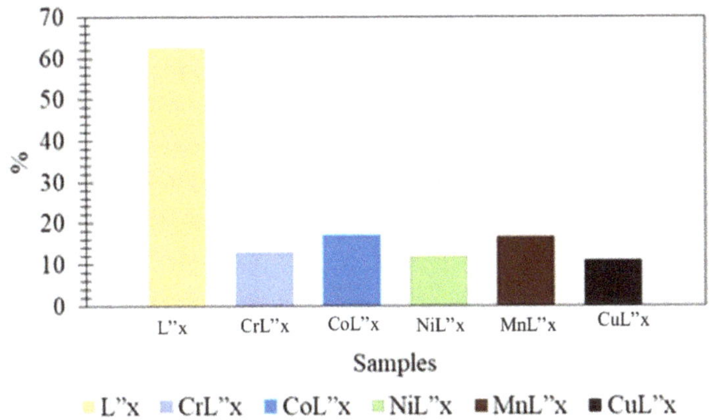

Figure 8. Graphical Representation of Antioxidant Activities of Compounds **3–8**.

3.12. Antifungal Activity

The fungal strains *A. niger*, *A. flavus*, *A. fumigatus*, and *C. albicans* were selected to determine the antifungal potential of compounds **3–8**. The quantitative agar well diffusion method was employed [7] for this purpose, and the results have been reported in Figure 9. Out of these compounds, only compound **3** presented antifungal activity. In contrast, the other compounds were found inactive. The highest activity was achieved against *A. fumigatus* (88.6%). For *C. albicans*, the movement found was 60%, whereas it was 61.90% for *A. niger*. The remaining fungal strains have presented comparatively low percentages.

$$\text{Inhibition of mycelial growth } \% = \frac{\Delta \text{D}}{\text{Dc}} \times 100 \tag{4}$$

where,

ΔD = Dc − Dt
Dc = average diameter of fungal colony in negative control
Dt = average diameter of fungal colony in experimental plates

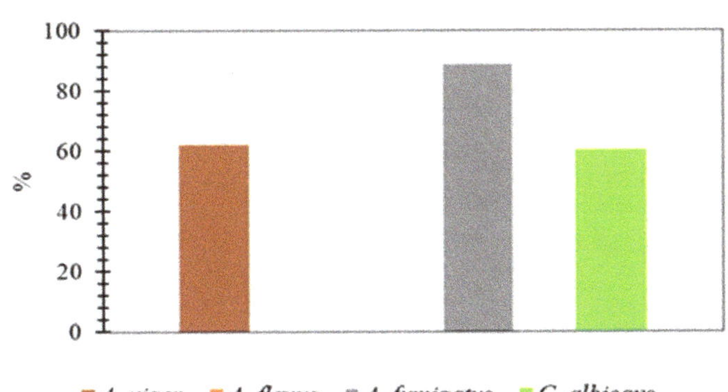

Figure 9. Antifungal Activity of Compound **3** Against Some Fungi.

3.13. Docking Studies

To check the binding ability of the synthesized ligand and its complexes towards certain antibacterial enzymes, molecular docking studies were performed using the ligand-bound crystal structures of *E. coli*, *S. aureus*, and *S. typhi* from PDB. Results from docking studies agree with the obtained antibacterial activities of ligand and metal complexes. Figure 10A–C panels are related to the synthesized MBH adduct ligand (L''_x), CoL''_x, and NiL''_x binding with the ATP active site of *E. coli* DNA gyrase B. The ATPase binding site residues of *E. coli* DNA gyrase B from PDB-ID: 1AJ6 are N46, D73, R76, V120, R136, and T165 and are found to be occupied with the well-known antibacterial compound novobiocin. Ligand (L''_x), CoL''_x, and NiL''_x are found well settled inside the ATPase binding site of *E. coli* DNA gyrase B. Figure 10D is related to the NiL''_x binding with *S. aureus*. The ATPase binding site residues of *S. aureus* DNA-gyrase from PDB-ID: 4URO are S55, A64, N65, V79, D89, T164, and T173 and they were found engaged with novobiocin. NiL''_x is found bound inside the ATPase binding site of *S. aureus* DNA gyrase B. Figure 10E panel is related to the MBH adduct ligand (L''_x) binding with *S. typhi*. The crystal structure presents the CDP-D-glucose 4,6-dehydratase from *S. typhi* complexed with CDP-D-xylose. The substrate binding site residues of *S. typhi* dehydratase from PDB-ID: 1WVG are S134, D135, K136, Y159, N197, and R208. The ligand (L''_x) was found active and occupied the xylose binding site of *S. typhi* dehydratase.

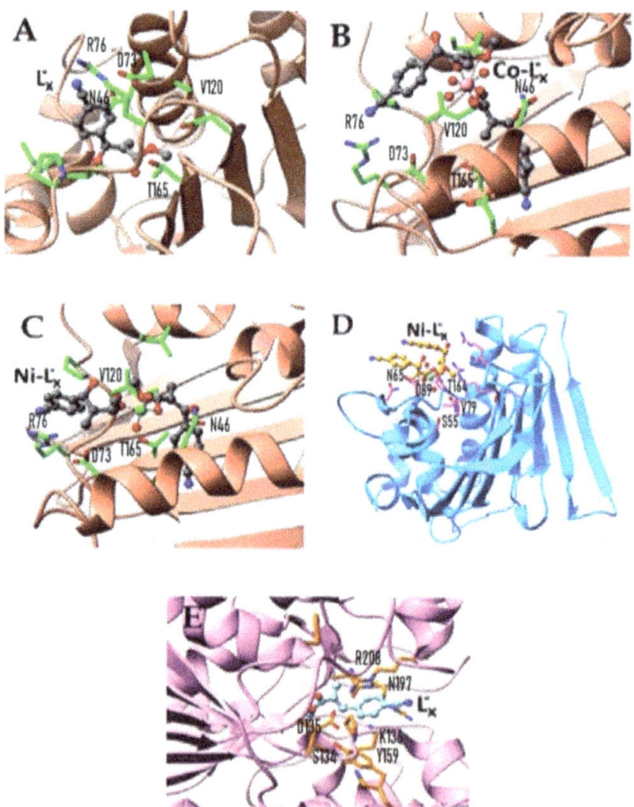

Figure 10. The Binding Conformations of Ligand and Corresponding Metal Complexes Active against (**A–C**) *E. coli*, (**D**) *S. aureaus* and (**E**) *S. typhi*.

4. Conclusions

A well-recognized MBH (Morita-Baylis-Hillman) reaction method has been utilized in the current study to prepare an aromatic adduct, methyl 2-((4-cyanophenyl)(hydroxy)methyl) acrylate (compound **3**) presented in Scheme 1. The prepared ligand was characterized by physical, analytical, and spectral analysis, and its molecular and structural formulas were determined. Moreover, the ligand's geometrical optimization was achieved using DFT B3LYP method and 6-311++ G (d,p) basis set. FT-IR spectrum of the synthesized ligand (L''_x) was resolved computationally and found in good agreement with the observed FT-IR spectrum. The five novel transition metal complexes (Cr^{3+}, Co^{3+}, Ni^{2+}, Mn^{2+}, Cu^{2+}) were synthesized successfully (Scheme 2) by utilizing this bioactive adduct subsequently (compounds **4**–**8**). These metal complexes were further analyzed by physical, analytical, and spectral analyses to confirm their proposed structures. Semi-empirical PM6 optimization and molecular docking studies of metal complexes provided their reasonable geometric shapes and binding conformations well correlated with our experimental findings. The results have suggested that compounds **4** and **5** have four water molecules in respective complexes (Scheme 2). Whereas compounds **6**–**8** have two water molecules in their structures. XRD-Powder diffraction analysis confirmed that all the synthesized metal complexes are crystalline. Additionally, chromium and cobalt metal complexes (compounds **4** and **5**) with the same oxidation state (3+) were found in cubic crystalline nature. Nickel, Manganese, and Copper (oxidation state = 2+) were in the hexagonal, orthorhombic, and monoclinic crystal class, respectively (compounds **6**–**8**). Further, the antibacterial activity has been performed to check the comparative potency of all synthesized compounds (compounds **3**–**8**) in contrast to *S. aureus*, *E. coli*, *B. pumilis*, and *S. typhi* bacterial strains. It was concluded that Cobalt and Nickel complexes (compounds **5** and **6**) exhibited the highest antibacterial potential compared to MBH adduct (L''_x) against *S. aureus* and *E. coli*. Additionally, against the remaining two strains (*B. pumilis* and *S. typhi*) they also showed positive results. However, both ligand (L''_x) and its Chromium-based metal complex (compounds **3** and **4**) are inactive against *S. aureus*, while, active against remaining three bacterial strains (*E. coli*, *B. pumilis* and *S. typhi*). Likewise, our studies demonstrated that both Manganese and Copper-based complexes (compounds **7** and **8**) were non-active against the four selected bacterial strains. In addition, the antioxidant activity (DPPH radical scavenging assay) of compounds **3**–**8** verified the positive inhibition with perspective to the ascorbic acid (standard). Furthermore, it has been observed that the MBH adduct L''_x (compound **3**) is an excellent antifungal drug; besides it, our newly synthesized metal complexes are non-active against these fungal strains (*A. niger*, *A. flavus*, *A. fumigatus*, and *C. albicans*). This research can be continued by synthesizing new MBH adduct ligands and their novel metal complexes to recognize the most suitable drugs as medication in treating infectious disorders.

Author Contributions: Conceptualization, S.I. (Shazia Ishfaq), S.N. and A.S.A.; methodology, S.I. (Shazia Ishfaq) and M.S.J.; software, S.I. (Sadaf Iqbal); validation, A.Q., N.F. and F.A.A.; formal analysis, S.I. (Sadaf Iqbal) and A.S.A.; investigation, S.I. (Shazia Ishfaq) and A.S.A.; resources, A.S.A.; data curation, E.M.T.E.D.; writing—original draft preparation, S.I. (Shazia Ishfaq); writing—review and editing, S.N. and A.S.A.; visualization, F.A.A. and M.S.J.; supervision, S.N.; project administration, P.B. and F.A.A.; funding acquisition, E.M.T.E.D. and M.S.J. All authors have read and agreed to the published version of the manuscript.

Funding: This work was funded by the Researchers Supporting Project Number (RSP-2021/259) King Saud University, Riyadh, Saudi Arabia.

Institutional Review Board Statement: Not applicable.

Informed Consent Statement: Not applicable.

Data Availability Statement: Not applicable.

Acknowledgments: The authors are thankful to University of Karachi for providing research laboratory and other necessary facilities to accomplish this project. We are extremely grateful to School of

Pharmacy University of Karachi, PCSIR laboratories complex-Karachi Pakistan and NED University of Engineering and Technology for their cooperation in TGA, bioactivity studies and XRD analysis. Authors are thankful to the Supercomputing Center of Lanzhou University. This work was funded by the Researchers Supporting Project Number (RSP-2021/259) King Saud University, Riyadh, Saudi Arabia.

Conflicts of Interest: All authors declare that they have no conflict of interest.

References

1. Basavaiah, D.; Rao, K.V.; Reddy, R.J. The Baylis–Hillman Reaction: A Novel Source of Attraction, Opportunities, and Challenges in Synthetic Chemistry. *Chem. Soc. Rev.* **2007**, *36*, 1581–1588. [CrossRef] [PubMed]
2. Junior, C.G.L.; De Assis, P.A.C.; Silva, F.P.L.; Sousa, S.C.O.; De Andrade, N.G.; Barbosa, T.P.; Nerís, P.L.N.; Segundo, L.V.G.; Anjos, Í.C.; Carvalho, G.A.U.; et al. Efficient Synthesis of 16 Aromatic Morita-Baylis-Hillman Adducts: Biological Evaluation on Leishmania Amazonensis and Leishmania Chagasi. *Bioorg. Chem.* **2010**, *38*, 279–284. [CrossRef] [PubMed]
3. Sousa, B.A.; Dos Santos, A.A. A Facile, Versatile, and Mild Morita-Baylis-Hillman-Type Reaction for the Modular One-Pot Synthesis of Highly Functionalized MBH Adducts. *Eur. J. Org. Chem.* **2012**, 3431–3436. [CrossRef]
4. Du, J.; Ma, Y.; Meng, F.; Zhang, R.; Wang, R.; Shi, H.; Wang, Q.; Fan, Y.; Huang, H.; Cui, J.; et al. Lewis Base-Catalyzed [4 + 3] Annulation of Ortho -Quinone Methides and MBH Carbonates: Synthesis of Functionalized Benzo[*b*]Oxepines Bearing Oxindole ScaffOlds. *Org. Lett.* **2019**, *21*, 465–468. [CrossRef]
5. Ketata, E.; Elleuch, H.; Neifar, A.; Mihoubi, W.; Ayadi, W.; Marrakchi, N.; Rezgui, F.; Gargouri, A. Anti-Melanogenesis Potential of a New Series of Morita-Baylis-Hillman Adducts in B16F10 Melanoma Cell Line. *Bioorg. Chem.* **2019**, *84*, 17–23. [CrossRef]
6. Mohan, R.; Rastogi, N.; Namboothiri, I.N.N.; Mobin, S.M.; Panda, D. Synthesis and Evaluation of α-Hydroxymethylated Conjugated Nitroalkenes for Their Anticancer Activity: Inhibition of Cell Proliferation by Targeting Microtubules. *Bioorg. Med. Chem.* **2006**, *14*, 8073–8085. [CrossRef] [PubMed]
7. Lima-Junior, C.G.; Vasconcellos, M.L.A.A. Morita-Baylis-Hillman Adducts: Biological Activities and Potentialities to the Discovery of New Cheaper Drugs. *Bioorg. Med. Chem.* **2012**, *20*, 3954–3971. [CrossRef]
8. Dadwal, M.; Mohan, R.; Panda, D.; Mobin, S.M.; Namboothiri, I.N.N. The Morita-Baylis-Hillman Adducts of β-Aryl Nitroethylenes with Other Activated Alkenes: Synthesis and Anticancer Activity Studies. *Chem. Commun.* **2006**, *3*, 338–340. [CrossRef]
9. Elleuch, H.; Mihoubi, W.; Mihoubi, M.; Ketata, E.; Gargouri, A.; Rezgui, F. Potential Antioxidant Activity of Morita-Baylis-Hillman Adducts. *Bioorg. Chem.* **2018**, *78*, 24–28. [CrossRef]
10. de Souza, R.O.M.A.; Pereira, V.L.P.; Muzitano, M.F.; Falcão, C.A.B.; Rossi-Bergmann, B.; Filho, E.B.A.; Vasconcellos, M.L.A.A. High Selective Leishmanicidal Activity of 3-Hydroxy-2-Methylene-3-(4-Bromophenyl) Propanenitrile and Analogous Compounds. *Eur. J. Med. Chem.* **2007**, *42*, 99–102. [CrossRef]
11. Amarante, G.W.; Cavallaro, M.; Coelho, F. Hyphenating the Curtius Rearrangement with Morita-Baylis-Hillman Adducts: Synthesis of Biologically Active Acyloins and Vicinal Aminoalcohols. *J. Braz. Chem. Soc.* **2011**, *22*, 1568–1584. [CrossRef]
12. Santos, M.S.; Fernandes, D.C.; Rodrigues, M.T.; Regiani, T.; Andricopulo, A.D.; Ruiz, A.L.T.G.; Vendramini-Costa, D.B.; De Carvalho, J.E.; Eberlin, M.N.; Coelho, F. Diastereoselective Synthesis of Biologically Active Cyclopenta[b]Indoles. *J. Org. Chem.* **2016**, *81*, 6626–6639. [CrossRef]
13. Pirovani, R.V.; Ferreira, B.R.V.; Coelho, F. Highly Functionalized Spirocyclohexadienones from Morita-Baylis-Hillman Adducts. *Synlett* **2009**, *14*, 2333–2337. [CrossRef]
14. Calvo, B.C.; Buter, J.; Minnaard, A.J. Applications to the synthesis of natural products. In *Copper-Catalyzed Asymmetric Synthesis*; Wiley Online Library: Hoboken, NJ, USA, 2014; Volume 9783527332, pp. 373–448. [CrossRef]
15. Rabello, A.; Rubinger, M.; Souza, R.; Guilardi, S.; de Lima, G.; Tavares, E.; Zanon, É.; Silva, G.; Zambolim, L.; Ellena, J. Molecular Structure Studies on Allyl Sulfonamides: Synthesis, Theoretical Treatment and Evaluation of Biological Activity. *J. Braz. Chem. Soc.* **2021**, *32*, 2033–2046. [CrossRef]
16. Amarante, G.W.; Cavallaro, M.; Coelho, F. Highly Diastereoselective Total Synthesis of the Anti-Tumoral Agent (±)-Spisulosine (ES285) from a Morita-Baylis-Hillman Adduct. *Tetrahedron Lett.* **2010**, *51*, 2597–2599. [CrossRef]
17. Frezza, M.; Hindo, S.; Chen, D.; Davenport, A.; Schmitt, S.; Tomco, D.; Ping Dou, Q. Novel Metals and Metal Complexes as Platforms for Cancer Therapy. *Curr. Pharm. Des.* **2010**, *16*, 1813–1825. [CrossRef]
18. Hanif, M.; Hartinger, C.G. Anticancer Metallodrugs: Where Is the next Cisplatin? *Future Med. Chem.* **2018**, *10*, 615–617. [CrossRef]
19. Narang, R.; Narasimhan, B.; Sharma, S. A Review on Biological Activities and Chemical Synthesis of Hydrazide Derivatives. *Curr. Med. Chem.* **2012**, *19*, 569–612. [CrossRef]
20. Creaven, B.S.; Egan, D.A.; Kavanagh, K.; McCann, M.; Mahon, M.; Noble, A.; Thati, B.; Walsh, M. Synthesis and Antimicrobial Activity of Copper(II) and Silver(I) Complexes of Hydroxynitrocoumarins: X-Ray Crystal Structures of $[Cu(Hnc)_2(H_2O)_2] \cdot 2H_2O$ and [Ag(Hnc)] (HncH = 4-Hydroxy-3-Nitro-2H-Chromen-2-One). *Polyhedron* **2005**, *24*, 949–957. [CrossRef]
21. Ahmad, S.; Wang, S.; Wu, W.; Yang, K.; Zhang, Y.F.; Tumukunde, E.; Wang, S.; Wang, Y. Functional Analysis of Peptidyl-Prolyl Cis-Trans Isomerase from Aspergillus Flavus. *Int. J. Mol. Sci.* **2019**, *20*, 2206. [CrossRef]

22. Wu, W.Z.; Ahmad, S.; Wang, S.; Zhang, Y.F.; Yang, H.; Wang, S.H.; Wang, Y. Expression and Antibody Preparation of Small Ubiquitin-like Modifier (SUMO) from Aspergillus Flavus. *IOP Conf. Ser. Earth Environ. Sci.* **2019**, *346*. [CrossRef]
23. Abdi, Y.; Bensouilah, N.; Siziani, D.; Hamdi, M.; Silva, A.M.S.; Boutemeur-Kheddis, B. New Complexes of Manganese (II) and Copper (II) Derived from the Two New Furopyran-3, 4-Dione Ligands: Synthesis, Spectral Characterization, ESR, DFT Studies and Evaluation of Antimicrobial Activity. *J. Mol. Struct.* **2020**, *1202*, 127307. [CrossRef]
24. Zhang, C.; Han, X.; Korshin, G.V.; Kuznetsov, A.M.; Yan, M. Interpretation of the Differential UV–Visible Absorbance Spectra of Metal-NOM Complexes Based on the Quantum Chemical Simulations for the Model Compound Esculetin. *Chemosphere* **2021**, *276*, 130043. [CrossRef]
25. Brito, V.B.M.; Santos, G.F.; Silva, T.D.S.; Souza, J.L.C.; Militão, G.C.G.; Martins, F.T.; Silva, F.P.L.; Oliveira, B.G.; Araújo, E.C.C.; Vasconcellos, M.L.A.A.; et al. Synthesis, Anti-Proliferative Activity, Theoretical and 1H NMR Experimental Studies of Morita–Baylis–Hillman Adducts from Isatin Derivatives. *Mol. Divers.* **2020**, *24*, 265–281. [CrossRef] [PubMed]
26. Carrasco-Sanchez, V.; Simirgiotis, M.J.; Santos, L.S. The Morita-Baylis-Hillman Reaction: Insights into Asymmetry and Reaction Mechanisms by Electrospray Ionization Mass Spectrometry. *Molecules* **2009**, *14*, 3989–4021. [CrossRef]
27. da Câmara Rocha, J.; da Franca Rodrigues, K.A.; do Nascimento Néris, P.L.; da Silva, L.V.; Almeida, F.S.; Lima, V.S.; Peixoto, R.F.; da Câmara Rocha, J.; de Azevedo, F.d.L.A.A.; Veras, R.C.; et al. Biological Activity of Morita-Baylis-Hillman Adduct Homodimers in *L. Infantum* and *L. Amazonensis*: Anti-Leishmania Activity and Cytotoxicity. *Parasitol. Res.* **2019**, *118*, 3067–3076. [CrossRef] [PubMed]
28. Liu, S.Y.; Hills, I.D.; Fu, G.C. The First General Method for the Synthesis of Transition-Metal π Complexes of an Electronically Diverse Family of 1,2-Azaborolyls. *Organometallics* **2002**, *21*, 4323–4325. [CrossRef]
29. Aiyelabola, T.; Akinkunmi, E.; Ojo, I.; Obuotor, E.; Adebajo, C.; Isabirye, D. Syntheses, Characterization, Resolution, and Biological Studies of Coordination Compounds of Aspartic Acid and Glycine. *Bioinorg. Chem. Appl.* **2017**, 2956145. [CrossRef]
30. Jeslin Kanaga Inba, P.; Annaraj, B.; Thalamuthu, S.; Neelakantan, M.A. Cu(II), Ni(II), and Zn(II) Complexes of Salan-Type Ligand Containing Ester Groups: Synthesis, Characterization, Electrochemical Properties, and in Vitro Biological Activities. *Bioinorg. Chem. Appl.* **2013**, *2013*. [CrossRef]
31. Kirbag, S.; Erecevit, P.; Zengin, F.; Guvenc, A.N. Antimicrobial Activities of Some Euphorbia Species. *Afr. J. Tradit. Complement. Altern. Med.* **2013**, *10*, 305–309. [CrossRef]
32. Harmon, K.G.; Clugston, J.R.; Dec, K.; Hainline, B.; Herring, S.; Kane, S.F.; Kontos, A.P.; Leddy, J.J.; McCrea, M.; Poddar, S.K.; et al. American Medical Society for Sports Medicine Position Statement on Concussion in Sport. *Br. J. Sports Med.* **2019**, *53*, 213–225. [CrossRef] [PubMed]
33. Rehman, S.; Ikram, M.; Subhan, F.; Sinnokrot, M.; Khan, W. Antibacterial Activities of Transition Metal Complexes of Mesocyclic Amidine 1,4-Diazacycloheptane (DACH). *Open Chem.* **2019**, *17*, 936–942. [CrossRef]
34. Alfredo Rodriguez, V.; Alfredo, V. Formulation of Nanoparticle Systems for Drug Delivery Application in Biomedical Sciences. Master's Thesis, The University of Texas at El Paso, El Paso, TX, USA, 2018.
35. Dawidowicz, A.L.; Wianowska, D.; Olszowy, M. On Practical Problems in Estimation of Antioxidant Activity of Compounds by DPPH Method (Problems in Estimation of Antioxidant Activity). *Food Chem.* **2012**, *131*, 1037–1043. [CrossRef]
36. Surapuram, V.; Setzer, W.N.; McFeeters, R.L.; McFeeters, H. Antifungal Activity of Plant Extracts against Aspergillus Niger and Rhizopus Stolonifer. *Nat. Prod. Commun.* **2014**, *9*, 1603–1605. [CrossRef] [PubMed]
37. Huang, W.; Yan, M.; Duan, H.; Bi, Y.; Cheng, X.; Yu, H. Synergistic Antifungal Activity of Green Synthesized Silver Nanoparticles and Epoxiconazole against Setosphaeria Turcica. *J. Nanomater.* **2020**, 9535432. [CrossRef]
38. Pusnik, M.; Imeri, M.; Deppierraz, G.; Bruinink, A.; Zinn, M. The Agar Diffusion Scratch Assay—A Novel Method to Assess the Bioactive and Cytotoxic Potential of New Materials and Compounds. *Sci. Rep.* **2016**, *6*, 20854. [CrossRef] [PubMed]
39. Frisch, M.J.; Trucks, G.W.; Schlegel, H.B.; Scuseria, G.E.; Robb, M.A.; Cheeseman, J.R.; Scalmani, G.; Barone, V.; Petersson, G.A.; Nakatsuji, H. Gaussian 16 2016. Available online: https://gaussian.com/ (accessed on 18 August 2022).
40. Ahmed, H.; Hashim, A.; Abduljalil, H. Analysis of Structural, Electrical and Electronic Properties of (Polymer Nanocomposites/Silicon Carbide) for Antibacterial Application. *Egypt. J. Chem.* **2019**, *62*, 767–776. [CrossRef]
41. Becke, A.D. The Effect of the Exchange-Only Gradient Gradient Correction. *J. Chem. Phys.* **1992**, *96*, 2155–2160. [CrossRef]
42. Azam, M.; Al-Resayes, S.I.; Alam, M.; Trzesowska-Kruszynska, A.; Kruszynski, R.; Siddiqui, M.R.H. A New Ladder-Type Dichloro(2,2-Dimethyl-1,3-Diaminopropane) Copper Complex: Synthesis, Structural Studies and Selective Sensing Behavior towards a Ketone Molecule. *Polyhedron* **2019**, *170*, 287–293. [CrossRef]
43. Stewart, J.J.P. Optimization of Parameters for Semiempirical Methods V: Modification of NDDO Approximations and Application to 70 Elements. *J. Mol. Model.* **2007**, *13*, 1173–1213. [CrossRef] [PubMed]
44. Holdgate, G.A.; Tunnicliffe, A.; Ward, W.H.J.; Weston, S.A.; Rosenbrock, G.; Barth, P.T.; Taylor, I.W.F.; Pauptit, R.A.; Timms, D. The Entropic Penalty of Ordered Water Accounts for Weaker Binding of the Antibiotic Novobiocin to a Resistant Mutant of DNA Gyrase: A Thermodynamic and Crystallographic Study. *Biochemistry* **1997**, *36*, 9663–9673. [CrossRef] [PubMed]
45. Bommer, M.; Kunze, C.; Fesseler, J.; Schubert, T.; Diekert, G.; Dobbek, H. Structural Basis for Organohalide Respiration. *Science* **2014**, *346*, 455–458. [CrossRef] [PubMed]
46. Koropatkin, N.M.; Holden, H.M. Structure of CDP-D-Glucose 4, 6-Dehydratase from Salmonella Typhi Complexed with CDP-D-Xylose. *Acta Crystallogr. Sect. D Biol. Crystallogr.* **2005**, *61*, 365–373. [CrossRef] [PubMed]

47. Trott, O.; Olson, A.J. AutoDock Vina: Improving the Speed and Accuracy of Docking with a New Scoring Function, Efficient Optimization, and Multithreading. *J. Comput. Chem.* **2010**, *31*, 455–461. [CrossRef] [PubMed]
48. Taft, C.A.; Da Silva, V.B. Current Topics in Computer-aided Drug Design. *J. Pharm. Sci.* **2008**, *97*, 1089–1098. [CrossRef] [PubMed]
49. El-Halim, H.F.A.; Mohamed, G.G.; El-Dessouky, M.M.I.; Mahmoud, W.H. Ligational Behaviour of Lomefloxacin Drug towards Cr(III), Mn(II), Fe(III), Co(II), Ni(II), Cu(II), Zn(II), Th(IV) and UO 2(VI) Ions: Synthesis, Structural Characterization and Biological Activity Studies. *Spectrochim. Acta Part A Mol. Biomol. Spectrosc.* **2011**, *82*, 8–19. [CrossRef] [PubMed]
50. Devi, J.; Batra, N. Synthesis, Characterization and Antimicrobial Activities of Mixed Ligand Transition Metal Complexes with Isatin Monohydrazone Schiff Base Ligands and Heterocyclic Nitrogen Base. *Spectrochim. Acta Part A Mol. Biomol. Spectrosc.* **2015**, *135*, 710–719. [CrossRef] [PubMed]
51. Desnoyer, A.N.; Nicolay, A.; Rios, P.; Ziegler, M.S.; Tilley, T.D. Bimetallics in a Nutshell: Complexes Supported by Chelating Naphthyridine-Based Ligands. *Acc. Chem. Res.* **2020**, *53*, 1944–1956. [CrossRef] [PubMed]
52. Gaber, M.; Khedr, A.M.; Elsharkawy, M. Characterization and Thermal Studies of Nano-Synthesized Mn(II), Co(II), Ni(II) and Cu(II) Complexes with Adipohydrazone Ligand as New Promising Antimicrobial and Antitumor Agents. *Appl. Organomet. Chem.* **2017**, *31*, 1–14. [CrossRef]
53. Köse, D.A. Synthesis and Characterization of Bis(Nicotinamide) m-Hydroxybenzoate Complexes of Co(II), Ni(II), Cu(II), and Zn(II). *Russ. J. Inorg. Chem.* **2007**, *52*, 1384–1390. [CrossRef]
54. Kang, Q.P.; Li, X.Y.; Wang, L.; Zhang, Y.; Dong, W.K. Containing-PMBP N2O2-Donors Transition Metal(II) Complexes: Synthesis, Crystal Structure, Hirshfeld Surface Analyses and Fluorescence Properties. *Appl. Organomet. Chem.* **2019**, *33*, e5013. [CrossRef]
55. Bruijnincx, P.C.; Sadler, P.J. New Trends for Metal Complexes with Anticancer Activity. *Curr. Opin. Chem. Biol.* **2008**, *12*, 197–206. [CrossRef] [PubMed]
56. Kumar, S. Spectroscopy of Organic Compounds. *Dept. Chem.* **2006**, *66*, 1–36.
57. Shaghaghi, Z. Spectroscopic Properties of Some New Azo–Azomethine Ligands in the Presence of Cu^{2+}, Pb^{2+}, Hg^{2+}, Co^{2+}, Ni^{2+}, Cd^{2+} and Zn^{2+} and Their Antioxidant Activity. *Spectrochim. Acta Part A Mol. Biomol. Spectrosc.* **2014**, *131*, 67–71. [CrossRef] [PubMed]
58. Khan, M.I.; Khan, A.; Hussain, I.; Khan, M.A.; Gul, S.; Iqbal, M.; Inayat-Ur-Rahman; Khuda, F. Spectral, XRD, SEM and Biological Properties of New Mononuclear Schiff Base Transition Metal Complexes. *Inorg. Chem. Commun.* **2013**, *35*, 104–109. [CrossRef]
59. Sundaraganesan, N.; Kalaichelvan, S.; Meganathan, C.; Joshua, B.D.; Cornard, J. FT-IR, FT-Raman Spectra and Ab Initio HF and DFT Calculations of 4-N,N′-Dimethylamino Pyridine. *Spectrochim. Acta Part A Mol. Biomol. Spectrosc.* **2008**, *71*, 898–906. [CrossRef] [PubMed]
60. Karabacak, M.; Cinar, M.; Kurt, M.; Sundaraganesan, N. Experimental and Theoretical FTIR and FT-Raman Spectroscopic Analysis of 1-Pyrenecarboxylic Acid. *Spectrochim. Acta Part A Mol. Biomol. Spectrosc.* **2013**, *114*, 509–519. [CrossRef] [PubMed]
61. Aiyelabola, T.; Akinkunmi, E.; Obuotor, E.; Olawuni, I.; Isabirye, D.; Jordaan, J. Synthesis Characterization and Biological Activities of Coordination Compounds of 4-Hydroxy-3-Nitro-2H-Chromen-2-One and Its Aminoethanoic Acid and Pyrrolidine-2-Carboxylic Acid Mixed Ligand Complexes. *Bioinorg. Chem. Appl.* **2017**, *2017*, 6426747. [CrossRef] [PubMed]
62. Anacona, J.R.; Santaella, J.; Al-shemary, R.K.R.; Amenta, J.; Otero, A.; Ramos, C.; Celis, F. Ceftriaxone-Based Schiff Base Transition Metal(II) Complexes. Synthesis, Characterization, Bacterial Toxicity, and DFT Calculations. Enhanced Antibacterial Activity of a Novel Zn(II) Complex against *S. aureus* and *E. coli*. *J. Inorg. Biochem.* **2021**, *223*, 111519. [CrossRef] [PubMed]
63. Manolov, I.; Kostova, I.; Netzeva, T.; Konstantinov, S.; Karaivanova, M. Cytotoxic Activity of Cerium Complexes with Coumarin Derivatives. Molecular Modeling of the Ligands. *Arch. der Pharm. Int. J. Pharm. Med. Chem.* **2000**, *333*, 93–98. [CrossRef]
64. Abdel-Monem, Y.K.; Abou El-Enein, S.A.; El-Sheikh-Amer, M.M. Design of New Metal Complexes of 2-(3-Amino-4,6-Dimethyl-1H-Pyrazolo[3,4-b]Pyridin-1-Yl)Aceto-Hydrazide: Synthesis, Characterization, Modelling and Antioxidant Activity. *J. Mol. Struct.* **2017**, *1127*, 386–396. [CrossRef]
65. Singh, S.K.; Eng, J.; Atanasov, M.; Neese, F. Covalency and Chemical Bonding in Transition Metal Complexes: An Ab Initio Based Ligand Field Perspective. *Coord. Chem. Rev.* **2017**, *344*, 2–25. [CrossRef]
66. Xu, F.; Huang, W.; You, X.Z. Novel Cyano-Bridged Mixed-Valent Copper Complexes Formed by Completely in Situ Synthetic Method via the Cleavage of C-C Bond in Acetonitrile. *Dalt. Trans.* **2010**, *39*, 10652–10658. [CrossRef] [PubMed]
67. Martí-Rujas, J. Structural Elucidation of Microcrystalline MOFs from Powder X-Ray Diffraction. *Dalt. Trans.* **2020**, *49*, 13897–13916. [CrossRef] [PubMed]
68. Tavares, E.C.; Rubinger, M.M.M.; Filho, E.V.; Oliveira, M.R.L.; Piló-Veloso, D.; Ellena, J.; Guilardi, S.; Souza, R.A.C.; Zambolim, L. Tetraphenylphosphonium Allyldithiocarbimates Derived from Morita-Baylis-Hillman Adducts: Synthesis, Characterization, Crystal Structure and Antifungal Activity. *J. Mol. Struct.* **2016**, *1106*, 130–140. [CrossRef]
69. Amarante, G.W.; Milagre, H.M.S.; Vaz, B.G.; Ferreira, B.R.V.; Eberlin, M.N.; Coelho, F. Dualistic Nature of the Mechanism of the Morita-Baylis-Hillman Reaction Probed by Electrospray Ionization Mass Spectrometry. *J. Org. Chem.* **2009**, *74*, 3031–3037. [CrossRef] [PubMed]
70. Szabó, P.T.; Kele, Z. Electrospray Mass Spectrometry of Hydrophobic Compounds Using Dimethyl Sulfoxide and Dimethylformamide as Solvents. *Rapid Commun. Mass Spectrom.* **2001**, *15*, 2415–2419. [CrossRef]
71. Borges, V.; Henion, J. Determination of Pharmaceutical Compounds in Aqueous Dimethyl Sulfoxide by Electrospray Ionization Mass Spectrometry. *Rapid Commun. Mass Spectrom.* **2005**, *19*, 415–423. [CrossRef]

72. Saad, F.A. Synthesis, Spectral, Electrochemical and X-Ray Single Crystal Studies on Ni(II) and Co(II) Complexes Derived from 1-Benzoyl-3-(4-Methylpyridin-2-Yl) Thiourea. *Spectrochim. Acta Part A Mol. Biomol. Spectrosc.* **2014**, *128*, 386–392. [CrossRef] [PubMed]
73. Şahin, Ö.; Özdemir, Ü.Ö.; Seferoğlu, N.; Genc, Z.K.; Kaya, K.; Aydıner, B.; Tekin, S.; Seferoğlu, Z. New Platinum (II) and Palladium (II) Complexes of Coumarin-Thiazole Schiff Base with a Fluorescent Chemosensor Properties: Synthesis, Spectroscopic Characterization, X-Ray Structure Determination, in Vitro Anticancer Activity on Various Human Carcinoma Ce. *J. Photochem. Photobiol. B Biol.* **2018**, *178*, 428–439. [CrossRef] [PubMed]
74. Atalay, V.E.; Ölüç, I.B.; Karahan, M. Modeling of BSA–Metal Ion-Acrylic Acid Complex by Theoretical Methods: Semi-Empirical PM6 and Docking Study. *Acta Phys. Pol. A* **2018**, *134*, 1200–1203. [CrossRef]
75. Pourjavid, M.R.; Sehat, A.A.; Arabieh, M.; Yousefi, S.R.; Hosseini, M.H.; Rezaee, M. Column Solid Phase Extraction and Flame Atomic Absorption Spectrometric Determination of Manganese(II) and Iron(III) Ions in Water, Food and Biological Samples Using 3-(1-Methyl-1H-Pyrrol-2-Yl)-1H-Pyrazole-5-Carboxylic Acid on Synthesized Graphene Oxide. *Mater. Sci. Eng. C* **2014**, *35*, 370–378. [CrossRef] [PubMed]
76. Abdel-Mottaleb, M.S.A.; Ismail, E.H. A Combined Experimental and Modelling Investigations on Mixed Bioligand Complexes of Divalent Cobalt and Copper in β-Cyclodextrin. *Appl. Organomet. Chem.* **2020**, *34*, e5280. [CrossRef]
77. Mahapatra, B.B.; Mishra, R.R.; Sarangi, A.K. Synthesis, Characterisation, XRD, Molecular Modelling and Potential Antibacterial Studies of Co(II), Ni(II), Cu(II), Zn(II), Cd(II) and Hg(II) Complexes with Bidentate Azodye Ligand. *J. Saudi Chem. Soc.* **2016**, *20*, 635–643. [CrossRef]
78. Bouhdada, M.; Amane, M.E.L.; El Hamzaoui, N. Synthesis, Spectroscopic Studies, X-Ray Powder Diffraction Data and Antibacterial Activity of Mixed Transition Metal Complexes with Sulfonate Azo Dye, Sulfamate and Caffeine Ligands. *Inorg. Chem. Commun.* **2019**, *101*, 32–39. [CrossRef]
79. Shukla, K.; Mishra, A.; Sharma, P. Synthesis, Characterization, XRD and EXAFS Studies of Fe(III) Complexes. *AIP Conf. Proc.* **2019**, *2100*, 020163. [CrossRef]
80. Prescimone, A.; Morien, C.; Allan, D.; Schlueter, J.A.; Tozer, S.W.; Manson, J.L.; Parsons, S.; Brechin, E.K.; Hill, S. Pressure-Driven Orbital Reorientations and Coordination-Sphere Reconstructions in [$CuF_2(H_2O)_2$(Pyz)]. *Angew. Chem.* **2012**, *124*, 7608–7612. [CrossRef]
81. Sinthuja, S.A.; Shaji, Y.C.; Rose, G.L. Synthesis, Characterization and Evaluation of Biological Properties of Transition Metal Chelates with Schiff Base Ligands Derived from Glutaraldehyde with L-Leucine. *IJSRST* **2018**, *4*, 587–593.
82. Sharfalddin, A.A.; Emwas, A.H.; Jaremko, M.; Hussien, M.A. Transition Metal Complexes of 6-Mercaptopurine: Characterization, Theoretical Calculation, DNA-Binding, Molecular Docking, and Anticancer Activity. *Appl. Organomet. Chem.* **2021**, *35*, e6041. [CrossRef]
83. Neha, M.; Biplab, M. TGA Analysis of Transition Metal Complexes Derived from Phenothiazine Ligands Introduction. *Int. J. Sci. Eng. Res.* **2018**, *6*, 47–57.
84. Mohammed Shafeeulla, R.; Krishnamurthy, G.; Bhojynaik, H.S.; Shivarudrappa, H.P.; Shiralgi, Y. Spectral Thermal Cytotoxic and Molecular Docking Studies of N′-2-Hydroxybenzoyl; Pyridine-4-Carbohydrazide Its Complexes. *Beni-Suef Univ. J. Basic Appl. Sci.* **2017**, *6*, 332–344. [CrossRef]
85. Kavitha, B.; Sravanthi, M.; Saritha Reddy, P. DNA Interaction, Docking, Molecular Modelling and Biological Studies of o-Vanillin Derived Schiff Base Metal Complexes. *J. Mol. Struct.* **2019**, *1185*, 153–167. [CrossRef]
86. Abu-Dief, A.M.; Abdel-Rahman, L.H.; Abdelhamid, A.A.; Marzouk, A.A.; Shehata, M.R.; Bakheet, M.A.; Almaghrabi, O.A.; Nafady, A. Synthesis and Characterization of New Cr(III), Fe(III) and Cu(II) Complexes Incorporating Multi-Substituted Aryl Imidazole Ligand: Structural, DFT, DNA Binding, and Biological Implications. *Spectrochim. Acta Part A Mol. Biomol. Spectrosc.* **2020**, *228*, 117700. [CrossRef] [PubMed]
87. Flieger, J.; Flieger, M. The [DPPH•/DPPH-H]-HPLC-DAD Method on Tracking the Antioxidant Activity of Pure Antioxidants and Goutweed (*Aegopodium podagraria* L.) Hydroalcoholic Extracts. *Molecules* **2020**, *25*, 6005. [CrossRef]
88. Ortiz, R.; Antilén, M.; Speisky, H.; Aliaga, M.E.; López-Alarcón, C.; Baugh, S. Application of a Microplate-Based Orac-Pyrogallol Red Assay for the Estimation of Antioxidant Capacity: First Action 2012.03. *J. AOAC Int.* **2012**, *95*, 1558–1561. [CrossRef]
89. Tsai, C.E.; Lin, L.H. DPPH Scavenging Capacity of Extracts from Camellia Seed Dregs Using Polyol Compounds as Solvents. *Heliyon* **2019**, *5*, e02315. [CrossRef]
90. Gülçin, I. Antioxidant Activity of Food Constituents: An Overview. *Arch. Toxicol.* **2012**, *86*, 345–391. [CrossRef]

separations

MDPI

Article

Ethyl Acetate Extract of *Dracocephalum heterophyllum* Benth Ameliorates Nonalcoholic Steatohepatitis and Fibrosis via Regulating Bile Acid Metabolism, Oxidative Stress and Inhibiting Inflammation

Yan Fang [1,2,†], Dandan Sun [3,4,†], Gang Li [2], Yue Lv [2], Jia Li [3], Qilan Wang [1,*] and Jun Dang [1,*]

1 Qinghai Provincial Key Laboratory of Tibetan Medicine Research, Key Laboratory of Tibetan Medicine Research, Northwest Institute of Plateau Biology, Chinese Academy of Sciences, Xining 810001, China
2 Center for Mitochondria and Healthy Aging, College of Life Sciences, Yantai University, Yantai 264005, China
3 School of Chinese Materia Medica, Nanjing University of Chinese Medicine, Nanjing 210023, China
4 State Key Laboratory of Drug Research, Shanghai Institute of Materia Medica, Chinese Academy of Sciences, Shanghai 201203, China
* Correspondence: wql@nwipb.cas.cn (Q.W.); dangjun@nwipb.cas.cn (J.D.)
† These authors contributed equally to this work.

Abstract: *Dracocephalum heterophyllum* Benth is well-known for its ability to alleviate liver heat. In this study, *Dracocephalum heterophyllum* Benth ethyl acetate extracts were evaluated on mouse models of nonalcoholic steatohepatitis and liver fibrosis. After 6 and 8 weeks of treatment, serum parameters and gene expressions in tissue samples, as well as stained tissue sections, demonstrated that the ethyl acetate extracts were effective in treating these liver diseases. The principal bioactive constituent (rosmarinic acid) was identified and screened by high pressure liquid chromatography-1,1-diphenyl-2-picrylhydrazyl and affinity ultrafiltration-HPLC. The rosmarinic acid was separated from extracts with high purity by medium- and high-pressure liquid chromatography. Finally, the interactions between rosmarinic acid and the key targets of lipid metabolism, oxidative stress and inflammation were verified by molecular docking. Thereby, an indirect regulation of lipid and cholesterol metabolism and inhibition of liver inflammation and liver fibrosis by the studied extract has been observed. This study demonstrated that *Dracocephalum heterophyllum* Benth ethyl acetate extracts have the potential to treat nonalcoholic steatohepatitis and liver fibrosis, revealing their multi-target and multi-pathway therapeutic characteristics.

Keywords: *Dracocephalum heterophyllum* benth; preparative separation; nonalcoholic steatohepatitis; liver fibrosis; molecular docking

1. Introduction

Nonalcoholic steatohepatitis (NASH) has been established as a chronic progressive nonalcoholic fatty liver disease (NAFLD) [1]. NASH occurs when the metabolism of fatty acids and the export of lipids are impaired [2–4]. The pathological mechanism of NASH is insufficiently explored, and there is no established treatment available for it. NASH-related clinical drugs result in the reduction of hepatocyte steatosis and the activation of hepatic stellate cells, which then inhibit the extracellular matrix synthesis [5,6]. Both inflammation and oxidative stress, as pivotal initiating and promoting factors for NASH and liver fibrosis, can certainly be selected as significant targets for the treatment [7,8], as metabolites produced by organisms through the evolutionary process of the survival of the fittest, natural products (NPs) have long been an indispensable resource for the development of new therapies [9–13].

Dracocephalum heterophyllum Benth (*D. heterophyllum*) is a traditional Tibetan medicine commonly used in ethnic areas. Its Tibetan name is "Jizi Qingbao". Jizi Qingbao represents the dry aerial part of the labiatae plant *Dracocephalum heterophyllum* Benth. In the Tibetan medicine system, it has a wide therapeutic application in the treatment of jaundice hepatitis, mouth ulcers, and other diseases [14,15]. According to findings in Jingzhu Materia Medica, this plant was reported to treat oral and dental diseases. Stappen et al. reported other pharmacological effects of *D. heterophyllum* such as anti-hypertension, cardiovascular protection and antiviral [16]. However, its effect on NASH and liver fibrosis is remaining elusive. Therefore, elucidating further mechanisms underlying its hepatoprotective activity remains a goal for future studies.

The traditional techniques for the isolation and purification of plant-derived compounds, namely column chromatography, in which gels (including sephadex, sepharose) and silica gel are used, are not suitable for the separation of high-purity standards. The key reason for the limitation of these techniques is that different compounds have different molecular weights or different capacities for adsorbing on silica gel [17]. On-line HPLC-1,1-diphenyl-2-picrylhydrazyl (HPLC-DPPH) is a technique for the current investigation and assessment of the antioxidant activity of separate components in multi-complex medicinal herbs. DPPH is a stable radical that can chemically interact with the reactive hydrogen of antioxidant substances and change their chemical structure [18]. The affinity ultrafiltration-HPLC coupling method uses an ultrafiltration technique to separate ligand-target complexes in the solution [19].

Molecular docking is an effective method enabling the study of the interactions between molecules, especially biomolecular complexes, which offer great insights in terms of binding conformation, site, and force of ligands and receptors [20]. With the fast progress of investigating computer simulation technology, the molecular docking technique has turned into an effective means for the interaction between proteins and small molecules. Molecular docking is composed of the following three components: identification of binding sites, an algorithm of conformational search, and a scoring function [21,22]. This gives molecular docking a tremendous value in terms of enhancing the effectiveness of virtual screening and minimizing the cost of drug development.

In the current study, acetyl acetate extracts of *D. heterophyllum* were prepared. Next, the methionine-choline deficient (MCD)-induced mouse NASH and CCl_4-induced liver fibrosis models were established to test the bioactivity of *D. heterophyllum*-derived acetyl acetate extracts on them. According to the obtained results, these extracts significantly improved liver function. Considering the importance of oxidative stress and inflammatory response in the development of NASH and liver fibrosis, DPPH and cyclooxygenase-2 (COX-2) were used as activity-directed compounds to rapidly determine the key constituents in the ethyl acetate extract of *D. heterophyllum*. Interestingly, the main component was found to be the functional component by HPLC-DPPH and the affinity ultrafiltration-HPLC screening. Subsequently, the main component was successfully isolated with >99% purity. We also managed to predict the key targets of rosmarinic acid against NASH and liver fibrosis by employing molecular docking. The combined analysis demonstrated that the enrichment of the main functional component of *D. heterophyllum* was achieved rapidly and efficiently by combining traditional extraction and medium- and high-pressure liquid chromatography. The findings of this study provide a framework for future quality control investigations and the expansion of *D. heterophyllum's* usefulness.

2. Materials and Methods

2.1. Apparatus and Reagents

Two prep-HPLC pumps from the NP7000 series, an NU3000 detector that detects in the UV-Vis range, and a manual 5 mL injector, were the main parts of the preparative MPC workstation (Hanbon Science & Technology Co., Ltd., Jiangsu, China) that were used for this study. A degasser DGU-20A_{3R} was utilized for the removal of gas in the samples, after which the Shimadzu Essentia LC-16A instrument enabled the performance of the HPLC analysis, which was supplied with an additional two tools such as a column thermostat and autosampler. ESI-MS spectra were obtained on the Agilent 6500 series

Q-TOF mass spectrometer. Using deuterated methanol as a solvent, the ^{1}H and ^{13}C nuclear magnetic resonance (NMR) spectroscopic data were recorded on the Bruker Avance NMR spectrometer at 600 MHz. Multimode Microplate Reader was purchased from Molecular Devices (Shanghai, China), while the BioMajesty® JCA-BM6010/C was supplied by the Sysmex (Wuxi, China). An automated quantitative pathology imaging system was purchased from PerkinElmer (Shanghai, China). Furthermore, the fluorescence quantitative PCR instrument was supplied by the Agilent Technologies (Palo Alto, CA, USA).

The MCD diet was provided by Research Diets (New Brunswick, NJ, USA). Concerning carbon tetrachloride (CCl_4), carboxymethylcellulose sodium (CMC-Na) and olive oil were obtained from the manufacturer Sinopharm Chemical Reagent Co., Ltd., Shanghai, China. RNAiso plus and PrimScriptTM RT Master Mix were obtained from the Takara Biomedical Technology, Co., Ltd. (Beijing, China). The dye synergy brand Green was purchased from Vazyme Medical Technology (Nanjing, China). Moreover, the aspartate aminotransferase (AST) test reagent R2 and alanine aminotransferase (ALT) w test reagent R1 were purchased from Sysmex (Wuxi, China). Shanghai FosunLong March Medical Science Co., Ltd. (Shanghai, China) provided the cholesterol and triglyceride total test regent kits. The Biotechnology company Shanghai Kehua bio-engineering (Shanghai, China) provided the total bile acid (TBA) and hydroxyproline (HYP) test regent kits. The separation material series MCI GEL® CHP20P (120 μm) was bought from a company named Mitsubishi Chemical Corporation (Tokyo, Japan). 7-X10 analytical and preparation columns were obtained from ACCHROM (Beijing, China). SunFire column was from Waters Corporation (Milford, MA, USA). Preparative and high-grade MeOH, EtOH, and ethyl acetate were from China KELON (Chengdu, China). Cyclooxygenase 2 was from Sigma-Aldrich (St. Louis, MO, USA) and PBS from Solarbio Science & Technology Co. Ltd. (Beijing, China). The ultrafiltration membranes (YM-30, 30 kDa) were from Millipore Co. Ltd. (Burlington, MA, USA). Moreover, the DPPH was purchased from Sigma–Aldrich (Steinheim, Germany). Moore Water Purifier was applied for ultra-pure HPLC water (Chongqing, China).

2.2. Sample Preparation

D. heterophyllum plants were collected from the North Mountain in Huzhu, Qinghai (2488 m, 36°50′15″ N, 101°57′06″ E) and were identified as *D. heterophyllum* by Prof. Lijuan Mei, Northwest Plateau Institute of Biology, Chinese Academy of Sciences. The sample (nwipb-2016-10-10) was preserved at the Tibetan Medicine Research Lab, Northwest Plateau Institute of Biology, Chinese Academy of Sciences.

The plant samples were air-dried and ground (8.6 kg) in a cool place. The extraction was followed with 95% of ethanol three times (3 h/each, material-liquid ratio: 1:5). The filtrates were combined, evaporated, and concentrated under reduced pressure to obtain 1026.00 g of ethanol crude extract (yield 11.93%), then diluted with a small amount of water (about 500 mL). Triple extractions for 2 h each with an equivalent volume of ethyl acetate were conducted, followed by drying to obtain the ethyl acetate extraction (132 g, yield 1.53%). The extract activity was evaluated on 32 g of the extracts. The remaining 100 g was mixed in methanol-water (1:1 v/v) and 170 g of silica gel (270 g in total) for subsequent isolation and purification.

2.3. Design and Treatment of Animal Experiments

Animal experimentations were permitted by the Animal Care and Use Committee affiliated with the Shanghai Institute of Materia Medica with approval number 2017-10-LJ-53 and 2018-11-LJ-66. Animal experiments were performed following the National Institutes of Health Guide for the Care and Use of Laboratory Animals (NIH Publication No. 85-23, revised in 1985). C57BL/6J males (Shanghai Lingchang Biotechnology Unit) were bred under controlled conditions, on a balanced diet for one week at a room temperature of 22 ± 2 °C, with normal circadian rhythm (12/12 h light/dark cycles), water use, and access to adequate food guaranteed.

2.3.1. Mouse MCD-Induced NASH Models

A standard diet or MCD (21% fat, 63% carbohydrate, and 16% protein, Research Diets Inc, A02082002BR) was fed to mice (10 weeks old). After 2 weeks, the animals were distributed into 5 groups (10 mice each): control (standard regime), vehicle (MCD diet and supplemented with the vehicle), and *D. heterophyllum* (DH) treatment group (MCD diet plus 240 mg/kg DH). Blood samples were collected from these animals after 2 or 4 weeks of treatment followed by a precise dissection and the weight of the levers. A portion of liver tissues was immediately frozen in liquid nitrogen and stored at −80 °C. Another part was preserved in 4% paraformaldehyde for further analysis.

2.3.2. Mouse CCl_4-Induced Liver Fibrosis Models

Mice at 8 weeks of age were intraperitoneally administrated 3 times/weekly with 10% CCl_4 (dissolved in olive oil, 2 mL/kg body weight) to cause liver fibrosis. Two weeks later these CCl_4-treated mice were divided into four groups of 10 mice each: the vehicle group (CCl_4 plus vehicle for 6 weeks), and the DH treatment (MCD diet and supplementation with 200 mg/kg, 400 mg/kg DH). The mice (n = 10) in the control cohort were treated with olive oil only. Blood samples were gathered 3- or 6-weeks post-treatment. Livers were precisely separated, pondered, frozen in liquid nitrogen, and stowed at −80 °C. Some of the biopsies were partly fixed in 4% paraformaldehyde for further analysis.

2.3.3. Testing Indicators and Methods

Basic Indicators

Body weight and wet liver weight were acquired by weighing them before and after sampling. The liver index was calculated following the formula: liver wet weight (g)/body weight (g) × 100%.

Biochemical Analysis

The Sysmex JCA-BM6010C measured the blood serum concentration of ALT, AST, triglycerides (TG), total cholesterol (TC) and TBA. Liver TG, TC, and Hyp concentrations were evaluated by a Folch withdrawal. The dehydrated lipid remainders were mixed in 800 μL of EtOH with 1% Triton X-100. The TG, TC, TBA, and Hyp contents were assayed under the instructions of the kits.

Quantitative Real-Time PCR

The total RNA was extracted from the livers by the TRIzol method (Invitrogen, Waltham, MA, USA). RNA samples were then reverse-transcribed using the PrimeScript Reverse Transcriptase kit (Takara). The cDNA amplification was carried out by 2 × SYBR Green qPCR Master Mix (Vazyme) and at a Stratagene Mx3005P PCR (Agilent Technologies). The housekeeping GAPDH gene is an internal standard. PCR primer pairs are shown in Table 1.

Table 1. Primer sequence for mice.

Gene	Forward Primer (5′-3′)	Reverse Primer (5′-3′)
α-SMA	CTGACAGAGGCACCACTGAA	CATCTCCAGAGTCCAGCACA
Col1α1	GAGCGGAGAGTACTGGATCG	TACTCGAACGGGAATCCATC
CD68	TACATGGCGGTGGAGTACAA	AGGTGGACAGCTGGTGAAAG
MCP-1	ACTGCATCTGCCCTAAGGTCT	AGGCATCACAGTCCGAGTCA
Col1α1	TGCCGTGACCTCAAGATGTG	CACAAGCGTGCTGTAGGTGA
GAPDH	TCTCCTGCGACTTCAACA	TGGTCCAGGGTTTCTTACT

Histological Analysis

Liver biopsies were paraffinized and were preserved in 4% paraformaldehyde for two days and fixed in paraffin. Hematoxylin-eosin (H&E)-staining and Sirius red dying followed.

H&E-stained paraffin samples were quantified for the NAFLD activity score (NAS). Data quantitation was conducted with the PerkinElmer software (Version, Shanghai, China).

2.4. DPPH Inhibitor Recognition and Screening of Anti-Inflammatory Active Component

DPPH inhibitors in the studied plant extracts of *D. heterophyllum* were evaluated with an online HPLC-DPPH technique. The technique was conducted on an analytical 7-X10 (4.6 × 250 mm, 5 μm) chromatographic column. MeOH (mobile phase B) was prepared in 0.1% *v*/*v* aqueous formic acid (HCOOH, mobile phase A) and was linearly increased from 0% B to 100% B by a gradient elution for 60 min. The eluate speed was 1.0 mL/min at an injection volume of 2 μL. DPPH (50 μg/mL) was applied in EtOH at a flow speed of 0.8 mL/min for post-column derivatization. The absorbance at 517 nm was observed.

Affinity ultrafiltration-HPLC-based evaluation of *D. heterophyllum* ethyl acetate extracts for potential anti-inflammatory active components was conducted by weighing 10.00 mg of *D. heterophyllum* ethyl acetate extracts, which were then dissolved in PBS (1 mL, pH 7.2). The sample solution (120 μL) was mixed with 200 μL COX-2 (2 U) in an incubator shaker for 30 min at 37 °C. The mixture was centrifuged at 12,000 rpm for 10 min and resuspended three times with PBS (200 μL). The filtrate was gathered to eliminate unbound ligands. The COX-2-linked ligand was unconstrained from the composite after mixing with MeOH (200 uL, 90%, *v*/*v*) for 10 min at room temperature and centrifuged at the same conditions described above. This step was performed in triplicate and the remains were gathered. It was desiccated by low temperature and dissolved in high-grade MeOH (50 μL). HPLC analyses followed. In the negative control samples, the enzyme was deactivated at 95 °C for 10 min, and the operation steps were the same as above. The relative binding affinity (RBA) was calculated following the formula:

$$\text{RBA} = A_1/A_2$$

where A_1 is the peak area of the sample with the activated enzyme and A_2 is the peak area of the sample with the inactivated enzyme.

Compounds with an RBA > 1.5 were taken as compounds' possible ligands for the enzyme.

2.5. Medium- and High-Pressure Liquid Chromatography Separation of the Main Functional Component from the Ethyl Acetate Extraction

The dried plant mixture (90.00 g) was mounted onto a small medium-pressure chromatography pylon (49 × 100 mm) and prepared in series with a medium-pressure chromatography column (49 × 460 mm) containing 1.2 L MCI GEL CHP20P stationary phase for dry sample charging. The elution was carried out with a MeOH/water system for 320 min. Isocratic elution with 0% MeOH was performed from 0 to 35 min, followed by gradient elution with increasing percentages of MeOH from 0 to 100% from 35 to 195 min, and finally with an isocratic elution of 100% MeOH for 125 min. A constant flow rate of 57.0 mL/min was applied. Next, the elution was observed by monitoring the absorbance at 210 nm. The process was conducted in triplicates at room temperature and finally, the mixture was concentrated and dried to yield a total of 5 fractions.

Furthermore, HPLC analysis demonstrated that the major functional component of the ethyl acetate extraction of *D. heterophyllum* was present in Fr3 (7.06 g with 7.06% recovery). For further preparative purification, the sample was mixed with MeOH/water solution and sieved through organic filter membranes (0.45 μm). Chromatographic conditions for HPLC have been described above in Section 2.5.

2.6. Purity and Activity Analysis of the Isolated Main Functional Component in the Studied Extracts

The purity and activity of the isolated compound were analyzed using a SunFire C18 (4.6 × 250 mm, 5 μm) analytical column. The mobile phases A and B were 0.1% *v*/*v* formic acid in water and MeOH. The linear gradient elution phase was 0–30 min at 10–90% B. The chromatogram was evaluated at 210 nm at a flow speed of 1.0 mL/min. The temperature of the column oven was 30 °C.

2.7. Molecular Docking Validation Analysis

To further valuate the effect of ethyl acetate extraction of *D. heterophyllum* on NASH and liver fibrosis, a molecular docking study was carried out on rosmarinic acid and 13 significant target protein molecules. These 13 3D structures of proteins were obtained from the Protein Data Bank (https://www.rcsb.org/, (assessed on 28 July 2022)) Their PDB IDs were 1UHL (liver x receptor (LXR)), 2JED (protein kinase C (PKC)), 1OT7 (farnesoid x receptor (FXR)), 1A9U (mitogen-activated protein kinase (MAPK)), 5CGJ (nuclear factor E2-related factor 2 (Nrf2)), 4I7B (kelch-like ECH-associated protein 1 (Keap1)), 1N3U (heme oxygenase-1 (HO-1)), 2GH5 (glutathione peroxidase (GSH-Px)), 4HJ2 (glutathione S-transferase (GST)), 5IKQ (COX-2), 3RZF (nuclear factor kappa-B (NF-κB)), 6CCY (protein kinase B (AKT) and 2CDU (nicotinamide adenine dinucleotide phosphate oxidase 2 (NOX2)). Chem3D version 16.0 was used to convert the 2D structure of the primary component rosmarinic acid into a 3D structure, and its low-energy stable conformation was produced using the semi-empirical AM1 method with geometric optimization and default parameters. The receptor protein was then optimized using PyMOL software (2.3.0, DeLano Scientific LLC, Sahnghai, China) for correlation, removing water molecules, hydrogen addition, force fields, and charges. Finding and defining the protein active site followed. As a final point, the compound and protein molecule formats are adapted to the "pdbqt" format by AutoDock. After docking, 100 docking conformations were generated and the best scored one was selected as the docking result for analysis. A docking binding energy < −5 kcal/mol indicates that the compound has some binding activity to the target protein, while a docking binding energy < −7 kcal/mol shows a good binding activity to the target protein. Molecular docking conformations were visualized and analyzed by Pymol and Discovery Studio programs.

2.8. Statistical Data Evaluation

The results are presented as the mean ± standard deviation. The unpaired Student's t-tests evaluated the differences between the two groups, while one-way ANOVA verified them among numerous assemblies. SPSS software (Version 20.0, SPSS, Chicago, IL, USA) was applied for the statistical data evaluations where $^{*}\, p < 0.05$, $^{**}\, p < 0.01$, $^{\#}\, p < 0.05$, and $^{\#\#}\, p < 0.01$ were accepted as statistically substantial.

3. Results and Discussion

3.1. Evaluation of the Therapeutic Effect of NASH and Liver Fibrosis

Hepatic fibrosis is represented by the abnormal proliferation of intrahepatic connective tissue during the repair process of chronic liver injuries [23]. In this study, used mouse models of NASH and liver fibrosis were established and treated with *D. heterophyllum* plant extracts. Their bioactivities were evaluated by measuring the animals' basal and biochemical indices such as body weight, liver wet weight, serum levels of ALT, AST, TG, TC, and TBA, liver TG, TC, and Hyp content, as well as the gene expression of α-SMA, col1α1, MCP-1, and CD68. Herein, these indicators were selected for NAHS and liver fibrosis, as data demonstrate that these pathologies are described by a discrepancy in the generation and degradation of the extracellular matrix (ECM), which leads to the excessive deposition of collagen type I alpha 1 (col1α1)-dominated ECM, and ultimately leads to the weakening of liver function [24,25]. The α-smooth muscle actin (α-SMA) is an indicator of hepatic stellate cell (HSC) stimulation. It is upregulated with the aggravation of organ fibrosis in the liver and other types of fibrosis [26]. The disruption of the released pro-inflammatory factors and tissue repair capacity caused by the macrophage hyperpolarization in immune regulation is an important factor correlated with liver fibrosis [23,27]. M1-type macrophages mainly mediate pro-inflammatory effects and secrete large amounts of TNF-α, which promotes the progression of liver fibrosis. The monocyte chemotactic protein 1 (MCP-1) is a cytokine from the CC chemokine family and represents an important pro-inflammatory cytokine with the specific chemotactic activation of macrophages [28,29]. CD68 is a cytoplasmic glycoprotein that can be used to assess the degree of the polarization of macrophages that are type M1 [30,31].

3.1.1. Effects of *D. Heterophyllum* Plant Extracts on Mouse MCD-Induced NASH Model

Liver injury in the mouse models was assessed by measuring the liver index and the blood serum concentrations of ALT and AST. The obtained results have been shown in Figure 1A,B. It has been revealed that in the MCD model group (Vehicle), the body weight of mice decreased continuously in comparison to the normal control group, however, no significant variations in this indicator were observed in the subject (DH 240 mg/kg) compared with the vehicle. In the MCD model group, the mice had a decreased liver index, while there were no important variations in the subject group. As revealed in Figure 1C,D, the blood plasma levels of ALT and AST in the vehicle animal cohorts were significantly increased. Our results further demonstrated that DH (240 mg/kg) groups were significantly reduced after 4 weeks of administration.

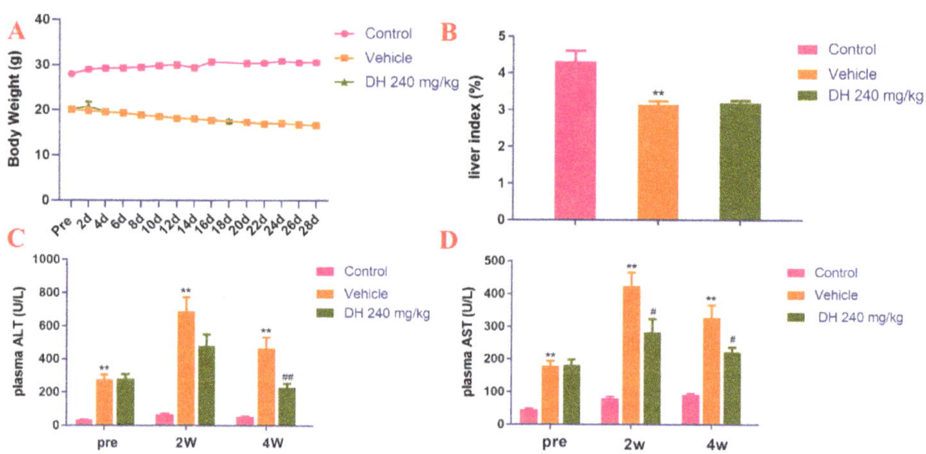

Figure 1. Investigation of the blood plasma concentrations of ALT and AST in NASH mouse model after supplementation of mice with ethyl acetate extraction of *D. heterophyllum*. Body weight (**A**), liver index (**B**), plasma levels of ALT (**C**) and AST (**D**). Pre: preparation; 2 d–28 d: 2 days–28 days; 2W: 2 weeks, 4W: 4 weeks. DH 240 mg/kg: 240 mg/kg ethyl acetate extract. Values are presented as the mean ± SD (n = 10). ** $p < 0.01$ vs. the control group; # $p < 0.05$, ## $p < 0.01$ vs. the vehicle group.

Liver biopsies from the three groups of mice were stained with H&E and the results are displayed in Figure 2A. Data quantitation was conducted by calculating the NAS score (Figure 2B). The results demonstrated that the liver cells in the control group had a regular morphology with clear borders of the liver lobules, without lipid droplet distribution and inflammatory cell infiltration. The NAS score was the lowest NAS. The distribution of hepatocytes in the vehicle group was recorded, with a large number of lipid droplet vacuoles in the cytoplasm, while the hepatocytes showed bullous diffuse steatosis. Furthermore, inflammatory cell infiltration was found, with the highest NAS score. However, in the DH (240 mg/kg) mice, there were more lipid droplets and lamellar balloon-like lesions in the hepatocytes. Their NAS score was slightly lower than that of the vehicle group. This revealed that DH (240 mg/kg) had a lesser effect on steatosis but a tendency to reduce lobular inflammation.

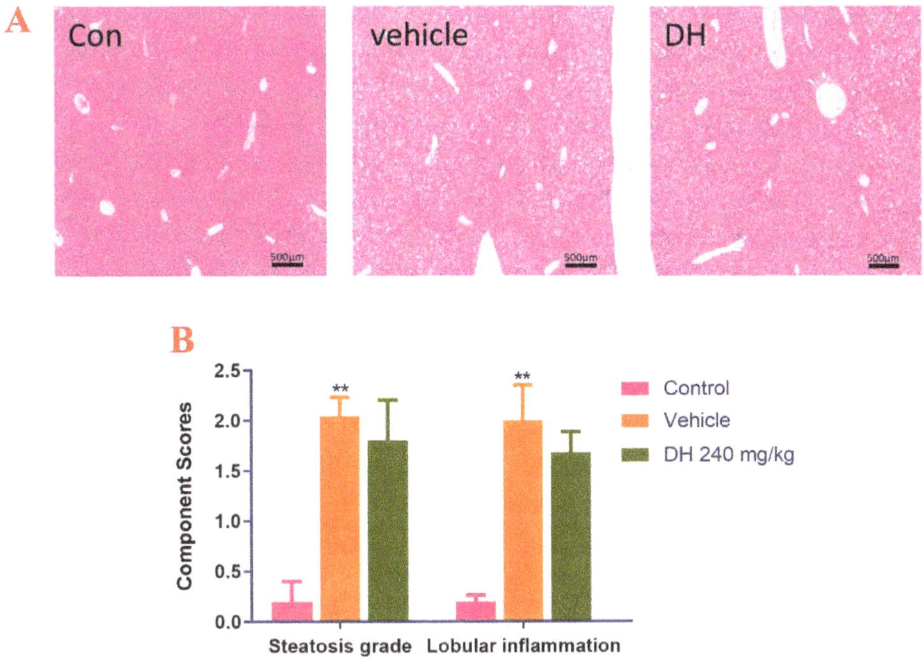

Figure 2. Investigation of steatosis in NASH mouse model after supplementation of mice with ethyl acetate extraction of *D. heterophyllum* extract supplementation of mice had no obvious effect on steatosis. We detected that steatosis is not obvious, but there is a certain tendency to alleviate lobular inflammation in the NASH mice. (**A**) HE staining results (500×), (**B**) NAS score. Con: control group; DH: 240 mg/kg ethyl acetate extract. Values are presented as the mean ± SD (n = 10). ** $p < 0.01$ vs. the control group.

Based on the histopathological findings, the parameters related to lipid metabolism (TG and TC) were further evaluated. Their blood serum concentrations were significantly reduced in the vehicle group after 2 and 4 weeks of administration (Figure 3A,B) compared with the normal control group. In the liver, they were also significantly increased after 4 weeks of administration (Figure 3C,D). DH (240 mg/kg) had some therapeutic effect on it, but there was no statistically significant difference (Figure 3A–D).

Differential expression of related genes was investigated by quantitative real-time PCR and the obtained results are displayed in Figure 3E–H. Herein, the obtained data suggested that compared with the normal control group, the expression of liver col1α1, α-SMA, MCP-1, and CD68 genes were found to be considerably upregulated in the vehicle group after 4 weeks of administration. In the subject DH (240 mg/kg) group, a significant decrease in the expression levels of genes including col1α1, α-SMA, MCP-1, and CD68 was observed.

3.1.2. Effects on Mice CCl_4-Induced Liver Fibrosis Model in Mice

As depicted in Figure 4A,B, there were no major dissimilarities in body weight measurements among mice. The CCl_4 model group (vehicle) demonstrated significant differences in the liver index compared to the normal group. The subjects (DH 200 mg/kg, 600 mg/kg) did not affect the liver index 6 weeks post-administration compared to the vehicle group.

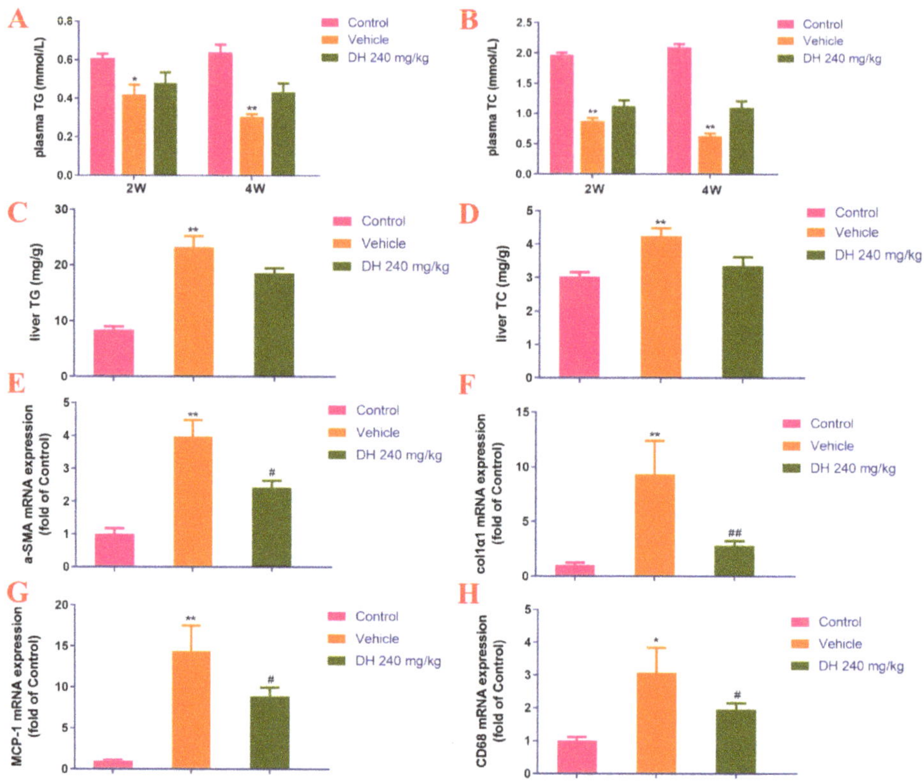

Figure 3. Effect of the ethyl acetate extract of *D. heterophyllum* supplementation on the blood serum levels of TC and TG, and the expression of related genes. Levels of TG (**A**), TC (**B**), liver levels of TG (**C**), and TC (**D**), collα1 mRNA expression in the NASH mice. α-SMA mRNA expression (**E**), collα1 mRNA expression (**F**), MCP-1 mRNA expression (**G**), and CD68 mRNA expression (**H**). DH 240 mg/kg: 240 mg/kg ethyl acetate extract. Values are presented as the mean $\pm$ SD (n = 10). * $p < 0.05$, ** $p < 0.01$ vs. the control group; # $p < 0.05$, ## $p < 0.01$ vs. the vehicle group.

Biochemical markers of liver function are the key basis for determining the extent of liver injury. The blood serum concentrations of ALT, AST, and TBA in mice from the vehicle group were significantly higher in comparison with the control group (Figure 4C–E). On the contrary, the blood serum concentrations of these biochemical markers in the DH (600 mg/kg) groups were found to be considerably lower after 6 weeks of administration but did not affect liver Hyp (Figure 4C–F).

The gene expression levels of liver fibrosis-associated biomarkers, α-SMA and colα1 were probed by quantitative real-time PCR. Figure 4G,H showed the results from these experiments. The hepatic α-SMA and collα1 expression rates were considerably upregulated in the vehicle group 6 weeks post-administration, while the subject DH mice had significantly downregulated α-SMA and collα1 gene expression rates in a concentration-dependent manner. The comparisons are related to the control group of mice and their expression levels of these genes.

Next, the liver pathological sections stained with Sirius red were examined. Figure 5 shows that the mice in the vehicle group had clear presinusoidal fibrosis in their liver tissues and that some of them exhibited bridging formation and considerably diminished ECM deposition around the central vein. The liver fibrosis in the DH (600 mg/kg) groups was still obvious, with no significant improvement effect.

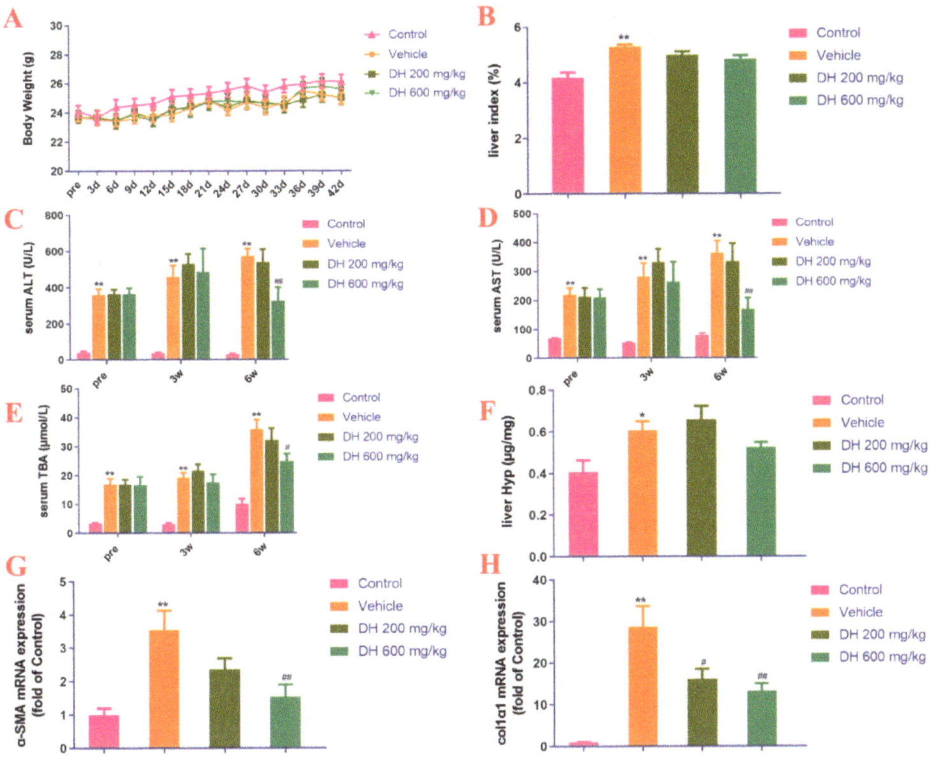

Figure 4. Investigation of the effect of *D. heterophyllum* treatment on the blood serum levels of ALT, AST, and TBA production, as well as its impact on the gene expression of α-SMA and col1α1 mRNA expression in the CCl_4-induced liver fibrosis mice. Body weight (**A**), liver index (**B**), serum levels of ALT (**C**), AST (**D**), TBA (**E**), liver levels of Hyp (**F**), α-SMA mRNA expression (**G**) and col1α1 mRNA expression (**H**). Pre: preparation; 3 d–42 d: 3 days–42 days; 3W: 3 weeks, 6W: 6 weeks. DH 200 mg/kg: 200 mg/kg ethyl acetate extract; DH 600 mg/kg: 600 mg/kg ethyl acetate extract. Values are presented as the mean ± SD (n = 10). * $p < 0.05$, ** $p < 0.01$ vs. the control group; # $p < 0.05$, ## $p < 0.01$ vs. the vehicle group.

Combining the experimental results of the two mice models, it was found that the ethyl acetate extraction of *D. heterophyllum* significantly reduced the TBA concentration in the liver, as well as influenced the expression of α-SMA and CD68 genes. It decreased the liver NAS score and reduced the formation of inflammatory foci in the liver. Moreover, it inhibited the expression of the col1α1 gene in type I collagen, reduced ECM formation, and exhibited antifibrotic properties. However, there was no significant improvement in the concentrations of Hyp neither in liver tissues, nor in the concentrations of TG and TC in liver tissues, which were indicators of liver fat metabolism in the model. Based on these results, it seems that the pharmacological effects of *D. heterophyllum* extract on liver fibrosis may come from reducing inflammation or affecting the activation of stellate cells at a later stage.

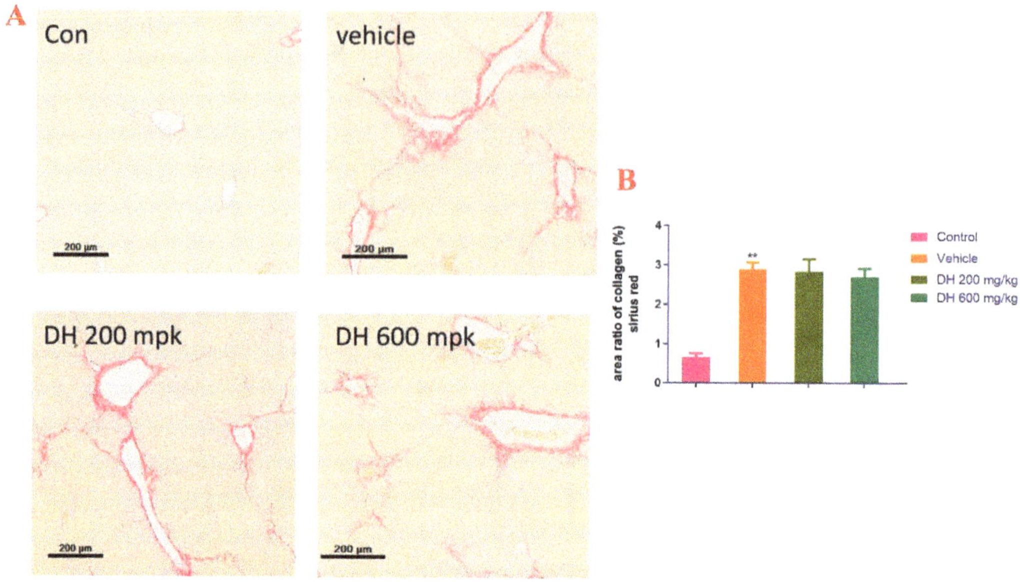

Figure 5. Pathological investigation of liver tissue sections in the CCl_4-induced liver fibrosis mice stained with Sirius red. (**A**) Sirius red stained representative micrographs of liver sections from the studied groups of mice (200×), the (**B**) area ratio of collagen. DH 200 mg/kg: 200 mg/kg ethyl acetate extract; DH 600 mg/kg: 600 mg/kg ethyl acetate extract. Values are presented as mean ± SD (n = 10). ** $p < 0.01$ vs. the control group.

3.2. *Isolation of DPPH Inhibitor and Anti-Inflammatory Active Component in Ethyl Acetate Extract Using Medium- and High-Pressure Liquid Chromatography*

D. heterophyllum ethyl acetate extracts (100 mg) were mixed with 100 µL MeOH-water (1:1 v/v) and sieved through a 0.45 µm filter membrane. It was analyzed on a 7-X10 analytical column using an online HPLC-DPPH system under optimized chromatographic conditions, as shown in Figure 6. Herein, the data obtained from isolation studies suggested that the main part of the *D. heterophyllum* ethyl acetate extract had a negative peak at 517 nm. This meant that the main part had strong antioxidant activity. The affinity ultrafiltration-HPLC analysis Figure was shown in Figure 7. Peak areas were obtained by HPLC integration. RBA values obtained by comparing the peak area ratio of the main component of *D. heterophyllum* ethyl acetate extract with the active and inactivated enzyme after incubation was greater than 1.5 [32], indicating that the main component of *D. heterophyllum* ethyl acetate extracts have a good binding affinity to COX-2 and possess a certain anti-inflammatory activity (RBA = 1.79). This is a significant finding and may serve as a candidate, considering that COX-2 controls inflammation. It is abundantly expressed when cells are stimulated by inflammation and rapidly respond to a series of pro-inflammatory mediators and cytokines [33].

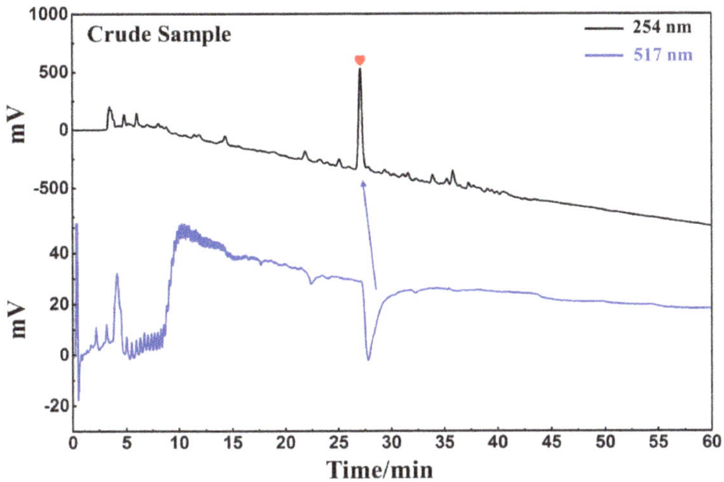

Figure 6. Analytical chromatogram on a 7-X10 analytical column and DPPH inhibitory activity profile of the extract of the ethyl acetate extraction of *D. heterophyllum*. Antioxidant peak marked with red heart. Conditions for HPLC1: mobile phase A: 0.1% v/v formic acid in water, B: MeOH; gradient elution: 0–60 min, 0–100% B; monitoring wavelength: 210 nm; flow rate: 1.0 mL/min; injection volume: 5 µL; column temperature: 30 °C. Conditions for HPLC2: monitoring wavelength: 517 nm; DPPH solution flow rate: 0.8 mL/min.

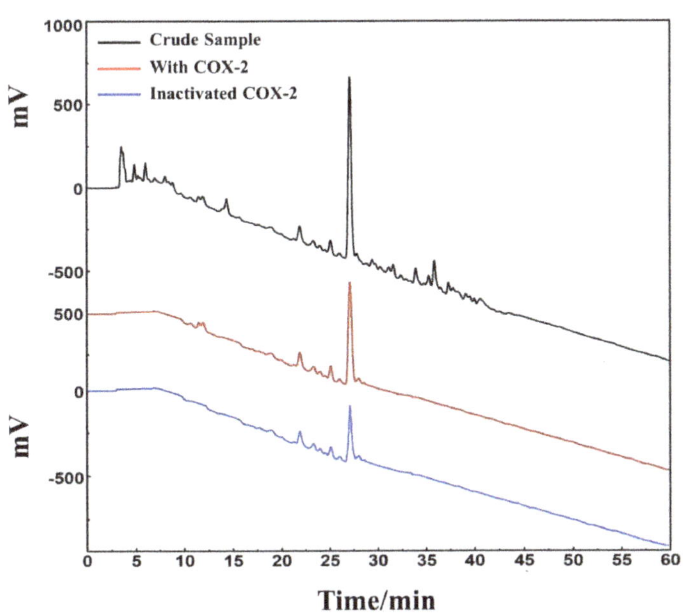

Figure 7. An affinity ultrafiltration-HPLC chromatogram for potential COX-2 ligands present in the ethyl acetate extraction of *D. heterophyllum*. The black, red, and blue lines, respectively, correspond to the HPLC chromatograms of the ethyl acetate extraction of *D. heterophyllum* without COX-2, with activated COX-2, and with inactivated COX-2. Conditions: mobile phase A: 0.1% v/v formic acid in water, B: MeOH; gradient elution: 0–60 min, 0–100% B; flow rate: 1.0 mL/min; monitoring wavelength: 210 nm; injection volume: 2 µL; column temperature: 30 °C.

The following phase involved the fast and efficient preparative separation of the primary functional component using medium- and high-pressure liquid chromatography in accordance with the activity-oriented results. The ethyl acetate extraction of *D. heterophyllum* contained a massive quantity of chlorophyll and lipophilic compounds, which were easily adsorbed on the stationary stage of the preparative column, causing column contamination and therefore had to be removed by pretreatment before further preparative separation experiments. MCI GEL® CHP20P packing is stable and can achieve good reproducibility for target compounds during purification [34,35]. Using it as a stationary phase for medium-pressure liquid chromatography can achieve high resolution for sample enrichment and high product recovery. In this view, 90.00 g of silica mix sample to a small medium-pressure tower (49 × 100 mm) was attached to a medium-pressure column packed with MCI GEL® CHP20P for dry loading sample preparation. The prepared enrichment chromatogram is shown in Figure 8A. Five fractions (Fr1, Fr2, Fr3, Fr4, and Fr5) were gathered after three repeated cycles using methanol–water as an eluent.

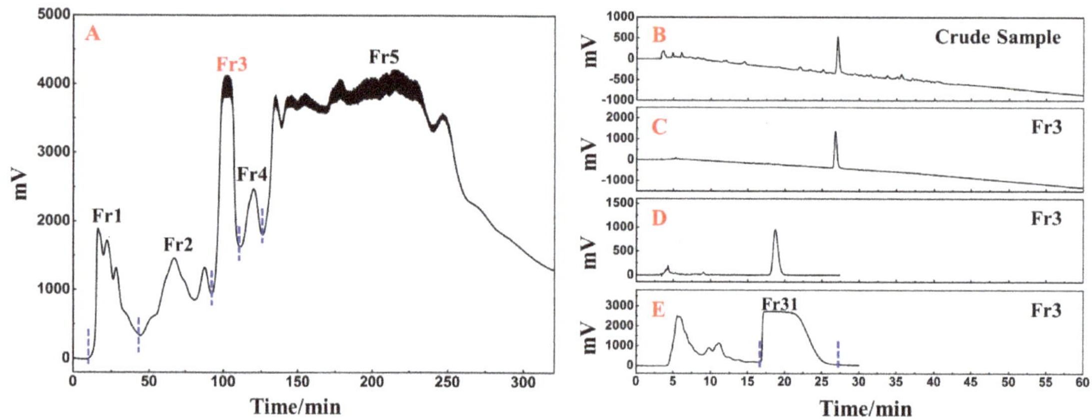

Figure 8. Separation chromatograms of *D. heterophyllum* ethyl acetate extracts mixed with amorphous silica gel (**A**). Conditions: mobile phase A: water and B: MeOH; gradient: 0–35 min, 0% B, 35–195 min, 0–100% B, 195–320 min, 100% B; monitoring wavelength: 210 nm; flow rate: 57.0 mL/min; sample loading: 90.0 g of *D. heterophyllum* ethyl acetate extract amorphous silica gel combination; column temperature: room temperature. The analytical chromatogram of the *D. heterophyllum* ethyl acetate extraction (**B**) and fraction Fr3 (**C**,**D**) on a 7-X10 analytical column. Preparative chromatogram (**E**) of the main component Fr31 sample on a 7-X10 preparative column. Conditions: mobile phase A: 0.1% formic acid in water, B: MeOH; gradient elution for (**B**,**C**): 0–60 min, 0–100% B; isocratic elution for (**D**,**E**): 0–30 min, 30% B; flow rate for (**B**–**D**): 1.0 mL/min, for (**E**): 19.0 mL/min; monitoring wavelength: 210 nm; injection volume for (**B**,**D**): 2 μL, for (**E**): 1.0 mL; column temperature for (**B**–**D**): 30 °C, for (**E**): room temperature.

As a highly engineered process, NPs' quality control is a system of considerable complexity. The efficient preparative separation of its main functional component can provide an important basis for its quality control studies. Therefore, the high-resolution screening and purification of the extract were performed. The liquid phase analysis chromatograms of the current study analyses are presented in Figure 8B,C. The main functional component from the *D. heterophyllum* to be in fraction Fr3 (7.06 g with 7.06% recovery). To achieve a high-purity preparative separation of its main functional component and to save preparation separation time and organic solvents, we optimized the separation conditions of Fr3 on a 7-X10 analytical column (4.6 × 250 mm, 5 μm). By adjusting the elution settings we prepared the main component of Fr3 by a 30% isocratic elution of MeOH in a mix of MeOH/0.1% *v*/*v* formic acid in the water system. Figure 8D contains the analysis diagram. The optimized isocratic elution conditions allowed the separation of the main functional component of the ethyl acetate *D. heterophyllum* extract. After linear amplification, 500.00 mg of Fr31 were further separated on the 7-X10 preparative column (20 × 250 mm, 5 μm) after 60 cycles, with a net recovery of 7.08%. The preparation diagram is shown in Figure 8E.

3.3. Purity Analysis and Structural Characterization of the Target Compound

Using a SunFire C18 analytical column, the separated Fr31 was re-evaluated for purity and activity. Figure 9B reveals the purity of the main functional component isolated from the ethyl acetate extraction of *D. heterophyllum*, which was above 99%. This indicated that its high purity preparation was successfully achieved. The comparison with the chromatogram of the crude extract (Figure 9A) demonstrated that Fr31 was indeed the main functional compound present in the ethyl acetate extraction of *D. heterophyllum*. Its structure was further studied by ESI-MS, ^{1}H, and ^{13}C NMR spectral analyses and data were documented and identified in comparison with the present information in the literature. Below, we list all spectra of the original spectra records, while the raw spectra are shown in the supporting materials (Figures S1–S3). Our results proved that the key component isolated from the ethyl acetate extraction of *D. heterophyllum* was the rosmarinic acid. Its chemical structure is shown in Figure 9C.

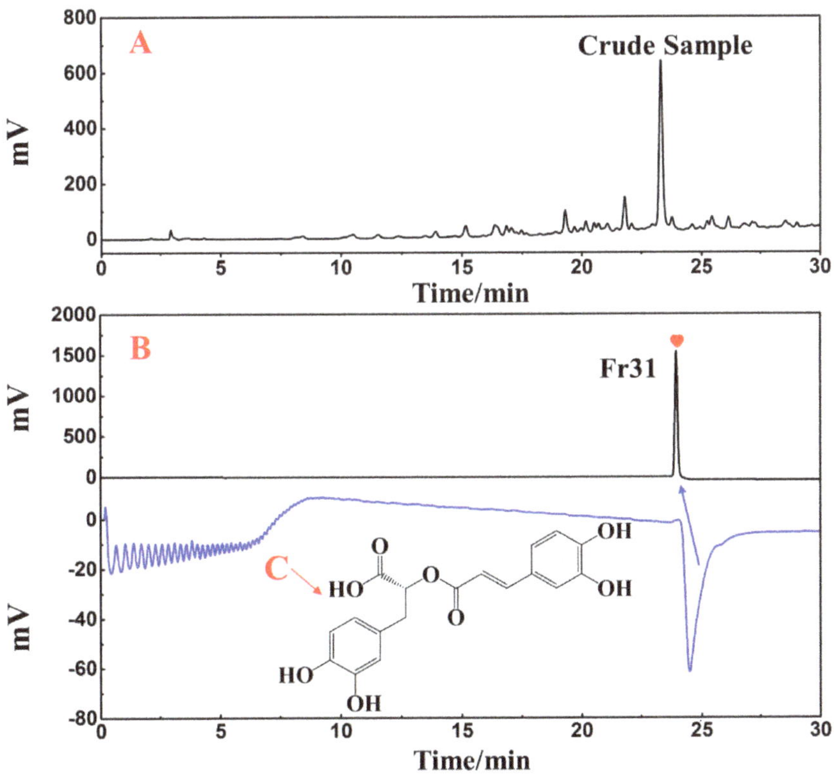

Figure 9. Purity and activity analysis comparison figures of the isolated main component Fr31 (**A**,**B**) on the SunFire analytical column. (**C**) is the chemical structure of the isolated compound. Antioxidant peak marked with red heart. Conditions: 0.1% formic acid in water, B: MeOH; gradient: 0–30 min, 10–90% B; monitoring wavelength: 210 nm; flow rate: 1.0 mL/min; injection volume: 1 μL; column temperature: 30 °C.

The principal bioactive compound isolated from the ethyl acetate extraction of *D. heterophyllum* include: (rosmarinic acid, 500.0 mg, white powder, ESI-MS m/z 359.25 $[M\text{-}H]^-$, calcd for $C_{18}H_{16}O_8$ m/z 360.25): ^{1}H NMR (600 MHz, MeOH-d_4) 7.54 (1H, d, *J* = 15.9 Hz, 7′-H), 7.03 (1H, d, *J* = 2.1 Hz, 2′-H), 6.94 (1H, dd, *J* = 8.1, 2.1 Hz, 6′-H), 6.77 (1H, d, *J* = 8.2 Hz, 5′-H), 6.74 (1H, d, *J* = 2.1 Hz, 2-H), 6.69 (1H, d, *J* = 8.0 Hz, 5-H), 6.60 (1H, dd, *J* = 8.0, 2.1 Hz, 6-H), 6.26 (1H, d, *J* = 15.9 Hz, 8′-H), 5.18 (1H, m, 8-H), 3.09 (1H, dd, *J* = 14.4, 4.3 Hz, 7b-H), 3.00 (1H, dd, *J* = 14.4, 8.5 Hz, 7a-H); ^{13}C NMR (151 MHz, MeOH-d_4) 173.4 (C-9), 168.4 (C-9′), 149.8 (C-4′), 147.7 (C-7′), 146.8 (C-3′), 146.2 (C-3), 145.3 (C-4), 129.2 (C-1), 127.7 (C-1′), 123.2 (C-6′), 121.8 (C-6), 117.6 (C-2), 116.5 (C-5′), 116.3 (C-5), 115.2 (C-8′), 114.4 (C-2′), 74.6 (C-8), 37.9 (C-7). These data corresponded to rosmarinic acid [36].

3.4. Prediction of the Therapeutic Potential of Rosmarinic Acid for Liver Diseases by Molecular Docking

The binding strength of the *D. heterophyllum* ethyl acetate extraction main functional component rosmarinic acid to important proteins of interest was evaluated by the molecular modeling of interactions by docking. After the analysis and visualization of the obtained results are shown in Figures 10–12, we found that the possible action mechanism of rosmarinic acid could be discussed from the perspectives of lipid metabolism, oxidative stress, and inflammation.

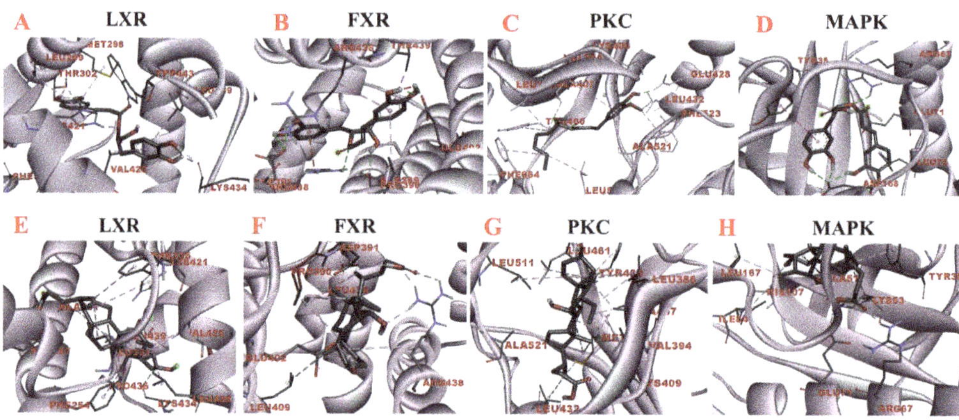

Figure 10. Molecular docking models of rosmarinic acid and obeticholic acid binding to LXR, FXR, PKC, and MAPK. (**A–D**) correspond to the binding models of rosmarinic acid with LXR, FXR, PKC, and MAPK, respectively. (**E–H**) correspond to the binding models of obeticholic acid with LXR, FXR, PKC, and MAPK, respectively.

LXR and FXR are members of the nuclear receptor supergene family encoding transcription factors, which are key transcriptional regulators of lipid metabolism genes and prospective therapeutic targets for the prevention and treatment of numerous diseases. FXR activity inhibits the ab initio synthesis of hepatic lipids, increases insulin sensitivity, and overcomes bile acid-induced cytotoxicity. It also results in the inhibition of adipogenic factor expression, which affects the transcription of key enzymes contributing to lipid production, such as ACC, FAS, and SCD-1 [37]. The MAPK signaling pathway is a signaling network consisting of a series of catalytic cascades that together regulate a variety of cellular processes including proliferation, differentiation, and migration. FXR can antagonize the MAPK signaling pathway, thereby inhibiting the expression of its downstream genes and other inflammation-related genes [38]. The PKC family includes about ten isoforms, which are involved in many important physiological responses in the body, including apoptosis, lipid metabolism, and the development of cardiovascular diseases. Unsaturated fatty acids can activate the PKC activity, which inhibits LXR activity and causes intracellular lipid accumulation, leading to hepatic metabolic disorders. The blockade of LXRα/β genes results in more lipid droplets stored in hepatocytes and increased expression of fibrotic genes, including Acta2 (the gene encoding α-SMA) and Col1a1 [39]. To maintain the liver's nutrient/energy balance, FXR and LXR are involved in processes including lipid, glucose, and inflammatory activation metabolism. Based on the above results, four proteins LXR, PKC, FXR, and MAPK were selected to establish the functional correlation between experiments and bioinformatics in this study. The obtained molecular models of the docking experiments are displayed in Tables 2 and 3 and Figure 10. The prediction models of this study demonstrated that the rosmarinic acid binds to the receptors of the above-discussed proteins via conventional hydrogen bonds, pi-sigma, pi-alkyl, pi-pi stacked and pi-cation. The relative binding affinities were −7.77 kcal/mol, −5.89 kcal/mol, −7.17 kcal/mol, and −6.86 kcal/mol, respectively, indicating that rosmarinic acid had the strongest binding affinity to LXR, further corroborating the data from previous animal model experiments. Further molecular docking results demonstrated that rosmarinic acid has multiple binding sites to LXR, PKC, FXR, and MAPK, advocating that rosmarinic acid regulates lipid metabolism by directly binding LXR, PKC, FXR, and MAPK.

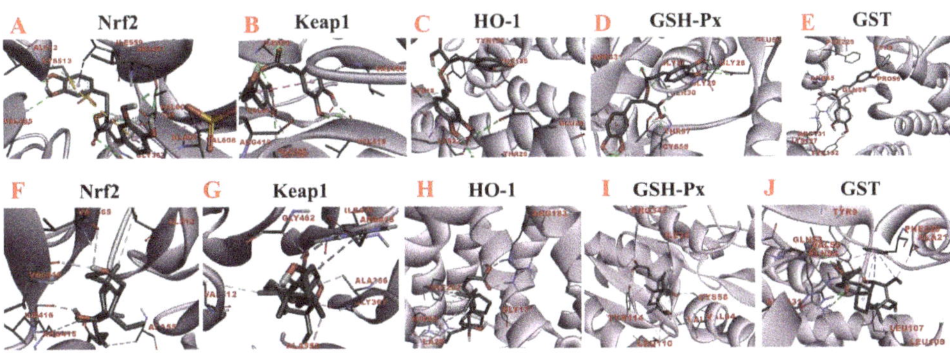

Figure 11. Molecular docking analysis of rosmarinic acid and obeticholic acid binding to Nrf2, Keap1, HO-1, GSH-Px, and GST. (**A–E**) correspond to the binding models of rosmarinic acid with Nrf2, Keap1, HO-1, GSH-Px and GST, respectively. (**F–J**) correspond to the binding models of obeticholic acid with Nrf2, Keap1, HO-1, GSH-Px, and GST, respectively.

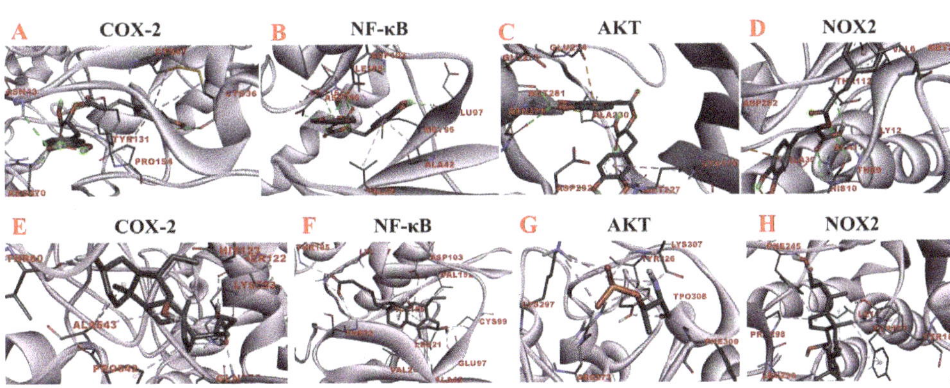

Figure 12. Molecular docking analysis of rosmarinic acid and obeticholic acid binding to COX-2, NF-κB, AKT and NOX2. (**A–D**) correspond to the binding models of rosmarinic acid with COX-2, NF-κB, AKT and NOX2, respectively. (**E–H**) correspond to the binding models of obeticholic acid with Nrf2, Keap1, HO-1, GSH-Px and GST, respectively.

Table 2. Intermolecular interactions between rosmarinic acid and LXR, PKC, FXR, and MAPK.

Proteins	Binding Energy (kcal/mol)	Binding Residues	Type
LXR	−7.77	LEU-439	Pi-Sigma
		LYS-434	Conventional Hydrogen Bond
		TRP-433	Conventional Hydrogen Bond
		HIS-421	Conventional Hydrogen Bond
		HIS-421	Pi-Sigma
		HIS-421	Pi-Alkyl
		VAL-425	Pi-Alkyl
		LEU-299	Pi-Alkyl
		PHE-335	Pi-Alkyl
		THR-302	Conventional Hydrogen Bond
		MET-298	Pi-Alkyl
PKC	−5.89	PHE-664	Pi-Alkyl
		LEU-511	Pi-Alkyl
		TYR-460	Pi-Alkyl
		ALA-407	Pi-Alkyl
		LEU-386	Pi-Alkyl
		ALA-521	Pi-Alkyl
		GLU-428	Conventional Hydrogen Bond
		PHE-523	Pi-Alkyl
		VAL-394	Pi-Alkyl
		LEU-432	Pi-Alkyl
		LYS-409	Pi-Alkyl
FXR	−7.17	SER-389	Conventional Hydrogen Bond
		ARG-438	Conventional Hydrogen Bond
		ARG-438	Pi-Cation
		ASP-391	Conventional Hydrogen Bond
		PRO-390	Pi-Alkyl
		THR-439	Pi-Sigma
		ARG-438	Pi-Alkyl
		GLU-402	Conventional Hydrogen Bond
MAPK	−5.87	TYR-35	Pi-Pi Stacked
		ASP-168	Conventional Hydrogen Bond
		GLU-71	Conventional Hydrogen Bond
		ARG-67	Conventional Hydrogen Bond
		LEU-75	Pi-Alkyl

Oxidative stress is a state of redox imbalance in the body, which is one of the risk factors for NASH and liver pathologies such as liver fibrosis. Data demonstrate that the Nrf2-Keap1 signaling pathway is not only an important defense system against oxidative stress damage but also is a key signaling pathway to enhance the antioxidant capacity of the body. The imbalance of oxidants and antioxidants in the body induces conformational changes in the cysteine residues of Keap1, resulting in the release of Nrf2 from the nucleus. There, it builds a heterodimer with Maf and interacts with the antioxidant response element, inducing the expression of downstream antioxidant molecules such as HO-1, GSH-Px, and GST [40,41]. Based on the activity-directed isolation results, we hypothesized that rosmarinic acid may bind to Nrf2, Keap1, HO-1, GSH-Px, and GST to regulate oxidative stress in the organism. As shown in Figure 11, the rosmarinic acid can enter the binding pockets of these five receptors through the conventional hydrogen bond, carbon hydrogen bond, pi-sigma, pi-alkyl, pi-pi stacked, pi-sulfur, and pi-anion. In addition, Tables 4 and 5 shows data that prove that the binding affinity of rosmarinic acid to these targets was below −6.5 kcal/mol, especially with GSH-Px, GST reaching −8.11 kcal/mol and −8.41 kcal/mol accordingly. Additionally, it was found that when the binding affinity was below −5.5 kcal/mol it is considered that the bioactive compound had a good binding activity to the target, whereas affinity values less than −7.0 kcal/mol indicated strong adhesion of the receptor to the ligand. In this view, rosmarinic acid is likely a good antioxidant, which is supported by the results of the preliminary HPLC-DPPH screening experiments.

Table 3. Intermolecular interactions between obeticholic acid and LXR, PKC, FXR, and MAPK.

Proteins	Binding Energy (kcal/mol)	Binding Residues	Type
LXR	−9.44	PRO-436	Pi-Alkyl
		LEU-439	Pi-Alkyl
		LYS-434	Carbon Hydrogen Bond
		VAL-425	Pi-Alkyl
		PHE-254	Pi-Alkyl
		LEU-428	Pi-Alkyl
		LEU-331	Pi-Alkyl
		PHE-335	Pi-Alkyl
		PHE-257	Conventional Hydrogen Bond
		HIS-421	Pi-Alkyl
PKC	−8.39	PHE-664	Pi-Lone Pair
		LEU-461	Pi-Alkyl
		LEU-386	Pi-Alkyl
		LEU-511	Pi-Alkyl
		TYR-460	Pi-Alkyl
		VAL-394	Pi-Alkyl
		ALA-407	Pi-Alkyl
		ALA-521	Pi-Alkyl
		LEU-432	Pi-Alkyl
		MET-458	Pi-Alkyl
		GLU-428	Conventional Hydrogen Bond
		LYS-409	Conventional Hydrogen Bond
FXR	−8.76	LEU-434	Pi-Alkyl
		ARG-438	Pi-Alkyl
		ARG-438	Conventional Hydrogen Bond
		ASP-391	Conventional Hydrogen Bond
		LEU-409	Pi-Alkyl
		PRO-390	Pi-Alkyl
		GLU-402	Conventional Hydrogen Bond
MAPK	−7.34	TYR-35	Pi-Alkyl
		GLU-71	Conventional Hydrogen Bond
		ARG-67	Conventional Hydrogen Bond
		ALA-51	Pi-Alkyl
		LYS-53	Conventional Hydrogen Bond
		ILE-84	Pi-Alkyl
		LEU-167	Pi-Alkyl
		HIS-107	Conventional Hydrogen Bond

The inflammatory response is one of the major factors contributing to most chronic liver diseases and liver fibrosis. COX-2 initiates cellular reactions against inflammation, promotes cell proliferation, and inhibits apoptosis. COX-2 expression was found to be elevated after the onset of liver fibrosis. Additionally, the activation of HSC was significantly reduced after the application of COX-2 inhibitors [42]. NOX is a transmembrane complex composed of multiple protein subunits and a major source of ROS in hepatocytes, which drives the progression of liver fibrosis. NOX PI3K/AKT activity is linked with induced IκBα phosphorylation, which dissociates the NF-κB p65 subunit from it and translocates it to the nucleus, thereby activating the transcriptional activity of NF-κB [43]. NF-κB is considered to be a core molecule in several inflammatory signaling pathways. NF-κB leads to elevated expression levels of various downstream inflammatory factors and exacerbates inflammatory damage, and long-term inflammatory stimulation leads to liver fibrosis [44]. Consequently, the molecular docking analysis of rosmarinic acid with inflammation-related targets was performed to explore the possible interactions between rosmarinic acid and COX-2, NF-κB, AKT, and NOX2. The results are shown in Figure 12. The data revealed that the rosmarinic acid and COX-2, NF-κB, AKT, and NOX2 interacted via a conventional hydrogen bond, pi-sigma, pi-alkyl, pi-sulfur, and pi-anion, respectively, showing −6.21 kcal/mol, −6.94 kcal/mol, −6.73 kcal/mol and −6.67 kcal/mol binding energies. Detailed molecular docking information is summarized in Tables 6 and 7. It shows that the binding affinity is excellent and is consistent with the results of the preliminary affinity ultrafiltration-HPLC guided separation.

Table 4. Intermolecular interactions between rosmarinic acid and Nrf2, Keap1, HO-1, GSH-Px, and GST.

Proteins	Binding Energy (kcal/mol)	Binding Residues	Type
Nrf2	−7.61	GLY-367	Conventional Hydrogen Bond
		VAL-606	Conventional Hydrogen Bond
		VAL-465	Conventional Hydrogen Bond
		GLY-605	Carbon Hydrogen Bond
		ILE-559	Pi-Sigma
		VAL-608	Pi-Alkyl
		ALA-607	Pi-Alkyl
		VAL-561	Conventional Hydrogen Bond
		VAL-512	Conventional Hydrogen Bond
		CYS-513	Pi-Sulfur
Keap1	−7.96	ARG-415	Carbon Hydrogen Bond
		VAL-465	Carbon Hydrogen Bond
		VAL-418	Conventional Hydrogen Bond
		GLY-367	Conventional Hydrogen Bond
		VAL-606	Conventional Hydrogen Bond
		ALA-366	Pi-Alkyl
		ILE-559	Conventional Hydrogen Bond
HO-1	−6.57	THR-135	Conventional Hydrogen Bond
		TYR-134	Conventional Hydrogen Bond
		ARG-183	Conventional Hydrogen Bond
		LYS-18	Carbon Hydrogen Bond
		LYS-22	Pi-Sigma
		GLU-29	Conventional Hydrogen Bond
		THR-26	Conventional Hydrogen Bond
GSH-Px	−8.11	GLY-31	Conventional Hydrogen Bond
		THR-57	Conventional Hydrogen Bond
		THR-57	Carbon Hydrogen Bond
		SER-30	Conventional Hydrogen Bond
		CYS-58	Conventional Hydrogen Bond
		GLY-29	Carbon Hydrogen Bond
		ASP-331	Pi-Anion
		ASP-331	Pi-Alkyl
		CYS-63	Pi-Alkyl
		CYS-63	Conventional Hydrogen Bond
		GLY-28	Conventional Hydrogen Bond
		GLU-50	Conventional Hydrogen Bond
GST	−8.41	TYR-132	Conventional Hydrogen Bond
		LYS-127	Conventional Hydrogen Bond
		ARG-131	Conventional Hydrogen Bond
		GLN-54	Conventional Hydrogen Bond
		ARG-45	Conventional Hydrogen Bond
		TYR-9	Conventional Hydrogen Bond
		PRO-56	Carbon Hydrogen Bond
		PHE-220	Pi-Pi Stacked

Table 5. Intermolecular interactions between obeticholic acid and Nrf2, Keap1, HO-1, GSH-Px, and GST.

Proteins	Binding Energy (kcal/mol)	Binding Residues	Type
Nrf2	−9.42	VAL-418	Conventional Hydrogen Bond
		VAL-465	Conventional Hydrogen Bond
		VAL-512	Pi-Alkyl
		ILE-416	Conventional Hydrogen Bond
		ARG-415	Pi-Alkyl
		ALA-556	Pi-Alkyl
Keap1	−9.25	GLY-367	Conventional Hydrogen Bond
		VAL-512	Conventional Hydrogen Bond
		ALA-366	Pi-Alkyl
		ALA-556	Pi-Alkyl
		ILE-416	Pi-Alkyl
		GLY-462	Carbon Hydrogen Bond
		ARG-415	Pi-Alkyl
		ARG-415	Carbon Hydrogen Bond
		ARG-415	Conventional Hydrogen Bond
HO-1	−8.65	ARG-183	Conventional Hydrogen Bond
		PHE-207	Pi-Alkyl
		HIS-25	Pi-Alkyl
		GLY-139	Conventional Hydrogen Bond
		ALA-28	Pi-Alkyl
		PHE-207	Pi-Alkyl
GSH-Px	−8.67	ILE-343	Pi-Alkyl
		ARG-347	Conventional Hydrogen Bond
		TYR-114	Conventional Hydrogen Bond
		TYR-114	Pi-Sigma
		VAL-64	Pi-Alkyl
		LEU-110	Pi-Alkyl
		CYS-58	Conventional Hydrogen Bond
		CYS-58	Pi-Alkyl
GST	−8.47	ALA-216	Pi-Alkyl
		LEU-107	Conventional Hydrogen Bond
		LEU-107	Pi-Alkyl
		LEU-108	Pi-Alkyl
		TYR-9	Conventional Hydrogen Bond
		PHE-220	Pi-Sigma
		PHE-220	Conventional Hydrogen Bond
		VAL-55	Pi-Alkyl
		GLN-53	Conventional Hydrogen Bond
		ARG-131	Conventional Hydrogen Bond
		GLN-54	Conventional Hydrogen Bond

Taken together, the predicted results of molecular docking further suggest that rosmarinic acid, the main functional component of *D. heterophyllum* ethyl acetate extract isolated by activity-directed screening, does possess favorable antioxidant, anti-inflammatory, and lipid metabolism modulating activities. It mainly reduces intracellular lipids and free radicals to react to form lipid peroxides by activating peroxidase, which constitutes a multi-level reduced organic hydroperoxide system specific to different substrates. Furthermore, this compound activates peroxidase to form a multi-level reduction organic hydroperoxide system specific to different substrates, thereby reducing the reaction of lipids and free radicals in cells to form lipid peroxides. This provides a scientific basis for the development and exploitation of the *D. heterophyllum* medicinal value.

Table 6. Intermolecular interactions between rosmarinic acid and COX-2, NF-κB, AKT, and NOX2.

Proteins	Binding Energy (kcal/mol)	Binding Residues	Type
COX-2	−6.21	ARG-470	Conventional Hydrogen Bond
		TYR-131	Conventional Hydrogen Bond
		ASN-43	Conventional Hydrogen Bond
		CYS-47	Pi-Alkyl
		PRO-154	Pi-Alkyl
		CYS-36	Pi-Alkyl
		CYS-36	Conventional Hydrogen Bond
		ASN-43	Conventional Hydrogen Bond
NF-κB	−6.94	GLU-97	Conventional Hydrogen Bond
		LEU-167	Conventional Hydrogen Bond
		ASP-166	Conventional Hydrogen Bond
		ASP-103	Conventional Hydrogen Bond
		MET-96	Pi-Sulfur
		ALA-42	Pi-Alkyl
		VAL-29	Pi-Alkyl
		ILE-165	Pi-Sigma
AKT	−6.73	GLU-198	Conventional Hydrogen Bond
		ASP-292	Conventional Hydrogen Bond
		ALA-230	Conventional Hydrogen Bond
		MET-227	Pi-Sigma
		LYS-179	Pi-Alkyl
		MET-281	Pi-Sulfur
		GLU-234	Pi-Anion
		ASN-279	Conventional Hydrogen Bond
		GLU-278	Conventional Hydrogen Bond
NOX2	−6.67	HIS-10	Conventional Hydrogen Bond
		ALA-11	Conventional Hydrogen Bond
		GLY-12	Conventional Hydrogen Bond
		THR-112	Conventional Hydrogen Bond
		THR-9	Conventional Hydrogen Bond
		ASP-282	Pi-Anion
		ALA-303	Pi-Alkyl
		MET-33	Pi-Sulfur
		VAL-81	Conventional Hydrogen Bond
		VAL-6	Pi-Alkyl

Table 7. Intermolecular interactions between rosmarinic acid and COX-2, NF-κB, AKT, and NOX2.

Proteins	Binding Energy (kcal/mol)	Binding Residues	Type
COX-2	−8.15	GLN-373	Conventional Hydrogen Bond
		LYS-533	Conventional Hydrogen Bond
		SER-122	Conventional Hydrogen Bond
		PRO-542	Pi-Alkyl
		ALA-543	Pi-Alkyl
		HIS-123	Pi-Alkyl
		THR-60	Conventional Hydrogen Bond

Table 7. *Cont.*

Proteins	Binding Energy (kcal/mol)	Binding Residues	Type
NF-κB	−8.81	LYA-147	Conventional Hydrogen Bond
		THR-185	Conventional Hydrogen Bond
		THR-23	Conventional Hydrogen Bond
		ASP-103	Carbon Hydrogen Bond
		VAL-152	Pi-Alkyl
		VAL-29	Pi-Alkyl
		LEU-21	Pi-Alkyl
		ILE-165	Pi-Alkyl
		ALA-42	Pi-Alkyl
		GLU-97	Conventional Hydrogen Bond
		CYS-99	Conventional Hydrogen Bond
AKT	−7.56	ARG-273	Attractive Charge
		LYS-297	Attractive Charge
		LYS-297	Conventional Hydrogen Bond
		LYS-307	Conventional Hydrogen Bond
NOX2	−8.71	TYR-188	Pi-Alkyl
		PHE-245	Pi-Alkyl
		PHE-245	Conventional Hydrogen Bond
		LEU-299	Pi-Alkyl
		TYR-159	Pi-Alkyl
		PRO-298	Pi-Alkyl
		ILE-160	Pi-Alkyl

4. Conclusions

The structural diversity of NPs and their characteristics that easily combine with those of biological macromolecules determine their incomparable advantages in participating in the physiological processes of life. These characteristics afford them an indispensable and pivotal position in the development of innovative drugs and drug-led structures. Therefore, the quality control research of NPs is a top priority in NPs' research.

Herein, ethyl acetate was used as the organic solvent to isolate the active constituents of *D. heterophyllum*. The obtained extract was subjected to efficacy evaluation in a mouse model of NASH and liver fibrosis. The analysis results revealed that *D. heterophyllum* ethyl acetate extracts improved liver function by reducing cholestasis and decreasing the inflammatory response. Because oxidative stress and inflammation are key factors in the development of NASH and liver fibrosis, the main component rosmarinic acid with a purity of >99% was isolated. The potential functions of the rosmarinic acid were demonstrated by molecular docking followed by in vivo studies using mice models. The results demonstrated that the rosmarinic acid exhibited lipid-modulating effects and has a role in several antioxidant- and anti-inflammatory-related signaling pathways, revealing a multi-target and multi-pathway therapeutic profile in NASH and liver fibrosis. Taken together, the approach taken in this study to extract and purify NPs paves the way for the discovery of more pharmacologically active NPs in natural sources and further investigation into them, with the ultimate goal of developing novel therapeutics.

We understand that certain mechanistic investigations are required to determine the interactions of the various molecular pathways involved, which should be subject to future explorations.

Supplementary Materials: The following supporting information can be downloaded at: https://www.mdpi.com/article/10.3390/separations9100273/s1, Figure S1: ESI mass spectrum of rosmarinic acid; Figure S2: ^{1}H NMR Spectrum (600 MHz) of rosmarinic acid (in MeOH-d_4); Figure S3: ^{13}C NMR Spectrum (151 MHz) of rosmarinic acid (in MeOH-d_4).

Author Contributions: Writing—original draft, methodology, Y.F.; writing—review and editing, methodology, D.S.; formal analysis, investigation, G.L.; data curation, Y.L.; conceptualization, visualization, J.L.; conceptualization, project administration, and funding acquisition, Q.W. and J.D. All authors have read and agreed to the published version of the manuscript.

Funding: This research was funded by the International Cooperation Project of Qinghai Province (2020-HZ-804).

Institutional Review Board Statement: The study was conducted in accordance with the Animal Care and Use Committee affiliated with the Shanghai Institute of Materia Medica with approval number 2017-10-LJ-53 and 2018-11-LJ-66. The study was also conducted in following the National Institutes of Health Guide for the Care and Use of Laboratory Animals (NIH Publication No. 85-23, revised in 1985).

Informed Consent Statement: Not applicable.

Data Availability Statement: All data generated or analyzed during this study are included in this published article (and its Supplementary Information file).

Conflicts of Interest: The authors have stated that they have no known conflicting financial interest or personal ties that may have influenced the work presented in this publication.

References

1. Eslam, M.; Valenti, L.; Romeo, S. Genetics and epigenetics of NAFLD and NASH: Clinical impact. *J. Hepatol.* **2019**, *68*, 268–279. [CrossRef]
2. Duan, X.; Meng, Q.; Wang, C.; Liu, Z.; Liu, Q.; Sun, H.; Sun, P.; Yang, X.; Huo, X.; Peng, J.; et al. Calycosin attenuates triglyceride accumulation and hepatic fibrosis in murine model of non-alcoholic steatohepatitis via activating farnesoid X receptor. *Phytomedicine* **2017**, *25*, 83–92. [CrossRef]
3. Xu, J.; Dai, L.; Zhang, Y.; Wang, A.; Li, H.; Wang, Y.; Meng, X.; Wu, S.; Wang, Y. Severity of Nonalcoholic Fatty Liver Disease and Risk of Future Ischemic Stroke Events. *Stroke* **2021**, *52*, 103–110. [CrossRef]
4. Younossi, Z.; Anstee, Q.M.; Marietti, M.; Hardy, T.; Henry, L.; Eslam, M.; George, J.; Bugianesi, E. Global burden of NAFLD and NASH: Trends, predictions, risk factors and prevention. *Nat. Rev. Gastroenterol. Hepatol.* **2018**, *15*, 11–20. [CrossRef] [PubMed]
5. Schuppan, D.; Surabattula, R.; Wang, X.Y. Determinants of fibrosis progression and regression in NASH. *J. Hepatol.* **2018**, *68*, 238–250. [CrossRef]
6. Sheka, A.C.; Adeyi, O.; Thompson, J.; Hameed, B.; Crawford, P.A.; Ikramuddin, S. Nonalcoholic Steatohepatitis: A Review. *JAMA* **2020**, *323*, 1175–1183. [CrossRef]
7. Hua, Y.Q.; Zeng, Y.; Xu, J.; Xu, X.L. Naringenin alleviates nonalcoholic steatohepatitis in middle-aged Apoe-/-mice: Role of SIRT1. *Phytomedicine* **2021**, *81*, 153412. [CrossRef]
8. Li, S.; Li, X.; Chen, F.; Liu, M.; Ning, L.; Yan, Y.; Zhang, S.; Huang, S.; Tu, C. Nobiletin mitigates hepatocytes death, liver inflammation, and fibrosis in a murine model of NASH through modulating hepatic oxidative stress and mitochondrial dysfunction. *J. Nutr. Biochem.* **2022**, *100*, 108888. [CrossRef] [PubMed]
9. Rodrigues, T.; Reker, D.; Schneider, P.; Schneider, G. Counting on natural products for drug design. *Nat. Chem.* **2016**, *8*, 531–541. [CrossRef]
10. Harvey, A.L.; Edrada-Ebel, R.; Quinn, R.J. The re-emergence of natural products for drug discovery in the genomics era. *Nat. Rev. Drug Discov.* **2015**, *14*, 111–129. [CrossRef]
11. Gouveia, D.N.; Guimarães, A.G.; Santos, W.B.D.R.; Quintans-Júnior, L.J. Natural products as a perspective for cancer pain management: A systematic review. *Phytomedicine* **2019**, *58*, 152766. [CrossRef]
12. Chopra, B.; Dhingra, A.K. Natural products: A lead for drug discovery and development. *Phytother. Res.* **2021**, *35*, 4660–4702. [CrossRef] [PubMed]
13. Du, K.Z.; Sun, A.L.; Yan, C.; Liang, C.; Qi, L.; Wang, C.; Yang, R.; Cui, Y.; Shang, Y.; Li, J.; et al. Recent advances of green pretreatment techniques for quality control of natural products. *Electrophoresis* **2020**, *41*, 1469–1481. [CrossRef]
14. Bian, J.; Wang, K.; Wang, Q.L.; Wang, P.; Wang, T.; Shi, W.Y.; Ruan, Q.G. *Dracocephalum heterophyllum* (DH) Exhibits Potent Anti-Proliferative Effects on Autoreactive CD4+ T Cells and Ameliorates the Development of Experimental Autoimmune Uveitis. *Front. Immunol.* **2020**, *11*, 575669. [CrossRef]
15. Shi, Q.Q.; Dang, J.; Wen, H.X.; Yuan, X.; Tao, Y.D.; Wang, Q.L. Anti-hepatitis, antioxidant activities and bioactive compounds of *Dracocephalum heterophyllum* extracts. *Bot. Stud.* **2016**, *57*, 16. [CrossRef]
16. Stappen, I.; Wanner, J.; Tabanca, N.; Wedge, D.E.; Ali, A.; Kaul, V.K.; Lal, B.; Jaitak, V.; Gochev, V.K.; Schmidt, E.; et al. Chemical Composition and Biological Activity of Essential Oils of *Dracocephalum heterophyllum* and Hyssopus officinalis from Western Himalaya. *Nat. Prod. Commun.* **2015**, *10*, 133–138. [CrossRef] [PubMed]
17. Khoo, H.T.; Leow, C.H. Advancements in the preparation and application of monolithic silica columns for efficient separation in liquid chromatography. *Talanta* **2021**, *224*, 121777. [CrossRef]

18. Gulcin, İ. Antioxidants and antioxidant methods: An updated overview. *Arch. Toxicol.* **2020**, *94*, 651–715. [CrossRef]
19. Zhang, X.W.; Bian, G.L.; Kang, P.Y.; Cheng, X.J.; Yan, K.; Liu, Y.L.; Gao, Y.X.; Li, D.Q. Recent advance in the discovery of tyrosinase inhibitors from natural sources via separation methods. *J. Enzyme Inhib. Med. Chem.* **2021**, *36*, 2104–2117. [CrossRef] [PubMed]
20. Crampon, K.; Giorkallos, A.; Deldossi, M.; Baud, S.; Steffenel, L.A. Machine-learning methods for ligand-protein molecular docking. *Drug Discov. Today* **2022**, *27*, 151–164. [CrossRef]
21. Ballante, F.; Kooistra, A.J.; Kampen, S.; de Graaf, C.; Carlsson, J. Structure-Based Virtual Screening for Ligands of G Protein-Coupled Receptors: What Can Molecular Docking Do for You? *Pharmacol. Rev.* **2021**, *73*, 527–565. [CrossRef]
22. Batool, M.; Ahmad, B.; Choi, S. A Structure-Based Drug Discovery Paradigm. *Int. J. Mol. Sci.* **2019**, *20*, 2783. [CrossRef]
23. Tacke, F.; Zimmermann, H.W. Macrophage heterogeneity in liver injury and fibrosis. *J. Hepatol.* **2014**, *60*, 1090–1096. [CrossRef]
24. Parola, M.; Pinzani, M. Liver fibrosis: Pathophysiology, pathogenetic targets and clinical issues. *Mol. Asp. Med.* **2019**, *65*, 37–55. [CrossRef] [PubMed]
25. Schwabe, R.F.; Tabas, I.; Pajvani, U.B. Mechanisms of Fibrosis Development in Nonalcoholic Steatohepatitis. *Gastroenterology* **2020**, *158*, 1913–1928. [CrossRef] [PubMed]
26. Higashi, T.; Friedman, S.L.; Hoshida, Y. Hepatic stellate cells as key target in liver fibrosis. *Adv. Drug Deliv. Rev.* **2017**, *121*, 27–42. [CrossRef]
27. Wen, Y.; Lambrecht, J.; Ju, C.; Tacke, F. Hepatic macrophages in liver homeostasis and diseases-diversity, plasticity and therapeutic opportunities. *Cell. Mol. Immunol.* **2021**, *18*, 45–56. [CrossRef] [PubMed]
28. Wang, C.; Ma, C.; Gong, L.; Guo, Y.; Fu, K.; Zhang, Y.; Zhou, H.; Li, Y. Macrophage Polarization and Its Role in Liver Disease. *Front. Immunol.* **2021**, *12*, 803037. [CrossRef]
29. Mohammadi, A.; Blesso, C.N.; Barreto, G.E.; Banach, M.; Majeed, M.; Sahebkar, A. Macrophage plasticity, polarization and function in response to curcumin, a diet-derived polyphenol, as an immunomodulatory agent. *J. Nutr. Biochem.* **2019**, *66*, 1–16. [CrossRef] [PubMed]
30. Yamate, J.; Izawa, T.; Kuwamura, M. Histopathological Analysis of Rat Hepatotoxicity Based on Macrophage Functions: In Particular, an Analysis for Thioacetamide-induced Hepatic Lesions. *Food Saf.* **2016**, *4*, 61–73. [CrossRef]
31. Lin, C.C.; Yang, H.M. Fibrolamellar Carcinoma: A Concise Review. *Arch. Pathol. Lab. Med.* **2018**, *142*, 1141–1145. [CrossRef]
32. Xie, L.; Lee, D.Y.; Shang, Y.; Cao, X.; Wang, S.; Liao, J.; Zhang, T.; Dai, R. Characterization of spirostanol glycosides and furostanol glycosides from anemarrhenae rhizoma as dual targeted inhibitors of 5-lipoxygenase and Cyclooxygenase-2 by employing a combination of affinity ultrafiltration and HPLC/MS. *Phytomedicine* **2020**, *77*, 153284. [CrossRef]
33. Yang, H.; Xuefeng, Y.; Shandong, W.; Jianhua, X. COX-2 in liver fibrosis. *Clin. Chim. Acta* **2020**, *506*, 196–203. [CrossRef]
34. Dang, J.; Ma, J.; Du, Y.; Dawa, Y.; Wang, Q.; Chen, C.; Wang, Q.; Tao, Y.; Ji, T. Large-scale preparative isolation of bergenin standard substance from *Saxifraga atrata* using polyamide coupled with MCI GEL®CHP20P as stationary phases in medium pressure chromatography. *J. Chromatogr. B* **2021**, *1170*, 122617. [CrossRef]
35. Yuan, C.; Dang, J.; Han, Y.; Liu, C.; Yu, S.; Lv, Y.; Cui, Y.; Wang, Z.; Li, G. Preparative isolation of maltol glycoside from *Dianthus superbus* and its anti-inflammatory activity in vitro. *RSC Adv.* **2022**, *12*, 5031–5041. [CrossRef]
36. Dapkevicius, A.; van Beek, T.A.; Lelyveld, G.P.; van Veldhuizen, A.; de Groot, A.; Linssen, J.P.; Venskutonis, R. Isolation and structure elucidation of radical scavengers from Thymus vulgaris leaves. *J. Nat. Prod.* **2002**, *65*, 892–896. [CrossRef] [PubMed]
37. Panzitt, K.; Wagner, M. FXR in liver physiology: Multiple faces to regulate liver metabolism. *Biochim. Biophys. Acta Mol. Basis Dis.* **2021**, *1867*, 166133. [CrossRef] [PubMed]
38. Filali-Mouncef, Y.; Hunter, C.; Roccio, F.; Zagkou, S.; Dupont, N.; Primard, C.; Proikas-Cezanne, T.; Reggiori, F. The ménage à trois of autophagy, lipid droplets and liver disease. *Autophagy* **2022**, *18*, 50–72. [CrossRef] [PubMed]
39. Wang, B.; Tontonoz, P. Liver X receptors in lipid signalling and membrane homeostasis. *Nat. Rev. Endocrinol.* **2018**, *14*, 452–463. [CrossRef]
40. Lu, M.C.; Ji, J.A.; Jiang, Z.Y.; You, Q.D. The Keap1-Nrf2-ARE Pathway As a Potential Preventive and Therapeutic Target: An Update. *Med. Res. Rev. Sep.* **2016**, *36*, 924–963. [CrossRef]
41. Bhattacharjee, S.; Dashwood, R.H. Epigenetic Regulation of NRF2/KEAP1 by Phytochemicals. *Antioxidants* **2020**, *9*, 865. [CrossRef]
42. Alhouayek, M.; Muccioli, G.G. COX-2-derived endocannabinoid metabolites as novel inflammatory mediators. *Trends Pharmacol. Sci.* **2014**, *35*, 284–292. [CrossRef]
43. Lin, S.; Li, X.; Zhang, J.; Zhang, Y. Omentin-1: Protective impact on ischemic stroke via ameliorating atherosclerosis. *Clin. Chim. Acta* **2021**, *517*, 31–40. [CrossRef]
44. Yahfoufi, N.; Alsadi, N.; Jambi, M.; Matar, C. The Immunomodulatory and Anti-Inflammatory Role of Polyphenols. *Nutrients* **2018**, *10*, 1618. [CrossRef]

separations

MDPI

Article

Multiprotein Inhibitory Effect of Dietary Polyphenol Rutin from Whole Green Jackfruit Flour Targeting Different Stages of Diabetes Mellitus: Defining a Bio-Computational Stratagem

Tejaswini Maradesha [1], Shashank M. Patil [1], Bhaskar Phanindra [2], Raghu Ram Achar [3], Ekaterina Silina [4], Victor Stupin [5] and Ramith Ramu [1,*]

[1] Department of Biotechnology and Bioinformatics, JSS Academy of Higher Education and Research, Mysuru 570015, India
[2] Department of Pharmacology, JSS Medical College, JSS Academy of Higher Education and Research, Mysuru 570015, India
[3] Division of Biochemistry, School of Life Sciences, JSS Academy of Higher Education and Research, Mysuru 570015, India
[4] Institute of Biodesign and Modeling of Complex Systems, I.M. Sechenov First Moscow State Medical University (Sechenov University), 119991 Moscow, Russia
[5] Department of Hospital Surgery 1, N.I. Pirogov Russian National Research Medical University (RNRMU), 117997 Moscow, Russia
* Correspondence: ramith.gowda@gmail.com; Tel.: +91-99-8638-0920; Fax: +91-82-1254-8394

Abstract: The anti-diabetic potential of whole unripe jackfruit (peel with pulp, flake, and seed) was investigated using inhibitory assays for α-glucosidase, α-amylase, aldose reductase, and glycation at multiple stages. Using activity-guided repeated fractionation on a silica gel column chromatography, dietary flavonoid rutin with potent antihyperglycemic activity was extracted from the methanol extract of whole jackfruit flour (MJ). Rutin was found to inhibit both α-glucosidase (IC_{50}: 7.86 µg/mL) and α-amylase (IC_{50}: 22.00 µg/mL) in a competitive manner of inhibition with low Ki values. In addition, in vitro glycation experiments revealed that rutin prevented each stage of protein glycation as well as the production of intermediate molecules. Furthermore, rutin significantly inhibited aldose reductase (IC_{50}: 2.75 µg/mL) in a non-competitive manner. During in silico studies, molecular docking and molecular dynamics simulation studies have suggested that rutin has a high binding affinity for the enzymes studied, which could explain its inhibitory effects. Rutin interacted with the key residues of the target enzymes' inhibitor binding sites. Compared to the controls used, rutin had a higher binding efficiency as well as stability in the inhibitor binding pocket of the target enzymes. According to our findings, the presence of rutin is more likely to be associated with the potential of MJ in antihyperglycemic activity via inhibition of α-glucosidase and in anti-diabetic action via inhibition of the polyol pathway and protein glycation. The bio-computational study indicates rutin as a potential lead inhibitor of all the target enzymes used and could be used as an effective anti-diabetic drug in the near future.

Keywords: whole jackfruit; diabetes mellitus; dietary flavonoid; rutin; inhibition kinetics; molecular dynamics simulation; phyto-computational stratagem

1. Introduction

Type 2 diabetes mellitus (T2DM) is regarded as a serious concern of endocrine health, where altered body metabolism occurs due to an imbalance in insulin levels [1]. Over the past few decades, diabetes and obesity have increased at an unprecedented rate, affecting more than 10.5% and 13%, respectively, of the global adult population. In addition, it is also recognized as a pediatric medical problem [2,3]. In >90% of all instances, T2DM is reportedly more common than T1DM. There have been a few instances of it in children and teenagers, but adults are the ones who typically experience it [4]. Due to the increasing levels of fast urbanization, poor diets, tobacco consumption, obesity, environmental factors, aging populations, and sedentary lifestyles, the condition continues to pose a global danger [5]. Diabetes mellitus patients may develop a number of concomitant health maladies known as diabetic complications as a result of chronic hyperglycemia and insulin resistance. These include persistent deterioration and the dysfunction of bodily tissues, which results in diabetes cardiomyopathy, nephropathy, neuropathy, retinopathy, and diseases of the liver, pancreas, adipose tissue, and skeletal muscle [6].

The pathophysiology of diabetes mellitus is spread throughout different stages of human metabolism. Most of the events related to the development of diabetic conditions occur during the absorption of digested food. For instance, glycoside hydrolases are known as α-glucosidase (AG) and α-amylase (AM), which aid in the swift digestion of ingested carbohydrates into simpler monosaccharides, resulting in postprandial hyperglycemia (excess blood glucose). This is the first sign of diabetes, and glycoside inhibitors are widely acknowledged as an effective way to control postprandial hyperglycemia by preventing the release of free sugars, allowing for a stable glycemic profile [7,8].

By the action of aldose reductase (AR), high blood glucose levels produce a substantial flux of glucose into the polyol pathway, where it is converted to sorbitol [7,9]. Reduced metabolism or decreased membrane permeability of sorbitol dehydrogenase causes the overproduction of sorbitol, which in turn accumulates in tissues, such as nerves, retina, kidney, retina, and lens. Therefore, AR can act as a crucial target, which can be inhibited to prevent sorbitol accumulation, which is linked to a variety of microvascular problems and cardiovascular disorders [10]. In addition, protein glycation in diabetes mellitus results in a partial loss of activity as a result of persistent hyperglycemia. A non-enzymatic nucleophilic addition reaction of the carbonyl residue of sugar with the free amino group of proteins produces a reversible Schiff base, which ultimately yields a more stable Amadori product. The Amadori products are subsequently exposed to a series of dicarbonyl intermediate-mediated processes, yielding an unknown family of molecules known as advanced glycation end products (AGEs). These AGEs accumulate in tissues and are the source of micro- and macro-vascular problems in diabetics [11,12].

As a result, finding molecules that block all the stages of glycation and the synthesis of intermediary products in the route can aid in the development of new therapeutic approaches to delay or avoid harmful consequences. Furthermore, by interfering with the signal transduction cascade, glycated proteins and AGEs cause the production of reactive oxygen species (ROS), resulting in oxidative stress, which is a key factor in the advancement of numerous vascular problems in diabetes [11]. Antioxidants, which neutralize the produced free radicals, are the most effective way to defend against ROS-mediated damage. Overall, a medication with integrated antioxidant and anti-glycation characteristics, as well as potent AG inhibition and reduced AM inhibition, may be the most effective treatment for diabetes mellitus and its consequences [13].

In this context, the use of fruits and vegetables to prevent diabetes has been the center of focus. The effects exerted are mainly due to the enormous antioxidant and antihyperglycemic potentials present in fruits and vegetables, which indicates the pharmacological potential of phytochemicals to curb diabetes mellitus. [14,15]. Diabetes mellitus is a chronic metabolic syndrome produced by a shift in diet and lifestyle from traditional diets rich in plant-based foods, including legumes, grains, fruits, and vegetables, to more Western-style diets rich in fat, carbohydrates, and animal-source foods [16,17]. Therefore, traditional diets rich in bioactive compounds are indeed an effective mode of therapy to achieve long-term control of diabetes. Thus, the present era can be marked as the period of transition providing a better scientific basis for phytochemical therapies. It also paves newer avenues to the modern understanding of dietary interventions known as non-pharmacological interventions, in the treatment of chronic diseases such as diabetes mellitus [18,19].

To date, several plant species have been investigated for their anti-diabetic potential against multiple targets. *Artocarpus heterophyllus* (jackfruit), a member of the *Moraceae* family and a common household tree in India and Bangladesh, is the most well-known of these species. This tree is very popular for its fruit and timber and is commonly called "the poor man's food" because of its abundance and lower cost [20]. Studies have proved that the fruit contains carotenoids, flavonoids, volatile acids, sterols, and tannins with a robust antioxidant potential [20,21]. Although information is available on ripe jackfruit in terms of its composition and health benefits, there is scarce knowledge on its potential in the treatment of diabetes [20,22].

Therefore, we aim to investigate the anti-diabetic potential of methanol extract of whole unripe jackfruit flour (MJ) by inhibiting AG and AM, which cause hyperglycemia. We also aim to evaluate its effect on AR and protein glycation, which cause numerous diabetic complications. Glycation indicators were evaluated at each stage of glycation, including fructosamines (early stage), protein carbonyls (middle stage), and AGEs (late stage). Moreover, the isolation of active compounds responsible for the beneficial properties followed by computational approaches to evaluate their druggability and ability to bind to the target proteins was also carried out.

2. Materials and Methods

2.1. Plant Material

In May 2019, whole mature and unripe jackfruits (94–101 days) were collected in Chandra Bakke cultivar nurturing farms of Nanjangud, Karnataka, India (geographical coordinates: 12°9′12.88″ North 76°42′51.01″ East), and authenticated (MYS 457869) by the Department of Horticulture, Government of Karnataka, Mysore, India, which also housed voucher specimens. Before being sliced into bits, the samples were rinsed under running tap water. They were then shade-dried before being milled into flour and kept at 4 °C until needed.

2.2. Extraction

Using the Soxhlet apparatus (Borosil, Mumbai, Maharashtra, India), crude extracts of whole jackfruit flour were obtained by extracting 500 g of dried whole jackfruit (peel with pulp, flake, and seed) with solvents of increasing polarity (chloroform, ethyl acetate, acetone, methanol, and water). The solvents used for extraction were of analytical grade (99%) and were procured from Merck (Mumbai, India). The methanol extract was selected for further studies as it was found to be more active on the basis of antioxidant and anti-diabetic potential. The yield of the crude methanol extract was 70 g. This crude extract was fractionated using a series of column chromatography into petroleum ether, ethyl acetate, and n-butanol fractions. The active ethyl acetate soluble fraction was chromatographed on a silica gel column and successively eluted with stepwise linear gradients of chloroform: methanol. The most active fraction (90:10) was further chromatographed on a Sephadex LH-20 column (Mitsubishi Chemical Corporation, Tokyo, Japan) with methanol solvent to obtain rutin (Supplementary Materials Figure S1).

2.3. Inhibition Assay and Kinetics for AM, AG, and AR Inhibitory Activity

The crude extracts, fractions, and isolated rutin were evaluated for anti-diabetic target enzyme inhibition (AM, AG, and AR). All the test samples (crude extracts, fractions, and rutin) with varying concentrations (0–1000 μg/mL) were dissolved in dimethyl sulfoxide. Acarbose (AG and AM) and quercetin (AR) were used as the positive controls. The inhibition tests for AM (EC 3.2.1.1, type-VI B porcine pancreatic amylase), yeast AG (EC 3.2.1.20, type-1 α-glucosidase), and human recombinant AR were performed using starch (1%), pNPG (0.5 mM), and DL-glyceraldehyde (5 mM), respectively, as described earlier [7]. By comparing the absorbance change of the test samples to that of the control, the inhibitory activity was assessed. Using the formula below, the results were reported as a percentage of enzyme inhibition (AM, AG and AR).

$$\text{Inhibition (\%)} = A_{(control)} - A_{(sample)} / A_{(control)} \times 100$$

Each experiment was carried out three times with the necessary blanks. The inhibitory activity of the test samples were represented by the least-squares regression line of logarithmic concentrations plotted against percent inhibition, which yielded the IC_{50} values (μg/mL). When compared to the control, this number (IC_{50} values) shows the concentration of test samples that can inhibit enzyme activity by 50%. The inhibition kinetics of AM, AG, and AR were determined using the method described by Maradesha et al. (2022) [20].

2.4. Assay for Antioxidant Activity

According to a previous study by Razali et al., 2008 [23], the antioxidant activity was assessed under in vitro conditions using the DPPH (2,2-diphenyl-1-picryl-hydrazyl-hydrate), superoxide, and ABTS (2,2′-azino-bis(3-ethylbenzothiazoline-6-sulfonic acid)) radical scavenging activities. The tests were conducted in triplicates. Their potential radical scavenging capability was represented by EC_{50} values. An EC_{50} value implies scavenging of 50% of free, cation, and anion radicals.

2.5. Analysis of Phenolic Compounds and Ascorbic Acid by HPLC

With a few minor modifications in the protocol, the identification of phenolic compounds from methanol extract of whole jackfruit flour (MJ) was conducted according to Seal (2016) [24]. With a photodiode array (PDA) detector and a reverse phase C18 (250 mm 4.6 mm, Supelco) column, the HPLC system (Agilent Technologies, Santa Clara, CA, USA) was run at 37 °C with a flow rate of 0.8 mL/min and an injection volume of 20 μL. Methanol (solvent A) and 0.1% formic acid (*v*/*v*) in water (solvent B) made up the mobile phase. From 0 to 55 min, the elution gradient was 85% A and 15% B; from 55 to 57 min, 20% A and 80% B; from 57 to 60 min, 85% A and 15% B. The phenolic compounds peak areas were compared to those of the standards viz. ascorbic acid, gallic acid, catechin, methyl gallate, caffeic acid, syringic acid, rutin, p-coumaric acid, sinapic acid, ferulic acid, myricetin, quercetin, apigenin, and kaempferol (Supplementary Materials Figure S2).

2.6. Determination of Total Flavonoid Content (TFC) and Total Phenol Content (TPC)

The TFC was evaluated using a modified protocol by Ordon et al. (2006) [25]. Furthermore, 200 μL of a 0.5 mol/L sodium carbonate solution was mixed with one milliliter of MJ of different concentrations (0–1000 μg/mL). The mixture was added to 200 μL of 0.3 mol/L aluminum chloride crystalline after standing for 5 min, and the mixture was then incubated for an additional 5 min. The reaction system was then added with 1.0 mL of 1 M NaOH, and the absorbance was measured at 510 nm in comparison to a blank. Quercetin equivalents per gram of dry weight (QE/g) were used to calculate and express the results.

By the Folin–Ciocalteu method, the TPC in MJ was determined as per Shuxia et al. (2013) [26]. In brief, 5.9 mL of water was used to dilute MJ (100 μL) of different concentrations (0–1000 μg/mL) before they were mixed. In addition, 200 μL of Folin–Ciocalteu reagent was added, and 2 mL of sodium carbonate solution was added 1 min later to the mixture. A 120-min reaction at room temperature and dark conditions was given to the mixture before the absorbance at 735 nm was obtained. Results were represented in milligrams of gallic acid equivalents (GAE/g) and compared to a reference of gallic acid.

2.7. Separation and Identification of Rutin

The methanol extract was chosen for the extraction of bioactive constituents because of its inhibitory potential (AG, AM, and AR), yield, and antioxidant capabilities. The methanol extract of whole jackfruit flour (MJ) was subjected to phytochemical profiling [27]. First, 70 g of MJ was fractionated using column chromatography (90 cm × 3 cm) on silica gel (100–200 mesh) and eluted with analytical grade (99%) solvents such as ethyl acetate, petroleum ether, and n-butanol (500 mL). Next, the soluble fractions (petroleum ether: 7 g; ethyl acetate: 8 g; n-butanol: 6 g) were collected (21 fractions), concentrated (flash evaporation), and then tested for anti-diabetic and antioxidant activities. The active ethyl acetate soluble fraction (Fr. I-09–15) was chromatographed once more on a silica gel column (35 cm–2 cm) and successively eluted with stepwise linear gradients of chloroform: methanol (100:0; 95:5; 90:10; 80:20; 75:25; 50:50; 25:75; 0:100 v/v). Then, the fractions were gathered (51 fractions) and spotted on Merck's F254 pre-coated silica gel plates (20 × 20 cm). The optimum resolution was obtained in the solvent system of ethyl acetate: toluene: formic acid (4.5:5:0.5, v/v). Thin Layer Chromatography (TLC) plates were subjected to iodine fumes to visualize the spot. The fractions (Fr) in the TLC pattern that had a similar retention factor (Rf) were combined. The anti-diabetic and antioxidant activity of these fractions were evaluated. The most active ethyl acetate soluble fraction Fr. II (37–42) was again separated using silica gel column (30 cm × 2 cm) chromatography with a 90:10 mixture of chloroform and methanol, followed by re-chromatography using a Sephadex LH20 column with methanol as the eluting solvent to yield rutin (Supplementary Material Figure S1). Rutin (96 mg) was isolated from Fr. II (37–42) with a single spot-on TLC with ethyl acetate: toluene: formic acid (4.5:5:0.5, v/v) as the mobile phase.

2.8. Structural Elucidation

Fourier transform infrared (FT-IR) (Thermo Fisher Scientific, Rockford, IL, USA), LCMS2010A (Shimadzu, Tokyo, Japan), and the ^{1}H and ^{13}C Nuclear magnetic spectrometer (NMR) (Bruker Biospin Co., Karlsruhe, Germany) with deuterated chloroform or chloroform-d ($CDCl_3$) as a solvent were used to determine the chemical structure of rutin.

2.9. Multiple Stages of the Human Serum Albumin (HSA) Glycation Inhibition Assay

The antiglycation potential of rutin was examined at multiple stages, namely early glycation product (fructosamine), intermediate (protein carbonyls), and late-stage glycation end products (AGEs), according to the procedure published in our previous work [1].

2.10. Molecular Docking Simulation

Protein and ligand preparation, binding site prediction, and virtual screening of the phenolic compounds were conducted according to Patil et al. (2021) [28]. The AG protein sequence retrieved from UniProt (https://www.uniprot.org/) was used to construct a homology model using SWISS-MODEL (https://swissmodel.expasy.org/ accessed on 10 July 2022). The protein model was constructed using an x-ray crystal structure of Saccharomyces cerevisiae isomaltase (PDB ID: 3AXH), which showed 72% identical and 84% comparable sequences at a resolution of 1.8 Å [29]. The validation of protein structure using the Ramachandran plot revealed the presence of 94% of the 9362 residues in favorable regions [28]. In addition, the X-ray crystal protein structures of AM (PDB ID: 1DHK), human serum albumin (HSA) (PDB ID: 2BXG), and human AR (HAR) (PDB ID: 1IEI) were obtained from the RCSB PDB database (https://www.rcsb.org/ accessed on 10 July 2022). For these proteins, the binding site was predicted using the literature analysis. For AG, the binding site predicted in the previous study was used [22]. Binding pocket of AG was placed in a box of 40 Å × 40 Å × 40 Å positioned at x = −17.489 Å, y = −8.621 Å, and z = −19.658 Å using AutoDock Tools 1.5.6 (Center for Computational Structural Biology Logo) [28]. Similarly, for AM (22.48 Å × 22.48 Å × 22.48 Å positioned at x = 103.469 Å, y = 37.176 Å, z = 19.607 Å), HSA (15.02 Å × 15.02 Å × 15.02 Å positioned at x = 8.249 Å, y = 2.58 Å, and z = −14.75 Å), and HAR (8.25 Å × 8.25 Å × 8.25 Å positioned at x = −5.06 Å, y = 0.19 Å, and z = 9.94 Å), grid boxes consisting of binding residues were placed. In case of ligand preparation, phytochemical structures in 3D Spatial Data File (SDF) format obtained from PubChem (https://pubchem.ncbi.nlm.nih.gov/ accessed on 11 July 2022 were converted into PDBQT format using OpenBabel 2.3.1 [30]. After ligand preparation, the compounds were docked into their respective protein targets using AutoDock Vina 1.1.2. Acarbose was used as a control for both AG and AM, whereas aminoguanidine and quercetin were used as a control for HSA and HAR, respectively.

2.11. Molecular Dynamics Simulation

The docked conformations of target proteins and respective ligands with the most negative binding affinity were selected, and the molecular dynamics simulation was performed according to Patil et al. (2021) [31]. The GROMACS-2018.1 software package (The Biophysical Chemistry department of University of Groningen, Groningen, Poland) was used for the simulation [32]. The CHARMM36 force field was applied to all the protein–ligand complexes, subsequently obtaining the ligand topology using the CGenFF server [33]. Using the GROMACS pdb2gmx module, hydrogen atoms were added to the present heavy atoms. Subsequently, vacuum minimization of 5000 steps was performed utilizing the steepest descent algorithm. Both protein–rutin and protein–acarbose complexes were placed in a box of 10 Å distance to the edges. The solvent was added using the TIP3P water model. Further, by incorporating the appropriate number of Na^+ and Cl^- counter ions, all the systems were neutralized. The steepest descent and conjugate gradient methods were employed to minimize the energy of the systems. A short equilibration in constant number (N), volume (V), and temperature (T) or NVT and constant number (N), pressure (P), and temperature (T) or NPT ensembles (1000 ps each) were performed prior to the simulation run. In total, 12 simulations were run (4 bare protein atoms, 4 protein–rutin complexes, and 4 protein–standard drug complexes) for 100 ns time at 310K temperature and 1 bar pressure. The protein–ligand root-mean-square deviation (RMSD), root-mean-square fluctuation (RMSF), radius of gyration (Rg), and solvent accessible surface-area trajectory analysis (SASA) and ligand hydrogen bond trajectory analysis were conducted by plotting the respective graphs using XMGRACE 5.1.22 [34].

2.12. Binding Free Energy Calculations

Another application of molecular dynamics simulations and thermodynamics to analyze the extent of ligand binding with protein is the computation of binding free energy of a protein–ligand complex. The Molecular Mechanics/Poisson–Boltzmann Surface Area (MM-PBSA) technique was employed to calculate the binding free energy for each ligand–protein complex using the g_mmpbsa tool [35]. The binding free energy is calculated using three components in the g_mmpbsa tool: molecular mechanical energy, polar and apolar solvation energies, and molecular mechanical energy. The last 50 ns of molecular dynamics trajectories were used to compute ΔG with dt 1000 frames. The binding free energy is computed using Equation (1) below, while the free energy of individual complex components is obtained using Equation (2) below:

$$\Delta G_{binding} = G_{complex} - (G_{protein} + G_{ligand}) \tag{1}$$

$$G = (E_{MM})\text{-}TS + (G_{sol}) \tag{2}$$

$$E_{MM} = E_{bonded} + E_{nonbonded} \tag{3}$$

$$G_{sol} = G_{polar} + G_{nonpolar} \tag{4}$$

G_{sol} is the sum of the solvation-free energy, while E_{MM} is the average potential energy in vacuum. E_{bonde}d indicates the bond length, angle, and torsion angle in Equation (3), whereas non-bonded van der Waals and electrostatic are observed in Equation (3). The energy required to transport a solute from vacuum to a solvent is calculated using Equation (4). The electrostatic and non-electrostatic support for the solvation-free energy is represented by G_{polar} and $G_{nonpolar}$ [36].

2.13. Statistical Analysis

All three different sets of experiments were conducted in triplicates. The data is presented as a mean standard deviation (mean ± SE). The computer program SPSS 21.0 version for Windows (Version 21.0, Chicago, IL, USA) was used for statistical analysis. Duncan's multiple range tests were performed to establish the study's significance, followed by one-way ANOVA. The level of statistical significance was chosen at $p \leq 0.05$.

3. Results

3.1. Isolation and Identification of Rutin from MJ

The methanol extract was chosen for extraction and purification of the bioactive component responsible for whole jackfruit flour due to its high antioxidant and anti-diabetic potential (Table 1) in comparison to other solvents (viz. chloroform, ethyl acetate, acetone, and water). Further, the crude methanol extract was fractionated chromatographically into three different polarity extracts: petroleum ether, ethyl acetate, and n-butanol. Individual soluble fractions were then tested for radical scavenging activities (DPPH, ABTS, and superoxide) and enzyme inhibition (AG, AM, and AR) to calculate the anti-diabetic as well as antioxidant effects of the extract fractions. Ethyl acetate was found to be the most effective solvent (in comparison to petroleum ether and n-butanol) in radical scavenging and anti-diabetic activities, with the lowest IC_{50} and EC_{50} values (Table 1). The findings suggest that bioactive components derived from whole jackfruit flour are more abundant in the ethyl acetate fraction of the methanol extract. Using column chromatography, the bioactive component of the ethyl acetate fraction from whole jackfruit flour was extracted (Supplementary Figure S1).

Table 1. Antioxidant activity and inhibitory potential of crude extracts and its respective fractions of green jackfruit flour against α-amylase, α-glucosidase, and aldose reductase enzymes.

Extracts (Ext.)/Fractions (Fr.)	Enzyme Inhibition IC_{50} ^{x,y} (μg/mL)			Antioxidant Activity EC_{50} ^{x,z} (μg/mL)		
	α-Amylase	α-Glucosidase	Aldose Reductase	DPPH	ABTS	Superoxide
Chloroform (Ext.)	43.00 ± 0.86 ^{h}	24.09 ± 0.14 ^{f}	9.00 ± 0.15 ^{d}	35.65 ± 0.57 ^{h}	35.14 ± 1.25 ^{h}	66.25 ± 1.19 ^{i}
Ethyl Acetate (Ext.)	36.65 ± 0.14 ^{f}	15.00 ±0.88 ^{e}	9.68 ± 1.11 ^{e}	37.05 ± 1.23 ^{i}	32.00 ± 0.00 ^{g}	50.80 ± 0.08 ^{f}
Acetone (Ext.)	31.00 ± 0.50 ^{e}	14.45 ± 0.23 ^{e}	8.00 ± 0.04 ^{d}	30.66 ± 0.08 ^{f}	28.00 ± 0.94 ^{f}	52.99 ± 0.37 ^{g}
Methanol (Ext.)	27.95 ± 0.10 ^{c}	10.10 ± 0.20 ^{c}	3.80 ± 1.01 ^{b}	24.55 ± 1.52 ^{d}	21.00 ± 0.96 ^{c}	44.75 ± 1.23 ^{e}
Water (Ext.)	47.00 ± 0.86 ^{i}	31.15 ± 0.08 ^{g}	10.20 ± 1.41 ^{e}	44.50 ± 0.02 ^{k}	36.65 ± 0.10 ^{h}	57.88 ± 1.33 ^{h}
Petroleum ether (Fr.)	40.50 ± 1.44 ^{g}	30.50 ± 0.54 ^{g}	8.50 ± 0.30 ^{d}	32.50 ± 0.11 ^{g}	39.15 ± 0.88 ^{i}	57.00 ± 1.00 ^{h}
Ethyl Acetate (Fr.)	26.15 ± 0.15 ^{c}	09.00 ± 0.10 ^{b}	3.25 ± 0.70 ^{b}	23.50 ± 0.35 ^{d}	19.06 ± 1.74 ^{b}	40.75 ± 0.65 ^{d}
n-butanol (Fr.)	31.00 ± 0.77 ^{e}	14.50 ± 0.55 ^{e}	6.00 ± 1.01 ^{c}	28.50 ± 0.80 ^{e}	25.00 ± 0.90 ^{e}	46.14 ± 1.26 ^{e}
Cf:Me (22–30)	28.00 ± 0.34 ^{c}	12.00 ± 1.33 ^{d}	5.50 ± 0.33 ^{c}	27.05 ± 0.12 ^{e}	23.00 ± 0.12 ^{d}	41.50 ± 1.14 ^{d}
Cf:Me (31–36)	27.88 ± 1.87 ^{c}	10.75 ± 1.02 ^{c}	5.25 ± 0.55 ^{c}	27.10 ± 1.09 ^{e}	22.15 ± 1.73 ^{c}	37.75 ± 1.00 ^{c}
Cf:Me (37–42)—Rutin	22.00 ± 0.16 ^{a}	07.86 ± 0.33 ^{a}	2.75 ± 0.10 ^{a}	15.00 ± 0.18 ^{a}	10.70 ± 0.47 ^{a}	27.05 ± 1.00 ^{a}
Cf:Me (43–48)	25.00 ± 0.00 ^{b}	09.05 ± 0.40 ^{b}	6.33 ± 0.21 ^{c}	18.25 ± 1.88 ^{b}	18.55 ± 1.11 ^{b}	30.30 ± 0.04 ^{b}
Cf:Me (49–54)	28.20 ± 1.33 ^{c}	10.50 ± 0.66 ^{c}	6.00 ± 0.12 ^{c}	25.10 ± 1.01 ^{d}	25.40 ± 0.75 ^{e}	40.06 ± 0.15 ^{d}
Cf:Me (55–60)	28.13 ± 0.07 ^{c}	09.50 ± 1.10 ^{b}	6.50 ± 0.00 ^{c}	19.20 ± 1.02 ^{c}	20.65 ± 1.66 ^{c}	40.00 ± 0.26 ^{d}
Cf:Me (61–66)	27.77 ± 1.19 ^{c}	08.80 ± 0.56 ^{b}	5.05 ± 1.00 ^{c}	20.20 ± 1.08 ^{c}	23.35 ± 0.68 ^{d}	35.66 ± 0.14 ^{c}
Cf:Me (67–72)	28.75 ± 0.55 ^{d}	10.88 ± 0.16 ^{c}	3.90 ± 0.16 ^{b}	34.66 ± 0.09 ^{h}	26.11 ± 0.54 ^{e}	50.00 ± 0.44 ^{f}
Positive control *	29.00 ± 0.16 ^{d}	11.05 ± 0.23 ^{c}	4.00 ± 0.14 ^{b}	40.00 ± 0.18 ^{j}	31.25 ± 0.02 ^{g}	65.00 ± 0.10 ^{i}

^{x} Values are reported as mean ± SE. A significant variation between the extracts and fractions is indicated by the different superscript letters (a–k) are significantly different ($p \leq 0.05$) according to Duncan multiple range test. ^{y} The IC_{50} (μg/mL) value is the sample concentration at which 50% inhibition was achieved. ^{z} The effective concentration of samples required to show 50% antioxidant activity under assay conditions is defined as the EC_{50} (μg/mL) value. * In the α-amylase and α-glucosidase inhibition assays, acarbose was utilized as a positive control, but in the aldose reductase assay, quercetin was employed as a positive control.

The bioactive compound was characterized as rutin with the resulting characteristics: pale yellow amorphous powder. Melting point: 242 °C. UV (methanol): λmax 359 nm. IR (KBr): 3520–3610 cm $^{-1}$ (OH). ^{1}H NMR (DMSO): δ 1.21 (s, 3H, CH_3), 3.48 (m, 6H, 6-HO-CH), 3.75 (d, 2H, O-CH_2), 3.9 (d, 1H, -O-CH), 4.15 (bs, 6H, 6-OH), 4.2 (q, 1H, -O-CH-C), 5.1 (s, 2H, 2-O-CH), 5.55 (bs, 4H, 4-OH), 6.2–6.6 (m, 5H, Ar-H). ^{13}C NMR (DMSO): δ 16.8, 64.5, 70.6, 71.8, 73.2, 73.5, 73.6, 73.9, 75.9, 77.7, 92.7, 98.0, 98.3, 104.5, 105.5, 113.6, 117.2, 120.4, 124.4, 135.1, 146.5, 147.2, 154.9, 160.1, 163.9, 166.4, 178.3. MS: m/z 611 (M+1). Analytical calculated data for $C_{27}H_{30}O_{16}$ (610.15): C, 53.12; H, 4.95. Found: C, 53.15; H, 4.93%. On the basis of the previously mentioned findings (Supplementary Materials Figures S3 and S4), as well as comparisons with NMR and MS data in the literature, the identity of rutin was determined [37,38]. These results concur with our HPLC findings that rutin was found in the methanol extract (Table 2). Additionally, the total phenolic content (253.7 mg GAE per g) and total flavonoid content (602.20 mg QE per g) of MJ was found to be high.

Table 2. HPLC study of phenolic components in methanol extract of green jackfruit flour.

Sl. No.	Name	Ret. Time	Area	Height	Concentration (μg/mg)
1	Ascorbic acid	4.223	294,491	35,608	17.29
2	Gallic acid	5.712	96,769	16,767	5.69
3	Catechin	11.520	73,497	7891	4.32
4	Methyl gallate	12.436	30,776	3117	1.81
5	Caffeic acid	14.586	21,652	2539	1.27
6	Syringic acid	15.033	14,842	2119	0.87
7	Rutin	18.396	11,618	1976	0.68
8	p-Coumaric acid	19.068	15,034	2077	0.88
9	Sinapic acid	19.851	38,537	6079	2.26
10	Ferulic acid	20.996	55,995	6370	3.29
11	Myricetin	23.226	17,352	2102	1.02
12	Quercetin	28.368	11,515	1267	0.68
13	Apigenin	32.265	96,531	8183	5.67
14	Kaempferol	34.993	107,714	10,321	6.32

3.2. Effect of Isolated Fractions on Multiple Diabetic Enzyme Inhibition

Table 1 shows the inhibitory activity of isolated fractions derived from methanol extraction of green jackfruit flour on AG, AM, and AR. Rutin isolated from methanol extract inhibited all the enzymes (IC_{50}: 22.00 μg/mL (AM); IC_{50}: 7.86 μg/mL (AG); IC_{50}: 2.75 μg/mL (AR) more effectively than all other isolated fractions. Under the same conditions, acarbose and quercetin exhibited IC_{50} values of 29.00 μg/mL (AM), 11.05 μg/mL (AG), and 4.00 μg/mL (AR), respectively, indicating that MJ and its isolated fractions had a stronger inhibitory impact in this experiment. Rutin and all isolated fractions demonstrated considerably higher ($p \leq 0.05$) IC_{50} values than acarbose and quercetin on yeast AG, AM, and AR.

3.3. Enzyme Kinetics of Multiple Diabetic Enzyme Inhibition by Rutin

To elucidate the manner of AM, AG, and AR inhibition, kinetic analysis was performed for rutin by incubating with different doses of starch (0.5–8%), *p*NPG (4-Nitrophenyl-β-D-glucopyranoside) (0.25–4 mmol L^{-1}), and DL-glyceraldehyde (2.5–40 mmol L^{-1}), respectively, in the absence (control) or presence of rutin at IC_{20}, IC_{40}, and IC_{60} inhibitory concentrations (μg/mL). Lineweaver–Burk (LB) plots in the reaction were used to determine the mode of inhibition, Km, and Vmax values. Figure 1A–C illustrate LB plots of rutin against the inhibition of AM, AG, and AR, respectively. The results show that rutin caused a decrease in Vmax values compared to the control, with a corresponding increase in Km value (without substantial change in Km values), which is typical of reversible, mixed-type plots. Competitive and non-competitive inhibition are combined in mixed-type inhibition. The kinetic manner of inhibition of starch, pNPG, and DL-glyceraldehyde by rutin was mixed, with increasing concentrations resulting in a succession of lines on the y-axis with the same intercept but various gradients. Rutin exhibited a mixed-type of inhibition against all the enzymes tested viz. AM (K1: 8.80 μg/mL; K2: 12.34 μg/mL), AG (K1: 11.50 μg/mL; K2: 15.15 μg/mL), and AR (K1: 37.86 μg/mL; K2: 59.05μg/mL). K1 and K2 are two types of inhibitor constants used in mixed inhibition. The kinetics of rutin inhibition against all the enzymes revealed that K2 values of rutin were greater than K1, indicating that rutin has a stronger affinity for free enzymes than for enzyme–substrate complexes.

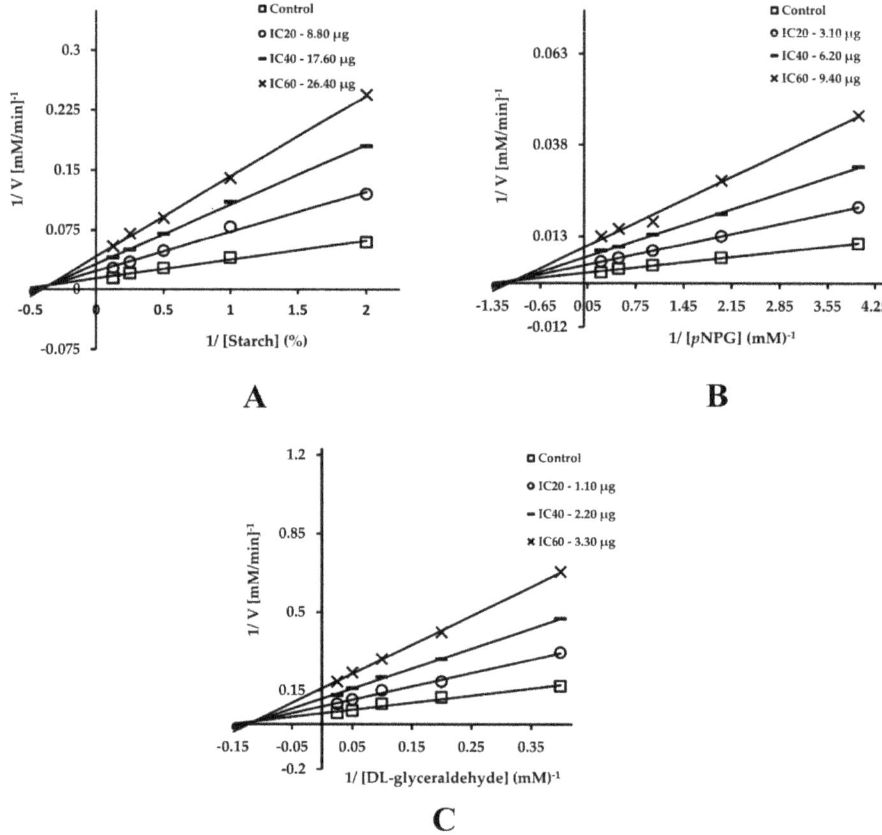

Figure 1. Rutin inhibitory potential of α-amylase (**A**), α-glucosidase (**B**), and aldose reductase (**C**) via Lineweaver–Burk plot of substrate-dependent enzyme kinetics. A-amylase, α-glucosidase, and aldose reductase were incubated with different doses of starch (0.5–8%), *p*NPG (0.25–4 mmol L^{-1}), and DL-glyceraldehyde (2.5–40 mmol L^{-1}), respectively, in the absence (control) or presence of rutin at IC_{20}, IC_{40}, and IC_{60} inhibitory concentrations (μgmL^{-1}).

3.4. Antioxidant Activities of the Isolated Fractions

DPPH, ABTS, and superoxide radical scavenging assay methodologies were used to assess the antioxidant properties of the separated MJ fractions (Table 1). In all parameters, rutin had stronger antioxidant activity than BHA (positive control). Additionally, in comparison to the positive control, all fractions examined had better radical scavenging properties (Table 1). The antioxidant activity of the investigated samples, as determined by DPPH, ABTS, and the superoxide radical scavenging method, might be ordered as follows: Rutin > MJ > ethyl acetate fractions > BHA in terms of EC_{50} values.

3.5. Antiglycation Potential of Rutin

In the antiglycation assay, HSA comprising fructose, rutin, or aminoguanidine (positive control) at varying concentrations was utilized. In sterile circumstances, the reaction mixture was incubated at 37 °C for 21 days. After 21 days, it was clear that rutin had strong inhibitory actions (at all stages) compared with the positive control with various concentrations. Rutin (88%) and aminoguanidine (68%) were found to suppress the synthesis of fructosamines at a concentration of 100 μg/mL, whilst protein carbonyl compounds were inhibited at 91% and 70%, respectively. Rutin and aminoguanidine have been shown to reduce the production of AGE by 51% and 74%, respectively. In the presence of rutin, thiol shielding values were found to be 82% (concentration 100 μg/mL). Under the same assay conditions, aminoguanidine (concentration 100 μg/mL) exhibited 75% thiol group protection.

3.6. Molecular Docking Simulation

Molecular docking simulation results show that rutin had the higher (most negative) binding affinity among all the ten phenolic compounds screened for the four target proteins, whereas the controls had a lesser binding affinity. The virtual screening of the compounds based on the binding affinity and the total number of bonds formed is been detailed in Table 3. While interacting with AG, rutin also formed the highest non-bonding interactions (thirteen); nine turned out to be hydrogen bonds. The hydrogen bonds formed by rutin included ARG 439 (2.71 Å), ASP 349 (2.18 Å and 2.17 Å), HIS 279 (2.95 Å), GLU 276 (2.63 Å), THR 307 (2.29 Å), ARG 312 (3.15 Å), PHE 157 (1.85 Å), and HIS 245 (2.97 Å). Two hydrophobic interactions, including a pi–pi stacked bond with HIS 279 (5.53 Å), and a pi–sigma bond with PRO 309 (2.46 Å) were formed. There were two electrostatic pi-anion bonds formed with GLU 304 (4.17 Å and 3.72 Å). With all these binding interactions, rutin had a binding affinity of −10.5 kcal/mol, whereas acarbose was found to have only seven non-bonding interactions with all of them being hydrogen bonds. These include GLU 304 (2.36 Å), SER 308 (1.92 Å), HIS 279 (2.49 Å), THR 307 (2.55 Å), PHE 157 (3.56 Å), HIS 239 (3.02 Å), and PRO 309 (1.77 Å). With these binding interactions, acarbose was predicted with −8.2 kcal/mol binding affinity. The binding interactions of rutin and acarbose with AG are visualized in Figure 2. In the case of AM, rutin bound with the key residue was involved with the catalytic mechanism, GLU 233 with two hydrogen bonds (2.85 Å) and (2.16 Å). In total, rutin was predicted with ten non-bonding interactions, in which seven of them were found to be hydrogen bonds. Apart from GLU 233, it formed five hydrogen bonds with HIS 101 (2.42 Å), HIS 299 (2.94 Å), ARG 195 (2.11 Å), TYR 151 (1.93 Å), and HIS 201 (2.04 Å). It also formed hydrophobic pi–pi bonds with TRP 59 (5.13 Å and 4.53 Å) and TYR 62 (4.65 Å). With these interactions, rutin had a binding affinity of −10.2 kcal/mol. While binding with AM, acarbose interacted with the GLU 233 with a single hydrogen bond (2.40 Å). However, apart from this, it was predicted with only four hydrogen bonds with HIS 101 (2.71 Å), TRP 59 (2.68 Å), ASP 300 (2.78 Å), and ASN 298 (2.75 Å). Acarbose did not form any hydrophobic or electrostatic bonds, and it had a binding affinity of −8.9 kcal/mol. The binding interactions of rutin and acarbose with AM are visualized in Figure 3. Both rutin and aminoguanidine are bound with the same binding site in the case of HSA, which is located at the subdomain IIIA, bound with co-crystallized ligand ibuprofen. Rutin formed a total of fourteen non-bonding interactions, where six of them were found to be hydrogen bonds. In the subdomain IIIA, rutin was predicted to bind with the key residues such as ASN 489 (2.39 Å), ARG 410 (2.19 Å), TYR 411 (2.57 Å), and VAL 433 (2.55 Å) with hydrogen bonds. Two hydrophobic pi–alkyl bonds were formed with VAL 433 (4.64 Å) and LEU 430 (5.44 Å). In addition, rutin formed a pi–sigma bond with LEU 453 (4.61 Å). Apart from these interactions, rutin bound with ASN 391 with two hydrogen bonds (1.87 Å and 3.26 Å), CYS 438 (4.94 Å) with a pi–sulfur bond, and ALA 449 (4.66 Å) with a pi–alkyl bond. With these interactions, rutin had a binding affinity of −9.9 kcal/mol. However, aminoguanidine was not able to bind properly with HSA. It had formed only two hydrogen bonds with ARG 485 (2.93 Å and 2.86 Å). There were two unfavorable bonds present, LYS 414 (3.04 Å and TYR 411 Å). With these bonds, aminoguanidine had a binding affinity of −6.4 kcal/mol. The visualization of binding interactions of rutin and aminoguanidine with HSA is given in Figure 4. In addition, both rutin and quercetin occupied the same binding site of the co-crystallized ligand zenarestat, which is located near to the NADPH binding site. Rutin formed a total of ten non-bonding interactions with HAR, including six hydrogen bonds. The hydrogen bonds included TYR 48 (1.81 Å), TRP 111 (1.78 Å), TRP 20 (2.52 Å), VAL 47 (2.93 Å), GLN 49 (2.45 Å), and PHE 122 (2.14 Å). It also formed three pi–alkyl bonds with CYS 298 (3.58 Å), TRP 219 (4.98 Å), and PRO 218 (5.48 Å). Altogether, rutin's binding affinity was −10.2 kcal/mol with these interactions, whereas quercetin formed a total of eight non-bonding interactions, which included a single hydrogen bond. It is bound with TRP 20 (5.03 Å) and TRP 111 (5.74 Å and 5.22 Å) with hydrophobic pi–pi bonds. It is also bound with LEU 300 with (5.13 Å and 3.63 Å). However, two unfavorable bonds with CYS 298 (2.39 Å) and TYR 309 (2.42 Å) were also present. With these interactions, quercetin was found with a binding affinity of −7.8 kcal/mol. The visualization of binding interactions of rutin and quercetin with HAR is depicted in Figure 5.

Table 3. Binding affinity, total number of non-bonding interactions, and hydrogen bonds formed by phenolic compounds during docking simulation.

Sl. No.	Name of the Compound	α-Glucosidase			α-Amylase			HSA			HAR		
		BA	NB	HB	BA	NB	HB	BA	NB	HB	BA	NB	HB
1	Ascorbic acid	−5.2	3	2	−7.5	7	2	−8.1	8	2	−6.2	5	1
2	Gallic acid	−6.4	3	2	−8.2	8	1	−7.7	7	2	−7.8	6	0
3	Catechin	−6.4	2	1	−9.1	5	2	−7.1	6	2	−8.3	8	2
4	Methyl gallate	−8.2	5	4	−8.1	6	3	−6.4	9	3	−7.2	4	3
5	Caffeic acid	−5.9	8	5	−6.2	5	1	−7.0	8	4	−8.2	7	1
6	Syringic acid	−8.4	11	6	−9.1	9	4	−8.9	10	5	−9.0	8	4
7	Rutin	−10.5	13	9	−10.2	10	7	−9.9	14	6	−10.2	10	6
8	p-Coumaric acid	−5.8	7	5	−8.3	9	6	−9.1	7	1	−9.7	9	3
9	Sinapic acid	−5.6	8	4	−7.2	7	3	−8.4	8	2	−8.2	5	2
10	Ferulic acid	−8.0	6	5	−6.5	8	3	−7.1	8	2	−6.2	8	3
11	Myricetin	−9.1	5	5	−8.9	5	2	−9.2	7	4	−7.8	6	5
12	Apigenin	−8.1	6	2	−7.2	8	2	−8.1	5	2	−8.6	5	2
13	Kaempferol	−8.5	7	3	−8.0	7	5	−7.4	6	3	−9.1	7	6
14	Acarbose	−8.2	7	7	−8.9	5	5	-	-	-	-	-	-
15	Amino-guanidine	-	-	-	-	-	-	−6.4	2	2	-	-	-
16	Quercetin	-	-	-	-	-	-	-	-	-	−7.8	8	1

Note: BA: binding affinity in kcal/mol, NB: Total number of non-bonding interactions, HB: Total number of hydrogen bonds, HSA: human serum albumin, HAR: human aldose reductase.

3.7. Molecular Dynamics Simulation

Since rutin had the highest number of interactions and the most negative binding affinity, it was selected for simulation. Based on the results obtained from the simulations that were run for 100 ns, trajectories were plotted in terms of RMSD, RMSF, Rg, SASA, and ligand hydrogen bonds. The stability of the protein–ligand complexes is depicted in the RMSD plot of the simulation. The Rg plot plots illustrate the structural compactness of the molecules by calculating their RMSD with respect to the central axis of rotation. The RMSF plots show a particle's average deviation from a reference point over time. It examines the regions of the protein–ligand complex or protein backbone structure that differ the most/least from the mean. Furthermore, the area around the hydrophobic core created between protein–ligand complexes is shown in the SASA plots. Since few hydrogen bonds were concurrently disrupted and rebuilt, it is critical to calculate the number of hydrogen bonds produced during the simulation.

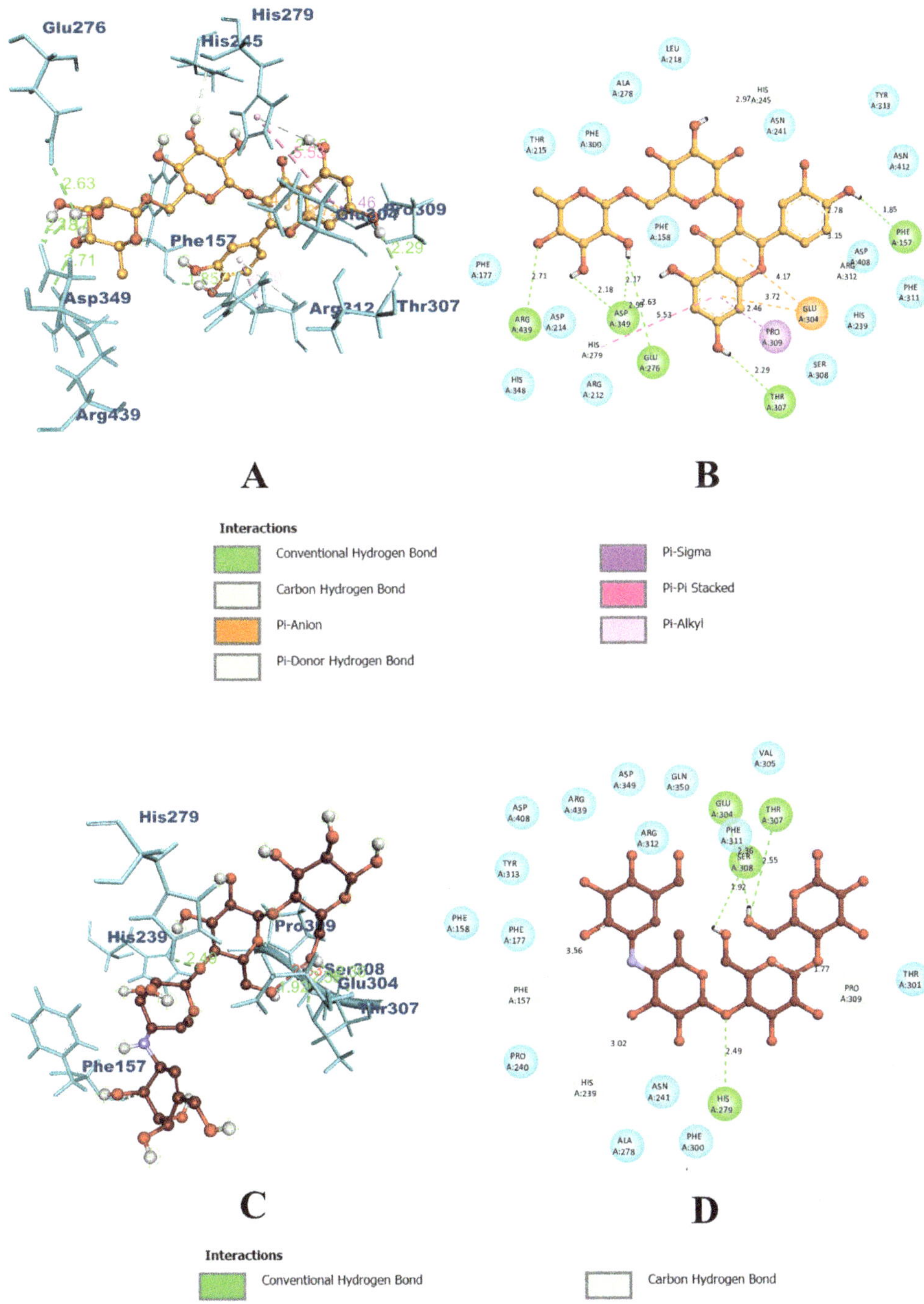

Figure 2. Visualization of docking simulation of experimental compounds with α-glucosidase. (**A**,**B**) Interaction of rutin acid visualized in 3D and 2D; (**C**,**D**) Interaction of acarbose visualized in 3D and 2D, respectively. Colored: bound residues, turquoise blue: surrounding residues.

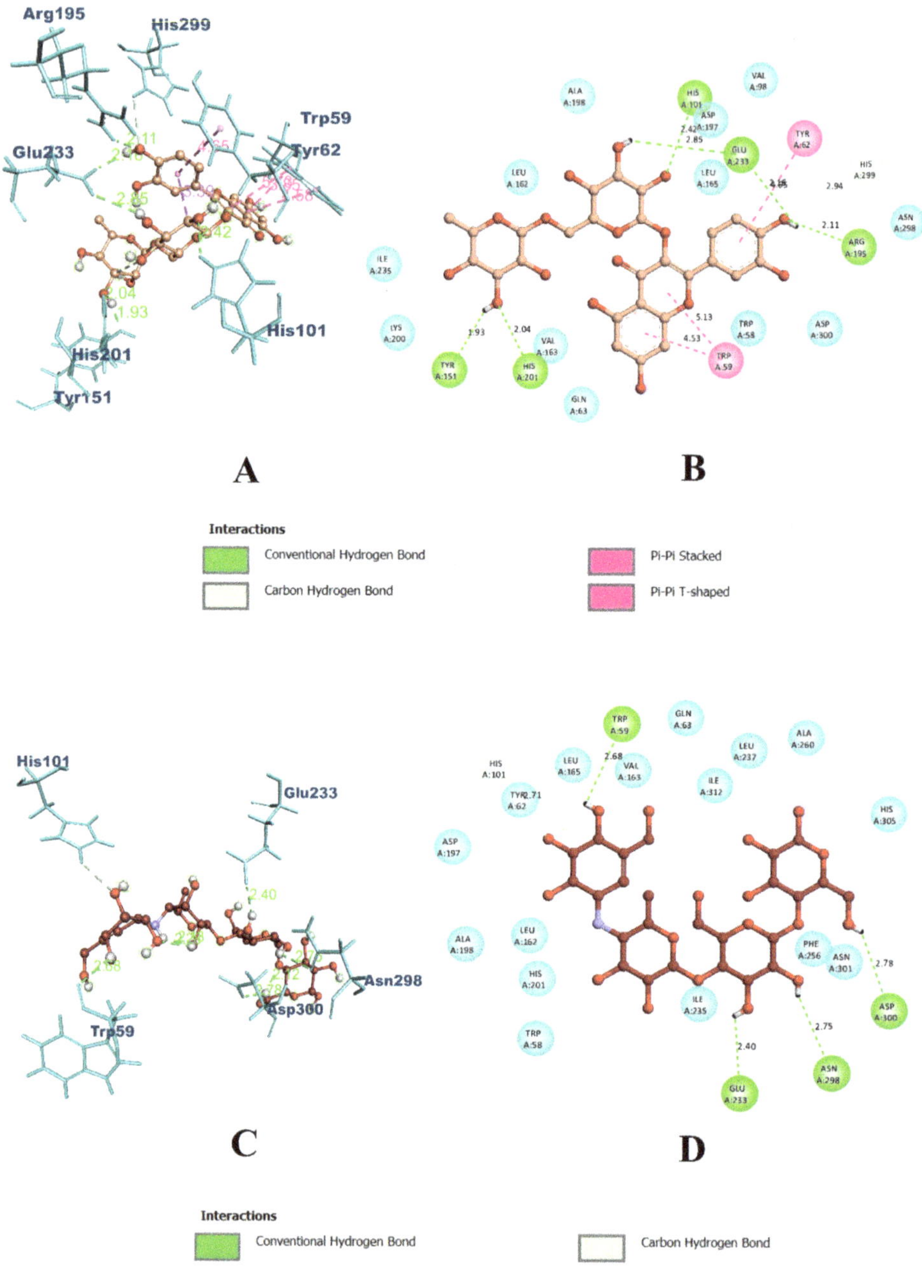

Figure 3. Visualization of docking simulation of experimental compounds with α-amylase. (**A**,**B**) Interaction of rutin visualized in 3D and 2D; (**C**,**D**) Interaction of acarbose visualized in 3D and 2D, respectively. Colored: bound residues, turquoise blue: surrounding residues.

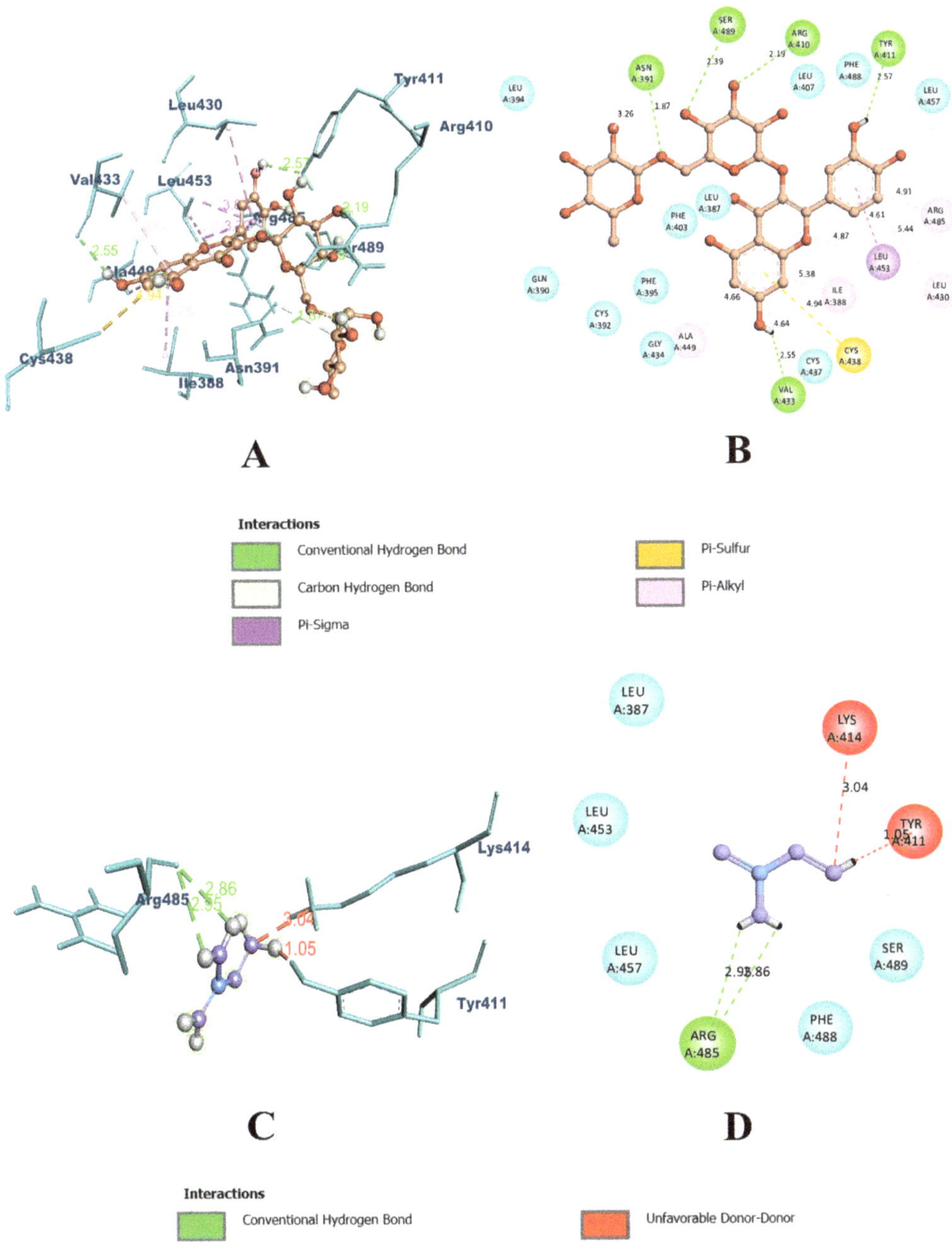

Figure 4. Visualization of docking simulation of experimental compounds with HSA. (**A**,**B**) Interaction of rutin visualized in 3D and 2D; (**C**,**D**) Interaction of aminoguanidine visualized in 3D and 2D, respectively. Colored: bound residues, turquoise blue: surrounding residues.

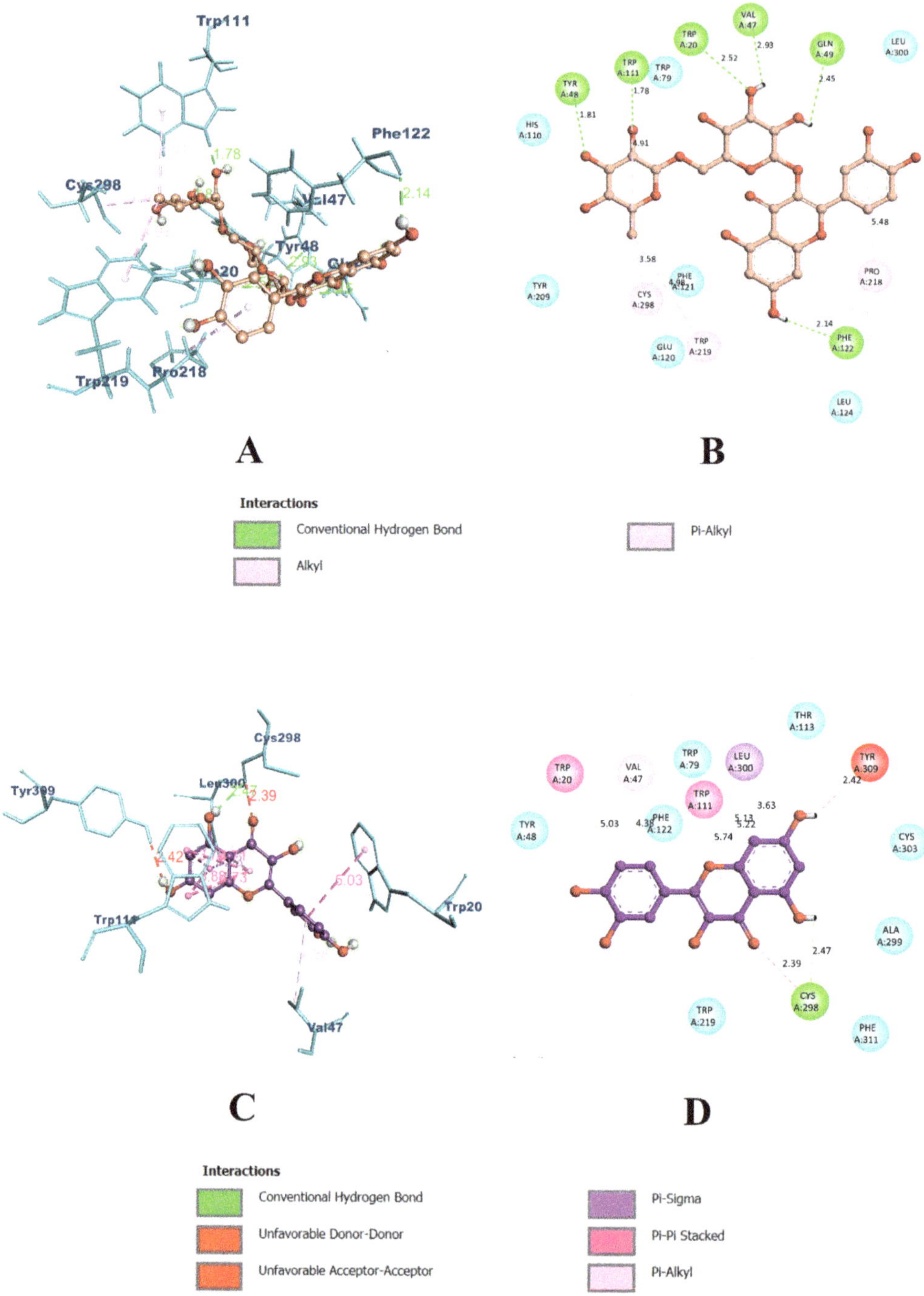

Figure 5. Visualization of docking simulation of experimental compounds with HAR. (**A**,**B**) Interaction of rutin visualized in 3D and 2D; (**C**,**D**) Interaction of quercetin visualized in 3D and 2D, respectively. Colored: bound residues, turquoise blue: surrounding residues.

The simulation trajectories obtained for AG complexed with rutin and acarbose revealed that all the RMSD plots become stabilized after 20 ns, reaching equilibrium after initial fluctuations. The RMSD value of bare protein atoms and the protein–rutin complex was found to range between ~0.35 and 0.40 nm. On the other hand, the RMSD of the protein–acarbose complex was found to be between ~0.30 and 0.35 nm. In the case of bare protein atoms, Rg value was found to be ~3.3 nm, whereas both protein–rutin and protein–acarbose showed the Rg value ranging between ~2.3 and 2.4 nm. In the case of RMSF analysis, bare protein atoms were predicted with fluctuations at terminal and loop regions. However, the protein–acarbose complex showed higher fluctuations than the protein–rutin complex (200–300 and 400–500 residues). Further, in the case of bare protein atoms, the SASA value was found to range between 350 and 375 nm^2. Both protein–rutin and protein–acarbose showed similar patterns, with the SASA value of 225 nm^2. In the case of ligand hydrogen bonds, rutin formed a maximum number of nine bonds, whereas acarbose was able to form only five of them. This indicates the stronger binding affinity and stability of rutin with the protein compared to acarbose. Even though similar patterns were observed in case of RMSF, SASA, and Rg, rutin poses a better ligand in comparison with acarbose during other trajectory analyses. Results from molecular dynamics simulation reveal rutin as a stable and stronger inhibitor of AG in comparison with acarbose. The visualization of simulation results for AG is summed up in Figure 6A1–A4.

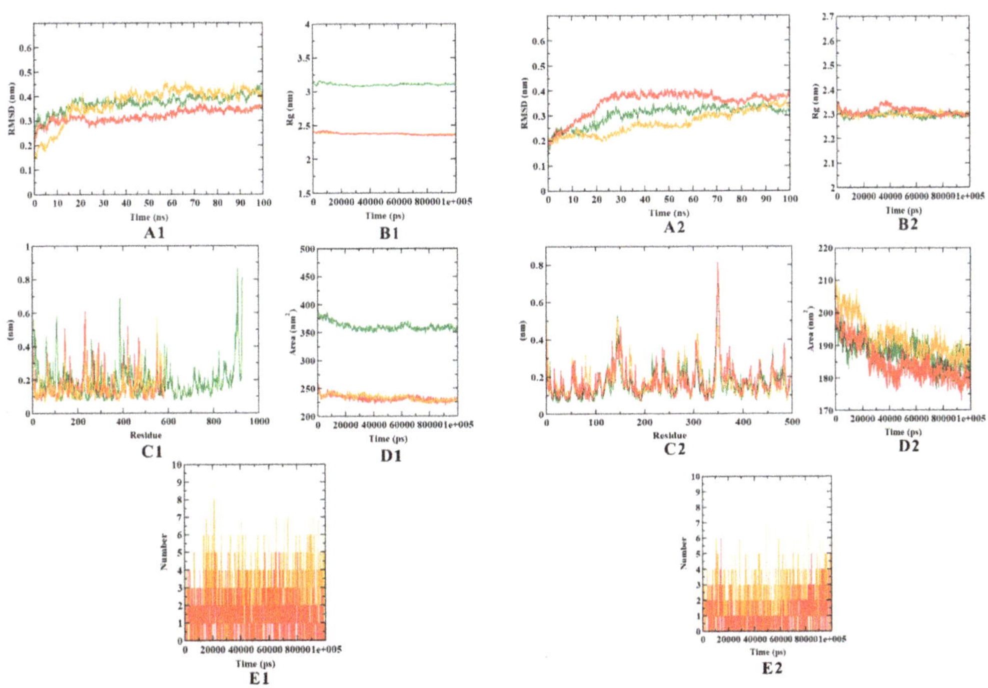

Figure 6. *Cont.*

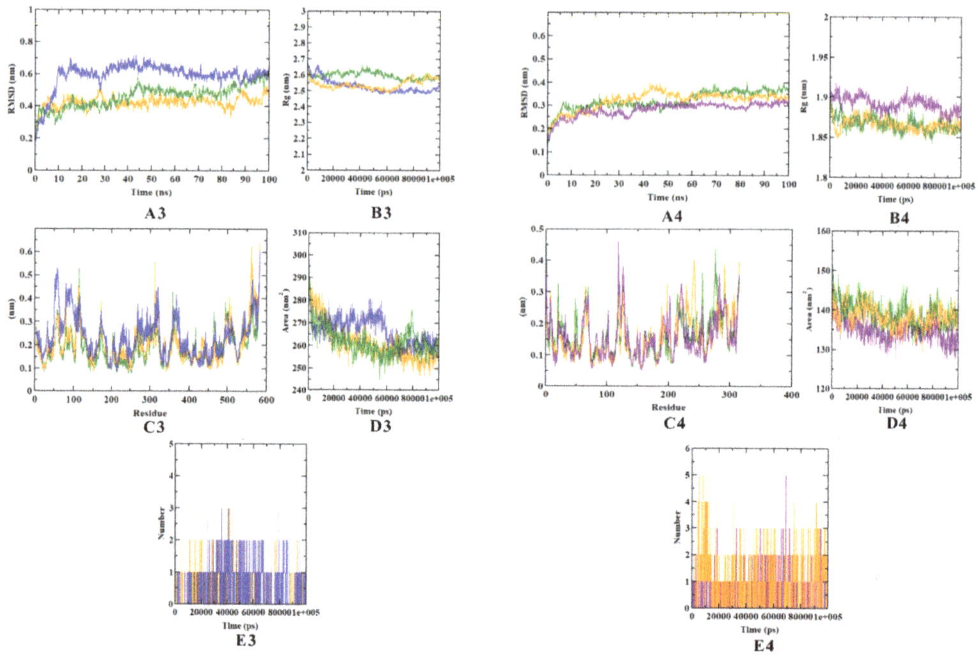

Figure 6. Visualization of trajectories obtained from molecular dynamics simulation. (**A1–A4**): RMSDs of proteins and protein–ligand complexes for α-glucosidase, α-amylase, HSA, and HAR, respectively. (**B1–B4**): Rg, (**C1–C4**): RMSF, (**D1–D4**): SASA, and (**E1–E4**): ligand hydrogen bonds. Green: protein backbone atoms, orange: protein–rutin complex, red: protein–acarbose complex, blue: protein–aminoguanidine complex, violet: protein–quercetin complex.

In the case of AM, the RMSD plots reveal that protein backbone and protein–acarbose complex becomes stabilized at 30 ns, whereas the protein–rutin complex becomes stabilized at 35 ns. However, both bare protein atoms and protein–rutin complexes become equilibrated at between 0.3 and 0.35 ns, and the protein–acarbose complex becomes equilibrated at between 0.35 and 0.40 ns. Meanwhile, the RMSD plots of the protein backbone and protein–acarbose complex are not found to be as concurrent as that of the protein–rutin RMSD plot. The Rg plots also depict the same pattern, where all the plots equilibrate at 2.3 nm. However, plots of the protein–rutin complex and bare protein atoms are more concurrent with each other. The RMSF plots depict the comparative instability of the protein–acarbose complex, where the fluctuations at loop regions (about 350th residue) were found to be higher (0.8 nm) than that of the protein–rutin complex plots (0.45 nm). The SASA plots reveal that both protein backbone atoms and protein–rutin complex become equilibrated at between 185 and 190 nm^2, whereas the protein–acarbose complex becomes equilibrated at 180 nm^2. This brings interference in the concurrency between the plots of bare protein atoms and the protein–acarbose complex. Further, acarbose was predicted to form five hydrogen atoms during MD simulation, whereas rutin was found with seven of them. Results from these simulations depict that rutin had comparatively higher stability than acarbose. The visualization of MD trajectories of AM complexed with experimental molecules is given in Figure 6B1–B4. During the analysis of MD simulation results of HSA with rutin and aminoguanidine, it was found that the RMSD of plots of both bare protein atoms become stabilized after 15 ns. Moreover, the protein–aminoguanidine complex becomes stabilized after 40 ns. The concurrency between the RMSD plots of protein backbone atoms and protein–rutin complexes was found to be higher in comparison with that of the protein–acarbose complex and bare protein atoms. The Rg plots also reveal the structural compactness of the protein–rutin complex over the protein–aminoguanidine complex, where both bare protein atoms and protein–rutin complexes become equilibrated at 2.6 nm and the protein–aminoguanidine complex at between 2.5 and 2.6 nm. The RMSF plots show that the protein–aminoguanidine complex had higher fluctuations in comparison with that of the protein–rutin complex throughout the simulation run. However, protein–rutin was found with fluctuations only in the loop regions (about 300th residue) and c-terminal regions. In the case of the SASA plots, all the plots become equilibrated at between 250 and 265 nm^2. However, the SASA plot of the protein–aminoguanidine complex was not in concurrence with that of the bare protein atoms. Further, aminoguanidine formed only three hydrogen bonds at the maximum during the simulation, whereas rutin formed four of them during the same. Figure 6C1–C4 detail the visualization of the MD trajectories obtained for the HSA complexed with rutin and aminoguanidine. In the case of HAR, the RMSD plots of bare protein atoms, protein–rutin complex, and protein–quercetin complex became stabilized after the initial fluctuation at 5 ns. All the plots become equilibrated in the range from 0.3–0.4 nm. However, the RMSD plot of the protein–rutin complex appears to have more concurrency with that of the bare protein atoms, in comparison with the protein–quercetin plot. The Rg plots also depict the same pattern, where bare protein atoms and the protein–rutin complex equilibrate at between 1.85 and 1.875 nm, whereas the protein–quercetin complex equilibrates at between 1.875 and 1.90 nm. In the case of RMSF plots, the protein–quercetin plot shows more fluctuations at loop regions (100–150 residues, 200–250 residues), in comparison with the protein–rutin complex. However, at terminal regions, fluctuations of the protein–rutin complex were found to be high. Moreover, the protein–rutin complex was predicted with minimal fluctuations throughout the simulation. The same pattern was continued with the SASA plots, where bare protein atoms and protein–rutin complexes were predicted with the SASA value of between 135 and 140 nm^2, yet the protein–quercetin complex was found with the SASA value of between 130 and 135 nm^2. In the case of ligand hydrogen bonds, both quercetin and rutin were able to form an equal number of hydrogen bonds (five) during the course of MD simulation. Visualization of MD trajectories obtained for HAR complexed with rutin and quercetin is depicted in Figure 6D1–D4.

3.8. Binding Free Energy Calculations

The extent of binding is represented by the binding free energy of ligands bound to protein structures. Binding free energy is released during the creation of a protein–ligand complex and is used to determine whether or not the complex is stable. The creation of a stable complex is better described by binding free energy with a lower value. Van der Waal's, electrostatic, polar solvation, SASA, and binding energy were used to calculate the binding free energy in this case. In this experiment, the AG–rutin complex (−324.712 kj/mol) showed the highest binding free energy in comparison with all the other complexes. It significantly used van der Waal's force to form. In comparison with the other binding free energies, van der Waal's was found to be the major contributor to the protein–ligand complexes. In addition, all the protein–rutin complexes were found to have higher (more negative) binding free energies in comparison with all the protein–control drug complexes. Results from binding free energy calculations support the results obtained from MD simulations in terms of stability and binding efficiency. Types of binding free energies and standard deviations of all protein–ligand complexes have been summarized in Table 4.

Table 4. Binding free energy calculations of target proteins complexed with experimental ligands.

Protein-Ligand Complexes	Values and Standard Deviations	Types of Binding Free Energies				
		Van der Waal's Energy (kj/mol)	Electrostatic Energy (kj/mol)	Polar Solvation Energy (kj/mol)	SASA Energy (kj/mol)	Binding Energy (kj/mol)
α-glucosidase-rutin	EV	−324.712	−5.382	92.618	−24.746	−260.222
	SD	±21.580	±4.082	±13.384	±1.441	±21.396
α-glucosidase-acarbose	EV	−134.192	−4.813	62.125	−9.310	−90.102
	SD	±180.341	±9.475	±58.801	±14.719	±145.076
α-amylase-rutin	EV	−204.258	−2.931	42.572	−16.289	−180.906
	SD	±117.430	±4.057	±39.446	±9.495	±118.715
α-amylase-acarbose	EV	−130.161	−2.106	39.340	−9.564	−87.109
	SD	±100.269	±22.186	±54.310	±6.998	±61.672
HSA-rutin	EV	−161.503	−5.499	55.663	−9.513	−99.851
	SD	±41.895	±6.908	±34.324	±3.103	±22.691
HSA-aminoguanidine	EV	−150.719	−5.127	47.498	−7.981	−81.872
	SD	±99.469	±10.298	±57.619	±8.124	±79.501
HAR-rutin	EV	−184.694	−6.705	97.407	−9.678	−93.670
	SD	±81.018	±6.141	±30.480	±7.049	±70.236
HAR-quercetin	EV	−171.669	−3.291	81.102	−8.781	−85.768
	SD	±110.361	±34.678	±79.539	±15.786	±92.766

Note: EV: Energy values, SD: standard deviation, HSA: human serum albumin, HAR: human aldose reductase.

4. Discussion

Successful hyperglycemia intervention is critical for reducing the frequency, progression, and severity of diabetes complications. On the other hand, using a single therapy technique has not been successful in preventing all of the negative consequences of high blood glucose levels [39]. As a result, AG inhibitors, AR inhibitors, antiglycation medications, and antioxidants may be viable choices for lowering the negative impact exerted by persistent circulating glucose. Numerous studies have demonstrated that basic plant extract as well as bioactive combinations produced from it can aid in the reduction of blood glucose levels [40,41]. Enumerable studies have shown that the unrefined plant concentrate, as well as its bioactive molecules present in these extracts, are effective in lowering blood glucose levels. In this regard, several bioactive ingredients isolated from plants have been identified for their potential glucose-lowering abilities [41]. Rutin is one such plant flavonoid that has anti-diabetic activity induced via reducing the expression of insulin-resistant molecules, enabling the interaction between insulin and its receptors, inducing adipose tissue peroxisome proliferator-activated receptor (PPAR) expression and adipocyte-derived protein production, according to studies through molecular and physiological mechanisms [42]. Chen et al. (2020) demonstrated in an animal study that rutin-containing formulations significantly improved serum insulin and C-peptide concentrations, hexokinase, hyperlipidemia, liver glycogen content, hyperglycemia, glucose-6-phosphatase, and glycogen phosphorylase activities in type 2 diabetes mellitus (DM) rats that were orally treated with rutin [43]. Rutin caused a significant improvement in peripheral glucose levels in rat diaphragm studies. It has demonstrated potent antioxidant properties observed by its lowering abilities on lipid peroxidation and the generation of thiobarbutiric acid reactive species (TBARS).

The metabolic process in the body is initiated by the conversion of dietary glucose into energy, which is utilized primarily by AM and AG [44]. In the present study, rutin extracted from jackfruit flour was discovered to be a potent AG and AM inhibitor. An LB plot obtained from the kinetics data to explore the mechanism underlying this inhibition demonstrated a reversible, mixed pattern of inhibition. Mixed-type inhibition is a cross between competitive and non-competitive inhibition, with two different types of equilibrium constants, K1 and K2. The higher the inhibition, the lower the equilibrium constant.

The inhibition constants (K1 and K2) were found to have lower values in this study, and K1 values were always smaller than K2 values. From the study, it was revealed that rutin inhibits both AM and glucosidase, which is in line with earlier research [45]. The mixed form of inhibition was previously observed in flavonoids with comparable results [46].

When diabetes persists, excessive free glucose units cause a number of secondary problems, which must be considered while developing an optimal anti-diabetic treatment. In addition, the polyol pathway, which is a part of the intermediate metabolism, is harmed when glucose levels are too high [47]. According to studies, roughly 3% of glucose is metabolized through this route in normoglycemic situations, whereas glucose consumption increases to more than 30% in hyperglycemic states [48]. The AR catalyzes the conversion of glucose to sorbitol and serves as the pathway's rate-limiting step. Despite evidence that AR has a role in the detoxification of aldehydes, a by-product of lipid peroxidation, its role in carbohydrate metabolism is unknown. However, its inhibition has been known to prevent the development of diabetic retinopathy, which constitutes one of the serious complications of diabetes [49]. In the present study, rutin showed to be a potent AR inhibitor faring better than the reference standard quercetin. The LB plot demonstrated that the compound inhibited AR in a mixed-type manner. Flavonoids have been reported to alter carbohydrate digestion, insulin generation, insulin signaling, and glucose absorption in insulin-sensitive organs via interacting with several intracellular signaling pathways [50]. The link between flavonoid structure and AR inhibitory function has been discovered through various studies on flavonoid structure. In agreement with these studies, rutin also demonstrated an inhibitory effect of AR, and, in turn, exerting its effect on the polyol pathway.

Protein glycation is considered to possess some of the serious complications of diabetes [51]. Glycation of various proteins occurs when there is too much glucose in the bloodstream, rendering them inactive. Fructose has recently been discovered in glycation, either directly or through promoting fructose formation from glucose by activating the polyol pathway [7]. Fructose participates in glycation at a quicker pace than glucose, meaning greater adverse effects. The nucleophilic addition reaction between the free amino group of proteins and the carbonyl group of the reducing sugar initiates the creation of a Schiff's base, which results in irreversible Amadori products, such as fructosamines [7,20]. In the second stage of glycation, fructosamines are converted to a range of carbonyl compounds, including deoxyglucosones glyoxal and methylglyoxals, resulting in the formation of carbonyl proteins. The progression of this condition results in the formation of protein thiols. Overall, the progressive glycation process results in the formation of advanced glycation end products (AGE), the insoluble luminous products that bind to glycated proteins and accumulate in cells. They hinder normal protein function within the cells and create irregular cross-linking of the extracellular matrix, preventing it from performing its normal function [20]. Aside from causing vascular problems, AGEs also cause the development of reactive oxygen species (ROS), which has been related to the majority of diabetes problems [20,52].

With this background, in the present study, the initial stage of protein glycation was performed under in vitro conditions by exposing HSA to high fructose concentrations, which was expected to glycate HSA. Fructosamine levels were higher than non-glycated HSA levels in our study, as expected, and rutin therapy significantly reduced this, exceeding the standard inhibitor aminoguanidine [7,20]. The increased protein carbonyl groups generated after the exposure to a high fructose load, as well as the similarly low levels of protein thiols, demonstrated the second stage of protein glycation. Treatment with rutin reduced this to approximately 82%, showing that it has a protective effect. Finally, the compounds' ability to create fluorescent products was employed to measure AGE development in this study; the results revealed that AGE formation was significantly reduced [7,20]. As a result, the potential role of rutin in avoiding each stage of protein glycation has been confirmed, indicating that they may be effective in reducing the different complications arising due to diabetes. Conversely, aminoguanidine, an anti-glycation experimental drug, was found to be less effective than the compound tested [20].

Plant extracts have been well-known for their potential antioxidant properties owing to the presence of several bioactive components [53]. In this regard, in the present study, the antioxidant potential of rutin was evaluated using some of the standard assays, namely DPPH, ABTS, and superoxide. Our findings proved that rutin had improved free radical scavenging activity in all of the tests employed in the study, showing that it has a protective role against free radical-mediated damage. Several researchers have proven the remarkable antioxidant potential of flavonoids present in plant extracts [54]. In all of the investigations, the extracts containing the greatest phenolic compounds and flavonoids were found to be the most powerful antioxidants, protecting against oxidative damage caused by free radicals in diseases such as cancer, diabetes, asthma, dementia, Parkinson's disease, and others [54]. In agreement with the previous studies, rutin showed noteworthy antioxidant ability in comparison with that of standard ascorbic acid.

Molecular docking simulations are used to determine the molecular interactions between ligands and target proteins; they determine the extent of ligand binding, which indicates whether or not a protein is inhibited or activated [55]. We chose rutin, a flavonoid found in jackfruit flour to target the inhibition of AG, AM, HSA, and HAR in this work. Rutin exhibited the highest binding affinity with all of the target proteins, according to the docking simulation results.

All experimental compounds were bound deep within the binding pocket during the docking simulation of AG. According to a previous study by Patil et al. (2021), the docking was accurate [28]. The interaction of rutin was found to be superior to that of acarbose, despite the fact that both the ligands were found docked inside the binding pocket. The binding affinity of rutin was high because the number of hydrophobic linkages (pi–pi and pi–alkyl) was deemed higher than the number of hydrogen bonds [56]. In the case of AM, HSA, and HAR, rutin showed the same pattern. When compared to other non-bonding interactions, all four proteins bound with rutin employed more hydrophobic bonds. In all the four target proteins, control drugs were not able to form more hydrophobic bonds, and their binding efficiency was not up to the mark of rutin. The binding interaction analysis of compounds docked with AM shows that both rutin and acarbose were bound to the key residue GLU 233. However, due to the hydrophobic bonds and other non-bonding interactions, such as hydrogen bonds, rutin was found to have more binding affinity than acarbose. Binding to this catalytic residue (GLU 233) would effectively reduce the activity of AM, as indicated in recent studies [57,58]. Moreover, the binding of rutin to both the carbohydrate digestion enzymes was in accordance with a previous study conducted by Osman et al. (2021) [59] and Jhong et al. (2015) [60]; these studies used different sources of rutin, yet the docking results are similar.

In case of HSA, all the compounds were bound to binding site II, which is made of 6 helices of subdomain III. Binding site II consists of a polar patch, which consists of key residues ARG 410, TYR 411, SER 489 LEU 430, and LEU 453. These residues are present in the vicinity of fatty acid site 4 (FA4), which accommodates the methylene tails of lipids bound to this site [61]. Moreover, the ligands occupied the same binding site of the co-crystallized ligand ibuprofen. According to a study, binding into the polar patch of the binding pocket induces conformational changes in the protein [62]. As rutin was bound to these key residues of the polar patch of binding site II, it is expected to induce conformational changes in HSA. However, aminoguanidine was not able to bind to these residues. The docking results were in accordance with the study performed by Isogai and Hirayama (2013) [61] and Ali et al. (2022) [63]. While binding with HAR, both rutin and quercetin occupy the same binding site as the co-crystallized ligand zenarestat, which is present in the proximity of the NADPH binding site. The NADPH-dependent conversion of glucose to sorbitol, which is the initial step in the polyol pathway of glucose metabolism, is catalyzed by HAR [64].

We performed the MD simulations for all the protein–ligand complexes formed as a result of molecular docking. The overall stability of the protein–ligand combination kept in a particular environment for a specific period of time is assessed using molecular dynamics simulation. Simulating experimental molecules with their target proteins has given variable results in this study.

In the case of AG, rutin acid is the most stable compound according to all graphs. In none of the plots was the protein–rutin acid complex predicted with aberrant variations (RMSD, RMSF, Rg, SASA, and ligand hydrogen bonds). Protein–acarbose complex plots, on the other hand, were not as similar as the protein–rutin complex with the bare protein atoms. The simulations of all four target proteins showed the same pattern in case of rutin. During the simulation study, the concurrent plots of the protein–ligand complex with the bare protein atoms show a greater binding affinity [65,66]. In the case of AM, protein–acarbose complex was found to be relatively unstable in comparison with the protein–rutin complex. Simulated plots of a protein–rutin acid complex were consistent with earlier research by Kumar et al. (2021) [67].

Further, dynamics simulation trajectory analysis of HSA complexed with caffeic acid and aminoguanidine showed similar patterns of instability compared with that of the protein–syringic acid complex. However, a study by Soltanabadi et al. (2018) depicted the binding stability of cinnamaldehyde [68]. Since the simulation was performed for only 20 ns, it was difficult to predict the overall stability of the protein–cinnamaldehyde complex. Moreover, our study clearly established the protein–syringic acid complex as the stable complex through 100 ns simulation. This result was in accordance with a study that evaluated the stability of the HSA–phycocyanobilin complex [69]. Furthermore, the relative instability of the protein–quercetin complex is depicted in the dynamics simulation results of HAR complexed with the experimental molecules. The protein–rutin complex has been considered stable in comparison with the protein–quercetin complex. The outcomes of the HAR simulation were consistent with a study that suggested kusunokinin as a potential HAR inhibitor [70].

We have also evaluated the binding free energy calculations using the MMPBSA program to determine the type of binding free energies contributing to the protein–ligand complex formation during MD simulation. All the complexes significantly used van der Waal's energy to form. This was followed by binding and SASA energies. Results from binding free energy calculations indicate that the formation of protein–ligand complexes is in accordance with molecular docking and dynamics simulations. Additionally, all the binding free energy calculations indicate that rutin binds effectively with all the target proteins in comparison with the control drugs. In the case of AG, rutin had the highest van der Waal's binding free energy of −324.712 kJ/mol, which was in accordance with the study conducted by Adinortey et al. (2022) [71], while binding with AM it had a van der Waal's binding free energy of −204.258 kJ/mol. The values obtained in our study were in accordance with the study by Lolok et al. (2021) for the inhibition of AM [72]. In another study, Yu et al. (2016) performed binding free energy calculations for the HSA–paclitaxel complex [73]. The results obtained from our calculations for HSA are found to be consistent with those given by Yu et al. (2016) [73]. In addition, a similar pattern of results was obtained for HAR complexed with rutin, which was found to be in accordance with Ciccone et al. (2022), where nature-inspired o-benzyl oxime-based derivatives bound with HAR were evaluated for the binding free energy calculations [74].

By the virtue of results obtained in our in vitro and in silico experiments, we propose rutin as the multi-target inhibitor of diabetes mellitus. In these experiments, it has been revealed that rutin can effectively inhibit all the enzymes (AG, AM, HSA, and HAR) effectively. Therefore, rutin would have the same effects in the in vivo studies. Rutin would decrease blood glucose levels, superoxide ions, and AGE levels. It would also reduce the production of sorbitol by interfering with the polyol pathway. Overall, it would reduce the characteristics of diabetes mellitus at different stages. While most phytochemical-based studies only focus on dual inhibition or single inhibition of target proteins [8], our study involves the inhibition of multiple proteins using a single phytochemical. Therefore, in the near future, rutin could be used as a potential inhibitor of the above-mentioned target enzymes in vivo and in clinical trials.

5. Conclusions

This study investigates the antihyperglycemic properties of the complete unripe jackfruit, as well as the polyphenol compound (rutin) that makes it up. Furthermore, MJ inhibits both the carbohydrate digesting enzymes, in addition to aldose reductase inhibition and anti-glycation potential. The extract also showed significant antioxidant activity by reducing the superoxide levels. The positive effects of MJ match those of isolated rutin, suggesting that rutin could be employed as anti-diabetic medication. Our data clearly demonstrate the antioxidant properties of MJ and rutin, proposing a link to their anti-diabetic properties. Furthermore, the presence of large levels of rutin in MJ provided support for a robust chemical basis for MJ's anti-diabetic properties. Since rutin is largely present in the extract, we propose rutin as a potential lead inhibitor of all the target enzymes used in this study. In computational studies, rutin outperformed all other phytochemicals and control drugs to become a ubiquitous inhibitor of all target proteins. Based on the findings of this investigation, a further experimental effort will hopefully be prioritized, resulting in the effective design and development of novel antihyperglycaemic drugs from different jackfruit extracts.

Supplementary Materials: The following supporting information can be downloaded at: https://www.mdpi.com/article/10.3390/separations9090262/s1, Figure S1: Purification outline of rutin from methanol extract of whole jackfruit flour and its structure; Figure S2: HPLC Chromatogram of standard phenolic compounds viz., (1) Ascorbic acid, (2) Gallic acid, (3) Catechin, (4) Methyl gallate, (5) Caffeic acid, (6) Syringic acid, (9) Rutin, (10) p-Coumaric acid, (11) Sinapic acid, (12) Ferrulic acid, (14) Myrecetin, (15) Quercetin, (16) Apigenin, and (17) Kaempferol (A). HPLC Chromatogram of methanol extract of whole jackfruit flour (B); Figure S3: NMR Assignments of Rutin; Figure S4: LC-MS Chromatogram of Rutin.

Author Contributions: R.R. planned and conceptualized the manuscript; T.M. and S.M.P. were involved in data analysis and method development; B.P., R.R.A., V.S. and E.S. were involved in supervision, editing and preparation of the manuscript draft. All authors have read and agreed to the published version of the manuscript.

Funding: This research received no external funding.

Institutional Review Board Statement: Not applicable.

Informed Consent Statement: Not applicable.

Data Availability Statement: Not applicable.

Acknowledgments: All the authors thank JSS Academy of Higher Education and Research (Mysore, Karnataka, India) for their kind support with the university research grant for faculty (REG/DIR (R)/URG/54/2011-12/9800), encouragement, and providing the necessary facilities.

Conflicts of Interest: All authors declare no conflict of interest.

References

1. Rachdaoui, N. Insulin: The friend and the foe in the development of type 2 diabetes mellitus. *Int. J. Mol. Sci.* **2020**, *21*, 1770. [CrossRef] [PubMed]
2. Sinha, R.; Fisch, G.; Teague, B.; Tamborlane, W.V.; Banyas, B.; Allen, K.; Savoye, M.; Rieger, V.; Taksali, S.; Barbetta, G.; et al. Prevalence of impaired glucose tolerance among children and adolescents with marked obesity. *N. Engl. J. Med.* **2002**, *346*, 802–810. [CrossRef] [PubMed]
3. Rocchini, A.P. Childhood obesity and a diabetes epidemic. *N. Engl. J. Med.* **2002**, *346*, 854–855. [CrossRef] [PubMed]
4. Tuomi, T.; Santoro, N.; Caprio, S.; Cai, M.; Weng, J.; Groop, L. The many faces of diabetes: A disease with increasing heterogeneity. *Lancet* **2014**, *383*, 1084–1094. [CrossRef]
5. Ramu, R.; Patil, S.M. A perspective on the effective conduction of functional-based coaching program on diabetic Indonesian communities. *Oman Med. J.* **2021**, *36*, e281. [CrossRef] [PubMed]
6. Harding, J.L.; Pavkov, M.E.; Magliano, D.J.; Shaw, J.E.; Gregg, E.W. Global trends in diabetes complications: A review of current evidence. *Diabetologia* **2019**, *62*, 3–16. [CrossRef]

7. Ramu, R.; Shirahatti, P.S.; Zameer, F.; Nagendra, P.M.N. Inhibitory effect of banana (Musa sp. var. Nanjangud rasa bale) flower extract and its constituents umbelliferone and lupeol on α-glucosidase; aldose reductase and glycation at multiple stages. *S. Afr. J. Bot.* **2014**, *95*, 54–63. [CrossRef]
8. Ramu, R.S.; Shirahatti, P.; Zameer, F.; Lakkappa, D.B.; Prasad, N.P.N. Assessment of in vivo anti-diabetic properties of umbelliferone and lupeol constituents of banana (Musa sp. var. Nanjangud Rasa Bale) flower in hyperglycaemic rodent model. *PLoS ONE* **2016**, *11*, e0151135.
9. Tang, W.; Martin, K.A.; Hwa, J. Aldose reductase, oxidative stress, and diabetic mellitus. *Front. Pharmacol.* **2012**, *3*, 87. [CrossRef]
10. Jannapureddy, S.; Sharma, M.; Yepuri, G.; Schmidt, A.M.; Ramasamy, R. Aldose reductase: An emerging target for development of interventions for diabetic cardiovascular complications. *Front. Endocrinol.* **2021**, *12*, 636267. [CrossRef]
11. Singh, V.P.; Bali, A.; Singh, N.; Jaggi, A.S. Advanced glycation end products and diabetic complications. *Korean. J. Physiol. Pharmacol.* **2014**, *18*, 1–4. [CrossRef] [PubMed]
12. Rungratanawanich, W.; Qu, Y.; Wang, X.; Essa, M.M.; Song, B.J. Advanced glycation end products (AGEs) and other adducts in aging-related diseases and alcohol-mediated tissue injury. *Exp. Mol. Med.* **2021**, *53*, 168–188. [CrossRef] [PubMed]
13. Prathapan, A.; Nampoothiri, S.V.; Mini, S.; Raghu, K.G. Antioxidant, antiglycation and inhibitory potential of Saraca ashoka flowers against the enzymes linked to type 2 diabetes and LDL oxidation. *Eur. Rev. Med. Pharmacol. Sci.* **2012**, *16*, 57–65. [PubMed]
14. Patil, S.M.; Shirahatti, P.S.; Ramu, R. Azadirachta indica A. Juss (neem) against diabetes mellitus: A critical review on its phytochemistry, pharmacology, and toxicology. *J. Pharm. Pharmacol.* **2022**, *74*, 681–710. [CrossRef]
15. Patil, S.M.; Kumari, V.C.; Sumana, K.; Sujay, S.; Tejaswini, M.; Shirahatti, P.S.; Ramu, R. Sustainable development of plant tissue culture industry: The Indian scenario. *J. Appl. Biol. Biotechnol.* **2021**, *9*, 18–27.
16. Patil, S.M.; Ramu, R.; Shirahatti, P.S.; Shivamallu, C.; Amachawadi, R.G. A systematic review on ethnopharmacology; phytochemistry and pharmacological aspects of *Thymus vulgaris Linn. Heliyon* **2021**, *7*, e07054. [CrossRef]
17. Patil, S.M.; Shirahatti, P.S.; Kumari, V.B.C.; Ramu, R.; Prasad, N. Azadirachta indica A. Juss (neem) as a contraceptive: An evidence-based review on its pharmacological efficiency. *Phytomedicine* **2021**, *88*, 153596. [CrossRef]
18. Pushpa, V.H.; Jayanthi, M.K.; Rashmi, H.R.; Shivamurthy, V.K.; Patil, S.M.; Shirahatti, P.S.; Ramu, R. New insights on the phytochemical intervention for the treatment of neuropsychiatric disorders using the leaves of *Michelia champaca*: An in vivo and in silico approach. *Pharm Biol.* **2022**, *60*, 1656–1668.
19. Mozaffarian, D. Dietary and policy priorities for cardiovascular disease, diabetes, and obesity: A comprehensive review. *Circulation* **2016**, *133*, 187–225. [CrossRef]
20. Maradesha, T.; Patil, S.M.; Al-Mutairi, K.A.; Ramu, R.; Madhunapantula, S.V.; Alqadi, T. Inhibitory effect of polyphenols from the whole green jackfruit flour against α-glucosidase, α-amylase, aldose reductase and glycation at multiple stages and their interaction: Inhibition kinetics and molecular simulations. *Molecules* **2022**, *27*, 1888. [CrossRef]
21. Baliga, M.S.; Shivashankara, A.R.; Haniadka, R.; Dsouza, J.; Bhat, H.P. Phytochemistry; nutritional and pharmacological properties of *Artocarpus heterophyllus* Lam. (jackfruit): A review. *Food Res. Int.* **2011**, *44*, 1800–1811. [CrossRef]
22. Swami, S.B.; Thakor, N.J.; Haldankar, P.M.; Kalse, S.B. Jackfruit and its many functional components as related to human health: A review. *Compr. Rev. Food Sci. Food Saf.* **2012**, *11*, 565–576. [CrossRef]
23. Razali, N.; Razab, R.; Junit, S.M.; Aziz, A.A. Radical scavenging and reducing properties of extracts of cashew shoots (*Anacardium occidentale*). *Food. Chem.* **2008**, *111*, 38–44. [CrossRef]
24. Seal, T. Quantitative HPLC analysis of phenolic acids; flavonoids and ascorbic acid in four different solvent extracts of two wild edible leaves; *Sonchus arvensis* and *Oenanthe linearis* of North-Eastern region in India. *J. Appl. Pharm. Sci.* **2016**, *6*, 157–166. [CrossRef]
25. Ordon-Ez, A.A.; Gomez, J.D.; Vattuone, M.A.; Isla, M.I. Antioxidant activities of Sechiumedule (Jacq.) Swart extracts. *Food Chem.* **2006**, *97*, 452–458. [CrossRef]
26. Shuxia, C.; Xiaoqing, S.; Siqiong, C.; Panpan, L.; Junna, D.; Yanxia, C.; Huanwen, M. Evaluation of garlic cultivars for polyphenolic content and antioxidant properties. *PLoS ONE* **2013**, *8*, e79730.
27. Harbone, J.B. *Phytochemical Methods*, 1st ed.; Chapman and Hall Ltd.: London, UK, 1973; pp. 49–188.
28. Patil, S.M.; Martiz, R.M.; Ramu, R.; Shirahatti, P.S.; Prakash, A.; Kumar, B.P.; Kumar, N. Evaluation of flavonoids from banana pseudostem and flower (quercetin and catechin) as potent inhibitors of α-glucosidase: An in-silico perspective. *J. Biomol. Struct. Dyn.* **2021**, *7*, 1–5. [CrossRef]
29. Shivanna, C.; Patil, S.M.; Mallikarjunaswamy, M.; Ramu, R.; Akhileshwari, P.; Nagaraju, L.R.; Sridhar, M.A.; Khanum, S.A.; Ranganatha, L.; Silina, E.; et al. Synthesis, characterization, Hirschfeld surface analysis, crystal structure and molecular modeling studies of 1-(4-(Methoxy(phenyl)methyl)-2-methylphenoxy)butan-2-one derivative as a novel α-glucosidase inhibitor. *Crystals* **2022**, *12*, 960. [CrossRef]
30. Martiz, R.M.; Patil, S.M.; Ramu, R.; Mallappa Kumar, J.; Ranganatha, L.V.; Khanum, S.A.; Silina, E.; Stupin, V.; Achar, R.R. Discovery of novel benzophenone integrated derivatives as anti-Alzheimer's agents targeting presenilin-1 and presenilin-2 inhibition: A computational approach. *PLoS ONE* **2022**, *17*, e0265022. [CrossRef]
31. Patil, S.M.; Martiz, R.M.; Ramu, R.; Shirahatti, P.S.; Prakash, A.; Chandra, J.S.; Ranganatha, L.V. In silico identification of novel benzophenone-coumarin derivatives as SARS-CoV-2 RNA dependent RNA polymerase (RdRp) inhibitors. *J. Biomol. Struct. Dyn.* **2021**, *11*, 1–17. [CrossRef]

32. Kumar, V.; Shetty, P.; Arunodaya, H.S.; Chandra, K.S.; Ramu, R.; Patil, S.M.; Baliga, A.; Rai, V.M.; Shalini Shenoy, M.; Udupi, V.; et al. Potential fluorinated anti-MRSA thiazolidinone derivatives with antibacterial, antitubercular activity and molecular docking studies. *Chem. Biodivers.* **2022**, *19*, e202100532. [CrossRef] [PubMed]
33. Sajal, H.; Patil, S.M.; Raj, R.; Shbeer, A.M.; Ageel, M.; Ramu, R. Computer-aided screening of phytoconstituents from ocimum tenuiflorum against diabetes mellitus targeting dpp4 inhibition: A combination of molecular docking, molecular dynamics, and pharmacokinetics approaches. *Molecules* **2022**, *27*, 5133. [CrossRef] [PubMed]
34. Gurupadaswamy, H.D.; Ranganatha, V.L.; Ramu, R.; Patil, S.M.; Khanum, S.A. Competent synthesis of biaryl analogs via asymmetric Suzuki–Miyaura cross-coupling for the development of anti-inflammatory and analgesic agents. *J. Iran. Chem. Soc.* **2022**, *1*, 2421–2436. [CrossRef]
35. Patil, S.M.; Maruthi, K.R.; Bajpe, N.S.; Vyshali, V.M.; Sushmitha, S.; Chagalamari, A.; Ramith, R. Comparative molecular docking and simulation analysis of molnupiravir and remdesivir with SARS-CoV-2 RNA dependent RNA polymerase (RdRp). *Bioinformation* **2021**, *7*, 932–939.
36. Martiz, R.M.; Patil, S.M.; Abdulaziz, M.; Babalghith, A.; Al-Areefi, M.; Al-Ghorbani, M.; Mallappa Kumar, J.; Prasad, A.; Mysore Nagalingaswamy, N.P.; Ramu, R. Defining the Role of Isoeugenol from Ocimum tenuiflorum against Diabetes Mellitus-Linked Alzheimer's Disease through Network Pharmacology and Computational Methods. *Molecules* **2022**, *27*, 2398. [CrossRef]
37. Shukla, P.; Gopalkrishna, B.; Shukla, P. Isolation of rutin from *Phyllanthus amarus*. *Int. J. Pharm. Sci. Res.* **2012**, *3*, 1198–1201.
38. Lin, L.J.; Huang, X.B.; Lv, Z.C. Isolation and identification of flavonoids components from *Pteris vittata* L. *Springer Plus.* **2016**, *5*, 1649. [CrossRef]
39. D'Aiuto, F.; Gkranias, N.; Bhowruth, D.; Khan, T.; Orlandi, M.; Suvan, J.; Masi, S.; Tsakos, G.; Hurel, S.; Hingorani, A.D.; et al. Systemic effects of periodontitis treatment in patients with type 2 diabetes: A 12 month, single-centre, investigator-masked, randomised trial. *Lancet. Diabetes. Endocrinol.* **2018**, *6*, 954–965. [CrossRef]
40. Zafar, A.; Alruwaili, N.K.; Panda, D.S.; Imam, S.S.; Alharbi, K.S.; Afzal, M.; Shalaby, K.; Kazmi, I.; Alshehri, S. Potential of Natural Bioactive Compounds in Management of Diabetes: Review of Preclinical and Clinical Evidence. *Curr. Pharmacol. Rep.* **2021**, *7*, 107–122. [CrossRef]
41. Piña-Contreras, N.; Martínez-Moreno, A.G.; Ramírez-Anaya, J.D.P.; Espinoza-Gallardo, A.C.; Valdés, E.H.M. Raspberry (*Rubus idaeus* L.), a Promising Alternative in the Treatment of Hyperglycemia and Dyslipidemias. *J. Med. Food.* **2022**, *25*, 121–129. [CrossRef]
42. Savych, A.; Milian, I. Total flavonoid content in the herbal mixture with anti-diabetic activity. *PharmacologyOnLine* **2021**, *2*, 68–75.
43. Chen, L.Y.; Huang, C.N.; Liao, C.K.; Chang, H.M.; Kuan, Y.H.; Tseng, T.J.; Yen, K.J.; Yang, K.L.; Lin, H.C. Effects of rutin on wound healing in hyperglycemic rats. *Antioxidants* **2020**, *9*, 1122. [CrossRef] [PubMed]
44. Barik, S.K.; Russell, W.R.; Moar, K.M.; Cruickshank, M.; Scobbie, L.; Duncan, G.; Hoggard, N. The anthocyanins in black currants regulate postprandial hyperglycaemia primarily by inhibiting α-glucosidase while other phenolics modulate salivary α-amylase, glucose uptake and sugar transporters. *J. Nutr. Biochem.* **2020**, *78*, 108325. [CrossRef]
45. Dubey, S.; Ganeshpurkar, A.; Ganeshpurkar, A.; Bansal, D.; Dubey, N. Glycolytic enzyme inhibitory and antiglycation potential of rutin. *Future. J. Pharm. Sci.* **2017**, *3*, 158–162. [CrossRef]
46. Tadera, K.; Minami, Y.; Takamatsu, K.; Matsuoka, T. Inhibition of α-glucosidase and α-amylase by flavonoids. *J. Nutr. Sci. Vitaminol.* **2006**, *52*, 149–153. [CrossRef]
47. Niimi, N.; Yako, H.; Takaku, S.; Chung, S.K.; Sango, K. Aldose Reductase and the polyol pathway in schwann cells: Old and new problems. *Int. J. Mol. Sci.* **2021**, *22*, 1031. [CrossRef]
48. Kumar, A.A.; Satheesh, G.; Vijayakumar, G.; Chandran, M.; Prabhu, P.R.; Simon, L.; Kutty, V.R.; Kartha, C.C.; Jaleel, A. Postprandial metabolism is impaired in overweight normoglycemic young adults without family history of diabetes. *Sci. Rep.* **2020**, *10*, 353. [CrossRef] [PubMed]
49. Benlarbi, M.; Jemai, H.; Hajri, K.; Mbarek, S.; Amri, E.; Jebbari, M.; Hammoun, I.; Baccouche, B.; Boudhrioua Mihoubi, N.; Zemmal, A.; et al. Neuroprotective effects of oleuropein on retina photoreceptors cells primary culture and olive leaf extract and oleuropein inhibitory effects on aldose reductase in a diabetic model: Meriones shawi. *Arch. Physiol. Biochem.* **2020**, *1*, 593–600. [CrossRef]
50. Hussain, T.; Tan, B.; Murtaza, G.; Liu, G.; Rahu, N.; Kalhoro, M.S.; Kalhoro, D.H.; Adebowale, T.O.; Mazhar, M.U.; ur Rehman, Z.; et al. Flavonoids and type 2 diabetes: Evidence of efficacy in clinical and animal studies and delivery strategies to enhance their therapeutic efficacy. *Pharmacol. Res.* **2020**, *152*, 104629. [CrossRef]
51. Dariya, B.; Nagaraju, G.P. Advanced glycation end products in diabetes, cancer and phytochemical therapy. *Drug Discov. Today* **2020**, *25*, 1614–1623. [CrossRef]
52. Fournet, M.; Bonté, F.; Desmoulière, A. Glycation damage: A possible hub for major pathophysiological disorders and aging. *Aging. Dis.* **2018**, *9*, 880. [CrossRef] [PubMed]
53. Cepas, V.; Collino, M.; Mayo, J.C.; Sainz, R.M. Redox signaling and advanced glycation endproducts (AGEs) in diet-related diseases. *Antioxidants* **2020**, *9*, 142. [CrossRef] [PubMed]
54. Zhou, J.; Zhang, L.; Li, Q.; Jin, W.; Chen, W.; Han, J.; Zhang, Y. Simultaneous optimization for ultrasound-assisted extraction and antioxidant activity of flavonoids from *Sophora flavescens* using response surface methodology. *Molecules* **2018**, *24*, 112. [CrossRef] [PubMed]

55. Patil, S.M.; Al-Mutairi, K.A.; Firdose, N.; Ramu, R.; Martiz, R.M.; Ashwini, P. Pharmacoinformatics based screening discovers swertianolin from Lavandula angustifolia as a novel neuromodulator targeting epilepsy, depression, and anxiety. *South. Afr. J. Bot* **2022**, *149*, 712–730. [CrossRef]
56. Jyothi, M.; Khamees, H.A.; Patil, S.M.; Ramu, R.; Khanum, S.A. Microwave-assisted synthesis, characterization, docking studies and molecular dynamic of some novel phenyl thiazole analogs as xanthine oxidase inhibitor. *J. Iran. Chem. Soc.* **2022**, *10*, 1–5. [CrossRef]
57. Shahzad, D.; Saeed, A.; Larik, F.A.; Channar, P.A.; Abbas, Q.; Alajmi, M.F.; Arshad, M.I.; Erben, M.F.; Hassan, M.; Raza, H.; et al. Novel C-2 symmetric molecules as α-glucosidase and α-amylase inhibitors: Design; synthesis; kinetic evaluation; molecular docking and pharmacokinetics. *Molecules* **2019**, *24*, 1511. [CrossRef]
58. Ganavi, D.; Ramu, R.; Kumar, V.; Patil, S.M.; Martiz, R.M.; Shirahatti, P.S.; Sathyanarayana, R.; Poojary, B.; Holla, B.S.; Poojary, V.; et al. In vitro and in silico studies of fluorinated 2; 3-disubstituted thiazolidinone-pyrazoles as potential α-amylase inhibitors and antioxidant agents. *Arch. Pharm.* **2021**, *12*, e2100342. [CrossRef]
59. Osman, W.; Ismail, E.M.; Shantier, S.W.; Mohammed, M.S.; Mothana, R.A.; Muddathir, A.; Khalid, H.S. In silico assessment of potential leads identified from *Bauhinia rufescens* Lam. as α-glucosidase and α-amylase inhibitors. *J. Recept. Signal Transduct. Res.* **2021**, *41*, 159–169. [CrossRef]
60. Jhong, C.H.; Riyaphan, J.; Lin, S.H.; Chia, Y.C.; Weng, C.F. Screening alpha-glucosidase and alpha-amylase inhibitors from natural compounds by molecular docking in silico. *Biofactors* **2015**, *41*, 242–251. [CrossRef]
61. Isogai, H.; Hirayama, N. In silico prediction of interactions between site II on human serum albumin and profen drugs. *Int. Sch. Res. Not.* **2013**, *2013*, 818364. [CrossRef]
62. Ghuman, J.; Zunszain, P.A.; Petitpas, I.; Bhattacharya, A.A.; Otagiri, M.; Curry, S. Structural basis of the drug-binding specificity of human serum albumin. *J Mol. Biol.* **2005**, *353*, 38–52. [CrossRef] [PubMed]
63. Ali, M.S.; Al-Lohedan, H.A. Experimental and Computational Investigation on the Interaction of Anticancer Drug Gemcitabine with Human Plasma Protein: Effect of Copresence of Ibuprofen on the Binding. *Molecules* **2022**, *27*, 1635. [CrossRef] [PubMed]
64. Ramu, R.; Shirahatti, P.S.; Deepika, T.H.; Bajpe, S.N.; Sreepathi, N.; Patil, S.M.; Prasad, N. Investigating *Musa paradisiaca* (Var. Nanjangud rasa bale) pseudostem in preventing hyperglycemia along with improvement of diabetic complications. *J. Appl. Biol. Biotechnol.* **2022**, *10*, 56–65. [CrossRef]
65. Kufareva, I.; Abagyan, R. Methods of protein structure comparison. *Methods Mol. Biol.* **2012**, *857*, 231–257. [PubMed]
66. Medina-Franco, J.L.; Méndez-Lucio, O.; Martinez-Mayorga, K. The interplay between molecular modeling and chemoinformatics to characterize protein–ligand and protein–protein interactions landscapes for drug discovery. *Adv. Protein Chem. Struct. Biol.* **2014**, *96*, 1–37. [PubMed]
67. Kumar, V.; Ramu, R.; Shirahatti, P.S.; Kumari, V.C.; Sushma, P.; Mandal, S.P.; Patil, S.M. α-glucosidase, α-amylase inhibition, kinetics and docking studies of novel (2-chloro-6-(trifluoromethyl)benzyloxy) arylidene) based rhodanine and rhodanine acetic acid derivatives. *ChemistrySelect* **2021**, *6*, 9637–9644. [CrossRef]
68. Soltanabadi, O.; Atri, M.S.; Bagheri, M. Spectroscopic analysis; docking and molecular dynamics simulation of the interaction of cinnamaldehyde with human serum albumin. *J Incl Phenom Macrocycl Chem.* **2018**, *91*, 189–197. [CrossRef]
69. Radibratovic, M.; Minic, S.; Stanic-Vucinic, D.; Nikolic, M.; Milcic, M.; CirkovicVelickovic, T. Stabilization of human serum albumin by the binding of phycocyanobilin; a bioactive chromophore of blue-green alga Spirulina: Molecular dynamics and experimental study. *PLoS ONE* **2016**, *11*, e0167973. [CrossRef]
70. Tanawattanasuntorn, T.; Thongpanchang, T.; Rungrotmongkol, T.; Hanpaibool, C.; Graidist, P.; Tipmanee, V. (−)-Kusunokinin as a Potential AR Inhibitor: Equivalency Observed via AKR1B1 Dynamics Simulation. *ACS Omega* **2020**, *6*, 606–614. [CrossRef]
71. Adinortey, C.A.; Kwarko, G.B.; Koranteng, R.; Boison, D.; Obuaba, I.; Wilson, M.D.; Kwofie, S.K. Molecular Structure-Based Screening of the Constituents of Calotropis procera Identifies Potential Inhibitors of Diabetes Mellitus Target Alpha Glucosidase. *Curr. Issues Mol. Biol.* **2022**, *44*, 963–987. [CrossRef]
72. Lolok, N.; Sumiwi, S.A.; Muhtadi, A.; Susilawati, Y.; Hendriani, R.; Ramadhan, D.S.; Levita, J.; Sahidin, I. Molecular docking and molecular dynamics studies of bioactive compounds contained in noni fruit (*Morinda citrifolia* L.) against human pancreatic α-amylase. *J. Biomol. Struct. Dyn.* **2021**, *3*, 7091–7098. [CrossRef] [PubMed]
73. Yu, H.; Li, D.; Xu, F.; Pan, Q.; Chai, P.; Liu, B.; Chen, C. The binding affinity of human serum albumin and paclitaxel through MMPBSA based on docked complex. *Mol. Simul.* **2016**, *42*, 1460–1467. [CrossRef]
74. Ciccone, L.; Petrarolo, G.; Barsuglia, F.; Fruchart-Gaillard, C.; Cassar Lajeunesse, E.; Adewumi, A.T.; Soliman, M.E.S.; La Motta, C.; Orlandini, E.; Nencetti, S. Nature-Inspired O-Benzyl Oxime-Based Derivatives as New Dual-Acting Agents Targeting Aldose Reductase and Oxidative Stress. *Biomolecules* **2022**, *12*, 448. [CrossRef] [PubMed]

separations

MDPI

Article

Combination of Medium- and High-Pressure Liquid Chromatography for Isolation of L-tryptophan (Q-marker) from *Medicago sativa* Extract

Shixuan Zhang [1,2], Yonggui Ma [3], Ronghua Ma [4], Qilan Wang [1,2,*] and Jun Dang [1,2,*]

1 Qinghai Provincial Key Laboratory of Tibetan Medicine Research, Chinese Academy of Sciences, Northwest Institute of Plateau Biology, Xining 810001, China
2 Key Laboratory of Tibetan Medicine Research, Chinese Academy of Sciences, Northwest Institute of Plateau Biology, Xining 810001, China
3 Key Laboratory of Medicinal Animal and Plant Resources of Qinghai-Tibetan Plateau in Qinghai Province, College of Life Science, Qinghai Normal University, Xining 810001, China
4 Qinghai Provincial People's Hospital, Xining 810000, China
* Correspondence: wql@nwipb.cas.cn (Q.W.); dangjun@nwipb.cas.cn (J.D.); Tel.: +86-971-614-3282 (J.D.)

Abstract: *Medicago sativa* (alfalfa) is a widely used animal feed. However, its quality has been difficult to control due to the lack of appropriate marker compounds. Therefore, it is very necessary to select an appropriate quality marker (Q-marker) to control its quality. In this study, medium-pressure liquid chromatography and high-pressure liquid chromatography were employed to effectively prepare the separation of the Q-marker (L-tryptophan) from *Medicago sativa*. Firstly, using MCI GEL® CHP20P as the stationary phase, 2.5 g of the target fraction Fr3 was enriched from crude *Medicago sativa* extract (2.9 kg) by medium-pressure liquid chromatography. Secondly, Sephadex LH-20 was used to further separate Fr3 fractions, and the Fr34 fraction (358.3 mg) was enriched after 14 repetitions. Lastly, using the ReproSil-Pur C18 AQ preparative column, 63.4 mg of L-tryptophan was obtained by high-pressure liquid chromatography, and the purity was above 95%. The results showed that medium-pressure liquid chromatography (MCI GEL® CHP20P and Sephadex LH-20) combined with high-pressure liquid chromatography (ReproSil-Pur C18 AQ) could be used to effectively prepare the Q-marker from natural products with satisfactory purity.

Keywords: *Medicago sativa*; medium-pressure liquid chromatography; high-pressure liquid chromatography; quality marker; L-tryptophan

1. Introduction

Medicago sativa (alfalfa), called "Queen of the forages", is a widely cultivated perennial leguminous plant used as animal feed [1,2]. It is mainly cultivated in temperate regions of the northern and southern hemispheres, with an area of about 32 million hectares [3]. Firdaous et al. studied compounds of *Medicago sativa* and found that they were beneficial to the feed industry [4]. Because of its high protein content and the full range of amino acids, it was a good source of available protein and amino acids for livestock [5–7]. In addition, *Medicago sativa* cultivation required low inputs of herbicides and pesticides. This was the reason for the choice of *Medicago sativa* as the main commercially grown source of forage and fodder in many countries [8]. These countries not only focused on yield, but the quality of *Medicago sativa* was also an important factor for them to consider. However, there were many factors that can affect the quality of *Medicago sativa*, including soil moisture, ambient temperature, and mode of transportation, making the quality difficult to control [9–11]. Therefore, it was necessary to choose an appropriate quality standard to control its quality. However, there was no related research on the quality control system of *Medicago sativa*. The quality control index of traditional Chinese medicine is Q-marker. As the main component, Q-marker could reflect the safety and efficacy of traditional Chinese medicine [12,13]. Because the quality control system of Chinese medicine and forage is similar, this study hence focused on isolating the key indicator of quality control of *Medicago sativa*—Q-marker.

The conventional method for preparation, separation, and purification was silica-gel column chromatography because of its cheapness and simple operation [14–16], whereas this method still had the problem of poor reproducibility, instability, and low recovery [17,18]. Another technique was high-speed countercurrent chromatography (HSCCC), which was utilized for preparative separation and purification of diverse natural products [19]. This liquid–liquid partition chromatography technology, unaffected by solid support matrices, could eliminate the irreversible adsorption of samples onto stationary phases that occurs with traditional column chromatography [20,21]. Nonetheless, there were significant drawbacks to this approach, such as low separation resolution, the ability to separate only moderately polar molecules, and the requirement to calculate partition coefficients.

Many laboratories have used high-pressure liquid chromatography to isolate milligram-scale target compounds. Dang et al. used this method to prepare and isolate gallic acid derivatives and 1,1-diphenyl-2-picrylhydrazine inhibitors from *Saxifraga tangutica*. Vichapong et al. used HPLC to optimize the conditions for the extraction of phenolic compounds from rice [22–25]. Hence, the Q-marker could be separated and quantitatively determined by high-pressure liquid chromatography. However, high-pressure liquid chromatography carried the risk of contamination of the stationary phase, for example, chlorophyll in plants adsorbs to the stationary phase [26]. Therefore, a technique for pretreatment of the crude sample was required to remove non-target compounds. Due to medium-pressure liquid chromatography having the advantages of automation, high reproducibility of separation, and durable stationary phase materials, it was widely used for the enrichment of high-purity compounds [27–30]. Therefore, medium-pressure liquid chromatography could be used to remove non-target compounds. The stationary phase materials included various forms of silica gel, MCI GEL® CHP20P, and Sephadex LH-20 [22,31,32]. On this basis, the combination of medium-pressure liquid chromatography with different stationary phases could better enrich the target compounds [33]. As a result, for sample preparative separation, we used two steps of medium-pressure liquid chromatography in conjunction with high-pressure liquid chromatography. This method could not only solve the problem of easy contamination of the high-pressure liquid chromatography stationary phase but also separate higher-purity compounds through different stationary phases.

The aim of this research was to utilize a combination of high-pressure liquid chromatography and medium-pressure liquid chromatography to extract L-tryptophan in *Medicago sativa* and use it as a Q-marker for this forage grass. First, MCI GEL® CHP20P and Sephadex LH-20 (Mitsubishi Chemical Corporation, Tokyo, Japan) were used as stationary phases for medium-pressure liquid chromatography to enrich the target fractions. Subsequently, a ReproSil-Pur C18 AQ (Hanau, Hessen, Germany) high-pressure preparative column was used to purify the target fractions. This method could be used to determine the Q-marker of other crops and establish the quality control system.

2. Materials and Methods

2.1. Equipment and Chemicals

The preparative medium-pressure liquid chromatography workstation (Hanbon Science & Technology Co., Ltd., Jiangsu, China) consisted of two NP7000 prep-high-performance liquid chromatography pumps, an NU3000 UV–Vis detector, a 5 mL manual injector, and an LC workstation. High-performance liquid chromatography with an Essentia LC-16 (Shimadzu Instruments Co., Kyoto, Japan) was used to analyze the samples. This system consisted of two binary gradient pumps, a UV–Vis detector, a 5 mL manual injector, and an LC workstation. ESI-MS spectra were acquired as mass spectrometer instruments. 1H and 13CNMR spectra were recorded on the Bruker Avance 600 MHz spectrometer (Bruker Instruments, Karlsruhe, Germany) with DMSO-*d6* as the solvent.

The separation material MCI GEL®CHP20P (120 μm) and Sephadex LH-20 were purchased from Mitsubishi Chemical Corporation (Tokyo, Japan) and GE Healthcare (Chicago, IL, USA), respectively. The analytical column ReproSil-Pur C18 AQ (4.6 × 250 mm, 5 μm) and ReproSil-Pur C18 AQ preparative column (20 × 250 mm, 5 μm) were purchased from Maisch Corporation (Hanau, Hessen, Germany).

The chromatographic and analytical-grade methanol (MeOH) was bought from Kelon Chemical Reagent Factory (Chengdu, China). Chromatographic-grade water was prepared by Moore water purification station (Chongqing, China).

2.2. Preparation of Extract of Medicago Sativa

The whole *Medicago sativa* was planted in the Northwest Plateau Institute of Biology and validated by Prof. Lijuan Mei of Northwest Institute of Plateau Biology. A sample had been stored in the Key Laboratory of Tibetan Medicine Research, the Chinese Academy of Sciences.

The dried *Medicago* sativa was cut into 1 cm pieces (2.9 kg) and extracted twice with 25.0 L MeOH (12 h each time). The 50.0 L extract was collected, filtered, and concentrated with a 45 °C rotary evaporator. After the extract was concentrated to 10.0 L, 1.0 mL of the extract was taken out and analyzed on a ReproSil-Pur C18 AQ analytical column (4.6 × 250 mm, 5 μm). With 0.1% v/v formic acid in water as mobile phase A and methanol as mobile phase B, the flow rate was 1.0 mL/min. The linear gradient elution settings were as follows: 0–50 min, 0–100% B; 50–60 min, 100% B. An amount of 920.0 g of amorphous silica gel was added to the remaining concentrated solution and dried in an oven at 40 °C. Finally, 1.2 kg of a mixture of dried silica gel and the sample was obtained (262.4 g of the sample).

2.3. Medium-Pressure Liquid Chromatography Sample Pretreatment

The dried silica gel mixture (104.4 g) was placed in another small medium-pressure chromatogram column (49 × 100 mm) and connected to a medium-pressure column (49 × 460 mm) equipped with MCI GEL® CHP20P as a stationary phase, and a MeOH/H2O combination was used for elution. Chromatographic pure water was mobile phase A, and methanol was mobile phase B. The linear elution gradient was: 0–40 min, 0% B; 40–340 min, 0–100% B; 340–540 min, 100% B. During this process, the flow rate was kept constant at 50.0 mL/min. The chromatogram record was obtained at 210 nm. After 11 repetitions, 12 fractions were obtained, which were rotary evaporated and weighed. The final fraction, fraction 3 (Fr3), was selected for further enrichment.

Fr3 (30.0 mg) was dissolved in methanol and analyzed on Resilpur C18 AQ (20 × 250 mm, 5 μm), and 0.1% v/v formic acid in water was used as mobile phase A, methanol solution was used as mobile phase B, and the flow rate was 1.0 mL/min. Linear gradient elution settings were as follows: 0–50 min, 0–100% B; 50–60 min, 100% B. Subsequently, the conditions were further optimized, and the optimized conditions were: 5–65% MeOH for 60 min at a flow rate of 1.0 mL/min.

The remaining Fr3 (70.0 mg per injection, 978.7 mg total weight) was dissolved in methanol and added to the medium-pressure chromatography column equipped with Sephadex LH-20. It was eluted with MeOH for 5000 min, with a flow rate of 0.3 mL/min at 210 nm. After repeating the separation 14 times, fraction 34 (Fr34) was collected, combined, and then concentrated by rotary evaporation and dried and weighed (538.3 mg). Fr34 was analyzed with ReproSil-Pur C18 AQ (20 × 250 mm, 5 μm) analytical column. The chromatographic conditions: mobile phase A was 0.1% v/v formic acid in water, mobile phase B was chromatographic methanol, the gradient elution condition was 0–60 min, 5–65% B, the flow rate was 1.0 mL/min, and detection wavelength was 210 nm.

2.4. High-Pressure Liquid Chromatography Purification Quality Marker

The ReproSil-Pur C18 AQ analytical column (4.6 × 250 mm, 5 μm) was used to re-analyze Fr34. Fr34 (538.3 mg) was dissolved and filtered through a 0.45 μm membrane. Mobile phase A was 0.1% *v/v* formic acid in water, and mobile phase B was methanol; the isocratic elution condition was 0–60 min 8% B, the flow rate was 1.0 mL/min, and the detection wavelength was 210 nm.

After analysis, the ReproSil-Pur C18 AQ preparative column (20 × 250 mm, 5 μm) was used to separate Fr34. The mobile phase is composed of methanol and 0.1% *v/v* formic acid in water. Before separation, the system was equilibrated for 10.0 min followed by isocratic elution with 8% methanol for 60 min. Each test is based on injecting 0.5 mL of Fr34 sample solution. The flow rate of the eluent is continuously maintained at 19.0 mL/min, and the elution process is tracked at 210 nm. Finally, 62.6 mg of fraction 341 (Fr341) was prepared.

2.5. Purity Evaluation of the Obtained Quality Marker

The purity of the separated Fr341 was evaluated using ReproSil-Pur C18 AQ analytical column (4.6 × 250 mm, 5 μm). The mobile phases were 0.1% *v/v* formic acid in water (A) and methanol (B). The isocratic elution was based on 8% B, the flow rate was 1.0 mL/min, the elution time was 60 min, and the absorbance was 210 nm.

The ReproSil-Pur C18 AQ analytical column (4.6 × 250 mm, 5 μm) was used to analyze Fr341 and the *Medicago sativa* crude sample. Mobile phase A was 0.1% *v/v* formic acid in water, and mobile phase B was methanol. The linear gradient elution was based on 0–60% B, the flow rate was 1.0 mL/min, the elution time was 60 min, and the absorbance was 210 nm.

3. Results

3.1. Medium-Pressure Chromatography for Enrichment of the Quality Marker Faction

An analytical ReproSil-Pur C18 AQ column (4.6 × 250 mm, 5 μm) was used to examine a crude sample of *Medicago sativa* extracted with MeOH. The extract includes the main component (approximately 17 min peak), as shown by the analytical chromatogram in Figure 1A. It is evident from the analytical chromatogram in Figure 1A that the crude MeOH extract of *Medicago sativa* contains a main compound. About 10.0 L of the concentrated extract obtained by rotary evaporation was mixed with silica gel (781.6 g, 100–200 mesh), dried, and weighed. About 262.4 g of crude sample was obtained from 2.9 kg of *Medicago sativa* in a yield of 9.2%. Before the MCI GEL® CHP20P pretreatment, the dried silica gel combination (104.4 g) was put in another small medium-pressure chromatographic tower (49 × 100 mm). The connection of the medium-pressure liquid chromatography was shown in Figure 1D, connecting two medium-pressure columns (49 × 100 mm and 49 × 460 mm) to the preparative liquid chromatography. After 11 repetitions, the crude extract was separated into 12 fractions (Fr1–Fr12) by MCI GEL® CHP20P medium-pressure liquid chromatography, yielding the chromatogram in Figure 1B. The ReproSil-Pur C18 AQ analytical column was used to analyze Fr3 (the same mobile phase and chromatographic conditions as the crude sample), resulting in the chromatogram in Figure 1C.

For better separation of target compounds from complex crude extracts, the elution conditions of Fr3 needed to be optimized before further preparation at medium-pressure liquid chromatography. Subsequently, the analysis was performed on a ReproSil-Pur C18 AQ analytical column with the optimized conditions to obtain the analytical chromatogram in Figure 2A. The red-hearted marked peak in this chromatogram was the main compound's peak. As shown in Figure 2D, the medium-pressure column (26 × 1000 mm) filled with separation material Sephadex LH-20 was connected to preparative liquid chromatography. The Fr3 (70.0 mg) sample was dissolved with 3 mL methanol and injected on a Sephadex LH-20 medium-pressure liquid chromatography column. It was eluted with isocratic MeOH for 5000 min at a flow rate of 0.3 mL/min. The resulting chromatogram is shown in Figure 2B, and six fractions (Fr31–Fr36) were obtained. Fr34 as the main fraction was collected, concentrated, and weighed (358.3 mg), with 17.0% recovery. Subsequently,

Fr34 was analyzed using the same chromatographic conditions as the optimized Fr3 on a ReproSil-Pur C18 AQ analytical column, resulting in the chromatogram in Figure 2C.

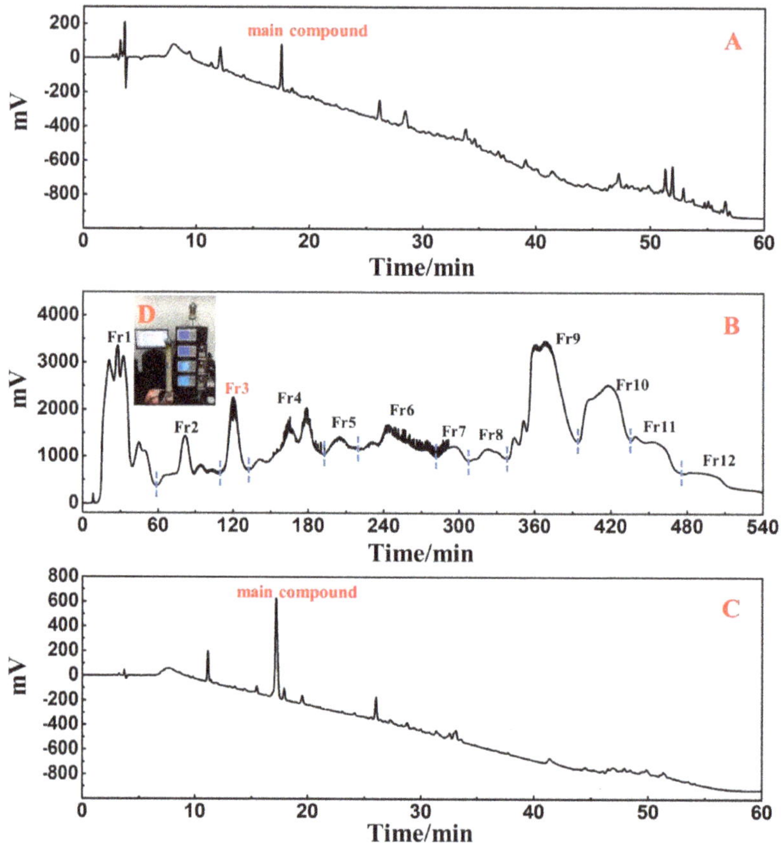

Figure 1. (**A**) The analytical chromatogram of crude Medicago sativa sample on the ReproSil−Pur C18 AQ analytical column. (**B**) The crude extract chromatogram of medium-pressure liquid chromatography pretreatment with MCI GEL® CHP20P as the stationary phase. (**C**) The analytical chromatogram of fraction Fr3 on the ReproSil-Pur C18 AQ analytical column. (**D**) The actual MCI GEL® CHP20P medium-pressure liquid chromatography system.

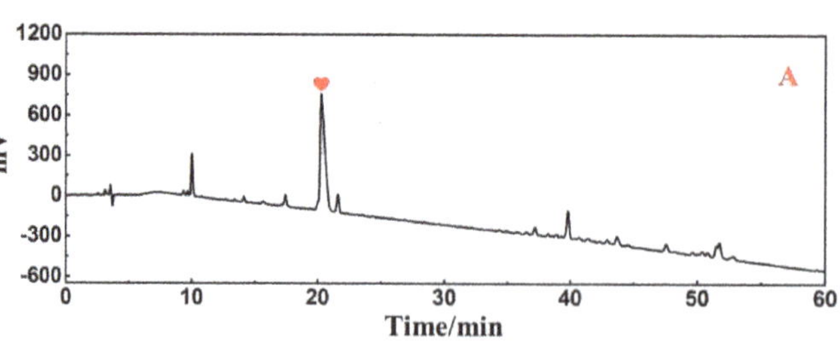

Figure 2. *Cont.*

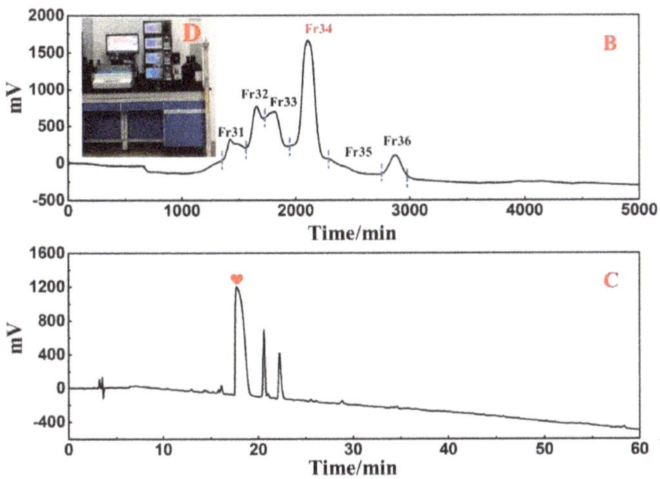

Figure 2. (**A**) The analytical chromatogram of fraction Fr3 on the ReproSil−Pur C18 AQ analytical column. (**B**) The fraction Fr3 chromatogram of medium-pressure liquid chromatography pretreatment with Sephadex LH-20 as the stationary phase. (**C**) The analytical chromatogram of fraction Fr34 on the ReproSil-Pur C18 AQ analytical column. (**D**) The actual Sephadex LH-20 medium-pressure liquid chromatography system.

3.2. High-Pressure Preparation and Purity Analysis of the Isolated Quality Marker

After optimizing the chromatographic conditions for the analysis of Fr34, the ReproSil-Pur C18 AQ analytical column was selected to further analyze Fr34 under the optimized chromatographic conditions. The resulting chromatogram is shown in Figure 3A. Thus, the subsequent preparation was more convenient and time-saving. The red-hearted peak in this chromatogram was the main compound's peak. Subsequently, the main compound was prepared on a high-pressure ReproSil-Pur C18 AQ preparative column with optimized chromatographic conditions for Fr34. The resulting chromatogram was Figure 3B. A sample of 63.4 mg of Fr341 (blue marked peaks) was prepared with a recovery of 17.6%. In order to clarify the purity of the target compound Fr341, the ReproSil-Pur C18 AQ analytical column was used to analyze Fr341. It could be seen from Figure 3C that the purity of the target compound is above 95%.

In order to confirm that the prepared Fr341 was the main compound in the crude extract, the ReproSil-Pur C18 AQ column was used to analyze and compare the crude extract and Fr341 under the same chromatographic conditions. The obtained chromatograms, Figure 4A,B, corresponded to the crude extract and Fr341, respectively.

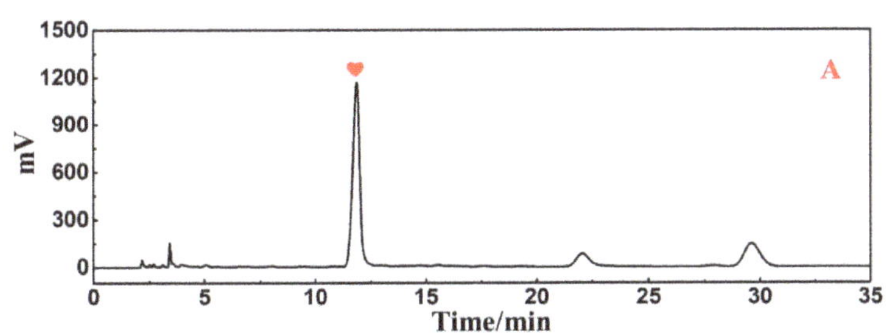

Figure 3. *Cont.*

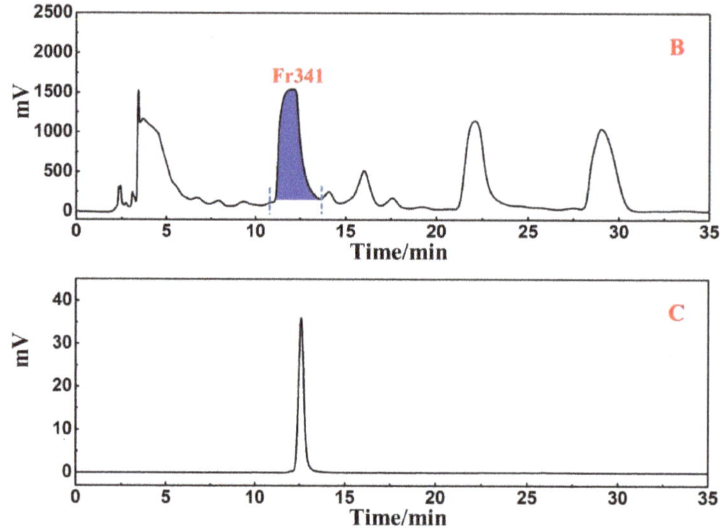

Figure 3. (**A**)The analytical chromatogram of fraction Fr34 on the ReproSil-Pur C18 AQ. (**B**) High-pressure preparative fraction Fr34 chromatogram using a ReproSil-Pur C18 AQ preparative column. (**C**) The analytical chromatogram of fraction Fr341 on the ReproSil-Pur C18 AQ.

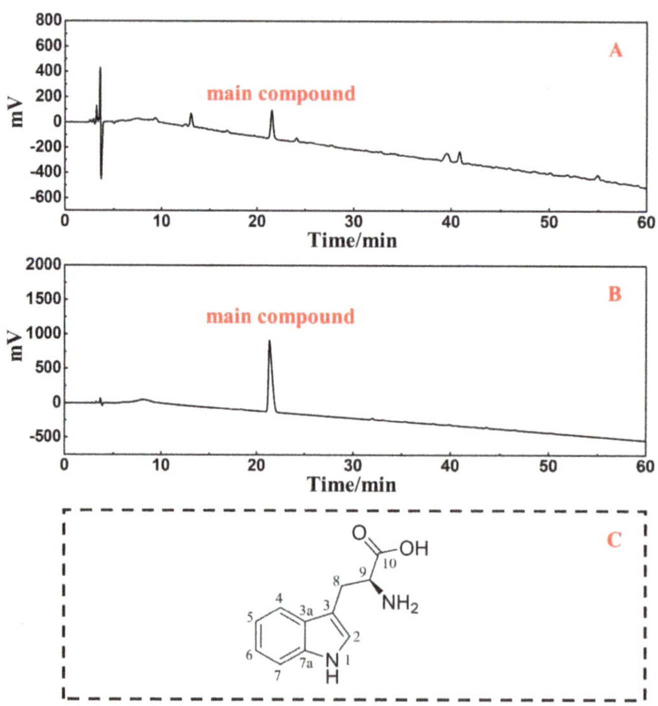

Figure 4. (**A**) The analytical chromatogram of fraction of crude Medicago sativa sample on the ReproSil-Pur C18 AQ analytical column. (**B**) The analytical chromatogram of fraction Fr341 on the ReproSil-Pur C18 AQ analytical column. (**C**) Structural formula of L-tryptophan.

3.3. Structural Characterization of the Isolated Quality Marker

In order to clarify the structure of Fr341, ESI-MS (Figure 5A,B), ^{1}H NMR (Figure 5C), and ^{13}C NMR (Figure 5D) spectra were obtained and matched with the published literature. According to all the spectral data, the target compound was L-tryptophan (see the list of NMR peaks and molecular ions below). The resulting L-tryptophan structural formula is shown in Figure 4C.

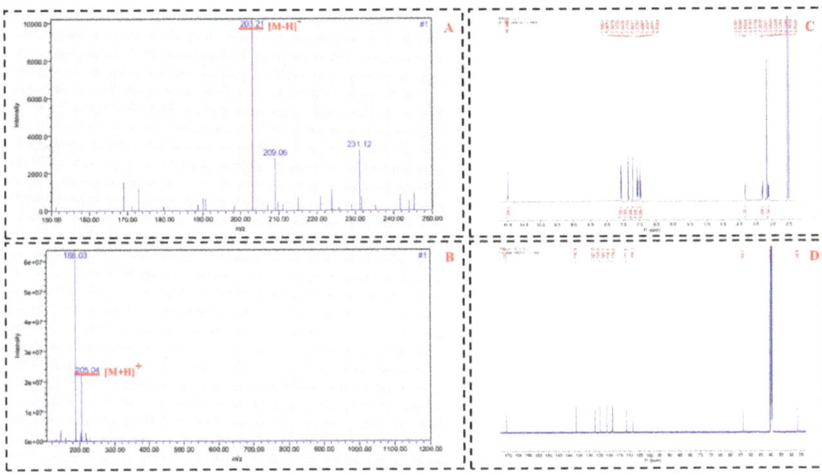

Figure 5. (**A**,**B**) Q−TOF−MS spectra of Fr341; (**C**) ^{1}H NMR spectra of Fr341; (**D**) ^{13}C NMR spectra of Fr341.

Fraction Fr341 (L-tryptophan, light-yellow powder, ESI-MS *m/z* 203.21, $[M-H]^-$: ^{1}H NMR (600 MHz, DMSO-d_6): δ 10.98 (1H, d, NH-1), 7.57 (1H, d, J = 7.9 Hz, H-4), 7.36 (1H, d, J = 7.9 Hz, H-7), 7.22 (1H, d, J = 2.4 Hz, H-2), 7.08 (1H, t, J = 7.4 Hz, H-6), 6.99 (1H, t, J = 7.4 Hz, H-5), 3.82 (1H, dd, J = 7.3, 5.1 Hz, H-9), 3.30 (1H, dd, J = 15.1, 5.1 Hz, H-8a), 3.12 (1H, dd, J = 15.1, 7.3 Hz, H-8b); ^{13}C NMR (125 MHz, DMSO-d_6): δ 170.7 (C-10), 136.3 (C-7a), 127.2 (C-3a), 124.5 (C-2), 121.1 (C-6), 118.5 (C-5), 118.3 (C-4), 111.4 (C-7), 108.1 (C-3), 53.7 (C-9), 26.6 (C-8). The data were in agreement with that of L-tryptophan in the literature [34].

4. Discussion

MeOH was chosen as the extraction solvent because of its high solubility and low cost. Dried *Medicago sativa* was cut into one-centimeter pieces to facilitate MeOH extraction of *Medicago sativa*. The purpose of mixing the concentrated extract obtained by rotary evaporation with silica gel was to consider the complexity and poor solubility of the extract. After mixing with silica gel and drying, it could be used for subsequent medium-pressure liquid chromatography pretreatment. The purpose of the MCI GEL® CHP20P pretreatment was to remove the chlorophyll in the methanol extract of *Medicago sativa* and at the same time achieve enrichment of the fraction. Because chlorophyll could be adsorbed on the preparative column's stationary phase, this would not contaminate the subsequent chromatographic columns we used. Because MCI GEL® CHP20P fillers were predominantly styrene–divinylbenzene copolymers, it was chosen as the stationary phase for this medium-pressure liquid chromatography procedure. This polymeric filler maintained a stable spherical structure in organic solvents, which could enable high reproducibility during purification of target compounds. This achieved high resolution and product recovery in this study. The analytical chromatogram in Figure 1C showed that with the same chromatographic conditions, the retention time of the main compound Fr3 was similar to that of the crude sample, i.e., the major compound Fr3 was significantly enriched in the crude sample. Accordingly, we chose Fr3 as the target fraction for further separation.

Since the components in Fr3 were still relatively complex, to separate the peaks of the primary components, medium-pressure liquid chromatography was utilized. The stationary phase was Sephadex LH-20, because this stationary phase has been widely used because of its convenience and efficiency. It was a novel technique that facilitates the isolation of compounds from certain plant sources. Subsequently, the Fr34 obtained by the medium-pressure liquid chromatography in this step was analyzed using the same chromatographic conditions that were optimized to analyze Fr3. The resulting analytical chromatogram in Figure 2C was compared with Fr3 (Figure 2A). The comparison results showed that the retention time of the main compound Fr34 was similar to that of Fr3 (red heart marked peaks) with the same chromatographic conditions. This means that the main compound, Fr34, was significantly enriched in the crude sample. Accordingly, we chose Fr34 for the next high-pressure liquid chromatography preparation.

For more convenient preparation, the chromatographic conditions for analyzing Fr34 need to be further optimized before high-pressure liquid chromatography preparation. The final optimized chromatographic condition was 8% methanol isocratic. This isocratic chromatographic condition means that there was no need to set an equilibration time during the preparation to restore the system to the desired mobile phase ratio. Fr341 and crude extracts prepared under these chromatographic conditions were analyzed on a ReproSil-Pur C18 AQ column under the same chromatographic conditions. By comparing these two chromatograms (Figure 4A,B), it was found that the retention time of the Fr341 peak was similar to the peak time of the main compound in the crude extract. This proved that the prepared Fr341 was the main compound of alfalfa *Medicago sativa*. As a result, Fr341 can be used as the Q-marker of *Medicago sativa* for quality control.

These results could show that the combination of medium- and high-pressure chromatography can effectively separate tryptophan from *Medicago sativa*. In addition, this method can filter out other redundant components and focus on the key indicators (Q-markers) of quality control. The selected Q-marker has the best comprehensive characteristics of content and stability among the many complex components of the forage and can comprehensively characterize the intrinsic quality of the forage. Yang et al. provide a successful case of setting scientific quality standards based on Q-markers [13]. According to these cases, it was known that HPLC could be used to determine the characteristic components of traditional Chinese medicine and other products, which could also confirm the accuracy of our results based on MPLC and HPLC. Finally, this method enables large-scale separation and purification of reference materials from other forages.

5. Conclusions

In this study, medium-pressure liquid chromatography and high-pressure liquid chromatography were used to separate L-tryptophan. Medium-pressure liquid chromatography with MCI GEL® CHP20P as the stationary phase removed chlorophyll to enrich the target fraction. Sephadex LH-20 was used for further purification by isocratic methanol elution. After analysis and preparation by ReproSil-Pur C18 AQ, L-tryptophan was obtained, with a purity of more than 95%. From the conclusions, it can be shown that the method combined with medium- and high-pressure chromatography can separate and purify Q-markers from other forages on a large scale. In conclusion, the new method established in this study provides a valuable perspective on forage quality control. The method could be used for relevant commercial cultivation such as forage and feed and can isolate and purify reference compounds of quality markers for quality control from these commercial forages on a large scale.

Author Contributions: Conceptualization, J.D. and Q.W.; methodology, S.Z.; validation, S.Z., Y.M., and R.M.; investigation, S.Z.; resources, J.D.; writing—original draft preparation, R.M.; writing—review and editing, S.Z.; visualization, J.D.; supervision, Q.W.; project administration, Y.M.; funding acquisition, J.D. All authors have read and agreed to the published version of the manuscript.

Funding: The study was sponsored by the Young Scholars in Western China, Chinese Academy of Sciences (2022), the Kunlun Talent and High-end Innovation and Entrepreneurship Talents (2021), Key Laboratory of Medicinal Animal and Plant Resources of Qinghai-Tibetan Plateau in Qinghai Province (2020-ZJ-Y04), the Joint Research Project of Three-River Headwaters National Park, Chinese Academy of Sciences, and the People's Government of Qinghai Province (LHZX-2021-02).

Data Availability Statement: Data are available upon request from the authors.

Conflicts of Interest: The authors declare that they have no known competing financial interests or personal relationships that could have appeared to influence the work reported in this paper.

References

1. Meng, Y.; Hou, Y.; Wang, H.; Ji, R.; Liu, B.; Wen, J.; Niu, L.; Lin, H. Targeted mutagenesis by CRISPR/Cas9 system in the model legume Medicago truncatula. *Plant Cell Rep.* **2017**, *36*, 371–374. [CrossRef]
2. Zhou, Q.; Luo, D.; Chai, X.; Wu, Y.; Wang, Y.; Nan, Z.; Yang, Q.; Liu, W.; Liu, Z. Multiple regulatory networks are activated during cold stress in *Medicago sativa* L. *Int. J. Mol. Sci.* **2018**, *19*, 3169. [CrossRef] [PubMed]
3. Ventroni, L.M.; Volenec, J.J.; Cangiano, C.A. Fall dormancy and cutting frequency impact on alfalfa yield and yield components. *Field Crops Res.* **2010**, *119*, 252–259. [CrossRef]
4. Firdaous, L.; Fertin, B.; Khelissa, O.; Dhainaut, M.; Nedjar, N.; Chataigné, G.; Ouhoud, L.; Lutin, F.; Dhulster, P. Adsorptive removal of polyphenols from an alfalfa white proteins concentrate: Adsorbent screening, adsorption kinetics and equilibrium study. *Sep. Purif. Technol.* **2017**, *178*, 29–39. [CrossRef]
5. Fan, W.; Ge, G.; Liu, Y.; Wang, W.; Liu, L.; Jia, Y. Proteomics integrated with metabolomics: Analysis of the internal causes of nutrient changes in alfalfa at different growth stages. *BMC Plant Biol.* **2018**, *18*, 1–15. [CrossRef] [PubMed]
6. Lei, Y.; Hannoufa, A.; Yu, P. The use of gene modification and advanced molecular structure analyses towards improving alfalfa forage. *Int. J. Mol. Sci.* **2017**, *18*, 298. [CrossRef]
7. Sahni, P.; Sharma, S.; Surasani, V.K.R. Influence of processing and pH on amino acid profile, morphology, electrophoretic pattern, bioactive potential and functional characteristics of alfalfa protein isolates. *Food Chem.* **2020**, *333*, 127503. [CrossRef]
8. Kulkarni, K.P.; Tayade, R.; Asekova, S.; Song, J.T.; Shannon, J.G.; Lee, J.D. Harnessing the potential of forage legumes, alfalfa, soybean, and cowpea for sustainable agriculture and global food security. *Front. Plant Sci.* **2018**, *9*, 1314. [CrossRef]
9. Kaliyan, N.; Morey, R.V. Factors affecting strength and durability of densified biomass products. *Biomass Bioenergy* **2009**, *33*, 337–359. [CrossRef]
10. Testa, G.; Gresta, F.; Cosentino, S.L. Dry matter and qualitative characteristics of alfalfa as affected by harvest times and soil water content. *Eur. J. Agron.* **2011**, *34*, 144–152. [CrossRef]
11. Romero-Pérez, G.A.; Ominski, K.H.; McAllister, T.A.; Krause, D.O. Effect of environmental factors and influence of rumen and hindgut biogeography on bacterial communities in steers. *Appl. Environ. Microbiol.* **2011**, *77*, 258–268. [CrossRef] [PubMed]
12. Jiang, Z.; Yang, J.; Wang, Y. Discrimination and identification of Q-markers based on 'Spider-web' mode for quality control of traditional Chinese medicine. *Phytomedicine* **2018**, *44*, 98–102. [CrossRef] [PubMed]
13. Yang, W.; Zhang, Y.; Wu, W.; Huang, L.; Guo, D.; Liu, C. Approaches to establish Q-markers for the quality standards of traditional Chinese medicines. *Acta Pharm. Sin. B* **2017**, *7*, 439–446. [CrossRef]
14. Kiasat, A.R.; Mouradzadegun, A.; Elahi, S.; Fallah-Mehrjardi, M. $Al(HSO_4)_3$/silica gel as a novel catalytic system for the ring opening of epoxides with thiocyanate anion under solvent-free conditions. *Chin. Chem. Lett.* **2010**, *21*, 146–150. [CrossRef]
15. Uckoo, R.M.; Jayaprakasha, G.K.; Patil, B.S. Rapid separation method of polymethoxyflavones from citrus using flash chromatography. *Sep. Purif. Technol.* **2011**, *81*, 151–158. [CrossRef]
16. Zhang, Y.; Jiao, J.; Liu, C.; Wu, X.; Zhang, Y. Isolation and purification of four flavone C-glycosides from antioxidant of bamboo leaves by macroporous resin column chromatography and preparative high-performance liquid chromatography. *Food Chem.* **2008**, *107*, 1326–1336. [CrossRef]
17. Han, W.; Wang, S.; Huang, H.; Luo, L.; Zhang, S. Simultaneous determination of brominated phenols in soils. *J. Environ. Sci.* **2013**, *25*, 2306–2312. [CrossRef]
18. Wang, L.; Longo, W.M.; Dillon, J.T.; Zhao, J.; Zheng, Y.; Moros, M.; Huang, Y. An efficient approach to eliminate steryl ethers and miscellaneous esters/ketones for gas chromatographic analysis of alkenones and alkenoates. *J. Chromatogr. A* **2019**, *1596*, 175–182. [CrossRef]
19. Xü, K.; Lü, H.; Qü, B.; Shan, H.; Song, J. High-speed counter-current chromatography preparative separation and purification of phloretin from apple tree bark. *Sep. Purif. Technol.* **2010**, *72*, 406–409. [CrossRef]
20. Huang, X.Y.; Fu, J.F.; Di, D.L. Preparative isolation and purification of steviol glycosides from Stevia rebaudiana Bertoni using high-speed counter-current chromatography. *Sep. Purif. Technol.* **2010**, *71*, 220–224. [CrossRef]
21. Ito, Y. Golden rules and pitfalls in selecting optimum conditions for high-speed counter-current chromatography. *J. Chromatogr. A* **2005**, *1065*, 145–168. [CrossRef] [PubMed]
22. Dang, J.; Wang, Q.; Wang, Q.; Yuan, C.; Li, G.; Ji, T. Preparative isolation of antioxidative gallic acid derivatives from Saxifraga tangutica using a class separation method based on medium-pressure liquid chromatography and reversed-phase liquid chromatography. *J. Sep. Sci.* **2021**, *44*, 3734–3746. [CrossRef] [PubMed]

23. Frenich, A.G.; del Mar Aguilera-Luiz, M.; Vidal, J.L.M.; Romero-González, R. Comparison of several extraction techniques for multiclass analysis of veterinary drugs in eggs using ultra-high pressure liquid chromatography–tandem mass spectrometry. *Anal. Chim. Acta* **2010**, *661*, 150–160. [CrossRef] [PubMed]
24. Motilva, M.J.; Serra, A.; Macià, A. Analysis of food polyphenols by ultra high-performance liquid chromatography coupled to mass spectrometry: An overview. *J. Chromatogr. A* **2013**, *1292*, 66–82. [CrossRef]
25. Vichapong, J.; Sookserm, M.; Srijesdaruk, V.; Swatsitang, P.; Srijaranai, S. High performance liquid chromatographic analysis of phenolic compounds and their antioxidant activities in rice varieties. *LWT-Food Sci. Technol.* **2010**, *43*, 1325–1330. [CrossRef]
26. Dawa, Y.; Du, Y.; Wang, Q.; Chen, C.; Zou, D.; Qi, D.; Ma, J.; Dang, J. Targeted isolation of 1, 1-diphenyl-2-picrylhydrazyl inhibitors from *Saxifraga atrata* using medium-and high-pressure liquid chromatography combined with online high performance liquid chromatography-1, 1-diphenyl-2-picrylhydrazyl detection. *J. Chromatogr. A* **2021**, *1635*, 461690. [CrossRef]
27. Cheng, Y.; Liang, Q.; Hu, P.; Wang, Y.; Jun, F.W.; Luo, G. Combination of normal-phase medium-pressure liquid chromatography and high-performance counter-current chromatography for preparation of ginsenoside-Ro from panax ginseng with high recovery and efficiency. *Sep. Purif. Technol.* **2010**, *73*, 397–402. [CrossRef]
28. Dang, J.; Ma, J.; Du, Y.; Dawa, Y.; Wang, Q.; Chen, C.; Wang, Q.; Tao, Y.; Ji, T. Large-scale preparative isolation of bergenin standard substance from Saxifraga atrata using polyamide coupled with MCI GEL®CHP20P as stationary phases in medium pressure chromatography. *J. Chromatogr. B* **2021**, *1170*, 122617. [CrossRef]
29. Qiu, Y.K.; Chen, F.F.; Zhang, L.L.; Yan, X.; Chen, L.; Fang, M.J.; Wu, Z. Two-dimensional preparative liquid chromatography system for preparative separation of minor amount components from complicated natural products. *Anal. Chim. Acta* **2014**, *820*, 176–186. [CrossRef]
30. Wiesenberg, G.L.; Schwark, L.; Schmidt, M.W. Improved automated extraction and separation procedure for soil lipid analyses. *Eur. J. Soil Sci.* **2004**, *55*, 349–356. [CrossRef]
31. Ebada, S.S.; Edrada, R.A.; Lin, W.; Proksch, P. Methods for isolation, purification and structural elucidation of bioactive secondary metabolites from marine invertebrates. *Nat. Protoc.* **2008**, *3*, 1820–1831. [CrossRef] [PubMed]
32. Mottaghipisheh, J.; Iriti, M. Sephadex® LH-20, isolation, and purification of flavonoids from plant species: A comprehensive review. *Molecules* **2020**, *25*, 4146. [CrossRef] [PubMed]
33. Zhang, H.; Shao, Q.; Wang, W.; Zhang, J.; Zhang, Z.; Liu, Y.; Yang, Y. Characterization of compounds with tumor–cell proliferation inhibition activity from mushroom (Phellinus baumii) mycelia produced by solid-state fermentation. *Molecules* **2017**, *22*, 698. [CrossRef] [PubMed]
34. Rho, T.; Yoon, K.D. Chemical constituents of Nelumbo nucifera seeds. *Nat. Prod. Sci.* **2017**, *23*, 253–257. [CrossRef]

MDPI AG
Grosspeteranlage 5
4052 Basel
Switzerland
Tel.: +41 61 683 77 34

MDPI Books Editorial Office
E-mail: books@mdpi.com
www.mdpi.com/books

www.ingramcontent.com/pod-product-compliance
Lightning Source LLC
Chambersburg PA
CBHW041934260926
51850CB00018B/164